# Student Solutions Manual

*Cindy Trimble & Associates*

# Intermediate Algebra

## FIFTH EDITION

*Elayn Martin-Gay*

**PEARSON**

Prentice
Hall

Upper Saddle River, NJ 07458

Editorial Director, Mathematics: Christine Hoag
Editor-in-Chief: Paul Murphy
Sponsoring Editor: Mary Beckwith
Assistant Editor: Georgina Brown
Senior Managing Editor: Linda Mihatov Behrens
Project Manager: Kristy S. Mosch
Art Director: Heather Scott
Supplement Cover Manager: Paul Gourhan
Supplement Cover Designer: Victoria Colotta
Operations Specialist: Ilene Kahn
Senior Operations Supervisor: Diane Peirano

© 2009 Pearson Education, Inc.
Pearson Prentice Hall
Pearson Education, Inc.
Upper Saddle River, NJ 07458

The author and publisher of this book have used their best efforts in preparing this book. These efforts include the development, research, and testing of the theories and programs to determine their effectiveness. The author and publisher make no warranty of any kind, expressed or implied, with regard to these programs or the documentation contained in this book. The author and publisher shall not be liable in any event for incidental or consequential damages in connection with, or arising out of, the furnishing, performance, or use of these programs.

Printed in the United States of America

10  9  8  7  6  5  4  3  2  1

ISBN-13:  978-0-13-603052-2   Standalone

ISBN-10:      0-13-603052-1   Standalone

ISBN-13:  978-0-13-603053-9   Value Pack

ISBN-10:      0-13-603053-X   Value Pack

Pearson Education Ltd., London
Pearson Education Singapore, Pte. Ltd.
Pearson Education Canada, Inc.
Pearson Education—Japan
Pearson Education Australia PTY, Limited
Pearson Education North Asia, Ltd., Hong Kong
Pearson Educación de Mexico, S.A. de C.V.
Pearson Education Malaysia, Pte. Ltd.
Pearson Education Upper Saddle River, New Jersey

# Contents

# Chapter 1

## Section 1.2

### Practice Exercises

1. Let $b = 3.5$ and $h = 8$.
$$A = \frac{1}{2}bh$$
$$A = \frac{1}{2}(3.5)(8) = 14$$
The area is 14 square centimeters.

2. Let $p = 17$ and $q = 3$.
$2p - q = 2(17) - 3 = 34 - 3 = 31$

3. a. $\{6, 7, 8, 9\}$

   b. $\{41, 42, 43, ...\}$

4. a. True, since 7 is a natural number and therefore an element of the set.

   b. True, since 6 is not an element of the set $\{1, 3, 5, 7\}$.

5. a. True; every integer is a real number.

   b. False; $\sqrt{8}$ is an irrational number.

   c. True; every whole number is a rational number.

   d. False; since the element 2 in the first set is not an element of the second set.

6. a. $|4| = 4$ since 4 is located 4 units from 0 on the number line.

   b. $\left|-\frac{1}{2}\right| = \frac{1}{2}$ since $-\frac{1}{2}$ is $\frac{1}{2}$ unit from 0 on the number line.

   c. $|1| = 1$ since 1 is 1 unit from 0 on the number line.

   d. $-|6.8| = -6.8$
   The negative sign outside the absolute value bars means to take the opposite of the absolute value of 6.8.

   e. $-|-4| = -4$
   Since $|-4| = 4$, $-|-4| = -4$.

7. a. The opposite of 5.4 is $-5.4$.

   b. The opposite of $-\frac{3}{5}$ is $\frac{3}{5}$.

   c. The opposite of 18 is $-18$.

8. a. $3 \cdot x$ or $3x$

   b. $2x - 5$

   c. $3\frac{5}{8} + x$

   d. $\frac{x}{2}$

   e. $x - 14$

   f. $5(x + 10)$

### Vocabulary and Readiness Check

1. Letters that represent numbers are called <u>variables</u>.

2. Finding the <u>value</u> of an expression means evaluating the expression.

3. The <u>absolute value</u> of a number is that number's distance from 0 on the number line.

4. An <u>expression</u> is formed by numbers and variables connected by operations such as addition, subtraction, multiplication, division, raising to powers, and/or taking roots.

5. The <u>natural numbers</u> are $\{1, 2, 3, ...\}$.

6. The <u>whole numbers</u> are $\{0, 1, 2, 3, ...\}$.

7. The <u>integers</u> are $\{..., -3, -2, -1, 0, 1, 2, 3, ...\}$.

8. The number $\sqrt{5}$ is an <u>irrational number</u>.

9. The number $\frac{5}{7}$ is a <u>rational number</u>.

10. The opposite of $a$ is <u>$-a$</u>.

### Exercise Set 1.2

1. $5x = 5(7) = 35$

1

**3.** $9.8z = 9.8(3.1) = 30.38$

**5.** $ab = \left(\dfrac{1}{2}\right)\left(\dfrac{3}{4}\right) = \dfrac{3}{8}$

**7.** $3x + y = 3(6) + (4) = 18 + 4 = 22$

**9.** $400t = 400(5) = 2000$ miles

**11.** $lw = (5.1)(4) = 20.4$
The display needs 20.4 sq ft of floor space.

**13.** $2948t = 2948(3.6) = \$10{,}612.80$

**15.** $\{1, 2, 3, 4, 5\}$

**17.** $\{11, 12, 13, 14, 15, 16\}$

**19.** $\{0\}$

**21.** $\{0, 2, 4, 6, 8\}$

**23.** 

**25.**

**27.**

**29.** Answers may vary

**31.** $\left\{3, 0, \sqrt{36}\right\}$

**33.** $\left\{3, \sqrt{36}\right\}$

**35.** $\left\{\sqrt{7}\right\}$

**37.** $-11 \in \{x \mid x \text{ is an integer}\}$

**39.** $-6 \notin \{2, 4, 6, ...\}$

**41.** $12 \subseteq \{1, 3, 5, ...\}$

**43.** $\dfrac{1}{2} \notin \{x \mid x \text{ is an irrational number}\}$

**45.** True; every integer is a real number.

**47.** True; $-1$ is an integer.

**49.** False; 0 is not a natural number.

**51.** False; $\sqrt{5}$ is an irrational number.

**53.** True; every natural number is an integer.

**55.** False; the number $\sqrt{7}$, for example, is a real number, but it is not a rational number.

**57.** Answers may vary

**59.** $-|2| = -2$ (the opposite of $|2|$)

**61.** $|-4| = 4$ since $-4$ is located 4 units from 0 on the number line.

**63.** $|0| = 0$ since 0 is located 0 units from 0 on the number line.

**65.** $-|-3| = -3$ (the opposite of $|-3|$)

**67.** Answers may vary

**69.** The opposite of $-6.2$ is $-(-6.2) = 6.2$.

**71.** The opposite of $\dfrac{4}{7}$ is $-\dfrac{4}{7}$.

**73.** The opposite of $-\dfrac{2}{3}$ is $\dfrac{2}{3}$.

**75.** The opposite of 0 is 0.

**77.** $2x$

**79.** $2x + 5$

**81.** $x - 10$

**83.** $x + 2$

**85.** $\dfrac{x}{11}$

**87.** $12 - 3x$

**89.** $x + 2.3$ or $x + 2\dfrac{3}{10}$

**91.** $1\dfrac{1}{3} - x$

**93.** $\dfrac{5}{4 - x}$

**95.** $2(x + 3)$

**97.** The height of the bar representing China is about 137. Therefore, 137 million tourists are predicted for China.

**99.** The height of the bar representing Spain is about 69. Therefore, 69 million tourists are predicted for Spain.

**101.** Answers may vary

## Section 1.3

**Practice Exercises**

**1. a.** $-6 + (-2) = -(6 + 2) = -8$

   **b.** $5 + (-8) = -3$

   **c.** $-4 + 9 = 5$

   **d.** $(-3.2) + (-4.9) = -8.1$

   **e.** $-\dfrac{3}{5} + \dfrac{2}{3} = -\dfrac{9}{15} + \dfrac{10}{15} = \dfrac{1}{15}$

**2. a.** $3 - 11 = 3 + (-11) = -8$

   **b.** $-6 - (-3) = -6 + (3) = -3$

   **c.** $-7 - 5 = -7 + (-5) = -12$

   **d.** $4.2 - (-3.5) = 4.2 + 3.5 = 7.7$

   **e.** $\dfrac{5}{7} - \dfrac{1}{3} = \dfrac{5 \cdot 3}{7 \cdot 3} - \dfrac{1 \cdot 7}{3 \cdot 7} = \dfrac{15}{21} + \left(-\dfrac{7}{21}\right) = \dfrac{8}{21}$

   **f.** $3 - 1.2 = 3 + (-1.2) = 1.8$

   **g.** $2 - 9 = 2 + (-9) = -7$

**3. a.** $13 + 5 - 6 = 18 - 6 = 12$

   **b.** $-6 - 2 + 4 = -8 + 4 = -4$

**4. a.** Since the signs of the two numbers are different or unlike, the product is negative. $(-5)(3) = -15$

   **b.** Since the signs of the two numbers are the same, the product is positive.
$(-7)\left(-\dfrac{1}{14}\right) = \dfrac{7}{14} = \dfrac{1}{2}$

   **c.** $5.1(-2) = -10.2$

   **d.** $14(0) = 0$

   **e.** $\left(-\dfrac{1}{4}\right)\left(\dfrac{8}{13}\right) = -\dfrac{8}{52} = -\dfrac{2}{13}$

   **f.** $6(-1)(-2)(3) = -6(-2)(3) = 12(3) = 36$

   **g.** $5(-2.3) = -11.5$

**5. a.** Since the signs are different or unlike, the quotient is negative.
$\dfrac{-16}{8} = -2$

   **b.** Since the signs are the same, the quotient is positive.
$\dfrac{-15}{-3} = 5$

   **c.** $-\dfrac{2}{3} \div 4 = -\dfrac{2}{3} \cdot \dfrac{1}{4} = -\dfrac{1}{6}$

   **d.** $\dfrac{54}{-9} = -6$

   **e.** $-\dfrac{1}{12} \div \left(-\dfrac{3}{4}\right) = -\dfrac{1}{12} \cdot -\dfrac{4}{3} = \dfrac{1}{9}$

   **f.** $\dfrac{0}{-7} = 0$

**6. a.** $2^3 = 2 \cdot 2 \cdot 2 = 8$

   **b.** $\left(\dfrac{1}{3}\right)^2 = \left(\dfrac{1}{3}\right)\left(\dfrac{1}{3}\right) = \dfrac{1}{9}$

   **c.** $-6^2 = -(6 \cdot 6) = -36$

   **d.** $(-6)^2 = (-6)(-6) = 36$

   **e.** $-4^3 = -(4 \cdot 4 \cdot 4) = -64$

   **f.** $(-4)^3 = (-4)(-4)(-4) = -64$

**7. a.** $\sqrt{49} = 7$ since 7 is positive and $7^2 = 49$.

   **b.** $\sqrt{\dfrac{1}{16}} = \dfrac{1}{4}$ since $\left(\dfrac{1}{4}\right)^2 = \dfrac{1}{16}$.

**c.** $-\sqrt{64} = -8$

**d.** $\sqrt{-64}$ is not a real number.

**e.** $\sqrt{100} = 10$ since $10^2 = 100$.

**8. a.** $\sqrt[3]{64} = 4$ since $4^3 = 64$.

**b.** $\sqrt[5]{-1} = -1$ since $(-1)^5 = -1$.

**c.** $\sqrt[4]{10,000} = 10$ since $10^4 = 10,000$.

**9. a.** $14 - 3 \cdot 4 = 14 - 12 = 2$

**b.** $3(5-8)^2 = 3(-3)^2 = 3(9) = 27$

**c.** $\dfrac{|-5|^2 + 4}{\sqrt{4}-3} = \dfrac{5^2+4}{2-3} = \dfrac{25+4}{-1} = \dfrac{29}{-1} = -29$

**10.** $5 - [(3-5) + 6(2-4)] = 5 - [-2 + 6(-2)]$
$= 5 - [-2 + (-12)]$
$= 5 - [-14]$
$= 5 + 14$
$= 19$

**11.** $\dfrac{-2\sqrt{12+4} - (-3)^2}{6^2 + |1-9|} = \dfrac{-2\sqrt{16} - (-3)^2}{6^2 + |-8|}$
$= \dfrac{-2(4) - 9}{36 + 8}$
$= \dfrac{-8 - 9}{44}$
$= -\dfrac{17}{44}$

**12.** For each expression, replace $x$ with 16 and $y$ with $-5$.

**a.** $2x - 7y = 2(16) - 7(-5) = 32 + 35 = 67$

**b.** $-4y^2 = -4(-5)^2 = -4(25) = -100$

**c.** $\dfrac{\sqrt{x}}{y} - \dfrac{y}{x} = \dfrac{\sqrt{16}}{-5} - \dfrac{-5}{16}$
$= -\dfrac{4}{5} + \dfrac{5}{16}$
$= -\dfrac{4}{5} \cdot \dfrac{16}{16} + \dfrac{5}{16} \cdot \dfrac{5}{5}$
$= -\dfrac{64}{80} + \dfrac{25}{80}$
$= -\dfrac{39}{80}$

**13.** When $x = -5$,
$\dfrac{9}{5}x + 32 = \dfrac{9}{5}(-5) + 32 = -9 + 32 = 23.$
When $x = 10$,
$\dfrac{9}{5}x + 32 = \dfrac{9}{5}(10) + 32 = 18 + 32 = 50.$
When $x = 25$,
$\dfrac{9}{5}x + 32 = \dfrac{9}{5}(25) + 32 = 45 + 32 = 77.$
The completed table is

| Degrees Celsius | $x$ | $-5$ | 10 | 25 |
|---|---|---|---|---|
| Degrees Fahrenheit | $\frac{9}{5}x + 32$ | 23 | 50 | 77 |

**Vocabulary and Readiness Check**

**1.** $-\dfrac{1}{7} = \dfrac{-1}{7} = \dfrac{1}{-7}$; b, c

**2.** $\dfrac{-x}{y} = \dfrac{x}{-y} = -\dfrac{x}{y}$; a, b

**3.** $\dfrac{5}{-(x+y)} = \dfrac{-5}{(x+y)} = -\dfrac{5}{(x+y)}$; b, d

**4.** $-\dfrac{(y+z)}{3y} = \dfrac{-(y+z)}{3y} = \dfrac{(y+z)}{-3y}$; a, d

**5.** $\dfrac{-9x}{-2y} = \dfrac{9x}{2y}$; b

**6.** $\dfrac{-a}{-b} = \dfrac{a}{b}$; a

**7.** $0 \cdot a = \underline{0}$

4

**8.** $\frac{0}{4}$ simplifies to $\underline{0}$ while $\frac{4}{0}$ is <u>undefined</u>.

**9.** The <u>reciprocal</u> of the nonzero number $b$ is $\frac{1}{b}$.

**10.** The fraction $-\frac{a}{b} = \frac{-a}{\underline{b}} = \frac{a}{\underline{-b}}$.

**11.** An <u>exponent</u> is a shorthand notation for repeated multiplication of the same number.

**12.** In $(-5)^2$, the 2 is the <u>exponent</u> and the $-5$ is the <u>base</u>.

**13.** The opposite of squaring a number is taking the <u>square root</u> of a number.

**14.** Using order of operations, $9 \div 3 \cdot 3 = \underline{9}$.

**Exercise Set 1.3**

**1.** $-3 + 8 = 5$

**3.** $-14 + (-10) = -24$

**5.** $-4.3 - 6.7 = -11$

**7.** $13 - 17 = -4$

**9.** $\frac{11}{15} - \left(-\frac{3}{5}\right) = \frac{11}{15} + \frac{9}{15} = \frac{20}{15} = \frac{4}{3}$

**11.** $19 - 10 - 11 = 9 - 11 = -2$

**13.** $-\frac{4}{5} - \left(-\frac{3}{10}\right) = -\frac{4}{5} + \frac{3}{10} = -\frac{8}{10} + \frac{3}{10} = -\frac{5}{10} = -\frac{1}{2}$

**15.** $8 - 14 = -6$

**17.** $-5 \cdot 12 = -60$

**19.** $-7 \cdot 0 = 0$

**21.** $\frac{0}{-2} = 0$

**23.** $\frac{-9}{3} = -3$

**25.** $\frac{-12}{-4} = 3$

**27.** $3\left(-\frac{1}{18}\right) = -\frac{3}{18} = -\frac{1}{6}$

**29.** $(-0.7)(-0.8) = 0.56$

**31.** $9.1 \div -1.3 = \frac{9.1}{1} \cdot \frac{1}{-1.3} = -7$

**33.** Multiplying from left to right gives $(-4)(-2)(-1) = 8(-1) = -8$.

**35.** $-7^2 = -(7 \cdot 7) = -49$

**37.** $(-6)^2 = (-6)(-6) = 36$

**39.** $(-2)^3 = (-2)(-2)(-2) = 4(-2) = -8$

**41.** $\left(-\frac{1}{3}\right)^3 = \left(-\frac{1}{3}\right)\left(-\frac{1}{3}\right)\left(-\frac{1}{3}\right) = -\frac{1}{27}$

**43.** $\sqrt{49} = 7$ since 7 is positive and $7^2 = 49$.

**45.** $-\sqrt{\frac{4}{9}} = -\frac{2}{3}$ since $\left(\frac{2}{3}\right)^2 = \frac{4}{9}$.

**47.** $\sqrt[3]{64} = 4$ since $4^3 = 64$.

**49.** $\sqrt[4]{81} = 3$ since $3^4 = 81$.

**51.** $\sqrt{-100}$ is not a real number.

**53.** $3(5 - 7)^4 = 3(-2)^4 = 3(16) = 48$

**55.** $-3^2 + 2^3 = -9 + 8 = -1$

**57.** $\frac{3.1 - (-1.4)}{-0.5} = \frac{3.1 + 1.4}{-0.5} = \frac{4.5}{-0.5} = -9$

**59.** $(-3)^2 + 2^3 = 9 + 8 = 17$

**61.** $-8 \div 4 \cdot 2 = -2 \cdot 2 = -4$

**63.** $-8\left(-\frac{3}{4}\right) - 8 = 6 - 8 = -2$

**65.** $2 - [(7 - 6) + (9 - 19)] = 2 - [1 + (-10)]$
$= 2 - (-9)$
$= 11$

**67.** $\dfrac{(-9+6)(-1^2)}{-2-2} = \dfrac{(-3)(-1)}{-4} = \dfrac{3}{-4} = -\dfrac{3}{4}$

**69.** $\left(\sqrt[3]{8}\right)(-4) - \left(\sqrt{9}\right)(-5) = (2)(-4) - (3)(-5)$
$$= -8 - (-15)$$
$$= -8 + 15$$
$$= 7$$

**71.** $25 - [(3-5) + (14-18)]^2 = 25 - [(-2) + (-4)]^2$
$$= 25 - (-6)^2$$
$$= 25 - 36$$
$$= -11$$

**73.** $\dfrac{\left(3 - \sqrt{9}\right) - (-5 - 1.3)}{-3} = \dfrac{(3-3) - (-6.3)}{-3}$
$$= \dfrac{0 + 6.3}{-3}$$
$$= \dfrac{6.3}{-3}$$
$$= -2.1$$

**75.** $\dfrac{|3-9| - |-5|}{-3} = \dfrac{6-5}{-3} = \dfrac{1}{-3} = -\dfrac{1}{3}$

**77.** $\dfrac{3(-2+1)}{5} - \dfrac{-7(2-4)}{1-(-2)} = \dfrac{3(-1)}{5} - \dfrac{-7(-2)}{1+2}$
$$= \dfrac{-3}{5} - \dfrac{14}{3}$$
$$= -\dfrac{9}{15} - \dfrac{70}{15}$$
$$= -\dfrac{79}{15}$$

**79.** $\dfrac{\frac{1}{3}\cdot 9 - 7}{3 + \frac{1}{2}\cdot 4} = \dfrac{3-7}{3+2} = \dfrac{-4}{5} = -\dfrac{4}{5}$

**81.** $3\{-2 + 5[1 - 2(-2+5)]\} = 3\{-2 + 5[1 - 2(3)]\}$
$$= 3\{-2 + 5[1-6]\}$$
$$= 3\{-2 + 5[-5]\}$$
$$= 3\{-2 + [-25]\}$$
$$= 3\{-27\}$$
$$= -81$$

**83.** $\dfrac{-4\sqrt{80+1} + (-4)^2}{3^3 + |-2(3)|} = \dfrac{-4\sqrt{81} + (-4)^2}{3^3 + |-6|}$
$$= \dfrac{-4(9) + 16}{27 + 6}$$
$$= \dfrac{-36 + 16}{27 + 6}$$
$$= \dfrac{-20}{33}$$
$$= -\dfrac{20}{33}$$

**85.** Let $x = 9$, $y = -2$.
$$9x - 6y = 9(9) - 6(-2) = 81 + 12 = 93$$

**87.** Let $y = -2$.
$$-3y^2 = -3(-2)^2 = -3(4) = -12$$

**89.** Let $x = 9$, $y = -2$.
$$\dfrac{\sqrt{x}}{y} - \dfrac{y}{x} = \dfrac{\sqrt{9}}{-2} - \dfrac{-2}{9}$$
$$= \dfrac{3}{-2} + \dfrac{2}{9}$$
$$= -\dfrac{27}{18} + \dfrac{4}{18}$$
$$= -\dfrac{23}{18}$$

**91.** Let $x = 9$, $y = -2$.
$$\dfrac{3 + 2|x - y|}{x + 2y} = \dfrac{3 + 2|9 - (-2)|}{9 + 2(-2)}$$
$$= \dfrac{3 + 2|9 + 2|}{9 + 2(-2)}$$
$$= \dfrac{3 + 2|11|}{9 + (-4)}$$
$$= \dfrac{3 + 22}{5}$$
$$= \dfrac{25}{5}$$
$$= 5$$

**93.** Let $x = 9$, $y = -2$.

$$\frac{y^3 + \sqrt{x-5}}{|4x - y|} = \frac{(-2)^3 + \sqrt{9-5}}{|4 \cdot 9 - (-2)|}$$

$$= \frac{-8 + \sqrt{4}}{|36 + 2|}$$

$$= \frac{-8 + 2}{|38|}$$

$$= \frac{-6}{38}$$

$$= -\frac{3}{19}$$

**95. a.**　$y = 5$: $8 + 2y = 8 + 2(5) = 8 + 10 = 18$
　　　$y = 7$: $8 + 2y = 8 + 2(7) = 8 + 14 = 22$
　　　$y = 10$: $8 + 2y = 8 + 2(10) = 8 + 20 = 28$
　　　$y = 100$: $8 + 2y = 8 + 2(100) = 8 + 200 = 208$
　　　The completed table is:

| Length | $y$ | 5 | 7 | 10 | 100 |
|---|---|---|---|---|---|
| Perimeter | $8 + 2y$ | 18 | 22 | 28 | 208 |

**b.**　The perimeter increases as length increases; answers may vary.

**97. a.**　$x = 10$: $\dfrac{100x + 5000}{x} = \dfrac{100(10) + 5000}{10}$

$$= \frac{1000 + 5000}{10}$$

$$= \frac{6000}{10}$$

$$= 600$$

　　　$x = 100$: $\dfrac{100x + 5000}{x} = \dfrac{100(100) + 5000}{100}$

$$= \frac{10,000 + 5000}{100}$$

$$= \frac{15,000}{100}$$

$$= 150$$

　　　$x = 1000$: $\dfrac{100x + 5000}{x} = \dfrac{100(1000) + 5000}{1000}$

$$= \frac{100,000 + 5000}{1000}$$

$$= \frac{105,000}{1000}$$

$$= 105$$

The completed table is:

| Number of Bookshelves | $x$ | 10 | 100 | 1000 |
|---|---|---|---|---|
| Cost per Bookshelf | $\frac{100x+5000}{x}$ | 600 | 150 | 105 |

    **b.** The cost per bookshelf decreases as the number of bookshelves increases; answers may vary.

**99.** Let $x_1 = 2$, $x_2 = 4$, $y_1 = -3$, $y_2 = 2$.
$$\frac{y_2 - y_1}{x_2 - x_1} = \frac{2 - (-3)}{4 - 2} = \frac{2 + 3}{4 - 2} = \frac{5}{2}$$

**101.** $1 - \frac{1}{5} - \frac{3}{7} = \frac{35}{35} - \frac{7}{35} - \frac{15}{35} = \frac{13}{35}$

**103.** $10{,}203 - 5998 = 4205$ meters

**105.** $(2 + 7) \cdot (1 + 3) = 9 \cdot 4 = 36$

**107.** Answers may vary

**109.** $\sqrt{10} \approx 3.1623$

**111.** $\sqrt{7.9} \approx 2.8107$

**113.** $\frac{-1.682 - 17.895}{(-7.102)(-4.691)} \approx -0.5876$

**115.** Look for the bar representing 15 years. Choose the positive number, 15.6%.

**117.** Look for the bar representing 15 years. Find the difference.
$15.6 - (-2.1) = 15.6 + 2.1 = 17.7\%$

**119.** This type of investment is recommended for long term investments. Short term investing appears to be very volatile.

**Integrated Review**

  **1.** Let $z = -4$.
$$z^2 = (-4)^2 = (-4)(-4) = 16$$

  **2.** Let $z = -4$.
$$-z^2 = -(-4)^2 = -(-4)(-4) = -16$$

**3.** Let $x = -1$, $y = 3$, $z = -4$.
$$\frac{4x - z}{2y} = \frac{4(-1) - (-4)}{2(3)} = \frac{-4 + 4}{6} = \frac{0}{6} = 0$$

**4.** Let $x = -1$, $y = 3$, $z = -4$.
$$\begin{aligned} x(y - 2z) &= -1[3 - 2(-4)] \\ &= -1[3 + 8] \\ &= -1[11] \\ &= -11 \end{aligned}$$

**5.** $-7 - (-2) = -7 + 2 = -5$

**6.** $\frac{9}{10} - \frac{11}{12} = \frac{9}{10} \cdot \frac{6}{6} - \frac{11}{12} \cdot \frac{5}{5} = \frac{54}{60} - \frac{55}{60} = -\frac{1}{60}$

**7.** $\frac{-13}{2 - 2} = \frac{-13}{0}$ is undefined.

**8.** $(1.2)^2 - (2.1)^2 = 1.44 - 4.41 = -2.97$

**9.** $\sqrt{64} - \sqrt[3]{64} = 8 - 4 = 4$

**10.** $-5^2 - (-5)^2 = -25 - 25 = -50$

**11.** $\begin{aligned} 9 + 2[(8 - 10)^2 + (-3)^2] &= 9 + 2[(-2)^2 + (-3)^2] \\ &= 9 + 2(4 + 9) \\ &= 9 + 2(13) \\ &= 9 + 26 \\ &= 35 \end{aligned}$

**12.** $\begin{aligned} 8 - 6\left[\sqrt[3]{8}(-2) + \sqrt{4}(-5)\right] &= 8 - 6[2(-2) + 2(-5)] \\ &= 8 - 6[(-4) + (-10)] \\ &= 8 - 6(-14) \\ &= 8 + 84 \\ &= 92 \end{aligned}$

**13.** $-15 - 2x$

**14.** $3x + 5$

**15.** 0 is a whole number that is not a natural number.

**16.** True

**Section 1.4**

**Practice Exercises**

  **1.** $\underbrace{\text{The product of } -4 \text{ and } x}_{-4x} \ \ \underset{=}{\overset{\downarrow}{\text{is}}} \ \ \underset{20}{\overset{\downarrow}{20}}$

**2.** $\underbrace{\text{Three times}}\ \underbrace{\text{the difference of } z \text{ and } 3}\ \underbrace{\text{equals}}\ \underbrace{9.}$

$\quad\quad 3 \quad\quad\quad\quad (z-3) \quad\quad\quad\quad = \quad\quad 9$

**3.** $\underbrace{\text{The sum of } x \text{ and } 5}\ \underbrace{\text{is the same as}}\ \underbrace{3 \text{ less than twice } x.}$

$\quad\quad x+5 \quad\quad\quad\quad = \quad\quad\quad\quad 2x-3$

**4.** $\underbrace{\text{The sum of } y \text{ and } 2}\ \underbrace{\text{is}}\ \underbrace{4 \text{ more than the quotient of } z \text{ and } 8.}$

$\quad\quad y+2 \quad\quad\quad\quad = \quad\quad\quad\quad 4+\dfrac{z}{8}$

**5. a.** $-6 < -5$ since $-6$ lies to the left of $-5$ on the number line.

$$-10\ {-9}\ {-8}\ {-7}\ {-6}\ {-5}\ {-4}\ {-3}\ {-2}\ {-1}\ 0\ 1$$

    **b.** $\dfrac{24}{3} = 8$

    **c.** $0 > -7$ since $0$ lies to the right of $-7$ on the number line.

$$-9\ {-8}\ {-7}\ {-6}\ {-5}\ {-4}\ {-3}\ {-2}\ {-1}\ 0\ 1\ 2$$

    **d.** $2.76 > 2.67$ since $2.76$ lies to the right of $2.67$ on the number line.

$$2.67\quad 2.76$$
$$1\quad\quad 2\quad\quad 3$$

**6. a.** $x - 3 \le 5$

    **b.** $y \ne -4$

    **c.** $2 < 4+\dfrac{1}{2}z$

**7. a.** The opposite of $-7$ is $-(-7) = 7$.

    **b.** The opposite of $4.7$ is $-4.7$.

    **c.** The opposite of $-\dfrac{3}{8}$ is $-\left(-\dfrac{3}{8}\right) = \dfrac{3}{8}$.

**8. a.** The reciprocal of $-\dfrac{5}{3}$ is $-\dfrac{3}{5}$ because $-\dfrac{5}{3}\left(-\dfrac{3}{5}\right) = 1$.

    **b.** The reciprocal of $14$ is $\dfrac{1}{14}$.

    **c.** The reciprocal of $-2$ is $-\dfrac{1}{2}$.

**9.** $8 + 13x = 13x + 8$

**10.** $3 \cdot (11b) = (3 \cdot 11)b = 33b$

**11. a.** $4(x + 5y) = 4 \cdot x + 4 \cdot 5y = 4x + 20y$

**b.** $-(3 - 2z) = -1(3 - 2z)$
$\qquad = -1 \cdot 3 + (-1)(-2z)$
$\qquad = -3 + 2z$

**c.** $0.3x(y - 3) = 0.3x \cdot y - 0.3x \cdot 3$
$\qquad = 0.3xy - 0.9x$

**12. a.** In words:   Value of a dime   ·   number of dimes

                       ↓                  ↓

        Translate:    0.10                $x$       , or $0.10x$

**b.** In words:   number of grams of   ·   number of
                     carbohydrates in one      cookies
                     cookie

                         ↓                  ↓

        Translate:    26                 $y$       , or $26y$

**c.** In words:   cost of one   ·   number of cards
                     birthday card

                       ↓                  ↓

        Translate:    1.75                $z$       , or $1.75z$

**d.** In words:   Discount   ·   purchase price

                       ↓                  ↓

        Translate:    0.15                $t$       , or $0.15t$

**13. a.** If two numbers have a sum of 16 and one number is $x$, the other number is the rest of 16.

       In words:   Sixteen   minus   $x$

                    ↓       ↓    ↓

       Translate:   16       –      $x$

**b.** In words:   One hundred   minus   one angle, $x$
                     eighty

                    ↓         ↓        ↓

       Translate:   180      –      $x$

c. The next consecutive even integer is always two more than the previous even integer.

| In words: | first integer | plus | two |
|---|---|---|---|
| | ↓ | ↓ | ↓ |
| Translate: | $x$ | + | 2 |

d.

| In words: | younger brother's age | plus | nine |
|---|---|---|---|
| | ↓ | ↓ | ↓ |
| Translate: | $x$ | + | 9 |

**14. a.** $6ab - ab = 6ab - 1ab = (6-1)ab = 5ab$

**b.** $4x - 5 + 6x = 4x + 6x - 5$
$= (4+6)x - 5$
$= 10x - 5$

**c.** $17p - 9$ cannot be simplified further since $17p$ and $-9$ are not like terms.

**15. a.** $5pq - 2pq - 11 - 4pq + 18$
$= 5pq - 2pq - 4pq - 11 + 18$
$= (5 - 2 - 4)pq + (-11 + 18)$
$= -1pq + (7)$
$= -pq + 7$

**b.** $3x^2 + 7 - 2(x^2 - 6) = 3x^2 + 7 - 2x^2 + 12$
$= 3x^2 - 2x^2 + 7 + 12$
$= x^2 + 19$

**c.** $(3.7x + 2.5) - (-2.1x - 1.3)$
$= 3.7x + 2.5 + 2.1x + 1.3$
$= 3.7x + 2.1x + 2.5 + 1.3$
$= 5.8x + 3.8$

**d.** $\dfrac{1}{5}(15c - 25d) - \dfrac{1}{2}(8c + 6d + 1) + \dfrac{3}{4}$
$= 3c - 5d - 4c - 3d - \dfrac{1}{2} + \dfrac{3}{4}$
$= -c - 8d + \dfrac{1}{4}$

**Vocabulary and Readiness Check**

| | Symbol | Meaning |
|---|---|---|
| **1.** | < | is less than |
| **2.** | > | is greater than |
| **3.** | ≠ | is not equal to |
| **4.** | = | is equal to |
| **5.** | ≥ | is greater than or equal to |
| **6.** | ≤ | is less than or equal to |

**7.** The opposite of nonzero number $a$ is $\underline{-a}$.

**8.** The reciprocal of nonzero number $a$ is $\underline{\dfrac{1}{a}}$.

**9.** The <u>commutative</u> property has to do with "order."

**10.** The <u>associative</u> property has to do with "grouping."

**11.** $a(b + c) = ab + ac$ illustrates the <u>distributive</u> property.

**12.** Terms with the same variable(s) raised to the same powers are called <u>like</u> terms.

**13.** The <u>terms</u> of an expression are the addends of the expression.

**14.** The process of adding or subtracting like terms is called <u>combining</u> like terms.

**Exercise Set 1.4**

**1.** The sum of 10 and $x$ is −12.
$10 + x$ = −12
or $10 + x = -12$

**3.** Twice $x$ plus 5 is the same as −14.
$2x + 5$ = −14
or $2x + 5 = -14$

5. The quotient of $n$ and 5 is 4 times $n$.

$$\frac{n}{5} \quad = \quad 4n$$

or $\frac{n}{5} = 4n$

7. The difference of $z$ and one-half is the same as the product of $z$ and one-half.

$$z - \frac{1}{2} \qquad = \qquad \frac{1}{2}z$$

or $z - \frac{1}{2} = \frac{1}{2}z$

9. The product of 7 and $x$ is less than or equal to $-21$.

$$7x \qquad \leq \qquad -21$$

or $7x \leq -21$

11. Twice the difference of $x$ and 6 is greater than the reciprocal of 11.

$$2(x-6) \qquad > \qquad \frac{1}{11}$$

or $2(x-6) > \frac{1}{11}$

13. Twice the difference of $x$ and 6 is $-27$.

$$2(x-6) \qquad = -27$$

or $2(x-6) = -27$

15. $-16 > -17$ since $-16$ is to the right of $-17$ on the number line.

17. $7.4 = 7.40$

19. $\frac{7}{11} < \frac{9}{11}$ since $7 < 9$.

21. $\frac{1}{2} < \frac{5}{8}$ since $\frac{1}{2}$ is to the left of $\frac{5}{8}$ on the number line.

23. $-7.9 < -7.09$ since $-7.9$ is to the left of $-7.09$ on the number line.

|  | Number | Opposite | Reciprocal |
|---|---|---|---|
| **25.** | 5 | –5 | $\frac{1}{5}$ |
| **27.** | –8 | 8 | $-\frac{1}{8}$ |
| **29.** | $-\frac{1}{7}$ | $\frac{1}{7}$ | –7 |
| **31.** | 0 | 0 | Undefined |
| **33.** | $\frac{7}{8}$ | $-\frac{7}{8}$ | $\frac{8}{7}$ |

**35.** Zero; for every real number $x$, $0 \cdot x \neq 1$, so 0 has no reciprocal. It is the only real number that has no reciprocal because if $x \neq 0$, then $x \cdot \dfrac{1}{x} = 1$ by definition.

**37.** $7x + y = y + 7x$

**39.** $z \cdot w = w \cdot z$

**41.** $\dfrac{1}{3} \cdot \dfrac{x}{5} = \dfrac{x}{5} \cdot \dfrac{1}{3}$

**43.** No, subtraction is not commutative. Answers may vary (for example, $8 - 5 \neq 5 - 8$).

**45.** $5 \cdot (7x) = (5 \cdot 7)x$

**47.** $(x + 1.2) + y = x + (1.2 + y)$

**49.** $(14z) \cdot y = 14(z \cdot y)$

**51.** $12 - (5 - 3) = 10$; $(12 - 5) - 3 = 4$; subtraction is not associative.

**53.** $3(x + 5) = 3 \cdot x + 3 \cdot 5 = 3x + 15$

**55.** $-(2a + b) = -1(2a + b)$
$= -1 \cdot 2a + (-1) \cdot b$
$= -2a - b$

**57.** $2(6x + 5y + 2z) = 2 \cdot 6x + 2 \cdot 5y + 2 \cdot 2z$
$= 12x + 10y + 4z$

**59.** $-4(x - 2y + 7) = -4 \cdot x + (-4)(-2y) + (-4)(7)$
$= -4x + 8y - 28$

**61.** $0.5x(6y - 3) = 0.5x \cdot 6y - 0.5x \cdot 3 = 3xy - 1.5x$

**63.** $3x + 6 = 6 + 3x$

**65.** $\dfrac{2}{3} + \left(-\dfrac{2}{3}\right) = 0$

**67.** $7 \cdot 1 = 7$

**69.** $10(2y) = (10 \cdot 2)y$

**71.** $a(b + c) = ab + ac$

**73.** In words: $\boxed{\text{Value of a dime}} \cdot \boxed{\text{Number of dimes}}$
Translate: $0.1 \cdot d$ or $0.1d$

**75.** If two numbers have a sum of 112 and one number is $x$, then the other number is the "rest of 112." So, in other words, we have
$\boxed{\text{One hundred twelve}} - \boxed{x}$
Translate: $112 - x$

**77.** In words: $\boxed{\text{Ninety}} - \boxed{5x}$
Translate: $90 - 5x$

**79.** In words: $\boxed{\text{Cost of a book}} \cdot \boxed{\text{Number of books}}$
Translate: $\$35.61y$

**81.** The next even integer would be 2 more than the given even integer. In words:
$\boxed{\text{Even integer}} + \boxed{\text{Two}}$
Translate: $2x + 2$

**83.** $5y - 14 + 7y - 20y = 5y + 7y - 20y - 14$
$= (5 + 7 - 20)y - 14$
$= -8y - 14$

**85.** $-11c - (4 - 2c) = -11c - 4 + 2c$
$= -11c + 2c - 4$
$= (-11 + 2)c - 4$
$= -9c - 4$

**87.** $(8 - 5y) - (4 + 3y) = 8 - 5y - 4 - 3y$
$= -5y - 3y + 8 - 4$
$= (-5 - 3)y + 4$
$= -8y + 4$ or $4 - 8y$

**89.** $-4(yz + 3) - 7yz + 1 + y^2$
$= -4yz - 12 - 7yz + 1 + y^2$
$= y^2 - 4yz - 7yz - 11$
$= y^2 + (-4 - 7)yz - 11$
$= y^2 - 11yz - 11$

**91.** $-(8-t)+(2t-6) = -8+t+2t-6$
$$= t+2t-8-6$$
$$= (1+2)t-14$$
$$= 3t-14$$

**93.** $5(2z^3-6)+10(3-z^3) = 10z^3-30+30-10z^3$
$$= 10z^3-10z^3-30+30$$
$$= (10-10)z^3+0$$
$$= 0$$

**95.** $7n+3(2n-6)-2 = 7n+6n-18-2$
$$= (7+6)n-20$$
$$= 13n-20$$

**97.** $6.3y-9.7+2.2y-11.1 = 6.3y+2.2y-9.7-11.1$
$$= (6.3+2.2)y-20.8$$
$$= 8.5y-20.8$$

**99.** $\dfrac{7}{8}a-\dfrac{11}{12}-\dfrac{1}{2}a+\dfrac{5}{6} = \dfrac{7}{8}a-\dfrac{1}{2}a-\dfrac{11}{12}+\dfrac{5}{6}$
$$= \left(\dfrac{7}{8}-\dfrac{1}{2}\right)a-\dfrac{11}{12}+\dfrac{10}{12}$$
$$= \left(\dfrac{7}{8}-\dfrac{4}{8}\right)a-\dfrac{1}{12}$$
$$= \dfrac{3}{8}a-\dfrac{1}{12}$$

**101.** $4(5y+12) = 20y+48$

**103.** $\dfrac{1}{2}(10x-2)-\dfrac{1}{6}(60x-5y) = 5x-1-10x+\dfrac{5}{6}y$
$$= 5x-10x+\dfrac{5}{6}y-1$$
$$= -5x+\dfrac{5}{6}y-1$$

**105.** $\dfrac{1}{3}(6x-33y)-\dfrac{1}{8}(24x-40y+1)-\dfrac{1}{3}$
$$= 2x-11y-3x+5y-\dfrac{1}{8}-\dfrac{1}{3}$$
$$= 2x-3x-11y+5y-\dfrac{3}{24}-\dfrac{8}{24}$$
$$= (2-3)x+(-11+5)y-\dfrac{11}{24}$$
$$= -x-6y-\dfrac{11}{24}$$

**107.** $5(7y) = (5\cdot 7)y$

**109.** $6.5y-4.4(1.8x-3.3)+10.95$
$$= 6.5y-7.92x+14.52+10.95$$
$$= 6.5y-7.92x+25.47$$

**111.** It is not the case that two rectangles with the same perimeter will necessarily have the same area. Take a rectangle that is 5 in. by 5 in. and another that is 8 in. by 2 in. Both have the same perimeter, but the areas are 25 square inches and 16 square inches, respectively.

**113.** Locate 2050 on the 'Year' axis. Travel up vertically until you hit the line. Travel left horizontally until you hit the 'Population'-axis. Read the value. The predicted population over 65 in 2050 is 80 million.

**115.** Locate 2000 on the 'Year'-axis. Travel up vertically until you hit the line. Travel left horizontally until you hit the 'Population'-axis. Read the value. The population over 65 in 2000 was 35 million.

**117.** $(2.5)(8.1\%) = 20.25\%$

**Chapter 1 Vocabulary Check**

1. An <u>algebraic expression</u> is formed by numbers and variables connected by the operations of addition, subtraction, multiplication, division, raising to powers, and/or taking roots.

2. The <u>opposite</u> of a number $a$ is $-a$.

3. $3(x-6) = 3x-18$ by the <u>distributive</u> property.

4. The <u>absolute value</u> of a number is the distance between the number and 0 on the number line.

5. An <u>exponent</u> is a shorthand notation for repeated multiplication of the same factor.

6. A letter that represents a number is called a <u>variable</u>.

7. The symbols $<$ and $>$ are called <u>inequality</u> symbols.

8. If $a$ is not 0, then $a$ and $\dfrac{1}{a}$ are called <u>reciprocals</u>.

9. $A+B = B+A$ by the <u>commutative</u> property.

10. $(A+B)+C = A+(B+C)$ by the <u>associative</u> property.

**11.** The numbers 0, 1, 2, 3, ... are called <u>whole</u> numbers.

**12.** If a number corresponds to a point on the number line, we know that number is a <u>real</u> number.

## Chapter 1 Review

**1.** $7x = 7(3) = 21$

**2.** $st = (1.6)(5) = 8$

**3.** One hour is $60(60) = 3600$ seconds.
$90t = 90(3600) = 324{,}000$
324,000 wing beats per hour.

**4.** $\{x|x$ is an odd integer between $-2$ and $4\}$
$= \{-1, 1, 3\}$

**5.** $\{x|x$ is an even integer between $-3$ and $7\}$
$= \{-2, 0, 2, 4, 6\}$

**6.** There are no whole numbers that are negative.
$\varnothing$

**7.** All natural numbers are rational numbers.
$\varnothing$

**8.** $\{x|x$ is a whole number greater than 5$\}$
$= \{6, 7, 8, ...\}$

**9.** $\{x|x$ is an integer less than 3$\} = \{..., -1, 0, 1, 2\}$

**10.** Since $D = \{2, 4, 6, 8, 10, ..., 16\}$, $10 \in D$ is true.

**11.** Since $B = \{5, 9, 11\}$, $B \in 9$ is false.

**12.** $\sqrt{169} = 13$, which is a rational number. So $\sqrt{169} \notin G$ is true.

**13.** Since $F = \{\ \ \}$ and 0 is not an element of the empty set, then $0 \notin F$ is true.

**14.** Since $E = \{x|x$ is a rational number$\}$ and $\pi$ is irrational, then $\pi \in E$ is false.

**15.** Since $H = \{x|x$ is a real number$\}$ and $\pi$ is a real number, then $\pi \in H$ is true.

**16.** Since $\sqrt{4} = 2$ and $G = \{x|x$ is an irrational number$\}$, and 2 is a rational number, then $\sqrt{4} \in G$ is false.

**17.** Since $E = \{x|x$ is a rational number$\}$ and $-9$ is a rational number, then $-9 \in E$ is true.

**18.** Since $A = \{6, 10, 12\}$ and $D = \{2, 4, 6, 8, 10, 12, 14, 16\}$, then $A \subseteq D$ is true.

**19.** Since $C = \{..., -3, -2, -1, 0, 1, 2, 3, ...\}$ and $B = \{5, 9, 11\}$, then $C \not\subseteq B$ is true.

**20.** Since $C = \{..., -3, -2, -1, 0, 1, 2, 3, ...\}$ and $E = \{x|x$ is a rational number$\}$, and all integers are rational numbers, then $C \not\subseteq E$ is false.

**21.** Since $F = \{\ \ \}$ and $H = \{x|x$ is a real number$\}$, and the empty set is a subset of all sets, then $F \subseteq H$ is true.

**22.** A set is always a subset of itself, so $B \subseteq B$ is true.

**23.** $D = \{2, 4, 6, ..., 16\}$ and
$C = \{..., -3, -2, -1, 0, 1, 2, 3, ...\}$
Every element of $D$ is also an element of $C$, so $D \subseteq C$ is true.

**24.** $C = \{..., -3, -2, -1, 0, 1, 2, 3, ...\}$ and $H = \{x|x$ is a real number$\}$.
Every integer is a real number, so $C \subseteq H$ is true.

**25.** $G = \{x|x$ is an irrational number$\}$ and $H = \{x|x$ is a real number$\}$
Every irrational number is also a real number, so $G \subseteq H$ is true.

**26.** Since $B = \{5, 9, 11\}$, and $B$ does not contain the set $\{5\}$, then $\{5\} \in B$ is false.

**27.** Since $B = \{5, 9, 11\}$, and $\{5\}$ is a subset of $B$, then $\{5\} \subseteq B$ is true.

**28.** Whole numbers: $\left\{5, \dfrac{8}{2}, \sqrt{9}\right\}$

**29.** Natural numbers: $\left\{5, \dfrac{8}{2}, \sqrt{9}\right\}$

**30.** Rational numbers: $\left\{5, -\dfrac{2}{3}, \dfrac{8}{2}, \sqrt{9}, 0.3, 1\dfrac{5}{8}, -1\right\}$

**31.** Irrational numbers: $\left\{\sqrt{7}, \pi\right\}$

**32.** Real numbers:
$$\left\{5, -\frac{2}{3}, \frac{8}{2}, \sqrt{9}, 0.3, \sqrt{7}, 1\frac{5}{8}, -1, \pi\right\}$$

**33.** Integers: $\left\{5, \frac{8}{2}, \sqrt{9}, -1\right\}$

**34.** The opposite of $-\frac{3}{4}$ is $-\left(-\frac{3}{4}\right) = \frac{3}{4}$.

**35.** The opposite of 0.6 is –0.6.

**36.** The opposite of 0 is –0 = 0.

**37.** The opposite of 1 is –1.

**38.** The reciprocal of $-\frac{3}{4}$ is $\dfrac{1}{\left(-\frac{3}{4}\right)} = -\frac{4}{3}$.

**39.** The reciprocal of 0.6 is $\dfrac{1}{0.6}$.

**40.** The reciprocal of 0 is $\dfrac{1}{0}$ which is undefined.

**41.** The reciprocal of 1 is $\dfrac{1}{1} = 1$.

**42.** $-7 + 3 = -4$

**43.** $-10 + (-25) = -35$

**44.** $5(-0.4) = -2$

**45.** $(-3.1)(-0.1) = 0.31$

**46.** $-7 - (-15) = -7 + 15 = 8$

**47.** $9 - (-4.3) = 9 + 4.3 = 13.3$

**48.** $(-6)(-4)(0)(-3) = 0$

**49.** $(-12)(0)(-1)(-5) = 0$

**50.** $(-24) \div 0$ is undefined.

**51.** $0 \div (-45) = 0$

**52.** $(-36) \div (-9) = 4$

**53.** $60 \div (-12) = -5$

**54.** $\left(-\frac{4}{5}\right) - \left(-\frac{2}{3}\right) = -\frac{4}{5} + \frac{2}{3} = -\frac{12}{15} + \frac{10}{15} = -\frac{2}{15}$

**55.** $\left(\frac{5}{4}\right) - \left(-2\frac{3}{4}\right) = \frac{5}{4} + \frac{11}{4} = \frac{16}{4} = 4$

**56.** $1 - \frac{1}{4} - \frac{1}{3} = \frac{12}{12} - \frac{3}{12} - \frac{4}{12} = \frac{5}{12}$

**57.** $-5 + 7 - 3 - (-10) = 2 - 3 + 10 = -1 + 10 = 9$

**58.** $8 - (-3) + (-4) + 6 = 8 + 3 - 4 + 6$
$$= 11 - 4 + 6$$
$$= 7 + 6$$
$$= 13$$

**59.** $3(4 - 5)^4 = 3(-1)^4 = 3(1) = 3$

**60.** $6(7 - 10)^2 = 6(-3)^2 = 6(9) = 54$

**61.** $\left(-\frac{8}{15}\right) \cdot \left(-\frac{2}{3}\right)^2 = -\frac{8}{15} \cdot \frac{4}{9} = -\frac{32}{135}$

**62.** $\left(-\frac{3}{4}\right)^2 \cdot \left(-\frac{10}{21}\right) = \left(\frac{9}{16}\right)\left(-\frac{10}{21}\right) = -\frac{15}{56}$

**63.** $\dfrac{-\frac{6}{15}}{\frac{8}{25}} = -\frac{6}{15} \div \frac{8}{25} = -\frac{6}{15} \cdot \frac{25}{8} = -\frac{150}{120} = -\frac{5}{4}$

**64.** $\dfrac{\frac{4}{9}}{-\frac{8}{45}} = \frac{4}{9} \div \left(-\frac{8}{45}\right) = \frac{4}{9} \cdot \left(-\frac{45}{8}\right) = -\frac{180}{72} = -\frac{5}{2}$

**65.** $-\frac{3}{8} + 3(2) \div 6 = -\frac{3}{8} + 6 \div 6 = -\frac{3}{8} + 1 = -\frac{3}{8} + \frac{8}{8} = \frac{5}{8}$

**66.** $5(-2) - (-3) - \frac{1}{6} + \frac{2}{3} = -10 + 3 - \frac{1}{6} + \frac{2}{3}$
$$= -7 - \frac{1}{6} + \frac{2}{3}$$
$$= -\frac{42}{6} - \frac{1}{6} + \frac{4}{6}$$
$$= -\frac{39}{6}$$
$$= -6\frac{1}{2}$$

**67.** $\left| 2^3 - 3^2 \right| - \left| 5 - 7 \right| = \left| 8 - 9 \right| - \left| -2 \right|$
$$= \left| -1 \right| - 2$$
$$= 1 - 2$$
$$= -1$$

**68.** $\left| 5^2 - 2^2 \right| + \left| 9 \div (-3) \right| = \left| 25 - 4 \right| + \left| -3 \right|$
$$= \left| 21 \right| + 3$$
$$= 21 + 3$$
$$= 24$$

**69.** $(2^3 - 3^2) - (5 - 7) = (8 - 9) - (-2) = -1 + 2 = 1$

**70.** $(5^2 - 2^4) + [9 \div (-3)] = (25 - 16) + (-3)$
$$= 9 + (-3)$$
$$= 6$$

**71.** $\dfrac{(8-10)^3 - (-4)^2}{2 + 8(2) \div 4} = \dfrac{(-2)^3 - 16}{2 + 16 \div 4}$
$$= \dfrac{-8 - 16}{2 + 4}$$
$$= \dfrac{-24}{6}$$
$$= -4$$

**72.** $\dfrac{(2+4)^2 + (-1)^5}{12 \div 2 \cdot 3 - 3} = \dfrac{(6)^2 + (-1)}{6 \cdot 3 - 3}$
$$= \dfrac{36 - 1}{18 - 3}$$
$$= \dfrac{35}{15}$$
$$= \dfrac{7}{3}$$

**73.** $\dfrac{(4-9) + 4 - 9}{10 - 12 \div 4 \cdot 8} = \dfrac{(-5) + 4 - 9}{10 - 3 \cdot 8}$
$$= \dfrac{-1 - 9}{10 - 24}$$
$$= \dfrac{-10}{-14}$$
$$= \dfrac{5}{7}$$

**74.** $\dfrac{3 - 7 - (7 - 3)}{15 + 30 \div 6 \cdot 2} = \dfrac{-4 - (4)}{15 + 5 \cdot 2} = \dfrac{-8}{15 + 10} = \dfrac{-8}{25} = -\dfrac{8}{25}$

**75.** $\dfrac{\sqrt{25}}{4 + 3 \cdot 7} = \dfrac{5}{4 + 21} = \dfrac{5}{25} = \dfrac{1}{5}$

**76.** $\dfrac{\sqrt{64}}{24 - 8 \cdot 2} = \dfrac{8}{24 - 16} = \dfrac{8}{8} = 1$

**77.** Let $x = 0$, $y = 3$, $z = -2$.
$$x^2 - y^2 + z^2 = (0)^2 - (3)^2 + (-2)^2$$
$$= 0 - 9 + 4$$
$$= -5$$

**78.** Let $x = 0$, $y = 3$, $z = -2$.
$$\dfrac{5x + z}{2y} = \dfrac{5(0) + (-2)}{2(3)} = \dfrac{0 - 2}{6} = \dfrac{-2}{6} = -\dfrac{1}{3}$$

**79.** Let $y = 3$, $z = -2$.
$$\dfrac{-7y - 3z}{-3} = \dfrac{-7(3) - 3(-2)}{-3} = \dfrac{-21 + 6}{-3} = \dfrac{-15}{-3} = 5$$

**80.** Let $x = 0$, $y = 3$, $z = -2$.
$$(x - y + z)^2 = (0 - 3 + (-2))^2$$
$$= (-3 - 2)^2$$
$$= (-5)^2$$
$$= 25$$

**81. a.** When $r = 1$, $2\pi r = 2\pi(1) = 2(3.14) = 6.28$.
When $r = 10$,
$2\pi r = 2\pi(10) = 20(3.14) = 62.8$.
When $r = 100$,
$2\pi r = 2\pi(100) = 200(3.14) = 628$.

| $r$ | 1 | 10 | 100 |
|---|---|---|---|
| $2\pi r$ | 6.28 | 62.8 | 628 |

**b.** As the radius increases, the circumference increases.

**82.** $5xy - 7xy + 3 - 2 + xy = 5xy - 7xy + xy + 3 - 2$
$$= (5 - 7 + 1)xy + (3 - 2)$$
$$= (-1)xy + 1$$
$$= -xy + 1$$

**83.** $4x + 10x - 19x + 10 - 19$
$$= (4 + 10 - 19)x + (10 - 19)$$
$$= -5x + (-9)$$
$$= -5x - 9$$

**84.**  $6x^2 + 2 - 4(x^2 + 1) = 6x^2 + 2 - 4x^2 - 4$
$$= 6x^2 - 4x^2 + 2 - 4$$
$$= (6 - 4)x^2 + (2 - 4)$$
$$= 2x^2 + (-2)$$
$$= 2x^2 - 2$$

**85.**  $-7(2x^2 - 1) - x^2 - 1 = -14x^2 + 7 - x^2 - 1$
$$= -14x^2 - x^2 + 7 - 1$$
$$= (-14 - 1)x^2 + (7 - 1)$$
$$= -15x^2 + 6$$

**86.**  $(3.2x - 1.5) - (4.3x - 1.2) = 3.2x - 1.5 - 4.3x + 1.2$
$$= 3.2x - 4.3x - 1.5 + 1.2$$
$$= (3.2 - 4.3)x - 0.3$$
$$= -1.1x - 0.3$$

**87.**  $(7.6x + 4.7) - (1.9x + 3.6) = 7.6x + 4.7 - 1.9x - 3.6$
$$= 7.6x - 1.9x + 4.7 - 3.6$$
$$= (7.6 - 1.9)x + 4.7 - 3.6$$
$$= 5.7x + 1.1$$

**88.**  Twelve is the product of $x$ and negative 4.

   $12 \quad = \qquad\qquad -4x$

   or $12 = -4x$

**89.**  The sum of $n$ and twice $n$ is negative fifteen.

   $n + 2n \qquad = \qquad -15$

**90.**  Four times the sum of $y$ and three is $-1$.

   $4 \quad \cdot \qquad (y + 3) \qquad = -1$

   or $4(y + 3) = -1$

**91.**  The difference of $t$ and 5, multiplied by six is four.

   $(t - 5) \qquad\qquad \cdot \qquad 6 = 4$

   or $6(t - 5) = 4$

**92.**  Seven subtracted from $z$ is six.

   $z - 7 \qquad = 6$

   or $z - 7 = 6$

**93.**  Ten less than the product of $x$ and nine is five.

   $9x - 10 \qquad\qquad = 5$

   or $9x - 10 = 5$

**94.** $\underbrace{\text{The difference of } x \text{ and 5}}\ \underbrace{\text{is at least}}\ \underset{\downarrow}{12}\ .$

$\qquad\quad x-5 \qquad\qquad\quad \geq \quad\ \ 12$

or $x - 5 \geq 12$

**95.** $\underbrace{\text{The opposite of four}}\ \underbrace{\text{is less than}}\ \underbrace{\text{the product of } y \text{ and seven}}\ .$

$\qquad\quad -4 \qquad\qquad\quad < \qquad\qquad 7y$

or $-4 < 7y$

**96.** $\underbrace{\text{Two-thirds}}\ \underbrace{\text{is not equal to}}\ \underbrace{\text{twice}}\ \underbrace{\text{the sum of } n \text{ and one-fourth}}\ .$

$\qquad \dfrac{2}{3} \qquad\quad \neq \qquad 2\cdot \qquad \left(n+\dfrac{1}{4}\right)$

or $\dfrac{2}{3} \neq 2\left(n+\dfrac{1}{4}\right)$

**97.** $\underbrace{\text{The sum of } t \text{ and six}}\ \underbrace{\text{is not more than}}\ \underbrace{\text{negative twelve}}\ .$

$\qquad\quad t+6 \qquad\qquad \leq \qquad\qquad -12$

or $t + 6 \leq -12$

**98.** $(M + 5) + P = M + (5 + P)$: Associative Property of Addition

**99.** $5(3x - 4) = 15x - 20$: Distributive Property

**100.** $(-4) + 4 = 0$: Additive Inverse Property

**101.** $(3 + x) + 7 = 7 + (3 + x)$: Commutative Property of Addition

**102.** Associative and Commutative Properties of Multiplication
To see this: $(XY)Z = X(YZ) = (YZ)X$

**103.** $\left(-\dfrac{3}{5}\right)\cdot\left(-\dfrac{5}{3}\right) = 1$: Multiplicative Inverse Property

**104.** $T \cdot 0 = 0$: Multiplication Property of Zero

**105.** $(ab)c = a(bc)$: Associative Property of Multiplication

**106.** $A + 0 = A$: Additive Identity Property

**107.** $8 \cdot 1 = 8$: Multiplicative Identity Property

**108.** $5x - 15z = 5(x - 3z)$

**109.** $(7 + y) + (3 + x) = (3 + x) + (7 + y)$

**110.** $0 = 2 + (-2)$, for example

**111.** $1 = 2 \cdot \dfrac{1}{2}$, for example

**112.** $[(3.4)(0.7)]5=(3.4)[(0.7)(5)]$

**113.** $7 = 7 + 0$

**114.** $-9 > -12$, since $-9$ is to the right of $-12$ on the number line.

**115.** $0 > -6$, since $0$ is to the right of $-6$ on the number line.

**116.** $-3 < -1$, since $-3$ is to the left of $-1$ on the number line.

**117.** $7 = |-7|$

**118.** $-5 < -(-5)$, since $-(-5) = 5$.

**119.** $-(-2) > -2$, since $-(-2) = 2$.

**120.** The opposite of $-\dfrac{3}{4}$ is $\dfrac{3}{4}$.

The reciprocal of $-\dfrac{3}{4}$ is $-\dfrac{4}{3}$.

**121.** If the opposite of the number is $-5$, then the number is $-(-5) = 5$. The reciprocal of 5 is $\dfrac{1}{5}$.

**122.** 
$$-2\left(5x + \frac{1}{2}\right) + 7.1 = -2 \cdot 5x + (-2) \cdot \frac{1}{2} + 7.1$$
$$= -10x - 1 + 7.1$$
$$= -10x + 6.1$$

**123.** $\sqrt{36} \div 2 \cdot 3 = 6 \div 2 \cdot 3 = 3 \cdot 3 = 9$

**124.** $-\dfrac{7}{11} - \left(-\dfrac{1}{11}\right) = -\dfrac{7}{11} + \dfrac{1}{11} = -\dfrac{6}{11}$

**125.** 
$$10 - (-1) + (-2) + 6 = 10 + 1 + (-2) + 6$$
$$= 11 + (-2) + 6$$
$$= 9 + 6$$
$$= 15$$

**126.** 
$$\left(-\frac{2}{3}\right)^3 \div \frac{10}{9} = -\frac{8}{27} \div \frac{10}{9}$$
$$= -\frac{8}{27} \cdot \frac{9}{10}$$
$$= -\frac{2 \cdot 4 \cdot 9}{3 \cdot 9 \cdot 2 \cdot 5}$$
$$= -\frac{4}{15}$$

**127.** 
$$\frac{(3-5)^2 + (-1)^3}{1 + 2(3 - (-1))^2} = \frac{(-2)^2 + (-1)^3}{1 + 2(3+1)^2}$$
$$= \frac{4 + (-1)}{1 + 2(4)^2}$$
$$= \frac{3}{1 + 2(16)}$$
$$= \frac{3}{1 + 32}$$
$$= \frac{3}{33}$$
$$= \frac{1}{11}$$

**128.** 
$$\frac{1}{3}(9x - 3y) - (4x - 1) + 4y$$
$$= \frac{1}{3} \cdot 9x - \frac{1}{3} \cdot 3y - 4x + 1 + 4y$$
$$= 3x - y - 4x + 1 + 4y$$
$$= 3x - 4x - y + 4y + 1$$
$$= -x + 3y + 1$$

**129.** 1976: $76.8 - 75 = 1.8$
1981: $77.8 - 76.8 = 1.0$
1986: $78.2 - 77.8 = 0.4$
1991: $78.9 - 78.2 = 0.7$
1996: $79.1 - 78.9 = 0.2$
2001: $79.8 - 79.1 = 0.7$
2006: $80.8 - 79.8 = 1.0$

| Year | Increase in Life Expectancy (in Years) from 5 Years Earlier |
|------|------------------------------------------------------------|
| 1976 | 1.8 |
| 1981 | 1.0 |
| 1986 | 0.4 |
| 1991 | 0.7 |
| 1996 | 0.2 |
| 2001 | 0.7 |
| 2006 | 1.0 |

**Chapter 1 Test**

**1.** True; $-2.3$ lies to the right of $-2.33$ on the number line.

**2.** False; $-6^2 = -36$, while $(-6)^2 = 36$.

**3.** False; $-5 - 8 = -13$, while $-(5 - 8) = -(-3) = 3$.

**4.** False; $(-2)(-3)(0) = 0$, while $\dfrac{(-4)}{0}$ is undefined.

**5.** True

**6.** False; for example, $\dfrac{1}{2}$ is a rational number that is not an integer.

**7.** $5 - 12 \div 3(2) = 5 - 4(2) = 5 - 8 = -3$

**8.** $5^2 - 3^4 = 25 - 81 = -56$

**9.**
$$(4-9)^3 - |-4-6|^2 = (-5)^3 - |-10|^2$$
$$= -125 - 10^2$$
$$= -125 - 100$$
$$= -225$$

**10.**
$$12 + \{6 - [5 - 2(-5)]\} = 12 + \{6 - [5 + 10]\}$$
$$= 12 + (6 - 15)$$
$$= 12 + (-9)$$
$$= 12 - 9$$
$$= 3$$

**11.**
$$\frac{6(7-9)^3 + (-2)}{(-2)(-5)(-5)} = \frac{6(-2)^3 - 2}{10(-5)}$$
$$= \frac{6(-8) - 2}{-50}$$
$$= \frac{-48 - 2}{-50}$$
$$= \frac{-50}{-50}$$
$$= 1$$

**12.**
$$\frac{\left(4 - \sqrt{16}\right) - (-7 - 20)}{-2(1-4)^2} = \frac{(4-4) - (-27)}{-2(-3)^2}$$
$$= \frac{0 + 27}{-2(9)}$$
$$= \frac{27}{-18}$$
$$= -\frac{3}{2}$$

**13.** Let $q = 4$ and $r = -2$.
$$q^2 - r^2 = (4)^2 - (-2)^2 = 16 - 4 = 12$$

**14.** Let $q = 4$, $r = -2$, and $t = 1$.
$$\frac{5t - 3q}{3r - 1} = \frac{5(1) - 3(4)}{3(-2) - 1} = \frac{5 - 12}{-6 - 1} = \frac{-7}{-7} = 1$$

**15. a.** When $x = 1$, $5.75x = 5.75(1) = 5.75$.
When $x = 3$, $5.75x = 5.75(3) = 17.25$.
When $x = 10$, $5.75x = 5.75(10) = 57.50$.
When $x = 20$, $5.75x = 5.75(20) = 115.00$.

| $x$ | 1 | 3 | 10 | 20 |
|---|---|---|---|---|
| $5.75x$ | 5.75 | 17.25 | 57.50 | 115.00 |

   **b.** As the number of adults increases the total cost increases.

**16.** Twice the sum of $x$ and five is 30.

$$2 \cdot (x+5) = 30$$

or $2(x + 5) = 30$

**17.** The square of the difference of six and $y$ divided by seven is not equal to 10.

$$(6-y)^2 \qquad\qquad \div \quad 7 \quad \neq \quad 10$$

or $\dfrac{(6-y)^2}{7} \neq 10$

**18.** The product of nine and $z$, divided by the absolute value of $-12$ is not equal to 10.

$$9z \qquad\qquad \div \qquad |-12| \qquad\qquad \neq \qquad 10$$

or $\dfrac{9z}{|-12|} \neq 10$

**19.** Three times the quotient of $n$ and five is the opposite of $n$.

$$3 \qquad \cdot \qquad \frac{n}{5} \qquad = \qquad -n$$

or $3\left(\dfrac{n}{5}\right) = -n$

**20.** Twenty is equal to 6 subtracted from twice $x$.

$$20 \qquad = \qquad 2x - 6$$

or $20 = 2x - 6$

**21.** Negative two is equal to $x$ divided by the sum of $x$ and five.

$$-2 \qquad = \quad x \quad \div \qquad (x+5)$$

or $-2 = \dfrac{x}{x+5}$

**22.** $6(x - 4) = 6x - 24$: Distributive Property

**23.** $(4 + x) + z = 4 + (x + z)$: Associative Property of Addition

**24.** $(-7) + 7 = 0$: Additive Inverse Property

**25.** $(-18)(0) = 0$: Multiplication Property of Zero

**26.** Let 0.05 be the value of each nickel and 0.1 be the value of each dime. If there are $n$ nickels, and $d$ dimes, then the total amount of money is $0.05n + 0.1d$.

**27.** $-2(3x + 7) = -6x - 14$

**28.** $\dfrac{1}{3}a - \dfrac{3}{8} + \dfrac{1}{6}a - \dfrac{3}{4} = \dfrac{1}{3}a + \dfrac{1}{6}a - \dfrac{3}{8} - \dfrac{3}{4}$

$= \left(\dfrac{1}{3} + \dfrac{1}{6}\right)a - \dfrac{3}{8} - \dfrac{3}{4}$

$= \left(\dfrac{2}{6} + \dfrac{1}{6}\right)a - \dfrac{3}{8} - \dfrac{6}{8}$

$= \left(\dfrac{3}{6}\right)a - \dfrac{9}{8}$

$= \dfrac{1}{2}a - \dfrac{9}{8}$

**29.** $4y + 10 - 2(y + 10) = 4y + 10 - 2y - 20$

$= 4y - 2y + 10 - 20$

$= (4 - 2)y - 10$

$= 2y - 10$

**30.** $(8.3x - 2.9) - (9.6x - 4.8)$

$= 8.3x - 2.9 - 9.6x + 4.8$

$= 8.3x - 9.6x - 2.9 + 4.8$

$= (8.3 - 9.6)x + 1.9$

$= -1.3x + 1.9$

# Chapter 2

## Section 2.1

## Practice Exercises

**1.**
$$3x + 7 = 22$$
$$3x + 7 - 7 = 22 - 7$$
$$3x = 15$$
$$\frac{3x}{3} = \frac{15}{3}$$
$$x = 5$$

**2.**
$$2.5 = 3 - 2.5t$$
$$2.5 - 3 = 3 - 2.5t - 3$$
$$-0.5 = -2.5t$$
$$\frac{-0.5}{-2.5} = \frac{-2.5t}{-2.5}$$
$$0.2 = t$$

**3.**
$$-8x - 4 + 6x = 5x + 11 - 4x$$
$$-2x - 4 = x + 11$$
$$-2x - 4 - x = x + 11 - x$$
$$-3x - 4 = 11$$
$$-3x - 4 + 4 = 11 + 4$$
$$-3x = 15$$
$$\frac{-3x}{-3} = \frac{15}{-3}$$
$$x = -5$$

**4.**
$$3(x - 5) = 6x - 3$$
$$3x - 15 = 6x - 3$$
$$3x - 15 - 6x = 6x - 3 - 6x$$
$$-3x - 15 = -3$$
$$-3x - 15 + 15 = -3 + 15$$
$$-3x = 12$$
$$\frac{-3x}{-3} = \frac{12}{-3}$$
$$x = -4$$

**5.**
$$\frac{y}{2} - \frac{y}{5} = \frac{1}{4}$$
$$20\left(\frac{y}{2} - \frac{y}{5}\right) = 20\left(\frac{1}{4}\right)$$
$$20\left(\frac{y}{2}\right) - 20\left(\frac{y}{5}\right) = 5$$
$$10y - 4y = 5$$
$$6y = 5$$
$$\frac{6y}{6} = \frac{5}{6}$$
$$y = \frac{5}{6}$$

**6.**
$$x - \frac{x - 2}{12} = \frac{x + 3}{4} + \frac{1}{4}$$
$$12\left(x - \frac{x - 2}{12}\right) = 12\left(\frac{x + 3}{4} + \frac{1}{4}\right)$$
$$12 \cdot x - 12\left(\frac{x - 2}{12}\right) = 12\left(\frac{x + 3}{4}\right) + 12 \cdot \frac{1}{4}$$
$$12x - (x - 2) = 3(x + 3) + 3$$
$$12x - x + 2 = 3x + 9 + 3$$
$$11x + 2 = 3x + 12$$
$$11x + 2 - 3x = 3x + 12 - 3x$$
$$8x + 2 = 12$$
$$8x + 2 - 2 = 12 - 2$$
$$8x = 10$$
$$\frac{8x}{8} = \frac{10}{8}$$
$$x = \frac{5}{4}$$

**7.**
$$0.15x - 0.03 = 0.2x + 0.12$$
$$100(0.15x - 0.03) = 100(0.2x + 0.12)$$
$$100(0.15x) - 100(0.03) = 100(0.2x) + 100(0.12)$$
$$15x - 3 = 20x + 12$$
$$15x - 20x = 12 + 3$$
$$-5x = 15$$
$$\frac{-5x}{-5} = \frac{15}{-5}$$
$$x = -3$$

**8.**
$$4x - 3 = 4(x + 5)$$
$$4x - 3 = 4x + 20$$
$$4x - 3 - 4x = 4x + 20 - 4x$$
$$-3 = 20$$
This equation is false no matter what value the variable $x$ might have. Thus, there is no solution. The solution set is { } or $\varnothing$.

24

**9.**
$$5x - 2 = 3 + 5(x - 1)$$
$$5x - 2 = 3 + 5x - 5$$
$$5x - 2 = -2 + 5x$$
$$5x - 2 + 2 = -2 + 5x + 2$$
$$5x = 5x$$
$$5x - 5x = 5x - 5x$$
$$0 = 0$$
Since $0 = 0$ is a true statement for every value of $x$, all real numbers are solutions. The solution set is $\{x | x$ is a real number$\}$.

**Vocabulary and Readiness Check**

**1.** Equations with the same solution set are called <u>equivalent</u> equations.

**2.** A value for the variable in an equation that makes the equation a true statement is called a <u>solution</u> of the equation.

**3.** By the <u>addition</u> property of equality, $y = -3$ and $y - 7 = -3 - 7$ are equivalent equations.

**4.** By the <u>multiplication</u> property of equality, $2y = -3$ and $\dfrac{2y}{2} = \dfrac{-3}{2}$ are equivalent equations.

**5.** $\dfrac{1}{3}x - 5$  <u>expression</u>

**6.** $2(x - 3) = 7$  <u>equation</u>

**7.** $\dfrac{5}{9}x + \dfrac{1}{3} = \dfrac{2}{9} - x$  <u>equation</u>

**8.** $\dfrac{5}{9}x + \dfrac{1}{3} - \dfrac{2}{9} - x$  <u>expression</u>

**9.** $2x + 3 = 2x + 3$
Since the two sides of the equation are identical, the equation is true for any value of $x$. All real numbers are solutions.

**10.** $2x + 1 = 2x + 3$
Adding 1 to a number and adding 3 to the same number will not result in equal numbers for any value of $x$. There is no solution.

**11.** $5x - 2 = 5x - 7$
Subtracting 2 from a number and subtracting 7 from the same number will not result in equal numbers for any value of $x$. There is no solution.

**12.** $5x - 3 = 5x - 3$
Since the two sides of the equation are identical, the equation is true for any value of $x$. All real numbers are solutions.

**Exercise Set 2.1**

**1.** $-5x = -30$
$$\dfrac{-5x}{-5} = \dfrac{-30}{-5}$$
$$x = 6$$
Check:  $-5x = -30$
$$-5(6) \overset{?}{=} -30$$
$$-30 = -30 \quad \text{True}$$
The solution is 6.

**3.** $-10 = x + 12$
$$-10 - 12 = x + 12 - 12$$
$$-22 = x$$
Check:  $-10 = x + 12$
$$-10 \overset{?}{=} -22 + 12$$
$$-10 = -10 \quad \text{True}$$
The solution is $-22$.

**5.** $x - 2.8 = 1.9$
$$x - 2.8 + 2.8 = 1.9 + 2.8$$
$$x = 4.7$$
Check:  $x - 2.8 = 1.9$
$$4.7 - 2.8 \overset{?}{=} 1.9$$
$$1.9 = 1.9 \quad \text{True}$$
The solution is 4.7.

**7.** $5x - 4 = 26 + 2x$
$$5x - 2x = 26 + 4$$
$$3x = 30$$
$$\dfrac{3x}{3} = \dfrac{30}{3}$$
$$x = 10$$
Check:  $5x - 4 = 26 + 2x$
$$5(10) - 4 \overset{?}{=} 26 + 2(10)$$
$$50 - 4 \overset{?}{=} 26 + 20$$
$$46 = 46 \quad \text{True}$$
The solution is 10.

**9.**
$$-4.1 - 7z = 3.6$$
$$-4.1 - 7z + 4.1 = 3.6 + 4.1$$
$$-7z = 7.7$$
$$\frac{-7z}{-7} = \frac{7.7}{-7}$$
$$z = -1.1$$

Check:
$$-4.1 - 7z = 3.6$$
$$-4.1 - 7(-1.1) \stackrel{?}{=} 3.6$$
$$-4.1 + 7.7 \stackrel{?}{=} 3.6$$
$$3.6 = 3.6 \quad \text{True}$$

The solution is $-1.1$.

**11.**
$$5y + 12 = 2y - 3$$
$$5y + 12 - 2y = 2y - 3 - 2y$$
$$3y + 12 = -3$$
$$3y + 12 - 12 = -3 - 12$$
$$3y = -15$$
$$\frac{3y}{3} = \frac{-15}{3}$$
$$y = -5$$

Check:
$$5y + 12 = 2y - 3$$
$$5(-5) + 12 \stackrel{?}{=} 2(-5) - 3$$
$$-25 + 12 \stackrel{?}{=} -10 - 3$$
$$-13 = -13 \quad \text{True}$$

The solution is $-5$.

**13.**
$$3x - 4 - 5x = x + 4 + x$$
$$-4 - 2x = 2x + 4$$
$$-2x - 2x = 4 + 4$$
$$-4x = 8$$
$$x = -2$$

Check:
$$3x - 4 - 5x = x + 4 + x$$
$$3(-2) - 4 - 5(-2) \stackrel{?}{=} -2 + 4 - 2$$
$$-6 - 4 + 10 \stackrel{?}{=} 0$$
$$0 = 0 \quad \text{True}$$

The solution is $-2$.

**15.**
$$8x - 5x + 3 = x - 7 + 10$$
$$3x + 3 = x + 3$$
$$2x = 0$$
$$x = 0$$

Check:
$$8x - 5x + 3 = x - 7 + 10$$
$$8(0) - 5(0) + 3 \stackrel{?}{=} (0) - 7 + 10$$
$$0 + 3 \stackrel{?}{=} 3$$
$$3 = 3 \quad \text{True}$$

The solution is 0.

**17.**
$$5x + 12 = 2(2x + 7)$$
$$5x + 12 = 4x + 14$$
$$x + 12 = 14$$
$$x = 2$$

Check:
$$5x + 12 = 2(2x + 7)$$
$$5(2) + 12 \stackrel{?}{=} 2(2(2) + 7)$$
$$10 + 12 \stackrel{?}{=} 2(4 + 7)$$
$$22 \stackrel{?}{=} 2(11)$$
$$22 = 22 \quad \text{True}$$

The solution is 2.

**19.**
$$3(x - 6) = 5x$$
$$3x - 18 = 5x$$
$$-18 = 2x$$
$$-9 = x$$

Check:
$$3(x - 6) = 5x$$
$$3((-9) - 6) \stackrel{?}{=} 5(-9)$$
$$3(-15) \stackrel{?}{=} -45$$
$$-45 = -45 \quad \text{True}$$

The solution is $-9$.

**21.**
$$-2(5y - 1) - y = -4(y - 3)$$
$$-10y + 2 - y = -4y + 12$$
$$-7y + 2 = 12$$
$$-7y = 10$$
$$y = -\frac{10}{7}$$

Check:
$$-2(5y - 1) - y = -4(y - 3)$$
$$-2\left(5\left(-\frac{10}{7}\right) - 1\right) - \left(-\frac{10}{7}\right) \stackrel{?}{=} -4\left(\left(-\frac{10}{7}\right) - 3\right)$$
$$-2\left(-\frac{50}{7} - 1\right) + \frac{10}{7} \stackrel{?}{=} -4\left(-\frac{31}{7}\right)$$
$$-2\left(-\frac{57}{7}\right) + \frac{10}{7} \stackrel{?}{=} \frac{124}{7}$$
$$\frac{114}{7} + \frac{10}{7} \stackrel{?}{=} \frac{124}{7}$$
$$\frac{124}{7} = \frac{124}{7} \quad \text{True}$$

The solution is $-\frac{10}{7}$.

**23.**
$$\frac{x}{2} + \frac{x}{3} = \frac{3}{4}$$
$$12\left(\frac{x}{2} + \frac{x}{3}\right) = 12\left(\frac{3}{4}\right)$$
$$6x + 4x = 9$$
$$10x = 9$$
$$x = \frac{9}{10}$$

Check:
$$\frac{x}{2} + \frac{x}{3} = \frac{3}{4}$$
$$\frac{9}{10} \cdot \frac{1}{2} + \frac{9}{10} \cdot \frac{1}{3} \stackrel{?}{=} \frac{3}{4}$$
$$\frac{9}{20} + \frac{3}{10} \stackrel{?}{=} \frac{3}{4}$$
$$\frac{3}{4} = \frac{3}{4} \quad \text{True}$$

The solution is $\frac{9}{10}$.

**25.**
$$\frac{3t}{4} - \frac{t}{2} = 1$$
$$4\left(\frac{3t}{4} - \frac{t}{2}\right) = 4(1)$$
$$3t - 2t = 4$$
$$t = 4$$

Check:
$$\frac{3t}{4} - \frac{t}{2} = 1$$
$$\frac{3(4)}{4} - \frac{(4)}{2} \stackrel{?}{=} 1$$
$$3 - 2 \stackrel{?}{=} 1$$
$$1 = 1 \quad \text{True}$$

The solution is 4.

**27.**
$$\frac{n-3}{4} + \frac{n+5}{7} = \frac{5}{14}$$
$$28\left(\frac{n-3}{4}\right) + 28\left(\frac{n+5}{7}\right) = 28\left(\frac{5}{14}\right)$$
$$7(n-3) + 4(n+5) = 2(5)$$
$$7n - 21 + 4n + 20 = 10$$
$$11n - 1 = 10$$
$$11n = 11$$
$$n = 1$$

Check:
$$\frac{n-3}{4} + \frac{n+5}{7} = \frac{5}{14}$$
$$\frac{(1)-3}{4} + \frac{(1)+5}{7} \stackrel{?}{=} \frac{5}{14}$$
$$\frac{-2}{4} + \frac{6}{7} \stackrel{?}{=} \frac{5}{14}$$
$$\frac{-1}{2} + \frac{6}{7} \stackrel{?}{=} \frac{5}{14}$$
$$-\frac{7}{14} + \frac{12}{14} \stackrel{?}{=} \frac{5}{14}$$
$$\frac{5}{14} = \frac{5}{14} \quad \text{True}$$

The solution is 1.

**29.**
$$0.6x - 10 = 1.4x - 14$$
$$-0.8x - 10 = -14$$
$$-0.8x = -4$$
$$x = 5$$

Check:
$$0.6x - 10 = 1.4x - 14$$
$$0.6(5) - 10 \stackrel{?}{=} 1.4(5) - 14$$
$$3 - 10 \stackrel{?}{=} 7 - 14$$
$$-7 = -7 \quad \text{True}$$

The solution is 5.

**31.**
$$\frac{3x-1}{9} + x = \frac{3x+1}{3} + 4$$
$$9\left(\frac{3x-1}{9} + x\right) = 9\left(\frac{3x+1}{3} + 4\right)$$
$$(3x-1) + 9x = 3(3x+1) + 36$$
$$3x - 1 + 9x = 9x + 3 + 36$$
$$12x = 9x + 40$$
$$3x = 40$$
$$x = \frac{40}{3}$$

Check:
$$\frac{3x-1}{9} + x = \frac{3x+1}{3} + 4$$
$$\frac{3\left(\frac{40}{3}\right)-1}{9} + \frac{40}{3} \stackrel{?}{=} \frac{3\left(\frac{40}{3}\right)+1}{3} + 4$$
$$\frac{39}{9} + \frac{120}{9} \stackrel{?}{=} \frac{41}{3} + \frac{12}{3}$$
$$\frac{53}{3} = \frac{53}{3} \quad \text{True}$$

The solution is $\frac{40}{3}$.

**33.**
$$1.5(4-x) = 1.3(2-x)$$
$$10[1.5(4-x)] = 10[1.3(2-x)]$$
$$15(4-x) = 13(2-x)$$
$$60 - 15x = 26 - 13x$$
$$-2x = -34$$
$$x = 17$$
Check: $1.5(4-x) = 1.3(2-x)$
$$1.5(4-17) \overset{?}{=} 1.3(2-17)$$
$$1.5(-13) \overset{?}{=} 1.3(-15)$$
$$-19.5 = -19.5 \quad \text{True}$$
The solution is 17.

**35.** $4(n+3) = 2(6+2n)$
$$4n + 12 = 12 + 4n$$
$$0 = 0$$
This is true for all $x$. Therefore, all real numbers are solutions.

**37.** $3(x+1) + 5 = 3x + 2$
$$3x + 3 + 5 = 3x + 2$$
$$3x + 8 = 3x + 2$$
$$8 = 2$$
This is false for any $x$. Therefore, no solution exists, $\varnothing$.

**39.** $2(x-8) + x = 3(x-6) + 2$
$$2x - 16 + x = 3x - 18 + 2$$
$$3x - 16 = 3x - 16$$
$$0 = 0$$
This is true for all $x$. Therefore, all real numbers are solutions.

**41.** $4(x+5) = 3(x-4) + x$
$$4x + 20 = 3x - 12 + x$$
$$4x + 20 = 4x - 12$$
$$20 = -12$$
This is false for any $x$. Therefore, no solution exists, $\varnothing$.

**43.**
$$\frac{3}{8} + \frac{b}{3} = \frac{5}{12}$$
$$24\left(\frac{3}{8}\right) + 24\left(\frac{b}{3}\right) = 24\left(\frac{5}{12}\right)$$
$$9 + 8b = 10$$
$$8b = 1$$
$$b = \frac{1}{8}$$

**45.** $x - 10 = -6x - 10$
$$x + 6x = -10 + 10$$
$$7x = 0$$
$$x = 0$$

**47.** $5(x-2) + 2x = 7(x+4) - 38$
$$5x - 10 + 2x = 7x + 28 - 38$$
$$7x - 10 = 7x - 10$$
$$0 = 0$$
This is true for all $x$. Therefore, all real numbers are solutions.

**49.** $y + 0.2 = 0.6(y+3)$
$$y + 0.2 = 0.6y + 1.8$$
$$0.4y = 1.6$$
$$y = 4$$

**51.**
$$\frac{1}{4}(a+2) = \frac{1}{6}(5-a)$$
$$\frac{1}{4}a + \frac{1}{2} = \frac{5}{6} - \frac{1}{6}a$$
$$\frac{1}{4}a + \frac{1}{6}a = \frac{5}{6} - \frac{1}{2}$$
$$\frac{3}{12}a + \frac{2}{12}a = \frac{5}{6} - \frac{3}{6}$$
$$\frac{5}{12}a = \frac{2}{6}$$
$$a = \frac{2}{6} \cdot \frac{12}{5}$$
$$a = \frac{4}{5}$$

**53.** $2y + 5(y-4) = 4y - 2(y-10)$
$$2y + 5y - 20 = 4y - 2y + 20$$
$$7y - 20 = 2y + 20$$
$$7y - 2y = 20 + 20$$
$$5y = 40$$
$$y = 8$$

**55.** $6x - 2(x-3) = 4(x+1) + 4$
$$6x - 2x + 6 = 4x + 4 + 4$$
$$4x + 6 = 4x + 8$$
$$4x - 4x = 8 - 6$$
$$0 = 2$$
This is false for any $x$. Therefore, the solution set is $\varnothing$.

**57.**
$$\frac{m-4}{3} - \frac{3m-1}{5} = 1$$
$$15\left(\frac{m-4}{3}\right) - 15\left(\frac{3m-1}{5}\right) = 15(1)$$
$$5(m-4) - 3(3m-1) = 15$$
$$5m - 20 - 9m + 3 = 15$$
$$-4m - 17 = 15$$
$$-4m = 32$$
$$m = -8$$

**59.** $8x - 12 - 3x = 9x - 7$
$5x - 12 = 9x - 7$
$5x - 9x = -7 + 12$
$-4x = 5$
$x = -\dfrac{5}{4}$

**61.** $-(3x - 5) - (2x - 6) + 1 = -5(x - 1) - (3x + 2) + 3$
$-3x + 5 - 2x + 6 + 1 = -5x + 5 - 3x - 2 + 3$
$-5x + 12 = -8x + 6$
$3x = -6$
$x = -2$

**63.** $\dfrac{1}{3}(y + 4) + 6 = \dfrac{1}{4}(3y - 1) - 2$
$12\left[\dfrac{1}{3}(y + 4) + 6\right] = 12\left[\dfrac{1}{4}(3y - 1) - 2\right]$
$4(y + 4) + 12 \cdot 6 = 3(3y - 1) - 12 \cdot 2$
$4y + 16 + 72 = 9y - 3 - 24$
$4y + 88 = 9y - 27$
$-5y = -115$
$y = 23$

**65.** $2[7 - 5(1 - n)] + 8n = -16 + 3[6(n + 1) - 3n]$
$2[7 - 5 + 5n] + 8n = -16 + 3[6n + 6 - 3n]$
$2(2 + 5n) + 8n = -16 + 3(3n + 6)$
$4 + 10n + 8n = -16 + 9n + 18$
$4 + 18n = 2 + 9n$
$9n = -2$
$n = -\dfrac{2}{9}$

**67.** Quotient means to divide. The quotient of 8 and a number: $\dfrac{8}{x}$

**69.** Product means to multiply. The product of 8 and a number: $8x$

**71.** Five subtracted from twice a number: $2x - 5$

**73.** Subtract 19 instead of adding;
$3x + 19 = 13$
$2x = -6$
$\dfrac{2x}{2} = \dfrac{-6}{2}$
$x = -3$

**75.** $0.4 - 1.6 = -1.2$, not $1.2$;
$9x + 1.6 = 4x + 0.4$
$5x = -1.2$
$\dfrac{5x}{5} = \dfrac{-1.2}{5}$
$x = -0.24$

**77. a.** $4(x + 1) + 1 = 4x + 4 + 1 = 4x + 5$

    **b.** $4(x + 1) + 1 = -7$
$4x + 4 + 1 = -7$
$4x + 5 = -7$
$4x = -12$
$x = -3$
The solution is $-3$.

    **c.** Answers may vary

**79.** Answers may vary

**81.** $3.2x + 4 = 5.4x - 7$
$3.2x + 4 - 4 = 5.4x - 7 - 4$
$3.2x = 5.4x - 11$
From this we see that $K = -11$.

**83.** $\dfrac{7}{11}x + 9 = \dfrac{3}{11}x - 14$
$\dfrac{7}{11}x + 9 - 9 = \dfrac{3}{11}x - 14 - 9$
$\dfrac{7}{11}x = \dfrac{3}{11}x - 23$
From this we see that $K = -23$.

**85.** Answers may vary

**87.** $x(x - 6) + 7 = x(x + 1)$
$x^2 - 6x + 7 = x^2 + x$
$-6x + 7 = x$
$7 = 7x$
$1 = x$

**89.** $3x(x + 5) - 12 = 3x^2 + 10x + 3$
$3x^2 + 15x - 12 = 3x^2 + 10x + 3$
$15x - 12 = 10x + 3$
$5x = 15$
$x = 3$

**91.** $2.569x = -12.48534$

$$\frac{2.569x}{2.569} = \frac{-12.48534}{2.569}$$

$$x = -4.86$$

Check:     $2.569x = -12.48534$

$2.569(-4.86) \stackrel{?}{=} -12.48534$

$-12.48534 = -12.48534$   True

The solution is $-4.86$.

**93.** $2.86z - 8.1258 = -3.75$

$$2.86z = 4.3758$$

$$\frac{2.86z}{2.86} = \frac{4.3758}{2.86}$$

$$z = 1.53$$

Check:     $2.86z - 8.1258 = -3.75$

$2.86(1.53) - 8.1258 \stackrel{?}{=} -3.75$

$-3.75 = -3.75$   True

The solution is $1.53$.

## Section 2.2

## Practice Exercises

**1. a.**   In words:

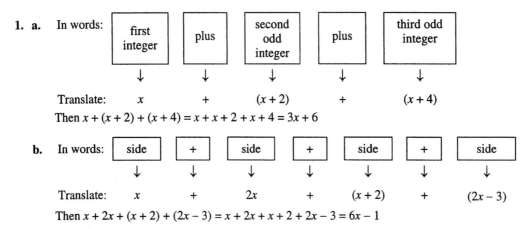

Translate:     $x$     $+$     $(x + 2)$     $+$     $(x + 4)$

Then $x + (x + 2) + (x + 4) = x + x + 2 + x + 4 = 3x + 6$

**b.**   In words:

| side | + | side | + | side | + | side |

Translate:     $x$     $+$     $2x$     $+$     $(x + 2)$     $+$     $(2x - 3)$

Then $x + 2x + (x + 2) + (2x - 3) = x + 2x + x + 2 + 2x - 3 = 6x - 1$

**2.**   If $x$ = number of arrivals and departures at Frankfurt airport,
then $x + 15.7$ = number at London, and $x + 1.6$ = number at Paris.

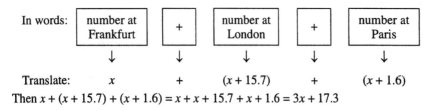

Translate:     $x$     $+$     $(x + 15.7)$     $+$     $(x + 1.6)$

Then $x + (x + 15.7) + (x + 1.6) = x + x + 15.7 + x + 1.6 = 3x + 17.3$

3. Let $x$ = the first number, then $3x - 8$ = the second number, and $5x$ = the third number.
   The sum of the three numbers is 118.
   $$x + (3x - 8) + 5x = 118$$
   $$x + 3x + 5x - 8 = 118$$
   $$9x - 8 = 118$$
   $$9x = 126$$
   $$x = 14$$
   The numbers are 14, $3x - 8 = 3(14) - 8 = 34$, and $5x = 5(14) = 70$.

4. Let $x$ = the original price. Then $0.4x$ = the discount. The original price, minus the discount, is equal to $270.
   $$x - 0.4x = 270$$
   $$0.6x = 270$$
   $$x = \frac{270}{0.6} = 450$$
   The original price was $450.

5. Let $x$ = width, then $2x - 16$ = length.
   The perimeter is 160 inches.
   $$2(x) + 2(2x - 16) = 160$$
   $$2x + 4x - 32 = 160$$
   $$6x - 32 = 160$$
   $$6x = 192$$
   $$x = 32$$
   $$2x - 16 = 2(32) - 16 = 48$$
   The width is 32 inches and the length is 48 inches.

6. Let $x$ = first odd integer, then $x + 2$ = second odd integer, and $x + 4$ = third odd integer.
   The sum of the integers is 81.
   $$x + (x + 2) + (x + 4) = 81$$
   $$3x + 6 = 81$$
   $$3x = 75$$
   $$x = 25$$
   $$x + 2 = 27$$
   $$x + 4 = 29$$
   The integers are 25, 27, and 29.

## Vocabulary and Readiness Check

1. 130% of a number  $\underline{\;>\;}$  the number.

2. 70% of a number  $\underline{\;<\;}$  the number.

3. 100% of a number  $\underline{\;=\;}$  the number.

4. 200% of a number  $\underline{\;>\;}$  the number.

| | First Integer | All Described Integers |
|---|---|---|
| **5.** Four consecutive integers | 31 | 31, 32, 33, 34 |
| **6.** Three consecutive odd integers | 31 | 31, 33, 35 |
| **7.** Three consecutive even integers | 18 | 18, 20, 22 |
| **8.** Four consecutive even integers | 92 | 92, 94, 96, 98 |
| **9.** Three consecutive integers | $y$ | $y, y+1, y+2$ |
| **10.** Three consecutive even integers | $z$ ($z$ is even) | $z, z+2, z+4$ |
| **11.** Four consecutive integers | $p$ | $p, p+1, p+2, p+3$ |
| **12.** Three consecutive odd integers | $s$ ($s$ is odd) | $s, s+2, s+4$ |

## Exercise Set 2.2

**1.** The perimeter is the sum of the lengths of the four sides.
$$y+y+y+y=4y$$

**3.** Let $z$ = first integer, then $z + 1$ = second integer, and $z + 2$ = third integer.
$$z+(z+1)+(z+2)=z+z+z+1+2=3z+3$$

**5.** Find the sum of $x$ nickels worth 5¢ each, and $(x + 3)$ dimes worth 10¢ each, and $2x$ quarters worth 25¢ each.
$$5x+10(x+3)+25(2x)=5x+10x+30+50x$$
$$=65x+30$$
The total amount is $(65x + 30)$ cents.

**7.** $4x + 3(2x + 1) = 4x + 6x + 3 = 10x + 3$

**9.** The length of the side denoted by ? is $10 - 2 = 8$. Similarly, the length of the unmarked side is
$(x - 3) - (x - 10) = x - 3 - x + 10 = 7$.
Thus the perimeter of the floor plan is given by $(x - 10) + 2 + 7 + 8 + (x - 3) + 10 = 2x + 14$.

**11.** Let $x$ = the number.
$$4(x-2)=2+4x+2x$$
$$4x-8=2+6x$$
$$-2x=10$$
$$x=-5$$
The number is $-5$.

**13.** Let $x$ = the first number, then
$5x$ = the second number, and
$x + 100$ = the third number.
$$x + 5x + (x + 100) = 415$$
$$7x + 100 = 415$$
$$7x = 315$$
$$x = 45$$
$5x = 225$
$x + 100 = 145$
The numbers are 45, 225, and 145.

**15.** 29% of $2271 = 0.29 \cdot 2271 = 658.59$;
$2271 - 658.59 = 1612.41$.
Approximately 1612.41 million acres are not federally owned.

**17.** 85.3% of $2748 = 0.853 \cdot 2748 \approx 2344$
Approximately 2344 minor earthquakes occurred in 2006.

**19.** 15% of $1500 = 0.15 \cdot 1500 = 225$
$1500 - 225 = 1275$
1275 are willing to do business with any size retailer.

**21.** $100\% - (55\% + 7\% + 9\% + 7\%) = 100\% - 78\%$
$$= 22\%$$

**23.** 7% of $5957 = 0.07 \cdot 5957 = 416.99$
About 417 employees spend more than 3 hours per day using e-mail.

**25.** Let $x$ = population in 2001.
$$x + 0.054x = 31.6$$
$$1.054x = 31.6$$
$$x \approx 29.98$$
The population of Canada in 2001 was about 29.98 million.

**27.** $$x + 4x + (x + 6) = 180$$
$$6x + 6 = 180$$
$$6x = 174$$
$$x = 29$$
$4x = 4(29) = 116$
$x + 6 = 29 + 6 = 35$
The angles measure 29°, 35°, and 116°.

**29.** $$(4x) + (5x + 1) + (5x + 3) = 102$$
$$14x + 4 = 102$$
$$14x = 98$$
$$x = 7$$
$4x = 4(7) = 28$
$5x + 1 = 5(7) + 1 = 36$
$5x + 3 = 5(7) + 3 = 38$
The sides measure 28 meters, 36 meters, and 38 meters.

**31.** $$x + (2.5x - 9) + x + 1.5x = 99$$
$$6x - 9 = 99$$
$$6x = 108$$
$$x = 18$$
$1.5x = 1.5(18) = 27$
$2.5x - 9 = 2.5(18) - 9 = 36$
The sides measure 18 inches, 18 inches, 27 inches, and 36 inches.

**33.** Let $x$ = first integer; then
$x + 1$ = next integer and
$x + 2$ = third integer.
$$x + (x + 1) + (x + 2) = 228$$
$$3x + 3 = 228$$
$$3x = 225$$
$$x = 75$$
$x + 1 = 75 + 1 = 76$
$x + 2 = 75 + 2 = 77$
The integers are 75, 76, and 77.

**35.** Let $x$ = first even integer, then
$x + 2$ = second even integer, and
$x + 4$ = third even integer.
$$2x + (x + 4) = 268,222$$
$$3x + 4 = 268,222$$
$$3x = 268,218$$
$$x = 89,406$$
$x + 2 = 89,408$
$x + 4 = 89,410$
Fallon's zip code is 89406, Fernley's zip code is 89408, and Gardnerville Ranchos's zip code is 89410.

**37.** $$(2x - 51) + \left(\frac{3}{2}x + 3\right) + x = 780$$
$$\frac{9}{2}x - 48 = 780$$
$$\frac{9}{2}x = 828$$
$$x = 828 \cdot \frac{2}{9}$$
$$x = 184$$
$2x - 51 = 2(184) - 51 = 317$
$\frac{3}{2}x + 3 = \frac{3}{2}(184) + 3 = 279$

| Occupation | Increase in Number of Jobs (in thousands) from 2000 to 2012 |
|---|---|
| Security guards | 317 thousand |
| Home health aides | 279 thousand |
| Computer system analysts | 184 thousand |
| Total | 780 thousand |

**39.** Let $x$ = number of medical assistant jobs (in thousands), then $2x + 173$ = number of postsecondary teacher jobs (in thousands), and $3x - 22$ = number of registered nurse jobs (in thousands).
$$x + (2x + 173) + (3x - 22) = 1441$$
$$6x + 151 = 1441$$
$$6x = 1290$$
$$x = 215$$
$$2x + 173 = 2(215) + 173 = 603$$
$$3x - 22 = 3(215) - 22 = 623$$
The predicted job growth:
medical assistant: 215 thousand;
postsecondary teacher jobs: 603 thousand;
registered nurses: 623 thousand

**41.** Let $x$ = no. of seats in the 737-200;
then $x + 21$ = no. in the 737-300 and
$2x - 36$ = no. in the 757-200.
$$x + (x + 21) + (2x - 36) = 437$$
$$4x - 15 = 437$$
$$4x = 452$$
$$x = 113$$
$$x + 21 = 113 + 21 = 134$$
$$2x - 33 = 2(113) - 36 = 190$$
The 737-200 has 113 seats. The 737-300 has 134 seats. The 757-200 has 190 seats.

**43.** Let $x$ = price before taxes.
$$x + 0.08x = 464.40$$
$$1.08x = 464.40$$
$$x = 430$$
The price was \$430 before taxes.

**45.** Let $x$ = expected population.
$$x = 44.2 - 0.056(44.2)$$
$$x = 44.2 - 2.4752$$
$$x \approx 41.7$$
The expected population of South Africa in 2050 is 41.7 million.

**47.** Let $x$ = measure of the angle; then
$180 - x$ = measure of its supplement.
$$x = 3(180 - x) + 20$$
$$x = 540 - 3x + 20$$
$$4x = 560$$
$$x = 140$$
$$180 - x = 180 - 140 = 40$$
The angles measure 140° and 40°.

**49.** Let $x$ = measure of second angle; then
$2x$ = measure of first angle and
$3x - 12$ = measure of third angle.
$$x + 2x + (3x - 12) = 180$$
$$6x - 12 = 180$$
$$6x = 192$$
$$x = 32$$
$$2x = 2(32) = 64$$
$$3x - 12 = 3(32) - 12 = 84$$
The angles measure 64°, 32°, and 84°.

**51.** Let $x$ = the length of a side of the square. Then $x + 6$ = the length of a side of the triangle.
$$4x = 3(x + 6)$$
$$4x = 3x + 18$$
$$x = 18$$
The sides of the square are 18 cm and the sides of the triangle are 24 cm.

**53.** Let $x$ = first even integer, then
$x + 2$ = second even integer, and
$x + 4$ = third even integer.
$$x + (x + 4) = 156$$
$$2x + 4 = 156$$
$$2x = 152$$
$$x = 76$$
$$x + 2 = 78$$
$$x + 4 = 80$$
The integers are 76, 78, and 80.

**55.** $$x + 5x + (6x - 3) = 483$$
$$12x - 3 = 483$$
$$12x = 486$$
$$x = 40.5$$
$$5x = 5(40.5) = 202.5$$
$$6x - 3 = 6(40.5) - 3 = 240$$
The sides measure 40.5 feet, 202.5 feet, and 240 feet.

**57.** $$3x + 14.6 = 197.6$$
$$3x = 183.0$$
$$x = 61.0$$
The arrivals and departures are as follows:
Los Angeles: $x = 61.0$ million
Atlanta: $x + 13.3 = 61.0 + 13.3 = 74.3$ million
Chicago: $x + 1.3 = 61.0 + 1.3 = 62.3$ million

**59.** Let $x$ = hours for halogen; then
$25x$ = hours for fluorescent and
$x - 2500$ = hours for incandescent.
$$x + 25x + (x - 2500) = 105,500$$
$$27x - 2500 = 105,500$$
$$27x = 108,000$$
$$x = 4000$$
$25x = 100,000$; $x - 2500 = 1500$
The halogen has 4000 bulb hours.
The fluorescent has 100,000 bulb hours.
The incandescent has 1500 bulb hours.

**61.** Let $x$ = height, then $2x + 12$ = length.
$$2(x) + 2(2x + 12) = 312$$
$$2x + 4x + 24 = 312$$
$$6x + 24 = 312$$
$$6x = 288$$
$$x = 48$$
$2x + 12 = 2(48) + 12 = 108$
The height is 48 inches and the length is
108 inches.

**63. a.** $4.7 + 0.05 \cdot 4.7 = 4.7 + 0.235 \approx 4.9$
The total sales in 2006 were \$4.9 billion.

    **b.** $0.25 \cdot 4.9 \approx 1.23$
The amount spent on running shoes in 2006
was \$1.23 billion.

**65.** Let $x$ = subscribers in Russia, then
$4x - 3.1$ = subscribers in China, and
$x + 4.3$ = subscribers in United States.
$$x + (4x - 3.1) + (x + 4.3) = 34.8$$
$$6x + 1.2 = 34.8$$
$$6x = 33.6$$
$$x = 5.6$$
$4x - 3.1 = 4(5.6) - 3.1 = 19.3$
$x + 4.3 = 5.6 + 4.3 = 9.9$
The percents of world subscribers are as follows:
Russia: 5.6%, China: 19.3%; U.S.: 9.9%.

**67.** Let $x$ = pages in first book.
$x + 1.54x$ = pages in final book
$$x + 1.54x = 784$$
$$2.54x = 784$$
$$x \approx 309$$
There are 309 pages in *Harry Potter and the Sorcerer's Stone*.

**69.** Let $x$ = first odd integer (Canada), then
$x + 2$ = second odd integer (U.S.), and
$x + 4$ = third odd integer (Germany).
$$x + 2(x + 2) + 4(x + 4) = 69$$
$$x + 2x + 4 + 4x + 16 = 69$$
$$7x + 20 = 69$$
$$7x = 49$$
$$x = 7$$
$x + 2 = 9$
$x + 4 = 11$
The number of gold medals won are as follows:
Germany: 11; U.S.: 9; Canada: 7

**71.** $ab + 6bc = 0(-1) + 6(-1)(9) = 0 - 6(9) = -54$

**73.** $2n^2 + 3m^2 = 2(-2)^2 + 3(7)^2$
$$= 2(4) + 3(49)$$
$$= 8 + 147$$
$$= 155$$

**75.** $\dfrac{1}{3}lwh = \dfrac{1}{3}(37.8)(5.6)(7.9) = 557.424$

**77.** Answers may vary

**79.** $180 - x = 2(90 - x) + 50$
$$180 - x = 180 - 2x + 50$$
$$180 - x = 230 - 2x$$
$$x = 50$$
The angle is 50°.

**81. a.** $y = -49.4x + 1756.8$
$$0 = -49.4x + 1756.8$$
$$-1756.8 = -49.4x$$
$$35 \approx x$$
$1997 + 35 = 2032$
The average annual number of cigarettes
smoked will be 0 during the year 2032.

    **b.** $y = -49.4x + 1756.8$
$y = -49.4(15) + 1756.8$
$y = 1015.8$
The predicted average annual number of
cigarettes smoked by an American adult in
2012 is 1015.8.

    **c.** $1015.8 \div 365 \approx 3$
An American adult will smoke an average
of 3 cigarettes a day in 2012.
No; answers may vary; possible answer:
This is the daily number of cigarettes for all
American adults—smokers and non-
smokers.

**83.**     $R = C$

$60x = 50x + 5000$

$10x = 5000$

$x = 500$

$R = 60x = 60(500) = 30,000$

$C = 50x + 5000 = 50(500) + 5000 = 30,000$

To break even, 500 boards must be sold. You need $30,000 to produce the 500 boards.

**85.** The company makes a profit.

**Section 2.3**

**Practice Exercises**

**1.**     $I = Prt$

$\dfrac{I}{Pr} = \dfrac{Prt}{Pr}$

$\dfrac{I}{Pr} = t$ or $t = \dfrac{I}{Pr}$

**2.**     $7x - 2y = 5$

$7x - 2y - 7x = 5 - 7x$

$-2y = 5 - 7x$

$\dfrac{-2y}{-2} = \dfrac{5 - 7x}{-2}$

$y = \dfrac{7}{2}x - \dfrac{5}{2}$

**3.**     $A = P + Prt$

$A - P = P + Prt - P$

$A - P = Prt$

$\dfrac{A - P}{Pt} = \dfrac{Prt}{Pt}$

$\dfrac{A - P}{Pt} = r$ or $r = \dfrac{A - P}{Pt}$

**4.** Let $P = 8000$, $r = 6\% = 0.06$, $t = 4$, $n = 2$.

$A = P\left(1 + \dfrac{r}{n}\right)^{nt}$

$A = 8000\left(1 + \dfrac{0.06}{2}\right)^{2\cdot 4}$

$A = 8000(1.03)^8$

$A \approx 8000(1.266770081)$

$A \approx 10{,}134.16$

Russ will have $10,134.16 in his account.

**5.** Let $d = 192$ and $r = 7.5$.

$d = rt$

$192 = 7.5t$

$\dfrac{192}{7.5} = \dfrac{7.5t}{7.5}$

$25.6t = t$

They spent 25.6 hours cycling, or 25 hours 36 minutes.

**Exercise Set 2.3**

**1.**     $D = rt$

$\dfrac{D}{r} = \dfrac{rt}{r}$

$\dfrac{D}{r} = t$

$t = \dfrac{D}{r}$

**3.**     $I = PRT$

$\dfrac{I}{PT} = \dfrac{PRT}{PT}$

$\dfrac{I}{PT} = R$

$R = \dfrac{I}{PT}$

**5.**     $9x - 4y = 16$

$9x - 4y - 9x = 16 - 9x$

$-4y = 16 - 9x$

$\dfrac{-4y}{-4} = \dfrac{16 - 9x}{-4}$

$y = \dfrac{9x - 16}{4}$

**7.**     $P = 2L + 2W$

$P - 2L = 2W$

$\dfrac{P - 2L}{2} = \dfrac{2W}{2}$

$\dfrac{P - 2L}{2} = W$

$W = \dfrac{P - 2L}{2}$

**9.**
$$J = AC - 3$$
$$J + 3 = AC$$
$$\frac{J+3}{C} = \frac{AC}{C}$$
$$\frac{J+3}{C} = A$$
$$A = \frac{J+3}{C}$$

**11.**
$$W = gh - 3gt^2$$
$$W = g(h - 3t^2)$$
$$\frac{W}{h - 3t^2} = \frac{g(h - 3t^2)}{h - 3t^2}$$
$$\frac{W}{h - 3t^2} = g$$
$$g = \frac{W}{h - 3t^2}$$

**13.**
$$T = C(2 + AB)$$
$$T = 2C + ABC$$
$$T - 2C = 2C + ABC - 2C$$
$$T - 2C = ABC$$
$$\frac{T - 2C}{AC} = \frac{ABC}{AC}$$
$$\frac{T - 2C}{AC} = B$$
$$B = \frac{T - 2C}{AC}$$

**15.**
$$C = 2\pi r$$
$$\frac{C}{2\pi} = \frac{2\pi r}{2\pi}$$
$$\frac{C}{2\pi} = r$$
$$r = \frac{C}{2\pi}$$

**17.**
$$E = I(r + R)$$
$$E = Ir + IR$$
$$E - IR = Ir + IR - IR$$
$$E - IR = Ir$$
$$\frac{E - IR}{I} = \frac{Ir}{I}$$
$$\frac{E - IR}{I} = r$$
$$r = \frac{E - IR}{I}$$

**19.**
$$s = \frac{n}{2}(a + L)$$
$$2s = 2 \cdot \frac{n}{2}(a + L)$$
$$2s = n(a + L)$$
$$2s = na + nL$$
$$2s - na = na + nL - na$$
$$2s - na = nL$$
$$\frac{2s - na}{n} = \frac{nL}{n}$$
$$\frac{2s - na}{n} = L$$
$$L = \frac{2s - na}{n}$$

**21.**
$$N = 3st^4 - 5sv$$
$$N - 3st^4 = 3st^4 - 5sv - 3st^4$$
$$N - 3st^4 = -5sv$$
$$\frac{N - 3st^4}{-5s} = \frac{-5sv}{-5s}$$
$$\frac{3st^4 - N}{5s} = v$$
$$v = \frac{3st^4 - N}{5s}$$

**23.**
$$S = 2LW + 2LH + 2WH$$
$$S - 2LW = 2LW + 2LH + 2WH - 2LW$$
$$S - 2LW = 2LH + 2WH$$
$$S - 2LW = H(2L + 2W)$$
$$\frac{S - 2LW}{2L + 2W} = \frac{H(2L + 2W)}{2L + 2W}$$
$$\frac{S - 2LW}{2L + 2W} = H$$
$$H = \frac{S - 2LW}{2L + 2W}$$

**25.** $A = P\left(1 + \dfrac{r}{n}\right)^{nt} = 3500\left(1 + \dfrac{0.03}{n}\right)^{10n}$

| $n$ | 1 | 2 | 4 |
|---|---|---|---|
| $A$ | \$4703.71 | \$4713.99 | \$4719.22 |

| $n$ | 12 | 365 |
|---|---|---|
| $A$ | \$4722.74 | \$4724.45 |

**27.** $A = P\left(1+\dfrac{r}{n}\right)^{nt} = 6000\left(1+\dfrac{0.04}{n}\right)^{5n}$

**a.** $n = 2$

$A = 6000\left(1+\dfrac{0.04}{2}\right)^{5\cdot2} \approx 7313.97$

$7313.97

**b.** $n = 4$

$A = 6000\left(1+\dfrac{0.04}{4}\right)^{5\cdot4} \approx 7321.14$

$7321.14

**c.** $n = 12$

$A = 6000\left(1+\dfrac{0.04}{12}\right)^{5\cdot12} \approx 7325.98$

$7325.98

**29.** $C = \dfrac{5}{9}(F-32)$

$C = \dfrac{5}{9}(104-32)$

$C = \dfrac{5}{9}(72)$

$C = 40°$

The day's high temperature was 40°C.

**31.** $d = rt$

$2(90) = 50t$

$180 = 50t$

$\dfrac{180}{50} = t$

$t = 3.6$

She takes 3.6 hours or 3 hours, 36 minutes to make the round trip.

**33.** $A = s^2 = (64)^2 = 4096$ ft$^2$; $\dfrac{4096}{24} \approx 171$

There should be 171 packages of tiles bought.

**35.** $A = \dfrac{1}{2}bh$

$18 = \dfrac{1}{2}(4)h$

$18 = 2h$

$9 = h$

The height is 9 feet.

**37.** The area of one pair of walls is $2\cdot14\cdot8 = 224$ ft$^2$ and the area of the other walls is $2\cdot16\cdot8 = 256$ ft$^2$ for a total of $480$ ft$^2$. Multiplying by 2, the number of coats, yields $960$ ft$^2$. Dividing this by 500 yields 1.92. Thus, 2 gallons should be purchased.

**39. a.** $V = \pi r^2 h$

$V = \pi(4.2)^2(2.12)$

$V \approx 1174.86$

The volume of the cylinder is 1174.86 cubic meters.

**b.** $V = \dfrac{4}{3}\pi r^3$

$V = \dfrac{4}{3}\pi(4.2)^3$

$V \approx 310.34$

The volume of the sphere is 310.34 cubic meters.

**c.** $V = 1174.86 + 310.34 = 1485.20$

The volume of the tank is 1485.20 cubic meters.

**41.** 19 hours 5 minutes $= 19\dfrac{5}{60}$ hours

$d = rt$

$2447.8 = r\left(19\dfrac{5}{60}\right)$

$128.3 \approx r$

Her average speed was 128.3 miles per hour.

**43.** $V = \pi r^2 h$

1 mile = 5280 feet

1.3 miles = 6864 feet

$3800 = \pi r^2(6864)$

$0.42 \approx r$

The radius of the hole is 0.42 feet.

**45.** $C = \pi d = \pi(41.125) = 41.125\pi$ ft $\approx 129.1325$ ft

The circumference of Eartha is $41.125\pi \approx 129.1325$ feet.

**47.** $A = P\left(1+\dfrac{r}{n}\right)^{nt}$

$= 10,000\left(1+\dfrac{0.085}{4}\right)^{4\cdot2}$

$= 10,000(1+0.02125)^8$

$\approx \$11,831.96$

$\$11,831.96 - \$10,000 = \$1831.96$

**49.** $\quad C = 4h + 9f + 4p$

$C - 4h - 4p = 9f$

$\dfrac{C-4h-4p}{9} = f$

$f = \dfrac{C-4h-4p}{9}$

**51.** $C = 4h + 9f + 4p$

$C = 4(7) + 9(14) + 4(6)$

$C = 178$

There are 178 calories in this serving.

**53.** $\quad C = 4h + 9f + 4p$

$130 = 4(31) + 9(0) + 4p$

$130 = 124 + 4p$

$6 = 4p$

$\dfrac{6}{4} = p$

$p = 1.5$

There are 1.5 g of protein provided by this serving of raisins.

**55.** $-3, -2, -1$ satisfy $x < 0$.

**57.** $-3, -2, -1, 0, 1$ satisfy $x + 5 \le 6$ or $x \le 1$.

**59.** Answers may vary

**61.** $AU = \dfrac{\text{miles}}{92,900,000}$ or $\dfrac{\text{million miles}}{92.9}$

| Planet | AU from Sun |
|---|---|
| Mercury | 0.388 |
| Venus | 0.723 |
| Earth | 1.00 |
| Mars | 1.523 |
| Jupiter | 5.202 |
| Saturn | 9.538 |
| Uranus | 19.193 |
| Neptune | 30.065 |
| Pluto | 39.505 |

**63.** Answers may vary

$\dfrac{1,700,000,000}{250,000,000} = 6.8$

It cost \$6.80 per person to build the *Endeavor*.

**65.** 4 times a year; answers may vary

**67.** $\dfrac{168 \text{ mi}}{1 \text{ hr}} \cdot \dfrac{5280 \text{ ft}}{1 \text{ mi}} \cdot \dfrac{1 \text{ hr}}{60 \text{ min}} \cdot \dfrac{1 \text{ min}}{60 \text{ sec}} = 246.4 \text{ ft/sec}$

$d = rt$

$60.5 \text{ ft} = 246.6 \text{ ft/sec} \cdot t$

$0.25 \text{ sec} \approx t$

The ball would reach the plate in approximately 0.25 second.

**69.** $P(\text{yellow}) = \dfrac{2}{8} = \dfrac{1}{4}$

**71.** $P(\text{blue}) = \dfrac{3}{8}$

**73.** $P(\text{black or yellow}) = P(\text{black}) + P(\text{yellow})$

$= \dfrac{1}{8} + \dfrac{2}{8}$

$= \dfrac{3}{8}$

**75.** $P(\text{yellow, blue, or black})$

$= P(\text{yellow}) + P(\text{blue}) + P(\text{black})$

$= \dfrac{2}{8} + \dfrac{3}{8} + \dfrac{1}{8}$

$= \dfrac{6}{8}$

$= \dfrac{3}{4}$

**77.** $P(\text{red, yellow, green, blue, or black})$

$= P(\text{red}) + P(\text{yellow}) + P(\text{green}) + P(\text{blue}) + P(\text{black})$

$= \dfrac{1}{8} + \dfrac{2}{8} + \dfrac{1}{8} + \dfrac{3}{8} + \dfrac{1}{8}$

$= 1$

**79.** 1

**Section 2.4**

**Practice Problems**

**1. a.** $\{x|x < 3.5\}$   $(-\infty, 3.5)$

3.5

    **b.** $\{x|x \geq -3\}$   $[-3, \infty)$

−3

    **c.** $\{x|-1 \leq x < 4\}$   $[-1, 4)$

−1     4

**2.**    $x + 5 > 9$

     $x + 5 - 5 > 9 - 5$

         $x > 4$

     $(4, \infty)$

4

**3.**       $8x + 21 \leq 2x - 3$

    $8x + 21 - 2x \leq 2x - 3 - 2x$

       $6x + 21 \leq -3$

   $6x + 21 - 21 \leq -3 - 21$

          $6x \leq -24$

          $\dfrac{6x}{6} \leq \dfrac{-24}{6}$

            $x \leq -4$

   $(-\infty, -4]$

−4

**4. a.**     $\dfrac{2}{5}x \geq \dfrac{4}{15}$

     $\dfrac{5}{2} \cdot \dfrac{2}{5}x \geq \dfrac{5}{2} \cdot \dfrac{4}{15}$

         $x \geq \dfrac{2}{3}$

    $\left[\dfrac{2}{3}, \infty\right)$

$\dfrac{2}{3}$

    **b.**   $-2.4x < 9.6$

       $\dfrac{-2.4x}{-2.4} > \dfrac{9.6}{-2.4}$

         $x > -4$

     $(-4, \infty)$

−4

**5.**     $-(4x + 6) \leq 2(5x + 9) + 2x$

       $-4x - 6 \leq 10x + 18 + 2x$

         $-4x - 6 \leq 12x + 18$

    $-4x - 6 + 4x \leq 12x + 18 + 4x$

            $-6 \leq 16x + 18$

       $-6 - 18 \leq 16x + 18 - 18$

          $-24 \leq 16x$

          $\dfrac{-24}{16} \leq \dfrac{16x}{16}$

           $\dfrac{3}{2} \leq x$

   $\left[-\dfrac{3}{2}, \infty\right)$

$-\dfrac{3}{2}$

**6.**     $\dfrac{3}{5}(x - 3) \geq x - 7$

    $5\left[\dfrac{3}{5}(x - 3)\right] \geq 5(x - 7)$

       $3(x - 3) \geq 5(x - 7)$

         $3x - 9 \geq 5x - 35$

    $3x - 9 - 5x \geq 5x - 35 - 5x$

         $-2x - 9 \geq -35$

    $-2x - 9 + 9 \geq -35 + 9$

          $-2x \geq -26$

          $\dfrac{-2x}{-2} \leq \dfrac{-26}{-2}$

           $x \leq 13$

   $(-\infty, 13]$

13

**7.**     $4(x - 2) < 4x + 5$

        $4x - 8 < 4x + 5$

    $4x - 8 - 4x < 4x + 5 - 4x$

         $-8 < 5$

This is a true statement for all values of $x$. The solution set is $\{x|x$ is a real number$\}$ or $(-\infty, \infty)$.

0

**8.** In words: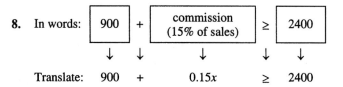

Translate:    900    +       $0.15x$      $\geq$     2400

$$900 + 0.15x \geq 2400$$
$$900 + 0.15x - 900 \geq 2400 - 900$$
$$0.15x \geq 1500$$
$$x \geq 10{,}000$$

Sales must be greater than or equal to $10,000 per month.

**9.** $-9.2t + 527.33 < 250$
$$-9.2t < -277.33$$
$$t > 30.14$$

The annual consumption of cigarettes will be less than 250 billion more than 30.14 years after 1990, or in approximately $31 + 1990 = 2021$ and after.

**Vocabulary and Readiness Check**

**1.** d. $(-\infty, -5)$

**2.** c. $[-11, \infty)$

**3.** b. $\left(-2.5, \dfrac{7}{4}\right]$

**4.** a. $\left[-\dfrac{10}{3}, 0.2\right)$

**5.** The set $\{x \mid x \geq -0.4\}$ written in interval notation is $\underline{[-0.4, \infty)}$.

**6.** The set $\{x \mid x < -0.4\}$ written in interval notation is $\underline{(-\infty, -0.4)}$.

**7.** The set $\{x \mid x \leq -0.4\}$ written in interval notation is $\underline{(-\infty, -0.4]}$.

**8.** The set $\{x \mid x > -0.4\}$ written in interval notation is $\underline{(-0.4, \infty)}$.

**9.** $3x > -14$   no

**10.** $-3x \leq 14$   yes

**11.** $-3x < -14$   yes

**12.** $-x \geq 23$   yes

**Exercise Set 2.4**

**1.** $\{x \mid x < -3\}$
$(-\infty, -3)$

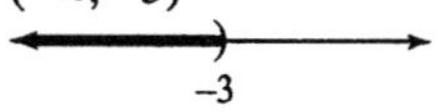

<!-- number line graph with open arrow pointing left from -3 -->
−3

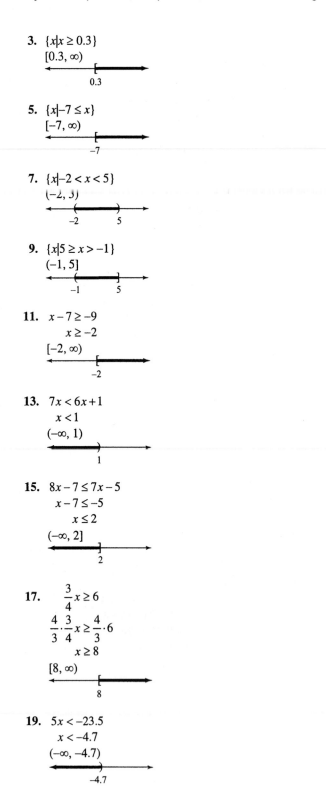

**3.** $\{x|x \ge 0.3\}$
$[0.3, \infty)$

**5.** $\{x|-7 \le x\}$
$[-7, \infty)$

**7.** $\{x|-2 < x < 5\}$
$(-2, 5)$

**9.** $\{x|5 \ge x > -1\}$
$(-1, 5]$

**11.** $x - 7 \ge -9$
$x \ge -2$
$[-2, \infty)$

**13.** $7x < 6x + 1$
$x < 1$
$(-\infty, 1)$

**15.** $8x - 7 \le 7x - 5$
$x - 7 \le -5$
$x \le 2$
$(-\infty, 2]$

**17.** $\frac{3}{4}x \ge 6$
$\frac{4}{3} \cdot \frac{3}{4}x \ge \frac{4}{3} \cdot 6$
$x \ge 8$
$[8, \infty)$

**19.** $5x < -23.5$
$x < -4.7$
$(-\infty, -4.7)$

**21.** $-3x \ge 9$
$x \le -3$
$(-\infty, -3]$

**23.** $-2x + 7 \ge 9$
$-2x \ge 2$
$x \le -1$
$(-\infty, -1]$

**25.** $15 + 2x \ge 4x - 7$
$15 \ge 2x - 7$
$22 \ge 2x$
$11 \ge x \text{ or } x \le 11$
$(-\infty, 11]$

**27.** $4(2x + 1) > 4$
$8x + 4 > 4$
$8x > 0$
$x > 0$
$(0, \infty)$

**29.** $3(x - 5) < 2(2x - 1)$
$3x - 15 < 4x - 2$
$-15 < x - 2$
$-13 < x$
$x > -13$
$(-13, \infty)$

**31.** $\frac{5x+1}{7} - \frac{2x-6}{4} \ge -4$
$28\left(\frac{5x+1}{7} - \frac{2x-6}{4}\right) \ge 28(-4)$
$4(5x+1) - 7(2x-6) \ge -112$
$20x + 4 - 14x + 42 \ge -112$
$6x + 46 \ge -112$
$6x \ge -158$
$x \ge -\frac{79}{3}$
$\left[-\frac{79}{3}, \infty\right)$

**33.**
$$-3(2x-1) < -4[2+3(x+2)]$$
$$-6x+3 < -4(2+3x+6)$$
$$-6x+3 < -4(8+3x)$$
$$-6x+3 < -32-12x$$
$$6x+3 < -32$$
$$6x < -35$$
$$x < -\frac{35}{6}$$
$$\left(-\infty, -\frac{35}{6}\right)$$

**35.**
$$x+9 < 3$$
$$x+9-9 < 3-9$$
$$x < -6$$
$$(-\infty, -6)$$

**37.**
$$-x < -4$$
$$\frac{-x}{-1} > \frac{-4}{-1}$$
$$x > 4$$
$$(4, \infty)$$

**39.**
$$-7x \leq 3.5$$
$$\frac{-7x}{-7} \geq \frac{3.5}{-7}$$
$$x \geq -0.5$$
$$[-0.5, \infty)$$

**41.**
$$\frac{1}{2}+\frac{2}{3} \geq \frac{x}{6}$$
$$6\left(\frac{1}{2}+\frac{2}{3}\right) \geq 6\left(\frac{x}{6}\right)$$
$$3+4 \geq x$$
$$7 \geq x$$
$$x \leq 7$$
$$(-\infty, 7]$$

**43.**
$$-5x+4 \leq -4(x-1)$$
$$-5x+4 \leq -4x+4$$
$$-x \leq 0$$
$$x \geq 0$$
$$[0, \infty)$$

**45.**
$$\frac{3}{4}(x-7) \geq x+2$$
$$4\left[\frac{3}{4}(x-7)\right] \geq 4(x+2)$$
$$3(x-7) \geq 4(x+2)$$
$$3x-21 \geq 4x+8$$
$$-x-21 \geq 8$$
$$-x \geq 29$$
$$x \leq -29$$
$$(-\infty, -29]$$

**47.**
$$0.8x+0.6x \geq 4.2$$
$$1.4x \geq 4.2$$
$$x \geq 3$$
$$[3, \infty)$$

**49.**
$$4(x-6)+2x-4 \geq 3(x-7)+10x$$
$$4x-24+2x-4 \geq 3x-21+10x$$
$$6x-28 \geq 13x-21$$
$$-28 \geq 7x-21$$
$$-7 \geq 7x$$
$$-1 \geq x$$
$$x \leq -1$$
$$(-\infty, -1]$$

**51.**
$$14-(5x-6) \geq -6(x+1)-5$$
$$14-5x+6 \geq -6x-6-5$$
$$-5x+20 \geq -6x-11$$
$$x+20 \geq -11$$
$$x \geq -31$$
$$[-31, \infty)$$

**53.**
$$\frac{1}{2}(3x-4) \leq \frac{3}{4}(x-6)+1$$
$$4\left[\frac{1}{2}(3x-4)\right] \leq 4\left[\frac{3}{4}(x-6)+1\right]$$
$$2(3x-4) \leq 3(x-6)+4$$
$$6x-8 \leq 3x-18+4$$
$$6x-8 \leq 3x-14$$
$$3x-8 \leq -14$$
$$3x \leq -6$$
$$x \leq -2$$
$$(-\infty, -2]$$

**55.**
$$\frac{-x+2}{2} - \frac{1-5x}{8} < -1$$
$$8\left(\frac{-x+2}{2} - \frac{1-5x}{8}\right) < 8(-1)$$
$$4(-x+2) - (1-5x) < -8$$
$$-4x+8-1+5x < -8$$
$$x+7 < -8$$
$$x < -15$$
$$(-\infty, -15)$$

**57.**
$$\frac{x+5}{5} - \frac{3+x}{8} \ge -\frac{3}{10}$$
$$40\left(\frac{x+5}{5} - \frac{3+x}{8}\right) \ge 40\left(-\frac{3}{10}\right)$$
$$8(x+5) - 5(3+x) \ge -12$$
$$8x+40-15-5x \ge -12$$
$$3x+25 \ge -12$$
$$3x \ge -37$$
$$x \ge -\frac{37}{3}$$
$$\left[-\frac{37}{3}, \infty\right)$$

**59.**
$$\frac{x+3}{12} + \frac{x-5}{15} < \frac{2}{3}$$
$$60\left(\frac{x+3}{12} + \frac{x-5}{15}\right) < 60\left(\frac{2}{3}\right)$$
$$5(x+3) + 4(x-5) < 20(2)$$
$$5x+15+4x-20 < 40$$
$$9x-5 < 40$$
$$9x < 45$$
$$x < 5$$
$$(-\infty, 5)$$

**61.**
$$0.4(4x-3) < 1.2(x+2)$$
$$10[0.4(4x-3)] < 10[1.2(x+2)]$$
$$4(4x-3) < 12(x+2)$$
$$16x-12 < 12x+24$$
$$4x-12 < 24$$
$$4x < 36$$
$$x < 9$$
$$(-\infty, 9)$$

**63.**
$$\frac{2}{5}x - \frac{1}{4} \le \frac{3}{10}x - \frac{4}{5}$$
$$20\left[\frac{2}{5}x - \frac{1}{4}\right] \le 20\left[\frac{3}{10}x - \frac{4}{5}\right]$$
$$4 \cdot 2x - 5 \le 2 \cdot 3x - 4 \cdot 4$$
$$8x-5 \le 6x-16$$
$$2x-5 \le -16$$
$$2x \le -11$$
$$x \le -\frac{11}{?}$$
$$\left(-\infty, -\frac{11}{2}\right]$$

**65.** $4(x-1) \ge 4x-8$
$$4x-4 \ge 4x-8$$
$$-4 \ge -8 \quad \text{(True for all } x\text{)}$$
All real numbers
$$(-\infty, \infty)$$

**67.** $7x < 7(x-2)$
$$7x < 7x-14$$
$$0 < -14 \quad \text{(False)}$$
No solution; $\varnothing$

**69.** Let $x$ = her score on the final.

a.  Then $\dfrac{72+67+82+79+2x}{6} \ge 77$
$$300+2x \ge 462$$
$$2x \ge 162$$
$$x \ge 81$$
$$\{x|x \ge 81\}$$

b.  A final exam grade of 81 or higher will result in an average of 77 or higher.

**71. a.** Let $x$ = weight of the luggage and cargo.
Then $6(160) + x \le 2000$
$$960 + x \le 2000$$
$$x \le 1040$$
$$\{x|x \le 1040\}$$

b.  The plane can carry a maximum of 1040 pounds of luggage and cargo.

**73. a.** Let $x$ be the number of boxes.
$$147 + 66x \le 1500$$
$$66x \le 1353$$
$$x \le \frac{1353}{66}$$
$$x \le 20.5$$
$$\{x|x \le 20\}$$

**b.** The number of boxes that can be moved at one time is at most 20.

**75.** Let $n$ = number of calls made in a given month.

    **a.** Then $\quad 25 < 13 + 0.06n$
$$12 < 0.06n$$
$$200 < n \text{ or } n > 200$$
$$\{n|n > 200\}$$

    **b.** Plan 1 is more economical than Plan 2 when 200 or more calls are made.

**77.** $F \ge \dfrac{9}{5}C + 32$

$\quad F \ge \dfrac{9}{5}(500) + 32$

$\quad F \ge 932°$

$\quad \{F|F \ge 932°\}$

Glass is a liquid at temperatures of 932°F or higher.

**79. a.** $\quad 651.2t + 28,472 > 42,000$
$$651.2t > 13,528$$
$$t > 20.8$$
$t$ is more than 20.8, so $t \ge 21$.
$1990 + 21 = 2011$
Salaries will be greater than \$42,000 in 2011.

    **b.** Answers may vary

**81.** The consumption of whole milk is decreasing. The graph of the line is going down over time.

**83.** $t = 2010 - 2000 = 10$
$y = -0.19t + 7.6$
$y = -0.19(10) + 7.6$
$y = -1.9 + 7.6$
$y = 5.7$
The consumption of whole milk in 2010 will be 5.7 gallons per person per year.

**85.** $\quad -0.19t + 7.6 < 6$
$$-0.19t < -1.6$$
$$t > 8.4$$
$2000 + 8 = 2008$
Consumption of whole milk will be less than 6 gallons per person per year during 2008.

**87.** Answers may vary

**89.** $x < 5$ and $x > 1$
The integers are 2, 3, and 4.

**91.** $x \ge -2$ and $x \ge 2$
The integers are 2, 3, 4, ....

**93.** $\quad 2x - 6 = 4$
$$2x - 6 + 6 = 4 + 6$$
$$2x = 10$$
$$\frac{2x}{2} = \frac{10}{2}$$
$$x = 5$$

**95.** $\quad -x + 7 = 5x - 6$
$$-x - 5x = -6 - 7$$
$$-6x = -13$$
$$\frac{-6x}{-6} = \frac{-13}{-6}$$
$$x = \frac{13}{6}$$

**97.** $\{x|x \ge 2\}, [2, \infty)$

**99.**

$(-\infty, 0)$

**101.** $\{x|-2 < x \le 1.5\}$

**103.** $\quad 2x - 3 = 5$
$$2x - 3 + 3 = 5 + 3$$
$$2x = 8$$
$$\frac{2x}{2} = \frac{8}{2}$$
$$x = 4$$
$\{4\}$

**105.** $\quad 2x - 3 > 5$
$$2x - 3 + 3 > 5 + 3$$
$$2x > 8$$
$$\frac{2x}{2} > \frac{8}{2}$$
$$x > 4$$
$(4, \infty)$

**107.** Answers may vary

**109.** Answers may vary

**111.** Answers may vary

**The Bigger Picture**

**1.**
$$3x - 4 = 3(2x - 1) + 7$$
$$3x - 4 = 6x - 3 + 7$$
$$3x - 4 = 6x + 4$$
$$3x - 4 - 6x = 6x + 4 - 6x$$
$$-3x - 4 = 4$$
$$-3x - 4 + 4 = 4 + 4$$
$$-3x = 8$$
$$\frac{-3x}{-3} = \frac{8}{-3}$$
$$x = -\frac{8}{3}$$

**2.**
$$5 + 2x = 5(x + 1)$$
$$5 + 2x = 5x + 5$$
$$5 + 2x - 5x = 5x + 5 - 5x$$
$$5 - 3x = 5$$
$$5 - 3x - 5 = 5 - 5$$
$$-3x = 0$$
$$\frac{-3x}{-3} = \frac{0}{-3}$$
$$x = 0$$

**3.**
$$\frac{x + 3}{2} > 1$$
$$2\left(\frac{x + 3}{2}\right) > 2(1)$$
$$x + 3 > 2$$
$$x + 3 - 3 > 2 - 3$$
$$x > -1$$
$$(-1, \infty)$$

**4.**
$$\frac{x - 2}{2} - \frac{x - 4}{3} = \frac{5}{6}$$
$$6\left(\frac{x - 2}{2} - \frac{x - 4}{3}\right) = 6\left(\frac{5}{6}\right)$$
$$3(x - 2) - 2(x - 4) = 5$$
$$3x - 6 - 2x + 8 = 5$$
$$x + 2 = 5$$
$$x + 2 - 2 = 5 - 2$$
$$x = 3$$

**5.**
$$\frac{7}{5} + \frac{y}{10} = 2$$
$$10\left(\frac{7}{5} + \frac{y}{10}\right) = 10(2)$$
$$2(7) + y = 20$$
$$14 + y = 20$$
$$14 + y - 14 = 20 - 14$$
$$y = 6$$

**6.**
$$5 + 2x = 2(x + 1)$$
$$5 + 2x = 2x + 2$$
$$5 + 2x - 2x = 2x + 2 - 2x$$
$$5 = 2 \quad \text{False}$$
This false statement indicates that there is no solution. The solution set is $\varnothing$.

**7.**
$$4(x - 2) + 3x \geq 9(x - 1) - 2$$
$$4x - 8 + 3x \geq 9x - 9 - 2$$
$$7x - 8 \geq 9x - 11$$
$$7x - 8 - 9x \geq 9x - 11 - 9x$$
$$-2x - 8 \geq -11$$
$$-2x - 8 + 8 \geq -11 + 8$$
$$-2x \geq -3$$
$$\frac{-2x}{-2} \leq \frac{-3}{-2}$$
$$x \leq \frac{3}{2}$$
$$\left(-\infty, \frac{3}{2}\right]$$

**8.**
$$6(x + 1) - 2 = 6x + 4$$
$$6x + 6 - 2 = 6x + 4$$
$$6x + 4 = 6x + 4$$
$$6x + 4 - 6x = 6x + 4 - 6x$$
$$4 = 4 \quad \text{True}$$
This true statement indicates that all real numbers are solutions of the equation. The solution set is $(-\infty, \infty)$.

**Integrated Review**

**1.**
$$-4x = 20$$
$$\frac{-4x}{-4} = \frac{20}{-4}$$
$$x = -5$$

**2.**
$$-4x < 20$$
$$\frac{-4x}{-4} > \frac{20}{-4}$$
$$x > -5$$
$$(-5, \infty)$$

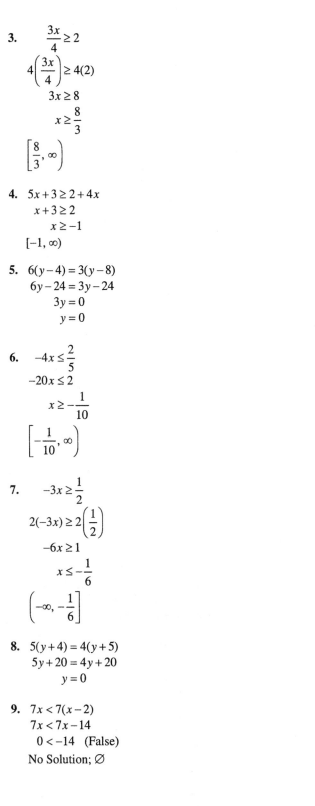

3.    $\dfrac{3x}{4} \geq 2$

$4\left(\dfrac{3x}{4}\right) \geq 4(2)$

$3x \geq 8$

$x \geq \dfrac{8}{3}$

$\left[\dfrac{8}{3}, \infty\right)$

4.    $5x + 3 \geq 2 + 4x$

$x + 3 \geq 2$

$x \geq -1$

$[-1, \infty)$

5.    $6(y - 4) = 3(y - 8)$

$6y - 24 = 3y - 24$

$3y = 0$

$y = 0$

6.    $-4x \leq \dfrac{2}{5}$

$-20x \leq 2$

$x \geq -\dfrac{1}{10}$

$\left[-\dfrac{1}{10}, \infty\right)$

7.    $-3x \geq \dfrac{1}{2}$

$2(-3x) \geq 2\left(\dfrac{1}{2}\right)$

$-6x \geq 1$

$x \leq -\dfrac{1}{6}$

$\left(-\infty, -\dfrac{1}{6}\right]$

8.    $5(y + 4) = 4(y + 5)$

$5y + 20 = 4y + 20$

$y = 0$

9.    $7x < 7(x - 2)$

$7x < 7x - 14$

$0 < -14$   (False)

No Solution; $\varnothing$

10.    $\dfrac{-5x + 11}{2} \leq 7$

$2\left(\dfrac{-5x + 11}{2}\right) \leq 2(7)$

$-5x + 11 \leq 14$

$-5x \leq 3$

$x \geq -\dfrac{3}{5}$

$\left[-\dfrac{3}{5}, \infty\right)$

11.    $-5x + 1.5 = -19.5$

$-5x + 1.5 - 1.5 = -19.5 - 1.5$

$-5x = -21$

$\dfrac{-5x}{-5} = \dfrac{-21}{-5}$

$x = 4.2$

12.    $-5x + 4 = -26$

$-5x = -30$

$x = 6$

13.    $5 + 2x - x = -x + 3 - 14$

$5 + x = -x - 11$

$5 + 2x = -11$

$2x = -16$

$x = -8$

14.    $12x + 14 < 11x - 2$

$x + 14 < -2$

$x < -16$

$(-\infty, -16)$

15.    $\dfrac{x}{5} - \dfrac{x}{4} = \dfrac{x - 2}{2}$

$20\left(\dfrac{x}{5} - \dfrac{x}{4}\right) = 20\left(\dfrac{x - 2}{2}\right)$

$4x - 5x = 10(x - 2)$

$-x = 10x - 20$

$-11x = -20$

$x = \dfrac{20}{11}$

16.    $12x - 12 = 8(x - 1)$

$12x - 12 = 8x - 8$

$4x - 12 = -8$

$4x = 4$

$x = 1$

**17.**  $2(x-3) > 70$
$\quad 2x - 6 > 70$
$\quad\quad 2x > 76$
$\quad\quad\quad x > 38$
$\quad (38, \infty)$

**18.**  $\quad -3x - 4.7 = 11.8$
$\quad -3x - 4.7 + 4.7 = 11.8 + 4.7$
$\quad\quad\quad -3x = 16.5$
$\quad\quad\quad \dfrac{-3x}{-3} = \dfrac{16.5}{-3}$
$\quad\quad\quad\quad x = -5.5$

**19.**  $-2(b-4) - (3b-1) = 5b + 3$
$\quad -2b + 8 - 3b + 1 = 5b + 3$
$\quad\quad\quad -5b + 9 = 5b + 3$
$\quad\quad\quad -10b = -6$
$\quad\quad\quad\quad b = \dfrac{-6}{-10} = \dfrac{3}{5}$

**20.**  $8(x+3) < 7(x+5) + x$
$\quad 8x + 24 < 7x + 35 + x$
$\quad 8x + 24 < 8x + 35$
$\quad\quad 24 < 35 \quad \text{(True for all } x)$
$\quad$ All real numbers; $(-\infty, \infty)$

**21.**  $\dfrac{3t+1}{8} = \dfrac{5+2t}{7} + 2$
$\quad 56\left(\dfrac{3t+1}{8}\right) = 56\left(\dfrac{5+2t}{7}\right) + 56(2)$
$\quad\quad 7(3t+1) = 8(5+2t) + 112$
$\quad\quad 21t + 7 = 40 + 16t + 112$
$\quad\quad 21t + 7 = 16t + 152$
$\quad\quad\quad 5t = 145$
$\quad\quad\quad t = 29$

**22.**  $4(x-6) - x = 8(x-3) - 5x$
$\quad 4x - 24 - x = 8x - 24 - 5x$
$\quad\quad 3x - 24 = 3x - 24$
$\quad\quad -24 = -24 \quad \text{(True for all } x)$
The solution is all real numbers.

**23.**  $\dfrac{x}{6} + \dfrac{3x-2}{2} < \dfrac{2}{3}$
$\quad 6\left(\dfrac{x}{6} + \dfrac{3x-2}{2}\right) < 6\left(\dfrac{2}{3}\right)$
$\quad\quad x + 3(3x-2) < 4$
$\quad\quad\quad x + 9x - 6 < 4$
$\quad\quad\quad 10x - 6 < 4$
$\quad\quad\quad 10x < 10$
$\quad\quad\quad\quad x < 1$
$\quad (-\infty, 1)$

**24.**  $\dfrac{y}{3} + \dfrac{y}{5} = \dfrac{y+3}{10}$
$\quad 30\left(\dfrac{y}{3}\right) + 30\left(\dfrac{y}{5}\right) = 30\left(\dfrac{y+3}{10}\right)$
$\quad\quad 10y + 6y = 3(y+3)$
$\quad\quad 16y = 3y + 9$
$\quad\quad 13y = 9$
$\quad\quad\quad y = \dfrac{9}{13}$

**25.**  $5(x-6) + 2x > 3(2x-1) - 4$
$\quad 5x - 30 + 2x > 6x - 3 - 4$
$\quad\quad 7x - 30 > 6x - 7$
$\quad\quad\quad x > 23$
$\quad (23, \infty)$

**26.**  $14(x-1) - 7x \le 2(3x-6) + 4$
$\quad 14x - 14 - 7x \le 6x - 12 + 4$
$\quad\quad 7x - 14 \le 6x - 8$
$\quad\quad\quad x \le 6$
$\quad (-\infty, 6]$

**27.**  $\dfrac{1}{4}(3x+2) - x \ge \dfrac{3}{8}(x-5) + 2$
$\quad 8\left[\dfrac{1}{4}(3x+2) - x\right] \ge 8\left[\dfrac{3}{8}(x-5) + 2\right]$
$\quad\quad 2(3x+2) - 8x \ge 3(x-5) + 16$
$\quad\quad 6x + 4 - 8x \ge 3x - 15 + 16$
$\quad\quad -2x + 4 \ge 3x + 1$
$\quad\quad 3 \ge 5x$
$\quad\quad \dfrac{3}{5} \ge x \quad \text{or} \quad x \le \dfrac{3}{5}$
$\quad \left(-\infty, \dfrac{3}{5}\right]$

**28.**    $\dfrac{1}{3}(x-10)-4x > \dfrac{5}{6}(2x+1)-1$

$$6\left[\dfrac{1}{3}(x-10)-4x\right] > 6\left[\dfrac{5}{6}(2x+1)-1\right]$$
$$2(x-10)-24x > 5(2x+1)-6$$
$$2x-20-24x > 10x+5-6$$
$$-22x-20 > 10x-1$$
$$-19 > 32x$$
$$-\dfrac{19}{32} > x \quad \text{or} \quad x < -\dfrac{19}{32}$$

$\left(-\infty, -\dfrac{19}{32}\right)$

## Section 2.5

### Practice Exercises

**1.** $A = \{1, 3, 5, 7, 9\}$ and $B = \{1, 2, 3, 4\}$
The numbers 1 and 3 are in sets $A$ and $B$.
The intersection is $\{1, 3\}$. $A \cap B = \{1, 3\}$.

**2.** $\begin{aligned} x+3 &< 8 \quad \text{and} \quad 2x-1 < 3 \\ x &< 5 \quad \text{and} \quad\quad 2x < 4 \\ x &< 5 \quad \text{and} \quad\quad\ x < 2 \end{aligned}$

$\{x \mid x < 5\}, (-\infty, 5)$

$\longleftarrow\!\!\!\!\!\!\!\!\!\!\!\!\!\!\!\!\!\!\!\!\!\!\!\!\!\!\!\!\!\!\!\!\!\!)\!\longrightarrow$
                5

$\{x \mid x < 2\}, (-\infty, 2)$

$\longleftarrow\!\!\!\!\!\!\!\!\!\!\!\!\!\!\!\!\!\!)\!\longrightarrow$
         2

$\{x \mid x < 5 \text{ and } x < 2\} = \{x \mid x < 2\}$

$\longleftarrow\!\!\!\!\!\!\!\!\!\!\!\!\!\!\!\!\!\!)\!\longrightarrow$
         2

The solution set is $(-\infty, 2)$.

**3.** $\begin{aligned} 4x &\le 0 \quad \text{and} \quad 3x+2 > 8 \\ x &\le 0 \quad \text{and} \quad\quad 3x > 6 \\ x &\le 0 \quad \text{and} \quad\quad\ x > 2 \end{aligned}$

$\{x \mid x \le 0\}, (-\infty, 0]$

$\longleftarrow\!\!\!\!\!\!\!\!\!\!\!\!\!\!\!\!\!\!]\!\longrightarrow$
         0

$\{x \mid x > 2\}, (2, \infty)$

$\longleftarrow\!(\!\!\!\!\!\!\!\!\!\!\!\!\!\!\!\!\!\!\longrightarrow$
         2

$\{x \mid 4x \le 0 \text{ and } 3x + 2 > 8\} = \{\ \} \text{ or } \varnothing$

$\longleftarrow\!\!\!\!\!\!\!\!\!\!\!\!\!\!\!\!\!\!\!\!\!\!\!\!\!\!\!\!\!\!\longrightarrow$

**4.** $\begin{aligned} 3 &< 5-x < 9 \\ 3-5 &< 5-x-5 < 9-5 \\ -2 &< -x < 4 \\ \dfrac{-2}{-1} &> \dfrac{-x}{-1} > \dfrac{4}{-1} \\ 2 &> x > -4 \end{aligned}$
or $-4 < x < 2$
The solution set is $(-4, 2)$.

**5.**    $-4 \le \dfrac{x}{2} - 1 \le 3$

$$2(-4) \le 2\left(\dfrac{x}{2} - 1\right) \le 2(3)$$
$$-8 \le x - 2 \le 6$$
$$-8+2 \le x-2+2 \le 6+2$$
$$-6 \le x \le 8$$
The solution set is $[-6, 8]$.

**6.** $A = \{1, 3, 5, 7, 9\}$ and $B = \{2, 3, 4, 5, 6\}$.
The numbers that are in either set or both sets are
$\{1, 2, 3, 4, 5, 6, 7, 9\}$. This set is the union,
$A \cup B$.

**7.** $\begin{aligned} 8x+5 &\le 8 \quad \text{or} \quad x-1 \ge 2 \\ 8x &\le 3 \quad \text{or} \quad\quad x \ge 3 \\ x &\le \dfrac{3}{8} \quad \text{or} \quad\quad x \ge 3 \end{aligned}$

$\left\{x \mid x \le \dfrac{3}{8}\right\}, \left(-\infty, \dfrac{3}{8}\right]$

$\longleftarrow\!\!\!\!\!\!\!\!\!\!\!\!\!\!\!\!\!\!]\!\longrightarrow$
        $\dfrac{3}{8}$

$\{x \mid x \ge 3\}, [3, \infty)$

$\longleftarrow\!\!\!\!\!\!\!\!\!\!\!\!\![\!\longrightarrow$
         3

$\left\{x \mid x \le \dfrac{3}{8} \text{ or } x \ge 3\right\} = \left(-\infty, \dfrac{3}{8}\right] \cup [3, \infty)$

$\longleftarrow\!\!\!\!\!\!\!\!\!\!\!\!]\!\!\!\!\!\!\!\![\!\longrightarrow$
      $\dfrac{3}{8}$    3

The solution set is $\left(-\infty, \dfrac{3}{8}\right] \cup [3, \infty)$.

**8.** $\begin{aligned} -3x-2 &> -8 \quad \text{or} \quad 5x > 0 \\ -3x &> -6 \quad \text{or} \quad\quad x > 0 \\ x &< 2 \quad \text{or} \quad\quad x > 0 \end{aligned}$

$\{x \mid x < 2\}, (-\infty, 2)$

$\longleftarrow\!\!\!\!\!\!\!\!\!\!\!\!\!\!\!\!\!\!)\!\longrightarrow$
         2

$\{x \mid x > 0\}, (0, \infty)$

$\longleftarrow\!(\!\!\!\!\!\!\!\!\!\!\!\!\!\!\!\!\!\!\longrightarrow$
         0

$\{x \mid x < 2 \text{ or } x > 0\}, (-\infty, \infty)$

$\longleftarrow\!\!\!\!\!\!\!\!\!\!\!\!\!\!\!\!\!\!\!\!\!\!\!\!\!\!\!\!\!\!\longrightarrow$

The solution set is $(-\infty, \infty)$.

### Vocabulary and Readiness Check

**1.** Two inequalities joined by the words "and" or
"or" are called <u>compound</u> inequalities.

**2.** The word <u>and</u> means intersection.

3.  The word <u>or</u> means union.

4.  The symbol $\cap$ means intersection.

5.  The symbol $\cup$ represents union.

6.  The symbol $\varnothing$ is the empty set.

7.  The inequality $-2 \le x < 1$ means $-2 \le x$ <u>and</u> $x < 1$.

8.  $\{x | x < 0 \text{ and } x > 0\} = \underline{\varnothing}$.

**Exercise Set 2.5**

1.  $C \cup D = \{2, 3, 4, 5, 6, 7\}$

3.  $A \cap D = \{4, 6\}$

5.  $A \cup B = \{..., -2, -1, 0, 1, ...\}$

7.  $B \cap D = \{5, 7\}$

9.  $B \cup C = \{x | x \text{ is an odd integer or } x = 2 \text{ or } x = 4\}$

11. $A \cap C = \{2, 4\}$

13. $x < 1 \text{ and } x > -3$
    $-3 < x < 1$
    $(-3, 1)$
    $-3 \qquad 1$

15. $x \le -3 \text{ and } x \ge -2$
    $\varnothing$

17. $x < -1 \text{ and } x < 1$
    $x < -1$
    $(-\infty, -1)$
    $-1$

19. $x + 1 \ge 7 \quad \text{and} \quad 3x - 1 \ge 5$
    $\quad x \ge 6 \quad \text{and} \qquad 3x \ge 6$
    $\qquad\qquad\qquad\qquad\qquad x \ge 2$
    $x \ge 6$
    $[6, \infty)$

21. $4x + 2 \le -10 \quad \text{and} \quad 2x \le 0$
    $\quad 4x \le -12 \quad \text{and} \qquad x \le 0$
    $\qquad x \le -3$
    $x \le -3$
    $(-\infty, -3]$

23. $-2x < -8 \quad \text{and} \quad x - 5 < 5$
    $\quad x > 4 \quad \text{and} \qquad x < 10$
    $(4, 10)$

25. $5 < x - 6 < 11$
    $11 < x < 17$
    $(11, 17)$

27. $-2 \le 3x - 5 \le 7$
    $3 \le 3x \le 12$
    $1 \le x \le 4$
    $[1, 4]$

29. $1 \le \dfrac{2}{3}x + 3 \le 4$
    $-2 \le \dfrac{2}{3}x \le 1$
    $-3 \le x \le \dfrac{3}{2}$
    $\left[-3, \dfrac{3}{2}\right]$

31. $-5 \le \dfrac{-3x + 1}{4} \le 2$
    $4(-5) \le 4\left(\dfrac{-3x + 1}{4}\right) \le 4(2)$
    $-20 \le -3x + 1 \le 8$
    $-21 \le -3x \le 7$
    $7 \ge x \ge -\dfrac{7}{3}$
    $-\dfrac{7}{3} \le x \le 7$
    $\left[-\dfrac{7}{3}, 7\right]$

33. $x < 4 \text{ or } x < 5$
    $(-\infty, 5)$
    $5$

35. $x \le -4 \text{ or } x \ge 1$
    $(-\infty, -4] \cup [1, \infty)$
    $-4 \qquad 1$

37. $x > 0 \text{ or } x < 3$
    $(-\infty, \infty)$

**39.** $-2x \le -4$   or   $5x - 20 \ge 5$
     $x \ge 2$   or     $5x \ge 25$
                      $x \ge 5$

  $x \ge 2$
  $[2, \infty)$

**41.** $x + 4 < 0$   or   $6x > -12$
     $x < -4$   or    $x > -2$
  $(-\infty, -4) \cup (-2, \infty)$

**43.** $3(x-1) < 12$   or   $x + 7 > 10$
     $x - 1 < 4$   or     $x > 3$
        $x < 5$

  $(-\infty, \infty)$

**45.** $x < \dfrac{2}{3}$ and $x > -\dfrac{1}{2}$

  $-\dfrac{1}{2} < x < \dfrac{2}{3}$

  $\left( -\dfrac{1}{2}, \dfrac{2}{3} \right)$

**47.** $x < \dfrac{2}{3}$ or $x > -\dfrac{1}{2}$

  $(-\infty, \infty)$

**49.** $0 \le 2x - 3 \le 9$
    $3 \le 2x \le 12$

  $\dfrac{3}{2} \le x \le 6$

  $\left[ \dfrac{3}{2}, 6 \right]$

**51.**     $\dfrac{1}{2} < x - \dfrac{3}{4} < 2$

  $4\left( \dfrac{1}{2} \right) < 4\left( x - \dfrac{3}{4} \right) < 4(2)$

      $2 < 4x - 3 < 8$

      $5 < 4x < 11$

    $\dfrac{5}{4} < x < \dfrac{11}{4}$

  $\left( \dfrac{5}{4}, \dfrac{11}{4} \right)$

**53.** $x + 3 \ge 3$   and   $x + 3 \le 2$
     $x \ge 0$   and     $x \le -1$
  No solution exists.
  $\varnothing$

**55.** $3x \ge 5$   or   $-\dfrac{5}{8}x - 6 > 1$

    $x \ge \dfrac{5}{3}$   or     $-\dfrac{5}{8}x > 7$

                     $x < -\dfrac{56}{5}$

  $\left( -\infty, -\dfrac{56}{5} \right) \cup \left[ \dfrac{5}{3}, \infty \right)$

**57.**    $0 < \dfrac{5 - 2x}{3} < 5$

    $0 < 5 - 2x < 15$

  $\dfrac{-5}{-2} > \dfrac{-2x}{-2} > \dfrac{10}{-2}$

    $\dfrac{5}{2} > x > -5$

    $-5 < x < \dfrac{5}{2}$

  $\left( -5, \dfrac{5}{2} \right)$

**59.** $-6 < 3(x - 2) \le 8$
    $-6 < 3x - 6 \le 8$
     $0 < 3x \le 14$

    $0 < x < \dfrac{14}{3}$

  $\left( 0, \dfrac{14}{3} \right]$

**61.** $-x + 5 > 6$   and   $1 + 2x \le -5$
    $-x > 1$   and     $2x \le -6$
     $x < -1$   and      $x \le -3$
  $x \le -3$
  $(-\infty, -3]$

**63.** $3x + 2 \le 5$   or   $7x > 29$

    $3x \le 3$   or     $x > \dfrac{29}{7}$

    $x \le 1$   or     $x > \dfrac{29}{7}$

  $(-\infty, 1] \cup \left( \dfrac{29}{7}, \infty \right)$

**65.** $5 - x > 7$   and   $2x + 3 \ge 13$
    $-x > 2$   and     $2x \ge 10$
    $x < -2$   and      $x \ge 5$
  No solution exists.
  $\varnothing$

**67.**
$$-\frac{1}{2} \le \frac{4x-1}{6} < \frac{5}{6}$$
$$6\left(-\frac{1}{2}\right) \le 6\left(\frac{4x-1}{6}\right) < 6\left(\frac{5}{6}\right)$$
$$-3 \le 4x-1 < 5$$
$$-2 \le 4x < 6$$
$$-\frac{1}{2} \le x < \frac{3}{2}$$
$$\left[-\frac{1}{2}, \frac{3}{2}\right)$$

**69.**
$$\frac{1}{15} < \frac{8-3x}{15} < \frac{4}{5}$$
$$15\left(\frac{1}{15}\right) < 15\left(\frac{8-3x}{15}\right) < 15\left(\frac{4}{5}\right)$$
$$1 < 8-3x < 12$$
$$-7 < -3x < 4$$
$$-\frac{4}{3} < x < \frac{7}{3}$$
$$\left(-\frac{4}{3}, \frac{7}{3}\right)$$

**71.** $0.3 < 0.2x - 0.9 < 1.5$
$$1.2 < 0.2x < 2.4$$
$$6 < x < 12$$
$$(6, 12)$$

**73.** $|-7| - |19| = 7 - 19 = -12$

**75.** $-(-6) - |-10| = 6 - 10 = -4$

**77.** $|x| = 7$
$$x = -7, 7$$

**79.** $|x| = 0$
$$x = 0$$

**81.** The years that the consumption of bottled water was greater than 20 gallons per person were 2003, 2004, and 2005. The years that consumption of diet soda was greater than 14 gallons per person were 2003, 2004, and 2005. The years in common are 2003, 2004, and 2005.

**83.**
$$-29 \le C \le 35$$
$$-29 \le \frac{5}{9}(F-32) \le 35$$
$$-52.5 \le F - 32 \le 63$$
$$-20.2 \le F \le 95$$
$$-20.2° \le F \le 95°$$

**85.**
$$70 \le \frac{68+65+75+78+2x}{6} \le 79$$
$$420 \le 286 + 2x \le 474$$
$$134 \le 2x \le 188$$
$$67 \le x \le 94$$
If Christian scores between 67 and 94 inclusive on his final exam, he will receive a C in the course.

**87.** $2x - 3 < 3x + 1 < 4x - 5$
$$2x-3 < 3x+1 \quad \text{and} \quad 3x+1 < 4x-5$$
$$-x < 4 \qquad \text{and} \qquad -x < -6$$
$$x > -4 \qquad \text{and} \qquad x > 6$$
$$x > 6$$
$$(6, \infty)$$

**89.** $-3(x-2) \le 3 - 2x \le 10 - 3x$
$$-3x+6 \le 3-2x \quad \text{and} \quad 3-2x \le 10-3x$$
$$-x \le -3 \qquad \text{and} \qquad x \le 7$$
$$x \ge 3$$
$$3 \le x \le 7$$
$$[3, 7]$$

**91.** $5x - 8 < 2(2 + x) < -2(1 + 2x)$
$$5x-8 < 4+2x \quad \text{and} \quad 4+2x < -2-4x$$
$$3x < 12 \qquad \text{and} \qquad 6x < -6$$
$$x < 4 \qquad \text{and} \qquad x < -1$$
$$x < -1$$
$$(-\infty, -1)$$

**The Bigger Picture**

**1.** $x - 2 \le 1$ and $3x - 1 \ge -4$
$$x \le 3 \quad \text{and} \quad 3x \ge -3$$
$$x \ge -1$$
$$-1 \le x \le 3$$
$$[-1, 3]$$

**2.**
$$-2 < x - 1 < 5$$
$$-2 + 1 < x - 1 + 1 < 5 + 1$$
$$-1 < x < 6$$
$$(-1, 6)$$

**3.** $-2x + 2.5 = -7.7$
$$-2x = -10.2$$
$$x = 5.1$$

**4.** $-5x > 20$

$$\frac{-5x}{-5} < \frac{20}{-5}$$

$$x < -4$$

$(-\infty, -4)$

**5.** $x \le -3$ or $x \le -5$

$x \le -3$

$(-\infty, -3]$

**6.** $5x < -10$ or $3x - 4 > 2$

$\quad x < -2$ or $\quad\quad 3x > 6$

$\quad\quad\quad\quad\quad\quad\quad x > 2$

$(-\infty, -2) \cup (2, \infty)$

**7.** $\quad \dfrac{5t}{2} - \dfrac{3t}{4} = 7$

$$4\left(\frac{5t}{2} - \frac{3t}{4}\right) = 4(7)$$

$$2(5t) - 3t = 28$$

$$10t - 3t = 28$$

$$7t = 28$$

$$t = 4$$

**8.** $5(x-3) + x + 2 \ge 3(x+2) + 2x$

$5x - 15 + x + 2 \ge 3x + 6 + 2x$

$\quad\quad\quad 6x - 13 \ge 5x + 6$

$\quad\quad\quad 6x - 5x \ge 13 + 6$

$\quad\quad\quad\quad\quad\quad x \ge 19$

$[19, \infty)$

## Section 2.6

### Practice Exercises

**1.** $|q| = 7$

$q = 7$ or $q = -7$

The solution set is $\{-7, 7\}$.

**2.** $|2x - 3| = 5$

$2x - 3 = 5$ or $2x - 3 = -5$

$\quad 2x = 8$ or $\quad\quad 2x = -2$

$\quad\quad x = 4$ or $\quad\quad\quad x = -1$

The solution set is $\{-1, 4\}$.

**3.** $\left|\dfrac{x}{5} + 1\right| = 15$

$\dfrac{x}{5} + 1 = 15$ or $\dfrac{x}{5} + 1 = -15$

$\quad \dfrac{x}{5} = 14$ or $\quad\quad \dfrac{x}{5} = -16$

$\quad\quad x = 70$ or $\quad\quad\quad x = -80$

The solutions are $-80$ and $70$.

**4.** $|3x| + 8 = 14$

$\quad |3x| = 6$

$3x = 6$ or $3x = -6$

$\quad x = 2$ or $\quad x = -2$

The solutions are $-2$ and $2$.

**5.** $|z| = 0$

The solution is $0$.

**6.** $3|z| + 9 = 7$

$\quad 3|z| = -2$

$\quad\quad |z| = -\dfrac{2}{3}$

The absolute value of a number is never negative, so there is no solution. The solution set is $\{ \ \}$ or $\varnothing$.

**7.** $\left|\dfrac{5x + 3}{4}\right| = -8$

The absolute value of a number is never negative, so there is no solution. The solution set is $\{ \ \}$ or $\varnothing$.

**8.** $|2x + 4| = |3x - 1|$

$2x + 4 = 3x - 1$ or $2x + 4 = -(3x - 1)$

$\quad -x + 4 = -1$       $2x + 4 = -3x + 1$

$\quad\quad -x = -5$          $5x + 4 = 1$

$\quad\quad\quad x = 5$            $5x = -3$

$\quad\quad\quad\quad\quad\quad\quad\quad\quad\quad x = -\dfrac{3}{5}$

The solutions are $-\dfrac{3}{5}$ and $5$.

**9.** $|x - 2| = |8 - x|$

$x - 2 = 8 - x$ or $x - 2 = -(8 - x)$

$2x - 2 = 8$         $x - 2 = -8 + x$

$\quad 2x = 10$         $-2 = -8$   False

$\quad\quad x = 5$

The solution is $5$.

**Vocabulary and Readiness Check**

1. $|x - 2| = 5$
   C. $x - 2 = 5$ or $x - 2 = -5$

2. $|x - 2| = 0$
   A. $x - 2 = 0$

3. $|x - 2| = |x + 3|$
   B. $x - 2 = x + 3$ or $x - 2 = -(x + 3)$

4. $|x + 3| = 5$
   E. $x + 3 = 5$ or $x + 3 = -5$

5. $|x + 3| = -5$
   D. $\varnothing$

**Exercise Set 2.6**

1. $|x| = 7$
   $x = 7$ or $x = -7$

3. $|3x| = 12.6$
   $3x = 12.6$ or $3x = -12.6$
   $x = 4.2$ or $x = -4.2$

5. $|2x - 5| = 9$
   $2x - 5 = 9$ or $2x - 5 = -9$
   $2x = 14$ or $2x = -4$
   $x = 7$ or $x = -2$

7. $\left|\dfrac{x}{2} - 3\right| = 1$

   $\dfrac{x}{2} - 3 = 1$ or $\dfrac{x}{2} - 3 = -1$

   $2\left(\dfrac{x}{2} - 3\right) = 2(1)$ or $2\left(\dfrac{x}{2} - 3\right) = 2(-1)$

   $x - 6 = 2$ or $x - 6 = -2$
   $x = 8$ or $x = 4$

9. $|z| + 4 = 9$
   $|z| = 5$
   $z = -5$ or $z = -5$

11. $|3x| + 5 = 14$
    $|3x| = 9$
    $3x = 9$ or $3x = -9$
    $x = 3$ or $x = -3$

13. $|2x| = 0$
    $2x = 0$
    $x = 0$

15. $|4n + 1| + 10 = 4$
    $|4n + 1| = -6$ which is impossible.
    The solution set is $\varnothing$.

17. $|5x - 1| = 0$
    $5x - 1 = 0$
    $5x = 1$
    $x = \dfrac{1}{5}$

19. $|x| = 5$

21. $|5x - 7| = |3x + 11|$
    $5x - 7 = 3x + 11$ or $5x - 7 = -(3x + 11)$
    $2x = 18$ or $5x - 7 = -3x - 11$
    $x = 9$ or $8x = -4$
    $x = -\dfrac{1}{2}$

23. $|z + 8| = |z - 3|$
    $z + 8 = z - 3$ or $z + 8 = -(z - 3)$
    $8 = -3$ or $z + 8 = -z + 3$
    $2z = -5$
    $z = -\dfrac{5}{2}$

    The only solution is $-\dfrac{5}{2}$.

25. Answers may vary

27. $|x| = 4$
    $x = 4$ or $x = -4$

29. $|y| = 0$; $y = 0$

31. $|z| = -2$ is impossible. The solution set is $\varnothing$.

33. $|7 - 3x| = 7$
    $7 - 3x = 7$ or $7 - 3x = -7$
    $-3x = 0$ or $-3x = -14$
    $x = 0$ or $x = \dfrac{14}{3}$

**35.** $|6x| - 1 = 11$

$\qquad |6x| = 12$

$\qquad 6x = 12 \quad$ or $\quad 6x = -12$

$\qquad\quad x = 2 \quad$ or $\qquad x = -2$

**37.** $|4p| = -8$ is impossible. The solution set is $\varnothing$.

**39.** $|x - 3| + 3 = 7$

$\qquad |x - 3| = 4$

$\qquad x - 3 = 4 \quad$ or $\quad x - 3 = -4$

$\qquad\quad x = 7 \quad$ or $\qquad x = -1$

**41.** $\left|\dfrac{z}{4} + 5\right| = -7$ is impossible. The solution set is $\varnothing$.

**43.** $|9v - 3| = -8$ is impossible. The solution set is $\varnothing$.

**45.** $|8n + 1| = 0$

$\qquad 8n + 1 = 0$

$\qquad\quad 8n = -1$

$\qquad\quad\; n = -\dfrac{1}{8}$

**47.** $|1 - 6c| - 7 = -3$

$\qquad |1 - 6c| = 4$

$\qquad 1 - 6c = 4 \quad$ or $\quad 1 - 6c = -4$

$\qquad\quad 6c = 3 \quad$ or $\qquad 6c = -5$

$\qquad\quad\; c = \dfrac{1}{2} \quad$ or $\qquad c = -\dfrac{5}{6}$

**49.** $|5x + 1| = 11$

$\qquad 5x + 1 = 11 \quad$ or $\quad 5x + 1 = -11$

$\qquad\quad 5x = 10 \quad$ or $\qquad 5x = -12$

$\qquad\quad\; x = 2 \quad$ or $\qquad\quad x = -\dfrac{12}{5}$

**51.** $|4x - 2| = |-10|$

$\quad |4x - 2| = 10$

$\qquad 4x - 2 = 10 \quad$ or $\quad 4x - 2 = -10$

$\qquad\quad 4x = 12 \quad$ or $\qquad 4x = -8$

$\qquad\quad\; x = 3 \quad$ or $\qquad\quad x = -2$

**53.** $|5x + 1| = |4x - 7|$

$\quad 5x + 1 = 4x - 7 \quad$ or $\quad 5x + 1 = -(4x - 7)$

$\qquad\quad x = -8 \qquad$ or $\quad 5x + 1 = -4x + 7$

$\qquad\qquad\qquad\qquad\qquad\qquad 9x = 6$

$\qquad\qquad\qquad\qquad\qquad\qquad\; x = \dfrac{2}{3}$

**55.** $|6 + 2x| = -|-7|$

$\quad |6 + 2x| = -7$ which is impossible. The solution set is $\varnothing$.

**57.** $|2x - 6| = |10 - 2x|$

$\quad 2x - 6 = 10 - 2x \quad$ or $\quad 2x - 6 = -(10 - 2x)$

$\qquad\quad 4x = 16 \qquad$ or $\quad 2x - 6 = -10 + 2x$

$\qquad\quad\; x = 4 \qquad\;$ or $\qquad -6 = -10$

$\quad -6 = -10$ is impossible. The only solution is 4.

**59.** $\left|\dfrac{2x - 5}{3}\right| = 7$

$\qquad \dfrac{2x - 5}{3} = 7 \quad$ or $\quad \dfrac{2x - 5}{3} = -7$

$\qquad 2x - 5 = 21 \quad$ or $\quad 2x - 5 = -21$

$\qquad\quad 2x = 26 \quad$ or $\qquad 2x = -16$

$\qquad\quad\; x = 13 \quad$ or $\qquad\quad x = -8$

**61.** $2 + |5n| = 17$

$\qquad |5n| = 15$

$\qquad 5n = 15 \quad$ or $\quad 5n = -15$

$\qquad\; n = 3 \quad$ or $\quad n = -3$

**63.** $\left|\dfrac{2x - 1}{3}\right| = |-5|$

$\quad \left|\dfrac{2x - 1}{3}\right| = 5$

$\qquad \dfrac{2x - 1}{3} = 5 \quad$ or $\quad \dfrac{2x - 1}{3} = -5$

$\qquad 2x - 1 = 15 \quad$ or $\quad 2x - 1 = -15$

$\qquad\quad 2x = 16 \quad$ or $\qquad 2x = -14$

$\qquad\quad\; x = 8 \quad$ or $\qquad\quad x = -7$

**65.** $|2y - 3| = |9 - 4y|$

$\quad 2y - 3 = 9 - 4y \quad$ or $\quad 2y - 3 = -(9 - 4y)$

$\qquad 6y = 12 \qquad$ or $\quad 2y - 3 = -9 + 4y$

$\qquad\; y = 2 \qquad\;$ or $\qquad -2y = -6$

$\qquad\qquad\qquad\qquad\qquad\qquad y = 3$

**67.** $\left|\dfrac{3n+2}{8}\right| = |-1|$

$\left|\dfrac{3n+2}{8}\right| = 1$

$\dfrac{3n+2}{8} = 1$ or $\dfrac{3n+2}{8} = -1$

$3n+2 = 8$ or $3n+2 = -8$

$3n = 6$ or $3n = -10$

$n = 2$ or $n = -\dfrac{10}{3}$

**69.** $|x+4| = |7-x|$

$x+4 = 7-x$ or $x+4 = -(7-x)$

$2x = 3$ or $x+4 = -7+x$

$x = \dfrac{3}{2}$ or $4 = -7$

$4 = -7$ is impossible. The only solution is $\dfrac{3}{2}$.

**71.** $\left|\dfrac{8c-7}{3}\right| = -|-5|$

$\left|\dfrac{8c-7}{3}\right| = -5$ which is impossible.

The solution set is $\varnothing$.

**73.** Answers may vary

**75.** 34% of cheese consumption came from cheddar cheese.

**77.** $33\% \cdot (120 \text{ pounds}) = 0.33(120 \text{ pounds})$
$= 39.6 \text{ pounds}$
We might expect they consumed 39.6 pounds.

**79.** $|x| \geq -2$
Answers may vary; 0, 1, 2, 3, 4, for example

**81.** $|y| < 0$
No solution

**83.** $|x-7| = 2$

**85.** $|2x-1| = 4$

**87.** $|ax+b| = c$

  **a.** one solution if $c = 0$

  **b.** no solutions if $c$ is a negative number

  **c.** two solutions if $c$ is a positive number

## Section 2.7

### Practice Exercises

**1.** $|x| < 2$
The solution set of this inequality contains all numbers whose distance from 0 is less than 2. The solution set is $(-2, 2)$.

**2.** $|b+1| < 3$
$-3 < b+1 < 3$
$-3-1 < b+1-1 < 3-1$
$-4 < b < 2$
$(-4, 2)$

**3.** $|3x-2| + 5 \leq 9$
$|3x-2| \leq 9-5$
$|3x-2| \leq 4$
$-4 \leq 3x-2 \leq 4$
$-4+2 \leq 3x-2+2 \leq 4+2$
$-2 \leq 3x \leq 6$
$-\dfrac{2}{3} \leq x \leq 2$
$\left[-\dfrac{2}{3}, 2\right]$

**4.** $\left|3x + \dfrac{5}{8}\right| < -4$
The absolute value of a number is always nonnegative and can never be less than −4. The solution set is { } or $\varnothing$.

**5.** $|y+4| \geq 6$
$y+4 \leq -6$ or $y+4 \geq 6$
$y+4-4 \leq -6-4$ or $y+4-4 \geq 6-4$
$y \leq -10$ or $y \geq 2$
$(-\infty, -10] \cup [2, \infty)$

**6.** $|4x+3| + 5 > 3$
$|4x+3| + 5 - 5 > 3 - 5$
$|4x+3| > -2$
The absolute value of any number is always nonnegative and thus is always greater than −2. $(-\infty, \infty)$

**7.**   $\left|\dfrac{x}{2}-3\right|-5>-2$

$\left|\dfrac{x}{2}-3\right|-5+5>-2+5$

$\left|\dfrac{x}{2}-3\right|>3$

$\dfrac{x}{2}-3<-3$    or    $\dfrac{x}{2}-3>3$

$2\left(\dfrac{x}{2}-3\right)<2(-3)$   or   $2\left(\dfrac{x}{2}-3\right)>2(3)$

$x-6<-6$    or    $x-6>6$

$x<0$    or    $x>12$

$(-\infty, 0)\cup(12, \infty)$

**8.**   $\left|\dfrac{3(x-2)}{5}\right|\le 0$

$\dfrac{3(x-2)}{5}=0$

$5\left[\dfrac{3(x-2)}{5}\right]=5(0)$

$3(x-2)=0$

$3x-6=0$

$3x=6$

$x=2$

The solution set is $\{2\}$.

**Vocabulary and Readiness Check**

**1.** D

**2.** E

**3.** C

**4.** B

**5.** A

**Exercise Set 2.7**

**1.**   $|x|\le 4$

$-4\le x\le 4$

$[-4, 4]$

**3.**   $|x-3|<2$

$-2<x-3<2$

$1<x<5$

$(1, 5)$

**5.**   $|x+3|<2$

$-2<x+3<2$

$-5<x<-1$

$(-5, -1)$

**7.**   $|2x+7|\le 3$

$-13\le 2x+7\le 13$

$-20\le 2x\le 6$

$-10\le x\le 3$

$[-10, 3]$

**9.**   $|x|+7\le 12$

$|x|\le 5$

$-5\le x\le 5$

$[-5, 5]$

**11.**   $|3x-1|<-5$

No real solutions; $\varnothing$

**13.**   $|x-6|-7\le -1$

$|x-6|\le 6$

$-6\le x-6\le 6$

$0\le x\le 12$

$[0, 12]$

**15.**   $|x|>3$

$x<-3$   or   $x>3$

$(-\infty, -3)\cup(3, \infty)$

**17.**   $|x+10|\ge 14$

$x+10\le -14$   or   $x+10\ge 14$

$x\le -24$   or   $x\ge 4$

$(-\infty, -24]\cup[4, \infty)$

**19.**   $|x|+2>6$

$|x|>4$

$x<-4$   or   $x>4$

$(-\infty, -4)\cup(4, \infty)$

**21.** $|5x| > -4$
All real numbers
$(-\infty, \infty)$

**23.** $|6x - 8| + 3 > 7$
$\qquad |6x - 8| > 4$

$\qquad 6x - 8 < -4 \quad$ or $\quad 6x - 8 > 4$
$\qquad\quad 6x < 4 \quad$ or $\qquad 6x > 12$
$\qquad\quad x < \dfrac{2}{3} \quad$ or $\qquad\quad x > 2$

$\qquad \left(-\infty, \dfrac{2}{3}\right) \cup (2, \infty)$

**25.** $|x| \le 0$
$\quad |x| = 0$
$\qquad x = 0$

**27.** $|8x + 3| > 0$ only excludes $|8x + 3| = 0$
$\quad 8x + 3 = 0$
$\qquad\quad 8x = -3$
$\qquad\quad x = -\dfrac{3}{8}$

All real numbers except $-\dfrac{3}{8}$.

$\left(-\infty, -\dfrac{3}{8}\right) \cup \left(-\dfrac{3}{8}, \infty\right)$

**29.** $|x| \le 2$
$\quad -2 \le x \le 2$
$\quad [-2, 2]$

**31.** $|y| > 1$
$\quad y < -1 \quad$ or $\quad y > 1$
$\quad (-\infty, -1) \cup (1, \infty)$

**33.** $|x - 3| < 8$
$\quad -8 < x - 3 < 8$
$\quad -5 < x < 11$
$\quad (-5, 11)$

**35.** $|0.6x - 3| > 0.6$
$\quad 0.6x - 3 < -0.6 \quad$ or $\quad 0.6x - 3 > 0.6$
$\qquad 0.6x < 2.4 \quad$ or $\qquad 0.6x > 3.6$
$\qquad\quad x < 4 \quad$ or $\qquad\quad x > 6$

$(-\infty, 4) \cup (6, \infty)$

**37.** $5 + |x| \le 2$
$\qquad |x| \le -3$
No real solution
$\varnothing$

**39.** $|x| > -4$
All real numbers
$(-\infty, \infty)$

**41.** $|2x - 7| \le 11$
$\quad -11 \le 2x - 7 \le 11$
$\qquad -4 \le 2x \le 18$
$\qquad -2 \le x \le 9$
$\quad [-2, 9]$

**43.** $|x + 5| + 2 \ge 8$
$\qquad |x + 5| \ge 6$

$\quad x + 5 \le -6 \quad$ or $\quad x + 5 \ge 6$
$\qquad x \le -11 \quad$ or $\qquad x \ge 1$
$\quad (-\infty, -11] \cup [1, \infty)$

**45.** $|x| > 0$ only excludes $|x| = 0$, or $x = 0$.
All real numbers except $x = 0$
$(-\infty, 0) \cup (0, \infty)$

**47.** $9 + |x| > 7$
$\qquad |x| > -2$
All real numbers
$(-\infty, \infty)$

**49.** $6 + |4x - 1| \le 9$

$|4x - 1| \le 3$

$-3 \le 4x - 1 \le 3$

$-2 \le 4x \le 4$

$-\dfrac{1}{2} \le x \le 1$

$\left[-\dfrac{1}{2}, 1\right]$

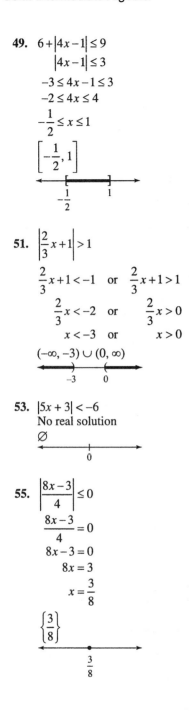

**51.** $\left|\dfrac{2}{3}x + 1\right| > 1$

$\dfrac{2}{3}x + 1 < -1$   or   $\dfrac{2}{3}x + 1 > 1$

$\dfrac{2}{3}x < -2$   or   $\dfrac{2}{3}x > 0$

$x < -3$   or   $x > 0$

$(-\infty, -3) \cup (0, \infty)$

**53.** $|5x + 3| < -6$

No real solution

$\varnothing$

**55.** $\left|\dfrac{8x - 3}{4}\right| \le 0$

$\dfrac{8x - 3}{4} = 0$

$8x - 3 = 0$

$8x = 3$

$x = \dfrac{3}{8}$

$\left\{\dfrac{3}{8}\right\}$

**57.** $|1 + 3x| + 4 < 5$

$|1 + 3x| < 1$

$-1 < 1 + 3x < 1$

$-2 < 3x < 0$

$-\dfrac{2}{3} < x < 0$

$\left(-\dfrac{2}{3}, 0\right)$

**59.** $\left|\dfrac{x + 6}{3}\right| > 2$

$\dfrac{x + 6}{3} < -2$     or     $\dfrac{x + 6}{3} > 2$

$x + 6 < -6$   or   $x + 6 > 6$

$x < -12$   or   $x > 0$

$(-\infty, -12) \cup (0, \infty)$

**61.** $-15 + |2x - 7| \le -6$

$|2x - 7| \le 9$

$-9 \le 2x - 7 \le 9$

$-2 \le 2x \le 16$

$-1 \le x \le 8$

$[-1, 8]$

**63.** $\left|2x + \dfrac{3}{4}\right| - 7 \le -2$

$\left|2x + \dfrac{3}{4}\right| \le 5$

$-5 \le 2x + \dfrac{3}{4} \le 5$

$-20 \le 8x + 3 \le 20$

$-23 \le 8x \le 17$

$-\dfrac{23}{8} \le x \le \dfrac{17}{8}$

$\left[-\dfrac{23}{8}, \dfrac{17}{8}\right]$

**65.** $|2x-3|<7$
$-7<2x-3<7$
$-4<2x<10$
$-2<x<5$
$(-2,5)$

**67.** $|2x-3|=7$
$2x-3=7$ or $2x-3=-7$
$2x=10$ or $2x=-4$
$x=5$ or $x=-2$

**69.** $|x-5|\geq 12$
$x-5\leq -12$ or $x-5\geq 12$
$x\leq -7$ or $x\geq 17$
$(-\infty,-7]\cup[17,\infty)$

**71.** $|9+4x|=0$
$9+4x=0$
$4x=-9$
$x=-\dfrac{9}{4}$

**73.** $|2x+1|+4<7$
$|2x+1|<3$
$-3<2x+1<3$
$-4<2x<2$
$-2<x<1$
$(-2,1)$

**75.** $|3x-5|+4=5$
$|3x-5|=1$
$3x-5=1$ or $3x-5=-1$
$3x=6$ or $3x=4$
$x=2$ or $x=\dfrac{4}{3}$

**77.** $|x+11|=-1$ is impossible. The solution set is $\varnothing$.

**79.** $\left|\dfrac{2x-1}{3}\right|=6$
$\dfrac{2x-1}{3}=6$ or $\dfrac{2x-1}{3}=-6$
$2x-1=18$ or $2x-1=-18$
$2x=19$ or $2x=-17$
$x=\dfrac{19}{2}$ or $x=-\dfrac{17}{2}$

**81.** $\left|\dfrac{3x-5}{6}\right|>5$
$\dfrac{3x-5}{6}<-5$ or $\dfrac{3x-5}{6}>5$
$3x-5<-30$ or $3x-5>30$
$3x<-25$ or $3x>35$
$x<-\dfrac{25}{3}$ or $x>\dfrac{35}{3}$
$\left(-\infty,-\dfrac{25}{3}\right)\cup\left(\dfrac{35}{3},\infty\right)$

**83.** $P(\text{rolling a 2})=\dfrac{1}{6}$

**85.** $P(\text{rolling a 7})=0$

**87.** $P(\text{rolling a 1 or 3})=\dfrac{1}{3}$

**89.** $3x-4y=12$
$3(2)-4y=12$
$6-4y=12$
$-4y=6$
$y=-\dfrac{3}{2}=-1.5$

**91.** $3x-4y=12$
$3x-4(-3)=12$
$3x+12=12$
$3x=0$
$x=0$

**93.** $|x|<7$

**95.** $|x|\leq 5$

**97.** Answers may vary

**99.** $|3.5-x|<0.05$
$-0.05<3.5-x<0.05$
$-3.55<-x<-3.45$
$3.55>x>3.45$
$3.45<x<3.55$

**The Bigger Picture**

**1.** $9x-14=11x+2$
$9x-11x=14+2$
$-2x=16$
$x=-8$

**2.** $|x - 4| = 17$
$$x - 4 = -17 \quad \text{or} \quad x - 4 = 17$$
$$x = -13 \quad \text{or} \quad\quad x = 21$$

**3.** $x - 1 \le 5 \quad \text{or} \quad 3x - 2 \le 10$
$$x \le 6 \quad \text{or} \quad\quad 3x \le 12$$
$$x \le 6 \quad \text{or} \quad\quad x \le 4$$

$(-\infty, 6]$

**4.** $-x < 7 \quad \text{and} \quad 4x \le 20$
$$x > -7 \quad \text{and} \quad x \le 5$$

$(-7, 5]$

**5.** $|x - 2| = |x + 15|$
$$x - 2 = x + 15 \quad\quad \text{or} \quad\quad x - 2 = -(x + 15)$$
$$-2 = 15 \quad \text{False} \quad\quad\quad x - 2 = -x - 15$$
$$2x - 2 = -15$$
$$2x = -13$$
$$x = -\frac{13}{2}$$

The only solution is $-\dfrac{13}{2}$.

**6.** $9y - 6y + 1 = 4y + 10 - y + 3$
$$3y + 1 = 3y + 13$$
$$1 = 13$$

$\varnothing$

**7.** $\quad 1.5x - 3 = 1.2x - 18$
$$1.5x - 1.2x = 3 - 18$$
$$0.3x = -15$$
$$x = -50$$

**8.** $\quad \dfrac{7x + 1}{8} - 3 = x + \dfrac{2x + 1}{4}$
$$8\left(\dfrac{7x + 1}{8} - 3\right) = 8\left(x + \dfrac{2x + 1}{4}\right)$$
$$7x + 1 - 8 \cdot 3 = 8x + 2(2x + 1)$$
$$7x + 1 - 24 = 8x + 4x + 2$$
$$7x - 23 = 12x + 2$$
$$7x - 12x = 2 + 23$$
$$-5x = 25$$
$$x = -5$$

**9.** $|5x+2|-10 \le -3$

$\quad |5x+2| \le 7$

$\quad -7 \le 5x+2 \le 7$

$\quad -9 \le 5x \le 5$

$\quad -\dfrac{9}{5} \le x \le 1$

$\quad \left[-\dfrac{9}{5}, 1\right]$

**10.** $|x+11| > 2$

$\quad x+11 > 2 \quad$ or $\quad x+11 < -2$

$\quad\quad x > -9 \quad$ or $\quad\quad\quad x < -13$

$\quad (-\infty, -13) \cup (-9, \infty)$

**11.** $|9x+2|-1 = 24$

$\quad |9x+2| = 25$

$\quad 9x+2 = -25 \quad$ or $\quad 9x+2 = 25$

$\quad\quad 9x = -27 \quad$ or $\quad\quad 9x = 23$

$\quad\quad\quad x = -3 \quad$ or $\quad\quad\quad x = \dfrac{23}{9}$

**12.** $\left|\dfrac{3x-1}{2}\right| = |2x+5|$

$\quad \dfrac{3x-1}{2} = -(2x+5) \quad$ or $\quad \dfrac{3x-1}{2} = 2x+5$

$\quad 2\left(\dfrac{3x-1}{2}\right) = 2[-(2x+5)] \quad$ or $\quad 2\left[\dfrac{3x-1}{2}\right] = 2(2x+5)$

$\quad\quad 3x-1 = -4x-10 \quad$ or $\quad\quad 3x-1 = 4x+10$

$\quad\quad 3x+4x = -10+1 \quad$ or $\quad\quad 3x-4x = 10+1$

$\quad\quad\quad 7x = -9 \quad$ or $\quad\quad\quad -x = 11$

$\quad\quad\quad x = -\dfrac{9}{7} \quad$ or $\quad\quad\quad x = -11$

## Chapter 2 Vocabulary Check

1. The statement "$x < 5$ or $x > 7$" is called a <u>compound inequality</u>.

2. An equation in one variable that has no solution is called a <u>contradiction</u>.

3. The <u>intersection</u> of two sets is the set of all elements common to both sets.

4. The <u>union</u> of two sets is the set of all elements that belong to either of the sets.

5. An equation in one variable that has every number (for which the equation is defined) as a solution is called an <u>identity</u>.

6. The equation $d = rt$ is also called a <u>formula</u>.

7. A number's distance from 0 is called its <u>absolute value</u>.

8. When a variable in an equation is replaced by a number and the resulting equation is true, then that number is called a <u>solution</u> of the equation.

9. The integers 17, 18, 19 are examples of <u>consecutive integers</u>.

10. The statement $5x - 0.2 < 7$ is an example of a <u>linear inequality in one variable</u>.

11. The statement $5x - 0.2 = 7$ is an example of a <u>linear equation in one variable</u>.

## Chapter 2 Review

1. $4(x - 5) = 2x - 14$
$4x - 20 = 2x - 14$
$2x = 6$
$x = 3$

2. $x + 7 = -2(x + 8)$
$x + 7 = -2x - 16$
$3x = -23$
$x = -\dfrac{23}{3}$

3. $3(2y - 1) = -8(6 + y)$
$6y - 3 = -48 - 8y$
$14y = -45$
$y = -\dfrac{45}{14}$

4. $-(z + 12) = 5(2z - 1)$
$-z - 12 = 10z - 5$
$-11z = 7$
$z = -\dfrac{7}{11}$

5. $n - (8 + 4n) = 2(3n - 4)$
$n - 8 - 4n = 6n - 8$
$-3n = 6n$
$-9n = 0$
$n = 0$

6. $4(9v + 2) = 6(1 + 6v) - 10$
$36v + 8 = 6 + 36v - 10$
$36v + 8 = 36v - 4$
$8 = -4$
No solution, or $\varnothing$

7. $0.3(x - 2) = 1.2$
$10[0.3(x - 2) = 10(1.2)$
$3(x - 2) = 12$
$3x - 6 = 12$
$3x = 18$
$x = 6$

8. $1.5 = 0.2(c - 0.3)$
$1.5 = 0.2c - 0.06$
$100(1.5) = 100(0.2c - 0.06)$
$150 = 20c - 6$
$156 = 20c$
$7.8 = c$

9. $-4(2 - 3x) = 2(3x - 4) + 6x$
$-8 + 12x = 6x - 8 + 6x$
$-8 + 12x = 12x - 8$
$-8 = -8$
All real numbers

10. $6(m - 1) + 3(2 - m) = 0$
$6m - 6 + 6 - 3m = 0$
$3m = 0$
$m = 0$

11. $6 - 3(2g + 4) - 4g = 5(1 - 2g)$
$6 - 6g - 12 - 4g = 5 - 10g$
$-6 - 10g = 5 - 10g$
$-6 = 5$
No solution, $\varnothing$

12. $20 - 5(p + 1) + 3p = -(2p - 15)$
$20 - 5p - 5 + 3p = -2p + 15$
$15 - 2p = -2p + 15$
$15 = 15$
All real numbers

13. $\dfrac{x}{3} - 4 = x - 2$
$3\left(\dfrac{x}{3} - 4\right) = 3(x - 2)$
$x - 12 = 3x - 6$
$-2x = 6$
$x = -3$

14.
$$\frac{9}{4}y = \frac{2}{3}y$$
$$12\left(\frac{9}{4}y\right) = 12\left(\frac{2}{3}y\right)$$
$$27y = 8y$$
$$19y = 0$$
$$y = 0$$

15.
$$\frac{3n}{8} - 1 = 3 + \frac{n}{6}$$
$$24\left(\frac{3n}{8} - 1\right) = 24\left(3 + \frac{n}{6}\right)$$
$$9n - 24 = 72 + 4n$$
$$5n = 96$$
$$n = \frac{96}{5}$$

16.
$$\frac{z}{6} + 1 = \frac{z}{2} + 2$$
$$6\left(\frac{z}{6} + 1\right) = 6\left(\frac{z}{2} + 2\right)$$
$$z + 6 = 3z + 12$$
$$-2z = 6$$
$$z = -3$$

17.
$$\frac{y}{4} - \frac{y}{2} = -8$$
$$4\left(\frac{y}{4} - \frac{y}{2}\right) = 4(-8)$$
$$y - 2y = -32$$
$$-y = -32$$
$$y = 32$$

18.
$$\frac{2x}{3} - \frac{8}{3} = x$$
$$2x - 8 = 3x$$
$$-8 = x$$

19.
$$\frac{b-2}{3} = \frac{b+2}{5}$$
$$5(b-2) = 3(b+2)$$
$$5b - 10 = 3b + 6$$
$$2b = 16$$
$$b = 8$$

20.
$$\frac{2t-1}{3} = \frac{3t+2}{15}$$
$$15\left(\frac{2t-1}{3}\right) = 15\left(\frac{3t+2}{15}\right)$$
$$5(2t - 1) = 3t + 2$$
$$10t - 5 = 3t + 2$$
$$7t = 7$$
$$t = 1$$

21.
$$\frac{2(t+1)}{3} = \frac{2(t-1)}{3}$$
$$3\left[\frac{2(t+1)}{3}\right] = 3\left[\frac{2(t-1)}{3}\right]$$
$$2(t+1) = 2(t-1)$$
$$2t + 2 = 2t - 2$$
$$2 = -2$$
No solution, $\varnothing$

22.
$$\frac{3a-3}{6} = \frac{4a+1}{15} + 2$$
$$30\left(\frac{3a-3}{6}\right) = 30\left(\frac{4a+1}{15} + 2\right)$$
$$5(3a - 3) = 2(4a + 1) + 30(2)$$
$$15a - 15 = 8a + 2 + 60$$
$$15a - 15 = 8a + 62$$
$$7a = 77$$
$$a = 11$$

23. Let $x$ = the number.
$$2(x - 3) = 3x + 1$$
$$2x - 6 = 3x + 1$$
$$-7 = x$$
The number is $-7$.

24. Let $x$ = smaller number, then
$x + 5$ = larger number.
$$x + x + 5 = 285$$
$$2x = 280$$
$$x = 140$$
$$x + 5 = 145$$
The numbers are 140 and 145.

25. $40\% \cdot 130 = 0.40 \cdot 130 = 52$

26. $1.5\% \cdot 8 = 0.015 \cdot 8 = 0.12$

27. Let $x$ = number of CDs sold in 2000.
$$x - 0.25x = 705.4$$
$$0.75x = 705.4$$
$$x \approx 940.5$$
There were 940.5 million music CDs sold by
U.S. manufacturers in 2000.

**28.** Let $n$ = the first integer, then
$n + 1$ = the second integer,
$n + 2$ = the third integer, and
$n + 3$ = the fourth integer.
$$(n+1) + (n+2) + (n+3) - 2n = 16$$
$$n + 6 = 16$$
$$n = 10$$
Therefore, the integers are 10, 11, 12, and 13.

**29.** Let $x$ = smaller odd integer, then
$x + 2$ = larger odd integer.
$$5x = 3(x+2) + 54$$
$$5x = 3x + 6 + 54$$
$$2x = 60$$
$$x = 30$$
Since this is not odd, no such consecutive odd integers exist.

**30.** Let $x$ = width of the playing field, then
$2x - 5$ = length of the playing field.
$$2x + 2(2x - 5) = 230$$
$$2x + 4x - 10 = 230$$
$$6x = 240$$
$$x = 40$$
Then $2x - 5 = 2(40) - 5 = 75$. The field is 75 meters long and 40 meters wide.

**31.** Let $m$ = number of miles of driven.
$$2(19.95) + 0.12(m - 200) = 46.86$$
$$39.90 + 0.12m - 24 = 46.86$$
$$0.12m + 15.90 = 46.86$$
$$0.12m = 30.96$$
$$m = 258$$

**32.** Solve $R = C$.
$$16.50x = 4.50x + 3000$$
$$12x = 3000$$
$$x = 250$$
Thus, 250 calculators must be produced and sold in order to break even.

**33.** $V = LWH$
$$W = \frac{V}{LH}$$

**34.** $C = 2\pi r$
$$\frac{C}{2\pi} = r$$

**35.** $5x - 4y = -12$
$$5x + 12 = 4y$$
$$y = \frac{5x + 12}{4}$$

**36.** $5x - 4y = -12$
$$5x = 4y - 12$$
$$x = \frac{4y - 12}{5}$$

**37.** $y - y_1 = m(x - x_1)$
$$m = \frac{y - y_1}{x - x_1}$$

**38.**
$$y - y_1 = m(x - x_1)$$
$$y - y_1 = mx - mx_1$$
$$y - y_1 + mx_1 = mx$$
$$\frac{y - y_1 + mx_1}{m} = x$$

**39.**
$$E = I(R + r)$$
$$E = IR + Ir$$
$$I - IR = Ir$$
$$\frac{E - IR}{I} = r$$

**40.**
$$S = vt + gt^2$$
$$S - vt = gt^2$$
$$\frac{S - vt}{t^2} = g$$

**41.** $T = gr + gvt$
$$T = g(r + vt)$$
$$g = \frac{T}{r + vt}$$

**42.**
$$I = Prt + P$$
$$I = P(rt + 1)$$
$$\frac{I}{rt + 1} = P$$

**43.** $A = P\left(1 + \dfrac{r}{n}\right)^{nt} = 3000\left(1 + \dfrac{0.03}{n}\right)^{7n}$

   **a.** $A = 3000\left(1 + \dfrac{0.03}{2}\right)^{14} \approx \$3695.27$

   **b.** $A = 3000\left(1 + \dfrac{0.03}{52}\right)^{364} \approx \$3700.81$

**44.** $C = \dfrac{5}{9}(F - 32)$

$C = \dfrac{5}{9}(90 - 32)$

$C = \dfrac{5}{9}(58)$

$C = \dfrac{290}{9} \approx 32.2$

90°F is $\left(\dfrac{290}{9}\right)$°C $\approx 32.2$°C.

**45.** Let $x =$ original width, then
$x + 2 =$ original length.
$(x + 4)(x + 2 + 4) = x(x + 2) + 88$

$(x + 4)(x + 6) = x^2 + 2x + 88$

$x^2 + 10x + 24 = x^2 + 2x + 88$

$8x = 64$

$x = 8$

$x + 2 = 10$
The original width is 8 in. and the original length is 10 in.

**46.** Area $= 18 \times 21 = 378 \text{ ft}^2$

Packages $= \dfrac{378}{24} = 15.75$

There are 16 packages needed.

**47.** $3(x - 5) > -(x + 3)$

$3x - 15 > -x - 3$

$4x > 12$

$x > 3$

$(3, \infty)$

**48.** $-2(x + 7) \geq 3(x + 2)$

$-2x - 14 \geq 3x + 6$

$-5x \geq 20$

$x \leq -4$

$(-\infty, -4]$

**49.** $4x - (5 + 2x) < 3x - 1$

$4x - 5 - 2x < 3x - 1$

$2x - 5 < 3x - 1$

$-x < 4$

$x > -4$

$(-4, \infty)$

**50.** $3(x - 8) < 7x + 2(5 - x)$

$3x - 24 < 7x + 10 - 2x$

$3x - 24 < 5x + 10$

$-2x < 34$

$x > -17$

$(-17, \infty)$

**51.** $24 \geq 6x - 2(3x - 5) + 2x$

$24 \geq 6x - 6x + 10 + 2x$

$24 \geq 10 + 2x$

$14 \geq 2x$

$7 \geq x$

$(-\infty, 7]$

**52.** $\dfrac{x}{3} + \dfrac{1}{2} > \dfrac{2}{3}$

$6\left(\dfrac{x}{3} + \dfrac{1}{2}\right) > 6\left(\dfrac{2}{3}\right)$

$2x + 3 > 4$

$2x > 1$

$x > \dfrac{1}{2}$

$\left(\dfrac{1}{2}, \infty\right)$

**53.** $x + \dfrac{3}{4} < -\dfrac{x}{2} + \dfrac{9}{4}$

$4\left(x + \dfrac{3}{4}\right) < 4\left(-\dfrac{x}{2} + \dfrac{9}{4}\right)$

$4x + 3 < -2x + 9$

$6x < 6$

$x < 1$

$(-\infty, 1)$

**54.** $\dfrac{x - 5}{2} \leq \dfrac{3}{8}(2x + 6)$

$8\left(\dfrac{x - 5}{2}\right) \leq 8\left[\dfrac{3}{8}(2x + 6)\right]$

$4(x - 5) \leq 3(2x + 6)$

$4x - 20 \leq 6x + 18$

$-2x \leq 38$

$x \geq -19$

$[-19, \infty)$

**55.** Let $n =$ number of pounds of laundry.

$15 < 0.5(10) + 0.4(n - 10)$

$15 < 5 + 0.4n - 4$

$15 < 1 + 0.4n$

$14 < 0.4n$

$35 < n$

It is more economical to use the housekeeper for more than 35 pounds of laundry per week.

**56.** $500 \le F \le 1000$

$$500 \le \frac{9}{5}C + 32 \le 1000$$

$$468 \le \frac{9}{5}C \le 968$$

$$260 \le C \le 538$$

Rounded to the nearest degree, firing temperatures range from 260°C to 538°C.

**57.** Let $x$ = the score from the last judge.

$$\frac{9.5 + 9.7 + 9.9 + 9.7 + 9.7 + 9.6 + 9.5 + x}{8} \ge 9.65$$

$$67.6 + x \ge 77.2$$

$$x \ge 9.6$$

The last judge must give Nana at least a 9.6 for her to win the silver medal.

**58.** Let $x$ = the amount saved each summer.

$4000 \le 2x + 500 \le 8000$

$3500 \le 2x \le 7500$

$1750 \le x \le 3750$

She must save between \$1750 and \$3750 each summer.

**59.** $1 \le 4x - 7 \le 3$

$8 \le 4x \le 10$

$$2 \le x \le \frac{5}{2}$$

$$\left[2, \frac{5}{2}\right]$$

**60.** $-2 \le 8 + 5x < -1$

$-10 \le 5x \le -9$

$$-2 \le x \le -\frac{9}{5}$$

$$\left[-2, \frac{9}{5}\right)$$

**61.** $-3 < 4(2x - 1) < 12$

$-3 < 8x - 4 < 12$

$1 < 8x < 16$

$$\frac{1}{8} < x < 2$$

$$\left(\frac{1}{8}, 2\right)$$

**62.** $-6 < x - (3 - 4x) < -3$

$-6 < x - 3 + 4x < -3$

$-6 < 5x - 3 < -3$

$-3 < 5x < 0$

$$-\frac{3}{5} < x < 0$$

$$\left(-\frac{3}{5}, 0\right)$$

**63.** $\dfrac{1}{6} < \dfrac{4x - 3}{3} \le \dfrac{4}{5}$

$$30\left(\frac{1}{6}\right) < 30\left(\frac{4x - 3}{3}\right) \le 30\left(\frac{4}{5}\right)$$

$$5 < 10(4x - 3) \le 24$$

$$5 < 40x - 30 \le 24$$

$$35 < 40x < 54$$

$$\frac{7}{8} < x \le \frac{27}{20}$$

$$\left(\frac{7}{8}, \frac{27}{20}\right]$$

**64.** $x \le 2$ and $x > -5$

$-5 < x \le 2$

$(-5, 2]$

**65.** $3x - 5 > 6$    or    $-x < -5$

      $3x > 11$    or    $x > 5$

$$x > \frac{11}{3} \quad \text{or} \quad x > 5$$

$$x > \frac{11}{3}$$

$$\left(\frac{11}{3}, \infty\right)$$

**66.** $|x - 7| = 9$

    $x - 7 = 9$    or    $x - 7 = -9$

       $x = 16$    or       $x = -2$

**67.** $|8 - x| = 3$

    $8 - x = 3$    or    $8 - x = -3$

      $-x = -5$    or      $-x = -11$

        $x = 5$    or        $x = 11$

**68.** $|2x + 9| = 9$

    $2x + 9 = 9$    or    $2x + 9 = -9$

       $2x = 0$    or       $2x = -18$

        $x = 0$    or        $x = -9$

**69.** $|-3x+4| = 7$

$-3x+4 = 7$    or    $-3x+4 = -7$

$-3x = 3$    or    $-3x = -11$

$x = -1$    or    $x = \dfrac{11}{3}$

**70.** $|3x-2| + 6 = 10$

$|3x-2| = 4$

$3x-2 = 4$    or    $3x-2 = -4$

$3x = 6$    or    $3x = -2$

$x = 2$    or    $x = -\dfrac{2}{3}$

**71.** $5 + |6x+1| = 5$

$|6x+1| = 0$

$6x+1 = 0$

$6x = -1$

$x = -\dfrac{1}{6}$

**72.** $-5 = |4x - 3|$

The solution set is $\varnothing$.

**73.** $|5-6x| + 8 = 3$

$|5-6x| = -5$

The solution set is $\varnothing$.

**74.** $-8 = |x-3| - 10$

$2 = |x-3|$

$x-3 = 2$    or    $x-3 = -2$

$x = 5$    or    $x = 1$

**75.** $\left|\dfrac{3x-7}{4}\right| = 2$

$\dfrac{3x-7}{4} = 2$    or    $\dfrac{3x-7}{4} = -2$

$3x-7 = 8$    or    $3x-7 = -8$

$3x = 15$    or    $3x = -1$

$x = 5$    or    $x = -\dfrac{1}{3}$

**76.** $|6x+1| = |15+4x|$

$6x+1 = 15+4x$    or    $6x+1 = -(15+4x)$

$2x = 14$    or    $6x+1 = -15-4x$

$x = 7$    or    $10x = -16$

$x = -\dfrac{8}{5}$

**77.** $|5x-1| < 9$

$-9 < 5x-1 < 9$

$-8 < 5x < 10$

$-\dfrac{8}{5} < x < 2$

$\left(-\dfrac{8}{5}, 2\right)$

**78.** $|6+4x| \geq 10$

$6+4x \leq -10$    or    $6+4x \geq 10$

$4x \leq -16$    or    $4x \geq 4$

$x \leq -4$    or    $x \geq 1$

$(-\infty, -4] \cup [1, \infty)$

**79.** $|3x| - 8 > 1$

$|3x| > 9$

$3x < -9$    or    $3x > 9$

$x < -3$    or    $x > 3$

$(-\infty, -3) \cup (3, \infty)$

**80.** $9 + |5x| < 24$

$|5x| < 15$

$-15 < 5x < 15$

$-3 < x < 3$

$(-3, 3)$

**81.** $|6x-5| \leq -1$

The solution set is $\varnothing$.

68

**82.** $\left|3x+\dfrac{2}{5}\right| \geq 4$

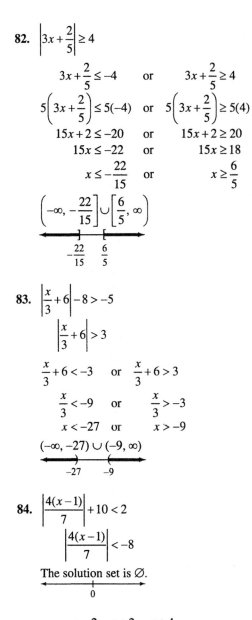

$$3x+\dfrac{2}{5} \leq -4 \quad \text{or} \quad 3x+\dfrac{2}{5} \geq 4$$

$$5\left(3x+\dfrac{2}{5}\right) \leq 5(-4) \quad \text{or} \quad 5\left(3x+\dfrac{2}{5}\right) \geq 5(4)$$

$$15x+2 \leq -20 \quad \text{or} \quad 15x+2 \geq 20$$

$$15x \leq -22 \quad \text{or} \quad 15x \geq 18$$

$$x \leq -\dfrac{22}{15} \quad \text{or} \quad x \geq \dfrac{6}{5}$$

$$\left(-\infty, -\dfrac{22}{15}\right] \cup \left[\dfrac{6}{5}, \infty\right)$$

**83.** $\left|\dfrac{x}{3}+6\right|-8 > -5$

$$\left|\dfrac{x}{3}+6\right| > 3$$

$$\dfrac{x}{3}+6 < -3 \quad \text{or} \quad \dfrac{x}{3}+6 > 3$$

$$\dfrac{x}{3} < -9 \quad \text{or} \quad \dfrac{x}{3} > -3$$

$$x < -27 \quad \text{or} \quad x > -9$$

$$(-\infty, -27) \cup (-9, \infty)$$

**84.** $\left|\dfrac{4(x-1)}{7}\right|+10 < 2$

$$\left|\dfrac{4(x-1)}{7}\right| < -8$$

The solution set is $\varnothing$.

**85.** $\dfrac{x-2}{5}+\dfrac{x+2}{2}=\dfrac{x+4}{3}$

$$30\left(\dfrac{x-2}{5}+\dfrac{x+2}{2}\right)=30\left(\dfrac{x+4}{3}\right)$$

$$6(x-2)+15(x+2)=10(x+4)$$

$$6x-12+15x+30=10x+40$$

$$21x+18=10x+40$$

$$11x=22$$

$$x=2$$

**86.** $\dfrac{2z-3}{4}-\dfrac{4-z}{2}=\dfrac{z+1}{3}$

$$12\left(\dfrac{2z-3}{4}-\dfrac{4-z}{2}\right)=12\left(\dfrac{z+1}{3}\right)$$

$$3(2z-3)-6(4-z)=4(z+1)$$

$$6z-9-24+6z=4z+4$$

$$12z-33=4z+4$$

$$8z=37$$

$$z=\dfrac{37}{8}$$

**87.** Let $x$ = number of tourists for France, then
$x + 9$ = number of tourists for United States, and
$x + 44$ = number of tourists for China.

$$x+(x+9)+(x+44)=332$$

$$3x+53=332$$

$$3x=279$$

$$x=93$$

$x+9=102$
$x+44=137$

China is predicted to have 137 million tourists, whereas the United States is predicted to have 102 million and France, 93 million.

**88.** $\qquad A=\dfrac{h}{2}(B+b)$

$$2A=hB+hb$$

$$2A-hb=hB$$

$$\dfrac{2A-hb}{h}=B$$

**89.** $\qquad V=\dfrac{1}{3}\pi r^2 h$

$$3V=\pi r^2 h$$

$$\dfrac{3V}{\pi r^2}=h$$

**90.** $V_{\text{box}}=lwh=8\cdot5\cdot3=120\ \text{in}^3$, while

$$V_{\text{cyl}}=\pi r^2 h=\pi\cdot 3^2\cdot 6=54\pi\approx 170\ \text{in}^3$$

Therefore, the cylinder holds more ice cream.

**91.** $d=rt$ or $r=\dfrac{d}{t}$

11:00 A.M. to 1:15 P.M. is 2.25 hours.

$$r=\dfrac{130}{2.25}\approx 58$$

His average speed was 58 mph.

**92.**  $48 + x \geq 5(2x + 4) - 2x$
$48 + x \geq 10x + 20 - 2x$
$48 + x \geq 8x + 20$
$28 \geq 7x$
$4 \geq x$
$(-\infty, 4]$

**93.**  $\dfrac{3(x-2)}{5} > \dfrac{-5(x-2)}{3}$

$15\left[\dfrac{3(x-2)}{5}\right] > 15\left[\dfrac{-5(x-2)}{3}\right]$

$9(x-2) > -25(x-2)$
$9x - 18 > -25x + 50$
$34x > 68$
$x > 2$
$(2, \infty)$

**94.**  $0 \leq \dfrac{2(3x+4)}{5} \leq 3$

$5(0) \leq 5\left[\dfrac{2(3x+4)}{5}\right] \leq 5(3)$

$0 \leq 2(3x+4) \leq 15$
$0 \leq 6x + 8 \leq 15$
$-8 \leq 6x \leq 7$
$-\dfrac{4}{3} \leq x \leq \dfrac{7}{6}$

$\left[-\dfrac{4}{3}, \dfrac{7}{6}\right]$

**95.**  $x \leq 2$  or  $x > -5$
$(-\infty, \infty)$

**96.**  $-2x \leq 6$   and   $-2x + 3 < -7$
$x \geq -3$   and        $-2x < -10$
$x \geq -3$   and            $x > 5$
$x > 5$
$(5, \infty)$

**97.**  $|7x| - 26 = -5$
$|7x| = 21$
$7x = 21$   or   $7x = -21$
$x = 3$   or   $x = -3$

**98.**  $\left|\dfrac{9-2x}{5}\right| = -3$
The solution set is $\varnothing$.

**99.**  $|x - 3| = |7 + 2x|$
$x - 3 = 7 + 2x$   or   $x - 3 = -(7 + 2x)$
$-10 = x$        or   $x - 3 = -7 - 2x$
$3x = -4$
$x = -\dfrac{4}{3}$

**100.**  $|6x - 5| \geq -1$
Since $|6x - 5|$ is nonnegative for all numbers $x$, the solution set is $(-\infty, \infty)$.

**101.**  $\left|\dfrac{4x-3}{5}\right| < 1$

$-1 < \dfrac{4x-3}{5} < 1$

$-5 < 4x - 3 < 5$
$-2 < 4x < 8$
$-\dfrac{1}{2} < x < 2$

$\left(-\dfrac{1}{2}, 2\right)$

**Chapter 2 Test**

**1.**  $8x + 14 = 5x + 44$
$3x = 30$
$x = 10$

**2.**  $9(x + 2) = 5[11 - 2(2 - x) + 3]$
$9x + 18 = 5[11 - 4 + 2x + 3]$
$9x + 18 = 5[10 + 2x]$
$9x + 18 = 50 + 10x$
$-x = 32$
$x = -32$

**3.**  $3(y - 4) + y = 2(6 + 2y)$
$3y - 12 + y = 12 + 4y$
$4y - 12 = 12 + 4y$
$-12 = 12$
No solution, $\varnothing$

**4.**  $7n - 6 + n = 2(4n - 3)$
$8n - 6 = 8n - 6$
$-6 = -6$
All real numbers

**5.** $\dfrac{7w}{4}+5=\dfrac{3w}{10}+1$

$20\left(\dfrac{7w}{4}+5\right)=20\left(\dfrac{3w}{10}+1\right)$

$35w+100=6w+20$

$29w=-80$

$w=-\dfrac{80}{29}$

**6.** $\dfrac{z+7}{9}+1=\dfrac{2z+1}{6}$

$18\left(\dfrac{z+7}{9}+1\right)=18\left(\dfrac{2z+1}{6}\right)$

$2(z+7)+18=3(2z+1)$

$2z+14+18=6z+3$

$2z+32=6z+3$

$2z-6z=3-32$

$-4z=-29$

$z=\dfrac{29}{4}$

**7.** $|6x-5|-3=-2$

$|6x-5|=1$

$6x-5=1$  or  $6x-5=-1$

$6x=6$  or  $6x=4$

$x=1$  or  $x=\dfrac{2}{3}$

**8.** $|8-2t|=-6$

No solution, $\varnothing$

**9.** $|2x-3|=|4x+5|$

$2x-3=4x+5$  or  $2x-3=-(4x+5)$

$2x-4x=5+3$  or  $2x-3=-4x-5$

$-2x=8$  or  $2x+4x=-5+3$

$x=-4$  or  $6x=-2$

$x=-4$  or  $x=-\dfrac{1}{3}$

**10.** $|x-5|=|x+2|$

$x-5=x+2$    or  $x-5=-(x+2)$

$-5=2$ False   or  $x-5=-x-2$

$2x=3$

$x=\dfrac{3}{2}$

Since $-5=2$ is not possible, the only solution is $\dfrac{3}{2}$.

**11.** $3x-4y=8$

$3x-8=4y$

$y=\dfrac{3x-8}{4}$

**12.** $S=gt^2+gvt$

$S=g(t^2+vt)$

$g=\dfrac{S}{t^2+vt}$

**13.** $F=\dfrac{9}{5}C+32$

$F-32=\dfrac{9}{5}C$

$C=\dfrac{5}{9}(F-32)$

**14.** $3(2x-7)-4x>-(x+6)$

$6x-21-4x>-x-6$

$2x-21>-x-6$

$3x>15$

$x>5$

$(5,\infty)$

**15.** $\dfrac{3x-2}{3}-\dfrac{5x+1}{4}\ge 0$

$12\left[\dfrac{3x-2}{3}-\dfrac{5x+1}{4}\right]\ge 12(0)$

$4(3x-2)-3(5x+1)\ge 0$

$12x-8-15x-3\ge 0$

$-3x-11\ge 0$

$-3x\ge 11$

$x\le -\dfrac{11}{3}$

$\left(-\infty,\ -\dfrac{11}{3}\right]$

**16.** $-3<2(x-3)\le 4$

$-3<2x-6\le 4$

$3<2x\le 10$

$\dfrac{3}{2}<x\le 5$

$\left(\dfrac{3}{2},\ 5\right]$

**17.** $|3x+1| > 5$

$3x+1 < -5 \quad\text{or}\quad 3x+1 > 5$

$3x < -6 \quad\text{or}\quad\quad 3x > 4$

$x < -2 \quad\text{or}\quad\quad x > \dfrac{4}{3}$

$\left(-\infty, -2\right) \cup \left(\dfrac{4}{3}, \infty\right)$

**18.** $|x-5| - 4 < -2$

$|x-5| < 2$

$-2 < x - 5 < 2$

$3 < x < 7$

$(3, 7)$

**19.** $x \geq 5$ and $x \geq 4$

$[5, \infty)$

**20.** $x \geq 5$ or $x \geq 4$

$[4, \infty)$

**21.** $-1 \leq \dfrac{2x-5}{3} < 2$

$3(-1) \leq 3\left(\dfrac{2x-5}{3}\right) < 3(2)$

$-3 \leq 2x - 5 < 6$

$-3 + 5 \leq 2x - 5 + 5 < 6 + 5$

$2 \leq 2x < 11$

$\dfrac{2}{2} \leq \dfrac{2x}{2} < \dfrac{11}{2}$

$1 \leq x < \dfrac{11}{2}$

$\left[1, \dfrac{11}{2}\right)$

**22.** $6x+1 > 5x+4 \quad\text{or}\quad 1-x > -4$

$\quad\quad x > 3 \quad\quad\text{or}\quad\quad 5 > x$

$(-\infty, \infty)$

**23.** $12\% \cdot 80 = 0.12 \cdot 80 = 9.6$

**24.** Let $x$ = number employed in 2004.

$x + 0.55x = 357,000$

$1.55x = 357,000$

$x \approx 230,323$

There were 230,323 employees in 2004.

**25.** Recall that $C = 2\pi r$. Here $C = 78.5$.

$78.5 = 2\pi r$

$r = \dfrac{78.5}{2\pi} = \dfrac{39.25}{\pi}$

Also, recall that $A = \pi r^2$.

$A = \pi\left(\dfrac{39.25}{\pi}\right)^2 \approx \dfrac{39.25^2}{3.14} \approx 490.63$

Dividing this by 60 yields approximately 8.18. Therefore, about 8 hunting dogs could safely be kept in the pen.

**26.** Solve $R > C$.

$7.4x > 3910 + 2.8x$

$4.6x > 3910$

$x > 850$

Therefore, more than 850 sunglasses must be produced and sold in order for them to yield a profit.

**27.** $A = P\left(1 + \dfrac{r}{n}\right)^{nt}$

$= 2500\left(1 + \dfrac{0.035}{4}\right)^{4\cdot10}$

$= \$3542.27$

**28.** Let $x$ = population of New York, then $x + 1.3$ = population of Seoul, Korea, and $2x - 10.2$ = population of Tokyo.

$x + (x+1.3) + (2x-10.2) = 78.3$

$4x - 8.9 = 78.3$

$4x = 87.2$

$x = 21.8$

$x + 1.3 = 23.1$

$2x - 10.2 = 33.4$

The populations are as follows:

New York: 21.8 million,

Seoul: 23.1 million,

Tokyo: 33.4 million.

**Chapter 2 Cumulative Review**

**1. a.** $\{101, 102, 103, ...\}$

**b.** $\{2, 3, 4, 5\}$

**2. a.** $\{-2, -1, 0, 1, 2, 3, 4\}$

**b.** $\{4\}$

**3. a.** $|3| = 3$

**b.** $\left|-\dfrac{1}{7}\right| = \dfrac{1}{7}$

**c.** $-|2.7| = -2.7$

**d.** $-|-8| = -8$

**e.** $|0| = 0$

**4. a.** The opposite of $\frac{2}{3}$ is $-\frac{2}{3}$.

   **b.** The opposite of $-9$ is $9$.

   **c.** The opposite of $1.5$ is $-1.5$.

**5. a.** $-3 + (-11) = -14$

   **b.** $3 + (-7) = -4$

   **c.** $-10 + 15 = 5$

   **d.** $-8.3 + (-1.9) = -10.2$

   **e.** $-\frac{2}{3} + \frac{3}{7} = -\frac{14}{21} + \frac{9}{21} = -\frac{5}{21}$

**6. a.** $-2 - (-10) = -2 + 10 = 8$

   **b.** $1.7 - 8.9 = -7.2$

   **c.** $-\frac{1}{2} - \frac{1}{4} = -\frac{2}{4} - \frac{1}{4} = -\frac{3}{4}$

**7. a.** $\sqrt{9} = 3$ since $3^2 = 9$.

   **b.** $\sqrt{25} = 5$ since $5^2 = 25$.

   **c.** $\sqrt{\frac{1}{4}} = \frac{1}{2}$ since $\left(\frac{1}{2}\right)^2 = \frac{1}{4}$.

   **d.** $-\sqrt{36} = -6$ since $6^2 = 36$.

   **e.** $\sqrt{-36}$ is not a real number.

**8. a.** $-3(-2) = 6$

   **b.** $-\frac{3}{4}\left(-\frac{4}{7}\right) = \frac{3}{7}$

   **c.** $\frac{0}{-2} = 0$

   **d.** $\frac{-20}{-2} = 10$

**9.** Let $x = 4$, $y = -3$.

   **a.** $3x - 7y = 3(4) - 7(-3) = 12 + 21 = 33$

   **b.** $-2y^2 = -2(-3)^2 = -2(9) = -18$

   **c.** $\dfrac{\sqrt{x}}{y} - \dfrac{y}{x} = \dfrac{\sqrt{4}}{-3} - \dfrac{-3}{4}$

$$= -\frac{2}{3} + \frac{3}{4}$$
$$= -\frac{8}{12} + \frac{9}{12}$$
$$= \frac{1}{12}$$

**10. a.** $\sqrt[4]{1} = 1$ since $1^4 = 1$.

   **b.** $\sqrt[3]{8} = 2$ since $2^3 = 8$.

   **c.** $\sqrt[4]{81} = 3$ since $3^4 = 81$.

**11. a.** $x + 5 = 20$

   **b.** $2(3 + y) = 4$

   **c.** $x - 8 = 2x$

   **d.** $\dfrac{z}{9} = 9 + z$

**12. a.** $-3 > -5$ since $-3$ is to the right of $-5$ on the number line.

   **b.** $\dfrac{-12}{-4} = 3$

   **c.** $0 > -2$ since $0$ is to the right of $-2$ on the number line.

**13.** $7x + 5 = 5 + 7x$

**14.** $5 \cdot (7x) = (5 \cdot 7)x = 35x$

**15.** $2x + 5 = 9$
$$2x = 4$$
$$x = 2$$

**16.** $11.2 = 1.2 - 5x$
$$10 = -5x$$
$$-2 = x$$

**17.** $6x - 4 = 2 + 6(x - 1)$
$6x - 4 = 2 + 6x - 6$
$6x - 4 = 6x - 4$
$-4 = -4$, which is always true.
All real numbers

**18.** $2x + 1.5 = -0.2 + 1.6x$
$0.4x = -1.7$
$x = -4.25$

**19. a.** Let $x =$ the first integer. Then
$x + 1 =$ the second integer and
$x + 2 =$ the third integer.
$x + (x + 1) + (x + 2) = 3x + 3$

**b.** $x + (5x) + (6x - 3) = 12x - 3$

**20. a.** Let $x =$ the first integer. Then
$x + 1 =$ the second integer and
$x + 2 =$ the third integer.
$x + (x + 1) + (x + 2) = 3x + 3$

**b.** $4(3x + 1) = 12x + 4$

**21.** Let $x =$ first number, then
$2x + 3 =$ second number and
$4x =$ third number.
$x + (2x + 3) + 4x = 164$
$7x + 3 = 164$
$7x = 161$
$x = 23$
$2x + 3 = 2(23) + 3 = 49$
$4x = 4(23) = 92$
The three numbers are 23, 49 and 92.

**22.** Let $x =$ first number, then
$3x + 2 =$ second number.
$(3x + 2) - x = 24$
$2x + 2 = 24$
$2x = 22$
$x = 11$
$3x + 2 = 3(11) + 2 = 35$
The two numbers are 11 and 35.

**23.** $3y - 2x = 7$
$3y = 2x + 7$
$y = \dfrac{2x + 7}{3}$, or $y = \dfrac{2x}{3} + \dfrac{7}{3}$

**24.** $7x - 4y = 10$
$7x = 4y + 10$
$x = \dfrac{4y + 10}{7}$, or $x = \dfrac{4y}{7} + \dfrac{10}{7}$

**25.** $A = \dfrac{1}{2}(B + b)h$
$2A = (B + b)h$
$2A = Bh + bh$
$2A - Bh = bh$
$\dfrac{2A - Bh}{h} = b$

**26.** $P = 2l + 2w$
$P - 2w = 2l$
$\dfrac{P - 2w}{2} = l$

**27. a.** $\{x | x \geq 2\}$
$[2, \infty)$

**b.** $\{x | x < -1\}$
$(-\infty, -1)$

**c.** $\{x | 0.5 < x \leq 3\}$
$(0.5, 3]$

**28. a.** $\{x | x \leq -3\}$
$(-\infty, -3]$

**b.** $\{x | -2 \leq x < 0.1\}$
$[-2, 0.1)$

**29.** $-(x - 3) + 2 \leq 3(2x - 5) + x$
$-x + 3 + 2 \leq 6x - 15 + x$
$-x + 5 \leq 7x - 15$
$20 \leq 8x$
$\dfrac{5}{2} \leq x$
$\left[\dfrac{5}{2}, \infty\right)$

**30.** $2(7x - 1) - 5x > -(-7x) + 4$
$14x - 2 - 5x > 7x + 4$
$9x - 2 > 7x + 4$
$2x > 6$
$x > 3$
$(3, \infty)$

**31.** $2(x+3) > 2x+1$
$2x+6 > 2x+1$
         $6 > 1$; True for all real numbers $x$.
$(-\infty, \infty)$

**32.** $4(x+1) - 3 < 4x+1$
   $4x+4-3 < 4x+1$
      $4x+1 < 4x+1$
         $1 < 1$   Never true
$\varnothing$

**33.** $A = \{2, 4, 6, 8\}$, $B = \{3, 4, 5, 6\}$; the numbers 4 and 6 are in both sets so the intersection of $A$ and $B$ is $\{4, 6\}$.

**34.** The elements in either set or both sets are $-2, -1,$ $0, 1, 2, 3, 4,$ and 5, so the union is $\{-2, -1, 0, 1, 2, 3, 4, 5\}$.

**35.** $x-7 < 2$   and   $2x+1 < 9$
     $x < 9$   and     $2x < 8$
                       $x < 4$
$x < 4$
$(-\infty, 4)$

**36.** $x+3 \le 1$    or   $3x-1 < 8$
     $x \le -2$   or      $3x < 9$
                       $x < 3$
$x < 3$
$(-\infty, 3)$

**37.** $A = \{2, 4, 6, 8\}$ and $B = \{3, 4, 5, 6\}$, so the union of $A$ and $B$ is $\{2, 3, 4, 5, 6, 8\}$.

**38.** $\varnothing$; there are no elements in common.

**39.** $-2x-5 < -3$   or   $6x < 0$
     $-2x < 2$     or     $x < 0$
       $x > -1$
All real numbers
$(-\infty, \infty)$

**40.** $-2x-5 < -3$   and   $6x < 0$
     $-2x < 2$    and     $x < 0$
       $x > -1$
$-1 < x < 0$
$(-1, 0)$

**41.** $|p| = 2$
  $p = 2$   or   $p = -2$

**42.** $|x| = 5$
  $x = 5$   or   $x = -5$

**43.** $\left| \dfrac{x}{2} - 1 \right| = 11$

   $\dfrac{x}{2} - 1 = 11$   or   $\dfrac{x}{2} - 1 = -11$

      $\dfrac{x}{2} = 12$   or      $\dfrac{x}{2} = -10$

        $x = 24$   or       $x = -20$

**44.** $\left| \dfrac{y}{3} + 2 \right| = 10$

   $\dfrac{y}{3} + 2 = 10$   or   $\dfrac{y}{3} + 2 = -10$

      $\dfrac{y}{3} = 8$    or      $\dfrac{y}{3} = -12$

       $y = 24$   or       $y = -36$

**45.** $|x - 3| = |5 - x|$
   $x-3 = 5-x$   or   $x-3 = -(5-x)$
      $2x = 8$     or   $x-3 = -5+x$
       $x = 4$      or      $-3 = -5$
Since $-3 = -5$ is not possible, the only solution is 4.

**46.** $|x + 3| = |7 - x|$
   $x+3 = 7-x$   or   $x+3 = -(7-x)$
      $2x = 4$     or   $x-3 = -7+x$
       $x = 2$      or      $-3 = -7$
Since $-3 = -7$ is not possible, the only solution is 2.

**47.** $|x| \le 3$
  $-3 \le x \le 3$
  $[-3, 3]$

**48.** $|x| > 1$
  $x < -1$   or   $x > 1$
  $(-\infty, -1) \cup (1, \infty)$

**49.** $|2x + 9| + 5 > 3$
     $|2x + 9| > -2$
Since $|2x + 9|$ is nonnegative for all numbers $x$, the solution set is $(-\infty, \infty)$.

**50.** $|3x + 1| + 9 < 1$
     $|3x + 1| < -8$
The solution set is $\varnothing$.

# Chapter 3

## Section 3.1

### Practice Exercises

**1.** The six points are graphed as shown.

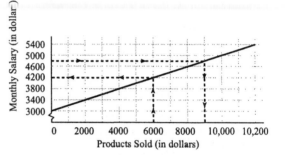

**a.** $(3, -4)$ lies in quadrant IV.

**b.** $(0, -2)$ is on the $y$-axis.

**c.** $(-2, 4)$ lies in quadrant II.

**d.** $(4, 0)$ is on the $x$-axis.

**e.** $\left(-1\frac{1}{2}, -2\right)$ is in quadrant III.

**f.** $(2.5, 3.5)$ is in quadrant I.

**2.** Let $x = 1$ and $y = 4$.

$$4x + y = 8$$
$$4(1) + 4 \overset{?}{=} 8$$
$$4 + 4 \overset{?}{=} 8$$
$$8 = 8 \quad \text{True}$$

Let $x = 0$ and $y = 6$.

$$4x + y = 8$$
$$4(0) + 6 \overset{?}{=} 8$$
$$0 + 6 \overset{?}{=} 8$$
$$6 = 8 \quad \text{False}$$

Let $x = 3$ and $y = -4$.

$$4x + y = 8$$
$$4(3) + (-4) \overset{?}{=} 8$$
$$12 - 4 \overset{?}{=} 8$$
$$8 = 8 \quad \text{True}$$

Thus, $(0, 6)$ is not a solution, but both $(1, 4)$ and $(3, -4)$ are solutions.

**3. a.** Since $x$ is products sold, find 6000 along the $x$-axis and move vertically up until you reach a point on the line. From this point on the line, move horizontally to the left until you reach the $y$-axis. Its value on the $y$-axis is 4200, which means if $6000 worth of products is sold, the salary for the month is $4200.

**b.** Since $y$ is monthly salary, find 4800 along the $y$-axis and move horizontally to the right until you reach a point on the line. Move vertically downward until you reach the $x$-axis. The corresponding $x$-value is 9000. This means that $9000 worth of products sold gives a salary of $4800 for the month. For the salary to be greater than $4800, products sold must be greater than $9000.

**4.** $y = -3x - 2$

This is a linear equation. (In standard form, it is $3x + y = -2$.) Since the equation is solved for $y$, we choose three $x$-values.

Let $x = 0$.
$$y = -3x - 2$$
$$y = -3 \cdot 0 - 2$$
$$y = -2$$

Let $x = -1$.
$$y = -3x - 2$$
$$y = -3(-1) - 2$$
$$y = 1$$

Let $x = -2$.
$$y = -3x - 2$$
$$y = -3(-2) - 2$$
$$y = 4$$

The three ordered pairs $(0, -2)$, $(-1, 1)$, and $(-2, 4)$ are listed in the table.

| $x$ | $y$ |
|-----|-----|
| 0 | −2 |
| −1 | 1 |
| −2 | 4 |

$y = -3x - 2$

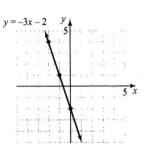

**5.** $y = -\dfrac{1}{2}x$

To avoid fractions, we choose $x$-values that are multiples of 2. To find the $y$-intercept, we let $x = 0$.

If $x = 0$, then $y = -\dfrac{1}{2}(0)$, or 0.

If $x = 2$, then $y = -\dfrac{1}{2}(2)$, or −1.

If $x = -2$, then $y = -\dfrac{1}{2}(-2)$, or 1.

| $x$ | $y$ |
|-----|-----|
| 0 | 0 |
| 2 | −1 |
| −2 | 1 |

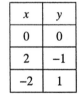

$y = -\dfrac{1}{2}x$

**6.** $y = 2x^2$

This equation is not linear because of the $x^2$ term. Its graph is not a line.

If $x = -3$, then $y = 2(-3)^2$, or 18.

If $x = -2$, then $y = 2(-2)^2$, or 8.

If $x = -1$, then $y = 2(-1)^2$, or 2.

If $x = 0$, then $y = 2(0)^2$, or 0.

If $x = 1$, then $y = 2(1)^2$, or 2.

If $x = 2$, then $y = 2(2)^2$, or 8.

If $x = 3$, then $y = 2(3)^2$, or 18.

| $x$ | $y$ |
|-----|-----|
| −3 | 18 |
| −2 | 8 |
| −1 | 2 |
| 0 | 0 |
| 1 | 2 |
| 2 | 8 |
| 3 | 18 |

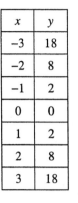

**7.** $y = -|x|$

This equation is not linear because it cannot be written in the form $Ax + By = C$. Its graph is not a line.

If $x = -3$, then $y = -|-3|$, or −3.

If $x = -2$, then $y = -|-2|$, or −2.

If $x = -1$, then $y = -|-1|$, or −1.

If $x = 0$, then $y = -|0|$, or 0.

If $x = 1$, then $y = -|1|$, or −1.

If $x = 2$, then $y = -|2|$, or −2.

If $x = 3$, then $y = -|3|$, or −3.

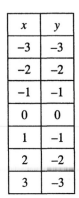

| x | y |
|----|----|
| −3 | −3 |
| −2 | −2 |
| −1 | −1 |
| 0 | 0 |
| 1 | −1 |
| 2 | −2 |
| 3 | −3 |

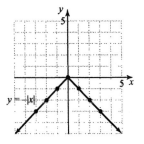

$y = -|x|$

## Graphing Calculator Explorations

**1.**

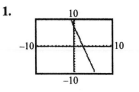

**2.**

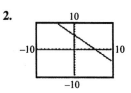

**3.**

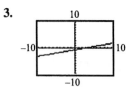

**4.**

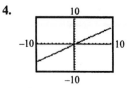

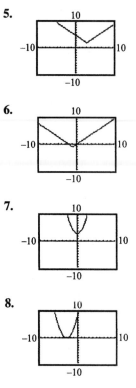

**5.**

**6.**

**7.**

**8.**

## Vocabulary and Readiness Check

**1.** Point *A* is (5, 2).

**2.** Point *B* is (2, 5).

**3.** Point *C* is (3, 0).

**4.** Point *D* is (−1, 3).

**5.** Point *E* is (−5, −2).

**6.** Point *F* is (−3, 5).

**7.** Point *G* is (−1, 0).

**8.** Point *H* is (0, −3).

**9.** (2, 3); QI

**10.** (0, 5); *y*-axis

**11.** (−2, 7); QII

**12.** (−3, 0); *x*-axis

**13.** (−1, −4); QIII

**14.** (4, −2); QIV

**15.** $(0, -100)$; $y$-axis

**16.** $(10, 30)$; QI

**17.** $(-10, -30)$; QIII

**18.** $(0, 0)$; $x$- and $y$-axis

**19.** $(-87, 0)$; $x$-axis

**20.** $(-42, 17)$; QII

**Exercise Set 3.1**

**1.** $(3, 2)$ is in quadrant I

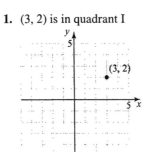

**3.** $(-5, 3)$ is in quadrant II.

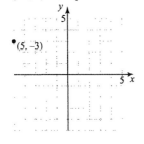

**5.** $\left(5\frac{1}{2}, -4\right)$ is in quadrant IV.

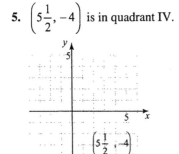

**7.** $(0, 3.5)$ is on the $y$-axis.

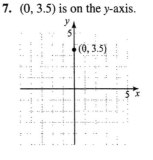

**9.** $(-2, -4)$ is in quadrant III.

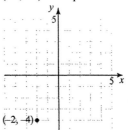

**11.** $(x, -y)$ lies in quadrant IV.

**13.** $(x, 0)$ lies on the $x$-axis.

**15.** $(-x, -y)$ lies in quadrant III.

**17.** Let $x = 0$, $y = 5$.
$$y = 3x - 5$$
$$5 = 3 \cdot 0 - 5$$
$$5 = -5$$
False; no

Let $x = -1$, $y = -8$.
$$y = 3x - 5$$
$$-8 = 3 \cdot (-1) - 5$$
$$-8 = -8$$
True; yes

**19.** Let $x = 1$, $y = 0$.
$$-6x + 5y = -6$$
$$-6(1) + 5(0) = -6$$
$$-6 = -6$$
True; yes

Let $x = 2$, $y = \frac{6}{5}$.
$$-6x + 5y = -6$$
$$-6(2) + 5\left(\frac{6}{5}\right) = -6$$
$$-6 = -6$$
True; yes

**21.** Let $x = 1$, $y = 2$.

$y = 2x^2$

$2 = 2(1)^2$

$2 = 2$

True; yes

Let $x = 3$, $y = 18$.

$y = 2x^2$

$18 = 2(3)^2$

$18 = 18$

True; yes

**23.** Let $x = 2$, $y = 8$.

$y = x^3$

$8 = (2)^3$

$8 = 8$

True; yes

Let $x = 3$, $y = 9$,

$y = x^3$

$9 = (3)^3$

$9 = 27$

False; no

**25.** Let $x = 1$, $y = 3$.

$y = \sqrt{x} + 2$

$3 = \sqrt{1} + 2$

$3 = 3$

True; yes

Let $x = 4$, $y = 4$.

$y = \sqrt{x} + 2$

$4 = \sqrt{4} + 2$

$4 = 4$

True; yes

**27.** $x + y = 3$

Linear

| $x$ | $y$ |
|-----|-----|
| 0 | 3 |
| 3 | 0 |
| 1 | 2 |

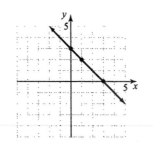

**29.** $y = 4x$

Linear

| $x$ | $y$ |
|-----|-----|
| $-1$ | $-4$ |
| 0 | 0 |
| 1 | 4 |

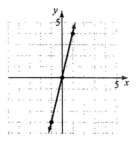

**31.** $y = 4x - 2$

Linear

| $x$ | $y$ |
|-----|-----|
| 0 | $-2$ |
| $\frac{1}{2}$ | 0 |
| 1 | 2 |

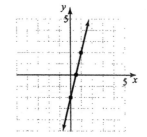

**33.** $y = |x| + 3$
Not linear

| $x$ | $y$ |
|-----|-----|
| $-2$ | 5 |
| $-1$ | 4 |
| 0 | 3 |
| 1 | 4 |
| 2 | 5 |

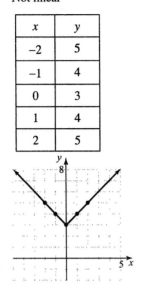

**35.** $2x - y = 5$
Linear

| $x$ | $y$ |
|-----|-----|
| $2\frac{1}{2}$ | 0 |
| 0 | $-5$ |
| 1 | $-3$ |

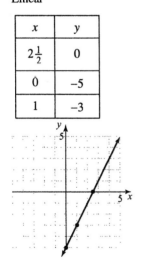

**37.** $y = 2x^2$
Not linear

| $x$ | $y$ |
|-----|-----|
| $-2$ | 8 |
| $-1$ | 2 |
| 0 | 0 |
| 1 | 2 |
| 2 | 8 |

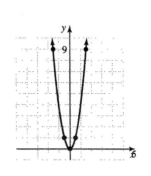

**39.** $y = x^2 - 3$
Not linear

| $x$ | $y$ |
|-----|-----|
| $-2$ | 1 |
| $-1$ | $-2$ |
| 0 | $-3$ |
| 1 | $-2$ |
| 2 | 1 |

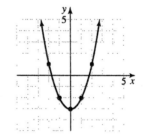

**41.** $y = -2x$
Linear

| $x$ | $y$ |
|-----|-----|
| $-1$ | 2 |
| 0 | 0 |
| 1 | $-2$ |

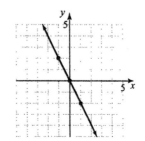

**43.** $y = -2x + 3$
Linear

| x | y |
|---|---|
| −1 | 5 |
| 0 | 3 |
| 1 | 1 |

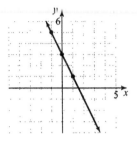

**45.** $y = |x + 2|$
Not linear

| x | y |
|---|---|
| −4 | 2 |
| −3 | 1 |
| −2 | 0 |
| −1 | 1 |
| 0 | 2 |

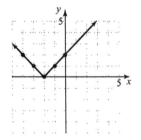

**47.** $y = x^3$
Not linear

| x | y |
|---|---|
| −3 | −27 |
| −2 | −8 |
| −1 | −1 |
| 0 | 0 |
| 1 | 1 |
| 2 | 8 |

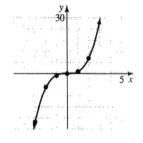

**49.** $y = -|x|$
Not linear

| x | y |
|---|---|
| −2 | −2 |
| −2 | −1 |
| 0 | 0 |
| 1 | −1 |
| 2 | −2 |

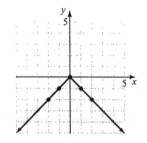

**51.** $y = \frac{1}{3}x - 1$

Linear

| x  | y  |
|----|----|
| −3 | −2 |
| 0  | −1 |
| 3  | 0  |

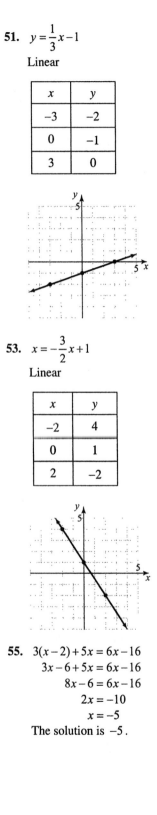

**53.** $x = -\frac{3}{2}x + 1$

Linear

| x  | y  |
|----|----|
| −2 | 4  |
| 0  | 1  |
| 2  | −2 |

**55.** $3(x-2) + 5x = 6x - 16$

$3x - 6 + 5x = 6x - 16$

$8x - 6 = 6x - 16$

$2x = -10$

$x = -5$

The solution is $-5$.

**57.** $3x + \frac{2}{5} = \frac{1}{10}$

$30x + 4 = 1$

$30x = -3$

$x = -\frac{1}{10}$

The solution is $-\frac{1}{10}$.

**59.** $3x \le -15$

$x \le -5$

$(-\infty, -5]$

**61.** $2x - 5 > 4x + 3$

$-2x > 8$

$x < -4$

$(-\infty, -4)$

**63.** The first coordinate, −1, indicates that the point is 1 unit to the left of the *y*-axis. The second coordinate, 5.3, indicates that the point is 5.3 units above the *x*-axis. The answer is b.

**65.** Look for the graph where the only nonzero *y*-values are 40 and 60. The answer is b.

**67.** Look for the graph where all the *y*-values are between 10 and 30. The answer is c.

**69.** The first segment in the graph with *y*-coordinate greater than 0.25 begins in February 1991. Thus, 1991 is the first year that the price of a first-class stamp rose above $0.25.

**71.** Answers may vary

**73.** $y = x^2 - 4x + 7$

| x | y |
|---|---|
| 0 | 7 |
| 1 | 4 |
| 2 | 3 |
| 3 | 4 |
| 4 | 7 |

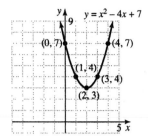

$y = x^2 - 4x + 7$

(0, 7)   (4, 7)
(1, 4)   (3, 4)
(2, 3)

**75.   a.   $y = 2x + 6$**

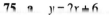

| $x$ | $y$ |
|-----|-----|
| 0   | 6   |
| 1   | 8   |
| 2   | 10  |

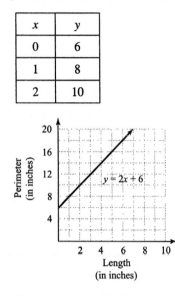

$y = 2x + 6$

Perimeter (in inches)

Length (in inches)

   **b.   When $x$ is 4, $y$ is 14. Thus, when the length
        is 4 inches, the perimeter is 14 inches.**

**77.   When $x = 0$, $y = 7$. Thus, the purchase price was
        $7000.**

**79.   $7000 - 6500 = \$500$**

**81.   Depreciation is the same from year to year.**

**83.   They are parallel.**

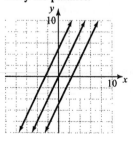

**85.   Answers may vary**

**87.   "The $y$-value is $-3$ decreased by twice the $x$-
        value" is written as $y = -3 - 2x$.**

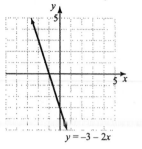

$y = -3 - 2x$

**89.   "The $y$-value is 5 decreased by the square of the
        $x$-value" is written as $y = 5 - x^2$.**

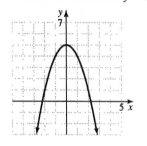

**91.**

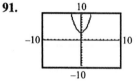

**93.**

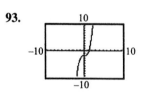

## Section 3.2

### Practice Exercises

**1.   a.   The domain is the set of all first coordinates,
            $\{4, 5\}$. The range is the set of all second
            coordinates, $\{1, -3, -2, 6\}$.**

   **b.   Ordered pairs are not listed here but are
            given in graph form. The relation is
            $\{(3, -4), (3, -3), (3, -2), (3, -1), (3, 0),
            (3, 1), (3, 2), (3, 3), (3, 4)\}$.
            The domain is $\{3\}$. The range is
            $\{-4, -3, -2, -1, 0, 1, 2, 3, 4\}$.**

**c.**  The domain is the set of inputs,
{Administrative Secretary, Game
Developer, Engineer, Restaurant Manager,
Marketing}. The range is comprised of the
numbers in the set of outputs that
correspond to elements in the set of inputs,
{27, 73, 50, 35}.

**2. a.**  Although the ordered pairs (3, 1) and (9, 1)
have the same *y*-value, each *x*-value is
assigned to only one *y*-value, so this set of
ordered pairs is a function.

**b.**  The *x*-value −2 is assigned to two *y*-values,
−3 and 4, in this graph, so this relation does
not define a function.

**c.**  This relation is a function because although
two different people may have the same
birth date, each person has only one birth
date. This means that each element in the
first set is assigned to only one element in
the second set.

**3.**  The relation $y = -3x + 5$ is a function if each *x*-
value corresponds to just one *y*-value. For each
*x*-value substituted into the equation
$y = -3x + 5$, the multiplication and addition
performed on each gives a single result, so only
one *y*-value will be associated with each *x*-value.
Thus, $y = -3x + 5$ is a function.

**4.**  The relation $y = -x^2$ is a function if each
*x*-value corresponds to just one *y*-value. For each
*x*-value substituted into the equation $y = -x^2$,
squaring each gives a single result, so only one
*y*-value will be associated with each *x*-value.
Thus, $y = -x^2$ is a function.

**5. a.**  Yes, this is the graph of a function since no
vertical line will intersect this graph more
than once.

**b.**  Yes, this is the graph of a function since no
vertical line will intersect this graph more
than once.

**c.**  No, this is not the graph of a function. Note
that vertical lines can be drawn that intersect
the graph in two points.

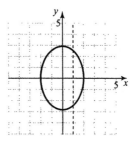

**d.**  Yes, this is the graph of a function since no
vertical line will intersect this graph more
than once.

**e.**  No, this is not the graph of a function. A
vertical line can be drawn that intersects this
line at every point.

**6. a.**  By the vertical line test, the graph is the
graph of a function. The *x*-values are
graphed from −1 to 2, so the domain is
[−1, 2]. The *y*-values are graphed from −2 to
9, so the range is [−2, 9].

**b.**  By the vertical line test, the graph is not the
graph of a function. The *x*-values are
graphed from −1 to 1, so the domain is
[−1, 1]. The *y*-values are graphed from −4 to
4, so the range is [−4, 4].

**c.**  By the vertical line test, the graph is the
graph of a function. The arrows indicate that
the graph continues forever. All *x*-values are
graphed, so the domain is (−∞, ∞). The
*y*-values for 4 and numbers less than 4 are
graphed, so the range is (−∞, 4].

**d.**  By the vertical line test, the graph is the
graph of a function. The arrows indicate that
the graph continues forever. All *x*-values
and all *y*-values are graphed, so the domain
is (−∞, ∞) and the range is (−∞, ∞).

**7. a.**  Substitute 1 for *x* in *f*(*x*).
$f(x) = 3x - 2$
$f(1) = 3(1) - 2 = 3 - 2 = 1$

**b.**  Substitute 1 for *x* in *g*(*x*).
$g(x) = 5x^2 + 2x - 1$
$g(1) = 5(1)^2 + 2(1) - 1$
$= 5 + 2 - 1 = 6$

**c.** Substitute 0 for *x* in *f*(*x*).
$$f(x) = 3x - 2$$
$$f(0) = 3(0) - 2 = 0 - 2 = -2$$

**d.** Substitute −2 for *x* in *g*(*x*).
$$g(x) = 5x^2 + 2x - 1$$
$$g(-2) = 5(-2)^2 + 2(-2) - 1$$
$$= 5(4) - 4 - 1$$
$$= 20 - 4 - 1 = 15$$

**8. a.** To find *f*(1), find the *y*-value when *x* = 1. We see from the graph that when *x* = 1, *y* or *f*(*x*) = −3. Thus, *f*(1) = −3.

**b.** *f*(0) = −2 from the ordered pair (0, −2).

**c.** *g*(−2) = 3 from the ordered pair (−2, 3).

**d.** *g*(0) = 1 from the ordered pair (0, 1).

**e.** To find *x*-values such that *f*(*x*) = 1, we are looking for any ordered pairs on the graph of *f* whose *f*(*x*) or *y*-value is 1. They are (−1, 1) and (3, 1). Thus, *f*(−1) = 1 and *f*(3) = 1. The *x*-values are −1 and 3.

**f.** Find ordered pairs on the graph of *g* whose *g*(*x*) or *y*-value is −2. There is one such ordered pair, (−3, −2). Thus, *g*(−3) = −2. The only *x*-value is −3.

**9.** Find the year 2003 and move upward until you reach the graph. From the point on the graph, move horizontally to the left until the other axis is reached. In 2003, approximately $35 billion was spent.

**10.** Find *f*(2012).
$$f(x) = 2.602x - 5178$$
$$f(2012) = 2.602(2012) - 5178$$
$$= 57.224$$
We predict that $57.224 billion will be spent in 2012.

### Graphing Calculator Explorations

**1.**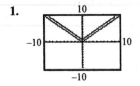

**2.** **3.** **4.** **5.** **6.**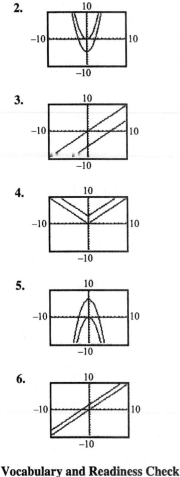

### Vocabulary and Readiness Check

**1.** The intersection of the *x*-axis and *y*-axis is a point, called the <u>origin</u>.

**2.** To find an *x*-intercept, let <u>y</u> = 0 and solve for <u>x</u>.

**3.** To find a *y*-intercept, let <u>x</u> = 0 and solve for <u>y</u>.

**4.** The graph of *Ax* + *By* = *C*, where *A* and *B* are not both 0 is a <u>line</u>.

**5.** The graph of *y* = |*x*| looks <u>V-shaped</u>.

**6.** The graph of *y* = *x*² is a <u>parabola</u>.

**7.** A <u>relation</u> is a set of ordered pairs.

**8.** The <u>range</u> of a relation is the set of all second components of the ordered pairs.

**9.** The <u>domain</u> of a relation is the set of all first components of the ordered pairs.

**10.** A <u>function</u> is a relation in which each first component in the ordered pairs corresponds to *exactly* one second component.

**11.** By the vertical line test, all linear equations are functions except those whose graphs are <u>vertical</u> lines.

**12.** If $f(-2) = 1.7$, the corresponding ordered pair is <u>(−2, 1.7)</u>.

**Exercise Set 3.2**

**1.** The domain is the set of all first coordinates and the range is the set of all second coordinates.
Domain = {−1, 0, −2, 5}
Range = {7, 6, 2}
Function since each *x*-value corresponds to exactly one *y*-value.

**3.** The domain is the set of all first coordinates and the range is the set of all second coordinates.
Domain = {−2, 6, −7}
Range = {4, −3, −8}
The relation is not a function since −2 is paired with both 4 and −3.

**5.** The domain is the set of all first coordinates and the range is the set of all second coordinates.
Domain = {1}
Range = {1, 2, 3, 4}
The relation is not a function since 1 is paired with both 1 and 2 for example.

**7.** The domain is the set of all first coordinates and the range is the set of all second coordinates.

Domain = $\left\{ \dfrac{3}{2}, 0 \right\}$

Range = $\left\{ \dfrac{1}{2}, -7, \dfrac{4}{5} \right\}$

The relation is not a function since $\dfrac{3}{2}$ is paired

with both $\dfrac{1}{2}$ and −7.

**9.** The domain is the set of all first coordinates and the range is the set of all second coordinates.
Domain = {−3, 0, 3}
Range = {−3, 0, 3}
Function since each *x*-value corresponds to exactly one *y*-value.

**11.** Points on graph: (−1, 2), (1, 1), (2, 1), (3, 1)
Domain = {−1, 1, 2, 3}
Range = {2, 1}
Function since each *x*-value corresponds to exactly one *y*-value.

**13.** Domain = {Iowa, Alaska, Delaware, Illinois, Connecticut, New York}
Range = {5, 1, 19, 29}
Function since each input corresponds to exactly one output.

**15.** Domain = {32°, 104°, 212°, 50°}
Range = {0°, 40°, 10°, 100°}
Function since each input corresponds to exactly one output.

**17.** Domain = {0}
Range = {2, −1, 5, 100}
Not a function since the input 0 corresponds to more than one output.

**19.** This relation is a function because although two different students may have the same final grade average, each student has only one final grade average. This means that each element in the first set is assigned to only one element in the second set.

**21.** This relation is not a function because more than one person in Cincinnati has blue eyes. This means that one element in the first set is assigned to more than one element in the second set.

**23.** Yes, this is the graph of a function since no vertical line will intersect this graph more than once.

**25.** No, this is not the graph of a function. Note that vertical lines can be drawn that intersect the graph in two points. The *y*-axis is such a vertical line.

**27.** Yes, this is the graph of a function since no vertical line will intersect this graph more than once.

**29.** The *x*-values are graphed from 0 to $+\infty$; domain = $[0, \infty)$

The arrows indicate the *y*-values continue forever; range = $(-\infty, \infty)$

The relation is not a function since it fails the vertical line test (try $x = 1$).

**31.** The $x$-values are graphed from $-1$ to $1$;
domain $= [-1, 1]$

The arrows indicate the $y$-values continue
forever; range $= (-\infty, \infty)$

The relation is not a function since it fails the
vertical line test (try $x = 0$).

**33.** The arrows indicate the $x$-values continue
forever; domain $= (-\infty, \infty)$

The $y$-values do not include $(-3, 3)$;
range $= (-\infty, -3] \cup [3, \infty)$

The relation is not a function since it fails the
vertical line test (try $x = 2$).

**35.** The $x$-values are graphed from $2$ to $7$;
domain $= [2, 7]$

The $y$-values are graphed from $1$ to $6$;
range $= [1, 6]$

The relation is not a function since it fails the
vertical line test (try $x = 4$).

**37.** The only $x$-value is 2; domain $= \{-2\}$
The $y$-values continue forever; range $= (-\infty, \infty)$
The relation is not a function since it fails the
vertical line test (try $x = -2$).

**39.** The $x$-values continue forever;
domain $= (-\infty, \infty)$

The $y$-values are 3 and less; range $= (-\infty, 3]$
Function since it passes the vertical line test.

**41.** Answers may vary

**43.** $y = x + 1$
For each $x$-value substituted into the equation
$y = x + 1$, the addition performed gives a single
result, so only one $y$-value will be associated
with each $x$-value. Thus, $y = x + 1$ is a function.

**45.** $x = 2y^2$
The $x$-value 8 is associated with two $y$-values, $-2$
and 2. Thus, $x = 2y^2$ is not a function.

**47.** $y - x = 7$
For each $x$-value substituted into the equation
$y - x = 7$, the process of solving for $y$ gives a
single result, so only one $y$-value will be
associated with each $x$-value. Thus, $y - x = 7$ is a
function.

**49.** $y = \dfrac{1}{x}$

For each $x$-value substituted into the equation
$y = \dfrac{1}{x}$, the division performed gives a single
result, so only one $y$-value will be associated
with each $x$-value. Thus, $y = \dfrac{1}{x}$ is a function.

**51.** $y = 5x - 12$

For each $x$-value substituted into the equation
$y = 5x - 12$, the multiplication and addition
performed on each gives a single result, so only
one $y$-value will be associated with each $x$-value.
Thus, $y = 5x - 12$ is a function.

**53.** $x = y^2$

The $x$-value 4 is associated with two $y$-values, $-2$
and 2. Thus, $x = y^2$ is not a function.

**55.** $f(x) = 3x + 3$
$f(4) = 3(4) + 3 = 12 + 3 = 15$

**57.** $h(x) = 5x^2 - 7$
$$\begin{aligned}
h(-3) &= 5(-3)^2 - 7 \\
&= 5(9) - 7 \\
&= 45 - 7 \\
&= 38
\end{aligned}$$

**59.** $g(x) = 4x^2 - 6x + 3$
$$\begin{aligned}
g(2) &= 4(2)^2 - 6(2) + 3 \\
&= 4(4) - 12 + 3 \\
&= 16 - 12 + 3 \\
&= 7
\end{aligned}$$

**61.** $g(x) = 4x^2 - 6x + 3$
$$\begin{aligned}
g(0) &= 4(0)^2 - 6(0) + 3 \\
&= 4(0) - 0 + 3 \\
&= 0 - 0 + 3 \\
&= 3
\end{aligned}$$

**63.** $f(x) = \dfrac{1}{2}x$

    **a.** $f(0) = \dfrac{1}{2}(0) = 0$

**b.** $f(2) = \frac{1}{2}(2) = 1$

**c.** $f(-2) = \frac{1}{2}(-2) = -1$

**65.** $g(x) = 2x^2 + 4$

  **a.** $g(-11) = 2(-11)^2 + 4$
$$= 2(121) + 4$$
$$= 242 + 4$$
$$= 246$$

  **b.** $g(-1) = 2(-1)^2 + 4$
$$= 2(1) + 4$$
$$= 2 + 4$$
$$= 6$$

  **c.** $g\left(\frac{1}{2}\right) = 2\left(\frac{1}{2}\right)^2 + 4$
$$= 2\left(\frac{1}{4}\right) + 4$$
$$= \frac{1}{2} + \frac{8}{2}$$
$$= \frac{9}{2}$$

**67.** $f(x) = -5$

  **a.** $f(2) = -5$

  **b.** $f(0) = -5$

  **c.** $f(606) = -5$

**69.** $f(x) = 1.3x^2 - 2.6x + 5.1$

  **a.** $f(2) = 1.3(2)^2 - 2.6(2) + 5.1$
$$= 1.3(4) - 5.2 + 5.1$$
$$= 5.2 - 5.2 + 5.1$$
$$= 5.1$$

  **b.** $f(-2) = 1.3(-2)^2 - 2.6(-2) + 5.1$
$$= 1.3(4) + 5.2 + 5.1$$
$$= 5.2 + 5.2 + 5.1$$
$$= 15.5$$

  **c.** $f(3.1) = 1.3(3.1)^2 - 2.6(3.1) + 5.1$
$$= 1.3(9.61) - 8.06 + 5.1$$
$$= 12.493 - 8.06 + 5.1$$
$$= 9.533$$

**71.** If $f(1) = -10$, then $y = -10$ when $x = 1$. The ordered pair is $(1, -10)$.

**73.** If $g(4) = 56$, then $y = 56$ when $x = 4$. The ordered pair is $(4, 56)$.

**75.** The ordered pair $(-1, -2)$ is on the graph of $f$. Thus, $f(-1) = -2$.

**77.** The ordered pair $(2, 0)$ is on the graph of $g$. Thus, $g(2) = 0$.

**79.** There are two ordered pairs on the graph of $f$ with a $y$-value of $-5$, $(-4, -5)$ and $(0, -5)$. The $x$-values are $-4$ and $0$.

**81.** To the right of the $y$-axis, there is one ordered pair on the graph of $g$ with a $y$-value of 4, $(3, 4)$. The $x$-value is 3.

**83.** Infinite number
The reason is that a graph is a function as long as it passes the vertical line test. So it does not matter if the equation of the graph takes on the value 0 many times.

**85. a.** Find the year 1996 and move upward until you reach the graph. From the point on the graph, move horizontally to the left until the other axis is reached. In 1996, approximately $17 billion was spent.

  **b.** Find $f(1996)$.
$$f(x) = 2.602x - 5178$$
$$f(1996) = 2.602(1996) - 5178$$
$$= 15.592$$
Approximately $15.592 billion was spent in 1996.

**87.** Since 2012 is 12 years after 2000, find $f(12)$.
$$f(x) = 0.42x + 10.5$$
$$f(12) = 0.42(12) + 10.5$$
$$= 15.54$$
We predict that diamond production will be $15.54 billion in 2012.

**89.** $f(x) = x + 7$

**91.** $A(r) = \pi r^2$

$A(5) = \pi(5)^2 = 25\pi$ square centimeters

**93.** $V(x) = x^3$

$V(14) = (14)^3 = 2744$ cubic inches

**95.** $H(f) = 2.59f + 47.24$

$H(46) = 2.59(46) + 47.24$

$\qquad = 166.38$ centimeters

**97.** $D(x) = \dfrac{136}{25}x$

$D(30) = \dfrac{136}{25}(30) = 163.2$ milligrams

**99.** $C(x) = 2.28x + 94.86$

**a.** $C(5) = 2.28(5) + 94.86 = 106.24$
The per capita consumption of poultry was about 106.26 lb in 2006.

**b.** 2007 gives $x = 6$.
$C(6) = 2.28(6) + 94.86 = 108.54$ pounds

**101.** $x - y = -5$

| $x$ | 0 | −5 | 1 |
|-----|---|----|---|
| $y$ | 5 | 0  | 6 |

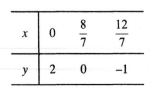

**103.** $7x + 4y = 8$

| $x$ | 0 | $\dfrac{8}{7}$ | $\dfrac{12}{7}$ |
|-----|---|----|----|
| $y$ | 2 | 0  | −1 |

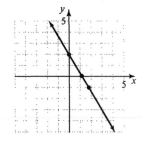

**105.** $y = 6x$

| $x$ | 0 | 0 | −1 |
|-----|---|---|----|
| $y$ | 0 | 0 | −6 |

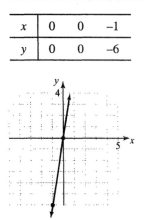

**107.** Yes, it is possible to find the perimeter. The sum of the lengths of the two sides parallel to the side measuring 45 meters is also 45 meters. The sum of the lengths of the two sides parallel to the side measuring 40 meters is also 40 meters. The perimeter is 45 + 45 + 40 + 40 = 170 meters.

**109.** $f(7) = 50$ means that $y = 50$ when $x = 7$. We conclude that the given statement is false, since it does not follow from $f(7) = 50$.

**111.** Since $f(7) = 50$ when $f(x) = 10x - 20$, the statement is true.

**113.** $g(x) = -3x + 12$

**a.** $g(s) = -3s + 12$

**b.** $g(r) = -3r + 12$

**115.** $f(x) = x^2 - 12$

**a.** $f(12) = (12)^2 - 12 = 144 - 12 = 132$

**b.** $f(a) = a^2 - 12$

**117.** Answers may vary

**Section 3.3**

**Practice Exercises**

**1.** $f(x) = 4x$, $g(x) = 4x - 3$

| $x$ | $f(x)$ | $g(x)$ |
|-----|--------|--------|
| 0 | 0 | –3 |
| –1 | –4 | –7 |
| 1 | 4 | 1 |

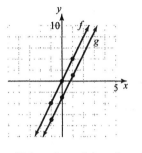

**2.** $f(x) = -2x$, $g(x) = -2x + 5$

| $x$ | $f(x)$ | $g(x)$ |
|-----|--------|--------|
| 0 | 0 | 5 |
| –1 | 2 | 7 |
| 1 | –2 | 3 |
| 2 | –4 | 1 |

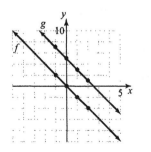

**3. a.** The *y*-intercept of $f(x) = \dfrac{3}{4}x - \dfrac{2}{5}$ is

$$\left(0, \ -\frac{2}{5}\right).$$

**b.** The *y*-intercept of $y = 2.6x + 4.1$ is $(0, 4.1)$.

**4.** $4x - 5y = -20$
Let $x = 0$.
$4x - 5y = -20$
$4 \cdot 0 - 5y = -20$
$-5y = -20$
$y = 4$
Let $y = 0$.
$4x - 5y = -20$
$4x - 5 \cdot 0 = -20$
$4x = -20$
$x = -5$
Let $x = -2$.
$4x - 5y = -20$
$4(-2) - 5y = -20$
$-8 - 5y = -20$
$-5y = -12$
$$y = \frac{12}{5} = 2\frac{2}{5}$$
The ordered pairs are in the table.

| $x$ | $y$ |
|-----|-----|
| 0 | 4 |
| –5 | 0 |
| –2 | $2\frac{2}{5}$ |

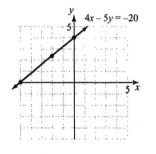

**5.** $y = -3x$
If $x = 0$, then $y = -3(0) = 0$.
If $x = 1$, then $y = -3(1) = -3$.
If $x = -1$, then $y = -3(-1) = 3$.
The ordered pairs are in the table.

| $x$ | $y$ |
|-----|-----|
| 0 | 0 |
| 1 | –3 |
| –1 | 3 |

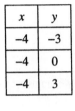

$y = -3x$

**Graphing Calculator Explorations**

**1.** $x = 3.5y$

$$y = \frac{x}{3.5}$$

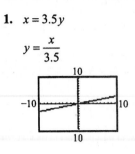

**6.** $x = -4$

The equation can be written as $x + 0y = -4$. For any $y$-value chosen, notice that $x$ is $-4$.

| x | y |
|----|----|
| -4 | -3 |
| -4 | 0 |
| -4 | 3 |

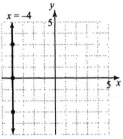

$x = -4$

**2.** $-2.7y = x$

$$y = \frac{x}{-2.7} = -\frac{x}{2.7}$$

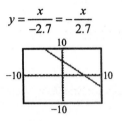

**3.** $5.78x + 2.31y = 10.98$

$2.31y = -5.78x + 10.98$

$$y = -\frac{5.78}{2.31}x + \frac{10.98}{2.31}$$

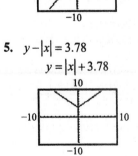

**7.** $y = 4$

The equation can be written as $0x + y = 4$. For any $x$-value chosen, notice that $y$ is 4.

| x | y |
|----|----|
| -3 | 4 |
| 0  | 4 |
| 3  | 4 |

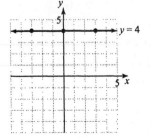

$y = 4$

**4.** $-7.22x + 3.89y = 12.57$

$3.89y = 7.22x + 12.57$

$$y = \frac{7.22}{3.89}x + \frac{12.57}{3.89}$$

**5.** $y - |x| = 3.78$

$$y = |x| + 3.78$$

**6.** $3y - 5x^2 = 6x - 4$

$$3y = 5x^2 + 6x - 4$$

$$y = \frac{5}{3}x^2 + 2x - \frac{4}{3}$$

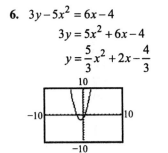

**7.** $y - 5.6x^2 = 7.7x + 1.5$

$$y = 5.6x^2 + 7.7x + 1.5$$

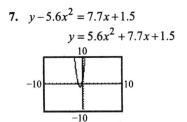

**8.** $y + 2.6|x| = -3.2$

$$y = -2.6|x| - 3.2$$

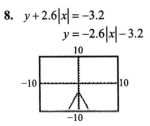

### Vocabulary and Readiness Check

**1.** A <u>linear</u> function can be written in the form $f(x) = mx + b$.

**2.** In the form $f(x) = mx + b$, the $y$-intercept is <u>(0, b)</u>.

**3.** The graph of $x = c$ is a <u>vertical</u> line with $x$-intercept <u>(c, 0)</u>.

**4.** The graph of $y = c$ is a <u>horizontal</u> line with $y$-intercept <u>(0, c)</u>.

**5.** To find an $x$-intercept, let $y = 0$ or <u>f(x)</u> = 0 and solve for <u>x</u>.

**6.** To find a $y$-intercept, let <u>x</u> = 0 and solve for <u>y</u>.

### Exercise Set 3.3

**1.** $f(x) = -2x$

| $x$ | 0 | −1 | 1 |
|---|---|---|---|
| $y$ | 0 | 2 | −2 |

Plot the points to obtain the graph.

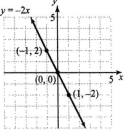

**3.** $f(x) = -2x + 3$

| $x$ | 0 | 1 | −1 |
|---|---|---|---|
| $y$ | 3 | 1 | 5 |

Plot the points to obtain the graph.

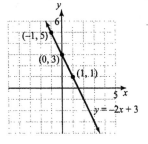

**5.** $f(x) = \frac{1}{2}x$

| $x$ | 0 | 2 | −2 |
|---|---|---|---|
| $y$ | 0 | 1 | −1 |

Plot the points to obtain the graph.

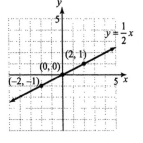

**7.** $f(x) = \frac{1}{2}x - 4$

| $x$ | 0 | 2 | 4 |
|---|---|---|---|
| $y$ | −4 | −3 | −2 |

Plot the points to obtain the graph.

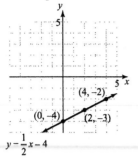

$y - \frac{1}{2}x - 4$

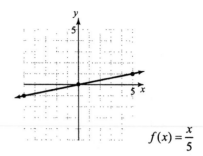

$$f(x) = \frac{x}{5}$$

9. The graph of $f(x) = 5x - 3$ is the graph of $f(x) = 5x$ shifted down 3 units. The correct graph is C.

11. The graph of $f(x) = 5x + 1$ is the graph of $f(x) = 5x$ shifted up 1 unit. The correct graph is D.

13. $x - y = 3$

Let $x = 0$.  Let $y = 0$.  Let $x = 2$.
$0 - y = 3$   $x - 0 = 3$   $2 - y = 3$
$y = -3$     $x = 3$     $y = -1$

| $x$ | 0 | 3 | 2 |
|---|---|---|---|
| $y$ | –3 | 0 | –1 |

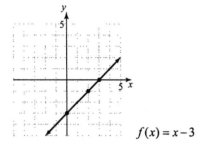

$$f(x) = x - 3$$

15. $x = 5y$

Let $x = 0$.  Let $x = 5$.  Let $x = -5$.
$0 = 5y$    $5 = 5y$    $-5 = 5y$
$y = 0$     $y = 1$     $y = -1$

| $x$ | 0 | 5 | –5 |
|---|---|---|---|
| $y$ | 0 | 1 | –1 |

17. $-x + 2y = 6$

Let $x = 0$.      Let $y = 0$.      Let $x = 2$.
$-0 + 2y = 6$   $-x + 2(0) = 6$   $-2 + 2y = 6$
$y = 3$         $x = -6$          $y = 4$

| $x$ | 0 | –6 | 2 |
|---|---|---|---|
| $y$ | 3 | 0 | 4 |

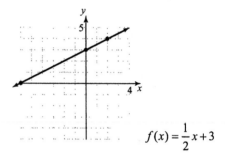

$$f(x) = \frac{1}{2}x + 3$$

19. $2x - 4y = 8$

Let $x = 0$.          Let $y = 0$.
$2(0) - 4y = 8$    $2x - 4(0) = 8$
$y = -2$           $x = 4$
Let $x = 2$.
$2(2) - 4y = 8$
$y = -1$

| $x$ | 0 | 4 | 2 |
|---|---|---|---|
| $y$ | –2 | 0 | –1 |

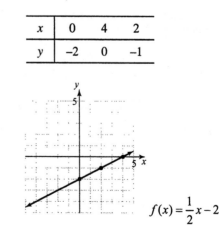

$$f(x) = \frac{1}{2}x - 2$$

**21.** Answers may vary

**23.** $x = -1$
Vertical line with $x$-intercept at $-1$

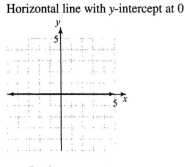

**25.** $y = 0$
Horizontal line with $y$-intercept at 0

**27.** $y + 7 = 0$
$y = -7$
Horizontal line with $y$-intercept at $-7$

**29.** The graph of $y = 2$ is a horizontal line with $y$-intercept $(0, 2)$. The correct graph is C.

**31.** The graph of $x - 2 = 0$ or $x = 2$ is a vertical line with $x$-intercept $(2, 0)$. The correct graph is A.

**33.** The vertical line $x = 0$ has $y$-intercepts.

**35.** $x + 2y = 8$

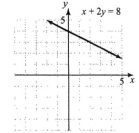

**37.** $3x + 5y = 7$

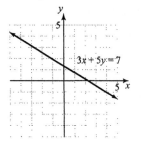

**39.** $x + 8y = 8$

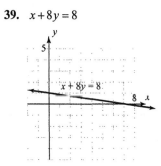

**41.** $5 = 6x - y$

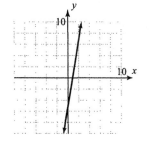

**43.** $-x + 10y = 11$

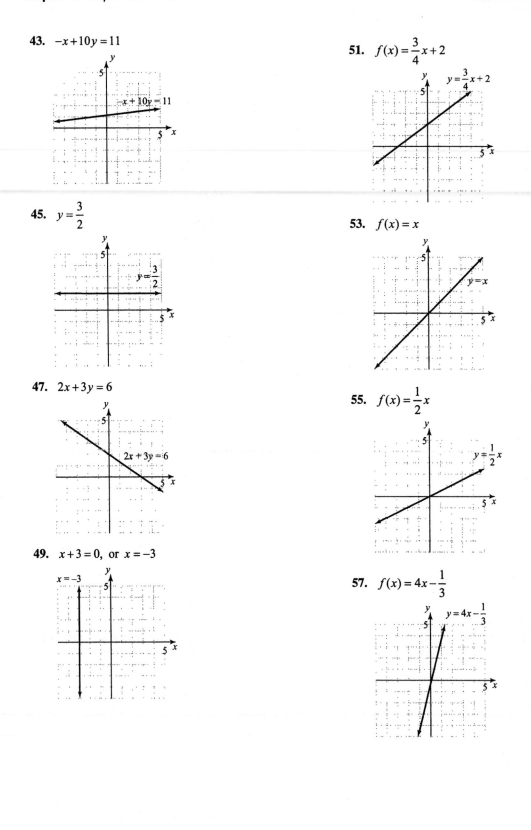

**45.** $y = \dfrac{3}{2}$

**47.** $2x + 3y = 6$

**49.** $x + 3 = 0$, or $x = -3$

**51.** $f(x) = \dfrac{3}{4}x + 2$

**53.** $f(x) = x$

**55.** $f(x) = \dfrac{1}{2}x$

**57.** $f(x) = 4x - \dfrac{1}{3}$

**59.** $x = -3$

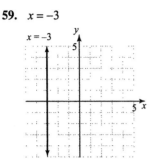

**61.** $|x - 3| = 6$

$x - 3 = 6$ or $x - 3 = -6$

$x = 9$ or $x = -3$

The solution set is $\{-3, 9\}$.

**63.** $|2x + 5| > 3$

$2x + 5 < -3$ or $2x + 5 > 3$

$2x < -8$ or $2x > -2$

$x < -4$ or $x > -1$

$(-\infty, -4) \cup (-1, \infty)$

**65.** $|3x - 4| \le 2$

$-2 \le 3x - 4 \le 2$

$2 \le 3x \le 6$

$\dfrac{2}{3} \le x \le 2$

$\left[ \dfrac{2}{3}, 2 \right]$

**67.** $\dfrac{-6 - 3}{2 - 8} = \dfrac{-9}{-6} = \dfrac{3}{2}$

**69.** $\dfrac{-8 - (-2)}{-3 - (-2)} = \dfrac{-8 + 2}{-3 + 2} = \dfrac{-6}{-1} = 6$

**71.** $\dfrac{0 - 6}{5 - 0} = \dfrac{-6}{5} = -\dfrac{6}{5}$

**73.** $2x + 3y = 1500$

 **a.** $2(0) + 3y = 1500$

 $3y = 1500$

 $y = 500$

 (0, 500); If no tables are produced, 500 chairs can be produced.

 **b.** $2x + 3(0) = 1500$

 $2x = 1500$

 $x = 750$

 (750, 0); If no chairs are produced, 750 tables can be produced.

 **c.** $2(50) + 3y = 1500$

 $100 + 3y = 1500$

 $3y = 1400$

 $y = 466.7$

 466 chairs

**75.** $C(x) = 0.2x + 24$

 **a.** $C(200) = 0.2(200) + 24$

 $= 40 + 24$

 $= 64$

 $64

 **b.**

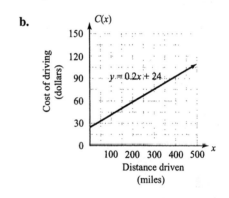

 **c.** The line moves upward from left to right.

**77.** $f(x) = 107.3x + 1245.62$

 **a.** Since 2015 is 15 years after 2000, find $f(15)$.

 $f(15) = 107.3(15) + 1245.62$

 $= 1609.5 + 1245.62$

 $= 2855.12$

 In 2015, the yearly cost of attending a two-year college will be approximately $2855.12.

 **b.** Let $f(x) = 2500$.

 $2500 = 107.3x + 1245.62$

 $1254.38 = 107.3x$

 $\dfrac{1254.38}{107.3} = x$

 $11.69 \approx x$

 Round up to 12. The yearly cost of attending a two-year college will first exceed $2500 in 2012, 12 years after 2000.

**c.** Answers may vary.

**79.**

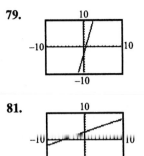

**81.**

**83. a.** $y = -4x + 2$ is a line parallel to $y = -4x$ but with $y$-intercept $(0, 2)$.

**b.** $y = -4x - 5$ is a line parallel to $y = -4x$ but with $y$-intercept $(0, -5)$.

**85.** The graph shows the graph of $y = |x|$ shifted up 1 unit. Its equation is $y = |x| + 1$. The correct answer is b.

**87.** The graph shows the graph of $y = |x|$ shifted down 1 unit. Its equation is $y = |x| - 1$. The correct answer is a.

## Section 3.4

### Practice Exercises

**1.** Let $(x_1, y_1) = (4, 0)$ and $(x_2, y_2) = (-2, 3)$.

$$m = \frac{y_2 - y_1}{x_2 - x_1}$$
$$= \frac{3 - 0}{-2 - 4}$$
$$= \frac{3}{-6}$$
$$= -\frac{1}{2}$$

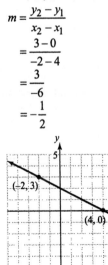

**2.** Let $(x_1, y_1) = (-5, -4)$ and $(x_2, y_2) = (5, 2)$.

$$m = \frac{y_2 - y_1}{x_2 - x_1}$$
$$= \frac{2 - (-4)}{5 - (-5)}$$
$$= \frac{6}{10}$$
$$= \frac{3}{5}$$

**3.** $f(x) = -4x + 6$ or $y = -4x + 6$

We need two points. We find the intercepts.
Let $x = 0$.
$$y = -4 \cdot 0 + 6 = 6$$
Let $y = 0$.
$$0 = -4x + 6$$
$$4x = 6$$
$$x = \frac{6}{4} = \frac{3}{2}$$

The intercepts are $(0, 6)$ and $\left(\frac{3}{2}, 0\right)$. Let

$(x_1, y_1) = (0, 6)$ and $(x_2, y_2) = \left(\frac{3}{2}, 0\right)$.

$$m = \frac{y_2 - y_1}{x_2 - x_1}$$
$$= \frac{0 - 6}{\frac{3}{2} - 0}$$
$$= \frac{-6}{\frac{3}{2}}$$
$$= -\frac{6}{1} \cdot \frac{2}{3}$$
$$= -\frac{12}{3}$$
$$= -4$$

**4.** $2x - 3y = 9$

Write the equation in slope-intercept form by solving for $y$.

$$2x - 3y = 9$$
$$-3y = -2x + 9$$
$$\frac{-3y}{-3} = \frac{-2x}{-3} + \frac{9}{-3}$$
$$y = \frac{2}{3}x - 3$$

The coefficient of $x$, $\frac{2}{3}$, is the slope, and the $y$-intercept is $(0, -3)$.

**5.** $f(x) = 2.7x + 38.64$

The year 2012 corresponds to $x = 16$.
$$f(16) = 2.7(16) + 38.64$$
$$= 43.2 + 38.64$$
$$= 81.84$$
We predict that in 2012 the price of an adult one-day pass will be about \$81.84.

**6.** $x = 4$

The graph of $x = 4$ is a vertical line. We choose two points on the line, $(4, 0)$ and $(4, 3)$. Let $(x_1, y_1) = (4, 0)$ and $(x_2, y_2) = (4, 3)$.

$$m = \frac{y_2 - y_1}{x_2 - x_1}$$
$$= \frac{3 - 0}{4 - 4}$$
$$= \frac{3}{0}$$

Since $\frac{3}{0}$ is undefined, the slope of the vertical line $x = 4$ is undefined.

**7.** $y = -3$

The graph of $y = -3$ is a horizontal line. We choose two points on the line, $(0, -3)$ and $(4, -3)$. Let $(x_1, y_1) = (0, -3)$ and $(x_2, y_2) = (4, -3)$.

$$m = \frac{y_2 - y_1}{x_2 - x_1}$$
$$= \frac{-3 - (-3)}{4 - 0}$$
$$= \frac{0}{4}$$
$$= 0$$

The slope of the horizontal line $y = -3$ is 0.

**8. a.** Find the slope of each line.

$$x - 2y = 3$$
$$-2y = -x + 3$$
$$\frac{-2y}{-2} = \frac{-x}{-2} + \frac{3}{-2}$$
$$y = \frac{1}{2}x - \frac{3}{2}$$

The slope is $\frac{1}{2}$.

$$2x + y = 3$$
$$y = -2x + 3$$

The slope is $-2$. The product of the slopes is $-1 \left[ \frac{1}{2}(-2) = -1 \right]$. The lines are perpendicular.

**b.** Find the slope of each line.

$$4x - 3y = 2$$
$$-3y = -4x + 2$$
$$\frac{-3y}{-3} = \frac{-4x}{-3} + \frac{2}{-3}$$
$$y = \frac{4}{3}x - \frac{2}{3}$$

The slope is $\frac{4}{3}$. The $y$-intercept is $\left( 0, \frac{2}{3} \right)$.

$$-8x + 6y = -6$$
$$6y = 8x - 6$$
$$\frac{6y}{6} = \frac{8x}{6} - \frac{6}{6}$$
$$y = \frac{4}{3}x - 1$$

The slope is $\frac{4}{3}$. The $y$-intercept is $(0, -1)$.

The slopes of both lines are $\frac{4}{3}$. The $y$-intercepts are different, so the lines are not the same. Therefore, the lines are parallel.

**Graphing Calculator Explorations**

**1.**

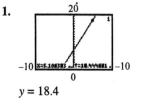

$y = 18.4$

**2.**

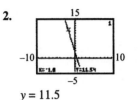

$y = 11.5$

**3.**

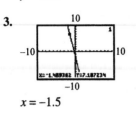

$x = -1.5$

**4.**

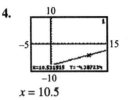

$x = 10.5$

**5.**

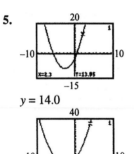

$y = 14.0$

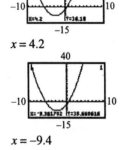

$x = 4.2$

$x = -9.4$

**6.**

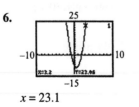

$x = 23.1$

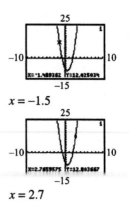

$x = -1.5$

$x = 2.7$

**Vocabulary and Readiness Check**

1. The measure of the steepness or tilt of a line is called <u>slope</u>.

2. The slope of a line through two points is measured by the ratio of <u>vertical</u> change to <u>horizontal</u> change.

3. If a linear equation is in the form $y = mx + b$, or $f(x) = mx + b$, the slope of the line is <u>$m$</u> and the $y$-intercept is <u>$(0, b)$</u>.

4. The form $y = mx + b$ or $f(x) = mx + b$ is the <u>slope-intercept</u> form.

5. The slope of a <u>horizontal</u> line is 0.

6. The slope of a <u>vertical</u> line is undefined.

7. Two perpendicular lines have slopes whose product is <u>$-1$</u>.

8. Two non-vertical lines are parallel if they have <u>the same</u> slope and different <u>$y$-intercepts</u>.

9. $m = \dfrac{7}{6}$ slants upward.

10. $m = -3$ slants downward.

11. Since $m = 0$, the line is horizontal.

12. Since the slope is undefined, the line is vertical.

**Exercise Set 3.4**

1. $m = \dfrac{11-2}{8-3} = \dfrac{9}{5}$

**3.** $m = \dfrac{8-1}{1-3} = \dfrac{7}{-2} = -\dfrac{7}{2}$

**5.** $m = \dfrac{3-8}{4-(-2)} = \dfrac{-5}{6} = -\dfrac{5}{6}$

**7.** $m = \dfrac{-4-(-6)}{4-(-2)} = \dfrac{-4+6}{4+2} = \dfrac{2}{6} = \dfrac{1}{3}$

**9.** $m = \dfrac{11-(-1)}{-12-(-3)} = \dfrac{12}{-9} = -\dfrac{4}{3}$

**11.** $m = \dfrac{5-5}{3-(-2)} = \dfrac{0}{5} = 0$

**13.** $m = \dfrac{-5-1}{-1-(-1)} = \dfrac{-6}{0}$

undefined slope

**15.** $m = \dfrac{0-6}{-3-0} = \dfrac{-6}{-3} = 2$

**17.** $m = \dfrac{4-2}{-3-(-1)} = \dfrac{2}{-2} = -1$

**19.** The slope of $l_1$ is negative, and the slope of $l_2$ is positive. Since a positive number is greater than any negative number, $l_2$ has the greater slope.

**21.** The slope of $l_1$ is negative, and the slope of $l_2$ is 0. Since 0 is greater than any negative number, $l_2$ has the greater slope.

**23.** Both lines have positive slope. Since $l_2$ is steeper, it has the greater slope.

**25.** $f(x) = 5x - 2$

$m = 5, b = -2$ so $y$-intercept is $(0, -2)$.

**27.** $2x + y = 7$

$\quad y = -2x + 7$

$m = -2, b = 7$ so $y$-intercept is $(0, 7)$.

**29.** $2x - 3y = 10$

$\quad -3y = -2x + 10$

$\quad y = \dfrac{2}{3}x - \dfrac{10}{3}$

$m = \dfrac{2}{3}, b = -\dfrac{10}{3}$ so $y$-intercept is $\left(0, -\dfrac{10}{3}\right)$.

**31.** $f(x) = \dfrac{1}{2}x$

$m = \dfrac{1}{2}, b = 0$ so $y$-intercept is $(0, 0)$.

**33.** $f(x) = 2x + 3$

The slope is 2, and the $y$-intercept is $(0, 3)$. The correct graph is A.

**35.** $f(x) = -2x + 3$

The slope is $-2$, and the $y$-intercept is $(0, 3)$. The correct graph is B.

**37.** $x = 1$ is a vertical line.

$m$ is undefined.

**39.** $y = -3$ is a horizontal line.

$m = 0$

**41.** $x + 2 = 0$

$\quad x = -2$

This is a vertical line. $m$ is undefined.

**43.** Answers may vary

**45.** $f(x) = -x + 5$ or $y = -1x + 5$

$m = -1, b = 5$ so $y$-intercept is $(0, 5)$.

**47.** $-6x + 5y = 30$

$\quad 5y = 6x + 30$

$\quad y = \dfrac{6}{5}x + 6$

$m = \dfrac{6}{5}, b = 6$ so $y$-intercept is $(0, 6)$.

**49.** $3x + 9 = y$

$\quad y = 3x + 9$

$m = 3, b = 9$ so $y$-intercept is $(0, 9)$.

**51.** $y = 4$

$m = 0, b = 4$ so $y$-intercept is $(0, 4)$.

**53.** $f(x) = 7x$

$m = 7, b = 0$ so $y$-intercept is $(0, 0)$.

**55.** $6 + y = 0$

$\quad y = -6$

$m = 0, b = -6$ so $y$-intercept is $(0, -6)$.

**57.** $2 - x = 3$

$\quad x = -1$

$m$ is undefined. There is no $y$-intercept.

**59.**  $f(x) = -3x + 6$          $g(x) = 3x + 5$
$m = -3$                    $m = 3$
Neither, since their slopes are not equal nor does their product equal $-1$.

**61.**  $-4x + 2y = 5$          $2x - y = 7$
$y = 2x + \dfrac{5}{2}$          $y = 2x - 7$
$m = 2$
$m = 2$
Parallel, since they have the same slope.

**63.**  $-2x + 3y = 1$          $3x + 2y = 12$
$y = \dfrac{2}{3}x + \dfrac{1}{3}$          $y = -\dfrac{3}{2}x + 6$
$m = \dfrac{2}{3}$          $m = -\dfrac{3}{2}$
Perpendicular, since the product of their slopes is $-1$.

**65.**  Answers may vary

**67.**  Two points on the line: $(0, 0)$, $(2, 3)$
$m = \dfrac{3 - 0}{2 - 0} = \dfrac{3}{2}$

**69.**  Two points on the line: $(4, 0)$, $(0, 2)$
$m = \dfrac{2 - 0}{0 - 4} = \dfrac{2}{-4} = -\dfrac{1}{2}$

**71.**  $m = \dfrac{8}{12} = \dfrac{2}{3}$

**73.**  $m = \dfrac{-1600 \text{ ft.}}{2.5 \text{ mi}}$
$= \dfrac{-1600 \text{ ft.}}{2.5(5280 \text{ ft.})}$
$= \dfrac{-1600}{13,200} \approx -0.12$

**75.**  $y = 694.9x + 43,884.9$

   **a.**  The year 2009 corresponds to $x = 9$.
$y = 694.9(9) + 43,884.9$
$= 6254.1 + 43,884.9$
$= 50,139$
We predict that in 2009 an American man with an associate's degree will earn $50,139.

   **b.**  The slope is 694.9. The annual income increases $694.90 every year.

   **c.**  The $y$-intercept is $(0, 43,884.9)$. When $x = 0$, or in 2000, the average annual income was $43,884.90.

**77.**  $-66x + 2y = 84$

   **a.**  Solve for $y$.
$-66x + 2y = 84$
$2y = 66x + 84$
$\dfrac{2y}{2} = \dfrac{66x}{2} + \dfrac{84}{2}$
$y = 33x + 42$
The slope is 33, and the $y$-intercept is $(0, 42)$.

   **b.**  The number of WiFi hotspots increases 33 thousand for every 1 year.

   **c.**  There were 42,000 WiFi hotspots in 2003.

**79.**  $f(x) = 291.5x + 2944.05$

   **a.**  The slope is 291.5. The yearly cost of tuition increases $291.50 every 1 year.

   **b.**  The $y$-intercept is $(0, 2944.05)$. The yearly cost of tuition when $x = 0$, or in 2000, was $2944.05.

**81.**  $y - 2 = 5(x + 6)$
$y - 2 = 5x + 30$
$y = 5x + 32$

**83.**  $y - (-1) = 2(x - 0)$
$y + 1 = 2x$
$y = 2x - 1$

**85.**  The denominator in the first fraction should be $7 - (-2)$.
$m = \dfrac{-14 - 6}{7 - (-2)} = \dfrac{-20}{9} = -\dfrac{20}{9}$

**87.**  The numerator in the first fraction should be $-10 - (-5)$. The denominator in the first fraction should be $-8 - (-11)$.
$m = \dfrac{-10 - (-5)}{-8 - (-11)} = \dfrac{-5}{3} = -\dfrac{5}{3}$

**89.** $f(x) = -\frac{7}{2}x - 6$ or $y = -\frac{7}{2}x - 6$

$m = -\frac{7}{2}$

The slope of a parallel line is $-\frac{7}{2}$.

**91.** $f(x) = -\frac{7}{2}x - 6$ or $y = -\frac{7}{2}x - 6$

$m = -\frac{7}{2}$

The slope of a perpendicular line is $\frac{2}{7}$.

**93.** $5x - 2y = 6 \Rightarrow y = \frac{5}{2}x - 3$

$m = \frac{5}{2}$

The slope of a parallel line is $\frac{5}{2}$.

**95.** $5x - 2y = 6 \Rightarrow y = \frac{5}{2}x - 3$

$m = \frac{5}{2}$

The slope of a perpendicular line is $-\frac{2}{5}$.

**97. a.** (6, 20)

**b.** (10, 13)

**c.** $m = \frac{13 - 20}{10 - 6} = \frac{-7}{4} = -\frac{7}{4} = -1.75$

The rate of change is –1.75 yd per sec.

**d.** $F(22, 2)$, $G(26, 8)$

$m = \frac{8 - 2}{26 - 22} = \frac{6}{4} = \frac{3}{2} = 1.5$

The rate of change is 1.5 yd per sec.

**99.** $-4x + 2y = 5$ or $y = 2x + \frac{5}{2}$

$2x - y = 7$ or $y = 2x - 7$

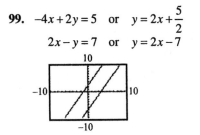

**101. a.** $y = \frac{1}{2}x + 1$

$y = x + 1$

$y = 2x + 1$

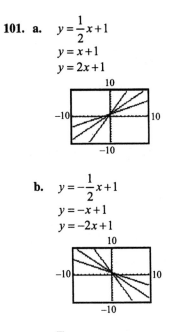

**b.** $y = -\frac{1}{2}x + 1$

$y = -x + 1$

$y = -2x + 1$

**c.** True

**Section 3.5**

**Practice Exercises**

**1.** We are given the slope, $-\frac{3}{4}$, and the $y$-intercept, (0, 4).

Let $m = -\frac{3}{4}$ and $b = 4$.

$y = mx + b$

$y = -\frac{3}{4}x + 4$

**2.** $y = \frac{3}{4}x + 2$

The slope is $\frac{3}{4}$, and the $y$-intercept is (0, 2). Plot (0, 2). Then plot a second point by starting at (0, 2), rising 3 units up, and running 4 units to the right. The second point is (4, 5).

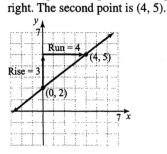

3. $x + 2y = 6$

   Solve for $y$.
   $$x + 2y = 6$$
   $$2y = -x + 6$$
   $$y = -\frac{1}{2}x + 3$$

   The slope is $-\frac{1}{2}$, and the $y$-intercept is $(0, 3)$.

   Plot $(0, 3)$. Then plot a second point by starting at $(0, 3)$, moving 1 unit down, and moving 2 units to the right. The second point is $(2, 2)$.

   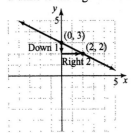

4. Use the point-slope form with $m = -4$ and $(x_1, y_1) = (-2, 5)$.
   $$y - y_1 = m(x - x_1)$$
   $$y - 5 = -4[x - (-2)]$$
   $$y - 5 = -4(x + 2)$$
   $$y - 5 = -4x - 8$$
   $$y = -4x - 3$$

5. First find the slope.
   $$m = \frac{0 - 2}{2 - (-1)} = \frac{-2}{3} = -\frac{2}{3}$$

   Use the slope and one of the points in the point-slope form. We use $(2, 0)$.
   $$y - y_1 = m(x - x_1)$$
   $$y - 0 = -\frac{2}{3}(x - 2)$$
   $$y = -\frac{2}{3}x + \frac{4}{3}$$
   $$f(x) = -\frac{2}{3}x + \frac{4}{3}$$

6. The points on the graph have coordinates $(-2, 3)$ and $(1, 1)$. Find the slope.
   $$m = \frac{1 - 3}{1 - (-2)} = \frac{-2}{3} = -\frac{2}{3}$$

   Use the slope and one of the points in the point-slope form. We use $(1, 1)$.

$$y - y_1 = m(x - x_1)$$
$$y - 1 = -\frac{2}{3}(x - 1)$$
$$3(y - 1) = -2(x - 1)$$
$$3y - 3 = -2x + 2$$
$$2x + 3y = 5$$

7. Let $x$ = the number of years after 2000 and $y$ = the number of houses sold in the year corresponding to $x$. We have two ordered pairs, $(2, 7513)$ and $(6, 9198)$. Find the slope.
   $$m = \frac{9198 - 7513}{6 - 2}$$
   $$= \frac{1685}{4}$$
   $$= 421.25$$

   Use the slope and one of the points in the point-slope form. We use $(2, 7513)$.
   $$y - y_1 = m(x - x_1)$$
   $$y - 7513 = 421.25(x - 2)$$
   $$y - 7513 = 421.25x - 842.5$$
   $$y = 421.25x + 6670.5$$

   The year 2014 corresponds to $x = 14$.
   $$y = 421.25(14) + 6670.5$$
   $$= 5897.5 + 6670.5$$
   $$= 12,568$$

   We predict that there will 12,568 house sales in 2014.

8. A horizontal line has an equation of the form $y = b$. Since the line contains the point $(6, -2)$, the equation is $y = -2$.

9. Since the line has undefined slope, the line must be vertical. A vertical line has an equation of the form $x = c$. Since the line contains the point $(6, -2)$, the equation is $x = 6$.

10. Solve the given equation for $y$.
    $$3x + 4y = 1$$
    $$4y = -3x + 1$$
    $$y = -\frac{3}{4}x + \frac{1}{4}$$

    The slope of this line is $-\frac{3}{4}$, so the slope of any line parallel to it is also $-\frac{3}{4}$. Use this slope and the point $(8, -3)$ in the point-slope form.

$$y - y_1 = m(x - x_1)$$
$$y - (-3) = -\frac{3}{4}(x - 8)$$
$$4(y + 3) = -3(x - 8)$$
$$4y + 12 = -3x + 24$$
$$3x + 4y = 12$$

**11.** Solve the given equation for $y$.
$$3x + 4y = 1$$
$$4y = -3x + 1$$
$$y = -\frac{3}{4}x + \frac{1}{4}$$

The slope of this line is $-\frac{3}{4}$, so the slope of any line perpendicular to it is the negative reciprocal of $-\frac{3}{4}$, or $\frac{4}{3}$. Use this slope and the point $(8, -3)$ in the point-slope form.
$$y - y_1 = m(x - x_1)$$
$$y - (-3) = \frac{4}{3}(x - 8)$$
$$3(y + 3) = 4(x - 8)$$
$$3y + 9 = 4x - 32$$
$$3y = 4x - 41$$
$$y = \frac{4}{3}x - \frac{41}{3}$$
$$f(x) = \frac{4}{3}x - \frac{41}{3}$$

**Vocabulary and Readiness Check**

**1.** $m = -4$, $b = 12$ so $y$-intercept is $(0, 12)$.

**2.** $m = \frac{2}{3}$, $b = -\frac{7}{2}$ so $y$-intercept is $\left(0, -\frac{7}{2}\right)$.

**3.** $m = 5$, $b = 0$ so $y$-intercept is $(0, 0)$.

**4.** $m = -1$, $b = 0$ so $y$-intercept is $(0, 0)$.

**5.** $m = \frac{1}{2}$, $b = 6$ so $y$-intercept is $(0, 6)$.

**6.** $m = -\frac{2}{3}$, $b = 5$ so $y$-intercept is $(0, 5)$.

**7.** The lines both have slope 12 and they have different $y$-intercepts, $(0, 6)$ and $(0, -2)$, so they are parallel.

**8.** The lines both have slope $-5$ and they have different $y$-intercepts, $(0, 8)$ and $(0, -8)$, so they are parallel.

**9.** The line have slopes $-9$ and $\frac{3}{2}$. The slopes are not equal and their product is not $-1$, so the lines are neither parallel nor perpendicular.

**10.** The line have slopes 2 and $\frac{1}{2}$. The slopes are not equal and their product is not $-1$, so the lines are neither parallel nor perpendicular.

**Exercise Set 3.5**

**1.** $m = -1$, $b = 1$
$$y = mx + b$$
$$y = -1x + 1$$
$$y = -x + 1$$

**3.** $m = 2$, $b = \frac{3}{4}$
$$y = mx + b$$
$$y = 2x + \frac{3}{4}$$

**5.** $m = \frac{2}{7}$, $b = 0$
$$y = mx + b$$
$$y = \frac{2}{7}x + 0$$
$$y = \frac{2}{7}x$$

**7.** $y = 5x - 2$
possible points: $(0, -2)$, $(1, 3)$

**9.** $4x + y = 7$

$\qquad y = -4x + 7$

possible points: $(0, 7)$, $(1, 3)$

**11.** $-3x + 2y = 3$

$\qquad 2y = 3x + 3$

$\qquad y = \dfrac{3}{2}x + \dfrac{3}{2}$

possible points: $\left(0, \dfrac{3}{2}\right)$, $\left(2, \dfrac{9}{2}\right)$

**13.** $y - y_1 = m(x - x_1)$

$\qquad y - 2 = 3(x - 1)$

$\qquad y - 2 = 3x - 3$

$\qquad y = 3x - 1$

**15.** $y - y_1 = m(x - x_1)$

$\qquad y - (-3) = -2(x - 1)$

$\qquad y + 3 = -2x + 2$

$\qquad y = -2x - 1$

**17.** $y - y_1 = m(x - x_1)$

$\qquad y - 2 = \dfrac{1}{2}[x - (-6)]$

$\qquad y - 2 = \dfrac{1}{2}(x + 6)$

$\qquad y - 2 = \dfrac{1}{2}x + 3$

$\qquad y = \dfrac{1}{2}x + 5$

**19.** $y - y_1 = m(x - x_1)$

$\qquad y - 0 = -\dfrac{9}{10}[x - (-3)]$

$\qquad y = -\dfrac{9}{10}(x + 3)$

$\qquad y = -\dfrac{9}{10}x - \dfrac{27}{10}$

**21.** $m = \dfrac{6 - 0}{4 - 2} = \dfrac{6}{2} = 3$

$\qquad y - 0 = 3(x - 2)$

$\qquad y = 3x - 6$

$\qquad f(x) = 3x - 6$

**23.** $m = \dfrac{13 - 5}{-6 - (-2)} = \dfrac{8}{-4} = -2$

$\qquad y - 5 = -2[x - (-2)]$

$\qquad y - 5 = -2(x + 2)$

$\qquad y - 5 = -2x - 4$

$\qquad y = -2x + 1$

$\qquad f(x) = -2x + 1$

**25.** $m = \dfrac{-3 - (-4)}{-4 - (-2)} = \dfrac{1}{-2} = -\dfrac{1}{2}$

$\qquad y - (-4) = -\dfrac{1}{2}[x - (-2)]$

$\qquad y + 4 = -\dfrac{1}{2}(x + 2)$

$\qquad 2y + 8 = -(x + 2)$

$\qquad 2y + 8 = -x - 2$

$\qquad 2y = -x - 10$

$\qquad y = -\dfrac{1}{2}x - 5$

$\qquad f(x) = -\dfrac{1}{2}x - 5$

**27.** $m = \dfrac{-9 - (-8)}{-6 - (-3)} = \dfrac{-1}{-3} = \dfrac{1}{3}$

$\qquad y - (-8) = \dfrac{1}{3}[x - (-3)]$

$\qquad y + 8 = \dfrac{1}{3}(x + 3)$

$\qquad 3y + 24 = x + 3$

$\qquad 3y = x - 21$

$\qquad y = \dfrac{1}{3}x - 7$

$\qquad f(x) = \dfrac{1}{3}x - 7$

**29.** $m = \dfrac{\frac{7}{10} - \frac{4}{10}}{-\frac{1}{5} - \frac{3}{5}} = \dfrac{\frac{3}{10}}{-\frac{4}{5}} = \dfrac{3}{10}\left(-\dfrac{5}{4}\right) = -\dfrac{3}{8}$

$$y - \dfrac{4}{10} = -\dfrac{3}{8}\left(x - \dfrac{3}{5}\right)$$
$$y - \dfrac{4}{10} = -\dfrac{3}{8}x + \dfrac{9}{40}$$
$$y = -\dfrac{3}{8}x + \dfrac{5}{8}$$
$$f(x) = -\dfrac{3}{8}x + \dfrac{5}{8}$$

**31.** $(0, 3), (1, 1)$

$$m = \dfrac{1-3}{1-0} = \dfrac{-2}{1} = -2$$
$$b = 3$$
$$y = -2x + 3$$
$$2x + y = 3$$

**33.** $(-2, 1), (4, 5)$

$$m = \dfrac{5-1}{4-(-2)} = \dfrac{4}{6} = \dfrac{2}{3}$$
$$y - 1 = \dfrac{2}{3}(x + 2)$$
$$3y - 3 = 2(x + 2)$$
$$3y - 3 = 2x + 4$$
$$2x - 3y - -7$$

**35.** $f(0) = -2$

**37.** $f(2) = 2$

**39.** $f(x) = -6$
$$f(-2) = -6$$
$$x = -2$$

**41.** $y = mx + b$
$$-4 = 0(-2) + b$$
$$-4 = b$$
$$y = -4$$

**43.** Every vertical line is in the form $x = c$. Since the line passes through the point $(4, 7)$, its equation is $x = 4$.

**45.** Every horizontal line is in the form $y = c$. Since the line passes through the point $(0, 5)$, its equation is $y = 5$.

**47.** $y = 4x - 2$ so $m = 4$
$$y - 8 = 4(x - 3)$$
$$y - 8 = 4x - 12$$
$$y = 4x - 4$$
$$f(x) = 4x - 4$$

**49.** $3y = x - 6$ or $y = \dfrac{1}{3}x - 2$ so

$$m = \dfrac{1}{3} \text{ and } m_\perp = -3$$
$$y - (-5) = -3(x - 2)$$
$$y + 5 = -3x + 6$$
$$y = -3x + 1$$
$$f(x) = -3x + 1$$

**51.** $3x + 2y = 5$
$$2y = -3x + 5$$
$$y = -\dfrac{3}{2}x + \dfrac{5}{2} \text{ so } m = -\dfrac{3}{2}$$
$$y - (-3) = -\dfrac{3}{2}[x - (-2)]$$
$$2(y + 3) = -3(x + 2)$$
$$2y + 6 = -3(x + 2)$$
$$2y + 6 = -3x - 6$$
$$y = -\dfrac{3}{2}x - 6$$
$$f(x) = -\dfrac{3}{2}x - 6$$

**53.** $y - 3 = 2[x - (-2)]$
$$y - 3 = 2(x + 2)$$
$$y - 3 = 2x + 4$$
$$2x - y = -7$$

**55.** $m = \dfrac{2-6}{5-1} = \dfrac{-4}{4} = -1$
$$y - 6 = -1(x - 1)$$
$$y - 6 = -x + 1$$
$$y = -x + 7$$
$$f(x) = -x + 7$$

**57.** $y = -\dfrac{1}{2}x + 11$
$$2y = -x + 22$$
$$x + 2y = 22$$

**59.** $m = \dfrac{-6-(-4)}{0-(-7)} = \dfrac{-2}{7} = -\dfrac{2}{7}$

$y = -\dfrac{2}{7}x - 6$

$7y = -2x - 42$

$2x + 7y = -42$

**61.** $y - 0 = -\dfrac{4}{3}[x - (-5)]$

$3y = -4(x+5)$

$3y = -4x - 20$

$4x + 3y = -20$

**63.** Every vertical line is in the form $x = c$. Since the line passes through the point $(-2, -10)$, its equation is $x = -2$.

**65.** $2x + 4y = 8$

$4y = -2x + 8$

$y = -\dfrac{1}{2}x + 2$ so $m = -\dfrac{1}{2}$

$y - (-2) = -\dfrac{1}{2}(x - 6)$

$2(y+2) = -(x-6)$

$2y + 4 = -x + 6$

$x + 2y = 2$

**67.** Lines with slopes of 0 are horizontal. Every horizontal line is in the form $y = c$. Since the line passes through $(-9, 12)$, its equation is $y = 12$.

**69.** $8x - y = 9$

$y = 8x - 9$ so $m = 8$

$y - 1 = 8(x - 6)$

$y - 1 = 8x - 48$

$8x - y = 47$

**71.** A line perpendicular to $y = 9$ will have the form $x = c$. Since the line passes through the point $(5, -6)$, its equation is $x = 5$.

**73.** $m = \dfrac{-5-(-8)}{-6-2} = \dfrac{3}{-8} = -\dfrac{3}{8}$

$y - (-8) = -\dfrac{3}{8}(x - 2)$

$8(y+8) = -3(x-2)$

$8y + 64 = -3x + 6$

$y = -\dfrac{3}{8}x - \dfrac{29}{4}$

$f(x) = -\dfrac{3}{8}x - \dfrac{29}{4}$

**75. a.** $(1, 30{,}000), (4, 66{,}000)$

$m = \dfrac{66{,}000 - 30{,}000}{4-1} = 12{,}000$

$y - 30{,}000 = 12{,}000(x-1)$

$y = 12{,}000x + 18{,}000$

$P(x) = 12{,}000x + 18{,}000$

**b.** $P(7) = 12{,}000(7) + 18{,}000$

$= \$102{,}000$

**c.** $126{,}000 = 12{,}000x + 18{,}000$

$x = \dfrac{126{,}000 - 18{,}000}{12{,}000}$

$x = 9$ years

**77. a.** $(3, 10{,}000), (5, 8000)$

$m = \dfrac{8000 - 10{,}000}{5-3} = -1000$

$y - 10{,}000 = -1000(x-3)$

$y - 10{,}000 = -1000x + 3{,}000$

$y = -1000x + 13{,}000$

**b.** $y = -1000(3.5) + 13{,}000$

$y = 9500$

9500 Fun Noodles

**79. a.** We have two ordered pairs, $(0, 150{,}900)$ and $(5, 222{,}000)$. Find the slope.

$m = \dfrac{222{,}000 - 150{,}900}{5-0}$

$= \dfrac{71{,}100}{5}$

$= 14{,}220$

Use the slope and the $y$-intercept, $(0, 150{,}900)$ to write the equation.

$y = mx + b$

$y = 14{,}220x + 150{,}900$

**b.** The year 2010 corresponds to $x = 9$.
$$y = 14,220(9) + 150,900$$
$$= 127,980 + 150,900$$
$$= 278,880$$
We predict that the median existing home price will be $278,880 in 2010.

**c.** The slope is 14,220. Every year the median price of a home increases by $14,220.

**81. a.** (0, 387), (10, 589)
$$m = \frac{589 - 387}{10 - 0} = \frac{202}{10} = 20.2$$
$$y - 387 = 20.2(x - 0)$$
$$y = 20.2x + 387$$

**b.** $x = 2013 - 2004 = 9$
$$y = 20.2(9) + 387$$
$$= 568.8 \text{ thousand people}$$

**83.** $2x - 7 \le 21$
$$2x \le 28$$
$$x \le 14$$
$$(-\infty, 14]$$

**85.** $5(x - 2) \ge 3(x - 1)$
$$5x - 10 \ge 3x - 3$$
$$2x \ge 7$$
$$x \ge \frac{7}{2}$$
$$\left[\frac{7}{2}, \infty\right)$$

**87.** $\dfrac{x}{2} + \dfrac{1}{4} < \dfrac{1}{8}$
$$8\left(\frac{x}{2} + \frac{1}{4}\right) < 8\left(\frac{1}{8}\right)$$
$$4x + 2 < 1$$
$$4x < -1$$
$$x < -\frac{1}{4}$$
$$\left(-\infty, -\frac{1}{4}\right)$$

**89.** Since any vertical line intersects any horizontal line in a right angle, the statement is true.

**91.** $m = \dfrac{1 - (-1)}{-5 - 3} = \dfrac{2}{-8} = -\dfrac{1}{4}$ so $m_\perp = 4$
$$M((3, -1), (5, 1)) = \left(\frac{3 - 5}{2}, \frac{-1 + 1}{2}\right) = (1, 0)$$
$$y - 0 = 4[x - (-1)]$$
$$y = 4(x + 1)$$
$$y = 4x + 4$$
$$-4x + y = 4$$

**93.** $m = \dfrac{-4 - 6}{-22 - (-2)} = \dfrac{-10}{-20} = \dfrac{1}{2}$ so $m_\perp = -2$
$$M((-2, 6), (-22, -4)) = \left(\frac{-2 - 22}{2}, \frac{6 - 4}{2}\right)$$
$$= (-12, 1)$$
$$y - 1 = -2[x - (-12)]$$
$$y - 1 = -2(x + 12)$$
$$y - 1 = -2x - 24$$
$$2x + y = -23$$

**95.** $m = \dfrac{7 - 3}{-4 - 2} = \dfrac{4}{-6} = -\dfrac{2}{3}$ so $m_\perp = \dfrac{3}{2}$
$$M((2, 3), (-4, 7)) = \left(\frac{2 - 4}{2}, \frac{3 + 7}{2}\right)$$
$$= (-1, 5)$$
$$y - 5 = \frac{3}{2}[x - (-1)]$$
$$2(y - 5) = 3(x + 1)$$
$$2y - 10 = 3x + 3$$
$$3x - 2y = -13$$

**97.** Answers may vary

**99.** $f(x) = -x + 7$

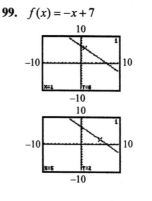

**101.** $4x + 3y = -20$

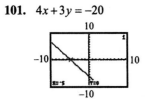

**103.** $y = 4x - 2$
$\quad\quad y = 4x - 4$

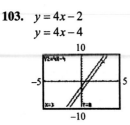

**Integrated Review**

**1.** $y = -2x$

| $x$ | $-1$ | $0$ | $1$ |
|---|---|---|---|
| $y$ | $2$ | $0$ | $-2$ |

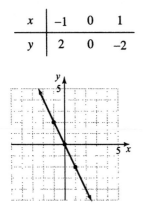

**2.** $3x - 2y = 6$

| $x$ | $0$ | $2$ | $4$ |
|---|---|---|---|
| $y$ | $-3$ | $0$ | $3$ |

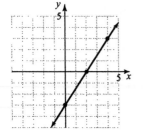

**3.** $x = -3$

The graph of $x = -3$ is a vertical line.

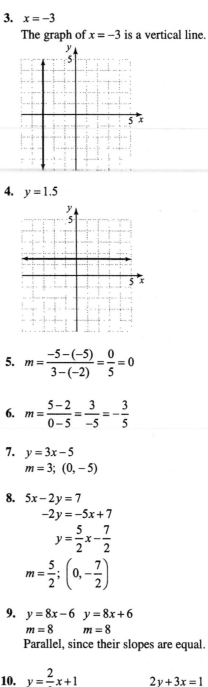

**4.** $y = 1.5$

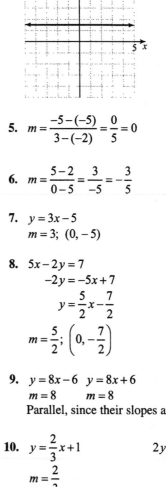

**5.** $m = \dfrac{-5 - (-5)}{3 - (-2)} = \dfrac{0}{5} = 0$

**6.** $m = \dfrac{5 - 2}{0 - 5} = \dfrac{3}{-5} = -\dfrac{3}{5}$

**7.** $y = 3x - 5$
$\quad m = 3; \ (0, -5)$

**8.** $5x - 2y = 7$
$\quad\quad -2y = -5x + 7$
$\quad\quad\quad y = \dfrac{5}{2}x - \dfrac{7}{2}$
$\quad\quad m = \dfrac{5}{2}; \ \left(0, -\dfrac{7}{2}\right)$

**9.** $y = 8x - 6 \quad y = 8x + 6$
$\quad m = 8 \quad\quad m = 8$
Parallel, since their slopes are equal.

**10.** $y = \dfrac{2}{3}x + 1 \quad\quad\quad 2y + 3x = 1$
$\quad\quad m = \dfrac{2}{3} \quad\quad\quad\quad\quad 2y = -3x + 1$
$\quad\quad\quad\quad\quad\quad\quad\quad\quad\quad y = -\dfrac{3}{2}x + \dfrac{1}{2}$
$\quad\quad\quad\quad\quad\quad\quad\quad\quad\quad m = -\dfrac{3}{2}$

Perpendicular, since the product of their slopes is $-1$.

**11.** $m = \dfrac{2-6}{5-1} = \dfrac{-4}{4} = -1$

$y - 6 = -1(x-1)$
$y - 6 = -x + 1$
$y = -x + 7$

**12.** Every vertical line is in the form $x = c$. Since the line passes through the point $(-2, -10)$, its equation is $x = -2$.

**13.** Every horizontal line is in the form $y = c$. Since the line passes through the point $(1, 0)$, its equation is $y = 0$.

**14.** $m = \dfrac{-5-(-9)}{-6-2} = \dfrac{4}{-8} = -\dfrac{1}{2}$

$y - (-9) = -\dfrac{1}{2}(x-2)$
$2(y+9) = -1(x-2)$
$2y + 18 = -x + 2$
$2y = -x - 16$
$y = -\dfrac{1}{2}x - 8$
$f(x) = -\dfrac{1}{2}x - 8$

**15.** $y - 4 = -5[x-(-2)]$
$y - 4 = -5(x+2)$
$y - 4 = -5x - 10$
$y = -5x - 6$
$f(x) = -5x - 6$

**16.** $y = -4x + \dfrac{1}{3}$
$f(x) = -4x + \dfrac{1}{3}$

**17.** $y = \dfrac{1}{2}x - 1$
$f(x) = \dfrac{1}{2}x - 1$

**18.** $y - 0 = 3\left(x - \dfrac{1}{2}\right)$
$y = 3x - \dfrac{3}{2}$

**19.** $3x - y = 5$
$y = 3x - 5$
$m = 3$
$y - (-5) = 3[x-(-1)]$
$y + 5 = 3(x+1)$
$y + 5 = 3x + 3$
$y = 3x - 2$

**20.** $4x - 5y = 10$
$-5y = -4x + 10$
$y = \dfrac{4}{5}x - 2;\ m = \dfrac{4}{5}$ so $m_\perp = -\dfrac{5}{4}$

Therefore, $y = -\dfrac{5}{4}x + 4$.

**21.** $4x + y = \dfrac{2}{3}$
$y = -4x + \dfrac{2}{3};\ m = -4$ so $m_\perp = \dfrac{1}{4}$
$y - (-3) = \dfrac{1}{4}(x-2)$
$4(y+3) = x - 2$
$4y + 12 = x - 2$
$4y = x - 14$
$y = \dfrac{1}{4}x - \dfrac{7}{2}$

**22.** $5x + 2y = 2$
$2y = -5x + 2$
$y = -\dfrac{5}{2}x + 1$
$m = -\dfrac{5}{2}$
$y - 0 = -\dfrac{5}{2}[x-(-1)]$
$y = -\dfrac{5}{2}(x+1)$
$2y = -5(x+1)$
$2y = -5x - 5$
$y = -\dfrac{5}{2}x - \dfrac{5}{2}$

**23.** A line having undefined slope is vertical. Therefore, the equation is $x = -1$.

**24.** $y - 3 = 0[x-(-1)]$
$y - 3 = 0$
$y = 3$

**Section 3.6**

**Practice Exercises**

1. $f(x) = \begin{cases} -4x-2 & \text{if } x \le 0 \\ x+1 & \text{if } x > 0 \end{cases}$

   Since $4 > 0$, $f(4) = 4+1 = 5$.

   Since $-2 \le 0$, $f(-2) = -4(-2)-2 = 8-2 = 6$.

   Since $0 \le 0$, $f(0) = -4(0)-2 = 0-2 = -2$.

2. $f(x) = \begin{cases} -4x-2 & \text{if } x \le 0 \\ x+1 & \text{if } x > 0 \end{cases}$

   For $x \le 0$:

   | $x$ | $f(x)$ |
   |-----|--------|
   | $-2$ | 6 |
   | $-1$ | 2 |
   | 0 | $-2$ |

   For $x > 0$:

   | $x$ | $f(x)$ |
   |-----|--------|
   | 1 | 2 |
   | 2 | 3 |
   | 3 | 4 |

   Graph a closed circle at (0, −2). Graph an open circle at (0, 1), which is found by substituting 0 for $x$ in $f(x) = x+1$.

   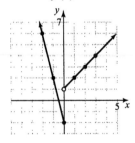

3. $f(x) = x^2$ and $g(x) = x^2 - 3$

   The graph of $g(x) = x^2 - 3$ is the graph of $f(x) = x^2$ moved downward 3 units.

   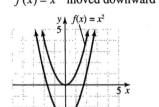

4. $f(x) = \sqrt{x}$ and $g(x) = \sqrt{x}+1$

   The graph of $g(x) = \sqrt{x}+1$ is the graph of $f(x) = \sqrt{x}$ moved upward 1 unit.

   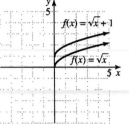

5. $f(x) = |x|$ and $g(x) = |x-3|$

   | $x$ | $f(x)$ | $g(x)$ |
   |-----|--------|--------|
   | $-2$ | 2 | 5 |
   | $-1$ | 1 | 4 |
   | 0 | 0 | 3 |
   | 1 | 1 | 2 |
   | 2 | 2 | 1 |
   | 3 | 3 | 0 |
   | 4 | 4 | 1 |
   | 5 | 5 | 2 |

   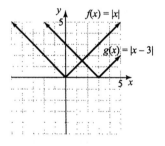

6. $f(x) = |x|$ and $g(x) = |x-2|+3$

   The graph of $g(x)$ is the same as the graph of $f(x)$ shifted 2 units to the right and 3 units up.

   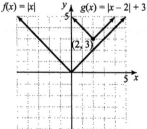

**7.** $h(x) = -(x+2)^2 - 1$

The graph of $h(x) = -(x+2)^2 - 1$ is the same as the graph of $f(x) = x^2$ reflected about the *x*-axis, then moved 2 units to the left and 1 unit downward.

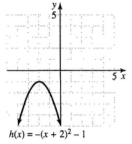

$h(x) = -(x+2)^2 - 1$

**Vocabulary and Readiness Check**

**1.** The graph that corresponds to $y = \sqrt{x}$ is C.

**2.** The graph that corresponds to $y = x^2$ is B.

**3.** The graph that corresponds to $y = x$ is D.

**4.** The graph that corresponds to $y = |x|$ is A.

**Exercise Set 3.6**

**1.** $f(x) = \begin{cases} 2x & \text{if } x < 0 \\ x+1 & \text{if } x \geq 0 \end{cases}$

For $x < 0$:      For $x \geq 0$:

| $x$ | $f(x)$ |
|---|---|
| $-3$ | $-6$ |
| $-2$ | $-4$ |
| $-1$ | $-2$ |

| $x$ | $f(x)$ |
|---|---|
| $0$ | $1$ |
| $1$ | $2$ |
| $2$ | $3$ |

Graph a closed circle at (0, 1). Graph an open circle at (0, 0), which is found by substituting 0 for *x* in $f(x) = 2x$.

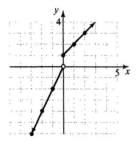

**3.** $f(x) = \begin{cases} 4x+5 & \text{if } x \leq 0 \\ \frac{1}{4}x+2 & \text{if } x > 0 \end{cases}$

For $x \leq 0$:      For $x > 0$:

| $x$ | $f(x)$ |
|---|---|
| $-2$ | $-3$ |
| $-1$ | $1$ |
| $0$ | $5$ |

| $x$ | $f(x)$ |
|---|---|
| $1$ | $2\frac{1}{4}$ |
| $2$ | $2\frac{1}{2}$ |
| $4$ | $3$ |

Graph a closed circle at (0, 5). Graph an open circle at (0, 2), which is found by substituting 0 for *x* in $f(x) = \frac{1}{4}x+2$.

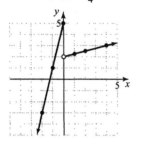

**5.** $g(x) = \begin{cases} -x & \text{if } x \leq 1 \\ 2x+1 & \text{if } x > 1 \end{cases}$

For $x \leq 1$:      For $x > 1$:

| $x$ | $g(x)$ |
|---|---|
| $-1$ | $1$ |
| $0$ | $0$ |
| $1$ | $-1$ |

| $x$ | $g(x)$ |
|---|---|
| $2$ | $5$ |
| $3$ | $7$ |
| $4$ | $9$ |

Graph a closed circle at (1, −1). Graph an open circle at (1, 3), which is found by substituting 1 for *x* in $g(x) = 2x+1$.

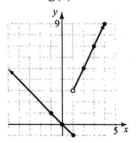

**7.** $f(x) = \begin{cases} 5 & \text{if } x < -2 \\ 3 & \text{if } x \geq -2 \end{cases}$

For $x < -2$:          For $x \geq -2$:

| $x$ | $f(x)$ |
|----|------|
| −5 | 5 |
| −4 | 5 |
| −3 | 5 |

| $x$ | $f(x)$ |
|----|------|
| −2 | 3 |
| −1 | 3 |
| 0 | 3 |

Graph a closed circle at (−2, 3). Graph an open circle at (−2, 5), which is found by substituting −2 for $x$ in $f(x) = 5$.

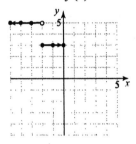

**9.** $f(x) = \begin{cases} -2x & \text{if } x \leq 0 \\ 2x+1 & \text{if } x > 0 \end{cases}$

For $x \leq 0$:          For $x > 0$:

| $x$ | $f(x)$ |
|----|------|
| −1 | 2 |
| 0 | 0 |

| $x$ | $f(x)$ |
|----|------|
| 1 | 3 |
| 2 | 5 |

Graph a closed circle at (0, 0). Graph an open circle at (0, 1), which is found by substituting 0 for $x$ in $f(x) = 2x+1$.

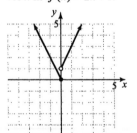

The function is defined for all real numbers, so the domain is $(-\infty, \infty)$. The function takes on all $y$-values greater than or equal to 0, so the range is $[0, \infty)$.

**11.** $h(x) = \begin{cases} 5x-5 & \text{if } x < 2 \\ -x+3 & \text{if } x \geq 2 \end{cases}$

For $x < 2$:          For $x \geq 2$:

| $x$ | $h(x)$ |
|----|------|
| 0 | −5 |
| 1 | 0 |

| $x$ | $h(x)$ |
|----|------|
| 2 | 1 |
| 3 | 0 |

Graph a closed circle at (2, 1). Graph an open circle at (2, 5), which is found by substituting 2 for $x$ in $h(x) = 5x-5$.

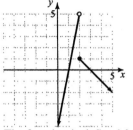

The function is defined for all real numbers, so the domain is $(-\infty, \infty)$. The function takes on all $y$-values less than 5, so the range is $(-\infty, 5)$.

**13.** $f(x) = \begin{cases} x+3 & \text{if } x < -1 \\ -2x+4 & \text{if } x \geq -1 \end{cases}$

For $x < -1$:          For $x \geq -1$:

| $x$ | $f(x)$ |
|----|------|
| −4 | −1 |
| −3 | 0 |
| −2 | 1 |

| $x$ | $f(x)$ |
|----|------|
| −1 | 6 |
| 0 | 4 |
| 1 | 2 |

Graph a closed circle at (−1, 6). Graph an open circle at (−1, 2), which is found by substituting −1 for $x$ in $f(x) = x+3$.

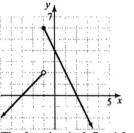

The function is defined for all real numbers, so the domain is $(-\infty, \infty)$. The function takes on all $y$-values less than or equal to 6, so the range is $(-\infty, 6]$.

15. $g(x) = \begin{cases} -2 & \text{if } x \le 0 \\ -4 & \text{if } x \ge 1 \end{cases}$

For $x \le 0$:         For $x \ge 1$:

| $x$ | $g(x)$ |
|-----|--------|
| −2  | −2     |
| −1  | −2     |
| 0   | −2     |

| $x$ | $g(x)$ |
|-----|--------|
| 1   | −4     |
| 2   | −4     |
| 3   | −4     |

Graph closed circles at (0, −2) and (1, −4).

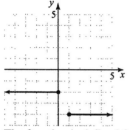

The function is defined for $x \le 0$ or $x \ge 1$, so the domain is (−∞, 0] ∪ [1, ∞). The function takes on two $y$-values, −2 and −4, so the range is {−2, −4}.

17. $f(x) = |x| + 3$

The graph of $f(x) = |x| + 3$ is the same as the graph of $y = |x|$ shifted up 3 units.

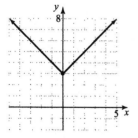

19. $f(x) = \sqrt{x} - 2$

The graph of $f(x) = \sqrt{x} - 2$ is the same as the graph of $y = \sqrt{x}$ shifted down 2 units.

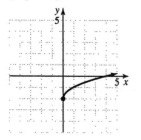

21. $f(x) = |x - 4|$

The graph of $f(x) = |x - 4|$ is the same as the graph of $y = |x|$ shifted right 4 units.

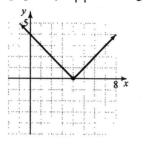

23. $f(x) = \sqrt{x + 2}$

The graph of $f(x) = \sqrt{x + 2}$ is the same as the graph of $y = \sqrt{x}$ shifted left 2 units.

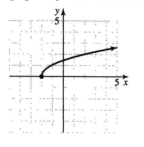

25. $y = (x - 4)^2$

The graph of $y = (x - 4)^2$ is the same as the graph of $y = x^2$ shifted right 4 units.

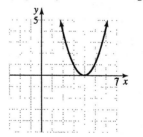

**27.** $f(x) = x^2 + 4$

The graph of $f(x) = x^2 + 4$ is the same as the graph of $y = x^2$ shifted up 4 units.

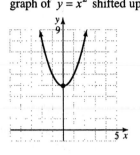

**29.** $f(x) = \sqrt{x-2} + 3$

The graph of $f(x) = \sqrt{x-2} + 3$ is the same as the graph of $y = \sqrt{x}$ shifted right 2 units and up 3 units.

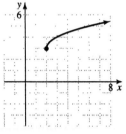

**31.** $f(x) = |x-1| + 5$

The graph of $f(x) = |x-1| + 5$ is the same as the graph of $y = |x|$ shifted right 1 unit and up 5 units.

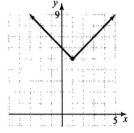

**33.** $f(x) = \sqrt{x+1} + 1$

The graph of $f(x) = \sqrt{x+1} + 1$ is the same as the graph of $y = \sqrt{x}$ shifted left 1 unit and up 1 unit.

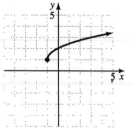

**35.** $f(x) = |x+3| - 1$

The graph of $f(x) = |x+3| - 1$ is the same as the graph of $y = |x|$ shifted left 3 units and down 1 unit.

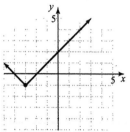

**37.** $g(x) = (x-1)^2 - 1$

The graph of $g(x) = (x-1)^2 - 1$ is the same as the graph of $y = x^2$ shifted right 1 unit and down 1 unit.

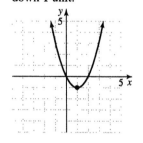

**39.** $f(x) = (x+3)^2 - 2$

The graph of $f(x) = (x+3)^2 - 2$ is the same as the graph of $y = x^2$ shifted left 3 units and down 2 units.

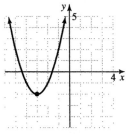

**41.** $f(x) = -(x-1)^2$

The graph of $f(x) = -(x-1)^2$ is the same as the graph of $y = x^2$ reflected about the *x*-axis and then shifted right 1 unit.

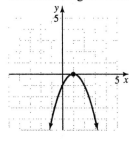

**43.** $h(x) = -\sqrt{x} + 3$

The graph of $h(x) = -\sqrt{x} + 3$ is the same as the graph of $y = \sqrt{x}$ reflected about the *x*-axis and then shifted up 3 units.

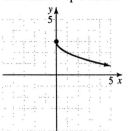

**45.** $h(x) = -|x+2| + 3$

The graph of $h(x) = -|x+2| + 3$ is the same as the graph of $y = |x|$ reflected about the *x*-axis and then shifted left 2 units and up 3 units.

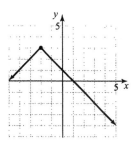

**47.** $f(x) = (x-3) + 2$

Since the function can be simplified to $f(x) = x - 1$, we see that its graph is a line with slope $m = 1$ and *y*-intercept $(0, -1)$.

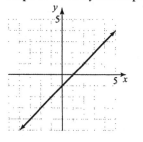

**49.** The graph of $y = -1$ is a horizontal line with *y*-intercept $(0, -1)$. The correct graph is A.

**51.** The graph of $x = 3$ is a vertical line with *x*-intercept $(3, 0)$. The correct graph is D.

**53.** Answers may vary

**55.** $f(x) = \begin{cases} -\frac{1}{2}x & \text{if } x \le 0 \\ x+1 & \text{if } 0 < x \le 2 \\ 2x-1 & \text{if } x > 2 \end{cases}$

Some points for $x \le 0$: $(-4, 2)$, $(-2, 1)$, $(0, 0)$
Closed dot at $(0, 0)$
Some points for $0 < x \le 2$: $(1, 2)$, $(2, 3)$
Open dot at $(0, 1)$, closed dot at $(2, 3)$
Some points for $x > 2$: $(3, 5)$, $(4, 7)$
There would be an open dot at $(2, 3)$ except that it gets filled by the middle piece of the graph.

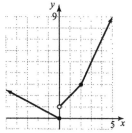

**57.** $f(x) = \sqrt{x-2} + 3$

The function is defined when $x - 2 \geq 0$, or $x \geq 2$, so the domain is $[2, \infty)$. The function takes on all $y$-values greater than or equal to 3, so the range is $[3, \infty)$.

**59.** $h(x) = -|x+2| + 3$

The function is defined for all real numbers, so the domain is $(-\infty, \infty)$. The function takes on all $y$-values less than or equal to 3, so the range is $(-\infty, 3]$.

**61.** $f(x) = 5\sqrt{x-20} + 1$

The function is defined when $x - 20 \geq 0$, or $x \geq 20$, so the domain is $[20, \infty)$.

**63.** $h(x) = 5|x - 20| + 1$

The function is defined for all real numbers, so the domain is $(-\infty, \infty)$.

**65.** $g(x) = 9 - \sqrt{x+103}$

The function is defined when $x + 103 \geq 0$, or $x \geq -103$, so the domain is $[-103, \infty)$.

**67.** $f(x) = \begin{cases} |x| & \text{if } x \leq 0 \\ x^2 & \text{if } x > 0 \end{cases}$

For $x \leq 0$:         For $x > 0$:

| $x$ | $f(x)$ |
|----|-----|
| $-2$ | 2 |
| $-1$ | 1 |
| $0$ | 0 |

| $x$ | $f(x)$ |
|----|-----|
| 1 | 1 |
| 2 | 4 |
| 3 | 9 |

Graph a closed circle at $(0, 0)$. The graph of $f(x) = x^2$ for $x > 0$ also approaches the point $(0, 0)$.

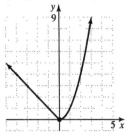

The function is defined for all real numbers, so the domain is $(-\infty, \infty)$. The function takes on all

$y$-values greater than or equal to 0, so the range is $[0, \infty)$.

**69.** $g(x) = \begin{cases} |x-2| & \text{if } x < 0 \\ -x^2 & \text{if } x \geq 0 \end{cases}$

For $x < 0$:                 For $x \geq 0$:

| $x$ | $g(x)$ |
|----|-----|
| $-3$ | 5 |
| $-2$ | 4 |
| $-1$ | 3 |

| $x$ | $g(x)$ |
|----|-----|
| 0 | 0 |
| 1 | $-1$ |
| 2 | $-4$ |

Graph an open circle at $(0, 2)$. Graph a closed circle at $(0, 0)$.

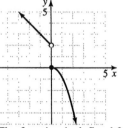

The function is defined for all real numbers, so the domain is $(-\infty, \infty)$. The function takes on all $y$-values such $y > 2$ or $y \leq 0$, so the range is $(-\infty, 0] \cup (2, \infty)$.

## Section 3.7

**Practice Exercises**

**1.** $3x + y < 8$

The boundary line is $3x + y = 8$. Graph a dashed boundary line because the inequality symbol is $<$. The point $(0, 0)$ is not on the boundary line, so we use it as a test point. Replace $x$ with 0 and $y$ with 0 in the original inequality.

$3x + y < 8$

$3(0) + 0 < 8$

$0 < 8$     True

Since $(0, 0)$ satisfies the inequality, shade the half-plane that contains $(0, 0)$. Every point in the shaded half-plane satisfies the original inequality.

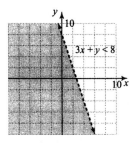

**2.** $x \geq 3y$

First graph the boundary line $x = 3y$. Graph a solid boundary line because the inequality symbol is $\geq$. We choose (0, 1) as a test point.

$x \geq 3y$

$0 \geq 3(1)$

$0 \geq 3$   False

Since this point does not satisfy the inequality, shade the half-plane on the opposite side of the boundary line from (0, 1). The graph of $x \geq 3y$ is the boundary line together with the shaded region.

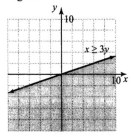

**3.** The intersection of $x \leq 3$ and $y \leq x - 2$

Graph each inequality. The intersection of the two graphs is all points common to both regions, as shown by the darker shading in the graph.

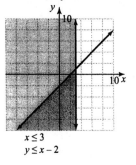

**4.** The union of $2x - 3y \leq -2$ or $y \geq 1$

Graph each inequality. The union of the two inequalities is both shaded regions, including the boundary lines, as shown in the graph.

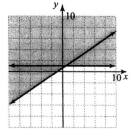

**Exercise Set 3.7**

**1.** $x < 2$

Graph $x = 2$ as a dashed line. Shade to the left of the line.

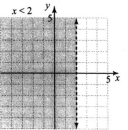

**3.** $x - y \geq 7$

Graph $x - y = 7$ as a solid line.
Test: (0, 0)
$0 - 0 \geq 7$
$0 \geq 7$   False
Shade the half-plane that does not contain (0, 0).

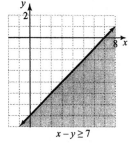

**5.** $3x + y > 6$

Graph $3x + y = 6$ as a dashed line.
Test: (0, 0)
$3(0) + 0 > 6$
$0 > 6$   False
Shade the half-plane that does not contain (0, 0).

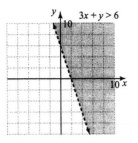

$3x + y > 6$

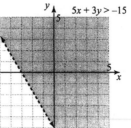

$5x + 3y > -15$

**7.** $y \le -2x$

Graph $y = -2x$ as a solid line.
Test: $(1, 1)$
$1 \le -2(1)$
$1 \le -2$   False
Shade the half-plane that does not contain $(1, 1)$.

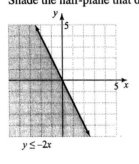

$y \le -2x$

**9.** $2x + 4y \ge 8$

Graph $2x + 4y = 8$ as a solid line.
Test: $(0, 0)$
$2(0) + 4(0) \ge 8$
$0 \ge 8$   False
Shade the half-plane that does not contain $(0, 0)$.

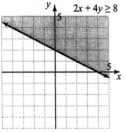

$2x + 4y \ge 8$

**11.** $5x + 3y > -15$

Graph $5x + 3y = -15$ as a dashed line.
Test: $(0, 0)$
$5(0) + 3(0) > -15$
$0 > -15$   True
Shade the half-plane that contains $(0, 0)$.

**13.** Answers may vary. A dashed boundary line should be used when the inequality contains a < or >.

**15.** $x \ge 3$ and $y \le -2$

The intersection is shown by the darker shading in the graph.

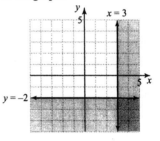

$x = 3$

$y = -2$

**17.** $x \le -2$ or $y \ge 4$

The union is both shaded regions, including the boundary line.

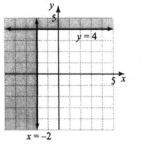

$y = 4$

$x = -2$

**19.** $x - y < 3$ and $x > 4$

The intersection is shown by the darker shading in the graph.

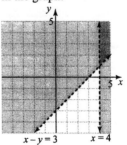

$x - y = 3$     $x = 4$

120

**21.** $x + y \le 3$ or $x - y \ge 5$

The union is both shaded regions, including the boundary lines.

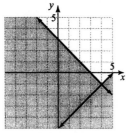

**23.** $y \ge -2$

Graph $y = -2$ as a solid line.
Test: (0, 0)
$0 \ge -2$ True
Shade the half-plane that contains (0, 0).

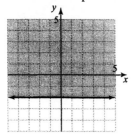

**25.** $x - 6y < 12$
$\qquad -6y < 12 - x$
$\qquad y > \dfrac{1}{6}x - 2$

Graph the boundary line as a dashed line.
Test: (0, 0)
$0 > \dfrac{1}{6}(0) - 2$ True

Shade the half-plane that contains (0, 0).

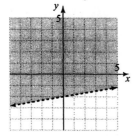

**27.** $x > 5$

Graph $x = 5$ as a dashed line.
Test: (0, 0)
$0 > 5$ False
Shade the half-plane that does not contain (0, 0).

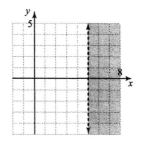

**29.** $-2x + y \le 4$
$\qquad y \le 2x + 4$

Graph the boundary line as a solid line.
Test: (0, 0)
$0 \le 2(0) + 4$ True
Shade the half-plane that contains (0, 0).

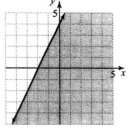

**31.** $x - 3y < 0$
$\qquad -3y < -x$
$\qquad y > \dfrac{x}{3}$

Graph the boundary line as a dashed line.
Test: (0, 1)
$1 > \dfrac{0}{3}$ True

Shade the half-plane that contains (0, 1).

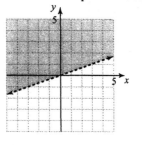
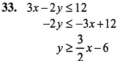

**33.** $3x - 2y \le 12$
$\qquad -2y \le -3x + 12$
$\qquad y \ge \dfrac{3}{2}x - 6$

Graph the boundary line as a solid line.
Test: (0, 0)
$3(0) - 2(0) \le 12$ True
Shade the half-plane that contains (0, 0).

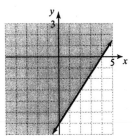

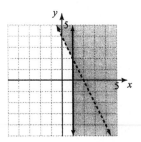

**35.** $x - y > 2$ 　 or $y < 5$
　　$y < x - 2$ or $y < 5$

Graph each inequality. The union of the two inequalities is both shaded regions, as shown by the shading in the graph below.

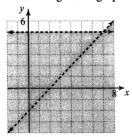

**41.** $x \geq -2$ and $x \leq 1$
　　$-2 \leq x \leq 1$

Graph each inequality. The intersection of the two inequalities is all points common to both regions, as shown by the shading in the graph below.

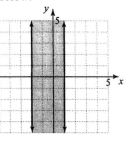

**37.** $x + y \leq 1$ 　　 and $y \leq -1$
　　$y \leq -x + 1$ and $y \leq -1$

Graph each inequality. The intersection of the two inequalities is all points common to both regions, as shown by the shading in the graph below.

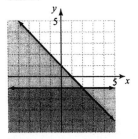

**39.** $2x + y > 4$ 　　 or $x \geq 1$
　　$y > -2x + 4$ or $x \geq 1$

Graph each inequality. The union of the two inequalities is both shaded regions, as shown by the shading in the graph below.

**43.** $x + y \leq 0$ 　 or $3x - 6y \geq 12$
　　$y \leq -x$ or 　 $-6y \geq -3x + 12$
　　$y \leq -x$ or 　　 $y \leq \frac{1}{2}x - 2$

Graph each inequality. The union of the two inequalities is both shaded regions, as shown by the shading in the graph below.

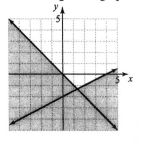

**45.** $2x - y > 3$ 　　 and $x > 0$
　　$y < 2x - 3$ and $x > 0$

Graph each inequality. The intersection of the two inequalities is all points common to both regions, as shown by the shading in the graph below.

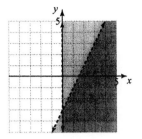

**47.** $y \le 2x+3$

The boundary line should be solid, and the half-plane below the boundary line should be shaded. The correct graph is D.

**49.** $y > 2x+3$

The boundary line should be dashed, and the half-plane above the boundary line should be shaded. The correct graph is A.

**51.** The boundary line, $x = 2$, is solid, and the half-plane with $x$-values greater than 2 is shaded. The inequality is $x \ge 2$.

**53.** The boundary line, $y = -3$, is solid, and the half-plane with $y$-values less than $-3$ is shaded. The inequality is $y \le -3$.

**55.** The boundary line, $y = 4$, is dashed, and the half-plane with $y$-values greater than 4 is shaded. The inequality is $y > 4$.

**57.** The boundary line, $x = 1$, is dashed, and the half-plane with $x$-values less than 1 is shaded. The inequality is $x < 1$.

**59.** $2^3 = 2 \cdot 2 \cdot 2 = 8$

**61.** $-5^2 = -(5 \cdot 5) = -25$

**63.** $(-2)^4 = (-2)(-2)(-2)(-2) = 16$

**65.** $\left(\dfrac{3}{5}\right)^3 = \dfrac{3^3}{5^3} = \dfrac{27}{125}$

**67.** Domain: [1, 5]
Range: [1, 3]
Since it fails the vertical line test it is not a function.

**69.** $x \le 20$ and $y \ge 10$

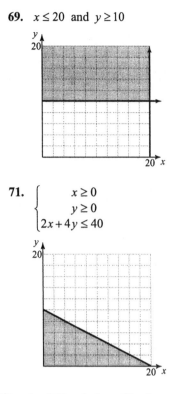

**71.** $\begin{cases} x \ge 0 \\ y \ge 0 \\ 2x+4y \le 40 \end{cases}$

**Chapter 3 Vocabulary Check**

1. A <u>relation</u> is a set of ordered pairs.

2. The graph of every linear equation in two variables is a <u>line</u>.

3. The statement $-x + 2y > 0$ is called a <u>linear inequality</u> in two variables.

4. <u>Standard</u> form of linear equation in two variables is $Ax + By = C$.

5. The <u>range</u> of a relation is the set of all second components of the ordered pairs of the relation.

6. <u>Parallel</u> lines have the same slope and different $y$-intercepts.

7. <u>Slope-intercept</u> form of a linear equation in two variables is $y = mx + b$.

8. A <u>function</u> is a relation in which each first component in the ordered pairs corresponds to exactly one second component.

9. In the equation $y = 4x - 2$, the coefficient of $x$ is the <u>slope</u> of its corresponding graph.

**10.** Two lines are <u>perpendicular</u> if the product of their slopes is –1.

**11.** To find the *x*-intercept of a linear equation, let <u>*y* = 0</u> and solve for the other variable.

**12.** The <u>domain</u> of a relation is the set of all first components of the ordered pairs of the relation.

**13.** A <u>linear function</u> is a function that can be written in the form $f(x) = mx + b$.

**14.** To find the *y*-intercept of a linear equation, let <u>*x* = 0</u> and solve for the other variable.

**15.** The equation $y - 8 = -5(x + 1)$ is written in <u>point-slope</u> form.

**Chapter 3 Review**

**1.** $A(2, -1)$, quadrant IV
$B(-2, 1)$, quadrant II
$C(0, 3)$, *y*-axis
$D(-3, -5)$, quadrant III

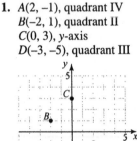

**2.** $A(-3, 4)$, quadrant II
$B(4, -3)$, quadrant IV
$C(-2, 0)$, *x*-axis
$D(-4, 1)$, quadrant II

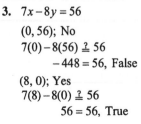

**3.** $7x - 8y = 56$
$(0, 56)$; No
$7(0) - 8(56) \stackrel{?}{=} 56$
$\quad\quad -448 = 56$, False
$(8, 0)$; Yes
$7(8) - 8(0) \stackrel{?}{=} 56$
$\quad\quad 56 = 56$, True

**4.** $-2x + 5y = 10$
$(-5, 0)$; Yes
$-2(-5) + 5(0) \stackrel{?}{=} 10$
$\quad\quad 10 = 10$, True
$(1, 1)$, No
$-2(1) + 5(1) \stackrel{?}{=} 10$
$\quad\quad 3 = 10$, False

**5.** $x = 13$
$(13, 5)$; Yes
$13 = 13$, True
$(13, 13)$; Yes
$13 = 13$, True

**6.** $y = 2$
$(7, 2)$; Yes
$2 = 2$, True
$(2, 7)$; No
$7 = 2$, False

**7.** $y = 3x$; Linear

| $x$ | –1 | 0 | 1 |
|---|---|---|---|
| $y$ | –3 | 0 | 3 |

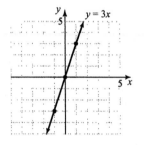

**8.** $y = 5x$; Linear

| $x$ | –1 | 0 | 1 |
|---|---|---|---|
| $y$ | –5 | 0 | 5 |

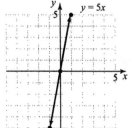

**9.** $3x - y = 4$; Linear

Find three ordered pair solutions, or find $x$- and $y$-intercepts, or find $m$ and $b$.

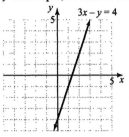

**10.** $x - 3y = 2$; Linear

Find three ordered pair solutions, or find $x$- and $y$-intercepts, or find $m$ and $b$.

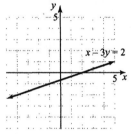

**11.** $y = |x| + 4$; Nonlinear

| $x$ | $-3$ | $-2$ | $-1$ | $0$ | $1$ | $2$ | $3$ |
|---|---|---|---|---|---|---|---|
| $y$ | $7$ | $6$ | $5$ | $4$ | $5$ | $6$ | $7$ |

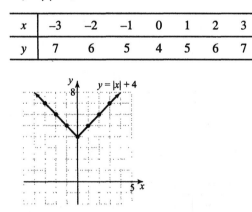

**12.** $y = x^2 + 4$; Nonlinear

| $x$ | $-3$ | $-2$ | $-1$ | $0$ | $1$ | $2$ | $3$ |
|---|---|---|---|---|---|---|---|
| $y$ | $13$ | $8$ | $5$ | $4$ | $5$ | $8$ | $13$ |

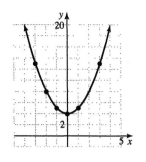

**13.** $y = -\dfrac{1}{2}x + 2$; Linear

Find three ordered pair solutions, or find $x$- and $y$-intercepts, or find $m$ and $b$.

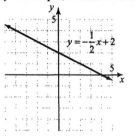

**14.** $y = -x + 5$; Linear

Find three ordered pair solutions, or find $x$- and $y$-intercepts, or find $m$ and $b$.

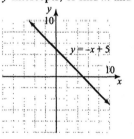

**15.** $y = 2x - 1$; Linear

Find three ordered pair solutions, or find $x$- and $y$-intercepts, or find $m$ and $b$.

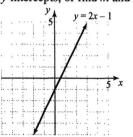

**16.** $y = \frac{1}{3}x + 1$; Linear

Find three ordered pair solutions, or find $x$- and $y$-intercepts, or find $m$ and $b$.

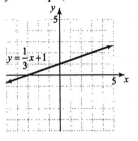

**17.** $y = -1.36x$; Linear

Find three ordered pair solutions, or find $x$- and $y$-intercepts, or find $m$ and $b$.

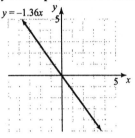

**18.** $y = 2.1x + 5.9$

Find three ordered pair solutions, or find $x$- and $y$-intercepts, or find $m$ and $b$.

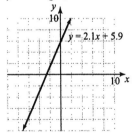

**19.** The domain is the set of all first coordinates (or inputs) and the range is the set of all second coordinates (or outputs).

Domain: $\left\{ -\frac{1}{2}, 6, 0, 25 \right\}$

Range: $\left\{ \frac{3}{4}, -12, 25 \right\}$

Function since each $x$-value corresponds to exactly one $y$-value.

**20.** The domain is the set of all first coordinates (or inputs) and the range is the set of all second coordinates (or outputs).

Domain: $\left\{ \frac{3}{4}, -12, 25 \right\}$

Range: $\left\{ -\frac{1}{2}, 6, 0, 25 \right\}$

Not a function since $\frac{3}{4}$ (or 0.75) is paired with both $-\frac{1}{2}$ and 6.

**21.** The domain is the set of all first coordinates (or inputs) and the range is the set of all second coordinates (or outputs).
Domain: {2, 4, 6, 8}
Range: {2, 4, 5, 6}
Not a function since 2 is paired with both 2 and 4.

**22.** The domain is the set of all first coordinates (or inputs) and the range is the set of all second coordinates (or outputs).
Domain: {Triangle, Square, Rectangle, Parallelogram}
Range: {3, 4}
Function since each input is paired with exactly one output.

**23.** Domain: $(-\infty, \infty)$
Range: $(-\infty, -1] \cup [1, \infty)$
Not a function since it fails the vertical line test.

**24.** Domain: $\{-3\}$
Range: $(-\infty, \infty)$
Not a function since it fails the vertical line test.

**25.** Domain: $(-\infty, \infty)$
Range: $\{4\}$
Function since it passes the vertical line test.

**26.** Domain: $[-1, 1]$
Range: $[-1, 1]$
Not a function since it fails the vertical line test.

**27.** $f(x) = x - 5$
$f(2) = (2) - 5 = -3$

**28.** $g(x) = -3x$
$g(0) = -3(0) = 0$

**29.** $g(x) = -3x$
$g(-6) = -3(-6) = 18$

**30.** $h(x) = 2x^2 - 6x + 1$
$h(-1) = 2(-1)^2 - 6(-1) + 1$
$= 2(1) + 6 + 1$
$= 9$

**31.** $h(x) = 2x^2 - 6x + 1$
$h(1) = 2(1)^2 - 6(1) + 1 = 2 - 6 + 1 = -3$

**32.** $f(x) = x - 5$
$f(5) = (5) - 5 = 0$

**33.** $J(x) = 2.54x$
$J(150) = 2.54(150) = 381$ pounds

**34.** $J(x) = 2.54x$
$J(2000) = 2.54(2000) = 5080$ pounds

**35.** The point $(-1, 0)$ is on the graph, so $f(-1) = 0$.

**36.** The point $(1, -2)$ is on the graph, so $f(1) = -2$.

**37.** $f(x) = 1$
$f(-2) = f(4) = 1$
$x = -2, 4$

**38.** $f(x) = -1$
$f(0) = f(2) = -1$
$x = 0, 2$

**39.** $f(x) = x$ or $y = x$
$m = 1, \ b = 0$

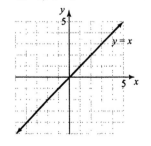

**40.** $f(x) = -\dfrac{1}{3}x$ or $y = -\dfrac{1}{3}x$
$m = -\dfrac{1}{3}, \ b = 0$

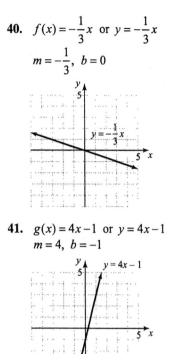

**41.** $g(x) = 4x - 1$ or $y = 4x - 1$
$m = 4, \ b = -1$

**42.** $f(x) = 3x + 1$
The *y*-intercept should be $(0, 1)$. The correct graph is C.

**43.** $f(x) = 3x - 2$
The *y*-intercept should be $(0, -2)$. The correct graph is A.

**44.** $f(x) = 3x + 2$
The *y*-intercept should be $(0, 2)$. The correct graph is B.

**45.** $f(x) = 3x - 5$
The *y*-intercept should be $(0, -5)$. The correct graph is D.

**46.** $4x + 5y = 20$

Let $x = 0$       Let $y = 0$

$4(0) + 5y = 20$       $4x + 5(0) = 20$

          $y = 4$               $x = 5$

$(0, 4)$           $(5, 0)$

**47.** $3x - 2y = -9$

Let $x = 0$       Let $y = 0$

$3(0) - 2y = -9$       $3x - 2(0) = -9$

          $y = \dfrac{9}{2}$            $x = -3$

                  $(-3, 0)$

$\left(0, \dfrac{9}{2}\right)$

**48.** $4x - y = 3$

Let $x = 0$       Let $y = 0$

$4(0) - y = 3$       $4x - (0) = 3$

          $y = -3$            $x = \dfrac{3}{4}$

$(0, -3)$

         $\left(\dfrac{3}{4}, 0\right)$

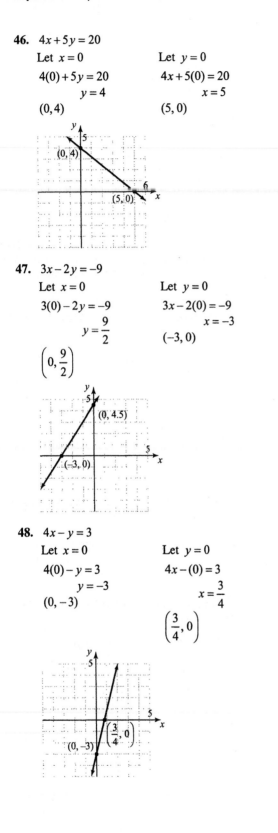

**49.** $2x + 6y = 9$

Let $x = 0$       Let $y = 0$

$2(0) + 6y = 9$       $2x + 6(0) = 9$

          $y = \dfrac{3}{2}$            $x = \dfrac{9}{2}$

$\left(0, \dfrac{3}{2}\right)$           $\left(\dfrac{9}{2}, 0\right)$

**50.** $y = 5$

Horizontal line with $y$-intercept 5.

**51.** $x = -2$

Vertical line with $x$-intercept $-2$.

**52.** $x - 2 = 0$

     $x = 2$

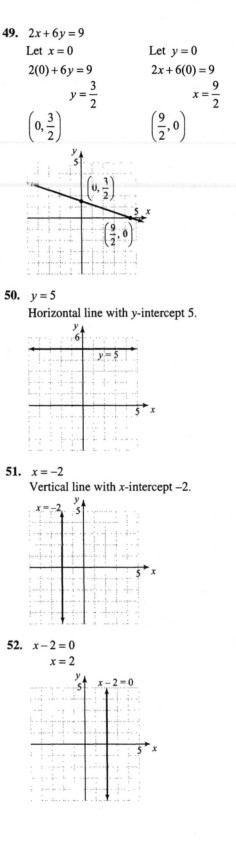

**53.** $y + 3 = 0$
$y = -3$

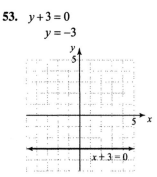

**54.** $C(x) = 0.3x + 42$

  **a.** $C(150) = 0.3(150) + 42$
  $= 45 + 42$
  $= 87$
  $\$87$

  **b.** $m = 0.3, \ b = 42$

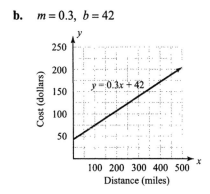

**55.** $m = \dfrac{-4 - 8}{6 - 2} = \dfrac{-12}{4} = -3$

**56.** $m = \dfrac{13 - 9}{5 - (-3)} = \dfrac{4}{8} = \dfrac{1}{2}$

**57.** $m = \dfrac{6 - (-4)}{-3 - (-7)} = \dfrac{10}{4} = \dfrac{5}{2}$

**58.** $m = \dfrac{7 - (-2)}{-5 - 7} = \dfrac{9}{-12} = -\dfrac{3}{4}$

**59.** $6x - 15y = 20$
$-15y = -6x + 20$
$y = \dfrac{2}{5}x - \dfrac{4}{3}$
$m = \dfrac{2}{5}, \ b = -\dfrac{4}{3}, \ y\text{-intercept} \left(0, -\dfrac{4}{3}\right)$

**60.** $4x + 14y = 21$
$14y = -4x + 21$
$y = -\dfrac{2}{7}x + \dfrac{3}{2}$
$m = -\dfrac{2}{7}, \ b = \dfrac{3}{2}, \ y\text{-intercept} \left(0, \dfrac{3}{2}\right)$

**61.** $y - 3 = 0$
$y = 3; \ \text{Slope} = 0$

**62.** $x = -5$ ; Vertical line
Slope is undefined.

**63.** The slope of $l_1$ is negative, and the slope of $l_2$ is positive. Since a positive number is greater than any negative number, $l_2$ has the greater slope.

**64.** The slope of $l_1$ is 0, and the slope of $l_2$ is positive. Since a positive number is greater than 0, $l_2$ has the greater slope.

**65.** The slope of $l_1$ and the slope of $l_2$ are both positive. Since $l_2$ is steeper, it has the greater slope.

**66.** The slope of $l_1$ is 0, and the slope of $l_2$ is negative. Since a negative number is less than 0, $l_1$ has the greater slope.

**67.** $y = 0.3x + 42$

  **a.** $m = 0.3$; the cost increases by \$0.30 for each additional mile driven.

  **b.** $b = 42$; the cost for 0 miles driven is $\$42$.

**68.** $f(x) = -2x + 6 \qquad g(x) = 2x - 1$
$m = -2 \qquad\qquad m = 2$
Neither; The slopes are not the same and their product is not $-1$.

**69.** $-x + 3y = 2 \qquad\qquad 6x - 18y = 3$
$\quad y = \dfrac{1}{3}x + \dfrac{2}{3} \qquad\quad y = \dfrac{1}{3}x - \dfrac{1}{6}$
$\quad m = \dfrac{1}{3} \qquad\qquad\quad m = \dfrac{1}{3}$
Parallel, since their slopes are equal.

**70.** $y = -x + 1$
$m = -1, \ b = 1$

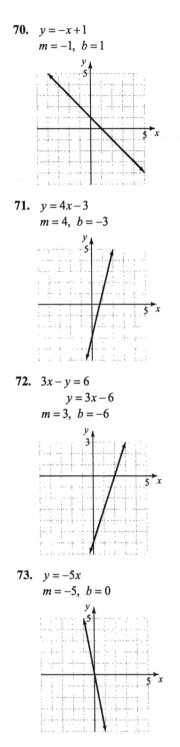

**71.** $y = 4x - 3$
$m = 4, \ b = -3$

**72.** $3x - y = 6$
$y = 3x - 6$
$m = 3, \ b = -6$

**73.** $y = -5x$
$m = -5, \ b = 0$

**74.** Every horizontal line is in the form $y = c$. Since the line passes through the point $(3, -1)$, its equation is $y = -1$.

**75.** Every vertical line has the form $x = c$. Since the line passes through the point $(-2, -4)$, its equation is $x = -2$.

**76.** A line parallel to $x = 6$ has the form $x = c$. Since the line passes through $(-4, -3)$, its equation is $x = -4$.

**77.** Lines with slope 0 are horizontal, and have the form $y = c$. Since it passes through $(2, 5)$, its equation is $y = 5$.

**78.** $y - y_1 = m(x - x_1)$
$y - 5 = 3[x - (-3)]$
$y - 5 = 3(x + 3)$
$y - 5 = 3x + 9$
$3x - y = -14$

**79.** $y - y_1 = m(x - x_1)$
$y - (-2) = 2(x - 5)$
$y + 2 = 2x - 10$
$2x - y = 12$

**80.** $m = \dfrac{-2 - (-1)}{-4 - (-6)} = \dfrac{-1}{2} = -\dfrac{1}{2}$
$y - y_1 = m(x - x_1)$
$y - (-1) = -\dfrac{1}{2}[x - (-6)]$
$2(y + 1) = -(x + 6)$
$2y + 2 = -x - 6$
$x + 2y = -8$

**81.** $m = \dfrac{-8 - 3}{-4 - (-5)} = \dfrac{-11}{1} = -11$
$y - y_1 = m(x - x_1)$
$y - 3 = -11[x - (-5)]$
$y - 3 = -11(x + 5)$
$y - 3 = -11x - 55$
$11x + y = -52$

**82.** $x = 4$ has undefined slope.
A line perpendicular to $x = 4$ has slope $= 0$ and is therefore horizontal.
$y = 3$

**83.** $y = 8$ has slope $= 0$
A line parallel to $y = 8$ has slope $= 0$.
$y = -5$

**84.** $y = mx + b$

$$y = -\frac{2}{3}x + 4$$

$$f(x) = -\frac{2}{3}x + 4$$

**85.** $y = mx + b$

$$y = -x - 2$$

$$f(x) = -x - 2$$

**86.** $6x + 3y = 5$

$$3y = -6x + 5$$

$$y = -2x + \frac{5}{3} \quad \text{so} \quad m = -2$$

$$y - y_1 = m(x - x_1)$$

$$y - (-6) = -2(x - 2)$$

$$y + 6 = -2x + 4$$

$$y = -2x - 2$$

$$f(x) = -2x - 2$$

**87.** $3x + 2y = 8$

$$2y = -3x + 8$$

$$y = -\frac{3}{2}x + 4 \quad \text{so} \quad m = -\frac{3}{2}$$

$$y - y_1 = m(x - x_1)$$

$$y - (-2) = -\frac{3}{2}[x - (-4)]$$

$$2(y + 2) = -3(x + 4)$$

$$2y + 4 = -3x - 12$$

$$2y = -3x - 16$$

$$y = -\frac{3}{2}x - 8$$

$$f(x) = -\frac{3}{2}x - 8$$

**88.** $4x + 3y = 5$

$$3y = -4x + 5$$

$$y = -\frac{4}{3}x + \frac{5}{3}$$

$$\text{so} \quad m = -\frac{4}{3} \quad \text{and} \quad m_\perp = \frac{3}{4}$$

$$y - y_1 = m(x - x_1)$$

$$y - (-1) = \frac{3}{4}[x - (-6)]$$

$$4(y + 1) = 3(x + 6)$$

$$4y + 4 = 3x + 18$$

$$4y = 3x + 14$$

$$y = \frac{3}{4}x + \frac{7}{2}$$

$$f(x) = \frac{3}{4}x + \frac{7}{2}$$

**89.** $2x - 3y = 6$

$$-3y = -2x + 6$$

$$y = \frac{2}{3}x - 2$$

$$\text{so} \quad m = \frac{2}{3} \quad \text{and} \quad m_\perp = -\frac{3}{2}$$

$$y - y_1 = m(x - x_1)$$

$$y - 5 = -\frac{3}{2}[x - (-4)]$$

$$2(y - 5) = -3(x + 4)$$

$$2y - 10 = -3x - 12$$

$$2y = -3x - 2$$

$$y = -\frac{3}{2}x - 1$$

$$f(x) = -\frac{3}{2}x - 1$$

**90. a.** Use ordered pairs (0, 71) and (5, 82)

$$m = \frac{82 - 71}{5 - 0} = \frac{11}{5} = 2.2 \quad \text{and} \quad b = 71$$

$$y = 2.2x + 71$$

**b.** $x = 2009 - 2000 = 9$

$y = 2.2(9) + 71 = 90.8$

About 91% of US drivers will be wearing seat belts.

**91. a.** Use ordered pairs (0, 43) and (22, 60)

$$m = \frac{60 - 43}{22 - 0} = \frac{17}{22} \quad \text{and} \quad b = 43$$

$$y = \frac{17}{22}x + 43$$

**b.** $x = 2010 - 1998 = 12$

$y = \dfrac{17}{22}(12) + 43 \approx 52.3$

There will be about 52 million people reporting arthritis.

**92.** $f(x) = \begin{cases} -3x & \text{if } x < 0 \\ x - 3 & \text{if } x \ge 0 \end{cases}$

For $x < 0$:　　　　For $x \ge 0$:

| $x$ | $f(x)$ |
|-----|--------|
| -3 | 9 |
| -2 | 6 |
| -1 | 3 |

| $x$ | $f(x)$ |
|-----|--------|
| 0 | -3 |
| 1 | -2 |
| 2 | -1 |

Graph a closed circle at $(0, -3)$. Graph an open circle at $(0, 0)$, which is found by substituting 0 for $x$ in $f(x) = -3x$.

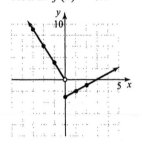

**93.** $g(x) = \begin{cases} -\dfrac{1}{5}x & \text{if } x \le -1 \\ -4x + 2 & \text{if } x > -1 \end{cases}$

For $x \le -1$:　　　　For $x > -1$:

| $x$ | $g(x)$ |
|-----|--------|
| -5 | 1 |
| -3 | $\frac{3}{5}$ |
| -1 | $\frac{1}{5}$ |

| $x$ | $g(x)$ |
|-----|--------|
| 0 | 2 |
| 1 | -2 |
| 2 | -6 |

Graph a closed circle at $\left(-1, \dfrac{1}{5}\right)$. Graph an open circle at $(-1, 6)$, which is found by substituting $-1$ for $x$ in $g(x) = -4x + 2$.

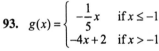

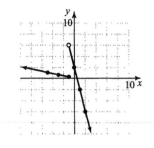

**94.** $y = \sqrt{x} - 4$

The graph of $f(x) = \sqrt{x} - 4$ is the same as the graph of $y = \sqrt{x}$ shifted down 4 units.

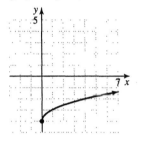

**95.** $f(x) = \sqrt{x - 4}$

The graph of $f(x) = \sqrt{x - 4}$ is the same as the graph of $y = \sqrt{x}$ shifted right 4 units.

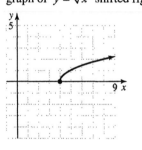

**96.** $g(x) = |x - 2| - 2$

The graph of $g(x) = |x - 2| - 2$ is the same as the graph of $y = |x|$ shifted right 2 units and down 2 units.

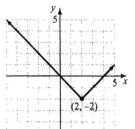

**97.** $h(x) = -(x+3)^2 - 1$

The graph of $h(x) = -(x+3)^2 - 1$ is the same as the graph of $y = x^2$ reflected about the $x$-axis and then shifted left 3 units and down 1 unit.

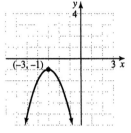

**98.** $3x + y > 4$
   $\quad y > -3x + 4$

Graph the boundary line as dashed.
Test: $(0, 0)$
$3(0) + 0 > 4$  False
Shade the half-plane that does not include $(0, 0)$.

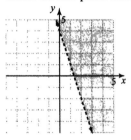

**99.** $\frac{1}{2}x - y < 2$

   $\quad y > \frac{1}{2}x - 2$

Graph the boundary line as dashed.
Test: $(0, 0)$

$\frac{1}{2}(0) - 0 < 2$  True

Shade the half-plane that contains $(0, 0)$.

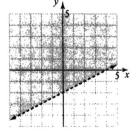

**100.** $5x - 2y \le 9$
   $\quad -2y \le -5x + 9$
   $\quad y \ge \frac{5}{2}x - \frac{9}{2}$

Graph the boundary line as solid.
Test: $(0, 0)$
$5(0) - 2(0) \le 9$  True
Shade the half-plane that contains $(0, 0)$.

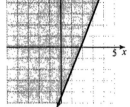

**101.** $3y \ge x$

   $\quad y \ge \frac{x}{3}$

Graph the boundary line as solid.
Test: $(0, 1)$
$3(1) \ge 0$  True
Shade the half-plane that contains $(0, 1)$.

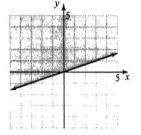

**102.** $y < 1$

Graph the boundary line as dashed. Shade the half-plane below $y = 1$.

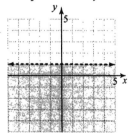

**103.** $x > -2$
Graph the boundary line as dashed. Shade the half-plane to the right of $x = -2$.

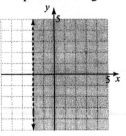

**104.** $y > 2x + 3$ or $x \leq -3$
Graph each inequality. The union of the two inequalities is both shaded regions, as shown by the graph below.

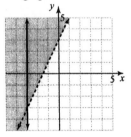

**105.** $2x < 3y + 8$ and $y \geq -2$
Graph each inequality. The intersection of the two inequalities is all points common to both regions, as shown by the shading in the graph below.

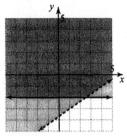

**106.** $3x - 2y = -9$

Let $x = 0$.
$3x - 2y = -9$
$3(0) - 2y = -9$
$-2y = -9$
$y = \dfrac{9}{2}$

Let $y = 0$.
$3x - 2y = -9$
$3x - 2(0) = -9$
$3x = -9$
$x = -3$

The intercepts are $\left(0, \dfrac{9}{2}\right)$ and $(-3, 0)$.

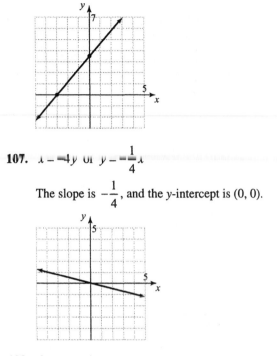

**107.** $x = -4y$ or $y = -\dfrac{1}{4}x$

The slope is $-\dfrac{1}{4}$, and the $y$-intercept is $(0, 0)$.

**108.** $3y \geq x$

Graph the boundary line $3y = x$ or $y = \dfrac{1}{3}x$ as a solid line.
Test $(0, 1)$.
$3y \geq x$
$3(1) \geq 0$
$3 \geq 0$   True
Shade the half-plane that contains $(0, 1)$.

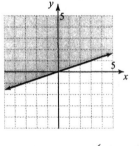

**109.** Vertical; through $\left(-7, -\dfrac{1}{2}\right)$

A vertical line has an equation of the form $x = a$, where $a$ is the $x$-coordinate of any point on the line. The equation is $x = -7$.

**110.** Slope 0; through $\left(-4, \dfrac{9}{2}\right)$

A line with slope 0 is horizontal, and a horizontal line has an equation of the form $y = b$, where $b$ is the $y$-coordinate of any point on the line. The equation is $y = \dfrac{9}{2}$.

**111.** Slope $\dfrac{3}{4}$; through $(-8, -4)$

$$y - y_1 = m(x - x_1)$$
$$y - (-4) = \dfrac{3}{4}(x - (-8))$$
$$y + 4 = \dfrac{3}{4}(x + 8)$$
$$4(y + 4) = 3(x + 8)$$
$$4y + 16 = 3x + 24$$
$$4y = 3x + 8$$
$$y = \dfrac{3}{4}x + 2$$

**112.** Through $(-3, 8)$ and $(-2, 3)$
Find the slope.
$$m = \dfrac{3 - 8}{-2 - (-3)} = \dfrac{-5}{1} = -5$$

Use the slope and one of the points in the point-slope form. We use $(-2, 3)$.
$$y - y_1 = m(x - x_1)$$
$$y - 3 = -5(x - (-2))$$
$$y - 3 = -5(x + 2)$$
$$y - 3 = -5x - 10$$
$$y = -5x - 7$$

**113.** Through $(-6, 1)$; parallel to $y = -\dfrac{3}{2}x + 11$

The slope of a line parallel to $y = -\dfrac{3}{2}x + 11$ will have the same slope, $-\dfrac{3}{2}$.

$$y - y_1 = m(x - x_1)$$
$$y - 1 = -\dfrac{3}{2}(x - (-6))$$
$$y - 1 = -\dfrac{3}{2}(x + 6)$$
$$2(y - 1) = -3(x + 6)$$
$$2y - 2 = -3x - 18$$
$$2y = -3x - 16$$
$$y = -\dfrac{3}{2}x - 8$$

**114.** Through $(-5, 7)$; perpendicular to $5x - 4y = 10$
Find the slope of $5x - 4y = 10$.
$$5x - 4y = 10$$
$$-4y = -5x + 10$$
$$y = \dfrac{5}{4}x - \dfrac{5}{2}$$

The slope is $\dfrac{5}{4}$. The slope of any line perpendicular to this line is the negative reciprocal of $\dfrac{5}{4}$, or $-\dfrac{4}{5}$.

$$y - y_1 = m(x - x_1)$$
$$y - 7 = -\dfrac{4}{5}(x - (-5))$$
$$y - 7 = -\dfrac{4}{5}(x + 5)$$
$$5(y - 7) = -4(x + 5)$$
$$5y - 35 = -4x - 20$$
$$5y = -4x + 15$$
$$y = -\dfrac{4}{5}x + 3$$

**115.** $f(x) = \begin{cases} x - 2 & \text{if } x \le 0 \\ -\dfrac{x}{3} & \text{if } x \ge 3 \end{cases}$

For $x \le 0$:        For $x > 3$:

| $x$ | $f(x)$ |
|-----|--------|
| $-2$ | $-4$ |
| $-1$ | $-3$ |
| $0$ | $-2$ |

| $x$ | $f(x)$ |
|-----|--------|
| $3$ | $-1$ |
| $4$ | $-\dfrac{4}{3}$ |
| $6$ | $-2$ |

Graph closed circles at $(0, -2)$ and $(3, -1)$.

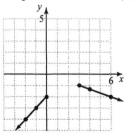

**116.** $g(x) = \begin{cases} 4x-3 & \text{if } x \le 1 \\ 2x & \text{if } x > 1 \end{cases}$

For $x \le 1$:          For $x > 1$:

| $x$ | $g(x)$ |
|-----|--------|
| $-1$ | $-7$ |
| $0$ | $-3$ |
| $1$ | $1$ |

| $x$ | $g(x)$ |
|-----|--------|
| $2$ | $4$ |
| $3$ | $6$ |
| $4$ | $8$ |

Graph a closed circle at (1, 1). Graph an open circle at (1, 2), which is found by substituting 1 for $x$ in $g(x) = 2x$.

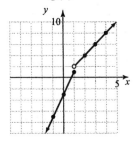

**117.** $f(x) = \sqrt{x-2}$

The graph of $f(x) = \sqrt{x-2}$ is the same as the graph of $y = \sqrt{x}$ shifted right 2 units.

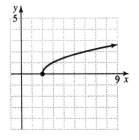

**118.** $f(x) = |x+1| - 3$

The graph of $f(x) = |x+1| - 3$ is the same as the graph of $y = |x|$ shifted left 1 unit and down 3 units.

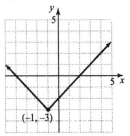

**Chapter 3 Test**

**1.**

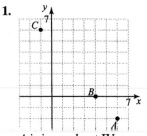

$A$ is in quadrant IV.
$B$ is on the $x$-axis, no quadrant.
$C$ is in quadrant II.

**2.**  $2x - 3y = -6$
$$-3y = -2x - 6$$
$$y = \frac{2}{3}x + 2$$
$$m = \frac{2}{3}, \ b = 2$$

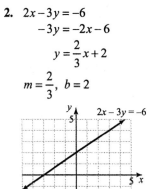

**3.**  $4x + 6y = 7$
$$6y = -4x + 7$$
$$y = -\frac{2}{3}x + \frac{7}{6}$$
$$m = -\frac{2}{3}, \ b = \frac{7}{6}$$

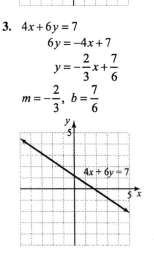

**4.** $f(x) = \dfrac{2}{3}x$ or $y = \dfrac{2}{3}x$

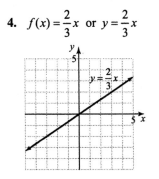

**5.** $y = -3$

Horizontal line with $y$-intercept at $-3$.

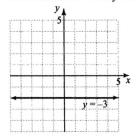

**6.** $m = \dfrac{10 - (-8)}{-7 - 5} = \dfrac{18}{-12} = -\dfrac{3}{2}$

**7.** $3x + 12y = 8$

$12y = -3x + 8$

$y = -\dfrac{1}{4}x + \dfrac{2}{3}$

$m = -\dfrac{1}{4}$, $b = \dfrac{2}{3}$, so $y$-intercept is $\left(0, \dfrac{2}{3}\right)$.

**8.** $f(x) = (x-1)^2$

| $x$ | $-2$ | $-1$ | 0 | 1 | 2 | 3 | 4 |
|---|---|---|---|---|---|---|---|
| $y$ | 9 | 4 | 1 | 0 | 1 | 4 | 9 |

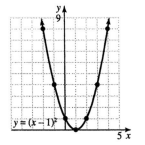

**9.** $f(x) = |x| + 2$

| $x$ | $-3$ | $-2$ | $-1$ | 0 | 1 | 2 | 3 |
|---|---|---|---|---|---|---|---|
| $y$ | 5 | 4 | 3 | 2 | 3 | 4 | 5 |

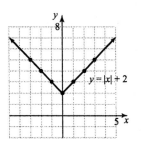

**10.** Horizontal; through $(2, -8)$

A horizontal line has an equation of the form $y = b$, where $b$ is the $y$-coordinate of any point on the line. The equation is $y = -8$.

**11.** Vertical; through $(-4, -3)$

A vertical line has an equation of the form $x = a$, where $a$ is the $x$-coordinate of any point on the line. The equation is $x = -4$.

**12.** Perpendicular to $x = 5$; through $(3, -2)$

The line $x = 5$ is vertical, so any line perpendicular to it is horizontal. A horizontal line has an equation of the form $y = b$, where $b$ is the $y$-coordinate of any point on the line. The equation is $y = -2$.

**13.**  $y - y_1 = m(x - x_1)$

$y - (-1) = -3(x - 4)$

$y + 1 = -3x + 12$

$3x + y = 11$

**14.**  $y - y_1 = m(x - x_1)$

$y - (-2) = 5(x - 0)$

$y + 2 = 5x$

$5x - y = 2$

**15.**  $m = \dfrac{-3-(-2)}{6-4} = \dfrac{-1}{2} = -\dfrac{1}{2}$

$y - y_1 = m(x - x_1)$

$y - (-2) = -\dfrac{1}{2}(x - 4)$

$2(y + 2) = -(x - 4)$

$2y + 4 = -x + 4$

$2y = -x$

$y = -\dfrac{1}{2}x$

$f(x) = -\dfrac{1}{2}x$

**16.**  $3x - y = 4$

$y = 3x - 4$

$m = 3$  so  $m_\perp = -\dfrac{1}{3}$

$y - y_1 = m(x - x_1)$

$y - 2 = -\dfrac{1}{3}[x - (-1)]$

$3(y - 2) = -(x + 1)$

$3y - 6 = -x - 1$

$3y = -x + 5$

$y = -\dfrac{1}{3}x + \dfrac{5}{3}$

$f(x) = -\dfrac{1}{3}x + \dfrac{5}{3}$

**17.**  $2y + x = 3$

$2y = -x + 3$

$y = -\dfrac{1}{2}x + 3$  so  $m = -\dfrac{1}{2}$

$y - y_1 = m(x - x_1)$

$y - (-2) = -\dfrac{1}{2}(x - 3)$

$2(y + 2) = -(x - 3)$

$2y + 4 = -x + 3$

$2y = -x - 1$

$y = -\dfrac{1}{2}x - \dfrac{1}{2}$

$f(x) = -\dfrac{1}{2}x - \dfrac{1}{2}$

**18.**  $2x - 5y = 8$

$-5y = -2x + 8$

$y = \dfrac{2}{5}x - \dfrac{8}{5}$  so  $m_1 = \dfrac{2}{5}$

$m_2 = \dfrac{-1-4}{-1-1} = \dfrac{-5}{-2} = \dfrac{5}{2}$

Therefore, lines $L_1$ and $L_2$ are neither parallel nor perpendicular since their slopes are not equal and the product of their slopes is not $-1$.

**19.**  $x \le -4$

Graph a solid boundary line and shade the half-plane to the left of $x = -4$.

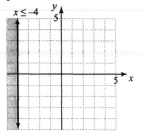

**20.**  $2x - y > 5$

$y < 2x - 5$

Graph the boundary line as a dashed line.
Test: (0, 0)
$2(0) - 0 > 5$  False
Shade the half-plane that does not contain the point (0, 0).

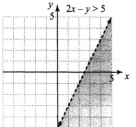

**21.**  $2x + 4y < 6$        and  $y \le 4$

$4y < -2x + 6$    and  $y \le 4$

$y < -\dfrac{1}{2}x + \dfrac{3}{2}$  and  $y \le 4$

Graph each inequality. The intersection of the two inequalities is all points common to both regions, as shown by the shading in the graph below.

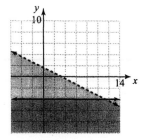

**22.** Domain: $(-\infty, \infty)$
Range: $\{5\}$
Function since it passes the vertical line test.

**23.** Domain: $\{-2\}$
Range: $(-\infty, \infty)$
Not a function since it fails the vertical line test.

**24.** Domain: $(-\infty, \infty)$
Range: $[0, \infty)$
Function since it passes the vertical line test.

**25.** Domain: $(-\infty, \infty)$
Range: $(-\infty, \infty)$
Function since it passes the vertical line test.

**26.** $f(x) = 1031x + 25{,}193$

    **a.**  $x = 0$
       $f(0) = 1031(0) + 25{,}193 = 25{,}193$
       The average earnings in 2000 were \$25,193.

    **b.**  $x = 2007 - 2000 = 7$
       $f(7) = 1031(7) + 25{,}193 = 32{,}410$
       The average earnings in 2007 were \$32,410.

    **c.**  $40{,}000 \le 1031x + 25{,}193$
       $14{,}807 \le 1031x$
         $14.4 \le x$
       $2000 + 15 = 2015$
       The average earnings will be greater than
       \$40,000 in 2015.

    **d.**  slope = 1031; the yearly earnings for high
       school graduates increases \$1031 per year.

    **e.**  (0, 25,193); the yearly earnings for a high
       school graduate in 2000 were \$25,193.

**27.** $f(x) = \begin{cases} -\frac{1}{2}x & \text{if } x \le 0 \\ 2x - 3 & \text{if } x > 0 \end{cases}$

For $x \le 0$:       For $x > 0$:

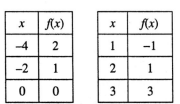

| $x$ | $f(x)$ |
|-----|--------|
| $-4$ | 2 |
| $-2$ | 1 |
| 0 | 0 |

| $x$ | $f(x)$ |
|-----|--------|
| 1 | $-1$ |
| 2 | 1 |
| 3 | 3 |

Graph a closed circle at (0, 0). Graph an open
circle at (0, −3), which is found by substituting 0
for $x$ in $f(x) = 2x - 3$.

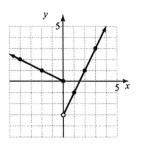

**28.** $f(x) = (x - 4)^2$

The graph of $f(x) = (x - 4)^2$ is the same as the
graph of $y = x^2$ shifted right 4 units.

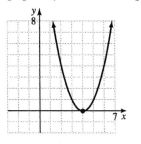

**29.** $g(x) = -|x + 2| - 1$

The graph of $g(x) = -|x + 2| - 1$ is the same as
the graph of $y = |x|$ reflected about the
$x$-axis and then shifted left 2 units and down
1 unit.

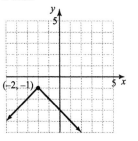

**30.** $h(x) = \sqrt{x} - 1$

The graph of $h(x) = \sqrt{x} - 1$ is the same as the
graph of $y = \sqrt{x}$ shifted down 1 unit.

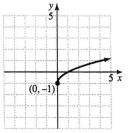

**Chapter 3 Cumulative Review**

1. $3x - y = 3(15) - (4) = 45 - 4 = 41$

2. **a.** $-4 + (-3) = -7$

   **b.** $\dfrac{1}{2} - \left(-\dfrac{1}{3}\right) = \dfrac{3}{6} + \dfrac{2}{6} = \dfrac{5}{6}$

   **c.** $7 - 20 = -13$

3. **a.** True, 3 is a real number

   **b.** False, $\dfrac{1}{5}$ is not an irrational number.

   **c.** False, every rational number is not an integer, for example, $\dfrac{2}{3}$.

   **d.** False, since 1 is not in the second set.

4. **a.** The opposite of $-7$ is 7.

   **b.** The opposite of 0 is 0.

   **c.** The opposite of $\dfrac{1}{4}$ is $-\dfrac{1}{4}$.

5. **a.** $2 - 8 = -6$

   **b.** $-8 - (-1) = -8 + 1 = -7$

   **c.** $-11 - 5 = -16$

   **d.** $10.7 - (-9.8) = 10.7 + 9.8 = 20.5$

   **e.** $\dfrac{2}{3} - \dfrac{1}{2} = \dfrac{4}{6} - \dfrac{3}{6} = \dfrac{1}{6}$

   **f.** $1 - 0.06 = 0.94$

   **g.** $4 - 7 = -3$

6. **a.** $\dfrac{-42}{-6} = 7$

   **b.** $\dfrac{0}{14} = 0$

   **c.** $-1(-5)(-2) = 5(-2) = -10$

7. **a.** $3^2 = 3 \cdot 3 = 9$

   **b.** $\left(\dfrac{1}{2}\right)^4 = \dfrac{1}{2^4} = \dfrac{1}{16}$

   **c.** $-5^2 = -(5 \cdot 5) = -25$

   **d.** $(-5)^2 = (-5)(-5) = 25$

   **e.** $-5^3 = -(5 \cdot 5 \cdot 5) = -125$

   **f.** $(-5)^3 = (-5)(-5)(-5) = -125$

8. **a.** Distributive Property

   **b.** Commutative Property of Addition

9. **a.** $-1 > -2$ since $-1$ is to the right of $-2$ on the number line.

   **b.** $\dfrac{12}{4} = 3$

   **c.** $-5 < 0$ since $-5$ is to the left of 0 on the number line.

   **d.** $-3.5 \le -3.05$ since $-3.5$ is to the left of $-3.05$ on the number line.

10. $2x^2$

   **a.** $2(7)^2 = 2(49) = 98$

   **b.** $2(-7)^2 = 2(49) = 98$

11. **a.** The reciprocal of 11 is $\dfrac{1}{11}$.

   **b.** The reciprocal of $-9$ is $-\dfrac{1}{9}$.

   **c.** The reciprocal of $\dfrac{7}{4}$ is $\dfrac{4}{7}$.

12. $-2 + 3[5 - (7 - 10)] = -2 + 3[5 - (-3)]$
    $= -2 + 3(8)$
    $= -2 + 24$
    $= 22$

**13.**   $0.6 = 2 - 3.5c$
$-1.4 = -3.5c$
$\dfrac{-1.4}{-3.5} = \dfrac{-3.5c}{-3.5}$
$0.4 = c$

**14.**   $2(x-3) = -40$
$2x - 6 = -40$
$2x = -34$
$x = -17$

**15.**   $3x + 5 = 3(x+2)$
$3x + 5 = 3x + 6$
$5 = 6$   False
The solution is $\varnothing$.

**16.**   $5(x-7) = 4x - 35 + x$
$5x - 35 = 5x - 35$
$-35 = -35$   True for any number
The solution is all real numbers.

**17.**  **a.**   If $x$ is the first integer, then the next two consecutive integers are $x + 1$ and $x + 2$. The sum is $x + (x+1) + (x+2) = 3x + 3$.

  **b.**   The perimeter is found by adding the lengths of the sides.
$x + 5x + (6x - 3) = 12x - 3$

**18.**   25% of $16 = 0.25(16) = 4$

**19.**   Let $x =$ the lowest of the scores. Then the other two scores are $x + 2$ and $x + 4$.
$x + (x+2) + (x+4) = 264$
$3x + 6 = 264$
$3x = 258$
$x = 86$
$x + 2 = 86 + 2 = 88$
$x + 4 = 86 + 4 = 90$
The scores are 86, 88, and 90.

**20.**   Let $x =$ first odd integer, then
$x + 2 =$ next odd integer and
$x + 4 =$ third odd integer.
$x + (x+2) + (x+4) = 213$
$3x + 6 = 213$
$3x = 207$
$x = 69$
$x + 2 = 69 + 2 = 71$
$x + 4 = 69 + 4 = 73$
The integers are 69, 71, and 73.

**21.**   $V = lwh$
$\dfrac{V}{lw} = \dfrac{lwh}{lw}$
$\dfrac{V}{lw} = h$

**22.**   $7x + 3y = 21$
$3y = -7x + 21$
$y = -\dfrac{7}{3}x + 7$

**23.**   $x - 2 < 5$
$x < 7$
$(-\infty, 7)$ or $\{x | x < 7\}$

**24.**   $-x - 17 \geq 9$
$-x \geq 26$
$x \leq -26$
$(-\infty, -26]$

**25.**   $\dfrac{2}{5}(x-6) \geq x - 1$
$5\left[\dfrac{2}{5}(x-6)\right] \geq 5[x-1]$
$2(x-6) \geq 5x - 5$
$2x - 12 \geq 5x - 5$
$-3x \geq 7$
$x \leq -\dfrac{7}{3}$
$\left(-\infty, -\dfrac{7}{3}\right]$

**26.**   $3x + 10 > \dfrac{5}{2}(x-1)$
$2(3x + 10) > 2\left[\dfrac{5}{2}(x-1)\right]$
$6x + 20 > 5(x-1)$
$6x + 20 > 5x - 5$
$x > -25$
$(-25, \infty)$

**27.**   $2x \geq 0$  and  $4x - 1 \leq -9$
$x \geq 0$  and     $4x \leq -8$
$x \geq 0$  and       $x \leq -2$
The solution set is $\varnothing$.

**28.** $x-2<6$ and $3x+1>1$
$\quad\quad x<8$ and $\quad 3x>0$
$\quad\quad x<8$ and $\quad\quad x>0$
$\quad 0<x<8$
$\quad (0,8)$

**29.** $5x-3\le 10$ or $x+1\ge 5$
$\quad\quad 5x\le 13$ or $\quad x\ge 4$
$\quad\quad x\le \dfrac{13}{5}$ or $\quad x\ge 4$
$\quad \left(-\infty, \dfrac{13}{5}\right]\cup[4,\infty)$

**30.** $x-2<6$ or $3x+1>1$
$\quad\quad x<8$ or $\quad\quad 3x>0$
$\quad\quad x<8$ or $\quad\quad x>0$
$\quad (-\infty,\infty)$

**31.** $|5w+3|=7$
$\quad 5w+3=7$ or $5w+3=-7$
$\quad\quad 5w=4$ or $\quad\quad 5w=-10$
$\quad\quad w=\dfrac{4}{5}$ or $\quad\quad w=-2$
$\quad$The solution set is $\left\{-2,\dfrac{4}{5}\right\}$.

**32.** $|5x-2|=3$
$\quad 5x-2=3$ or $5x-2=-3$
$\quad\quad 5x=5$ or $\quad\quad 5x=-1$
$\quad\quad x=1$ or $\quad\quad x=-\dfrac{1}{5}$
$\quad$The solution set is $\left\{-\dfrac{1}{5},1\right\}$.

**33.** $|3x+2|=|5x-8|$
$\quad 3x+2=5x-8$ or $3x+2=-(5x-8)$
$\quad -2x=-10$ or $3x+2=-5x+8$
$\quad\quad x=5$ or $\quad\quad 8x=6$
$\quad\quad\quad\quad\quad\quad x=\dfrac{3}{4}$
$\quad$The solution set is $\left\{\dfrac{3}{4},5\right\}$.

**34.** $|7x-2|=|7x+4|$
$\quad 7x-2=7x+4$ or $7x-2=-(7x+4)$
$\quad\quad -2=4$ or $7x-2=-7x-4$
$\quad\quad$False or $\quad 14x=-2$
$\quad\quad\quad\quad\quad\quad x=-\dfrac{1}{7}$
$\quad$The solution set is $\left\{-\dfrac{1}{7}\right\}$.

**35.** $|5x+1|+1\le 10$
$\quad |5x+1|\le 9$
$\quad -9\le 5x+1\le 9$
$\quad -10\le 5x\le 8$
$\quad -2\le x\le \dfrac{8}{5}$
$\quad \left[-2,\dfrac{8}{5}\right]$

**36.** $|-x+8|-2\le 8$
$\quad |-x+8|\le 10$
$\quad -10\le -x+8\le 10$
$\quad -18\le -x\le 2$
$\quad 18\ge x\ge -2$
$\quad -2\le x\le 18$
$\quad [-2,18]$

**37.** $|y-3|>7$
$\quad y-3<-7$ or $y-3>7$
$\quad\quad y<-4$ or $\quad y>10$
$\quad (-\infty,-4)\cup(10,\infty)$

**38.** $|x+3|>1$
$\quad x+3<-1$ or $x+3>1$
$\quad\quad x<-4$ or $\quad x>-2$
$\quad (-\infty,-4)\cup(-2,\infty)$

**39.** $3x-y=12$
$\quad 3(0)-(-12)\stackrel{?}{=}12$
$\quad\quad\quad 12=12$ True
$\quad (0,-12)$ is a solution.
$\quad 3(1)-9\stackrel{?}{=}12$
$\quad\quad\quad -6=12$ False
$\quad (1,9)$ is not a solution.
$\quad 3(2)-(-6)\stackrel{?}{=}12$
$\quad\quad\quad 6+6\stackrel{?}{=}12$
$\quad\quad\quad 12=12$ True
$\quad (2,-6)$ is a solution.

**40.** $7x + 2y = 10$
$$2y = -7x + 10$$
$$y = -\frac{7}{2}x + 5$$
$$m = -\frac{7}{2}, \ y\text{-intercept} = (0, 5)$$

**41.** Yes, $y = 2x + 1$ is a function (graph the function and use the vertical line test).

**42.** No, it is not a function (by the vertical line test).

**43. a.** $f(x) = \frac{1}{2}x + \frac{3}{7}$
$$y = mx + b$$
$$b = \frac{3}{7}$$
$$y\text{-intercept} = \left(0, \frac{3}{7}\right)$$

**b.** $y = -2.5x - 3.2$
$$y = mx + b$$
$$b = -3.2$$
$$y\text{-intercept} = (0, -3.2)$$

**44.** $m = \dfrac{y_2 - y_1}{x_2 - x_1} = \dfrac{9 - 6}{0 - (-1)} = \dfrac{3}{1} = 3$

**45.** $f(x) = \frac{2}{3}x + 4$
$y = mx + b$
The slope of the line is $m$, the coefficient of $x$,
$\frac{2}{3}$.

**46.** Vertical; through $\left(-2, \ -\frac{3}{4}\right)$

A vertical line has an equation of the form $x = a$, where $a$ is the $x$-coordinate of any point on the line. The equation is $x = -2$.

**47.** $y$-intercept = $(0, -3)$ means that $b = -3$. Using the equation $y = mx + b$, we have $y = \frac{1}{4}x - 3$.

**48.** Horizontal; through $\left(-2, \ -\frac{3}{4}\right)$

A horizontal line has an equation of the form $y = b$, where $b$ is the $y$-coordinate of any point on the line. The equation is $y = -\frac{3}{4}$.

**49.** $2x - y < 6$
Graph the boundary line as a dashed line.
Test: $(0, 0)$
$2(0) - 0 < 6$ True
Shade the half-plane that contains the point $(0, 0)$.

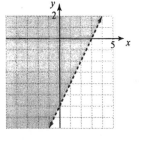

**50.** $m = \dfrac{7 - 5}{-4 - (-2)} = \dfrac{2}{-4 + 2} = \dfrac{2}{-2} = -1$
$$y - y_1 = m(x - x_1)$$
$$y - 5 = -1[x - (-2)]$$
$$y - 5 = -(x + 2)$$
$$y - 5 = -x - 2$$
$$x + y = 3$$

# Chapter 4

## Section 4.1

### Practice Exercises

1. a. $\begin{cases} -x - 4y = 1 \\ 2x + y = 5 \end{cases}$

   Replace $x$ with 3 and $y$ with $-1$ in each equation.
   $$-x - 4y = 1$$
   $$-3 - 4(-1) \stackrel{?}{=} 1$$
   $$-3 + 4 \stackrel{?}{=} 1$$
   $$1 = 1 \quad \text{True}$$

   $$2x + y = 5$$
   $$2(3) + (-1) \stackrel{?}{=} 5$$
   $$6 - 1 \stackrel{?}{=} 5$$
   $$5 = 5 \quad \text{True}$$

   Since $(3, -1)$ makes both equations true, it is a solution.

   b. $\begin{cases} 4x + y = -4 \\ -x + 3y = 8 \end{cases}$

   Replace $x$ with $-2$ and $y$ with 4 in each equation.
   $$4x + y = -4$$
   $$4(-2) + 4 \stackrel{?}{=} -4$$
   $$-8 + 4 \stackrel{?}{=} -4$$
   $$-4 = -4 \quad \text{True}$$

   $$-x + 3y = 8$$
   $$-(-2) + 3(4) \stackrel{?}{=} 8$$
   $$2 + 12 \stackrel{?}{=} 8$$
   $$14 = 8 \quad \text{False}$$

   Since $(-2, 4)$ does not make both equations true, it is not a solution.

2. a. $\begin{cases} 3x - 2y = 4 \\ -9x + 6y = -12 \end{cases}$

   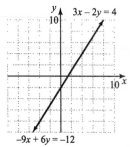

   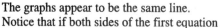

   The graphs appear to be the same line. Notice that if both sides of the first equation

are multiplied by $-3$, the result is the second equation. Any solution of one equation satisfies the other equation as well. There are an infinite number of solutions in the form $\{(x, y)|3x - 2y = 4\}$ or $\{(x, y)|-9x + 6y = -12\}$.

   b. $\begin{cases} y = 5x \\ 2x + y = 7 \end{cases}$

   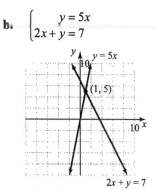

   These lines intersect at one point as shown in the graph. The coordinates of the point appear to be $(1, 5)$. Check by replacing $x$ with 1 and $y$ with 5 in both equations.

   $$y = 5x \qquad\qquad 2x + y = 7$$
   $$5 \stackrel{?}{=} 5(1) \qquad\qquad 2(1) + 5 \stackrel{?}{=} 7$$
   $$5 = 5 \quad \text{True} \qquad\qquad 2 + 5 \stackrel{?}{=} 7$$
   $$\qquad\qquad\qquad\qquad 7 = 7 \quad \text{True}$$

   Since $(1, 5)$ satisfies both equations, we conclude that $(1, 5)$ is the solution of the system.

   c. $\begin{cases} y = \dfrac{3}{4}x + 1 \\ 3x - 4y = 12 \end{cases}$

   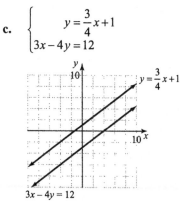

   The lines appear to be parallel. The first equation is in point-slope. Write the second equation in point-slope form.

$$3x - 4y = 12$$
$$-4y = -3x + 12$$
$$y = \frac{3}{4}x - 3$$

The graphs have the same slope, $\frac{3}{4}$, but different $y$-intercepts, so the lines are parallel. The system has no solution.

**3.** $\begin{cases} y = 4x + 7 \\ 2x + y = 4 \end{cases}$

In the first equation, we are told that $y$ is equal to $4x + 7$, so we substitute $4x + 7$ for $y$ in the second equation and solve for $x$.

$$2x + y = 4$$
$$2x + (4x + 7) = 4$$
$$6x + 7 = 4$$
$$6x = -3$$
$$x = \frac{-3}{6} = -\frac{1}{2}$$

To find the $y$-coordinate, we replace $x$ with $-\frac{1}{2}$ in the first equation.

$$y = 4x + 7$$
$$y = 4\left(-\frac{1}{2}\right) + 7$$
$$y = -2 + 7 = 5$$

The solution is $\left(-\frac{1}{2}, 5\right)$.

**4.** $\begin{cases} -\dfrac{x}{3} + \dfrac{y}{4} = \dfrac{1}{2} \\ \dfrac{x}{4} - \dfrac{y}{2} = -\dfrac{1}{4} \end{cases}$

Multiply each equation by its LCD to clear fractions.

$$\begin{cases} 12\left(-\dfrac{x}{3} + \dfrac{y}{4}\right) = 12\left(\dfrac{1}{2}\right) \\ 4\left(\dfrac{x}{4} - \dfrac{y}{2}\right) = 4\left(-\dfrac{1}{4}\right) \end{cases}$$

$$\begin{cases} -4x + 3y = 6 \\ x - 2y = -1 \end{cases}$$

Solve the second equation for $x$.

$$x - 2y = -1$$
$$x = 2y - 1$$

Replace $x$ with $2y - 1$ in the first equation.

$$-4x + 3y = 6$$
$$-4(2y - 1) + 3y = 6$$
$$-8y + 4 + 3y = 6$$
$$-5y + 4 = 6$$
$$-5y = 2$$
$$y = -\frac{2}{5}$$

To find the $x$-coordinate, replace $y$ with $-\frac{2}{5}$ in $x = 2y - 1$.

$$x = 2\left(-\frac{2}{5}\right) - 1 = -\frac{4}{5} - 1 = -\frac{4}{5} - \frac{5}{5} = -\frac{9}{5}$$

The solution is $\left(-\frac{9}{5}, -\frac{2}{5}\right)$.

**5.** $\begin{cases} 3x - y = 5 \\ 5x + y = 11 \end{cases}$

We add the equations.

$$3x - y = 5$$
$$\underline{5x + y = 11}$$
$$8x \quad\;\; = 16$$
$$x = 2$$

Replace $x$ with 2 in the second equation to find $y$.

$$5x + y = 11$$
$$5(2) + y = 11$$
$$10 + y = 11$$
$$y = 1$$

The solution is $(2, 1)$.

**6.** $\begin{cases} 3x - 2y = -6 \\ 4x + 5y = -8 \end{cases}$

We can eliminate $y$ if we multiply both sides of the first equation by 5 and both sides of the second equation by 2.

$$\begin{cases} 5(3x - 2y) = 5(-6) \\ 2(4x + 5y) = 2(-8) \end{cases}$$

$$\begin{cases} 15x - 10y = -30 \\ \underline{8x + 10y = -16} \end{cases}$$
$$23x \qquad\;\; = -46$$
$$x = -2$$

To find $y$, replace $x$ with $-2$ in either equation.

$$4x + 5y = -8$$
$$4(-2) + 5y = -8$$
$$-8 + 5y = -8$$
$$5y = 0$$
$$y = 0$$

The solution is $(-2, 0)$.

**7.** $\begin{cases} 8x + y = 6 \\ 2x + \dfrac{y}{4} = -2 \end{cases}$

If we multiply the second equation by $-4$, the coefficients of $x$ will be opposites.

$$\begin{cases} 8x + y = 6 \\ -4\left(2x + \dfrac{y}{4}\right) = -4(-2) \end{cases}$$

$$\begin{cases} 8x + y = 6 \\ -8x - y = 8 \end{cases}$$

$$\overline{\qquad\quad 0 = 14 \quad \text{False}}$$

The system has no solution. The solution set is $\{\ \}$ or $\varnothing$.

**8.** $\begin{cases} -3x + 2y = -1 \\ 9x - 6y = 3 \end{cases}$

To eliminate $x$, we multiply both sides of the first equation by 3.

$$\begin{cases} 3(-3x + 2y) = 3(-1) \\ 9x - 6y = 3 \end{cases}$$

$$\begin{cases} -9x + 6y = -3 \\ 9x - 6y = 3 \end{cases}$$

$$\overline{\qquad\quad 0 = 0 \quad \text{True}}$$

There are an infinite number of solutions. The solution set is $\{(x, y) \mid -3x + 2y = -1\}$ or $\{(x, y) \mid 9x - 6y = 3\}$.

**Graphing Calculator Explorations**

**1.**

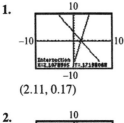

$(2.11, 0.17)$

**2.**

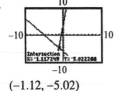

$(-1.12, -5.02)$

**3.**

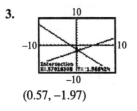

$(0.57, -1.97)$

**4.**

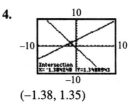

$(-1.38, 1.35)$

**Vocabulary and Readiness Check**

**1.** A system with no solution has lines that are parallel. The correct graph is B.

**2.** A system with an infinite number of solutions has lines that are the same. The correct graph is C.

**3.** A system with solution $(1, -2)$ has lines that intersect at $(1, -2)$. The correct graph is A.

**4.** A system with solution $(-3, 0)$ has lines that intersect at $(-3, 0)$. The correct graph is D.

**Exercise Set 4.1**

**1.** $\begin{cases} x - y = 3 \\ 2x - 4y = 8 \end{cases}$

$x - y = 3$

$2 - (-1) \overset{?}{=} 3$

$\qquad 3 = 3 \quad \text{True}$

$2x - 4y = 8$

$2(2) - 4(-1) \overset{?}{=} 8$

$4 + 4 \overset{?}{=} 8$

$\qquad\qquad 8 = 8 \quad \text{True}$

Yes, $(2, -1)$ is a solution.

**3.** $\begin{cases} 2x - 3y = -9 \\ 4x + 2y = -2 \end{cases}$

$2x - 3y = -9$

$2(3) - 3(5) \overset{?}{=} -9$

$6 - 15 \overset{?}{=} -9$

$\qquad -9 = -9 \quad \text{True}$

$4x + 2y = -2$

$4(3) + 2(5) \overset{?}{=} -2$

$12 + 10 \overset{?}{=} -2$

$\qquad 22 = -2 \quad \text{False}$

No, $(3, 5)$ is not a solution.

5. $\begin{cases} 3x + 7y = -19 \\ -6x \quad\quad = 5y + 8 \end{cases}$

$$3x + 7y = -19$$

$$3\left(\frac{2}{3}\right) + 7(-3) \overset{?}{=} -19$$

$$2 + (-21) \overset{?}{=} -19$$

$$-19 = -19 \quad \text{True}$$

$$-6x = 5y + 8$$

$$-6\left(\frac{2}{3}\right) \overset{?}{=} 5(-3) + 8$$

$$-4 \overset{?}{=} -15 + 8$$

$$-4 = -7 \quad \text{False}$$

No, $\left(\frac{2}{3}, -3\right)$ is not a solution.

7. $\begin{cases} x + y = 1 \\ x - 2y = 4 \end{cases}$

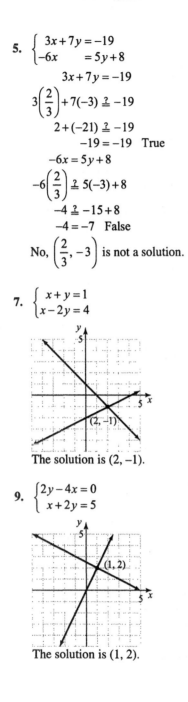

The solution is $(2, -1)$.

9. $\begin{cases} 2y - 4x = 0 \\ x + 2y = 5 \end{cases}$

The solution is $(1, 2)$.

11. $\begin{cases} 3x - y = 4 \\ 6x - 2y = 4 \end{cases}$

The solution set is $\varnothing$.

13. No; answers may vary

15. $\begin{cases} x + y = 10 \\ y = 4x \end{cases}$

Replace $y$ with $4x$ in E1.

$$x + (4x) = 10$$

$$5x = 10$$

$$x = 2$$

Replace $x$ with 2 in E2.

$$y = 4(2)$$

$$y = 8$$

The solution is $(2, 8)$.

17. $\begin{cases} 4x - y - 9 \\ 2x + 3y = -27 \end{cases}$

Solve E1 for $y$.

$$4x - y = 9$$

$$y = 4x - 9$$

Replace $y$ with $4x - 9$ in E2.

$$2x + 3(4x - 9) = -27$$

$$2x + 12x - 27 = -27$$

$$14x = 0$$

$$x = 0$$

Replace $x$ with 0 in E1.

$$4(0) - y = 9$$

$$y = -9$$

The solution is $(0, -9)$.

19. $\begin{cases} \dfrac{1}{2}x + \dfrac{3}{4}y = -\dfrac{1}{4} \\ \dfrac{3}{4}x - \dfrac{1}{4}y = 1 \end{cases}$

Clear fractions by multiplying each equation by 4.

$$\begin{cases} 2x + 3y = -1 \\ 3x - y = 4 \end{cases}$$

Now solve E2 for $y$.

$3x - y = 4$

$y = 3x - 4$

Replace $y$ with $3x - 4$ in E1.

$2x + 3(3x - 4) = -1$

$2x + 9x - 12 = -1$

$11x = 11$

$x = 1$

Replace $x$ with 1 in equation $y = 3x - 4$.

$y = 3(1) - 4$

$y = -1$

The solution is $(1, -1)$.

**21.** $\begin{cases} \dfrac{x}{3} + y = \dfrac{4}{3} \\ -x + 2y = 11 \end{cases}$

Clear fractions by multiplying the first equation by 3.

$\begin{cases} x + 3y = 4 \\ -x + 2y = 11 \end{cases}$

Solve E2 for $x$.

$2y - 11 = x$

$x = 2y - 11$

Replace $x$ with $2y - 11$ in E1.

$(2y - 11) + 3y = 4$

$5y = 15$

$y = 3$

Replace $y$ with 3 in equation $x = 2y - 11$.

$x = 2(3) - 11$

$x = -5$

The solution is $(-5, 3)$.

**23.** $\begin{cases} -x + 2y = 0 \\ x + 2y = 5 \end{cases}$

$\begin{array}{r} -x + 2y = 0 \\ x + 2y = 5 \\ \hline \end{array}$

E1 + E2:   $4y = 5$

$y = \dfrac{5}{4}$

Replace $y$ with $\dfrac{5}{4}$ in E1.

$-x + 2\left(\dfrac{5}{4}\right) = 0$

$-x + \dfrac{5}{2} = 0$

$\dfrac{5}{2} = x$

The solution is $\left(\dfrac{5}{2}, \dfrac{5}{4}\right)$.

**25.** $\begin{cases} 5x + 2y = 1 \\ x - 3y = 7 \end{cases}$

Multiply E2 by –5.

$\begin{cases} 5x + 2y = 1 \\ -5x + 15y = -35 \end{cases}$

E1 + E2:   $\begin{array}{r} 5x + 2y = 1 \\ -5x + 15y = -35 \\ \hline 17y = -34 \\ y = -2 \end{array}$

Replace $y$ with –2 in E2.

$x - 3(-2) = 7$

$x + 6 = 7$

$x = 1$

The solution is $(1, -2)$.

**27.** $\begin{cases} \dfrac{3}{4}x + \dfrac{5}{2}y = 11 \\ \dfrac{1}{16}x - \dfrac{3}{4}y = -1 \end{cases}$

Clear fractions by multiplying E1 by 4 and E2 by 16.

$\begin{cases} 3x + 10y = 44 \\ x - 12y = -16 \end{cases}$

Multiply E2 by –3.

$\begin{cases} 3x + 10y = 44 \\ -3x + 36y = 48 \end{cases}$

E1 + E2:   $\begin{array}{r} 3x + 10y = 44 \\ -3x + 36y = 48 \\ \hline 46y = 92 \\ y = 2 \end{array}$

Replace $y$ with 2 in the equation $x - 12y = -16$.

$x - 12(2) = -16$

$x - 24 = -16$

$x = 8$

The solution is $(8, 2)$.

**29.** $\begin{cases} 3x - 5y = 11 \\ 2x - 6y = 2 \end{cases}$

Multiply E1 by 2 and E2 by –3.

$\begin{cases} 6x - 10y = 22 \\ -6x + 18y = -6 \end{cases}$

E1 + E2:   $\begin{array}{r} 6x - 10y = 22 \\ -6x + 18y = -6 \\ \hline 8y = 16 \\ y = 2 \end{array}$

Replace $y$ with 2 in E2.

$$2x - 6(2) = 2$$
$$2x - 12 = 2$$
$$2x = 14$$
$$x = 7$$
The solution is (7, 2).

**31.** $\begin{cases} x - 2y = 4 \\ 2x - 4y = 4 \end{cases}$

Multiply E1 by –2.
$\begin{cases} -2x + 4y = -8 \\ 2x - 4y = 4 \end{cases}$

E1 + E2: $\begin{array}{r} -2x + 4y = -8 \\ 2x - 4y = 4 \\ \hline 0 = -4 \end{array}$ False

Inconsistent system; the solution set is $\varnothing$.

**33.** $\begin{cases} 3x + y = 1 \\ 2y = 2 - 6x \end{cases}$

$\begin{cases} 3x + y = 1 \\ 6x + 2y = 2 \end{cases}$

Multiply E1 by –2.
$\begin{cases} -6x - 2y = -2 \\ 6x + 2y = 2 \end{cases}$

E1 + E2: $\begin{array}{r} -6x - 2y = -2 \\ 6x + 2y = 2 \\ \hline 0 = 0 \end{array}$ True

Dependent system; the solution set is $\{(x, y)|3x + y = 1\}$.

**35.** $\begin{cases} 2x + 5y = 8 \\ 6x + y = 10 \end{cases}$

Multiply E1 by –3.
$\begin{cases} -6x - 15y = -24 \\ 6x + y = 10 \end{cases}$

E1 + E2: $\begin{array}{r} -6x - 15y = -24 \\ 6x + y = 10 \\ \hline -14y = -14 \\ y = 1 \end{array}$

Replace $y$ with 1 in E2.
$$6x + 1 = 10$$
$$6x = 9$$
$$x = \frac{9}{6} = \frac{3}{2}$$

The solution is $\left(\frac{3}{2}, 1\right)$.

**37.** $\begin{cases} x + y = 1 \\ x - 2y = 4 \end{cases}$

Multiply E1 by –1.
$\begin{cases} -x - y = -1 \\ x - 2y = 4 \end{cases}$

E1 + E2: $\begin{array}{r} -x - y = -1 \\ x - 2y = 4 \\ \hline -3y = 3 \\ y = -1 \end{array}$

Replace $y$ with –1 in E1.
$$x + (-1) = 1$$
$$x - 1 = 1$$
$$x = 2$$
The solution is (2, –1).

**39.** $\begin{cases} \dfrac{1}{3}x + y = \dfrac{4}{3} \\ -\dfrac{1}{4}x - \dfrac{1}{2}y = -\dfrac{1}{4} \end{cases}$

Clear fractions by multiplying E1 by 3 and E2 by 4.
$\begin{cases} x + 3y = 4 \\ -x - 2y = -1 \end{cases}$

E1 + E2: $\begin{array}{r} x + 3y = 4 \\ -x - 2y = -1 \\ \hline y = 3 \end{array}$

Replace $y$ with 3 in the equation $x + 3y = 4$.
$$x + 3(3) = 4$$
$$x + 9 = 4$$
$$x = -5$$
The solution is (–5, 3).

**41.** $\begin{cases} 2x + 6y = 8 \\ 3x + 9y = 12 \end{cases}$

Multiply E1 by –3 and E2 by 2.
$\begin{cases} -6x - 18y = -24 \\ 6x + 18y = 24 \end{cases}$

E1 + E2: $\begin{array}{r} -6x - 18y = -24 \\ 6x + 18y = 24 \\ \hline 0 = 0 \end{array}$ True

Dependent system; the solution is $\{(x, y)|3x + 9y = 12\}$.

**43.** $\begin{cases} 4x + 2y = 5 \\ 2x + y = -1 \end{cases}$

Multiply E2 by –2.
$\begin{cases} 4x + 2y = 5 \\ -4x - 2y = 2 \end{cases}$

E1 + E2: $\quad 4x+2y=5$
$$\underline{\phantom{4x+}-4x-2y=2}$$
$$\qquad\qquad 0=7\ \text{False}$$

Inconsistent system; the solution set is $\varnothing$.

**45.** $\begin{cases} 10y-2x=1 \\ \qquad 5y=4-6x \end{cases}$

$\begin{cases} 10y-2x=1 \\ \;\;5y+6x=4 \end{cases}$

Multiply E2 by $-2$.

$\begin{cases} \;\;\;10y-2x=1 \\ -10y-12x=-8 \end{cases}$

E1 + E2: $\quad 10y-2x=1$
$$\underline{\phantom{10y}-10y-12x=-8}$$
$$\qquad\qquad -14x=-7$$
$$\qquad\qquad x=\frac{1}{2}$$

Replace $x$ with $\dfrac{1}{2}$ in the equation $5y=4-6x$.

$$5y=4-6\left(\frac{1}{2}\right)$$
$$5y=4-3$$
$$5y=1$$
$$y=\frac{1}{5}$$

The solution is $\left(\dfrac{1}{2},\dfrac{1}{5}\right)$.

**47.** $\begin{cases} \;\;5x-2y=27 \\ -3x+5y=18 \end{cases}$

Multiply E1 by 3 and E2 by 5.

$\begin{cases} \;\;15x-6y=81 \\ -15x+25y=90 \end{cases}$

E1 + E2: $\quad 15x-6y=81$
$$\underline{\phantom{15x}-15x+25y=90}$$
$$\qquad\qquad 19y=171$$
$$\qquad\qquad y=9$$

Replace $y$ with 9 in E1.
$$5x-2(9)=27$$
$$5x-18=27$$
$$5x=45$$
$$x=9$$
The solution is $(9, 9)$.

**49.** $\begin{cases} \qquad x=3y+2 \\ 5x-15y=10 \end{cases}$

Replace $x$ with $3y+2$ in E2.

$$5(3y+2)-15y=10$$
$$15y+10-15y=10$$
$$\qquad\qquad 10=10\ \text{True}$$
The system is dependent. The solution is
$\{(x, y)|x = 3y + 2\}$.

**51.** $\begin{cases} 2x-y=-1 \\ \quad y=-2x \end{cases}$

Replace $y$ with $-2x$ in E1.
$$2x-(-2x)=-1$$
$$4x=-1$$
$$x=-\frac{1}{4}$$

Replace $x$ with $-\dfrac{1}{4}$ in E2.

$$y=-2\left(-\frac{1}{4}\right)$$
$$y=\frac{1}{2}$$

The solution is $\left(-\dfrac{1}{4},\dfrac{1}{2}\right)$.

**53.** $\begin{cases} 2x=6 \\ \;\;y=5-x \end{cases}$

E1 yields $x = 3$.
Replace $x$ with 3 in E2.
$$y=5-3$$
$$y=2$$
The solution is $(3, 2)$.

**55.** $\begin{cases} \dfrac{x+5}{2}=\dfrac{6-4y}{3} \\[2mm] \dfrac{3x}{5}=\dfrac{21-7y}{10} \end{cases}$

Multiply E1 by 6 and E2 by 10.
$\begin{cases} 3x+15=12-8y \\ \quad 6x=21-7y \end{cases}$

$\begin{cases} 3x+8y=-3 \\ 6x+7y=21 \end{cases}$

Multiply E1 by $-2$.
$\begin{cases} -6x-16y=6 \\ \;\;6x+7y=21 \end{cases}$

E1 + E2: $-6x-16y=6$
$$\underline{\phantom{-6x}6x+7y=21}$$
$$\qquad\qquad -9y=27$$
$$\qquad\qquad y=-3$$

Replace $y$ with $-3$ in the equation $3x + 8y = -3$.

$$3x + 8(-3) = -3$$
$$3x - 24 = -3$$
$$3x = 21$$
$$x = 7$$
The solution is (7, –3).

**57.** $\begin{cases} 4x - 7y = 7 \\ 12x - 21y = 24 \end{cases}$

Multiply E1 by –3.
$\begin{cases} -12x + 21y = -21 \\ 12x - 21y = 24 \end{cases}$

$\qquad\qquad\qquad 0 = 3 \quad$ False

Inconsistent system; the solution set is $\varnothing$.

**59.** $\begin{cases} \dfrac{2}{3}x - \dfrac{3}{4}y = -1 \\ -\dfrac{1}{6}x + \dfrac{3}{8}y = 1 \end{cases}$

Multiply E1 by 12 and E2 by 24.
$\begin{cases} 8x - 9y = -12 \\ -4x + 9y = 24 \end{cases}$

E1 + E2: $\quad 8x - 9y = -12$
$\qquad\qquad\quad \underline{-4x + 9y = 24}$
$\qquad\qquad\quad 4x \qquad\; = 12$
$\qquad\qquad\qquad\qquad x = 3$

Replace $x$ with 3 in the equation $-4x + 9y = 24$.
$$-4(3) + 9y = 24$$
$$-12 + 9y = 24$$
$$9y = 36$$
$$y = 4$$
The solution is (3, 4).

**61.** $\begin{cases} 0.7x - 0.2y = -1.6 \\ 0.2x - y = -1.4 \end{cases}$

Multiply both equations by 10.
$\begin{cases} 7x - 2y = -16 \\ 2x - 10y = -14 \end{cases}$

Multiply E1 by –5.
$\begin{cases} -35x + 10y = 80 \\ 2x - 10y = -14 \end{cases}$

E1 + E2: $-35x + 10y = 80$
$\qquad\qquad\quad \underline{2x - 10y = -14}$
$\qquad\qquad\; -33x \qquad = 66$
$\qquad\qquad\qquad\qquad x = -2$

Replace $x$ with –2 in the equation $7x - 2y = -16$.

$$7(-2) - 2y = -16$$
$$-14 - 2y = -16$$
$$-2y = -2$$
$$y = 1$$
The solution is (–2, 1).

**63.** $\begin{cases} 4x - 1.5y = 10.2 \\ 2x + 7.8y = -25.68 \end{cases}$

Multiply E2 by –2.
$\begin{cases} 4x - 1.5y = 10.2 \\ -4x - 15.6y = 51.36 \end{cases}$

E1 + E2: $\quad 4x - 1.5y = 10.2$
$\qquad\qquad\quad \underline{-4x - 15.6y = 51.36}$
$\qquad\qquad\qquad -17.1y = 61.56$
$\qquad\qquad\qquad\qquad y = -3.6$

Replace $y$ with –3.6 in E1.
$$4x - 1.5(-3.6) = 10.2$$
$$4x + 5.4 = 10.2$$
$$4x = 4.8$$
$$x = 1.2$$
The solution is (1.2, –3.6).

**65.** $\qquad 3x - 4y + 2z = 5$
$\qquad 3(1) - 4(2) + 2(5) \overset{?}{=} 5$
$\qquad\qquad 3 - 8 + 10 \overset{?}{=} 5$
$\qquad\qquad\qquad\qquad 5 = 5$

True

**67.** $\qquad -x - 5y + 3z = 15$
$\qquad -(0) - 5(-1) + 3(5) \overset{?}{=} 15$
$\qquad\qquad 0 + 5 + 15 \overset{?}{=} 15$
$\qquad\qquad\qquad\qquad 20 = 15$

False

**69.** $\quad 3x + 2y - 5z = 10$
$\qquad \underline{-3x + 4y + z = 15}$
$\qquad\qquad 6y - 4z = 25$

**71.** $\quad 10x + 5y + 6z = 14$
$\qquad \underline{-9x + 5y - 6z = -12}$
$\qquad\quad x + 10y \qquad = 2$

**73.** Find the coordinates of the equilibrium point, (5000, 21). This represents 5000 DVDs at \$21 per DVD.

**75.** Supply is greater than demand because the line representing supply is above that for demand.

**77.** $\begin{cases} y = 2.5x \\ y = 0.9x + 3000 \end{cases}$

Substitute.

$2.5x = 0.9x + 3000$

$1.6x = 3000$

$x = 1875$

$y = 2.5(1875) = 4687.5$

The point of intersection is $(1875, 4687.5)$.

**79.** Makes money because revenue is greater than cost at $x = 2000$.

**81.** For values of $x > 1875$ because the $x$-value at the intersection is 1875.

**83.** Answers may vary; one possibility:

$\begin{cases} -2x + y = 1 \\ x - 2y = -8 \end{cases}$

**85.** Red meat: $y = -0.3x + 113$
Poultry: $y = x + 68$

**a.** $m_{\text{red meat}} = -0.3$ and $m_{\text{poultry}} = 1$.

Consumption of red meat is decreasing while consumption of poultry is increasing.

**b.** $\begin{cases} y = -0.3x + 113 \\ y = x + 68 \end{cases}$

Substitute.

$-0.3x + 113 = x + 68$

$45 = 1.3x$

$35 = x$

$y = 35 + 68 = 103$

The solution is $(35, 103)$.

**c.** $x = 35 \Rightarrow 2000 + 35 = 2035$

In the year 2035, red meat and poultry consumption will each be about 103 pounds per person.

**87.** $\begin{cases} \dfrac{1}{x} + y = 12 \\ \dfrac{3}{x} - y = 4 \end{cases}$

Replacing $\dfrac{1}{x}$ with $a$, we have

$\begin{cases} a + y = 12 \\ 3a - y = 4 \end{cases}$

Adding the two new equations we get

$4a = 16$

$a = 4$

Replace $a$ with 4 in the equation $a + y = 12$.

$4 + y = 12$

$y = 8$

Since $a = 4$, $x = \dfrac{1}{4}$.

The solution is $\left( \dfrac{1}{4}, 8 \right)$.

**89.** $\begin{cases} \dfrac{1}{x} + \dfrac{1}{y} = 5 \\ \dfrac{1}{x} - \dfrac{1}{y} = 1 \end{cases}$

Replace $\dfrac{1}{x}$ with $a$ and $\dfrac{1}{y}$ with $b$.

$\begin{cases} a + b = 5 \\ a - b = 1 \end{cases}$

Adding the two new equations we get

$2a = 6$

$a = 3$

Replace $a$ with 3 in the equation $a + b = 5$.

$3 + b = 5$

$b = 2$

Since $a = 3$, $x = \dfrac{1}{3}$. Similarly, $y = \dfrac{1}{2}$.

The solution is $\left( \dfrac{1}{3}, \dfrac{1}{2} \right)$.

**91.** $\begin{cases} \dfrac{2}{x} + \dfrac{3}{y} = -1 \\ \dfrac{3}{x} - \dfrac{2}{y} = 18 \end{cases}$

Replace $\dfrac{1}{x}$ with $a$ and $\dfrac{1}{y}$ with $b$.

$\begin{cases} 2a + 3b = -1 \\ 3a - 2b = 18 \end{cases}$

Multiply E1 by 2 and E2 by 3 to obtain

$\begin{cases} 4a + 6b = -2 \\ 9a - 6b = 54 \end{cases}$

Adding these last two equations we have

$13a = 52$

$a = 4$

Replace $a$ with 4 in the equation $2a + 3b = -1$.

$2(4) + 3b = -1$

$3b = -9$

$b = -3$

Since $a = 4$, $x = \dfrac{1}{4}$. Similarly, $y = -\dfrac{1}{3}$.

The solution is $\left(\dfrac{1}{4}, -\dfrac{1}{3}\right)$.

**93.** $\begin{cases} \dfrac{2}{x} - \dfrac{4}{y} = 5 \\ \dfrac{1}{x} - \dfrac{2}{y} = \dfrac{3}{2} \end{cases}$

Replace $\dfrac{1}{x}$ with $a$ and $\dfrac{1}{y}$ with $b$.

$\begin{cases} 2a - 4b = 5 \\ a - 2b = \dfrac{3}{2} \end{cases}$

Multiply E2 by 2.

$\begin{cases} 2a - 4b = 5 \\ 2a - 4b = 3 \end{cases}$

This system is inconsistent. The solution set is $\varnothing$.

## Section 4.2

## Practice Exercises

**1.** $\begin{cases} 3x + 2y - z = 0 & (1) \\ x - y + 5z = 2 & (2) \\ 2x + 3y + 3z = 7 & (3) \end{cases}$

Multiply equation (2) by 2 and add to equation (1) to eliminate $y$.

$\begin{cases} 3x + 2y - z = 0 \\ 2(x - y + 5z) = 2(2) \end{cases}$

$\begin{cases} 3x - 2y \quad - z = 0 \\ 2x - 2y + 10z = 4 \end{cases}$

$\overline{\quad 5x \qquad + 9z = 4 \quad (4)}$

Multiply equation (2) by 3 and add to equation (3) to eliminate $y$ again.

$\begin{cases} 3(x - y + 5z) = 3(2) \\ 2x + 3y + 3z = 7 \end{cases}$

$\begin{cases} 3x - 3y + 15z = 6 \\ 2x + 3y \; + 3z = 7 \end{cases}$

$\overline{\quad 5x + \qquad 18z = 13 \quad (5)}$

Multiply equation (4) by $-1$ and add to equation (5) to eliminate $x$.

$\begin{cases} -1(5x + 9z) = -1(4) \\ 5x + 18z = 13 \end{cases}$

$\begin{cases} -5x \; - 9z = -4 \\ 5x + 18z = 13 \end{cases}$

$\overline{\qquad\qquad 9z = 9}$

$\qquad\qquad z = 1$

Replace $z$ with 1 in equation (4) or (5).

$5x + 9z = 4$

$5x + 9(1) = 4$

$5x = -5$

$x = -1$

Replace $x$ with $-1$ and $z$ with 1 in equation (1), (2), or (3).

$x - y + 5z = 2$

$-1 - y + 5(1) = 2$

$-y + 4 = 2$

$-y = -2$

$y = 2$

The solution is $(-1, 2, 1)$. To check, let $x = -1$, $y = 2$, and $z = 1$ in all three original equations of the system.

**2.** $\begin{cases} 6x - 3y + 12z = 4 & (1) \\ -6x + 4y - 2z = 7 & (2) \\ -2x + y - 4z = 3 & (3) \end{cases}$

Multiply equation (3) by 3 and add to equation (1) to eliminate $x$.

$\begin{cases} 6x - 3y + 12z = 4 \\ 3(-2x + y - 4z) = 3(3) \end{cases}$

$\begin{cases} 6x - 3y + 12z = 4 \\ -6x + 3y - 12z = 9 \end{cases}$

$\overline{\qquad\qquad\qquad 0 = 13 \quad \text{False}}$

Since the statement is false, this system is inconsistent and has no solution. The solution set is { } or $\varnothing$.

**3.** $\begin{cases} 3x + 4y \qquad = 0 & (1) \\ 9x \qquad - 4z = 6 & (2) \\ \qquad -2y + 7z = 1 & (3) \end{cases}$

Equation (2) has no term containing the variable $y$. Eliminate $y$ using equations (1) and (3). Multiply equation (3) by 2 and add to equation (1).

$\begin{cases} 3x + 4y = 0 \\ 2(-2y + 7z) = 2(1) \end{cases}$

$\begin{cases} 3x + 4y \qquad = 0 \\ \qquad -4y + 14z = 2 \end{cases}$

$\overline{\quad 3x \qquad + 14z = 2 \quad (4)}$

Multiply equation (4) by $-3$ and add to equation (2) to eliminate $x$.

$$\begin{cases} 9x - 4z = 6 \\ -3(3x + 14z) = -3(2) \end{cases}$$

$$\begin{cases} 9x\;\;\;-4z = 6 \\ -9x - 52z = -6 \end{cases}$$
$$\overline{\qquad\quad -56z = 0}$$
$$z = 0$$

Replace $z$ with 0 in equation (2) and solve for $x$.
$$9x - 4z = 6$$
$$9x - 4(0) = 6$$
$$9x = 6$$
$$x = \frac{6}{9} = \frac{2}{3}$$

Replace $z$ with 0 in equation (3) and solve for $y$.
$$-2y + 7z = 1$$
$$-2y + 7(0) = 1$$
$$-2y = 1$$
$$y = -\frac{1}{2}$$

The solution is $\left(\frac{2}{3}, -\frac{1}{2}, 0\right)$.

**4.** $\begin{cases} 2x + y - 3z = 6 & (1) \\ x + \frac{1}{2}y - \frac{3}{2}z = 3 & (2) \\ -4x - 2y + 6z = -12 & (3) \end{cases}$

Multiply both sides of equation (2) by 2 to eliminate fractions, and multiply both sides of equation (3) by $-\frac{1}{2}$ since all coefficients in equation (3) are divisible by 2 and the coefficient of $x$ is negative. The resulting system is
$$\begin{cases} 2x + y - 3z = 6 \\ 2x + y - 3z = 6 \\ 2x + y - 3z = 6 \end{cases}$$
Since the three equations are identical, there are infinitely many solutions of the system. The equations are dependent. The solution set can be written as $\{(x, y, z)|2x + y - 3z = 6\}$.

**5.** $\begin{cases} x + 2y + 4z = 16 & (1) \\ x\;\;\;\;\;\; + 2z = -4 & (2) \\ \;\;\;\;\;\; y - 3z = 30 & (3) \end{cases}$

Solve equation (2) for $x$ and equation (3) for $y$.
$$x + 2z = -4 \qquad\quad y - 3z = 30$$
$$x = -2z - 4 \qquad\quad y = 3z + 30$$

Substitute $-2z - 4$ for $x$ and $3z + 30$ for $y$ in equation (1) and solve for $z$.

$$x + 2y + 4z = 16$$
$$(-2z - 4) + 2(3z + 30) + 4z = 16$$
$$-2z - 4 + 6z + 60 + 4z = 16$$
$$8z + 56 = 16$$
$$8z = -40$$
$$z = -5$$

Use $x = -2z - 4$ to find $x$:
$x = -2(-5) - 4 = 10 - 4 = 6$.
Use $y = 3z + 30$ to find $y$:
$y = 3(-5) + 30 = -15 + 30 = 15$.
The solution is $(6, 15, -5)$.

**Exercise Set 4.2**

**1.** $\quad x + y + z = 3 \qquad\quad -x + y + z = 5$
$\quad (-1) + 3 + 1 \overset{?}{=} 3 \qquad -(-1) + 3 + 1 \overset{?}{=} 5$
$\qquad\qquad 3 = 3 \qquad\qquad\qquad 5 = 5$
a is true.      b is true.
$\quad -x + y + 2z = 0 \qquad x + 2y - 3z = 2$
$-(-1) + 3 + 2(1) \overset{?}{=} 0 \quad (-1) + 2(3) - 3(1) \overset{?}{=} 2$
$\qquad\qquad 6 = 0 \qquad\qquad\qquad 2 = 2$
c is false.      d is true.
Therefore, equations a, b, and d.

**3.** Yes; answers may vary

**5.** $\begin{cases} x - y + z = -4 & (1) \\ 3x + 2y - z = 5 & (2) \\ -2x + 3y - z = 15 & (3) \end{cases}$

Add E1 and E2.
$$4x + y = 1$$
Add E1 and E3.
$$-x + 2y = 11$$
Solve the new system:
$$\begin{cases} 4x + y = 1 \\ -x + 2y = 11 \end{cases}$$
Multiply the second equation by 4.
$$\begin{cases} 4x + y = 1 \\ -4x + 8y = 44 \end{cases}$$
Add the equations.
$$4x + y = 1$$
$$\underline{-4x + 8y = 44}$$
$$9y = 45$$
$$y = 5$$
Replace $y$ with 5 in the equation $4x + y = 1$.
$$4x + 5 = 1$$
$$4x = -4$$
$$x = -1$$
Replace $x$ with $-1$ and $y$ with 5 in E1.

$$(-1)-(5)+z=-4$$
$$-6+z=-4$$
$$z=2$$
The solution is $(-1, 5, 2)$.

**7.** $\begin{cases} x+y \quad\quad\; =3 \quad (1) \\ \quad\quad 2y \quad\; =10 \quad (2) \\ 3x+2y-3z=1 \quad (3) \end{cases}$

Solve E2 for $y$: $y=5$
Replace $y$ with 5 in E1.
$$x+5=3$$
$$x=-2$$
Replace $x$ with $-2$ and $y$ with 5 in E3.
$$3(-2)+2(5)-3z=1$$
$$-6+10-3z=1$$
$$4-3z=1$$
$$-3z=-3$$
$$z=1$$
The solution is $(-2, 5, 1)$.

**9.** $\begin{cases} 2x+2y+z=1 \quad (1) \\ -x+y+2z=3 \quad (2) \\ x+2y+4z=0 \quad (3) \end{cases}$

Add E2 and E3.
$$3y+6z=3 \text{ or } y+2z=1$$
Multiply E2 by 2 and add to E1.
$$-2x+2y+4z=6$$
$$\underline{2x+2y+z=1}$$
$$4y+5z=7$$
Solve the new system:
$$\begin{cases} y+2z=1 \\ 4y+5z=7 \end{cases}$$
Multiply the first equation by $-4$.
$$\begin{cases} -4y-8z=-4 \\ 4y+5z=7 \end{cases}$$
Add the equations.
$$-4y-8z=-4$$
$$\underline{4y+5z=7}$$
$$-3z=3$$
$$z=-1$$
Replace $z$ with $-1$ in the equation $y+2z=1$.
$$y+2(-1)=1$$
$$y-2=1$$
$$y=3$$
Replace $y$ with 3 and $z$ with $-1$ in E3.
$$x+2(3)+4(-1)=0$$
$$x+6-4=0$$
$$x+2=0$$
$$x=-2$$
The solution is $(-2, 3, -1)$.

**11.** $\begin{cases} x-2y+z=-5 \quad (1) \\ -3x+6y-3z=15 \quad (2) \\ 2x-4y+2z=-10 \quad (3) \end{cases}$

Multiply E2 by $-\dfrac{1}{3}$ and E3 by $\dfrac{1}{2}$.
$$\begin{cases} x-2y+z=-5 \\ x-2y+z=-5 \\ x-2y+z=-5 \end{cases}$$
All three equations are identical. There are infinitely many solutions. The solution set is $\{(x, y, z)\,|\,x-2y+z=-5\}$.

**13.** $\begin{cases} 4x-y+2z=5 \quad (1) \\ 2y+z=4 \quad (2) \\ 4x+y+3z=10 \quad (3) \end{cases}$

Multiply E1 by $-1$ and add to E3.
$$-4x+y-2z=-5$$
$$\underline{4x+y+3z=10}$$
$$2y+z=5 \quad (4)$$
Multiply E4 by $-1$ and add to E2.
$$-2y-z=-5$$
$$\underline{2y+z=4}$$
$$0=-1 \quad \text{False}$$
Inconsistent system; the solution set is $\varnothing$.

**15.** $\begin{cases} x+5z=0 \quad (1) \\ 5x+y=0 \quad (2) \\ y-3z=0 \quad (3) \end{cases}$

Multiply E3 by $-1$ and add to E2.
$$-y+3z=0$$
$$\underline{5x+y \quad\quad =0}$$
$$5x+3z=0 \quad (4)$$
Multiply E1 by $-5$ and add to E4.
$$-5x-25z=0$$
$$\underline{5x+3z=0}$$
$$-22z=0$$
$$z=0$$
Replace $z$ with 0 in E4.
$$5x+3(0)=0$$
$$5x=0$$
$$x=0$$
Replace $x$ with 0 in E2.
$$5(0)+y=0$$
$$y=0$$
The solution is $(0, 0, 0)$.

**17.** $\begin{cases} 6x - \quad 5z = 17 \quad (1) \\ 5x - y + 3z = -1 \quad (2) \\ 2x + y \quad\quad = -41 \quad (3) \end{cases}$

Add E2 and E3.
$7x + 3z = -42 \quad (4)$
Multiply E4 by 5, multiply E1 by 3, and add.
$35x + 15z = -210$
$\underline{18x - 15z = 51}$
$53x \quad\quad = -159$
$x = -3$
Replace $x$ with $-3$ in E1.
$6(-3) - 5z = 17$
$-18 - 5z = 17$
$-5z = 35$
$z = -7$
Replace $x$ with $-3$ in E3.
$2(-3) + y = -41$
$-6 + y = -41$
$y = -35$
The solution is $(-3, -35, -7)$.

**19.** $\begin{cases} x + y + z = 8 \quad (1) \\ 2x - y - z = 10 \quad (2) \\ x - 2y - 3z = 22 \quad (3) \end{cases}$

Add E1 and E2.
$3x = 18 \text{ or } x = 6$
Add twice E1 to E3.
$2x + 2y + 2z = 16$
$\underline{x - 2y - 3z = 22}$
$3x - \quad\quad z = 38$
Replace $x$ with 6 in this equation.
$3(6) - z = 38$
$18 - z = 38$
$-z = 20$
$z = -20$
Replace $x$ with 6 and $z$ with $-20$ in E1.
$6 + y + (-20) = 8$
$y - 14 = 8$
$y = 22$
The solution is $(6, 22, -20)$.

**21.** $\begin{cases} x + 2y - z = 5 \quad (1) \\ 6x + y + z = 7 \quad (2) \\ 2x + 4y - 2z = 5 \quad (3) \end{cases}$

Add E1 and E2.
$7x + 3y = 12 \quad (4)$
Add twice E2 to E3.

$12x + 2y + 2z = 14$
$\underline{2x + 4y - 2z = 5}$
$14x + 6y \quad\quad = 19 \quad (5)$
Multiply E4 by $-2$ and add to E5.
$-14x - 6y = -24$
$\underline{14x + 6y = 19}$
$0 = -5 \quad \text{False}$
Inconsistent system; the solution set is $\varnothing$.

**23.** $\begin{cases} 2x - 3y + z = 2 \quad (1) \\ x - 5y + 5z = 3 \quad (2) \\ 3x + y - 3z = 5 \quad (3) \end{cases}$

Add $-2$ times E2 to E1.
$2x - \quad 3y + \quad z = 2$
$\underline{-2x + 10y - 10z = -6}$
$7y - \quad 9z = -4 \quad (4)$
Add $-3$ times E2 to E3.
$-3x + 15y - 15z = -9$
$\underline{3x + \quad y - \quad 3z = 5}$
$16y - 18z = -4$
Solve the new system:
$\begin{cases} 7y - 9z = -4 \quad (4) \\ 16y - 18z = -4 \quad (5) \end{cases}$
Multiply E4 by $-2$ and add to E5.
$-14y + 18z = 8$
$\underline{16y - 18z = -4}$
$2y \quad\quad = 4$
$y = 2$
Replace $y$ with 2 in E4.
$7(2) - 9z = -4$
$-9z = -18$
$z = 2$
Replace $y$ with 2 and $z$ with 2 in E1.
$2x - 3(2) + 2 = 2$
$2x = 6$
$x = 3$
The solution is $(3, 2, 2)$.

**25.** $\begin{cases} -2x - 4y + 6z = -8 \quad (1) \\ x + 2y - 3z = 4 \quad (2) \\ 4x + 8y - 12z = 16 \quad (3) \end{cases}$

Add 2 times E2 to E1.
$2x + 4y - 6z = 8$
$\underline{-2x - 4y + 6z = -8}$
$0 = 0$
Add $-4$ times E2 to E3.

$$-4x - 8y + 12z = -16$$
$$\underline{4x + 8y - 12z = 16}$$
$$0 = 0$$

The system is dependent.
The solution set is $\{(x, y, z)|x + 2y - 3z = 4\}$.

**27.** $\begin{cases} 2x + 2y - 3z = 1 & (1) \\ y + 2z = -14 & (2) \\ 3x - 2y = -1 & (3) \end{cases}$

Add E1 to E3.
$$5x - 3z = 0 \ (4)$$

Add twice E2 to E3.
$$2y + 4z = -28$$
$$\underline{3x - 2y = -1}$$
$$3x + \quad 4z = -29 \ (5)$$

Multiply E4 by 4, multiply E5 by 3, and add.
$$20x - 12z = 0$$
$$\underline{9x + 12z = -87}$$
$$29x \quad = -87$$
$$x = -3$$

Replace $x$ with $-3$ in E4.
$$5(-3) - 3z = 0$$
$$3z = -15$$
$$z = -5$$

Replace $z$ with $-5$ in E2.
$$y + 2(-5) = -14$$
$$y - 10 = -14$$
$$y = -4$$

The solution is $(-3, -4, -5)$.

**29.** $\begin{cases} x + 2y - z = 5 & (1) \\ -3x - 2y - 3z = 11 & (2) \\ 4x + 4y + 5z = -18 & (3) \end{cases}$

Add E1 and E2.
$$-2x - 4z = 16 \ \text{ or } \ x + 2z = -8 \ (4)$$

Add twice E2 to E3.
$$-6x - 4y - 6z = 22$$
$$\underline{4x + 4y + 5z = -18}$$
$$-2x - \quad z = 4 \ (5)$$

Solve the new system:
$$\begin{cases} x + 2z = -8 & (4) \\ -2x - z = 4 & (5) \end{cases}$$

Add twice E4 to E5.
$$2x + 4z = -16$$
$$\underline{-2x - z = 4}$$
$$3z = -12$$
$$z = -4$$

Replace $z$ with $-4$ in E4.

$$x + 2(-4) = -8$$
$$x - 8 = -8$$
$$x = 0$$

Replace $x$ with 0 and $z$ with $-4$ in E1.
$$0 + 2y - (-4) = 5$$
$$2y = 1$$
$$y = \frac{1}{2}$$

The solution is $\left(0, \dfrac{1}{2}, -4\right)$.

**31.** $\begin{cases} \dfrac{3}{4}x - \dfrac{1}{3}y + \dfrac{1}{2}z = 9 & (1) \\ \dfrac{1}{6}x + \dfrac{1}{3}y - \dfrac{1}{2}z = 2 & (2) \\ \dfrac{1}{2}x - \ y + \dfrac{1}{2}z = 2 & (3) \end{cases}$

Multiply E1 by 12, multiply E2 by 6, and multiply E3 by 2.
$$\begin{cases} 9x - 4y + 6z = 108 & (4) \\ x + 2y - 3z = 12 & (5) \\ x - 2y + z = 4 & (6) \end{cases}$$

Add twice E5 to E4.
$$2x + 4y - 6z = 24$$
$$\underline{9x - 4y + 6z = 108}$$
$$11x \quad = 132$$
$$x = 12$$

Add E5 and E6.
$$2x - 2z = 16 \ \text{ or } \ x - z = 8$$

Replace $x$ with 12 in this equation.
$$12 - z = 8$$
$$z = 4$$

Replace $x$ with 12 and $z$ with 4 in E6.
$$12 - 2y + 4 = 4$$
$$12 - 2y = 0$$
$$-2y = -12$$
$$y = 6$$

The solution is $(12, 6, 4)$.

**33.** Let $x =$ the first number, then
$2x =$ the second number.
$$x + 2x = 45$$
$$3x = 45$$
$$x = 15$$
$$2x = 2(15) = 30$$

The numbers are 15 and 30.

**35.**  $2(x-1)-3x = x-12$
$2x-2-3x = x-12$
$-x-2 = x-12$
$-2x = -10$
$x = 5$

**37.**  $-y-5(y+5) = 3y-10$
$-y-5y-25 = 3y-10$
$-6y-25 = 3y-10$
$-9y = 15$
$y = -\dfrac{15}{9} = -\dfrac{5}{3}$

**39.** Answers may vary

**41.** Answers may vary

**43.**  $\begin{cases} x+\ y+\ \ z=1 & (1) \\ 2x-\ y+\ \ z=0 & (2) \\ -x+2y+2z=-1 & (3) \end{cases}$

Add E1 and E3.
$3y+3z = 0 \ \text{ or } \ y+z = 0 \ (4)$
Add –2 times E1 to E2.
$-2x-2y-2z = -2$
$\underline{2x-\ y+\ \ z = 0}$
$\quad\quad -3y-\ \ z = -2 \ (5)$
Add E4 and E5.
$-2y = -2$
$y = 1$
Replace $y$ with 1 in E4.
$1+z = 0$
$z = -1$
Replace $y$ with 1 and $z$ with –1 in E1.
$x+1+(-1) = 1$
$x = 1$
The solution is (1, 1, –1), and
$\dfrac{x}{8}+\dfrac{y}{4}+\dfrac{z}{3} = \dfrac{1}{8}+\dfrac{1}{4}-\dfrac{1}{3}$
$= \dfrac{3}{24}+\dfrac{6}{24}-\dfrac{8}{24}$
$= \dfrac{1}{24}.$

**45.**  $\begin{cases} x+y\ \ \ \ \ -w=0 & (1) \\ \ \ \ \ \ y+2z+w=3 & (2) \\ x\ \ \ \ \ -z\ \ \ \ =1 & (3) \\ 2x-y\ \ \ \ \ -w=-1 & (4) \end{cases}$

Add E1 and E2.
$x+2y+2z = 3 \ (5)$
Add E2 and E4.

$2x+2z = 2 \ \text{ or } \ x+z = 1 \ (6)$
Add E3 and E6.
$x-z = 1$
$\underline{x+z = 1}$
$2x\ \ \ \ = 2$

Replace $x$ with 1 in E3.
$1-z = 1$
$z = 0$
Replace $x$ with 1 and $z$ with 0 in E5.
$1+2y+2(0) = 3$
$1+2y = 3$
$2y = 2$
$y = 1$
Replace $y$ with 1, and $z$ with 0 in E2.
$1+2(0)+w = 3$
$1+w = 3$
$w = 2$
The solution is (1, 1, 0, 2).

**47.**  $\begin{cases} x+y+z+w=5 & (1) \\ 2x+y+z+w=6 & (2) \\ x+y+z\ \ \ \ =2 & (3) \\ x+y\ \ \ \ \ \ \ =0 & (4) \end{cases}$

Add –1 times E4 to E3.
$-x-y\ \ \ \ = 0$
$\underline{x+y+z = 2}$
$\quad\quad\quad z = 2$
Replace $z$ with 2 in E1 and E2.
$\begin{cases} x+y+w=3 & (5) \\ 2x+y+w=4 & (6) \end{cases}$
Add –1 times E5 to E6.
$-x-y-w = -3$
$\underline{2x+y+w = 4}$
$x\ \ \ \ \ \ \ = 1$
Replace $x$ with 1 in E4.
$1+y = 0$
$y = -1$
Replace $x$ with 1, $y$ with –1, and $z$ with 2 in E1.
$1+(-1)+2+w = 5$
$2+w = 5$
$w = 3$
The solution is (1, –1, 2, 3).

**49.** Answers may vary

**Section 4.3**

**Practice Exercises**

1.  **a.** We are given a system of equations.
$$\begin{cases} y = -0.16x + 113.9 \\ y = 1.06x + 62.3 \end{cases}$$
    We want to know the year $x$ in which the pounds $y$ are the same. Since both equations are solved for $y$, we use the substitution method. Substitute $-0.16x + 113.9$ for $y$ in the second equation.
$$-0.16x + 113.9 = 1.06x + 62.3$$
$$-1.22x = -51.6$$
$$x = \frac{-51.6}{-1.22} \approx 42.30$$
    Since we are only asked to give the year, we need only solve for $x$. The consumption of red meat and poultry will be the same about 42.30 years after 1995, or in about 2037.

    **b.** Yes; answers may vary.

2.  Let $x$ = first number
    $y$ = second number
    "A first number is five more than a second number" is translated as $x = y + 5$. "Twice the first number is 2 less than 3 times the second number" is translated as $2x = 3y - 2$.
    We solve the following system.
$$\begin{cases} x = y + 5 \\ 2x = 3y - 2 \end{cases}$$
    Since the first equation is solved for $x$, we use substitution. Substitute $y + 5$ for $x$ in the second equation.
$$2(y + 5) = 3y - 2$$
$$2y + 10 = 3y - 2$$
$$12 = y$$
    Replace $y$ with 12 in the equation $x = y + 5$ and solve for $x$.
$$x = 12 + 5 = 17$$
    The numbers are 12 and 17.

3.  Let $x$ = speed of the V150
    $y$ = speed of the Atlantique
    We summarize the information in a chart. Both trains have traveled two hours.

| | Rate | • | Time | = | Distance |
|---|---|---|---|---|---|
| V150 | $x$ | | 2 | | $2x$ |
| Atlantique | $y$ | | 2 | | $2y$ |

The trains are 2150 kilometers apart, so the sum of the distances is 2150: $2x + 2y = 2150$.
The V150 is 75 kph faster than the Atlantique: $x = y + 75$.
We solve the following system.
$$\begin{cases} 2x + 2y = 2150 \\ x = y + 75 \end{cases}$$
Since the second equation is solved for $x$, we use substitution. Substitute $y + 75$ for $x$ in the first equation.
$$2(y + 75) + 2y = 2150$$
$$2y + 150 + 2y = 2150$$
$$4y + 150 = 2150$$
$$4y = 2000$$
$$y = 500$$
To find $x$, we replace $y$ with 500 in the second equation.
$$x = 500 + 75 = 575$$
The speed of the V150 is 575 kph, and the speed of the Atlantique is 500 kph.

4.  Let $x$ = amount of 99% acid
    $y$ = amount of water (0%)
    Both $x$ and $y$ are measured in liters. We use a table to organize the given data.

| | Amount | Acid Strength | Amount of Pure Acid |
|---|---|---|---|
| 99% acid | $x$ | 99% | $0.99x$ |
| Water | $y$ | 0% | $0y$ |

The amount of 99% acid and water combined must equal 1 liter, so $x + y = 1$.
The amount of pure acid in the mixture must equal the sum of the amounts of pure acid in the 99% acid and in the water, so
$0.99x + 0y = 0.05(1)$, which simplifies to $0.99x = 0.05$.
We solve the following system.
$$\begin{cases} x + y = 1 \\ 0.99x = 0.05 \end{cases}$$
Since the second equation does not contain $y$, we solve it for $x$.
$$0.99x = 0.05$$
$$x = \frac{0.05}{0.99} \approx 0.05$$
To find $y$, we replace $x$ with 0.05 in the first equation.

$$x+y=1$$
$$0.05+y=1$$
$$y=0.95$$

The teacher should use 0.05 liter of the 99% HCL solution and 0.95 liter of water.

5. Let $x$ = the number of packages.
The firm charges the customer $4.50 for each package, so the revenue equation is $R(x)=4.5x$.
Each package costs $2.50 to produce and the equipment costs $3000, so the cost equation is $C(x)=2.5x+3000$.
Since the break-even point is when $R(x)=C(x)$, we solve the equation $4.5x=2.5x+3000$.
$$4.5x=2.5x+3000$$
$$2x=3000$$
$$x=1500$$
The company must sell 1500 packages to break even.

6. Let $x$ = measure of smallest angle
$y$ = measure of largest angle
$z$ = measure of third angle
The sum of the measures is 180°:
$x+y+z=180$.

The measure of the largest angle is 40° more than the measure of the smallest angle:
$y=x+40$.

The measure of the remaining angle is 20° more than the measure of the smallest angle:
$y=x+20$.

We solve the following system.
$$\begin{cases} x+y+z=1180 \\ y=x+40 \\ z=x+20 \end{cases}$$

We substitute $x+40$ for $y$ and $x+20$ for $z$ in the first equation.
$$x+(x+40)+(x+20)=180$$
$$3x+60=180$$
$$3x=120$$
$$x=40$$
Then $y=x+40=40+40=80$ and $z=x+20=40+20=60$.
The angle measures are 40°, 60°, and 80°.

### Exercise Set 4.3

1. Let $x$ = the first number, and $y$ = the second number.
$$\begin{cases} x=y+2 & (1) \\ 2x=3y-4 & (2) \end{cases}$$
Substitute $x=y+2$ in E2.

$$2(y+2)=3y-4$$
$$2y+4=3y-4$$
$$y=8$$
Replace $y$ with 8 in E1.
$$x=8+2=10$$
The numbers are 10 and 8.

3. a. Let $x$ = length of Enterprise, and $y$ = length of Nimitz.
$$\begin{cases} x+y=2193 & (1) \\ x-y=9 & (2) \end{cases}$$
Add E1 and E2.
$$2x=2202$$
$$x=1101$$
Replace $x$ with 1101 in E1.
$$1101+y=2193$$
$$y=1092$$
The Enterprise is 1101 feet long and the Nimitz is 1092 feet long.

b. Since 100 yards is equivalent to 300 feet, we divide the length of the Enterprise by 300 feet.
$$\frac{1101}{300}=3.67 \text{ football fields}$$

5. Let $p$ = the speed of the plane in still air, and $w$ = the speed of the wind.
$$\begin{cases} p+w=560 & (1) \\ p-w=480 & (2) \end{cases}$$
Add E1 and E2.
$$2p=1040$$
$$p=520$$
Replace $p$ with 520 in E1.
$$520+w=560$$
$$w=40$$
The speed of the plane in still air is 520 mph and the speed of the wind is 40 mph.

7. Let $x$ = number of quarts of 4% butterfat milk, and $y$ = number of quarts of 1% butterfat milk.
$$\begin{cases} x+y=60 & (1) \\ 0.04x+0.01y=0.02(60) & (2) \end{cases}$$
Multiply E2 by $-100$ and add to E1.
$$x+y=60$$
$$-4x-y=-120$$
$$\overline{-3x=-60}$$
$$x=20$$
Replace $x$ with 20 in E1.

$20 + y = 60$

$\quad\quad y = 40$

There should be 20 quarts of 4% butterfat used and 40 quarts of 1% butterfat used.

**9.** Let $x$ = number of students studied abroad in the United Kingdom and
$y$ = number of students studied abroad in Italy.

$$\begin{cases} x + \quad y = 56,929 \quad (1) \\ \quad\quad x = y + 7213 \quad (2) \end{cases}$$

Substitute $y + 7213$ for $x$ in E1.

$(y + 7213) + y = 56,929$

$\quad 2y + 7213 = 56,929$

$\quad\quad\quad 2y = 49,716$

$\quad\quad\quad\quad y = 24,858$

Replace $y$ with 24,858 in E2.

$x = 24,858 + 7213 = 32,071$

The United Kingdom had 32,071 students and Italy had 24,858 students.

**11.** Let $l$ = the number of large frames, and
$s$ = the number of small frames.

$$\begin{cases} \quad l + s = 22 \quad (1) \\ 15l + 8s = 239 \quad (2) \end{cases}$$

Multiply E1 by $-8$ and add to E2.

$-8l - 8s = -176$

$\underline{15l + 8s = 239}$

$\quad 7l \quad\quad = 63$

$\quad\quad\quad l = 9$

Replace $l$ with 9 in E1.

$9 + s = 22$

$\quad\quad s = 13$

She bought 9 large frames and 13 small frames.

**13.** Let $x$ = the first number, and
$y$ = the second number.

$$\begin{cases} \quad x = y - 2 \quad (1) \\ 2x = 3y + 4 \quad (2) \end{cases}$$

Substitute $x = y - 2$ in E2.

$2(y - 2) = 3y + 4$

$\quad 2y - 4 = 3y + 4$

$\quad\quad\quad y = -8$

Replace $y$ with $-8$ in E1.

$x = -8 - 2 = -10$

The numbers are $-10$ and $-8$.

**15.** $\begin{cases} y = 5.3x + 39.5 \quad (1) \\ y = 4.5x + 45.5 \quad (2) \end{cases}$

Substitute $5.3x + 39.5$ for $y$ in E2.

$5.3x + 39.5 = 4.5x + 45.5$

$\quad\quad 0.8x = 6$

$\quad\quad\quad x = 7.5$

$2000 + 7 = 2007$

The year was 2007.

**17.** Let $x$ = price of each tablet, and
$y$ = the price of each pen.

$$\begin{cases} 7x + \quad 4y = 6.40 \quad (1) \\ 2x + 19y = 5.40 \quad (2) \end{cases}$$

Multiply E1 by 2 and E2 by $-7$ and add.

$\quad 14x + \quad 8y = 12.8$

$\underline{-14x - 133y = -37.80}$

$\quad\quad\quad -125y = -25$

$\quad\quad\quad\quad\quad y = 0.20$

Replace $y$ with 0.20 in E1.

$7x + 4(0.20) = 6.40$

$\quad 7x + 0.80 = 6.40$

$\quad\quad\quad 7x = 5.60$

$\quad\quad\quad\quad x = 0.80$

Tablets cost \$0.80 each and pens cost \$0.20 each.

**19.** Let $p$ = the speed of the plane in still air, and
$w$ = the speed of the wind.

First note:

$$\frac{2160 \text{ mi}}{3 \text{ hr}} = 720 \text{ mph and } \frac{2160 \text{ mi}}{4 \text{ hr}} = 540 \text{ mph}$$

Now,

$$\begin{cases} p + w = 720 \\ p - w = 540 \end{cases}$$

Add E1 and E2.

$2p = 1260$

$\quad p = 630$

Replace $p$ with 630 in E1.

$630 + w = 720$

$\quad\quad\quad w = 90$

The speed of the plane in still air is 630 mph and the speed of the wind is 90 mph.

**21. a.** Answers may vary, but depend on the slope of each function.

**b.** $\begin{cases} y = -1379.4x + 150,604 \quad (1) \\ y = 478.4x + 157,838 \quad\quad\quad (2) \end{cases}$

Substitute $478.4x + 157,838$ for $y$ in E1.

$478.4x + 157,838 = -1379.4x + 150,604$
$1857.8x = -7234$
$x = \dfrac{-7234}{1857.8} \approx -3.89$
$1995 + (-3.89) = 1991.11$
They were the same in 1991.

**23.** Let $x$ = length of shortest two sides, and $y$ = length of the longest side.
$\begin{cases} 2x + y = 93 \ (1) \\ y = x + 9 \quad (2) \end{cases}$
Replace $y$ with $x + 9$ in E1.
$2x + (x + 9) = 93$
$3x + 9 = 93$
$3x = 84$
$x = 28$
Replace $x$ with 28 in E2.
$y = 28 + 9 = 37$
The three sides are 28 cm, 28 cm, and 37 cm.

**25.** Cost for Hertz: $H(x) = 25 + 0.10x$
Cost for Budget: $B(x) = 20 + 0.25x$
We want to find when $B(x) = 2 \cdot H(x)$
$20 + 0.25x = 2(25 + 0.10x)$
$20 + 0.25x = 50 + 0.20x$
$0.05x = 30$
$x = 600$
The Budget charge will be twice that of the Hertz charge at 600 miles.

**27.** $\begin{cases} x + y = 180 \\ x = y - 30 \end{cases}$
Replace $x$ with $y - 30$ in E1.
$(y - 30) + y = 180$
$2y - 30 = 180$
$2y = 210$
$y = 105$
Replace $y$ with 105 in E2.
$x = 105 - 30 = 75$
The value of $x$ is 75° and the value of $y$ is 105°.

**29.** $C(x) = 30x + 10,000$
$R(x) = 46x$
$46x = 30x + 10,000$
$16x = 10,000$
$x = 625$
625 units

**31.** $C(x) = 1.2x + 1500$
$R(x) = 1.7x$
$1.7x = 1.2x + 1500$
$0.5x = 1500$
$x = 3000$
3000 units

**33.** $C(x) = 75x + 160,000$
$R(x) = 200x$
$200x = 75x + 160,000$
$125x = 160,000$
$x = 1280$
1280 units

**35. a.** $R(x) = 450x$

**b.** $C(x) = 200x + 6000$

**c.** $R(x) = C(x)$
$450x = 200x + 6000$
$250x = 6000$
$x = 24$ desks

**37.** Let $x$ = units of Mix A, $y$ = units of Mix B, and $z$ = units of Mix C.
$\begin{cases} 4x + 6y + 4z = 30 \ (1) \\ 6x + y + z = 16 \ (2) \\ 3x + 2y + 12z = 24 \ (3) \end{cases}$
Multiply E2 by –6 and add to E1.
$-36x - 6y - 6z = -96$
$\underline{4x + 6y + 4z = 30}$
$-32x \quad\quad - 2z = -66$ or $16x + z = 33$ (4)
Multiply E2 by –2 and add to E3.
$-12x - 2y - 2z = -32$
$\underline{3x + 2y + 12z = 24}$
$-9x + \quad 10z = -8$ (5)
Multiply E4 by –10 and add to E5.
$-160x - 10z = -330$
$\underline{-9x + 10z = -8}$
$-169x \quad\quad = -338$
$x = 2$
Replace $x$ with 2 in E4.
$16(2) + z = 33$
$32 + z = 33$
$z = 1$
Replace $x$ with 2 and $z$ with 1 in E2.
$6(2) + y + 1 = 16$
$y = 3$
You need 2 units of Mix A, 3 units of Mix B, and 1 unit of Mix C.

**39.** Let $x$ = length of shortest side,
$y$ = length of longest side, and
$z$ = length of the other two sides
$$\begin{cases} x+y+2z = 29 & (1) \\ y = 2x & (2) \\ z = x+2 & (3) \end{cases}$$
Substitute $y = 2x$ and $z = x+2$ in E1.
$$x+(2x)+2(x+2) = 29$$
$$x+2x+2x+4 = 29$$
$$5x = 25$$
$$x = 5$$
Replace $x$ with 5 in E2 and E3.
$$y = 2(5) \qquad z = 5+2$$
$$y = 10 \qquad z = 7$$
The sides are 5 in., 7 in., 7 in., and 10 in.

**41.** Let $x$ = the first number
$y$ = the second number, and
$z$ = the third number.
$$\begin{cases} x+y+z = 40 \\ x = y+5 \\ x = 2z \end{cases}$$
$$\begin{cases} x+y+z = 40 & (1) \\ x-y = 5 & (2) \\ x-2z = 0 & (3) \end{cases}$$
Add E1 and E2.
$$2x+z = 45 \quad (4)$$
Multiply E3 by $-2$ and add to E4.
$$-2x+4z = 0$$
$$\underline{2x+z = 45}$$
$$5z = 45$$
$$z = 9$$
Replace $z$ with 9 in E3.
$$x-2(9) = 0$$
$$x = 18$$
Replace $x$ with 18 in E2.
$$18-y = 5$$
$$y = 13$$
The numbers are 18, 13, and 9.

**43.** Let $x$ = number of free throws,
$y$ = number of two-point field goals, and
$z$ = number of three-point field goals
$$\begin{cases} x+2y+3z = 860 \\ y = 2z-65 \\ x = y-34 \end{cases}$$
$$\begin{cases} x+2y+3z = 860 & (1) \\ y-2z = -65 & (2) \\ x-y = -34 & (3) \end{cases}$$
Multiply E3 by $-1$ and add to E1.

$$-x+y = 34$$
$$\underline{x+2y+3z = 860}$$
$$3y+3z = 894 \text{ or } y+z = 298 \ (4)$$
Multiply E4 by $-1$ and add to E2.
$$-y-z = -298$$
$$\underline{y-2z = -65}$$
$$-3z = -363$$
$$z = 121$$
Replace $z$ with 121 in E2.
$$y-2(121) = -65$$
$$y-242 = -65$$
$$y = 177$$
Replace $y$ with 177 in E3.
$$x-177 = -34$$
$$x = 143$$
She made 143 free throws, 177 two-point field goals, and 121 three-point field goals.

**45.** $$\begin{cases} x+y+z = 180 \\ y+2x+5 = 180 \\ z+2x-5 = 180 \end{cases}$$
$$\begin{cases} x+y+z = 180 & (1) \\ 2x+y = 175 & (2) \\ 2x+z = 185 & (3) \end{cases}$$
Multiply E1 by $-1$ and add to E2.
$$-x-y-z = -180$$
$$\underline{2x+y = 175}$$
$$x-z = -5 \ (4)$$
Add E3 and E4.
$$3x = 180$$
$$x = 60$$
Replace $x$ with 60 in E4.
$$60-z = -5$$
$$z = 65$$
Replace $x$ with 60 in E2.
$$2(60)+y = 175$$
$$120+y = 175$$
$$y = 55$$
$x = 60$, $y = 55$, and $z = 65$

**47.** $$\begin{cases} 3x-y+z = 2 & (1) \\ -x+2y+3z = 6 & (2) \end{cases}$$
Multiply E1 by 2 and add to E2.
$$6x-2y+2z = 4$$
$$\underline{-x+2y+3z = 6}$$
$$5x+5z = 10$$
$$5x+5z = 10$$

**49.** $\begin{cases} x+2y-z=0 & (1) \\ 3x+y-z=2 & (2) \end{cases}$

Multiply E1 by –3 and add to E2.
$-3x-6y+3z=0$
$\underline{3x+y-z=2}$
$-5y+2z=2$
$-5y+2z=2$

**51.** Let $x$ = number filed in 1996
$y$ = number filed in 2006
$\begin{cases} y=x+25,765 \\ x+y=2,144,653 \end{cases}$

Substitute $x+25{,}765$ for $y$ in E2.
$x+(x+25,765)=2,144,653$
$2x+25,765=2,144,653$
$2x=2,118,888$
$x=1,059,444$
Replace $x$ with 1,059,444 in E1.
$y=1,059,444+25,765=1,085,209$
There were 1,059,444 bankruptcy petitions filed in 1996 and 1,085,209 filed in 2006.

**53. a.** Replace $f(x)$ with $y$ in each equation.
$\begin{cases} y=0.85x+41.75 & (1) \\ y=1.13x+10.49 & (2) \end{cases}$
Substitute $0.85x+41.75$ for $y$ in E2.
$0.85x+41.75=1.13x+10.49$
$31.26=0.28x$
$\dfrac{31.26}{0.28}=x$
$112\approx x$
Replace $x$ with 112 in E1.
$y=0.85(112)+41.75\approx137$
The solution is (112, 137).

**b.** 112 months is 9 years, 4 months.
Since the first month is February 2007, the 112th month is 9 years and 4 months later, or June 2016.

**55.** $y=ax^2+bx+c$
$(1, 2)$: $2=a+b+c$   (1)
$(2, 3)$: $3=4a+2b+c$  (2)
$(-1, 6)$: $6=a-b+c$   (3)
Add E1 and E3 to obtain
$2a+2c=8$, or $a+c=4$ (4)
Multiply E3 by 2 and add to E2 to get
$15=6a+3c$, or $2a+c=5$ (5)
Multiply E4 by –1 and add to E5 to get $a=1$.
Replace $a$ with 1 in E4.

$1+c=4$ so $c=3$
Replace $a$ with 1 and $c$ with 3 in E1.
$2=1+b+3$
$-2=b$
Therefore, $a=1$, $b=-2$, and $c=3$.

**57.** $y=ax^2+bx+c$
$(4, 2.47)$: $2.47=16a+4b+c$ (1)
$(7, 0.6)$: $0.6=49a+7b+c$ (2)
$(8, 1.1)$: $1.1=64a+8b+c$ (3)
Multiply E1 by –1 and add to E2.
$-16a-4b-c=-2.47$
$\underline{49a+7b+c=0.6}$
$33a+3b=-1.87$ (4)
Multiply E1 by –1 and add to E3.
$-16a-4b-c=-2.47$
$\underline{64a+8b+c=1.1}$
$48a+4b=-1.37$ (5)
Multiply E4 by –4, E5 by 3, and add.
$-132a-12b=7.48$
$\underline{144a+12b=-4.11}$
$12a=3.37$
$a=\dfrac{3.37}{12}\approx0.2808$
Use this value in E4.
$33(0.2808)+3b=-1.87$
$3b=-11.1364$
$b=-3.7121$
From E1 we now have
$16(0.2808)+4(-3.7121)+c=2.47$
$-10.3556+c=2.47$
$c=12.8256$
So, $a=0.28$, $b=-3.71$, and $c=12.83$.
September is represented by $x=9$:
$y=0.28x^2-3.71x+12.83$
$=0.28(9)^2-3.71(9)+12.83$
$=2.12$ inches

## Integrated Review

**1.** A system with solution (1, 2) has lines that intersect at (1, 2). The correct graph is C.

**2.** A system with solution (–2, 3) has lines that intersect at (–2, 3). The correct graph is D.

**3.** A system with no solution has lines that are parallel. The correct graph is A.

**4.** A system with an infinite number of solutions has lines that are the same. The correct graph is B.

**5.** $\begin{cases} x+y=4 & (1) \\ y=3x & (2) \end{cases}$

Substitute $y=3x$ in E1.

$x+(3x)=4$

$4x=4$

$x=1$

Replace $x$ with 1 in E2.

$y=3x=3(1)=3$

The solution is (1, 3).

**6.** $\begin{cases} x-y=-4 & (1) \\ y=4x & (2) \end{cases}$

Substitute $y=4x$ in E1.

$x-(4x)=-4$

$-3x=-4$

$x=\dfrac{4}{3}$

Replace $x$ with $\dfrac{4}{3}$ in E2.

$y=4x=4\left(\dfrac{4}{3}\right)=\dfrac{16}{3}$

The solution is $\left(\dfrac{4}{3},\dfrac{16}{3}\right)$.

**7.** $\begin{cases} x+y=1 & (1) \\ x-2y=4 & (2) \end{cases}$

Multiply E1 by –1 and add to E2.

$-x-y=-1$

$\underline{x-2y=4}$

$-3y=3$

$y=-1$

Replace $y$ with –1 in E1.

$x+(-1)=1$

$x-1=1$

$x=2$

The solution is (2, –1).

**8.** $\begin{cases} 2x-y=8 & (1) \\ x+3y=11 & (2) \end{cases}$

Multiply E1 by 3 and add to E2.

$6x-3y=24$

$\underline{x+3y=11}$

$7x=35$

$x=5$

Replace $x$ with 5 in E1.

$2(5)-y=8$

$10-y=8$

$y=2$

The solution is (5, 2).

**9.** $\begin{cases} 2x+5y=8 & (1) \\ 6x+y=10 & (2) \end{cases}$

Multiply E2 by –5 and add to E1.

$2x+5y=8$

$\underline{-30x-5y=-50}$

$-28x=-42$

$x=\dfrac{3}{2}$

Replace $x$ with $\dfrac{3}{2}$ in E2.

$6\left(\dfrac{3}{2}\right)+y=10$

$9+y=8$

$y=1$

The solution is $\left(\dfrac{3}{2},1\right)$.

**10.** $\begin{cases} \dfrac{1}{8}x-\dfrac{1}{2}y=-\dfrac{5}{8} & (1) \\ -3x-8y=0 & (2) \end{cases}$

Multiply E1 by –16 and add to E2.

$-2x+8y=10$

$\underline{-3x-8y=0}$

$-5x=10$

$x=-2$

Replace $x$ with –2 in E2.

$-3(-2)-8y=0$

$6-8y=0$

$-8y=-6$

$y=\dfrac{-6}{-8}=\dfrac{3}{4}$

The solution is $\left(-2,\dfrac{3}{4}\right)$.

**11.** $\begin{cases} 4x-7y=7 & (1) \\ 12x-21y=24 & (2) \end{cases}$

Multiply E1 by –3 and add to E2.

$-12x+21y=-21$

$\underline{12x-21y=24}$

$0=3$ False

The system is inconsistent. The solution set is ∅.

**12.** $\begin{cases} 2x-5y=3 & (1) \\ -4x+10y=-6 & (2) \end{cases}$

Multiply E1 by 2 and add to E2.

$\begin{array}{r} 4x-10y=6 \\ -4x+10y=-6 \\ \hline 0=0 \quad \text{True} \end{array}$

The system is dependent. The solution set is $\{(x, y)|2x - 5y = 3\}$.

**13.** $\begin{cases} y=\dfrac{1}{3}x \\ 5x-3y=4 \end{cases}$

Substitute $\dfrac{1}{3}x$ for $y$ in E2.

$5x-3\left(\dfrac{1}{3}x\right)=4$

$5x-x=4$

$4x=4$

$x=1$

Replace $x$ with 1 in E1.

$y=\dfrac{1}{3}(1)=\dfrac{1}{3}$

The solution is $\left(1, \dfrac{1}{3}\right)$.

**14.** $\begin{cases} y=\dfrac{1}{4}x \\ 2x-4y=3 \end{cases}$

Substitute $\dfrac{1}{4}x$ for $y$ in E2.

$2x-4\left(\dfrac{1}{4}x\right)=3$

$2x-x=3$

$x=3$

Replace $x$ with 3 in E1.

$y=\dfrac{1}{4}(3)=\dfrac{3}{4}$

The solution is $\left(3, \dfrac{3}{4}\right)$.

**15.** $\begin{cases} x+y=2 & (1) \\ -3y+z=-7 & (2) \\ 2x+y-z=-1 & (3) \end{cases}$

Add E2 and E3.

$2x-2y=-8$ or $x-y=-4$ (4)

Add E1 and E4.

$2x=-2$

$x=-1$

Replace $x$ with $-1$ in E1.

$-1+y=2$

$y=3$

Replace $y$ with 3 in E2.

$-3(3)+z=-7$

$-9+z=-7$

$z=2$

The solution is $(-1, 3, 2)$.

**16.** $\begin{cases} y+2z=-3 & (1) \\ x-2y=7 & (2) \\ 2x-y+z=5 & (3) \end{cases}$

Multiply E2 by $-2$ and add to E3.

$\begin{array}{r} -2x+4y=-14 \\ 2x-y+z=5 \\ \hline 3y+z=-9 \quad (4) \end{array}$

Multiply E4 by $-2$ and add to E1.

$\begin{array}{r} -6y-2z=18 \\ y+2z=-3 \\ \hline -5y=15 \\ y=-3 \end{array}$

Replace $y$ with $-3$ in E4.

$3(-3)+z=-9$

$z=0$

Replace $y$ with $-3$ in E2.

$x-2(-3)=7$

$x+6=7$

$x=1$

The solution is $(1, -3, 0)$.

**17.** $\begin{cases} 2x+4y-6z=3 & (1) \\ -x+y-z=6 & (2) \\ x+2y-3z=1 & (3) \end{cases}$

Multiply E3 by $-2$ and add to E1.

$\begin{array}{r} -2x-4y+6z=-2 \\ 2x+4y-6z=3 \\ \hline 0=1 \quad \text{False} \end{array}$

The system is inconsistent. The solution set is $\varnothing$.

**18.** $\begin{cases} x-y+3z=2 & (1) \\ -2x+2y-6z=-4 & (2) \\ 3x-3y+9z=6 & (3) \end{cases}$

Multiply E1 by 2 and add to E2.

$\begin{array}{r} 2x-2y+6z=4 \\ -2x+2y-6z=-4 \\ \hline 0=0 \quad \text{True} \end{array}$

The system is dependent. The solution set is $\{(x, y)|x - y + 3z = 2\}$.

**19.** $\begin{cases} x + y - 4z = 5 & (1) \\ x - y + 2z = -2 & (2) \\ 3x + 2y + 4z = 18 & (3) \end{cases}$

Add E1 and E2.

$2x - 2z = 3 \quad (4)$

Multiply E2 by 2 and add to E3.

$2x - 2y + 4z = -4$
$\underline{3x + 2y + 4z = 18}$
$5x \qquad + 8z = 14 \quad (5)$

Multiply E4 by 4 and add to E5.

$8x - 8z = 12$
$\underline{5x + 8z = 14}$
$13x \qquad = 26$
$\qquad x = 2$

Replace $x$ with 2 in E4.

$2(2) - 2z = 3$
$\qquad -2z = -1$
$\qquad z = \dfrac{1}{2}$

Replace $x$ with 2 and $z$ with $\dfrac{1}{2}$ in E1.

$2 + y - 4\left(\dfrac{1}{2}\right) = 5$
$\quad 2 + y - 2 = 5$
$\qquad\quad y = 5$

The solution is $\left(2, 5, \dfrac{1}{2}\right)$.

**20.** $\begin{cases} 2x - y + 3z = 2 & (1) \\ x + y - 6z = 0 & (2) \\ 3x + 4y - 3z = 6 & (3) \end{cases}$

Add E1 and E3.

$5x + 3y = 8 \quad (4)$

Multiply E1 by 2 and add to E2.

$4x - 2y + 6z = 4$
$\underline{x + \; y - 6z = 0}$
$5x - y \qquad = 4 \quad (5)$

Multiply E5 by 3 and add to E4.

$15x - 3y = 12$
$\underline{5x + 3y = 8}$
$20x \qquad = 20$
$\qquad x = 1$

Replace $x$ with 1 in E5.

$5(1) - y = 4$
$\qquad -y = -1$
$\qquad y = 1$

Replace both $x$ and $y$ with 1 in E1.

$2(1) - 1 + 3z = 2$
$1 + 3z = 2$
$3z = 1$
$z = \dfrac{1}{3}$

The solution is $\left(1, 1, \dfrac{1}{3}\right)$.

**21.** Let $x =$ the first number and $y =$ the second number.

$\begin{cases} x = y - 8 & (1) \\ 2x = y + 11 & (2) \end{cases}$

Substitute $x = y - 8$ in E2.

$2(y - 8) = y + 11$
$2y - 16 = y + 11$
$y = 27$

Replace $y$ with 27 in E1.

$x = 27 - 8 = 19$

The numbers are 19 and 27.

**22.** Let $x =$ measure of the two smallest angles, $y =$ measure of the third angle, and $z =$ measure of the fourth angle.

$\begin{cases} 2x + y + z = 360 \\ y = x + 30 \\ z = x + 50 \end{cases}$

Substitute $y = x + 30$ and $z = x + 50$ in the first equation.

$2x + (x + 30) + (x + 50) = 360$
$4x + 80 = 360$
$4x = 280$
$x = 70$

so $y = 70 + 30 = 100$ and $z = 70 + 50 = 120$

The two smallest angles are 70°, the third angle is 100°, and the fourth angle is 120°.

## Section 4.4

**Practice Exercises**

**1.** $\begin{cases} x + 4y = -2 \\ 3x - y = 7 \end{cases}$

The corresponding matrix is $\begin{bmatrix} 1 & 4 & | & -2 \\ 3 & -1 & | & 7 \end{bmatrix}$. The element in the first row, first column is already 1. Multiply row 1 by −3 and add to row 2 to get a 0 below the 1.

$\begin{bmatrix} 1 & 4 & | & -2 \\ -3(1)+3 & -3(4)+(-1) & | & -3(-2)+7 \end{bmatrix}$

$$\begin{bmatrix} 1 & 4 & | & -2 \\ 0 & -13 & | & 13 \end{bmatrix}$$

We change $-13$ to a 1 by dividing row 2 by $-13$.

$$\begin{bmatrix} 1 & 4 & | & -2 \\ 0 & \frac{-13}{-13} & | & \frac{13}{-13} \end{bmatrix}$$

$$\begin{bmatrix} 1 & 4 & | & -2 \\ 0 & 1 & | & -1 \end{bmatrix}$$

The last matrix corresponds to $\begin{cases} x+4y = -2 \\ \quad\;\; y = -1 \end{cases}$

To find $x$, we let $y = -1$ in the first equation.

$$x+4y = -2$$
$$x+4(-1) = -2$$
$$x-4 = -2$$
$$x = 2$$

The solution is $(2, -1)$.

**2.** $\begin{cases} x - 3y = 3 \\ -2x + 6y = 4 \end{cases}$

The corresponding matrix is $\begin{bmatrix} 1 & -3 & | & 3 \\ -2 & 6 & | & 4 \end{bmatrix}$. The

element in the first row, first column is already 1. Multiply row 1 by 2 and add to row 2 to get a 0 below the 1.

$$\begin{bmatrix} 1 & -3 & | & 3 \\ 2(1)+(-2) & 2(-3)+6 & | & 2(3)+4 \end{bmatrix}$$

$$\begin{bmatrix} 1 & -3 & | & 3 \\ 0 & 0 & | & 10 \end{bmatrix}$$

The corresponding system is $\begin{cases} x - 3y = 3 \\ \quad\; 0 = 10 \end{cases}$

The equation $0 = 10$ is false. Hence, the system is inconsistent and has no solution. The solution set is $\varnothing$.

**3.** $\begin{cases} x + 3y - z = 0 \\ 2x + y + 3z = 5 \\ -x - 2y + 4z = 7 \end{cases}$

The corresponding matrix is $\begin{bmatrix} 1 & 3 & -1 & | & 0 \\ 2 & 1 & 3 & | & 5 \\ -1 & -2 & 4 & | & 7 \end{bmatrix}$.

The element in the first row, first column is already 1. Multiply row 1 by $-2$ and add to row 2 to get a 0 below the 1 in row 2. Add row 1 to row 3 to get a 0 below the 1 in row 3.

$$\begin{bmatrix} 1 & 3 & -1 & | & 0 \\ -2(1)+2 & -2(3)+1 & -2(-1)+3 & | & -2(0)+5 \\ 1+(-1) & 3+(-2) & -1+4 & | & 0+7 \end{bmatrix}$$

$$\begin{bmatrix} 1 & 3 & -1 & | & 0 \\ 0 & -5 & 5 & | & 5 \\ 0 & 1 & 3 & | & 7 \end{bmatrix}$$

Now we want a 1 where the $-5$ is now. Interchange rows 2 and 3.

$$\begin{bmatrix} 1 & 3 & -1 & | & 0 \\ 0 & 1 & 3 & | & 7 \\ 0 & -5 & 5 & | & 5 \end{bmatrix}$$

Now we want a 0 below the 1. Multiply row 2 by 5 and add to row 3.

$$\begin{bmatrix} 1 & 3 & -1 & | & 0 \\ 0 & 1 & 3 & | & 7 \\ 5(0)+0 & 5(1)+(-5) & 5(3)+5 & | & 5(7)+5 \end{bmatrix}$$

$$\begin{bmatrix} 1 & 3 & -1 & | & 0 \\ 0 & 1 & 3 & | & 7 \\ 0 & 0 & 20 & | & 40 \end{bmatrix}$$

Finally, divide row 3 by 20.

$$\begin{bmatrix} 1 & 3 & -1 & | & 0 \\ 0 & 1 & 3 & | & 7 \\ 0 & 0 & \frac{20}{20} & | & \frac{40}{20} \end{bmatrix}$$

$$\begin{bmatrix} 1 & 3 & -1 & | & 0 \\ 0 & 1 & 3 & | & 7 \\ 0 & 0 & 1 & | & 2 \end{bmatrix}$$

This matrix corresponds to the system

$$\begin{cases} x + 3y - z = 0 \\ \quad\;\; y + 3z = 7 \\ \qquad\quad\; z = 2 \end{cases}$$

The $z$-coordinate is 2. Replace $z$ with 2 in the second equation and solve for $y$.

$$y + 3z = 7$$
$$y + 3(2) = 7$$
$$y + 6 = 7$$
$$y = 1$$

To find $x$, we let $z = 2$ and $y = 1$ in the first equation.

$$x + 3y - z = 0$$
$$x + 3(1) - 2 = 0$$
$$x + 1 = 0$$
$$x = -1$$

The solution is $(-1, 1, 2)$.

**Vocabulary and Readiness Check**

1. A <u>matrix</u> is a rectangular array of numbers.

2. Each of the numbers in a matrix is called an <u>element</u>.

3. The numbers aligned horizontally in a matrix are in the same <u>row</u>.

4. The numbers aligned vertically in a matrix are in the same <u>column</u>.

5. Any two columns may be interchanged. <u>false</u>

6. Any two rows may be interchanged. <u>true</u>

7. The elements in a row may be added to their corresponding elements in another row. <u>true</u>

8. The elements of a column may be multiplied by any nonzero number. <u>false</u>

## Exercise Set 4.4

1. $\begin{cases} x + y = 1 \\ x - 2y = 4 \end{cases}$

$\begin{bmatrix} 1 & 1 & | & 1 \\ 1 & -2 & | & 4 \end{bmatrix}$

Multiply R1 by $-1$ and add to R2.

$\begin{bmatrix} 1 & 1 & | & 1 \\ 0 & -3 & | & 3 \end{bmatrix}$

Divide R2 by $-3$.

$\begin{bmatrix} 1 & 1 & | & 1 \\ 0 & 1 & | & -1 \end{bmatrix}$

This corresponds to $\begin{cases} x + y = 1 \\ y = -1 \end{cases}$.

$x + (-1) = 1$
$x - 1 = 1$
$x = 2$

The solution is $(2, -1)$.

3. $\begin{cases} x + 3y = 2 \\ x + 2y = 0 \end{cases}$

$\begin{bmatrix} 1 & 3 & | & 2 \\ 1 & 2 & | & 0 \end{bmatrix}$

Multiply R1 by $-1$ and add to R2.

$\begin{bmatrix} 1 & 3 & | & 2 \\ 0 & -1 & | & -2 \end{bmatrix}$

Multiply R2 by $-1$.

$\begin{bmatrix} 1 & 3 & | & 2 \\ 0 & 1 & | & 2 \end{bmatrix}$

This corresponds to $\begin{cases} x + 3y = 2 \\ y = 2 \end{cases}$.

$x + 3(2) = 2$
$x + 6 = 2$
$x = -4$

The solution is $(-4, 2)$.

5. $\begin{cases} x - 2y = 4 \\ 2x - 4y = 4 \end{cases}$

$\begin{bmatrix} 1 & -2 & | & 4 \\ 2 & -4 & | & 4 \end{bmatrix}$

Multiply R1 by $-2$ and add to R2.

$\begin{bmatrix} 1 & -2 & | & 4 \\ 0 & 0 & | & -4 \end{bmatrix}$

This corresponds to $\begin{cases} x - 2y = 4 \\ 0 = -4 \end{cases}$.

This is an inconsistent system. The solution is $\varnothing$.

7. $\begin{cases} 3x - 3y = 9 \\ 2x - 2y = 6 \end{cases}$

$\begin{bmatrix} 3 & -3 & | & 9 \\ 2 & -2 & | & 6 \end{bmatrix}$

Divide R1 by 3.

$\begin{bmatrix} 1 & -1 & | & 3 \\ 2 & -2 & | & 6 \end{bmatrix}$

Multiply R1 by $-2$ and add to R2.

$\begin{bmatrix} 1 & -1 & | & 3 \\ 0 & 0 & | & 0 \end{bmatrix}$

This corresponds to $\begin{cases} x - y = 3 \\ 0 = 0 \end{cases}$.

This is a dependent system. The solution is $\{(x, y) | x - y = 3\}$.

9. $\begin{cases} x + y = 3 \\ 2y = 10 \\ 3x + 2y - 4z = 12 \end{cases}$

$\begin{bmatrix} 1 & 1 & 0 & | & 3 \\ 0 & 2 & 0 & | & 10 \\ 3 & 2 & -4 & | & 12 \end{bmatrix}$

Multiply R1 by $-3$ and add to R3.

$\begin{bmatrix} 1 & 1 & 0 & | & 3 \\ 0 & 2 & 0 & | & 10 \\ 0 & -1 & -4 & | & 3 \end{bmatrix}$

Divide R2 by 2.

$\begin{bmatrix} 1 & 1 & 0 & | & 3 \\ 0 & 1 & 0 & | & 5 \\ 0 & -1 & -4 & | & 3 \end{bmatrix}$

Add R2 to R3.

$\begin{bmatrix} 1 & 1 & 0 & | & 3 \\ 0 & 1 & 0 & | & 5 \\ 0 & 0 & -4 & | & 8 \end{bmatrix}$

Divide R3 by $-4$.

$$\begin{bmatrix} 1 & 1 & 0 & | & 3 \\ 0 & 1 & 0 & | & 5 \\ 0 & 0 & 1 & | & -2 \end{bmatrix}$$

This corresponds to $\begin{cases} x + y = 3 \\ \quad\; y = 5 \\ \quad\quad z = -2 \end{cases}$.

$x + 5 = 3$
$\quad\;\; x = -2$
The solution is $(-2, 5, -2)$.

**11.** $\begin{cases} 2y - z = -7 \\ x + 4y + z = -4 \\ 5x - y + 2z = 13 \end{cases}$

$$\begin{bmatrix} 0 & 2 & -1 & | & -7 \\ 1 & 4 & 1 & | & -4 \\ 5 & -1 & 2 & | & 13 \end{bmatrix}$$

Interchange R1 and R2.

$$\begin{bmatrix} 1 & 4 & 1 & | & -4 \\ 0 & 2 & -1 & | & -7 \\ 5 & -1 & 2 & | & 13 \end{bmatrix}$$

Multiply R1 by −5 and add to R3.

$$\begin{bmatrix} 1 & 4 & 1 & | & -4 \\ 0 & 2 & -1 & | & -7 \\ 0 & -21 & -3 & | & 33 \end{bmatrix}$$

Divide R2 by 2.

$$\begin{bmatrix} 1 & 4 & 1 & | & -4 \\ 0 & 1 & -\frac{1}{2} & | & -\frac{7}{2} \\ 0 & -21 & -3 & | & 33 \end{bmatrix}$$

Multiply R2 by 21 and add to R3.

$$\begin{bmatrix} 1 & 4 & 1 & | & -4 \\ 0 & 1 & -\frac{1}{2} & | & -\frac{7}{2} \\ 0 & 0 & -\frac{27}{2} & | & -\frac{81}{2} \end{bmatrix}$$

Multiply R2 by $-\dfrac{2}{27}$.

$$\begin{bmatrix} 1 & 4 & 1 & | & -4 \\ 0 & 1 & -\frac{1}{2} & | & -\frac{7}{2} \\ 0 & 0 & 1 & | & 3 \end{bmatrix}$$

This corresponds to $\begin{cases} x + 4y + z = -4 \\ \quad\; y - \frac{1}{2}z = -\frac{7}{2} \\ \quad\quad\quad z = 3 \end{cases}$.

$y - \dfrac{1}{2}(3) = -\dfrac{7}{2}$

$y - \dfrac{3}{2} = -\dfrac{7}{2}$

$y = -2$

$x + 4(-2) + 3 = -4$
$x - 8 + 3 = -4$
$\quad\quad\;\; x = 1$
The solution is $(1, -2, 3)$.

**13.** $\begin{cases} x - 4 = 0 \\ x + y = 1 \end{cases}$ or $\begin{cases} x = 4 \\ x + y = 1 \end{cases}$

$$\begin{bmatrix} 1 & 0 & | & 4 \\ 1 & 1 & | & 1 \end{bmatrix}$$

Multiply R1 by −1 and add to R2.

$$\begin{bmatrix} 1 & 0 & | & 4 \\ 0 & 1 & | & -3 \end{bmatrix}$$

This corresponds to $\begin{cases} x = 4 \\ y = -3 \end{cases}$

The solution is $(4, -3)$.

**15.** $\begin{cases} x + y + z = 2 \\ 2x \quad\; - z = 5 \\ \quad\; 3y + z = 2 \end{cases}$

$$\begin{bmatrix} 1 & 1 & 1 & | & 2 \\ 2 & 0 & -1 & | & 5 \\ 0 & 3 & 1 & | & 2 \end{bmatrix}$$

Multiply R1 by −2 and add to R2.

$$\begin{bmatrix} 1 & 1 & 1 & | & 2 \\ 0 & -2 & -3 & | & 1 \\ 0 & 3 & 1 & | & 2 \end{bmatrix}$$

Divide R2 by −2.

$$\begin{bmatrix} 1 & 1 & 1 & | & 2 \\ 0 & 1 & \frac{3}{2} & | & -\frac{1}{2} \\ 0 & 3 & 1 & | & 2 \end{bmatrix}$$

Multiply R2 by −3 and add to R3.

$$\begin{bmatrix} 1 & 1 & 1 & | & 2 \\ 0 & 1 & \frac{3}{2} & | & -\frac{1}{2} \\ 0 & 0 & -\frac{7}{2} & | & \frac{7}{2} \end{bmatrix}$$

Multiply R3 by $-\dfrac{2}{7}$.

$$\begin{bmatrix} 1 & 1 & 1 & | & 2 \\ 0 & 1 & \frac{3}{2} & | & -\frac{1}{2} \\ 0 & 0 & 1 & | & -1 \end{bmatrix}$$

This corresponds to $\begin{cases} x+y+z=2 \\ y+\dfrac{3}{2}z=-\dfrac{1}{2} \\ \qquad z=-1 \end{cases}$.

$$y+\frac{3}{2}(-1)=-\frac{1}{2}$$
$$y-\frac{3}{2}=-\frac{1}{2}$$
$$y=1$$
$$x+1+(-1)=2$$
$$x=2$$

The solution is $(2, 1, -1)$.

**17.** $\begin{cases} 5x-2y=27 \\ -3x+5y=18 \end{cases}$

$$\begin{bmatrix} 5 & -2 & | & 27 \\ -3 & 5 & | & 18 \end{bmatrix}$$

Divide R1 by 5.

$$\begin{bmatrix} 1 & -\frac{2}{5} & | & \frac{27}{5} \\ -3 & 5 & | & 18 \end{bmatrix}$$

Multiply R1 by 3 and add to R2.

$$\begin{bmatrix} 1 & -\frac{2}{5} & | & \frac{27}{5} \\ 0 & \frac{19}{5} & | & \frac{171}{5} \end{bmatrix}$$

Multiply R2 by $\dfrac{5}{19}$.

$$\begin{bmatrix} 1 & -\frac{2}{5} & | & \frac{27}{5} \\ 0 & 1 & | & 9 \end{bmatrix}$$

This corresponds to $\begin{cases} x-\dfrac{2}{5}y=\dfrac{27}{5} \\ \qquad y=9 \end{cases}$.

$$x-\frac{2}{5}(9)=\frac{27}{5}$$
$$x-\frac{18}{5}=\frac{27}{5}$$
$$x=9$$

The solution is $(9, 9)$.

**19.** $\begin{cases} 4x-7y=7 \\ 12x-21y=24 \end{cases}$

$$\begin{bmatrix} 4 & -7 & | & 7 \\ 12 & -21 & | & 24 \end{bmatrix}$$

Divide R1 by 4.

$$\begin{bmatrix} 1 & -\frac{7}{4} & | & \frac{7}{4} \\ 12 & -21 & | & 24 \end{bmatrix}$$

Multiply R1 by $-12$ and add to R2.

$$\begin{bmatrix} 1 & -\frac{7}{4} & | & \frac{7}{4} \\ 0 & 0 & | & 3 \end{bmatrix}$$

This corresponds to $\begin{cases} x-\dfrac{7}{4}y=\dfrac{7}{4} \\ \qquad 0=3 \end{cases}$.

This is an inconsistent system. The solution set is $\varnothing$.

**21.** $\begin{cases} 4x-y+2z=5 \\ 2y+z=4 \\ 4x+y+3z=10 \end{cases}$

$$\begin{bmatrix} 4 & -1 & 2 & | & 5 \\ 0 & 2 & 1 & | & 4 \\ 4 & 1 & 3 & | & 10 \end{bmatrix}$$

Divide R1 by 4.

$$\begin{bmatrix} 1 & -\frac{1}{4} & \frac{1}{2} & | & \frac{5}{4} \\ 0 & 2 & 1 & | & 4 \\ 4 & 1 & 3 & | & 10 \end{bmatrix}$$

Multiply R1 by $-4$ and add to R3.

$$\begin{bmatrix} 1 & -\frac{1}{4} & \frac{1}{2} & | & \frac{5}{4} \\ 0 & 2 & 1 & | & 4 \\ 0 & 2 & 1 & | & 5 \end{bmatrix}$$

Divide R2 by 2.

$$\begin{bmatrix} 1 & -\frac{1}{4} & \frac{1}{2} & | & \frac{5}{4} \\ 0 & 1 & \frac{1}{2} & | & 2 \\ 0 & 2 & 1 & | & 5 \end{bmatrix}$$

Multiply R2 by $-2$ and add to R3.

$$\begin{bmatrix} 1 & -\frac{1}{4} & \frac{1}{2} & | & \frac{5}{4} \\ 0 & 1 & \frac{1}{2} & | & 2 \\ 0 & 0 & 0 & | & 1 \end{bmatrix}$$

This corresponds to $\begin{cases} x-\dfrac{1}{4}y+\dfrac{1}{2}z=\dfrac{5}{4} \\ \qquad y+\dfrac{1}{2}z=2 \\ \qquad 0=1 \end{cases}$.

This is an inconsistent system. The solution set is $\varnothing$.

**23.** $\begin{cases} 4x + y + z = 3 \\ -x + y - 2z = -11 \\ x + 2y + 2z = -1 \end{cases}$

$$\begin{bmatrix} 4 & 1 & 1 & 3 \\ -1 & 1 & -2 & -11 \\ 1 & 2 & 2 & -1 \end{bmatrix}$$

Interchange R1 and R3.

$$\begin{bmatrix} 1 & 2 & 2 & -1 \\ -1 & 1 & -2 & -11 \\ 4 & 1 & 1 & 3 \end{bmatrix}$$

Add R1 to R2. Multiply R1 by –4 and add to R3.

$$\begin{bmatrix} 1 & 2 & 2 & -1 \\ 0 & 3 & 0 & -12 \\ 0 & -7 & -7 & 7 \end{bmatrix}$$

Divide R2 by 3.

$$\begin{bmatrix} 1 & 2 & 2 & -1 \\ 0 & 1 & 0 & -4 \\ 0 & -7 & -7 & 7 \end{bmatrix}$$

Multiply R2 by 7 and add to R3.

$$\begin{bmatrix} 1 & 2 & 2 & -1 \\ 0 & 1 & 0 & -4 \\ 0 & 0 & -7 & -21 \end{bmatrix}$$

Divide R3 by –7.

$$\begin{bmatrix} 1 & 2 & 2 & -1 \\ 0 & 1 & 0 & -4 \\ 0 & 0 & 1 & 3 \end{bmatrix}$$

This corresponds to $\begin{cases} x + 2y + 2z = -1 \\ y = -4. \\ z = 3 \end{cases}$

$x + 2(-4) + 2(3) = -1$
$x - 8 + 6 = -1$
$x = 1$
The solution is (1, –4, 3).

**25.** No vertical line intersects the graph more than once. It is the graph of a function.

**27.** The *y*-axis is a vertical line that intersects the graph more than once. It is not the graph of a function.

**29.** $(-1)(-5) - (6)(3) = 5 - 18 = -13$

**31.** $(4)(-10) - (2)(-2) = -40 + 4 = -36$

**33.** $(-3)(-3) - (-1)(-9) = 9 - 9 = 0$

**35.** The matrix should have four columns, so (a) is not the correct matrix. The matrix should have a 0 in the first column, second row since the coefficient of *x* in the second equation is 0, so (b) is not the correct matrix. The correct matrix is (c).

**37. a.** Solve the system $\begin{cases} 2.3x + y = 52 \\ -5.4x + y = 14 \end{cases}$.

$$\begin{bmatrix} 2.3 & 1 & 52 \\ -5.4 & 1 & 14 \end{bmatrix}$$

Since getting 1 in the first column would lead to repeating decimals, we multiply R1 by –1 and add to R2.

$$\begin{bmatrix} 2.3 & 1 & 52 \\ -7.7 & 0 & -38 \end{bmatrix}$$

This corresponds to $\begin{cases} 2.3x + y = 52 \\ -7.7x = -38 \end{cases}$.

From the second equation,

$x = \dfrac{-3.8}{-7.7} \approx 4.935$.

Thus, the percent of U.S. households owning black-and-white television sets was the same as the percent of U.S. households owning a microwave oven in the end of 1984 (about 4.9 years after 1980).

**b.** Solve the television equation for *y*:
$y = -2.3x + 52$. Thus, for 1980,
$y = -2.3(0) + 52 = 52$, and for 1993,
$y = -2.3(13) + 52 = 22.1$.
Solve the microwave equation for *y*:
$y = 5.4x + 14$. Thus, for 1980
$y = 5.4(0) + 14 = 14$, and for 1993,
$y = 5.4(13) + 14 = 84.2$.
In 1980, a greater percent of (and hence more) U.S. households owned black-and-white television sets. In 1993, more households owned a microwave oven. The percent owning black-and-white television sets is decreasing and the percent owning a microwave oven is increasing.
Answers may vary.

**c.** Let $y = 0$ in the television equation.

$$2.3x + y = 52$$
$$2.3x + 0 = 52$$
$$x = \frac{52}{2.3} \approx 22.6$$

According to this model, the percent of U.S. households owning a black-and-white television set will be 0% about 22.6 years after 1980, or sometime in 2002.

**39.** Answers may vary

**Section 4.5**

**Practice Exercises**

**1.** $\begin{cases} 4x \geq y \\ x + 3y \geq 6 \end{cases}$

Graph both inequalities on the same set of axes. The solution is the intersection of the solution regions.

For $4x \geq y$, the boundary line is the graph of $4x = y$. The boundary line is solid since the inequality means $4x > y$ or $4x = y$. The test point $(1, 0)$ satisfies the inequality, so we shade the half-plane that includes $(1, 0)$.

For $x + 3y \geq 6$, sketch the solid boundary line $x + 3y = 6$. The test point $(0, 0)$ does not satisfy the inequality, so shade the half-plane that does not include $(0, 0)$.

The solution of the system is the darker shaded region. This solution includes parts of both boundary lines.

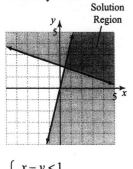

Solution Region

**2.** $\begin{cases} x - y < 1 \\ y < 4 \\ 3x + y > -3 \end{cases}$

Graph all three inequalities on the same set of axes. All boundary lines are dashed since the inequality symbols are < and >. The solution set of the system is the shaded region. The boundary

lines are not a part of the solution.

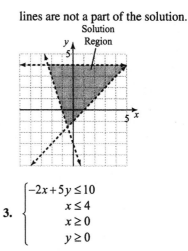

Solution Region

**3.** $\begin{cases} -2x + 5y \leq 10 \\ x \leq 4 \\ x \geq 0 \\ y \geq 0 \end{cases}$

Graph the inequalities on the same set of axes. The intersection of the inequalities is the solution region. It is the only shaded region in this graph and includes the portion of all four boundary lines that border the shaded region.

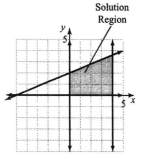

Solution Region

**Vocabulary and Readiness Check**

**1.** Two or more linear inequalities form a <u>system</u> of linear inequalities.

**2.** An ordered pair that satisfies each inequality in a system is a <u>solution</u> of the system.

**3.** The point where two boundary lines intersect is a <u>corner</u> point.

**4.** The solution region of a system of inequalities consists of the <u>intersection</u> of the solution regions of the inequalities in the system.

**Exercise Set 4.5**

**1.** $\begin{cases} y \geq x + 1 \\ y \geq 3 - x \end{cases}$

Graph both inequalities on the same set of axes. The solution is the intersection of the solution regions. The solution of the system is the darker shaded region. This solution includes parts of both boundary lines.

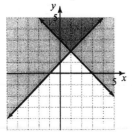

**3.** $\begin{cases} y < 3x - 4 \\ y \le x + 2 \end{cases}$

Graph both inequalities on the same set of axes. The solution is the intersection of the solution regions. The solution of the system is the darker shaded region. This solution includes the part of the solid boundary line that borders the region but not the dashed boundary line or the point where the boundary lines intersect.

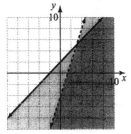

**5.** $\begin{cases} y < -2x - 2 \\ y > x + 4 \end{cases}$

Graph both inequalities on the same set of axes. The solution is the intersection of the solution regions. The solution of the system is the darker shaded region. The boundary lines are not a part of the solution.

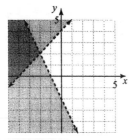

**7.** $\begin{cases} y \ge -x + 2 \\ y \le 2x + 5 \end{cases}$

Graph both inequalities on the same set of axes. The solution is the intersection of the solution regions. The solution of the system is the darker shaded region. This solution includes parts of

both boundary lines.

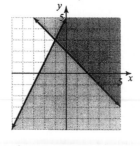

**9.** $\begin{cases} x \ge 3y \\ x + 3y \le 6 \end{cases}$

Graph both inequalities on the same set of axes. The solution is the intersection of the solution regions. The solution of the system is the darker shaded region. This solution includes parts of both boundary lines.

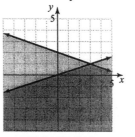

**11.** $\begin{cases} x \le 2 \\ y \ge -3 \end{cases}$

Graph both inequalities on the same set of axes. The solution is the intersection of the solution regions. The solution of the system is the darker shaded region. This solution includes parts of both boundary lines.

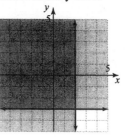

**13.** $\begin{cases} y \ge 1 \\ x < -3 \end{cases}$

Graph both inequalities on the same set of axes. The solution is the intersection of the solution regions. The solution of the system is the darker shaded region. This solution includes the part of the solid boundary line that borders the region but not the dashed boundary line or the point where the boundary lines intersect.

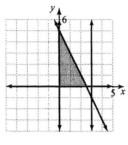

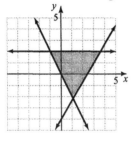

**15.** $\begin{cases} y + 2x \ge 0 \\ 5x - 3y \le 12 \\ \quad\; y \le 2 \end{cases}$

Graph all three inequalities on the same set of axes. The solution set of the system is the shaded region. The parts of the boundary lines that border the shaded region are part of the solution.

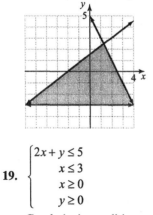

**17.** $\begin{cases} 3x - 4y \ge -6 \\ 2x + y \le 7 \\ \quad\; y \ge -3 \end{cases}$

Graph all three inequalities on the same set of axes. The solution set of the system is the shaded region. The parts of the boundary lines that border the shaded region are part of the solution.

**19.** $\begin{cases} 2x + y \le 5 \\ \quad\; x \le 3 \\ \quad\; x \ge 0 \\ \quad\; y \ge 0 \end{cases}$

Graph the inequalities on the same set of axes. The intersection of the inequalities is the solution region. It is the only shaded region in this graph and includes the portion of all four boundary lines that border the shaded region.

**21.** $\begin{cases} y < 5 \\ x > 3 \end{cases}$

Both boundary lines should be dashed. The region including (5, 0) should be shaded since (5, 0) satisfies both inequalities. The correct graph is C.

**23.** $\begin{cases} y \le 5 \\ x < 3 \end{cases}$

The boundary line $y = 5$ should be solid. The correct graph is D.

**25.** $(-3)^2 = (-3)(-3) = 9$

**27.** $\left(\dfrac{2}{3}\right)^2 = \dfrac{2}{3} \cdot \dfrac{2}{3} = \dfrac{2 \cdot 2}{3 \cdot 3} = \dfrac{4}{9}$

**29.** $\begin{aligned} (-2)^2 - (-3) + 2(-1) &= 4 - (-3) + 2(-1) \\ &= 4 - (-3) + (-2) \\ &= 4 + 3 - 2 \\ &= 7 - 2 \\ &= 5 \end{aligned}$

**31.** $\begin{aligned} 8^2 + (-13) - 4(-2) &= 64 + (-13) - 4(-2) \\ &= 64 + (-13) - (-8) \\ &= 64 - 13 + 8 \\ &= 51 + 8 \\ &= 59 \end{aligned}$

**33.** $\begin{cases} y \le 3 \\ y \ge 3 \end{cases}$

The only $y$-values that satisfy both inequalities are those that equal 3. The solution of the system is the line $y = 3$.

**35.** Answers may vary.

**Chapter 4 Vocabulary Check**

**1.** Two or more linear equations in two variables form a <u>system of equations</u>.

**2.** A <u>solution</u> of a system of two equations in two variables is an ordered pair that makes both equations true.

**3.** A <u>consistent</u> system of equations has at least one solution.

**4.** If a matrix has the same number of rows and columns, it is called a <u>square</u> matrix.

**5.** An <u>inconsistent</u> system of equations has no solution.

**6.** A <u>matrix</u> is a rectangular array of numbers.

## Chapter 4 Review

**1.** $\begin{cases} 3x+10y=1 & (1) \\ x+2y=-1 & (2) \end{cases}$

**(1)**

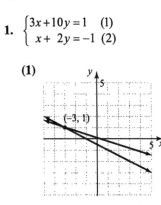

**(2)** From E2: $x=-2y-1$
Replace $x$ with $-2y-1$ in E1.
$3(-2y-1)+10y=1$
$-6y-3+10y=1$
$4y=4$
$y=1$
Replace $y$ with 1 in the equation $x=-2y-1$.
$x=-2(1)-1=-3$
The solution is $(-3, 1)$.

**(3)** Multiply E2 by $-3$ and add to E1.
$3x+10y=1$
$\underline{-3x-6y=3}$
$\phantom{3x+10}4y=4$
$\phantom{3x+10}y=1$
Replace $y$ with 1 in E2.
$x+2(1)=-1$
$x+2=-1$
$x=-3$
The solution is $(-3, 1)$.

**2.** $\begin{cases} y=\dfrac{1}{2}x+\dfrac{2}{3} & (1) \\ 4x+6y=4 & (2) \end{cases}$

**(1)**

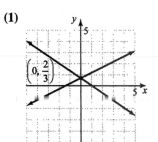

**(2)** Replace $y$ with $\dfrac{1}{2}x+\dfrac{2}{3}$ in E2.

$4x+6\left(\dfrac{1}{2}x+\dfrac{2}{3}\right)=4$

$4x+3x+4=4$

$x=0$

Replace $x$ with 0 in E1.

$y=\dfrac{1}{2}(0)+\dfrac{2}{3}=\dfrac{2}{3}$

The solution is $\left(0,\dfrac{2}{3}\right)$.

**(3)** Rewrite the system: $\begin{cases} -\dfrac{1}{2}x+y=\dfrac{2}{3} \\ 4x+6y=4 \end{cases}$.

Multiply the first equation by $-6$.

$\begin{cases} 3x-6y=-4 \\ 4x+6y=4 \end{cases}$

Add these equations.
$7x=0$
$x=0$
Replace $x$ with 0 in second equation.
$4(0)+6y=4$
$6y=4$
$y=\dfrac{4}{6}=\dfrac{2}{3}$

The solution is $\left(0,\dfrac{2}{3}\right)$.

**3.** $\begin{cases} 2x-4y=22 & (1) \\ 5x-10y=15 & (2) \end{cases}$

**(1)**

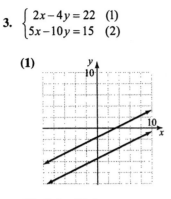

**(2)** Solve E1 for $x$.

$2x-4y=22$

$2x=4y+22$

$x=2y+11$

Replace $x$ with $2y+11$ in E2.

$5(2y+11)-10y=15$

$10y+55-10y=15$

$55=15$ False

This is an inconsistent system. The solution is $\varnothing$.

**(3)** Multiply E1 by 5 and E2 by –2.

$\begin{cases} 10x-20y=110 \\ -10x+20y=-30 \end{cases}$

Add these equations.

$10x-20y=110$

$\underline{-10x+20y=-30}$

$\phantom{10x-20y=}0=80$ False

This is an inconsistent system. The solution is $\varnothing$.

**4.** $\begin{cases} 3x-6y=12 & (1) \\ 2y=x-4 & (2) \end{cases}$

**(1)**

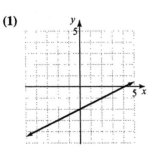

**(2)** Solve E2 for $x$.

$x=2y+4$

Replace $x$ with $2y+4$ in E1.

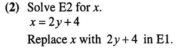

$3(2y+4)-6y=12$

$6y+12-6y=12$

$\phantom{6y+}12=12$ True

This is a dependent system. The solution is $\{(x,y)|3x-6y=12\}$.

**(3)** $\begin{cases} 3x-6y=12 & (1) \\ -x+2y=-4 & (2) \end{cases}$

Multiply E2 by 3.

$\begin{cases} 3x-6y=12 \\ -3x+6y=-12 \end{cases}$

Add these equations.

$3x-6y=12$

$\underline{-3x+6y=-12}$

$\phantom{3x-6y=12}0=0$ True

This is a dependent system. The solution is $\{(x,y)|3x-6y=12\}$.

**5.** $\begin{cases} \dfrac{1}{2}x-\dfrac{3}{4}y=-\dfrac{1}{2} & (1) \\ \dfrac{1}{8}x+\dfrac{3}{4}y=\dfrac{19}{8} & (2) \end{cases}$

**(1)**

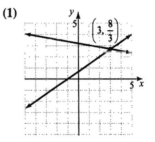

**(2)** Clear fractions by multiplying E1 by 4 and E2 by 8.

$\begin{cases} 2x-3y=-2 & (1) \\ x+6y=19 & (2) \end{cases}$

Solve the new E2 for $x$.

$x=-6y+19$

Replace $x$ with $-6y+19$ in new E1.

$2(-6y+19)-3y=-2$

$-12y+38-3y=-2$

$\phantom{-12y+38}-15y=-40$

$y=\dfrac{-40}{-15}=\dfrac{8}{3}$

Replace $y$ with $\dfrac{8}{3}$ in the equation

$x=-6y+19$.

$$x = -6\left(\frac{8}{3}\right) + 19$$
$$x = -16 + 19$$
$$x = 3$$

The solution is $\left(3, \frac{8}{3}\right)$.

**(3)** Add the equations.

$$\frac{1}{2}x - \frac{3}{4}y = -\frac{1}{2}$$
$$\frac{1}{8}x + \frac{3}{4}y = \frac{19}{8}$$
$$\overline{\frac{5}{8}x \qquad = \frac{15}{8}}$$
$$5x = 15$$
$$x = 3$$

Replace $x$ with 3 in E1.

$$\frac{1}{2}(3) - \frac{3}{4}y = -\frac{1}{2}$$
$$-\frac{3}{4}y = -2$$
$$-3y = -8$$
$$y = \frac{8}{3}$$

The solution is $\left(3, \frac{8}{3}\right)$.

**6.** $\begin{cases} y = 32x & (1) \\ y = 15x + 25,500 & (2) \end{cases}$

Multiply E1 by –1 and add to E2.

$$-y = -32$$
$$\underline{y = 15x + 25,500}$$
$$0 = -17x + 25,500$$
$$17x = 25,500$$
$$x = 1500$$

Replace $x$ with 1500 in E1.
$$y = 32(1500) = 48,000$$

The number of backpacks that the company must sell is 1500.

**7.** $\begin{cases} x + \quad z = 4 & (1) \\ 2x - y \quad = 4 & (2) \\ x + y - z = 0 & (3) \end{cases}$

Adding E2 and E3 gives $3x - z = 4$ (4)
Adding E1 and E4 gives $4x = 8$ or $x = 2$
Replace $x$ with 2 in E1.
$$2 + z = 4$$
$$z = 2$$
Replace $x$ with 2 and $z$ with 2 in E3.

$$2 + y - 2 = 0$$
$$y = 0$$
The solution is (2, 0, 2).

**8.** $\begin{cases} 2x + 5y \quad = 4 & (1) \\ x - 5y + z = -1 & (2) \\ 4x \quad - z = 11 & (3) \end{cases}$

Add E2 and E3.
$$5x - 5y = 10 \quad (4)$$
Add E1 and E4.
$$7x = 14$$
$$x = 2$$
Replace $x$ with 2 in E1.
$$2(2) + 5y = 4$$
$$4 + 5y = 4$$
$$5y = 0$$
$$y = 0$$
Replace $x$ with 2 in E3.
$$4(2) - z = 11$$
$$8 - z = 11$$
$$z = -3$$
The solution is (2, 0, –3).

**9.** $\begin{cases} 4y + 2z = 5 & (1) \\ 2x + 8y \quad = 5 & (2) \\ 6x \quad + 4z = 1 & (3) \end{cases}$

Multiply E1 by –2 and add to E2.
$$-8y - 4z = -10$$
$$\underline{2x + 8y \qquad = 5}$$
$$2x \qquad - 4z = -5 \quad (4)$$
Add E3 and E4.
$$8x = -4$$
$$x = -\frac{1}{2}$$

Replace $x$ with $-\frac{1}{2}$ in E2.
$$2\left(-\frac{1}{2}\right) + 8y = 5$$
$$-1 + 8y = 5$$
$$8y = 6$$
$$y = \frac{3}{4}$$

Replace $x$ with $-\frac{1}{2}$ in E3.

$$6\left(-\frac{1}{2}\right) + 4z = 1$$
$$-3 + 4z = 1$$
$$4z = 4$$
$$z = 1$$

The solution is $\left(-\frac{1}{2}, \frac{3}{4}, 1\right)$.

**10.** $\begin{cases} 5x + 7y \quad\quad = 9 \quad (1) \\ \quad\quad 14y - z = 28 \quad (2) \\ 4x \quad\quad + 2z = -4 \quad (3) \end{cases}$

Dividing E3 by 2 gives $2x + z = -2$.
Add this equation to E2.
$$2x \quad\quad + z = -2$$
$$\underline{\quad 14y - z = 28 \quad}$$
$$2x + 14y \quad = 26 \text{ or } x + 7y = 13 \quad (4)$$
Multiply E4 by $-1$ and add to E1.
$$-x - 7y = -13$$
$$\underline{5x + 7y = 9 \quad}$$
$$4x \quad\quad = -4$$
$$x = -1$$
Replace $x$ with $-1$ in E4.
$$-1 + 7y = 13$$
$$7y = 14$$
$$y = 2$$
Replace $x$ with $-1$ in E3.
$$4(-1) + 2z = -4$$
$$-4 + 2z = -4$$
$$2z = 0$$
$$z = 0$$
The solution is $(-1, 2, 0)$.

**11.** $\begin{cases} 3x - 2y + 2z = 5 \quad (1) \\ -x + 6y + z = 4 \quad (2) \\ 3x + 14y + 7z = 20 \quad (3) \end{cases}$

Multiply E2 by 3 and add to E1.
$$3x - 2y + 2z = 5$$
$$\underline{-3x + 18y + 3z = 12 \quad}$$
$$16y + 5z = 17 \quad (4)$$
Multiply E3 by $-1$ and add to E1.
$$3x - 2y + 2z = 5$$
$$\underline{-3x - 14y - 7z = -20 \quad}$$
$$-16y - 5z = -15 \quad (5)$$
Add E4 and E5.
$$16y + 5z = 17$$
$$\underline{-16y - 5z = -15 \quad}$$
$$0 = 2 \quad \text{False}$$
The system is inconsistent. The solution is $\varnothing$.

**12.** $\begin{cases} x + 2y + 3z = 11 \quad (1) \\ \quad\quad y + 2z = 3 \quad (2) \\ 2x \quad\quad + 2z = 10 \quad (3) \end{cases}$

Multiply E2 by $-2$ and add to E1.
$$x + 2y + 3z = 11$$
$$\underline{-2y - 4z = -6 \quad}$$
$$x \quad\quad - z = 5 \quad (4)$$
Multiply E4 by 2 and add to E3.
$$2x + 2z = 10$$
$$\underline{2x - 2z = 10 \quad}$$
$$4x \quad\quad = 20$$
$$x = 5$$
Replace $x$ with 5 in E3.
$$2(5) + 2z = 10$$
$$10 + 2z = 10$$
$$2z = 0$$
$$z = 0$$
Replace $z$ with 0 in E2.
$$y + 2(0) = 3$$
$$y + 0 = 3$$
$$y = 3$$
The solution is $(5, 3, 0)$.

**13.** $\begin{cases} 7x - 3y + 2z = 0 \quad (1) \\ 4x - 4y - z = 2 \quad (2) \\ 5x + 2y + 3z = 1 \quad (3) \end{cases}$

Multiply E2 by 2 and add to E1.
$$7x - 3y + 2z = 0$$
$$\underline{8x - 8y - 2z = 4 \quad}$$
$$15x - 11y \quad = 4 \quad (4)$$
Multiply E2 by 3 and add to E3.
$$12x - 12y - 3z = 6$$
$$\underline{5x + 2y + 3z = 1 \quad}$$
$$17x - 10y \quad = 7 \quad (5)$$
Solve the new system.
$$\begin{cases} 15x - 11y = 4 \quad (4) \\ 17x - 10y = 7 \quad (5) \end{cases}$$
Multiply E4 by $-10$, multiply E5 by 11, and add.
$$-150x + 110y = -40$$
$$\underline{187x - 110y = 77 \quad}$$
$$37x \quad\quad = 37$$
$$x = 1$$
Replace $x$ with 1 in E4.
$$15(1) - 11y = 4$$
$$15 - 11y = 4$$
$$-11y = -11$$
$$y = 1$$
Replace $x$ with 1 and $y$ with 1 in E1.

$$7(1) - 3(1) + 2z = 0$$
$$4 + 2z = 0$$
$$2z = -4$$
$$z = -2$$

The solution is $(1, 1, -2)$.

**14.** $\begin{cases} x - 3y - 5z = -5 & (1) \\ 4x - 2y + 3z = 13 & (2) \\ 5x + 3y + 4z = 22 & (3) \end{cases}$

Multiply E1 by $-4$ and add to E2.
$$-4x + 12y + 20z = 20$$
$$\underline{4x - 2y + 3z = 13}$$
$$10y + 23z = 33 \quad (4)$$

Multiply E1 by $-5$ and add to E3.
$$-5x + 15y + 25z = 25$$
$$\underline{5x + 3y + 4z = 22}$$
$$18y + 29z = 47 \quad (5)$$

Solve the new system.
$$\begin{cases} 10y + 23z = 33 & (4) \\ 18y + 29z = 47 & (5) \end{cases}$$

Multiply E4 by 9, multiply E5 by $-5$ and add.
$$90y + 207z = 297$$
$$\underline{-90y - 145z = -235}$$
$$62z = 62$$
$$z = 1$$

Replace $z$ with 1 in E4.
$$10y + 23(1) = 33$$
$$10y = 10$$
$$y = 1$$

Replace $y$ with 1 and $z$ with 1 in E1.
$$x - 3(1) - 5(1) = -5$$
$$x - 8 = -5$$
$$x = 3$$

The solution is $(3, 1, 1)$.

**15.** Let $x$ = the first number, $y$ = the second number, and $z$ = the third number.
$$\begin{cases} x + y + z = 98 & (1) \\ x + y = z + 2 & (2) \\ y = 4x & (3) \end{cases}$$

Replace $y$ with $4x$ in E1 and E2.
$$x + 4x + z = 98$$
$$5x + z = 98 \quad (4)$$
$$x + 4x = z + 2$$
$$5x - z = 2 \quad (5)$$

Add E4 and E5.

$$5x + z = 98$$
$$\underline{5x - z = 2}$$
$$10x \quad = 100$$
$$x = 10$$

Replace $x$ with 10 in E3.
$$y = 4(10) = 40$$

Replace $x$ with 10 and $y$ with 40 in E2.
$$10 + 40 = z + 2$$
$$50 = z + 2$$
$$48 = z$$

The numbers are 10, 40, and 48.

**16.** Let $x$ = the first number and $y$ = the second number.
$$\begin{cases} x = 3y & (1) \\ 2(x + y) = 168 & (2) \end{cases}$$

Replace $x$ with $3y$ in E2.
$$2(3y + y) = 168$$
$$8y = 168$$
$$y = 21$$

Replace $y$ with 21 in E1.
$$x = 3(21) = 63$$

The numbers are 63 and 21.

**17.** Let $x$ = speed of first car and $y$ = speed of the second car.
$$\begin{cases} 4x + 4y = 492 & (1) \\ y = x + 7 & (2) \end{cases}$$

Replace $y$ with $x + 7$ in E1.
$$4x + 4(x + 7) = 492$$
$$8x + 28 = 492$$
$$8x = 464$$
$$x = 58$$

Replace $x$ with 58 in E2.
$$y = 58 + 7 = 65$$

The cars are going 58 and 65 miles per hour.

**18.** Let $w$ = the width of the foundation and $l$ = the length of the foundation.
$$\begin{cases} l = 3w & (1) \\ 2w + 2l = 296 & (2) \end{cases}$$

Replace $l$ with $3w$ in E2.
$$2w + 2(3w) = 296$$
$$2w + 6w = 296$$
$$8w = 296$$
$$w = 37$$

Replace $w$ with 37 in E1.
$$l = 3(37) = 111$$

The foundation is 37 feet wide and 111 feet long.

**19.** Let $x$ = liters of 10% solution and
$y$ = liters of 60% solution.
$$\begin{cases} x+ \quad y = 50 \quad (1) \\ 0.10x + 0.60y = 0.40(50) \quad (2) \end{cases}$$
Solve E1 for $y$.
$y = 50 - x$
Replace $y$ with $50 - x$ in E2.
$$0.10x + 0.60(50-x) = 0.40(50)$$
$$10[0.10x + 0.60(50-x)] = 10[0.40(50)]$$
$$x + 6(50-x) = 4(50)$$
$$x + 300 - 6x = 200$$
$$-5x = -100$$
$$x = 20$$
Replace $x$ with 20 in the equation $y = 50 - x$.
$y = 50 - 20 = 30$
He should use 20 liters of 10% solution and
30 liters of 60% solution.

**20.** Let $c$ = pounds of chocolate used,
$n$ = pounds of nuts used, and
$r$ = pounds of raisins used.
$$\begin{cases} r = 2n \quad (1) \\ c + n + r = 45 \quad (2) \\ 3.00c + 2.70n + 2.25r = 2.80(45) \quad (3) \end{cases}$$
Replace $r$ with $2n$ in E2.
$c + n + 2n = 45$
$c + 3n = 45$
$c = -3n + 45$
Replace $r$ with $2n$ and $c$ with $-3n + 45$ in E3.
$$3.00(-3n+45) + 2.70n + 2.25(2n) = 126$$
$$-9n + 135 + 2.7n + 4.5n = 126$$
$$-1.8n + 135 = 126$$
$$-1.8n = -9$$
$$n = 5$$
Replace $n$ with 5 in E1.
$r = 2(5) = 10$
Replace $n$ with 5 and $r$ with 10 in E2.
$c + 5 + 10 = 45$
$c + 15 = 45$
$c = 30$
She should use 30 pounds of creme-filled
chocolates, 5 pounds of chocolate-covered nuts,
and 10 pounds of chocolate-covered raisins.

**21.** Let $x$ = the number of pennies,
$y$ = the number of nickels, and
$z$ = the number dimes.
$$\begin{cases} x + y + z = 53 \quad (1) \\ 0.01x + 0.05y + 0.10z = 2.77 \quad (2) \\ y = z + 4 \quad (3) \end{cases}$$

Clear the decimals from E2 by multiplying by
100.
$x + 5y + 10z = 277$ (4)
Replace $y$ with $z + 4$ in E1.
$x + z + 4 + z = 53$
$x + 2z = 49$ (5)
Replace $y$ with $z + 4$ in E4.
$x + 5(z+4) + 10z = 277$
$x + 15z = 257$ (6)
Solve the new system.
$$\begin{cases} x + 2z = 49 \quad (5) \\ x + 15z = 257 \quad (6) \end{cases}$$
Multiply E5 by –1 and add to E6.
$$\begin{array}{r} -x - 2z = -49 \\ x + 15z = 257 \\ \hline 13z = 208 \\ z = 16 \end{array}$$
Replace $z$ with 16 in E3.
$x + 2(16) = 49$
$x + 32 = 49$
$x = 17$
Replace $z$ with 16 in E3.
$y = 16 + 4 = 20$
He has 17 pennies, 20 nickels, and 16 dimes in
his jar.

**22.** Let $l$ = rate of interest on the larger investment
and $s$ = the rate of interest on the smaller
investment, both expressed as decimals.
$$\begin{cases} 10,000l + 4000s = 1250 \quad (1) \\ l = s + 0.02 \quad (2) \end{cases}$$
Replace $l$ with $s + 0.02$ in E1.
$$10,000(s + 0.02) + 4000s = 1250$$
$$10,000s + 200 + 4000s = 1250$$
$$14,000s = 1050$$
$$s = \frac{1050}{14,000} = 0.075$$
and $l = 0.075 + 0.02 = 0.095$.
The interest rate on the larger investment is 9.5%
and the rate on the smaller investment is 7.5%.

**23.** Let $x$ = length of the equal side and
$y$ = length of the third side.
$$\begin{cases} 2x + y = 73 \quad (1) \\ y = x + 7 \quad (2) \end{cases}$$
Replace $y$ with $x + 7$ in E1.
$2x + x + 7 = 73$
$3x = 66$
$x = 22$
Replace $x$ with 22 in E2.

$y = 22 + 7 = 29$

Two sides of the triangle have length 22 cm and the third side has length 29 cm.

24. Let $f$ = the first number, $s$ = the second number, and $t$ = the third number.

$$\begin{cases} f + s + t = 295 & (1) \\ f = s + 5 & (2) \\ f = 2t & (3) \end{cases}$$

Solve E2 for $s$ and E3 for $t$.

$s = f - 5$

$t = \dfrac{f}{2}$

Replace $s$ with $f - 5$ and $t$ with $\dfrac{f}{2}$ in E1.

$$f + f - 5 + \frac{f}{2} = 295$$

$$\frac{5}{2}f = 300$$

$$f = 120$$

Replace $f$ with 300 in the equation $s = f - 5$.

$s = 120 - 5 = 115$

Replace $f$ with 120 the equation $\dfrac{f}{2}$.

$$t = \frac{120}{2} = 60$$

The first number is 120, the second number is 115, and the third number is 60.

25. $\begin{cases} 3x + 10y = 1 \\ x + 2y = -1 \end{cases}$

$\begin{bmatrix} 3 & 10 & | & 1 \\ 1 & 2 & | & -1 \end{bmatrix}$

Interchange R1 and R2.

$\begin{bmatrix} 1 & 2 & | & -1 \\ 3 & 10 & | & 1 \end{bmatrix}$

Multiply R1 by $-3$ and add to R2.

$\begin{bmatrix} 1 & 2 & | & -1 \\ 0 & 4 & | & 4 \end{bmatrix}$

Divide R2 by 4.

$\begin{bmatrix} 1 & 2 & | & -1 \\ 0 & 1 & | & 1 \end{bmatrix}$

This corresponds to $\begin{cases} x + 2y = -1 \\ y = 1 \end{cases}$.

$x + 2(1) = -1$

$x = -3$

The solution is $(-3, 1)$.

26. $\begin{cases} 3x - 6y = 12 \\ 2y = x - 4 \end{cases}$, or $\begin{cases} 3x - 6y = 12 \\ -x + 2y = -4 \end{cases}$

$\begin{bmatrix} 3 & -6 & | & 12 \\ -1 & 2 & | & -4 \end{bmatrix}$

Divide R1 by 3.

$\begin{bmatrix} 1 & -2 & | & 4 \\ -1 & 2 & | & -4 \end{bmatrix}$

Add R1 to R2.

$\begin{bmatrix} 1 & -2 & | & 4 \\ 0 & 0 & | & 0 \end{bmatrix}$

This corresponds to $\begin{cases} x - 2y = 4 \\ 0 = 0 \end{cases}$.

This is a dependent system. The solution is $\{(x, y) | x - 2y = 4\}$.

27. $\begin{cases} 3x - 2y = -8 \\ 6x + 5y = 11 \end{cases}$

$\begin{bmatrix} 3 & -2 & | & -8 \\ 6 & 5 & | & 11 \end{bmatrix}$

Divide R1 by 3.

$\begin{bmatrix} 1 & -\frac{2}{3} & | & -\frac{8}{3} \\ 6 & 5 & | & 11 \end{bmatrix}$

Multiply R1 by $-6$ and add to R2.

$\begin{bmatrix} 1 & -\frac{2}{3} & | & -\frac{8}{3} \\ 0 & 9 & | & 27 \end{bmatrix}$

Divide R2 by 9.

$\begin{bmatrix} 1 & -\frac{2}{3} & | & -\frac{8}{3} \\ 0 & 1 & | & 3 \end{bmatrix}$

This corresponds to $\begin{cases} x - \dfrac{2}{3}y = -\dfrac{8}{3} \\ y = 3 \end{cases}$.

$$x - \frac{2}{3}(3) = -\frac{8}{3}$$

$$x - 2 = -\frac{8}{3}$$

$$x = -\frac{2}{3}$$

The solution is $\left(-\dfrac{2}{3}, 3\right)$.

28. $\begin{cases} 6x - 6y = -5 \\ 10x - 2y = 1 \end{cases}$

$\begin{bmatrix} 6 & -6 & | & -5 \\ 10 & -2 & | & 1 \end{bmatrix}$

Divide R1 by 6.

$$\begin{bmatrix} 1 & -1 & \vline & -\frac{5}{6} \\ 10 & -2 & \vline & 1 \end{bmatrix}$$

Multiply R1 by −10 and add to R2.

$$\begin{bmatrix} 1 & -1 & \vline & -\frac{5}{6} \\ 0 & 8 & \vline & \frac{28}{3} \end{bmatrix}$$

Divide R2 by 8.

$$\begin{bmatrix} 1 & -1 & \vline & -\frac{5}{6} \\ 0 & 1 & \vline & \frac{7}{6} \end{bmatrix}$$

Add R2 to R1.

$$\begin{bmatrix} 1 & 0 & \vline & \frac{1}{3} \\ 0 & 1 & \vline & \frac{7}{6} \end{bmatrix}$$

This corresponds to $\begin{cases} x = \dfrac{1}{3} \\ y = \dfrac{7}{6} \end{cases}$. The solution is

$\left( \dfrac{1}{3}, \dfrac{7}{6} \right)$.

**29.** $\begin{cases} 3x - 6y = 0 \\ 2x + 4y = 5 \end{cases}$

$$\begin{bmatrix} 3 & -6 & \vline & 0 \\ 2 & 4 & \vline & 5 \end{bmatrix}$$

Divide R1 by 3.

$$\begin{bmatrix} 1 & -2 & \vline & 0 \\ 2 & 4 & \vline & 5 \end{bmatrix}$$

Multiply R1 by −2 and add to R2.

$$\begin{bmatrix} 1 & -2 & \vline & 0 \\ 0 & 8 & \vline & 5 \end{bmatrix}$$

Divide R2 by 8.

$$\begin{bmatrix} 1 & -2 & \vline & 0 \\ 0 & 1 & \vline & \frac{5}{8} \end{bmatrix}$$

This corresponds to $\begin{cases} x - 2y = 0 \\ y = \dfrac{5}{8} \end{cases}$.

$x - 2\left( \dfrac{5}{8} \right) = 0$

$x - \dfrac{5}{4} = 0$

$x = \dfrac{5}{4}$

The solution is $\left( \dfrac{5}{4}, \dfrac{5}{8} \right)$.

**30.** $\begin{cases} 5x - 3y = 10 \\ -2x + y = -1 \end{cases}$

$$\begin{bmatrix} 5 & -3 & \vline & 10 \\ -2 & 1 & \vline & -1 \end{bmatrix}$$

Divide R1 by 5.

$$\begin{bmatrix} 1 & -\frac{3}{5} & \vline & 2 \\ -2 & 1 & \vline & -1 \end{bmatrix}$$

Multiply R1 by 2 and add to R2.

$$\begin{bmatrix} 1 & -\frac{3}{5} & \vline & 2 \\ 0 & -\frac{1}{5} & \vline & 3 \end{bmatrix}$$

Multiply R2 by −5.

$$\begin{bmatrix} 1 & -\frac{3}{5} & \vline & 2 \\ 0 & 1 & \vline & -15 \end{bmatrix}$$

This corresponds to $\begin{cases} x - \dfrac{3}{5}y = 2 \\ y = -15 \end{cases}$.

$x - \dfrac{3}{5}(-15) = 2$

$x + 9 = 2$

$x = -7$

The solution is $(-7, -15)$.

**31.** $\begin{cases} 0.2x - 0.3y = -0.7 \\ 0.5x + 0.3y = 1.4 \end{cases}$

$$\begin{bmatrix} 0.2 & -0.3 & \vline & -0.7 \\ 0.5 & 0.3 & \vline & 1.4 \end{bmatrix}$$

Multiply both rows by 10 to clear decimals.

$$\begin{bmatrix} 2 & -3 & \vline & -7 \\ 5 & 3 & \vline & 14 \end{bmatrix}$$

Divide R1 by 2.

$$\begin{bmatrix} 1 & -\frac{3}{2} & \vline & -\frac{7}{2} \\ 5 & 3 & \vline & 14 \end{bmatrix}$$

Multiply R1 by −5 and add to R2.

$$\begin{bmatrix} 1 & -\frac{3}{2} & \vline & -\frac{7}{2} \\ 0 & \frac{21}{2} & \vline & \frac{63}{2} \end{bmatrix}$$

Multiply R2 by $\dfrac{2}{21}$.

$$\begin{bmatrix} 1 & -\frac{3}{2} & \vline & -\frac{7}{2} \\ 0 & 1 & \vline & 3 \end{bmatrix}$$

This corresponds to $\begin{cases} x - \dfrac{3}{2}y = -\dfrac{7}{2} \\ y = 3 \end{cases}$.

$$x - \frac{3}{2}(3) = -\frac{7}{2}$$

$$x - \frac{9}{2} = -\frac{7}{2}$$

$$x = 1$$

The solution is (1, 3).

**32.** $\begin{cases} 3x + 2y = 8 \\ 3x - y = 5 \end{cases}$

$$\begin{bmatrix} 3 & 2 & | & 8 \\ 3 & -1 & | & 5 \end{bmatrix}$$

Divide R1 by 3.

$$\begin{bmatrix} 1 & \frac{2}{3} & | & \frac{8}{3} \\ 3 & -1 & | & 5 \end{bmatrix}$$

Multiply R1 by −3 and add to R2.

$$\begin{bmatrix} 1 & \frac{2}{3} & | & \frac{8}{3} \\ 0 & -3 & | & -3 \end{bmatrix}$$

Divide R2 by −3.

$$\begin{bmatrix} 1 & \frac{2}{3} & | & \frac{8}{3} \\ 0 & 1 & | & 1 \end{bmatrix}$$

This corresponds to $\begin{cases} x + \frac{2}{3}y = \frac{8}{3} \\ y = 1 \end{cases}$.

$$x + \frac{2}{3}(1) = \frac{8}{3}$$

$$x = 2$$

The solution is (2, 1).

**33.** $\begin{cases} x \quad + z = 4 \\ 2x - y \quad = 0 \\ x + y - z = 0 \end{cases}$

$$\begin{bmatrix} 1 & 0 & 1 & | & 4 \\ 2 & -1 & 0 & | & 0 \\ 1 & 1 & -1 & | & 0 \end{bmatrix}$$

Multiply R1 by −2 and add to R2. Multiply R1 by −1 and add to R3.

$$\begin{bmatrix} 1 & 0 & 1 & | & 4 \\ 0 & -1 & -2 & | & -8 \\ 0 & 1 & -2 & | & -4 \end{bmatrix}$$

Multiply R2 by −1.

$$\begin{bmatrix} 1 & 0 & 1 & | & 4 \\ 0 & 1 & 2 & | & 8 \\ 0 & 1 & -2 & | & -4 \end{bmatrix}$$

Multiply R2 by −1 and add to R3.

$$\begin{bmatrix} 1 & 0 & 1 & | & 4 \\ 0 & 1 & 2 & | & 8 \\ 0 & 0 & -4 & | & -12 \end{bmatrix}$$

Divide R3 by −4.

$$\begin{bmatrix} 1 & 0 & 1 & | & 4 \\ 0 & 1 & 2 & | & 8 \\ 0 & 0 & 1 & | & 3 \end{bmatrix}$$

This corresponds to $\begin{cases} x + z = 4 \\ y + 2z = 8 \\ z = 3 \end{cases}$.

$$y + 2(3) = 8$$

$$y + 6 = 8$$

$$y = 2$$

$$x + 3 = 4$$

$$x = 1$$

The solution is (1, 2, 3).

**34.** $\begin{cases} 2x + 5y \quad = 4 \\ x - 5y + z = -1 \\ 4x \quad - z = 11 \end{cases}$

$$\begin{bmatrix} 2 & 5 & 0 & | & 4 \\ 1 & -5 & 1 & | & -1 \\ 4 & 0 & -1 & | & 11 \end{bmatrix}$$

Interchange R1 and R2.

$$\begin{bmatrix} 1 & -5 & 1 & | & -1 \\ 2 & 5 & 0 & | & 4 \\ 4 & 0 & -1 & | & 11 \end{bmatrix}$$

Multiply R1 by −2 and add to R2. Multiply R1 by −4 and add to R3.

$$\begin{bmatrix} 1 & -5 & 1 & | & -1 \\ 0 & 15 & -2 & | & 6 \\ 0 & 20 & -5 & | & 15 \end{bmatrix}$$

Divide R2 by 15.

$$\begin{bmatrix} 1 & -5 & 1 & | & -1 \\ 0 & 1 & -\frac{2}{15} & | & \frac{2}{5} \\ 0 & 20 & -5 & | & 15 \end{bmatrix}$$

Multiply R2 by −20 and add to R3.

$$\begin{bmatrix} 1 & -5 & 1 & | & -1 \\ 0 & 1 & -\frac{2}{15} & | & \frac{2}{5} \\ 0 & 0 & -\frac{7}{3} & | & 7 \end{bmatrix}$$

Multiply R3 by $-\frac{3}{7}$.

$$\begin{bmatrix} 1 & -5 & 1 & | & -1 \\ 0 & 1 & -\frac{2}{15} & | & \frac{2}{5} \\ 0 & 0 & 1 & | & -3 \end{bmatrix}$$

This corresponds to $\begin{cases} x - 5y + z = -1 \\ y - \frac{2}{15}z = \frac{2}{5} \\ z = -3 \end{cases}$.

$$y - \frac{2}{15}(-3) = \frac{2}{5}$$
$$y + \frac{2}{5} = \frac{2}{5}$$
$$y = 0$$
$$x - 5(0) + (-3) = -1$$
$$x - 3 = -1$$
$$x = 2$$

The solution is $(2, 0, -3)$.

**35.** $\begin{cases} 3x - y \phantom{+2z} = 11 \\ x \phantom{-y} + 2z = 13 \\ \phantom{x} y - z = -7 \end{cases}$

$$\begin{bmatrix} 3 & -1 & 0 & | & 11 \\ 1 & 0 & 2 & | & 13 \\ 0 & 1 & -1 & | & -7 \end{bmatrix}$$

Interchange R1 and R2.

$$\begin{bmatrix} 1 & 0 & 2 & | & 13 \\ 3 & -1 & 0 & | & 11 \\ 0 & 1 & -1 & | & -7 \end{bmatrix}$$

Interchange R2 and R3.

$$\begin{bmatrix} 1 & 0 & 2 & | & 13 \\ 0 & 1 & -1 & | & -7 \\ 3 & -1 & 0 & | & 11 \end{bmatrix}$$

Multiply R1 by $-3$ and add to R3.

$$\begin{bmatrix} 1 & 0 & 2 & | & 13 \\ 0 & 1 & -1 & | & -7 \\ 0 & -1 & -6 & | & -28 \end{bmatrix}$$

Add R2 to R3.

$$\begin{bmatrix} 1 & 0 & 2 & | & 13 \\ 0 & 1 & -1 & | & -7 \\ 0 & 0 & -7 & | & -35 \end{bmatrix}$$

Divide R3 by $-7$.

$$\begin{bmatrix} 1 & 0 & 2 & | & 13 \\ 0 & 1 & -1 & | & -7 \\ 0 & 0 & 1 & | & 5 \end{bmatrix}$$

This corresponds to $\begin{cases} x + 2z = 13 \\ y - z = -7. \\ z = 5 \end{cases}$

$$y - 5 = -7$$
$$y = -2$$
$$x + 2(5) = 13$$
$$x = 3$$

The solution is $(3, -2, 5)$.

**36.** $\begin{cases} 5x + 7y + 3z = 9 \\ 14y - z = 28 \\ 4x \phantom{+7y} + 2z = -4 \end{cases}$

$$\begin{bmatrix} 5 & 7 & 3 & | & 9 \\ 0 & 14 & -1 & | & 28 \\ 4 & 0 & 2 & | & -4 \end{bmatrix}$$

Divide R1 by 5.

$$\begin{bmatrix} 1 & \frac{7}{5} & \frac{3}{5} & | & \frac{9}{5} \\ 0 & 14 & -1 & | & 28 \\ 4 & 0 & 2 & | & -4 \end{bmatrix}$$

Multiply R1 by $-4$ and add to R3.

$$\begin{bmatrix} 1 & \frac{7}{5} & \frac{3}{5} & | & \frac{9}{5} \\ 0 & 14 & -1 & | & 28 \\ 0 & -\frac{28}{5} & -\frac{2}{5} & | & -\frac{56}{5} \end{bmatrix}$$

Divide R2 by 14.

$$\begin{bmatrix} 1 & \frac{7}{5} & \frac{3}{5} & | & \frac{9}{5} \\ 0 & 1 & -\frac{1}{14} & | & 2 \\ 0 & -\frac{28}{5} & -\frac{2}{5} & | & -\frac{56}{5} \end{bmatrix}$$

Multiply R2 by $\dfrac{28}{5}$ and add to R3.

$$\begin{bmatrix} 1 & \frac{7}{5} & \frac{3}{5} & | & \frac{9}{5} \\ 0 & 1 & -\frac{1}{14} & | & 2 \\ 0 & 0 & -\frac{4}{5} & | & 0 \end{bmatrix}$$

Multiply R3 by $-\dfrac{5}{4}$.

$$\begin{bmatrix} 1 & \frac{7}{5} & \frac{3}{5} & | & \frac{9}{5} \\ 0 & 1 & -\frac{1}{14} & | & 2 \\ 0 & 0 & 1 & | & 0 \end{bmatrix}$$

This corresponds to $\begin{cases} x + \dfrac{7}{5}y + \dfrac{3}{5}z = \dfrac{9}{5} \\ y - \dfrac{1}{14}z = 2. \\ z = 0 \end{cases}$

$$y - \frac{1}{14}(0) = 2$$
$$y = 2$$
$$x + \frac{7}{5}(2) + \frac{3}{5}(0) = \frac{9}{5}$$
$$x + \frac{14}{5} = \frac{9}{5}$$
$$x = -1$$

The solution is $(-1, 2, 0)$.

**37.** $\begin{cases} 7x - 3y + 2z = 0 \\ 4x - 4y - z = 2 \\ 5x + 2y + 3z = 1 \end{cases}$

$$\begin{bmatrix} 7 & -3 & 2 & | & 0 \\ 4 & -4 & -1 & | & 2 \\ 5 & 2 & 3 & | & 1 \end{bmatrix}$$

Interchange R1 and R2.

$$\begin{bmatrix} 4 & -4 & -1 & | & 2 \\ 7 & -3 & 2 & | & 0 \\ 5 & 2 & 3 & | & 1 \end{bmatrix}$$

Divide R1 by 4.

$$\begin{bmatrix} 1 & -1 & -\frac{1}{4} & | & \frac{1}{2} \\ 7 & -3 & 2 & | & 0 \\ 5 & 2 & 3 & | & 1 \end{bmatrix}$$

Multiply R1 by –7 and add to R2. Multiply R1 by –5 and add to R3.

$$\begin{bmatrix} 1 & -1 & -\frac{1}{4} & | & \frac{1}{2} \\ 0 & 4 & \frac{15}{4} & | & -\frac{7}{2} \\ 0 & 7 & \frac{17}{4} & | & -\frac{3}{2} \end{bmatrix}$$

Divide R2 by 4.

$$\begin{bmatrix} 1 & -1 & -\frac{1}{4} & | & \frac{1}{2} \\ 0 & 1 & \frac{15}{16} & | & -\frac{7}{8} \\ 0 & 7 & \frac{17}{4} & | & -\frac{3}{2} \end{bmatrix}$$

Multiply R2 by –7 and add to R3.

$$\begin{bmatrix} 1 & -1 & -\frac{1}{4} & | & \frac{1}{2} \\ 0 & 1 & \frac{15}{16} & | & -\frac{7}{8} \\ 0 & 0 & -\frac{37}{16} & | & -\frac{37}{8} \end{bmatrix}$$

Multiply R3 by $-\dfrac{16}{37}$.

$$\begin{bmatrix} 1 & -1 & -\frac{1}{4} & | & \frac{1}{2} \\ 0 & 1 & \frac{15}{16} & | & -\frac{7}{8} \\ 0 & 0 & 1 & | & -2 \end{bmatrix}$$

This corresponds to $\begin{cases} x - y - \dfrac{1}{4}z = \dfrac{1}{2} \\ y + \dfrac{15}{16}z = -\dfrac{7}{8} \\ z = -2 \end{cases}$.

$$y + \frac{15}{16}(-2) = -\frac{7}{8}$$
$$y - \frac{15}{8} = -\frac{7}{8}$$
$$y = 1$$
$$x - 1 - \frac{1}{4}(-2) = \frac{1}{2}$$
$$x - 1 + \frac{1}{2} = \frac{1}{2}$$
$$x = 1$$

The solution is (1, 1, –2).

**38.** $\begin{cases} x + 2y + 3z = 14 \\ y + 2z = 3 \\ 2x \qquad - 2z = 10 \end{cases}$

$$\begin{bmatrix} 1 & 2 & 3 & | & 14 \\ 0 & 1 & 2 & | & 3 \\ 2 & 0 & -2 & | & 10 \end{bmatrix}$$

Multiply R1 by –2 and add to R3.

$$\begin{bmatrix} 1 & 2 & 3 & | & 14 \\ 0 & 1 & 2 & | & 3 \\ 0 & -4 & -8 & | & -18 \end{bmatrix}$$

Multiply R2 by 4 and add to R3.

$$\begin{bmatrix} 1 & 2 & 3 & | & 14 \\ 0 & 1 & 2 & | & 3 \\ 0 & 0 & 0 & | & -6 \end{bmatrix}$$

This corresponds to $\begin{cases} x + 2y + 3z = 14 \\ y + 2z = 3 \\ 0 = -6 \end{cases}$.

This system is inconsistent. The solution is $\varnothing$.

**39.** $\begin{cases} y \geq 2x - 3 \\ y \leq -2x + 1 \end{cases}$

Graph both inequalities on the same set of axes. The solution is the intersection of the solution regions. The solution of the system is the darker shaded region. This solution includes parts of both boundary lines.

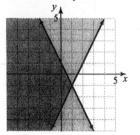

**40.** $\begin{cases} y \le -3x - 3 \\ y \le 2x + 7 \end{cases}$

Graph both inequalities on the same set of axes. The solution is the intersection of the solution regions. The solution of the system is the darker shaded region. This solution includes parts of both boundary lines.

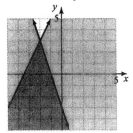

**41.** $\begin{cases} x + 2y > 0 \\ x - y \le 6 \end{cases}$

Graph both inequalities on the same set of axes. The solution is the intersection of the solution regions. The solution of the system is the darker shaded region. This solution includes the part of the solid boundary line that borders the region but not the dashed boundary line or the point where the boundary lines intersect.

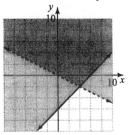

**42.** $\begin{cases} x - 2y \ge 7 \\ x + y \le -5 \end{cases}$

Graph both inequalities on the same set of axes. The solution is the intersection of the solution regions. The solution of the system is the darker shaded region. This solution includes parts of both boundary lines.

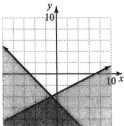

**43.** $\begin{cases} 3x - 2y \le 4 \\ 2x + y \ge 5 \\ y \le 4 \end{cases}$

Graph all three inequalities on the same set of axes. The solution set of the system is the shaded region. The parts of the boundary lines that border the shaded region are part of the solution.

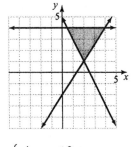

**44.** $\begin{cases} 4x - y \le 0 \\ 3x - 2y \ge -5 \\ y \ge -4 \end{cases}$

Graph all three inequalities on the same set of axes. The solution set of the system is the shaded region. The parts of the boundary lines that border the shaded region are part of the solution.

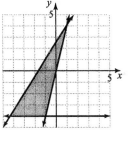

**45.** $\begin{cases} x + 2y \le 5 \\ x \le 2 \\ x \ge 0 \\ y \ge 0 \end{cases}$

Graph the inequalities on the same set of axes. The intersection of the inequalities is the solution region. It is the only shaded region in this graph and includes the portion of all four boundary lines that border the shaded region.

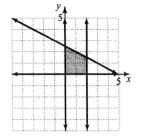

**46.** $\begin{cases} x+3y \le 7 \\ \quad y \le 5 \\ \quad x \ge 0 \\ \quad y \ge 0 \end{cases}$

Graph the inequalities on the same set of axes. The intersection of the inequalities is the solution region. It is the only shaded region in this graph and includes the portion of all four boundary lines that border the shaded region.

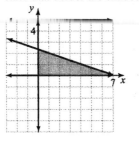

**47.** $\begin{cases} y = x-5 \\ y = -2x+2 \end{cases}$

We substitute $x-5$ for $y$ in the second equation.

$x-5 = -2x+2$

$3x = 7$

$x = \dfrac{7}{3}$

Replace $x$ with $\dfrac{7}{3}$ in the first equation.

$y = \dfrac{7}{3}-5 = \dfrac{7}{3}-\dfrac{15}{3} = -\dfrac{8}{3}$

The solution is $\left(\dfrac{7}{3},\ -\dfrac{8}{3}\right)$.

**48.** $\begin{cases} \dfrac{2}{5}x+\dfrac{3}{4}y = 1 \\ \quad x+3y = -2 \end{cases}$

Multiply both sides of the first equation by 20 to eliminate fractions.

$\begin{cases} 20\left(\dfrac{2}{5}x+\dfrac{3}{4}y\right) = 20(1) \\ \quad x+3y = -2 \end{cases}$

$\begin{cases} 8x+15y = 20 \\ \ x+3y = -2 \end{cases}$

Multiply both sides of the second equation by $-5$ and add to the first equation to eliminate $y$.

$\begin{cases} \ \ 8x+15y = 20 \\ -5x-15y = 10 \end{cases}$

$\begin{array}{r} 3x \qquad\quad = 30 \\ x = 10 \end{array}$

To find $y$, replace $x$ with 10 in the second equation.

$10+3y = -2$

$3y = -12$

$y = -4$

The solution is $(10, -4)$.

**49.** $\begin{cases} 5x-2y = 10 \\ \quad x = \dfrac{2}{5}y+2 \end{cases}$

Multiply both sides of the second equation by 5.

$\begin{cases} 5x-2y = 10 \\ 5x = 5\left(\dfrac{2}{5}y+2\right) \end{cases}$

$\begin{cases} 5x-2y = 10 \\ 5x = 2y+10 \end{cases}$

Subtract $2y$ from both sides of the second equation.

$\begin{cases} 5x-2y = 10 \\ 5x-2y = 10 \end{cases}$

The equations are the same. The system has an infinite number of solutions. The solution set can be written as $\{(x, y)|5x - 2y = 10\}$.

**50.** $\begin{cases} \ \ x-4y = 4 \\ \dfrac{1}{8}x-\dfrac{1}{2}y = 3 \end{cases}$

Multiply the second by $-8$ and add to the first equation to eliminate $x$.

$\begin{cases} \ \ x-4y = 4 \\ -x+4y = -24 \end{cases}$

The equation $0 = -20$ is false. The system has no solution. The solution set is { } or $\varnothing$.

**51.** $\begin{cases} x-3y+2z = 0 \\ \quad 9y-\ z = 22 \\ 5x \qquad +3z = 10 \end{cases}$

The corresponding matrix is $\begin{bmatrix} 1 & -3 & 2 & | & 0 \\ 0 & 9 & -1 & | & 22 \\ 5 & 0 & 3 & | & 10 \end{bmatrix}$

Multiply row 1 by $-5$ and add to row 3.

$\begin{bmatrix} 1 & -3 & 2 & | & 0 \\ 0 & 9 & -1 & | & 22 \\ 0 & 15 & -7 & | & 10 \end{bmatrix}$

Divide row 2 by 9.

$\begin{bmatrix} 1 & -3 & 2 & | & 0 \\ 0 & 1 & -\frac{1}{9} & | & \frac{22}{9} \\ 0 & 15 & -7 & | & 10 \end{bmatrix}$

Multiply row 2 by −15 and add to row 3.

$$\begin{bmatrix} 1 & -3 & 2 & | & 0 \\ 0 & 1 & -\frac{1}{9} & | & \frac{22}{9} \\ 0 & 0 & -\frac{48}{9} & | & -\frac{240}{9} \end{bmatrix}$$

Multiply row 3 by $-\frac{9}{48}$.

$$\begin{bmatrix} 1 & -3 & 2 & | & 0 \\ 0 & 1 & -\frac{1}{9} & | & \frac{22}{9} \\ 0 & 0 & 1 & | & 5 \end{bmatrix}$$

This matrix represents the system

$$\begin{cases} x - 3y + 2z = 0 \\ \quad y - \frac{1}{9}z = \frac{22}{9} \\ \qquad\qquad z = 5 \end{cases}.$$

Replace $z$ with 5 in the second equation to find $y$.

$$y - \frac{1}{9}(5) = \frac{22}{9}$$
$$y = \frac{22}{9} + \frac{5}{9} = \frac{27}{9} = 3$$

Replace $y$ with 3 and $z$ with 5 in the first equation to find $x$.

$$x - 3(3) + 2(5) = 0$$
$$x - 9 + 10 = 0$$
$$x + 1 = 0$$
$$x = -1$$

The solution is $(-1, 3, 5)$.

52. Let $x$ = the first number
    $y$ = the second number
    We solve the system

    $$\begin{cases} x = 3y - 5 \\ x + y = 127 \end{cases}$$

    We substitute $3y - 5$ for $x$ in the second equation.

    $$(3y - 5) + y = 127$$
    $$4y - 5 = 127$$
    $$4y = 132$$
    $$y = 33$$

    We replace $y$ with 33 in the first equation to find $x$.

    $$x = 3(33) - 5 = 99 - 5 = 94$$

    The numbers are 33 and 94.

53. Let $x$ = length of the shortest side
    $y$ = length of the second side
    $z$ = length of the third side
    We solve the system

    $$\begin{cases} x + y + z = 126 \\ \quad y = 2x \\ \quad z = x + 14 \end{cases}$$

    We substitute $2x$ for $y$ and $x + 14$ for $z$ in the first equation.

    $$x + 2x + (x + 14) = 126$$
    $$4x + 14 = 126$$
    $$4x = 112$$
    $$x = 28$$

    Now we find $y$ and $z$.
    $$y = 2x = 2(28) = 56$$
    $$z = x + 14 = 28 + 14 = 42$$

    The lengths are 28 units, 42 units, and 56 units.

54. $$\begin{cases} y \le 3x - \frac{1}{2} \\ 3x + 4y \ge 6 \end{cases}$$

    Graph both inequalities on the same set of axes. The solution is the intersection of the solution regions. The solution of the system is the darker shaded region. This solution includes parts of both boundary lines.

    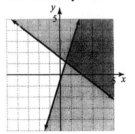

55. We solve the system

    $$\begin{cases} y = -443x + 2584 \\ y = 500x + 551 \end{cases}$$

    We substitute $-443x + 2584$ for $y$ in the second equation.

    $$-443x + 2584 = 500x + 551$$
    $$-994x = -2033$$
    $$x = \frac{-2033}{-994} \approx 2.05$$

    The amount spent on VCR decks and DVD players was the same about 2 years after 1998, or in 2000.

**Chapter 4 Test**

**1.** $\begin{cases} 2x - y = -1 & (1) \\ 5x + 4y = 17 & (2) \end{cases}$

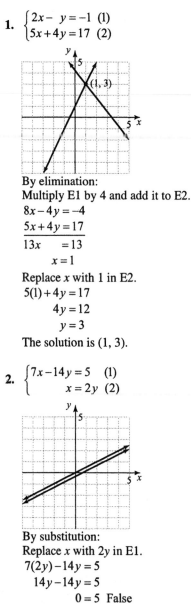

By elimination:
Multiply E1 by 4 and add it to E2.

$$8x - 4y = -4$$
$$\underline{5x + 4y = 17}$$
$$13x \qquad = 13$$
$$x = 1$$

Replace $x$ with 1 in E2.
$$5(1) + 4y = 17$$
$$4y = 12$$
$$y = 3$$
The solution is (1, 3).

**2.** $\begin{cases} 7x - 14y = 5 & (1) \\ x = 2y & (2) \end{cases}$

By substitution:
Replace $x$ with $2y$ in E1.
$$7(2y) - 14y = 5$$
$$14y - 14y = 5$$
$$0 = 5 \text{ False}$$

The system is inconsistent. The solution set is $\varnothing$.

**3.** $\begin{cases} 4x - 7y = 29 \\ 2x + 5y = -11 \end{cases}$

Multiply E2 by $-2$ and add to E1.
$$-4x - 10y = 22$$
$$\underline{4x - 7y = 29}$$
$$-17y = 51$$
$$y = -3$$
Replace $y$ with $-3$ in E1.

$$4x - 7(-3) = 29$$
$$4x + 21 = 29$$
$$4x = 8$$
$$x = 2$$
The solution is (2, $-3$).

**4.** $\begin{cases} 15x + 6y = 15 \\ 10x + 4y = 10 \end{cases}$

Divide E1 by 3 and E2 by 2.
$$\begin{cases} 5x + 2y = 5 \\ 5x + 2y = 5 \end{cases}$$
The system is dependent. The solution is
$\{(x, y) | 10x + 4y = 10\}$.

**5.** $\begin{cases} 2x - 3y \qquad = 4 & (1) \\ \quad 3y + 2z = 2 & (2) \\ x \qquad - z = -5 & (3) \end{cases}$

Add E1 and E2.
$$2x + 2z = 6 \text{ or } x + z = 3 \quad (4)$$
Add E3 and E4.
$$x + z = 3$$
$$\underline{x - z = -5}$$
$$2x \quad = -2$$
$$x = -1$$
Replace $x$ with $-1$ in E3.
$$-1 - z = -5$$
$$-z = -4 \text{ so } z = 4$$
Replace $x$ with $-1$ in E1.
$$2(-1) - 3y = 4$$
$$-2 - 3y = 4$$
$$-3y = 6$$
$$y = -2$$
The solution is ($-1$, $-2$, 4).

**6.** $\begin{cases} 3x - 2y - z = -1 & (1) \\ 2x - 2y \quad = 4 & (2) \\ 2x \quad - 2z = -12 & (3) \end{cases}$

Multiply E2 by $-1$ and add to E1.
$$3x - 2y - z = -1$$
$$\underline{-2x + 2y \quad = -4}$$
$$x \qquad - z = -5 \quad (4)$$
Multiply E4 by $-2$ and add to E3.
$$2x - 2z = -12$$
$$\underline{-2x + 2z = 10}$$
$$0 = -2 \text{ False}$$
The system is inconsistent. The solution set is $\varnothing$.

**7.** $\begin{cases} \dfrac{x}{2} + \dfrac{y}{4} = -\dfrac{3}{4} \\ x + \dfrac{3}{4}y = -4 \end{cases}$

Clear fractions by multiplying both equations by 4.

$\begin{cases} 2x + y = -3 \quad (1) \\ 4x + 3y = -16 \quad (2) \end{cases}$

Multiply E1 by –2 and add to E2.

$-4x - 2y = 6$
$\underline{4x + 3y = -16}$
$\qquad\qquad y = -10$

Replace $y$ with –10 in E1.

$2x + (-10) = -3$

$\qquad 2x = 7 \quad \text{so} \quad x = \dfrac{7}{2}$

The solution is $\left( \dfrac{7}{2}, -10 \right)$.

**8.** $\begin{cases} x - y = -2 \\ 3x - 3y = -6 \end{cases}$

$\begin{bmatrix} 1 & -1 & | & -2 \\ 3 & -3 & | & -6 \end{bmatrix}$

Multiply R1 by –3 and add to R2.

$\begin{bmatrix} 1 & -1 & | & -2 \\ 0 & 0 & | & 0 \end{bmatrix}$

This corresponds to $\begin{cases} x - y = -2 \\ \quad 0 = 0 \end{cases}$.

This is a dependent system. The solution is $\{(x, y) | x - y = -2\}$.

**9.** $\begin{cases} x + 2y = -1 \\ 2x + 5y = -5 \end{cases}$

$\begin{bmatrix} 1 & 2 & | & -1 \\ 2 & 5 & | & -5 \end{bmatrix}$

Multiply R1 by –2 and add to R2.

$\begin{bmatrix} 1 & 2 & | & -1 \\ 0 & 1 & | & -3 \end{bmatrix}$

This corresponds to $\begin{cases} x + 2y = -1 \\ \quad y = -3 \end{cases}$.

$x + 2(-3) = -1$
$\quad x - 6 = -1$
$\qquad\quad x = 5$

The solution is $(5, -3)$.

**10.** $\begin{cases} x - y - z = 0 \\ 3x - y - 5z = -2 \\ 2x + 3y = -5 \end{cases}$

$\begin{bmatrix} 1 & -1 & -1 & | & 0 \\ 3 & -1 & -5 & | & -2 \\ 2 & 3 & 0 & | & -5 \end{bmatrix}$

Multiply R1 by –3 and add to R2. Multiply R1 by –2 and add to R3.

$\begin{bmatrix} 1 & -1 & -1 & | & 0 \\ 0 & 2 & -2 & | & -2 \\ 0 & 5 & 2 & | & -5 \end{bmatrix}$

Divide R2 by 2.

$\begin{bmatrix} 1 & -1 & -1 & | & 0 \\ 0 & 1 & -1 & | & -1 \\ 0 & 5 & 2 & | & -5 \end{bmatrix}$

Multiply R2 by –5 and add to R3.

$\begin{bmatrix} 1 & -1 & -1 & | & 0 \\ 0 & 1 & -1 & | & -1 \\ 0 & 0 & 7 & | & 0 \end{bmatrix}$

Divide R3 by 7.

$\begin{bmatrix} 1 & -1 & -1 & | & 0 \\ 0 & 1 & -1 & | & -1 \\ 0 & 0 & 1 & | & 0 \end{bmatrix}$

This corresponds to $\begin{cases} x - y - z = 0 \\ \quad y - z = -1 \\ \qquad z = 0 \end{cases}$.

$y - 0 = -1$
$\quad y = -1$
$x - (-1) - 0 = 0$
$\qquad x + 1 = 0$
$\qquad\qquad x = -1$

The solution is $(-1, -1, 0)$.

**11.** Let $x$ = double occupancy rooms and $y$ = single occupancy rooms.

$\begin{cases} x + y = 80 \quad (1) \\ 90x + 80y = 6930 \quad (2) \end{cases}$

Multiply E1 by –80 and add to E2.

$-80x - 80y = -6400$
$\underline{90x + 80y = 6930}$
$\quad 10x \qquad\quad = 530$
$\qquad\qquad x = 53$

Replace $x$ with 53 in E1.

$53 + y = 80$
$\qquad y = 27$

53 double-occupancy and 27 single-occupancy rooms are occupied.

**12.** Let $x$ = gallons of 10% solution and
$y$ = gallons of 20% solution.
$$\begin{cases} x + y = 20 & (1) \\ 0.10x + 0.20y = 0.175(20) & (2) \end{cases}$$
Multiply E1 by $-0.10$ add to E2.
$$-0.10x - 0.10y = -2.0$$
$$\underline{0.10x + 0.20y = 3.5}$$
$$0.10y = 1.5$$
$$y = 15$$
Replace $y$ with 15 in E1.
$$x + 15 = 20$$
$$x = 5$$
They should use 5 gallons of 10% fructose
solution and 15 gallons of the 20% solution.

**13.** $R(x) = 4x$ and $C(x) = 1.5x + 2000$

Break even occurs when $R(x) = C(x)$.
$$4x = 1.5x + 2000$$
$$2.5x = 2000$$
$$x = 800$$
The company must sell 800 packages to break
even.

**14.** Let $x$ = measure of the smallest angle. Then the
largest angle has a measure of $5x - 3$, and the
remaining angle has a measure of $2x - 1$. The
sum of the three angles must add to 180°:
$$a + b + c = 180$$
$$x + (5x - 3) + (2x - 1) = 180$$
$$x + 5x - 3 + 2x - 1 = 180$$
$$8x - 4 = 180$$
$$8x = 184$$
$$x = 23$$
$$5x - 3 = 5(23) - 3 = 115 - 3 = 112$$
$$2x - 1 = 2(23) - 1 = 46 - 1 = 45$$
The angle measures are 23°, 45°, and 112°.

**15.** $\begin{cases} 2y - x \geq 1 \\ x + y \geq -4 \\ y \leq 2 \end{cases}$

Graph all three inequalities on the same set of
axes. The solution set of the system is the shaded
region. The parts of the boundary lines that
border the shaded region are part of the solution.

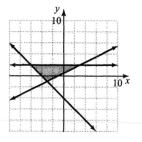

**Chapter 4 Cumulative Review**

**1. a.** Since 3 is a natural number, the statement is
true.

   **b.** Since 7 is not one of the three numbers
listed in the set, the statement is true.

**2. a.** Since 7 is not an element of the second set,
the first set is not a subset of the second set.
The statement is false.

   **b.** Since all three numbers in the first set are
also elements of the second set, the first set
is a subset of the second set. The statement
is true.

**3. a.** $11 + 2 - 7 = 13 - 7 = 6$

   **b.** $-5 - 4 + 2 = -9 + 2 = -7$

**4. a.** $-7 - (-2) = -7 + 2 = -5$

   **b.** $14 - 38 = -24$

**5. a.** The opposite of 4 is $-4$.

   **b.** The opposite of $\dfrac{3}{7}$ is $-\dfrac{3}{7}$.

   **c.** The opposite of $-11.2$ is $11.2$.

**6. a.** The reciprocal of 5 is $\dfrac{1}{5}$.

   **b.** The reciprocal of $-\dfrac{2}{3}$ is $-\dfrac{3}{2}$.

**7. a.** $3(2x + y) = 6x + 3y$

   **b.** $-(3x - 1) = -3x + 1$

   **c.** $0.7a(b - 2) = 0.7ab - 1.4a$

**8. a.** $7(3x - 2y + 4) = 21x - 14y + 28$

**b.** $-(-2s - 3t) = 2s + 3t$

**9. a.** $3x - 5x + 4 = (3 - 5)x + 4 = -2x + 4$

**b.** $7yz + yz = (7 + 1)yz = 8yz$

**c.** $4z + 6.1 = 4z + 6.1$

**10. a.** $5y^2 - 1 + 2(y^2 + 2) = 5y^2 - 1 + 2y^2 + 4$
$$= 7y^2 + 3$$

**b.** $(7.8x - 1.2) - (5.6x - 2.4)$
$$= 7.8x - 1.2 - 5.6x + 2.4$$
$$= 2.2x + 1.2$$

**11.** $-4x - 1 + 5x = 9x + 3 - 7x$
$$x - 1 = 2x + 3$$
$$-x = 4$$
$$x = -4$$

**12.** $8y - 14 = 6y - 14$
$$2y = 0$$
$$y = 0$$

**13.** $0.3x + 0.1 = 0.27x - 0.02$
$$0.03x = -0.12$$
$$x = -4$$

**14.** $2(m - 6) - m = 4(m - 3) - 3m$
$$2m - 12 - m = 4m - 12 - 3m$$
$$m - 12 = m - 12$$
$$0 = 0 \quad \text{Always True}$$
The solution is all real numbers.

**15.** Let $x$ = length of the third side, then
$2x + 12$ = length of the two equal sides.
$$x + (2x + 12) + (2x + 12) = 149$$
$$5x + 24 = 149$$
$$5x = 125$$
$$x = 25$$
$$2(25) + 12 = 50 + 12 = 62$$
The sides are 25 cm, 62 cm, and 62 cm.

**16.** Let $x$ = measure of the equal angles,
$x + 10$ = measure of the third angle, and
$\dfrac{1}{2}x$ = measure of the fourth angle.

$$x + x + (x + 10) + \frac{1}{2}x = 360$$
$$\frac{7}{2}x + 10 = 360$$
$$\frac{7}{2}x = 350$$
$$7x = 700$$
$$x = 100$$
$$x + 10 = 100 + 10 = 110$$
$$\frac{1}{2}x = \frac{1}{2}(100) = 50$$
The measure of the angles are 100°, 100°, 110°, and 50°.

**17.** $3x + 4 \geq 2x - 6$
$$x \geq -10$$

**18.** $5(2x - 1) > -5$
$$10x - 5 > -5$$
$$10x > 0$$
$$x > 0$$
$$(0, \infty)$$

**19.** $2 < 4 - x < 7$
$$-2 < -x < 3$$
$$2 > x > -3$$
$$-3 < x < 2$$
$$(-3, 2)$$

**20.** $-1 < \dfrac{-2x - 1}{3} < 1$
$$3(-1) < 3\left[\frac{-2x - 1}{3}\right] < 3(1)$$
$$-3 < -2x - 1 < 3$$
$$-2 < -2x < 4$$
$$1 > x > -2$$
$$-2 < x < 1$$
$$(-2, 1)$$

**21.** $|2x| + 5 = 7$
$$|2x| = 2$$
$$2x = 2 \quad \text{or} \quad 2x = -2$$
$$x = 1 \quad \text{or} \quad x = -1$$
The solution set is $\{-1, 1\}$.

**22.** $|x-5|=4$

$\quad x-5=4 \ \text{ or } \ x-5=-4$

$\qquad x=9 \ \text{ or } \qquad x=1$

The solution set is $\{1, 9\}$.

**23.** $|m-6|<2$

$\quad -2<m-6<2$

$\qquad 4<m<8$

$(4, 8)$

**24.** $|2x+1|>5$

$\quad 2x+1<-5 \ \text{ or } \ 2x+1>5$

$\qquad 2x<-6 \ \text{ or } \qquad 2x>4$

$\qquad x<-3 \ \text{ or } \qquad x>2$

$(-\infty, -3)\cup(2, \infty)$

**25.**

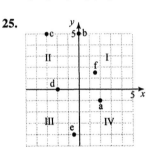

a.   $(2, -1)$ is in Quadrant IV.

b.   $(0, 5)$ is on the $y$-axis.

c.   $(-3, 5)$ is in Quadrant II.

d.   $(-2, 0)$ is on the $x$-axis.

e.   $\left(-\dfrac{1}{2}, -4\right)$ is in Quadrant III.

f.   $(1.5, 1.5)$ is in Quadrant I.

**26.**  a.   $(-1, -5)$ is in Quadrant III.

b.   $(4, -2)$ is in Quadrant IV.

c.   $(0, 2)$ is on the $y$-axis.

**27.**  No; for the input $x = 4$, there are two outputs, $y = \pm 2$.

**28.**   $-2x+\dfrac{1}{2}y=-2, \ \text{ or } \ y=4x-4$

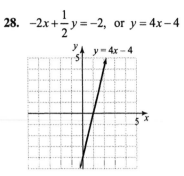

**29.**   $f(x)=7x^2-3x+1, \ g(x)=3x-2$

a.   $f(1)=7(1)^2-3(1)+1=7-3+1=5$

b.   $g(1)=3(1)-2=3-2=1$

c.   $f(-2)=7(-2)^2-3(-2)+1$

$\qquad\quad = 7(4)+6+1$

$\qquad\quad = 28+6+1$

$\qquad\quad = 35$

d.   $g(0)=3(0)-2=0-2=-2$

**30.**   $f(x)=3x^2$

a.   $f(5)=3(5)^2=3(25)=75$

b.   $f(-2)=3(-2)^2=3(4)=12$

**31.**   $g(x) = 2x + 1$ and $f(x) = 2x$

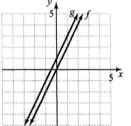

The graph of $g$ is the graph of $f$ shifted 1 unit up.

**32.**   $m=\dfrac{9-6}{0-(-2)}=\dfrac{3}{2}$

**33.** $3x - 4y = 4$
$$-4y = -3x + 4$$
$$y = \frac{3}{4}x - 1$$
$$m = \frac{3}{4}, \ y\text{-intercept} = (0, -1)$$

**34.** $y = 2$
$$m = 0, \ y\text{-intercept} = (0, 2)$$

**35. a.** $3x + 7y = 4$
$$7y = -3x + 4$$
$$y = -\frac{3}{7}x + \frac{4}{7}$$
$$m = -\frac{3}{7}$$
$$6x + 14y = 7$$
$$14y = -6x + 7$$
$$y = -\frac{3}{7}x + \frac{1}{2}$$
$$m = -\frac{3}{7}$$
Parallel, since the slopes are equal.

**b.** $-x + 3y = 2$
$$3y = x + 2$$
$$y = \frac{1}{3}x + \frac{2}{3}$$
$$m = \frac{1}{3}$$
$$2x + 6y = 5$$
$$6y = -2x + 5$$
$$y = -\frac{1}{3}x + \frac{5}{6}$$
$$m = -\frac{1}{3}$$
Neither, since the slopes are not equal and their product is not $-1$.

**36.** $y - (-9) = \frac{1}{5}(x - 0)$
$$y + 9 = \frac{1}{5}x$$
$$y = \frac{1}{5}x - 9$$

**37.** $m = \dfrac{-5 - 0}{-4 - 4} = \dfrac{-5}{-8} = \dfrac{5}{8}$
$$y - 0 = \frac{5}{8}(x - 4)$$
$$y = \frac{5}{8}x - \frac{5}{2}$$
$$f(x) = \frac{5}{8}x - \frac{5}{2}$$

**38.** $f(x) = \dfrac{1}{2}x - \dfrac{1}{3}$ or $y = \dfrac{1}{2}x - \dfrac{1}{3}$
$$m = \frac{1}{2} \ \text{ so } \ m_\perp = -2$$
$$y - 6 = -2[x - (-2)]$$
$$y - 6 = -2(x + 2)$$
$$y - 6 = -2x - 4$$
$$y = -2x + 2$$

**39.** $3x \geq y$, or $y \leq 3x$
Graph the boundary line $y = 3x$ with a solid line because the inequality symbol is $\leq$.
Test: $(0, 1)$
$$3x \geq y$$
$$3(0) \geq 1$$
$$0 \geq 1 \quad \text{False}$$
Shade the half-plane that does not contain $(0, 1)$.

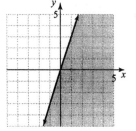

**40.** $x \geq 1$
Graph the boundary line $x = 1$ with a solid line because the inequality symbol is $\geq$.
Shade the half-plane that does not contain $(0, 0)$.

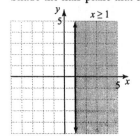

**41. a.** $\begin{cases} -x+y=2 \\ 2x-y=-3 \end{cases}$

$-(-1)+1=2$
$1+1=2$
$2=2$ True
$2(-1)-(1)=-3$
$-2-1=-3$
$-3=-3$ True
Yes, $(-1, 1)$ is a solution.

**b.** $\begin{cases} 5x+3y=-1 \\ x-y=1 \end{cases}$

$5(-2)+3(3)=-1$
$-10+9=-1$
$-1=-1$ True
$-2-3=-1$
$-5=-1$ False
No, $(-2, 3)$ is not a solution.

**42.** $\begin{cases} 5x+y=-2 \quad (1) \\ 4x-2y=-10 \quad (2) \end{cases}$

Multiply E1 by 2 and add to E2.
$10x+2y=-4$
$\underline{4x-2y=-10}$
$14x \quad\quad =-14$
$x=-1$
Replace $x$ with $-1$ in E1.
$5(-1)+y=-2$
$-5+y=-2$
$y=3$
The solution is $(-1, 3)$.

**43.** $\begin{cases} 3x-y+z=-15 \quad (1) \\ x+2y-z=1 \quad (2) \\ 2x+3y-2z=0 \quad (3) \end{cases}$

Add E1 and E2.
$4x+y=-14 \quad (4)$
Multiply E1 by 2 and add to E3.
$6x-2y+2z=-30$
$\underline{2x+3y-2z=0}$
$8x+y \quad =-30 \quad (5)$
Solve the new system:
$\begin{cases} 4x+y=-14 \quad (4) \\ 8x+y=-30 \quad (5) \end{cases}$
Multiply E4 by $-1$ and add to E5.
$-4x-y=14$
$\underline{8x+y=-30}$
$4x \quad =-16$
$x=-4$

Replace $x$ with $-4$ in E4.
$4(-4)+y=-14$
$-16+y=-14$
$y=2$
Replace $x$ with $-4$ and $y$ with 2 in E1.
$3(-4)-(2)+z=-15$
$-12-2+z=-15$
$-14+z=-15$
$z=-1$
The solution is $(-4, 2, -1)$.

**44.** $\begin{cases} x-2y+z=0 \quad (1) \\ 3x-y-2z=-15 \quad (2) \\ 2x-3y+3z=7 \quad (3) \end{cases}$

Multiply E1 by 2 and add to E2.
$2x-4y+2z=0$
$\underline{3x-y-2z=-15}$
$5x-5y \quad =-15$ or $x-y=-3 \quad (4)$
Multiply E1 by $-3$ and add to E3.
$-3x+6y-3z=0$
$\underline{2x-3y+3z=7}$
$-x+3y \quad =7 \quad (5)$
Add E4 and E5.
$2y=4$
$y=2$
Replace $y$ with 2 in E4.
$x-2=-3$
$x=-1$
Replace $x$ with $-1$ and $y$ with 2 in E1.
$-1-2(2)+z=0$
$-5+z=0$
$z=5$
The solution is $(-1, 2, 5)$.

**45.** $\begin{cases} x+3y=5 \\ 2x-y=-4 \end{cases}$

$\begin{bmatrix} 1 & 3 & | & 5 \\ 2 & -1 & | & -4 \end{bmatrix}$

Multiply R1 by $-2$ and add to R2.
$\begin{bmatrix} 1 & 3 & | & 5 \\ 0 & -7 & | & -14 \end{bmatrix}$

Divide R2 by $-7$.
$\begin{bmatrix} 1 & 3 & | & 5 \\ 0 & 1 & | & 2 \end{bmatrix}$

This corresponds to $\begin{cases} x+3y=5 \\ y=2 \end{cases}$.

$$x + 3(2) = 5$$
$$x + 6 = 5$$
$$x = -1$$
The solution is (–1, 2).

**46.** $\begin{cases} -6x + 8y = 0 & (1) \\ 9x - 12y = 2 & (2) \end{cases}$

Divide E1 by –2 and E2 by 3.

$\begin{cases} 3x - 4y = 0 \\ 3x - 4y = \dfrac{2}{3} \end{cases}$

This system is inconsistent. The solution set is
∅.

# Chapter 5

**Section 5.1**

**Practice Exercises**

1. **a.** $3^4 \cdot 3^2 = 3^{4+2} = 3^6$

   **b.** $x^5 \cdot x^2 = x^{5+2} = x^7$

   **c.** $y \cdot y^3 \cdot y^5 = (y^1 \cdot y^3) \cdot y^5 = y^4 \cdot y^5 = y^9$

2. **a.** $(5z^3)(7z) = 5(7)z^3 z^1 = 35z^4$

   **b.** $(-4.1t^5 q^3)(5tq^5) = -4.1(5)t^5 t^1 q^3 q^5$
   $$= -20.5t^6 q^8$$

3. **a.** $5^0 = 1$

   **b.** $-5^0 = -(5^0) = -(1) = -1$

   **c.** $(3x - 8)^0 = 1$

   **d.** $3x^0 = 3(1) = 3$

4. **a.** $\dfrac{z^8}{z^3} = z^{8-3} = z^5$

   **b.** $\dfrac{3^9}{3^3} = 3^{9-3} = 3^6$

   **c.** $\dfrac{45x^7}{5x^3} = 9x^{7-3} = 9x^4$

   **d.** $\dfrac{24a^{14}b^6}{18a^7 b^6} = \dfrac{4}{3}a^{14-7}b^{6-6}$
   $$= \dfrac{4}{3}a^7 b^0$$
   $$= \dfrac{4}{3}a^7 \text{ or } \dfrac{4a^7}{3}$$

5. **a.** $6^{-2} = \dfrac{1}{6^2} = \dfrac{1}{36}$

   **b.** $(-2)^{-6} = \dfrac{1}{(-2)^6} = \dfrac{1}{64}$

   **c.** $3x^{-5} = 3 \cdot \dfrac{1}{x^5} = \dfrac{3}{x^5}$

   **d.** $(5y)^{-1} = \dfrac{1}{(5y)^1} = \dfrac{1}{5y}$

   **e.** $\dfrac{k^4}{k^{11}} = k^{4-11} = k^{-7} = \dfrac{1}{k^7}$

   **f.** $\dfrac{5^3}{5^5} = 5^{3-5} = 5^{-2} = \dfrac{1}{5^2} = \dfrac{1}{25}$

   **g.** $5^{-1} + 2^{-2} = \dfrac{1}{5^1} + \dfrac{1}{2^2} = \dfrac{1}{5} + \dfrac{1}{4} = \dfrac{4}{20} + \dfrac{5}{20} = \dfrac{9}{20}$

   **h.** $\dfrac{1}{z^{-8}} = \dfrac{1}{\frac{1}{z^8}} = 1 \div \dfrac{1}{z^8} = 1 \cdot \dfrac{z^8}{1} = z^8$

6. **a.** $\dfrac{z^{-8}}{z^3} = z^{-8-3} = z^{-11} = \dfrac{1}{z^{11}}$

   **b.** $\dfrac{7t^3}{t^{-5}} = 7 \cdot t^{3-(-5)} = 7t^8$

   **c.** $\dfrac{3^{-2}}{3^{-4}} = 3^{-2-(-4)} = 3^{-2+4} = 3^2 = 9$

   **d.** $\dfrac{5a^{-5}b^3}{15a^2 b^{-4}} = \dfrac{a^{-5-2}b^{3-(-4)}}{3} = \dfrac{a^{-7}b^7}{3} = \dfrac{b^7}{3a^7}$

   **e.** $\dfrac{(2x^{-5})(x^6)}{x^5} = \dfrac{2x^{-5+6}}{x^5}$
   $$= \dfrac{2x^1}{x^5}$$
   $$= 2x^{1-5}$$
   $$= 2x^{-4}$$
   $$= \dfrac{2}{x^4}$$

7. **a.** $x^{3a} \cdot x^4 = x^{3a+4}$

   **b.** $\dfrac{x^{3t-2}}{x^{t-3}} = x^{(3t-2)-(t-3)} = x^{3t-2-t+3} = x^{2t+1}$

**8. a.** Move the decimal point until the number is between 1 and 10. The decimal point is moved 4 places and the original number is 10 or greater, so the count is positive 4.
$$65,000 = 6.5 \times 10^4$$

**b.** Move the decimal point until the number is between 1 and 10. The decimal point is moved 5 places and the original number is less than 1, so the count is $-5$.
$$0.000038 = 3.8 \times 10^{-5}$$

**9. a.** Since the exponent is positive, move the decimal point 5 places to the right.
$$6.2 \times 10^5 = 620,000$$

**b.** Since the exponent is negative, more the decimal point 2 places to the left.
$$3.109 \times 10^{-2} = 0.03109$$

**Graphing Calculator Explorations**

**1.** $(3 \times 10^{11})(2 \times 10^{32}) = 6 \times 10^{43}$

**2.** $(6 \times 10^{14}) \div (3 \times 10^9) = 2 \times 10^5$

**3.** $(5.2 \times 10^{23})(7.3 \times 10^4) = 3.796 \times 10^{28}$

**4.** $(4.38 \times 10^{41}) \div (3 \times 10^{17}) = 1.46 \times 10^{24}$

**Vocabulary and Readiness Check**

**1.** $9x^5$; base $x$

**2.** $yz^5$; base $z$

**3.** $-3^5$; base 3

**4.** $(-3)^5$; base $-3$

**5.** $(y^7)^5$; base $y^7$

**6.** $9 \cdot 2^5$; base 2

**7.** $5x^{-1}y^{-2} = \dfrac{5}{xy^2}$

**8.** $7xy^{-4} = \dfrac{7x}{y^4}$

**9.** $a^2 b^{-1} c^{-5} = \dfrac{a^2}{bc^5}$

**10.** $a^{-4} b^2 c^{-6} = \dfrac{b^2}{a^4 c^6}$

**11.** $\dfrac{y^{-2}}{x^{-4}} = \dfrac{x^4}{y^2}$

**12.** $\dfrac{x^{-7}}{z^{-3}} = \dfrac{z^3}{x^7}$

**Exercise Set 5.1**

**1.** $4^2 \cdot 4^3 = 4^{2+3} = 4^5$

**3.** $x^5 \cdot x^3 = x^{5+3} = x^8$

**5.** $m \cdot m^7 \cdot m^6 = m^{1+7+6} = m^{14}$

**7.** $(4xy)(-5x) = -20x^{1+1}y = -20x^2 y$

**9.** $(-4x^3 p^2)(4y^3 x^3) = -16x^{3+3}y^3 p^2$
$$= -16x^6 y^3 p^2$$

**11.** $-8^0 = -(8^0) = -1$

**13.** $(4x + 5)^0 = 1$

**15.** $-x^0 = -(x^0) = -(1) = -1$

**17.** $4x^0 + 5 = 4(1) + 5 = 4 + 5 = 9$

**19.** $\dfrac{a^5}{a^2} = a^{5-2} = a^3$

**21.** $-\dfrac{26z^{11}}{2z^7} = -13z^{11-7} = -13z^4$

**23.** $\dfrac{x^9 y^6}{x^8 y^6} = x^{9-8} y^{6-6} = x^1 y^0 = x$

**25.** $\dfrac{12x^4y^7}{9xy^5} = \dfrac{4x^{4-1}y^{7-5}}{3} = \dfrac{4}{3}x^3y^2$

**27.** $\dfrac{-36a^5b^7c^{10}}{6ab^3c^4} = -6a^{5-1}b^{7-3}c^{10-4} = -6a^4b^4c^6$

**29.** $4^{-2} = \dfrac{1}{4^2} = \dfrac{1}{16}$

**31.** $(-3)^{-3} = \dfrac{1}{(-3)^3} = \dfrac{1}{-27} = -\dfrac{1}{27}$

**33.** $\dfrac{x^7}{x^{15}} = x^{7-15} = x^{-8} = \dfrac{1}{x^8}$

**35.** $5a^{-4} = \dfrac{5}{a^4}$

**37.** $\dfrac{x^{-7}}{y^{-2}} = \dfrac{y^2}{x^7}$

**39.** $\dfrac{x^{-2}}{x^5} = x^{-2-5} - x^{-7} - \dfrac{1}{x^7}$

**41.** $\dfrac{8r^4}{2r^{-4}} = 4r^{4-(-4)} = 4r^8$

**43.** $\dfrac{x^{-9}x^4}{x^{-5}} = \dfrac{x^{-9+4}}{x^{-5}} = \dfrac{x^{-5}}{x^{-5}} = x^{-5-(-5)} = x^0 = 1$

**45.** $\dfrac{2a^{-6}b^2}{18ab^{-5}} = \dfrac{a^{-6-1}b^{2-(-5)}}{9} = \dfrac{a^{-7}b^7}{9} = \dfrac{b^7}{9a^7}$

**47.** $\dfrac{(24x^8)(x)}{20x^{-7}} = \dfrac{6x^{8+1}}{5x^{-7}} = \dfrac{6x^{9-(-7)}}{5} = \dfrac{6x^{16}}{5}$

**49.** $-7x^3 \cdot 20x^9 = -7 \cdot 20x^{3+9} = -140x^{12}$

**51.** $x^7 \cdot x^8 \cdot x = x^{7+8+1} = x^{16}$

**53.** $2x^3 \cdot 5x^7 = 2 \cdot 5x^{3+7} = 10x^{10}$

**55.** $(5x)^0 + 5x^0 = 1 + 5 \cdot 1 = 1 + 5 = 6$

**57.** $\dfrac{z^{12}}{z^{15}} = z^{12-15} = z^{-3} = \dfrac{1}{z^3}$

**59.** $3^0 - 3t^0 = 1 - 3 \cdot 1 = 1 - 3 = -2$

**61.** $\dfrac{y^{-3}}{y^{-7}} = y^{-3-(-7)} = y^4$

**63.** $4^{-1} + 3^{-2} = \dfrac{1}{4^1} + \dfrac{1}{3^2}$
$= \dfrac{1}{4} + \dfrac{1}{9}$
$= \dfrac{9}{36} + \dfrac{4}{36}$
$= \dfrac{13}{36}$

**65.** $3x^{-1} = \dfrac{3}{x^1} = \dfrac{3}{x}$

**67.** $\dfrac{r^4}{r^{-4}} = r^{4-(-4)} = r^8$

**69.** $\dfrac{x^{-7}y^{-2}}{x^2y^2} = x^{-7-2}y^{-2-2} = x^{-9}y^{-4} = \dfrac{1}{x^9y^4}$

**71.** $(-4x^2y)(3x^4)(-2xy^5)$
$= -4(3)(-2)x^2 \cdot x^4 \cdot x \cdot y \cdot y^5$
$= 24x^{2+4+1} \cdot y^{1+5}$
$= 24x^7y^6$

**73.** $2^{-4} \cdot x = \dfrac{x}{2^4} = \dfrac{x}{16}$

**75.** $\dfrac{5^{17}}{5^{13}} = 5^{17-13} = 5^4 = 625$

**77.** $\dfrac{8^{-7}}{8^{-6}} = 8^{-7-(-6)} = 8^{-7+6} = 8^{-1} = \dfrac{1}{8}$

**79.** $\dfrac{9^{-5}a^4}{9^{-3}a^{-1}} = 9^{-5-(-3)}a^{4-(-1)}$
$= 9^{-5+3}a^{4+1}$
$= 9^{-2}a^5$
$= \dfrac{a^5}{9^2}$
$= \dfrac{a^5}{81}$

**81.** $\dfrac{14x^{-2}yz^{-4}}{2xyz} = \dfrac{14}{2} \cdot x^{-2-1}y^{1-1}z^{-4-1}$

$\qquad = 7x^{-3}y^0z^{-5}$

$\qquad = \dfrac{7}{x^3z^5}$

**83.** $x^5 \cdot x^{7a} = x^{5+7a}$ or $x^{7a+5}$

**85.** $\dfrac{x^{3t-1}}{x^t} = x^{3t-1-t} = x^{2t-1}$

**87.** $x^{4a} \cdot x^7 = x^{4a+7}$

**89.** $\dfrac{z^{6x}}{z^7} = z^{6x-7}$

**91.** $\dfrac{x^{3t} \cdot x^{4t-1}}{x^t} = \dfrac{x^{3t+(4t-1)}}{x^t} = x^{7t-1-t} = x^{6t-1}$

**93.** $31,250,000 = 3.125 \times 10^7$

**95.** $0.016 = 1.6 \times 10^{-2}$

**97.** $67,413 = 6.7413 \times 10^4$

**99.** $0.0125 = 1.25 \times 10^{-2}$

**101.** $0.000053 = 5.3 \times 10^{-5}$

**103.** $344,992,000,000 = 3.44992 \times 10^{11}$

**105.** $3,500,00 = 3.5 \times 10^6$

**107.** $124,000,000,000 = 1.24 \times 10^{11}$

**109.** $0.001 = 1.0 \times 10^{-3}$

**111.** $3.6 \times 10^{-9} = 0.0000000036$

**113.** $9.3 \times 10^7 = 93,000,000$

**115.** $1.278 \times 10^6 = 1,278,000$

**117.** $7.35 \times 10^{12} = 7,350,000,000,000$

**119.** $4.03 \times 10^{-7} = 0.000000403$

**121.** $3.0 \times 10^8 = 300,000,000$

**123.** $1.53 \times 10^{11} = \$153,000,000,000$

**125.** $(5 \cdot 2)^2 = (10)^2 = 100$

**127.** $\left(\dfrac{3}{4}\right)^3 = \left(\dfrac{3}{4}\right)\left(\dfrac{3}{4}\right)\left(\dfrac{3}{4}\right) = \dfrac{3 \cdot 3 \cdot 3}{4 \cdot 4 \cdot 4} = \dfrac{27}{64}$

**129.** $(2^3)^2 = 8^2 = 64$

**131.** Answers may vary

**133.** Answers may vary

**135. a.** $x^a \cdot x^a = x^{a+a} = x^{2a}$

  **b.** $x^a + x^a = 2x^a$

  **c.** $\dfrac{x^a}{x^b} = x^{a-b}$

  **d.** $x^a \cdot x^b = x^{a+b}$

  **e.** $x^a + x^b = x^a + x^b$

**137.** $7^{13}$

**139.** $7^{-11}$

**Section 5.2**

**Practice Exercises**

**1. a.** $(z^3)^5 = z^{3 \cdot 5} = z^{15}$

  **b.** $(5^2)^2 = 5^{2 \cdot 2} = 5^4 = 625$

  **c.** $(3^{-1})^3 = 3^{-1 \cdot 3} = 3^{-3} = \dfrac{1}{3^3} = \dfrac{1}{27}$

  **d.** $(x^{-4})^{-6} = x^{-4(-6)} = x^{24}$

**2. a.** $(2x^3)^5 = 2^5 \cdot (x^3)^5 = 2^5 \cdot x^{3 \cdot 5} = 32x^{15}$

  **b.** $\left(\dfrac{3}{5}\right)^2 = \dfrac{3^2}{5^2} = \dfrac{9}{25}$

**c.** $\left(\dfrac{2a^5}{b^7}\right)^4 = \dfrac{(2a^5)^4}{(b^7)^4} = \dfrac{2^4\cdot(a^5)^4}{(b^7)^4} = \dfrac{16a^{20}}{b^{28}}$

**d.** $\left(\dfrac{3^{-2}}{x}\right)^{-1} = \dfrac{(3^{-2})^{-1}}{x^{-1}} = \dfrac{3^2}{x^{-1}} = 9x$

**e.** $(a^{-2}b^{-5}c^4)^{-2} = (a^{-2})^{-2}\cdot(b^{-5})^{-2}\cdot(c^4)^{-2}$
$= a^4 b^{10} c^{-8}$
$= \dfrac{a^4 b^{10}}{c^8}$

**3. a.** $(3ab^{-5})^{-3} = 3^{-3}a^{-3}(b^{-5})^{-3}$
$= 3^{-3}a^{-3}b^{15}$
$= \dfrac{b^{15}}{3^3 a^3}$
$= \dfrac{b^{15}}{27a^3}$

**b.** $\left(\dfrac{y^{-7}}{y^{-4}}\right)^{-5} = \dfrac{(y^{-7})^{-5}}{(y^{-4})^{-5}}$
$= \dfrac{y^{35}}{y^{20}}$
$= y^{35-20}$
$= y^{15}$

**c.** $\left(\dfrac{3}{8}\right)^{-2} = \dfrac{3^{-2}}{8^{-2}} = \dfrac{8^2}{3^2} = \dfrac{64}{9}$

**d.** $\dfrac{9^{-2}a^{-4}b^3}{a^2 b^{-5}} = 9^{-2}\left(\dfrac{a^{-4}}{a^2}\right)\left(\dfrac{b^3}{b^{-5}}\right)$
$= 9^{-2}a^{-4-2}b^{3-(-5)}$
$= 9^{-2}a^{-6}b^8$
$= \dfrac{b^8}{9^2 a^6}$
$= \dfrac{b^8}{81a^6}$

**4. a.** $\left(\dfrac{5a^4b}{a^{-8}c}\right)^{-3} = \left(\dfrac{5a^{12}b}{c}\right)^{-3}$
$= \dfrac{5^{-3}a^{-36}b^{-3}}{c^{-3}}$
$= \dfrac{c^3}{5^3 a^{36}b^3}$
$= \dfrac{c^3}{125a^{36}b^3}$

**b.** $\left(\dfrac{2x^4}{5y^{-2}}\right)^3\left(\dfrac{x^{-4}}{10y^{-2}}\right)^{-1} = \dfrac{8x^{12}}{125y^{-6}}\cdot\dfrac{x^4}{10^{-1}y^2}$
$= \dfrac{8\cdot10\cdot x^{12}x^4 y^6}{125y^2}$
$= \dfrac{16x^{16}y^4}{25}$

**5. a.** $x^{-2a}(3x^a)^3 = x^{-2a}\cdot3^3\cdot x^{a\cdot3}$
$= 27x^{-2a+3a}$
$= 27x^a$

**b.** $\dfrac{(y^{3b})^3}{y^{4b-3}} = \dfrac{y^{9b}}{y^{4b-3}}$
$= y^{9b-(4b-3)}$
$= y^{9b-4b+3}$
$= y^{5b+3}$

**6. a.** $(3.4\times10^4)(5\times10^{-7})$
$= 3.4\times5\times10^4\times10^{-7}$
$= 17.0\times10^{-3}$
$= (1.7\times10^1)\times10^{-3}$
$= 1.7\times10^{-2}$

**b.** $\dfrac{5.6\times10^8}{4\times10^{-2}} = \left(\dfrac{5.6}{4}\right)\left(\dfrac{10^8}{10^{-2}}\right)$
$= 1.4\times10^{8-(-2)}$
$= 1.4\times10^{10}$

**7.** $\dfrac{2400 \times 0.0000014}{800}$

$= \dfrac{(2.4 \times 10^3)(1.4 \times 10^{-6})}{8 \times 10^2}$

$= \dfrac{2.4(1.4)}{8} \cdot \dfrac{10^3 \cdot 10^{-6}}{10^2}$

$= 0.42 \times 10^{-5}$

$= (4.2 \times 10^{-1}) \times 10^{-5}$

$= 4.2 \times 10^{-6}$

**Vocabulary and Readiness Check**

**1.** $(x^4)^5 = x^{4(5)} = x^{20}$

**2.** $(5^6)^2 = 5^{6(2)} = 5^{12}$

**3.** $x^4 \cdot x^5 = x^{4+5} = x^9$

**4.** $x^7 \cdot x^8 = x^{7+8} = x^{15}$

**5.** $(y^6)^7 = y^{6(7)} = y^{42}$

**6.** $(x^3)^4 = x^{3(4)} = x^{12}$

**7.** $(z^4)^9 = z^{4(9)} = z^{36}$

**8.** $(z^3)^7 = z^{3(7)} = z^{21}$

**9.** $(z^{-6})^{-3} = z^{-6(-3)} = z^{18}$

**10.** $(y^{-4})^{-2} = y^{-4(-2)} = y^8$

**Exercise Set 5.2**

**1.** $(3^{-1})^2 = 3^{-1(2)} = 3^{-2} = \dfrac{1}{3^2} = \dfrac{1}{9}$

**3.** $(x^4)^{-9} = x^{4(-9)} = x^{-36} = \dfrac{1}{x^{36}}$

**5.** $(y)^{-5} = y^{-5} = \dfrac{1}{y^5}$

**7.** $(3x^2 y^3)^2 = 3^2 (x^2)^2 (y^3)^2$

$= 9x^{2(2)} y^{3(2)}$

$= 9x^4 y^6$

**9.** $\left(\dfrac{2x^5}{y^{-3}}\right)^4 = \dfrac{2^4 (x^5)^4}{(y^{-3})^4}$

$= \dfrac{16 x^{5(4)}}{y^{-3(4)}}$

$= \dfrac{16 x^{20}}{y^{-12}}$

$= 16 x^{20} y^{12}$

**11.** $(a^2 b c^{-3})^{-6} = (a^2)^{-6} b^{-6} (c^{-3})^{-6}$

$= a^{2(-6)} b^{-6} c^{-3(-6)}$

$= a^{-12} b^{-6} c^{18}$

$= \dfrac{c^{18}}{a^{12} b^6}$

**13.** $\left(\dfrac{x^7 y^{-3}}{z^{-4}}\right)^{-5} = \dfrac{(x^7)^{-5} (y^{-3})^{-5}}{(z^{-4})^{-5}}$

$= \dfrac{x^{-35} y^{15}}{z^{20}}$

$= \dfrac{y^{15}}{x^{35} z^{20}}$

**15.** $(5^{-1})^3 = 5^{-1(3)} = 5^{-3} = \dfrac{1}{5^3} = \dfrac{1}{125}$

**17.** $\left(\dfrac{x^{-9}}{x^{-4}}\right)^{-3} = \dfrac{(x^{-9})^{-3}}{(x^{-4})^{-3}} = \dfrac{x^{27}}{x^{12}} = x^{27-12} = x^{15}$

**19.** $\left(\dfrac{5x^7 y^4}{10 x^3 y^{-2}}\right)^{-3} = \left(\dfrac{x^4 y^6}{2}\right)^{-3}$

$= \dfrac{(x^4)^{-3} (y^6)^{-3}}{(2)^{-3}}$

$= (2)^3 x^{-12} y^{-18}$

$= \dfrac{8}{x^{12} y^{18}}$

**21.** $\dfrac{8^{-2} x^{-3} y^{11}}{x^2 y^{-5}} = \dfrac{x^{-3-2} y^{11-(-5)}}{8^2} = \dfrac{x^{-5} y^{16}}{64} = \dfrac{y^{16}}{64 x^5}$

**23.** $\left(\dfrac{4p^6}{p^9}\right)^3 = \left(\dfrac{4}{p^3}\right)^3 = \dfrac{4^3}{(p^3)^3} = \dfrac{64}{p^9}$

**25.** $(-xy^0x^2a^3)^{-3} = (-x^3a^3)^{-3}$
$$= (-1)^3(x^3)^{-3}(a^3)^{-3}$$
$$= -1x^{-9}a^{-9}$$
$$= -\frac{1}{x^9a^9}$$

**27.** $\left(\dfrac{x^{-1}y^{-2}}{5^{-3}}\right)^{-5} = \dfrac{(x^{-1})^{-5}(y^{-2})^{-5}}{(5^{-3})^{-5}} = \dfrac{x^5y^{10}}{5^{15}}$

**29.** $(x^7)^{-9} = x^{7(-9)} = x^{-63} = \dfrac{1}{x^{63}}$

**31.** $\left(\dfrac{7}{8}\right)^3 = \dfrac{7^3}{8^3} = \dfrac{343}{512}$

**33.** $(4x^2)^2 = 4^2(x^2)^2 = 16x^4$

**35.** $(-2^{-2}y)^3 = (-2^{-2})^3y^3$
$$= -2^{-6}y^3$$
$$= -\dfrac{y^3}{2^6}$$
$$= -\dfrac{y^3}{64}$$

**37.** $\left(\dfrac{4^{-4}}{y^3x}\right)^{-2} = \dfrac{(4^{-4})^{-2}}{(y^3)^{-2}x^{-2}} = \dfrac{4^8}{y^{-6}x^{-2}} = 4^8x^2y^6$

**39.** $\left(\dfrac{1}{4}\right)^{-3} = \dfrac{1^{-3}}{4^{-3}} = \dfrac{4^3}{1^3} = \dfrac{64}{1} = 64$

**41.** $\left(\dfrac{3x^5}{6x^4}\right)^4 = \left(\dfrac{x^{5-4}}{2}\right)^4 = \left(\dfrac{x}{2}\right)^4 = \dfrac{x^4}{2^4} = \dfrac{x^4}{16}$

**43.** $\dfrac{(y^3)^{-4}}{y^3} = \dfrac{y^{-12}}{y^3} = y^{-12-3} = y^{-15} = \dfrac{1}{y^{15}}$

**45.** $\left(\dfrac{2x^{-3}}{y^{-1}}\right)^{-3} = \dfrac{2^{-3}(x^{-3})^{-3}}{(y^{-1})^{-3}} = \dfrac{x^9}{2^3y^3} = \dfrac{x^9}{8y^3}$

**47.** $\dfrac{3^{-2}a^{-5}b^6}{4^{-2}a^{-7}b^{-3}} = \dfrac{4^2a^{-5-(-7)}b^{6-(-3)}}{3^2} = \dfrac{16a^2b^9}{9}$

**49.** $(4x^6y^5)^{-2}(6x^4y^3) = 4^{-2}(x^6)^{-2}(y^5)^{-2} \cdot 6x^4y^3$
$$= \dfrac{1}{4^2}x^{-12}y^{-10} \cdot 6x^4y^3$$
$$= \dfrac{6}{16}x^{-12+4}y^{-10+3}$$
$$= \dfrac{3x^{-8}y^{-7}}{8}$$
$$= \dfrac{3}{8x^8y^7}$$

**51.** $x^6(x^6bc)^{-6} = x^6(x^6)^{-6}b^{-6}c^{-6}$
$$= \dfrac{x^6x^{-36}}{b^6c^6}$$
$$= \dfrac{x^{-30}}{b^6c^6}$$
$$= \dfrac{1}{x^{30}b^6c^6}$$

**53.** $\dfrac{2^{-3}x^2y^{-5}}{5^{-2}x^7y^{-1}} = \dfrac{5^2x^{2-7}y^{-5-(-1)}}{2^3}$
$$= \dfrac{25x^{-5}y^{-4}}{8}$$
$$= \dfrac{25}{8x^5y^4}$$

**55.** $\left(\dfrac{2x^2}{y^4}\right)^3\left(\dfrac{2x^5}{y}\right)^{-2} = \dfrac{2^3x^{2(3)}2^{-2}x^{5(-2)}}{y^{4(3)}y^{-2}}$
$$= \dfrac{8x^6x^{-10}}{2^2y^{12}y^{-2}}$$
$$= \dfrac{2x^{-4}}{y^{10}}$$
$$= \dfrac{2}{x^4y^{10}}$$

**57.** $(x^{3a+6})^3 = x^{(3a+6)\cdot3} = x^{9a+18}$

**59.** $\dfrac{x^{4a}(x^{4a})^3}{x^{4a-2}} = \dfrac{x^{4a} \cdot x^{12a}}{x^{4a-2}}$
$$= \dfrac{x^{4a+12a}}{x^{4a-2}}$$
$$= x^{16a-(4a-2)}$$
$$= x^{12a+2}$$

**61.** $(b^{5x-2})^{2x} = b^{(5x-2)\cdot 2x} = b^{10x^2-4x}$

**63.** $\dfrac{(y^{2a})^8}{y^{a-3}} = \dfrac{y^{16a}}{y^{a-3}} = y^{16a-(a-3)} = y^{15a+3}$

**65.** $\left(\dfrac{2x^{3t}}{x^{2t-1}}\right)^4 = \dfrac{2^4 x^{3t(4)}}{x^{(2t-1)\cdot 4}}$

$= \dfrac{16x^{12t}}{x^{8t-4}}$

$= 16x^{12t-(8t-4)}$

$= 16x^{4t+4}$

**67.** $\dfrac{25x^{2a+1}y^{a-1}}{5x^{3a+1}y^{2a-3}} = \left(\dfrac{25}{5}\right)\left(\dfrac{x^{2a+1}}{x^{3a+1}}\right)\left(\dfrac{y^{a-1}}{y^{2a-3}}\right)$

$= 5x^{2a+1-(3a+1)}y^{a-1-(2a-3)}$

$= 5x^{2a+1-3a-1}y^{a-1-2a+3}$

$= 5x^{-a}y^{-a+2}$

**69.** $(5\times 10^{11})(2.9\times 10^{-3}) = 5\times 2.9\times 10^{11+(-3)}$

$= 14.5\times 10^8$

$= 1.45\times 10^1 \times 10^8$

$= 1.45\times 10^9$

**71.** $(2\times 10^5)^3 = 2^3\times 10^{5(3)} = 8\times 10^{15}$

**73.** $\dfrac{3.6\times 10^{-4}}{9\times 10^2} = \dfrac{3.6}{9}\times 10^{-4-2}$

$= 0.4\times 10^{-6}$

$= 4\times 10^{-1}\times 10^{-6}$

$= 4\times 10^{-7}$

**75.** $\dfrac{0.0069}{0.023} = \dfrac{6.9\times 10^{-3}}{2.3\times 10^{-2}}$

$= \dfrac{6.9}{2.3}\times 10^{-3-(-2)}$

$= 3\times 10^{-1}$

**77.** $\dfrac{18,200\times 100}{91,000} = \dfrac{1.82\times 10^4 \times 1\times 10^2}{9.1\times 10^4}$

$= \dfrac{1.82\times 10^6}{9.1\times 10^4}$

$= 0.2\times 10^{6-4}$

$= 2\times 10^{-1}\times 10^2$

$= 2\times 10^{-1+2}$

$= 2\times 10^1$

**79.** $\dfrac{6000\times 0.006}{0.009\times 400} = \dfrac{6\times 10^3 \times 6\times 10^{-3}}{9\times 10^{-3}\times 4\times 10^2}$

$= \dfrac{36\times 10^0}{36\times 10^{-1}}$

$= 1\times 10^{0-(-1)}$

$= 1\times 10^1$

**81.** $\dfrac{0.00064\times 2000}{16,000} = \dfrac{6.4\times 10^{-4}\times 2\times 10^3}{1.6\times 10^4}$

$= \dfrac{12.8\times 10^{-1}}{1.6\times 10^4}$

$= 8\times 10^{-1-4}$

$= 8\times 10^{-5}$

**83.** $\dfrac{66,000\times 0.001}{0.002\times 0.003} = \dfrac{6.6\times 10^4 \times 1\times 10^{-3}}{2\times 10^{-3}\times 3\times 10^{-3}}$

$= \dfrac{6.6\times 10^1}{6\times 10^{-6}}$

$= 1.1\times 10^{1-(-6)}$

$= 1.1\times 10^7$

**85.** $\dfrac{9.24\times 10^{15}}{(2.2\times 10^{-2})(1.2\times 10^{-5})}$

$= \dfrac{9.24}{(2.2)(1.2)}\cdot 10^{15-(-2)-(-5)}$

$= 3.5\times 10^{22}$

**87.** $200,000\times 10^{-8} = (2\times 10^5)\times 10^{-8}$

$= 2\times 10^{-3}$ second

**89.** $(3.8\times 10^{-6})(1.64\times 10^{-5}) = 6.232\times 10^{-11}$

The volume is $6.232\times 10^{-11}$ cubic meter.

**91.** $12m-14-15m-1 = -3m-15$

**93.** $-9y-(5-6y)=-9y-5+6y=-3y-5$

**95.** $5(x-3)-4(2x-5)=5x-15-8x+20$
$$=-3x+5$$

**97.** $\left(\dfrac{3x^{-1}}{y^{-3}}\right)\left(5x^{-7}\right)=\dfrac{3\cdot5x^{-1+(-7)}}{y^{-3}}$

$$=\dfrac{15x^{-8}}{y^{-3}}$$

$$=\dfrac{15y^3}{x^8}$$

The area is $\dfrac{15y^3}{x^8}$ square feet.

**99.**
$$D=\dfrac{M}{V}$$
$$3.12\times10^{-2}=\dfrac{M}{4.269\times10^{14}}$$
$$(3.12\times10^{-2})(4.269\times10^{14})=M$$
$$3.12\times4.269\times10^{-2+14}=M$$
$$13.31928\times10^{12}=M$$
$$1.331928\times10^1\times10^{12}=M$$
$$1.331928\times10^{13}=M$$

The mass is $1.331928\times10^{13}$ tons.

**101.** $a^{-2}=\dfrac{1}{a^2}$

Since 1 and $a^2$ are both positive, their quotient cannot be negative. Therefore, no, there is no such $a$.

**103.** $\dfrac{3.016\times10^8}{3.536\times10^6}=\dfrac{3.016}{3.536}\times10^{8-6}$
$$=0.85\times10^2$$
$$=85$$
The population density for the United States in 2007 was 85 people per square mile.

**105.** $\dfrac{2.82\times10^9}{4.44\times10^8}=\dfrac{2.82}{4.44}\times10^{9-8}$
$$=0.64\times10^1$$
$$=6.4$$
The Tokyo subway's volume is 6.4 times greater than that of Toronto's subway.

**107.** $\dfrac{4.87\times10^6}{15.38\times10^6}=\dfrac{4.87}{15.38}\times10^{6-6}$
$$=0.317\times10^0$$
$$=31.7\%$$
Therefore, 31.7% of the residents of Beijing could speak a foreign language.

**Section 5.3**

**Practice Exercises**

**1. a.** $4x^5$: The exponent on $x$ is 5, so the degree of the term is 5.

**b.** $-4^3y^3$: The exponent on $y$ is 3, so the degree of the term is 3.

**c.** The degree of $z$, or $z^1$, is 1.

**d.** $65a^3b^7c$: The degree is the sum of the exponents on the variables, or $3+7+1=11$.

**e.** The degree of 36, which can be written as $36x^0$, is 0.

**2.**

| | Polynomial | Degree | Classification |
|---|---|---|---|
| **a.** | $3x^4+2x^2-3$ | 4 | trinomial |
| **b.** | $9abc^3$ | 5 | monomial |
| **c.** | $8x^5+5x^3$ | 5 | binomial |

**3.**

| Term | Degree |
|---|---|
| $2x^3y$ | 4 |
| $-3x^3y^2$ | 5 |
| $-9y^5$ | 5 |
| $9.6$ | 0 |

The largest degree of any term is 5, so the degree of this polynomial is 5.

**4. a.** Substitute −1 for $x$ and simplify.
$$P(x) = -5x^2 + 2x - 8$$
$$P(-1) = -5(-1)^2 + 2(-1) - 8$$
$$= -5 - 2 - 8$$
$$= -15$$

**b.** Substitute 3 for $x$ and simplify.
$$P(x) = -5x^2 + 2x - 8$$
$$P(3) = -5(3)^2 + 2(3) - 8$$
$$= -45 + 6 - 8$$
$$= -47$$

**5.** $P(t) = -16t^2 + 290$

Let $t = 0$: $P(0) = -16(0)^2 + 290 = 290$

Let $t = 2$: $P(2) = -16(2)^2 + 290 = 226$

The height of the object at $t = 0$ second is 290 feet and the height at $t = 2$ seconds is 226 feet.

**6. a.** $8x^4 - 5x^4 - 5x = (8-5)x^4 - 5x$
$$= 3x^4 - 5x$$

**b.** $4ab - 5b + 3ab + 2b$
$$= 4ab + 3ab - 5b + 2b$$
$$= (4+3)ab + (-5+2)b$$
$$= 7ab - 3b$$

**7. a.** $(3a^4b - 5ab^2 + 7) + (9ab^2 - 12)$
$$= 3a^4b - 5ab^2 + 7 + 9ab^2 - 12$$
$$= 3a^4b - 5ab^2 + 9ab^2 + 7 - 12$$
$$= 3a^4b + 4ab^2 - 5$$

**b.** $(2x^5 - 3y + x - 6) + (4y - 2x - 3)$
$$= 2x^5 - 3y + x - 6 + 4y - 2x - 3$$
$$= 2x^5 - 3y + 4y + x - 2x - 6 - 3$$
$$= 2x^5 + y - x - 9$$

**8.** $(5x^3 - 3x^2 - 9x - 8) + (x^3 + 9x^2 + 2x)$
$$= 5x^3 + x^3 - 3x^2 + 9x^2 - 9x + 2x - 8$$
$$= 6x^3 + 6x^2 - 7x - 8$$

**9.** $(13a^4 - 7a^3 - 9) - (-2a^4 + 8a^3 - 12)$
$$= 13a^4 - 7a^3 - 9 + 2a^4 - 8a^3 + 12$$
$$= 13a^4 + 2a^4 - 7a^3 - 8a^3 - 9 + 12$$
$$= 15a^4 - 15a^3 + 3$$

**10.** $(11x^2y^2 - 7xy^2) - (5x^2y^2 - 3xy^2 + 5y^3)$
$$= 11x^2y^2 - 7xy^2 - 5x^2y^2 + 3xy^2 - 5y^3$$
$$= 6x^2y^2 - 4xy^2 - 5y^3$$

**11.** The degree of $f(x)$ is 3, which means that its graph has the shape of **C**.

**Graphing Calculator Explorations**

**1.** $(2x^2 + 7x + 6) + (x^3 - 6x^2 - 14)$
$$= x^3 - 4x^2 + 7x - 8$$

**2.** $(-14x^3 - x + 2) + (-x^3 + 3x^2 + 4x)$
$$= -15x^3 + 3x^2 + 3x + 2$$

**3.** $(1.8x^2 - 6.8x - 1.7) - (3.9x^2 - 3.6x)$
$$= -2.1x^2 - 3.2x - 1.7$$

**4.** $(-4.8x^2 + 12.5x - 7.8) - (3.1x^2 - 7.8x)$
$$= -7.9x^2 + 20.3x - 7.8$$

**5.** $(1.29x - 5.68) + (7.69x^2 - 2.55x + 10.98)$
$$= 7.69x^2 - 1.26x + 5.3$$

6. $(-0.98x^2 - 1.56x + 5.57) + (4.36x - 3.71)$
   $= -0.98x^2 + 2.8x + 1.86$

**Vocabulary and Readiness Check**

1. The numerical factor of a term is the <u>coefficient</u>.

2. A <u>polynomial</u> is a finite sum of terms in which all variables are raised to nonnegative integer powers and no variables appear in any denominator.

3. A <u>binomial</u> is a polynomial with 2 terms.

4. A <u>monomial</u> is a polynomial with 1 term.

5. A <u>trinomial</u> is a polynomial with 3 terms.

6. The degree of a term is the sum of the exponents on the <u>variables</u> in the term.

7. The <u>degree</u> of a polynomial is the largest degree of all its terms.

8. <u>Like</u> terms contain the same variables raised to the same powers.

9. $5x + x = 6x$

10. $5x - x = 4x$

11. $y + y = 2y$

12. $z^2 + z^2 = 2z^2$

13. $7xy^2 - y^2 = 7xy^2 - y^2$

14. $x^3 - 9x^3 = -8x^3$

**Exercise Set 5.3**

1. 4 has degree 0.

3. $5x^2$ has degree 2.

5. $-3xy^2$ has degree $1 + 2 = 3$.

7. $-8^7 y^3$ has degree 3 (note: the degree on the *variable* is 3).

9. $3.78ab^3c^5$ has degree $1 + 3 + 5 = 9$.

11. $6x + 0.3$ has degree 1 and is a binomial.

13. $3x^2 - 2x + 5$ has degree 2 and is a trinomial.

15. $-3^4 xy^2$ has degree $1 + 2 = 3$ and is a monomial.

17.

| Term | Degree |
|------|--------|
| $x^2 y$ | 3 |
| $-4xy^2$ | 3 |
| $5x$ | 1 |
| $y^4$ | 4 |

19. $P(x) = x^2 + x + 1$
    $P(7) = 7^2 + 7 + 1 = 49 + 7 + 1 = 57$

21. $Q(x) = 5x^2 - 1$
    $Q(-10) - 5(-10)^2 - 1$
    $= 5(100) - 1$
    $= 500 - 1$
    $= 499$

23. $Q(x) = 5x^2 - 1$
    $Q\left(\dfrac{1}{4}\right) = 5\left(\dfrac{1}{4}\right)^2 - 1$
    $= 5\left(\dfrac{1}{16}\right) - 1$
    $= \dfrac{5}{16} - \dfrac{16}{16}$
    $= -\dfrac{11}{16}$

25. $P(t) = -16t^2 + 1125$
    $P(2) = -16(2)^2 + 1125 = 1061$ feet

27. $P(t) = -16t^2 + 1125$
    $P(6) = -16(6)^2 + 1125 = 549$ feet

29. $5y + y = 6y$

**31.** $4x + 7x - 3 = 11x - 3$

**33.** $4xy + 2x - 3xy - 1 = xy + 2x - 1$

**35.** $7x^2 - 2xy + 5y^2 - x^2 + xy + 11y^2$
     $= 6x^2 - xy + 16y^2$

**37.** $(9y^2 - 8) + (9y^2 - 9) = 18y^2 - 17$

**39.** $\quad x^2 + \quad xy - \quad y^2$
     $\underline{2x^2 - 4xy + 7y^2}$
     $3x^2 - 3xy + 6y^2$

**41.** $\quad x^2 - 6x + 3$
     $\underline{+ \quad (2x + 5)}$
     $\quad x^2 - 4x + 8$

**43.** $(9y^2 - 7y + 5) - (8y^2 - 7y + 2)$
     $= 9y^2 - 7y + 5 - 8y^2 + 7y - 2$
     $= y^2 + 3$

**45.** $(4x^2 + 2x) - (6x^2 - 3x)$
     $= 4x^2 + 2x - 6x^2 + 3x$
     $= -2x^2 + 5x$

**47.** $\quad 3x^2 - 4x + 8$
     $\underline{-5x^2 \quad\quad + 7}$
     $-2x^2 - 4x + 15$

**49.** $(5x - 11) + (-x - 2) = 5x - 11 - x - 2$
                                    $= 4x - 13$

**51.** $(7x^2 + x + 1) - (6x^2 + x - 1)$
     $= 7x^2 + x + 1 - 6x^2 - x + 1$
     $= x^2 + 2$

**53.** $(7x^3 - 4x + 8) + (5x^3 + 4x + 8x)$
     $= 7x^3 - 4x + 8 + 5x^3 + 4x + 8x$
     $= 12x^3 + 8x + 8$

**55.** $\quad 9x^3 - 2x^2 + 4x - 7$
     $\underline{-2x^3 + 6x^2 + 4x - 3}$
     $\quad 7x^3 + 4x^2 + 8x - 10$

**57.** $(y^2 + 4yx + 7) + (-19y^2 + 7yx + 7)$
     $= y^2 + 4yx + 7 - 19y^2 + 7yx + 7$
     $= -18y^2 + 11yx + 14$

**59.** $(3x^3 - b + 2a - 6) + (-4x^3 + b + 6a - 6)$
     $= 3x^3 - b + 2a - 6 - 4x^3 + b + 6a - 6$
     $= -x^3 + 8a - 12$

**61.** $(4x^2 - 6x + 2) - (-x^2 + 3x + 5)$
     $= 4x^2 - 6x + 2 + x^2 - 3x - 5$
     $= 5x^2 - 9x - 3$

**63.** $(-3x + 8) + (-3x^2 + 3x - 5)$
     $= -3x + 8 - 3x^2 + 3x - 5$
     $= -3x^2 + 3$

**65.** $(-3 + 4x^2 + 7xy^2) + (2x^3 - x^2 + xy^2)$
     $= -3 + 4x^2 + 7xy^2 + 2x^3 - x^2 + xy^2$
     $= 2x^3 + 3x^2 + 8xy^2 - 3$

**67.** $\quad 6y^2 - 6y + 4$
     $\underline{\quad y^2 + 6y - 7}$
     $\quad 7y^2 \quad\quad\quad 3$

**69.** $\quad 3x^2 + 15x + 8$
     $\underline{2x^2 + \; 7x + 8}$
     $\quad 5x^2 + 22x + 16$

**71.** $\quad \dfrac{1}{2}x^2 - \dfrac{1}{3}x^2 y \quad\quad\quad\quad + 2y^3$
     $\underline{\dfrac{1}{4}x^2 \quad\quad\quad - \dfrac{8}{3}x^2 y^2 - \dfrac{1}{2}y^3}$
     $\dfrac{3}{4}x^2 - \dfrac{1}{3}x^2 y - \dfrac{8}{3}x^2 y^2 + \dfrac{3}{2}y^3$

**73.** $(5q^4 - 2q^2 - 3q) + (-6q^4 + 3q^2 + 5)$
     $= 5q^4 - 2q^2 - 3q - 6q^4 + 3q^2 + 5$
     $= -q^4 + q^2 - 3q + 5$

**75.** 
$$7x^2 + 4x + 9$$
$$+\ 8x^2 + 7x - 8$$
$$\overline{15x^2 + 11x + 1}$$
$$-\qquad\quad 3x + 7$$
$$\overline{15x^2 + 8x - 6}$$

**77.** $(4x^4 - 7x^2 + 3) + (2 - 3x^4)$
$$= 4x^4 - 7x^2 + 3 + 2 - 3x^4$$
$$= x^4 - 7x^2 + 5$$

**79.** $\left(\dfrac{2}{3}x^2 - \dfrac{1}{6}x + \dfrac{5}{6}\right) - \left(\dfrac{1}{3}x^2 + \dfrac{5}{6}x - \dfrac{1}{6}\right)$
$$= \dfrac{2}{3}x^2 - \dfrac{1}{6}x + \dfrac{5}{6} - \dfrac{1}{3}x^2 - \dfrac{5}{6}x + \dfrac{1}{6}$$
$$= \dfrac{1}{3}x^2 - x + 1$$

**81.** If $L = 5$, $W = 4$, and $H = 9$, then
$$2HL + 2LW + 2HW$$
$$= 2(9)(5) + 2(5)(4) + 2(9)(4)$$
$$= 90 + 40 + 72$$
$$= 202$$
The surface area is 202 square inches.

**83.** $P(t) = -16t^2 + 300t$

    **a.** $P(1) = -16(1)^2 + 300(1) = 284$ feet

    **b.** $P(2) = -16(2)^2 + 300(2) = 536$ feet

    **c.** $P(3) = -16(3)^2 + 300(3) = 756$ feet

    **d.** $P(4) = -16(4)^2 + 300(4) = 944$ feet

    **e.** Answers may vary

    **f.**
$$0 = -16t^2 + 300t$$
$$0 = -4t(4t - 75)$$
$$4t - 75 = 0$$
$$4t = 75$$
$$t = \dfrac{75}{4} = 18.75$$
        19 sec

**85.** $P(x) = 45x - 100,000$
$$P(4000) = 45(4000) - 100,000$$
$$= 80,000$$
The profit is $80,000.

**87.** $R(x) = 2x$
$$R(20,000) = 2(20,000)$$
$$= 40,000$$
The revenue is $40,000.

**89.** A: The degree of $f(x)$ is 2, so the graph has the shape of A or C. The coefficient of $x^2$ is a positive number, so the graph has the shape of A.

**91.** D: The degree of $g(x)$ is 3, so the graph has the shape of B or D. The coefficient of $x^3$ is a negative number, so the graph has the shape of D.

**93.** $5(3x - 2) = 15x - 10$

**95.** $-2(x^2 - 5x + 6) = -2x^2 + 10x - 12$

**97.** The opposite of $8x - 6$ is $-(8x - 6)$ or $-8x + 6$; a and c.

**99.** $(12x - 1.7) - (15x + 6.2)$
$$= 12x - 1.7 - 15x - 6.2$$
$$= -3x - 7.9$$

**101.** Answers may vary

**103.** Answers may vary

**105.** $(4x^{2a} - 3x^a + 0.5) - (x^{2a} - 5x^a - 0.2)$
$$= 4x^{2a} - 3x^a + 0.5 - x^{2a} + 5x^a + 0.2$$
$$= 3x^{2a} + 2x^a + 0.7$$

**107.** $(8x^{2y} - 7x^y + 3) + (-4x^{2y} + 9x^y - 14)$
$$= 8x^{2y} - 7x^y + 3 - 4x^{2y} + 9x^y - 14$$
$$= 4x^{2y} + 2x^y - 11$$

**109.** $P = 2l + 2w$
$$= 2(3x^2 - x + 2y) + 2(x + 5y)$$
$$= 6x^2 - 2x + 4y + 2x + 10y$$
$$= 6x^2 + 14y$$
The perimeter is $P = (6x^2 + 14y)$ units.

**111.** $P(x) + Q(x) = (3x + 3) + (4x^2 - 6x + 3)$
$$= 3x + 3 + 4x^2 - 6x + 3$$
$$= 4x^2 - 3x + 6$$

**113.** $Q(x) - R(x) = (4x^2 - 6x + 3) - (5x^2 - 7)$
$$= 4x^2 - 6x + 3 - 5x^2 + 7$$
$$= -x^2 - 6x + 10$$

**115.** $2[Q(x)] - R(x)$
$$= 2(4x^2 - 6x + 3) - (5x^2 - 7)$$
$$= 8x^2 - 12x + 6 - 5x^2 + 7$$
$$= 3x^2 - 12x + 13$$

**117.** $3[R(x)] + 4[P(x)] = 3(5x^2 - 7) + 4(3x + 3)$
$$= 15x^2 - 21 + 12x + 12$$
$$= 15x^2 + 12x - 9$$

**119.** $P(x) = 2x - 3$

     **a.** $P(a) = 2a - 3$

     **b.** $P(-x) = 2(-x) - 3 = -2x - 3$

     **c.** $P(x + h) = 2(x + h) - 3 = 2x + 2h - 3$

**121.** $P(x) = 4x$

     **a.** $P(a) = 4a$

     **b.** $P(-x) = 4(-x) = -4x$

     **c.** $P(x + h) = 4(x + h) = 4x + 4h$

**123.** $P(x) = 4x - 1$

     **a.** $P(a) = 4a - 1$

     **b.** $P(-x) = 4(-x) - 1 = -4x - 1$

     **c.** $P(x + h) = 4(x + h) - 1 = 4x + 4h - 1$

**125.** $f(x) = 0.07x^2 - 0.8x + 3.6$

     **a.** Jan 2004 means that $x = 1$.
$$f(1) = 0.07(1)^2 - 0.8(1) + 3.6$$
$$= 2.9 \text{ million}$$

     **b.** Oct 2006 means that $x = 34$.
$$f(34) = 0.07(34)^2 - 0.8(34) + 3.6$$
$$= 57.3 \text{ million}$$

     **c.** May 2009 means that $x = 65$.
$$f(65) = 0.07(65)^2 - 0.8(65) + 3.6$$
$$= 247.4 \text{ million}$$

     **d.** Answers may vary

**127.** $f(x) = -0.39x^2 + 2.49x + 38.7$

     **a.** 2003 means that $x = 4$.
$$f(4) = -0.39(4)^2 + 2.49(4) + 38.7$$
$$= 42.4 \text{ million}$$

     **b.** 2008 means that $x = 9$.
$$f(9) = -0.39(9)^2 + 2.49(9) + 38.7$$
$$= 29.5 \text{ million}$$

**129.** $f(x) = -0.005x^2 + 0.377x + 1.71$

     **a.** 2003 means that $x = 8$.
$$f(8) = -0.005(8)^2 + 0.377(8) + 1.71$$
$$= 4.4 \text{ million}$$

     **b.** 2010 means that $x = 15$.
$$f(15)$$
$$= -0.005(15)^2 + 0.377(15) + 1.71$$
$$= 6.2 \text{ million}$$

**Section 5.4**

**Practice Exercises**

**1. a.** $(3x^4)(2x^2) = 3(2)(x^4)(x^2) = 6x^6$

     **b.** $(-5m^4np^3)(-8mnp^5)$
$$= -5(-8)(m^4m)(n \cdot n)(p^3p^5)$$
$$= 40m^5n^2p^8$$

**2. a.** $3x(7x - 1) = 3x(7x) + 3x(-1)$
$$= 21x^2 - 3x$$

     **b.** $-5a^2(3a^2 - 6a + 5)$
$$= -5a^2(3a^2) + (-5a^2)(-6a)$$
$$\qquad + (-5a^2)(5)$$
$$= -15a^4 + 30a^3 - 25a^2$$

**c.**  $-mn^3(5m^2n^2 + 2mn - 5m)$
$= -mn^3(5m^2n^2) + (-mn^3)(2mn)$
$\qquad + (-mn^3)(-5m)$
$= -5m^3n^5 - 2m^2n^4 + 5m^2n^3$

**3. a.**  $(x+5)(2x+3) = x(2x+3) + 5(2x+3)$
$\qquad\qquad = 2x^2 + 3x + 10x + 15$
$\qquad\qquad = 2x^2 + 13x + 15$

**b.**  $(3x-1)(x^2 - 6x + 2)$
$= 3x(x^2 - 6x + 2) + (-1)(x^2 - 6x + 2)$
$= 3x^3 - 18x^2 + 6x - x^2 + 6x - 2$
$= 3x^3 - 19x^2 + 12x - 2$

**4.**
$$\begin{array}{r} x^2 - 4x - 5 \\ 3x^2 + 2 \\ \hline 2x^2 - 8x - 10 \\ 3x^4 - 12x^3 - 15x^2 \\ \hline 3x^4 - 12x^3 - 13x^2 - 8x - 10 \end{array}$$

**5.**  $(x-5)(x+3)$
$= x \cdot x + 3 \cdot x + (-5)x + (-5)(3)$
$= x^2 + 3x - 5x - 15$
$= x^2 - 2x - 15$

**6. a.**  $(3x-5)(2x-7)$
$= 3x(2x) + 3x(-7) + (-5)(2x)$
$\qquad + (-5)(-7)$
$= 6x^2 - 21x - 10x + 35$
$= 6x^2 - 31x + 35$

**b.**  $(2x^2 - 3y)(4x^2 + y)$
$= 8x^4 + 2x^2y - 12x^2y - 3y^2$
$= 8x^4 - 10x^2y - 3y^2$

**7. a.**  $(x+6)^2 = x^2 + 2 \cdot x \cdot 6 + 6^2$
$\qquad\qquad = x^2 + 12x + 36$

**b.**  $(x-2)^2 = x^2 - 2 \cdot x \cdot 2 + 2^2$
$\qquad\qquad = x^2 - 4x + 4$

**c.**  $(3x+5y)^2$
$= (3x)^2 + 2(3x)(5y) + (5y)^2$
$= 9x^2 + 30xy + 25y^2$

**d.**  $(3x^2 - 8b)^2$
$= (3x^2)^2 - 2(3x^2)(8b) + (8b)^2$
$= 9x^4 - 48x^2b + 64b^2$

**8. a.**  $(x-7)(x+7) = x^2 - 7^2 = x^2 - 49$

**b.**  $(2a+5)(2a-5) = (2a)^2 - 5^2$
$\qquad\qquad\qquad = 4a^2 - 25$

**c.**  $\left(5x^2 + \frac{1}{4}\right)\left(5x^2 - \frac{1}{4}\right) = (5x^2)^2 - \left(\frac{1}{4}\right)^2$
$\qquad\qquad\qquad = 25x^4 - \frac{1}{16}$

**d.**  $(a^3 - 4b^2)(a^3 + 4b^2) = (a^3)^2 - (4b^2)^2$
$\qquad\qquad\qquad = a^6 - 16b^4$

**9.**  $[2 + (3x - y)]^2$
$= 2^2 + 2(2)(3x - y) + (3x - y)^2$
$= 4 + 4(3x - y) + (3x)^2 - 2(3x) \cdot y + y^2$
$= 4 + 12x - 4y + 9x^2 - 6xy + y^2$

**10.**  $[(3x - y) - 5][(3x - y) + 5]$
$= (3x - y)^2 - 5^2$
$= (3x)^2 - 2(3x)(y) + y^2 - 25$
$= 9x^2 - 6xy + y^2 - 25$

**11.**  $(x+4)(x-4)(x^2 - 16)$
$= (x^2 - 16)(x^2 - 16)$
$= (x^2 - 16)^2$
$= x^4 - 32x^2 + 256$

**12.**  $f(x) = x^2 - 3x + 5$
$f(h+1) = (h+1)^2 - 3(h+1) + 5$
$\qquad = h^2 + 2h + 1 - 3h - 3 + 5$
$\qquad = h^2 - h + 3$

**Graphing Calculator Explorations**

**1.**  $(x+4)(x-4) = x^2 - 16$

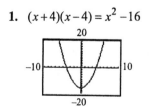

**2.** $(x+3)(x+3) = x^2 + 6x + 9$

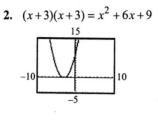

**3.** $(3x-7)^2 = 9x^2 - 42x + 49$

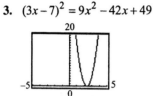

**4.** $(5x-2)^2 = 25x^2 - 20x + 4$

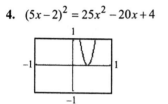

**5.** $(5x+1)(x^2 - 3x - 2) = 5x^3 - 14x^2 - 13x - 2$

**6.** $(7x+4)(2x^2 + 3x - 5) = 14x^3 + 29x^2 - 23x - 20$

**Vocabulary and Readiness Check**

**1.** $(6x^3)\left(\dfrac{1}{2}x^3\right) = \underline{3x^6}$

**2.** $(x+7)^2 = \underline{x^2 + 14x + 49}$

**3.** $(x+7)(x-7) = \underline{x^2 - 49}$

**4.** The product of $(3x-1)(4x^2 - 2x + 1)$ is a polynomial of degree 3.

**5.** If $f(x) = x^2 + 1$ then $f(a+1) = \underline{(a+1)^2 + 1}$.

**6.** $[x+(2y+1)]^2$
$= \underline{[x+(2y+1)][x+(2y+1)]}$

**Exercise Set 5.4**

**1.** $(-4x^3)(3x^2) = -4(3)x^5 = -12x^5$

**3.** $3x(4x+7) = 3x(4x) + 3x(7)$
$\qquad\qquad = 12x^2 + 21x$

**5.** $-6xy(4x+y) = -6xy(4x) - 6xy(y)$
$\qquad\qquad\qquad = -24x^2 y - 6xy^2$

**7.** $-4ab(xa^2 + ya^2 - 3)$
$= -4ab(xa^2) - 4ab(ya^2) - 4ab(-3)$
$= -4a^3 bx - 4a^3 by + 12ab$

**9.**
$$\begin{array}{r} 2x+4 \\ \times \quad\quad x-3 \\ \hline -6x-12 \\ 2x^2 + 4x \quad\quad\quad \\ \hline 2x^2 - 2x - 12 \end{array}$$

**11.** $(2x+3)(x^3 - x + 2)$
$= 2x(x^3 - x + 2) + 3(x^3 - x + 2)$
$= 2x^4 - 2x^2 + 4x + 3x^3 - 3x + 6$
$= 2x^4 + 3x^3 - 2x^2 + x + 6$

**13.**
$$\begin{array}{r} 3x-2 \\ \times \quad\quad 5x+1 \\ \hline 3x-2 \\ 15x^2 - 10x \quad\quad\quad \\ \hline 15x^2 - 7x - 2 \end{array}$$

**15.**
$$\begin{array}{r} 3m^2 + 2m - 1 \\ \times \quad\quad 5m + 2 \\ \hline 6m^2 + 4m - 2 \\ 15m^3 + 10m^2 - 5m \quad\quad\quad \\ \hline 15m^3 + 16m^2 - m - 2 \end{array}$$

**17.** $(x-3)(x+4) = x\cdot x + x(4) - 3\cdot x - 3(4)$
$\qquad\qquad\qquad = x^2 + 4x - 3x - 12$
$\qquad\qquad\qquad = x^2 + x - 12$

**19.** $(5x+8y)(2x-y)$
$= 5x \cdot 2x + 5x(-y) + 8y(2x) + 8y(-y)$
$= 10x^2 - 5xy + 16xy - 8y^2$
$= 10x^2 + 11xy - 8y^2$

**21.** $(3x-1)(x+3) = 3x \cdot x + 3x \cdot 3 - 1 \cdot x - 1 \cdot 3$
$= 3x^2 + 9x - x - 3$
$= 3x^2 + 8x - 3$

**23.** $\left(3x + \dfrac{1}{2}\right)\left(3x - \dfrac{1}{2}\right)$
$= 3x(3x) + 3x\left(-\dfrac{1}{2}\right) + \dfrac{1}{2}(3x) + \dfrac{1}{2}\left(-\dfrac{1}{2}\right)$
$= 9x^2 - \dfrac{3}{2}x + \dfrac{3}{2}x - \dfrac{1}{4}$
$= 9x^2 - \dfrac{1}{4}$

**25.** $(5x^2 - 2y^2)(x^2 - 3y^2)$
$= 5x^4 - 15x^2 y^2 - 2x^2 y^2 + 6y^4$
$= 5x^4 - 17x^2 y^2 + 6y^4$

**27.** $(x+4)^2 = x^2 + 2(x)(4) + 4^2$
$= x^2 + 8x + 16$

**29.** $(6y-1)(6y+1) = (6y)^2 - 1^2 = 36y^2 - 1$

**31.** $(3x - y)^2 = (3x)^2 - 2(3x)(y) + y^2$
$= 9x^2 - 6xy + y^2$

**33.** $(5b - 6y)(5b + 6y) = (5b)^2 - (6y)^2$
$= 25b^2 - 36y^2$

**35.** $[3 + (4b+1)]^2$
$= 3^2 + 2(3)(4b+1) + (4b+1)^2$
$= 9 + 6(4b+1) + (4b)^2 + 2(4b)(1) + 1^2$
$= 9 + 24b + 6 + 16b^2 + 8b + 1$
$= 16b^2 + 32b + 16$

**37.** $[(2s-3)-1][(2s-3)+1]$
$= (2s-3)^2 - 1^2$
$= (2s)^2 - 2(2s)(3) + 3^2 - 1$
$= 4s^2 - 12s + 9 - 1$
$= 4s^2 - 12s + 8$

**39.** $[(xy+4)-6]^2$
$= (xy+4)^2 - 2(xy+4)(6) + 6^2$
$= (xy)^2 + 2(xy)(4) + 4^2 - 12(xy+4) + 36$
$= x^2 y^2 + 8xy + 16 - 12xy - 48 + 36$
$= x^2 y^2 - 4xy + 4$

**41.** Answers may vary

**43.** $(x+y)(x-y)(x^2 - y^2) = (x^2 - y^2)(x^2 - y^2)$
$= (x^2)^2 - 2x^2 y^2 + (y^2)^2$
$= x^4 - 2x^2 y^2 + y^4$

**45.** $(x-2)^4 = (x-2)^2 (x-2)^2$
$= (x^2 - 4x + 4)(x^2 - 4x + 4)$

$$
\begin{array}{r}
x^2 - 4x + 4 \\
\times \quad x^2 - 4x + 4 \\
\hline
4x^2 - 16x + 16 \\
-4x^3 + 16x^2 - 16x \\
x^4 - 4x^3 + 4x^2 \\
\hline
x^4 - 8x^3 + 24x^2 - 32x + 16
\end{array}
$$

**47.** $(x-5)(x+5)(x^2+25) = (x^2 - 25)(x^2 + 25)$
$= (x^2)^2 - 25^2$
$= x^4 - 625$

**49.** $(3x+1)(3x+5)$
$= (3x)^2 + 3x(5) + 1(3x) + 1(5)$
$= 9x^2 + 15x + 3x + 5$
$= 9x^2 + 18x + 5$

**51.** $(2x^3 + 5)(5x^2 + 4x + 1)$
$= 2x^3(5x^2 + 4x + 1) + 5(5x^2 + 4x + 1)$
$= 10x^5 + 8x^4 + 2x^3 + 25x^2 + 20x + 5$

**53.** $(7x-3)(7x+3) = (7x)^2 - 3^2 = 49x^2 - 9$

**55.**

$$
\begin{array}{r}
3x^2 + 4x - 4 \\
\times \quad 3x + 6 \\
\hline
18x^2 + 24x - 24 \\
9x^3 + 12x^2 - 12x \\
\hline
9x^3 + 30x^2 + 12x - 24
\end{array}
$$

**57.** $\left(4x+\dfrac{1}{3}\right)\left(4x-\dfrac{1}{2}\right)$

$= (4x)^2 + 4x\left(-\dfrac{1}{2}\right) + \dfrac{1}{3}(4x) + \dfrac{1}{3}\left(-\dfrac{1}{2}\right)$

$= 16x^2 - 2x + \dfrac{4}{3}x - \dfrac{1}{6}$

$= 16x^2 - \dfrac{2}{3}x - \dfrac{1}{6}$

**59.** $(6x+1)^2 = (6x)^2 + 2(6x)(1) + 1^2$

$\qquad\qquad = 36x^2 + 12x + 1$

**61.** $(x^2+2y)(x^2-2y) = (x^2)^2 - (2y)^2$

$\qquad\qquad\qquad\qquad = x^4 - 4y^2$

**63.**

$\qquad\qquad 5a^2b^2 - 6a - 6b$

$\underline{\times \qquad\qquad -6a^2b^2}$

$-30a^4b^4 + 36a^3b^2 + 36a^2b^3$

**65.** $(a-4)(2a-4) = 2a^2 - 4a - 8a + 16$

$\qquad\qquad\qquad = 2a^2 - 12a + 16$

**67.** $(7ab+3c)(7ab-3c) = (7ab)^2 - (3c)^2$

$\qquad\qquad\qquad\qquad = 49a^2b^2 - 9c^2$

**69.** $(m-4)^2 = m^2 - 2(m)(4) + 4^2$

$\qquad\qquad = m^2 - 8m + 16$

**71.** $(3x+1)^2 = (3x)^2 + 2(3x)(1) + 1^2$

$\qquad\qquad = 9x^2 + 6x + 1$

**73.** $(y-4)(y-3) = y^2 - 3y - 4y + 12$

$\qquad\qquad\qquad = y^2 - 7y + 12$

**75.** $(x+y)(2x-1)(x+1)$

$= (x+y)(2x^2 + 2x - x - 1)$

$= (x+y)(2x^2 + x - 1)$

$= x(2x^2 + x - 1) + y(2x^2 + x - 1)$

$= 2x^3 + x^2 - x + 2x^2y + xy - y$

$= 2x^3 + 2x^2y + x^2 + xy - x - y$

**77.**

$\qquad\qquad 3x^2 + 2x - 1$

$\underline{\times \qquad\quad 3x^2 + 2x - 1}$

$\qquad\qquad -3x^2 - 2x + 1$

$\qquad 6x^3 + 4x^2 - 2x$

$\underline{9x^4 + 6x^3 - 3x^2}$

$9x^4 + 12x^3 - 2x^2 - 4x + 1$

**79.**

$\qquad\qquad 4x^2 - 2x + 5$

$\underline{\times \qquad\qquad 3x + 1}$

$\qquad\qquad 4x^2 - 2x + 5$

$\underline{12x^3 - 6x^2 + 15x}$

$12x^3 - 2x^2 + 13x + 5$

**81.** $f(x) = x^2 - 3x$

$\quad f(a) = a^2 - 3a$

**83.** $f(x) = x^2 - 3x$

$\quad f(a+h) = (a+h)^2 - 3(a+h)$

$\qquad\qquad = a^2 + 2ah + h^2 - 3a - 3h$

**85.** $f(x) = x^2 - 3x$

$\quad f(b-2) = (b-2)^2 - 3(b-2)$

$\qquad\qquad = b^2 - 4b + 4 - 3b + 6$

$\qquad\qquad = b^2 - 7b + 10$

**87.** $y = -2x + 7$

$\quad m = -2$

**89.** $3x - 5y = 14$

$\qquad -5y = -3x + 14$

$\qquad\quad y = \dfrac{3}{5}x - \dfrac{14}{5}$

$\quad m = \dfrac{3}{5}$

**91.** Since any vertical line crosses the graph at most once, it is a function.

**93.** $7y(3z - 2) + 1 = 21yz - 14y + 1$

**95.** Answers may vary

**97.** $F(x) = x^2 + 3x + 2$

    **a.**  $F(a+h) = (a+h)^2 + 3(a+h) + 2$
$$= a^2 + 2ah + h^2 + 3a + 3h + 2$$

    **b.**  $F(a) = a^2 + 3a + 2$

    **c.**  $F(a+h) - F(a)$
$$= a^2 + 2ah + h^2 + 3a + 3h + 2 - (a^2 + 3a + 2)$$
$$= 2ah + h^2 + 3h$$

**99.** $5x^2 y^n (6y^{n+1} - 2)$
$$= 5x^2 y^n (6y^{n+1}) + 5x^2 y^n (-2)$$
$$= 30x^2 y^{2n+1} - 10x^2 y^n$$

**101.** $(x^a + 5)(x^{2a} - 3)$
$$= x^a \cdot x^{2a} + x^a(-3) + 5(x^{2a}) + 5(-3)$$
$$= x^{3a} - 3x^a + 5x^{2a} - 15$$

**103.** Area $= \pi r^2$
$$= \pi(5x - 2)^2$$
$$= \pi(25x^2 - 20x + 4) \text{ square km}$$

**105.** Area $= (3x - 2)^2 - x^2$
$$= (9x^2 - 12x + 4) - x^2$$
$$= (8x^2 - 12x + 4) \text{ square inches}$$

**107.** One operation is addition, the other is multiplication.

    **a.**  $(3x + 5) + (3x + 7) = 6x + 12$

    **b.**  $(3x + 5)(3x + 7)$
$$= 9x^2 + 21x + 15x + 35$$
$$= 9x^2 + 36x + 35$$

**109.** $P(x) \cdot R(x) = (5x)(x + 5)$
$$= 5x \cdot x + 5x \cdot 5$$
$$= 5x^2 + 25x$$

**111.** $[Q(x)]^2 = (x^2 - 2)^2$
$$= (x^2)^2 - 2(x^2)(2) + 2^2$$
$$= x^4 - 4x^2 + 4$$

**113.** $R(x) \cdot Q(x) = (x + 5)(x^2 - 2)$
$$= x^3 - 2x + 5x^2 - 10$$
$$= x^3 + 5x^2 - 2x - 10$$

**Section 5.5**

**Practice Exercises**

**1.**  $32x^4 y^2 = 2 \cdot 2 \cdot 2 \cdot 2 \cdot 2 \cdot x^4 \cdot y \cdot y$
$$48x^3 y = 2 \cdot 2 \cdot 2 \cdot 2 \cdot 3 \cdot x^3 \cdot y$$
$$24y^2 = 2 \cdot 2 \cdot 2 \cdot 3 \cdot y \cdot y$$
$$\text{GCF} = 2 \cdot 2 \cdot 2 \cdot y = 8y$$

**2.**  **a.**  The GCF of $6x^2$, 9, and $15x$ is 3.
$$6x^2 + 9 + 15x = 3(2x^2) + 3(3) + 3(5x)$$
$$= 3(2x^2 + 3 + 5x)$$

    **b.**  There is no common factor of the terms $3x$ and $-8y^3$ other than 1 (or $-1$).
$$3x - 8y^3$$

    **c.**  The GCF of $8a^4$ and $-2a^3$ is $2a^3$.
$$8a^4 - 2a^3 = 2a^3 \cdot 4a - 2a^3 \cdot 1$$
$$= 2a^3(4a - 1)$$

**3.**  Factor out the GCF of the two terms, $8x^3 y^2$.
$$64x^5 y^2 - 8x^3 y^2 = 8x^3 y^2 \cdot 8x^2 - 8x^3 y^2 \cdot 1$$
$$= 8x^3 y^2 (8x^2 - 1)$$

**4.**  Factor out the GCF of the three terms, $-xy^2$.
$$-9x^4 y^2 + 5x^2 y^2 + 7xy^2$$
$$= -xy^2 \cdot 9x^3 - xy^2(-5x) - xy^2(-7)$$
$$= -xy^2(9x^3 - 5x - 7)$$

**5.**  The GCF is $(x + 4)$.
$$3(x + 4) + 5b(x + 4) = (x + 4)(3 + 5b)$$

**6.**  $8b(a^3 + 2y) - (a^3 + 2y)$
$$= 8b(a^3 + 2y) - 1(a^3 + 2y)$$
$$= (a^3 + 2y)(8b - 1)$$

**7.**  $xy + 2y - 10 - 5x = (xy + 2y) + (-10 - 5x)$
$$= y(x + 2) - 5(2 + x)$$
$$= y(x + 2) - 5(x + 2)$$
$$= (x + 2)(y - 5)$$

**8.**  $a^3 + 2a^2 + 5a + 10 = (a^3 + 2a^2) + (5a + 10)$
$$= a^2(a + 2) + 5(a + 2)$$
$$= (a + 2)(a^2 + 5)$$

**9.** $x^2y^2 + 3y^2 - 5x^2 - 15$
$= (x^2y^2 + 3y^2) + (-5x^2 - 15)$
$= y^2(x^2 + 3) - 5(x^2 + 3)$
$= (x^2 + 3)(y^2 - 5)$

**10.** $pq + 3p - q - 3 = (pq + 3p) + (-q - 3)$
$= p(q + 3) - 1(q + 3)$
$= (q + 3)(p - 1)$

**Vocabulary and Readiness Check**

**1.** The reverse of multiplying is <u>factoring</u>.

**2.** The greatest common factor (GCF) of $x^7, x^3, x^5$ is <u>$x^3$</u>.

**3.** In general, the GCF of a list of common variables raised to powers is the <u>least</u> exponent in the list.

**4.** Factoring means writing as a <u>product</u>.

**5.** True or false: A factored form of $2xy^3 + 10xy$ is $2xy \cdot y^2 + 2xy \cdot 5$. <u>false</u>

**6.** True or false: A factored form of $x^3 - 6x^2 + x$ is $x(x^2 - 6x)$. <u>false</u>

**7.** True or false: A factored form of $5x - 5y + x^3 - x^2y$ is $5(x - y) + x^2(x - y)$. <u>false</u>

**8.** True or false: A factored form of $5x - 5y + x^3 - x^2y$ is $(x - y)(5 + x^2)$. <u>true</u>

**9.** $6 = 2 \cdot 3$
$12 = 2 \cdot 2 \cdot 3$
$GCF = 2 \cdot 3 = 6$

**10.** $9 = 3 \cdot 3$
$27 = 3 \cdot 3 \cdot 3$
$GCF = 3 \cdot 3 = 9$

**11.** $15x = 3 \cdot 5 \cdot x$
$10 = 2 \cdot 5$
$GCF = 5$

**12.** $9x = 3 \cdot 3 \cdot x$
$12 = 2 \cdot 2 \cdot 3$
$GCF = 3$

**13.** $13x = 13 \cdot x$
$2x = 2 \cdot x$
$GCF = x$

**14.** $4y = 4 \cdot y$
$5y = 5 \cdot y$
$GCF = y$

**15.** $7x = 7 \cdot x$
$14x = 2 \cdot 7 \cdot x$
$GCF = 7x$

**16.** $8z = 2 \cdot 2 \cdot 2 \cdot z$
$4z = 2 \cdot 2 \cdot z$
$GCF = 2 \cdot 2 \cdot z = 4z$

**Exercise Set 5.5**

**1.** $a^8, a^5,$ and $a^3$; $GCF = a^3$

**3.** $x^2y^3z^3, y^2z^3,$ and $xy^2z^2$; $GCF = y^2z^2$

**5.** $6x^3y, 9x^2y^2,$ and $12x^2y$; $GCF = 3x^2y$

**7.** $10x^3yz^3, 20x^2z^5, 45xz^3$; $GCF = 5xz^3$

**9.** $18x - 12 - 6 \cdot 3x - 6 \cdot 2 = 6(3x \quad 2)$

**11.** $4y^2 - 16xy^3 = 4y^2 \cdot 1 - 4y^2 \cdot 4xy$
$= 4y^2(1 - 4xy)$

**13.** $6x^5 - 8x^4 + 2x^3 = 2x^3(3x^2) - 2x^3(4x) + 2x^3(1)$
$= 2x^3(3x^2 - 4x + 1)$

**15.** $8a^3b^3 - 4a^2b^2 + 4ab + 16ab^2$
$= 4ab(2a^2b^2) - 4ab(ab) + 4ab(1) + 4ab(4b)$
$= 4ab(2a^2b^2 - ab + 1 + 4b)$

**17.** $6(x + 3) + 5a(x + 3) = (x + 3)(6 + 5a)$

**19.** $2x(z + 7) + (z + 7) = (z + 7)(2x + 1)$

**21.** $3x(x^2 + 5) - 2(x^2 + 5) = (x^2 + 5)(3x - 2)$

**23.** Answers may vary

**25.** $ab + 3a + 2b + 6 = a(b + 3) + 2(b + 3)$
$= (a + 2)(b + 3)$

**27.** $ac + 4a - 2c - 8 = a(c + 4) - 2(c + 4)$
$$= (a - 2)(c + 4)$$

**29.** $2xy - 3x - 4y + 6 = x(2y - 3) - 2(2y - 3)$
$$= (x - 2)(2y - 3)$$

**31.** $12xy - 8x - 3y + 2 = 4x(3y - 2) - (3y - 2)$
$$= (4x - 1)(3y - 2)$$

**33.** $6x^3 + 9 = 3(2x^3) + 3(3) = 3(2x^3 + 3)$

**35.** $x^3 + 3x^2 = x^2(x) + x^2(3) = x^2(x + 3)$

**37.** $8a^3 - 4a = 4a(2a^2) - 4a(1) = 4a(2a^2 - 1)$

**39.** $-20x^2y + 16xy^3 = -4xy(5x) - 4xy(4y^2)$
$$= -4xy(5x - 4y^2)$$

**41.** $10a^2b^3 + 5ab^2 - 15ab^3$
$$= 5ab^2(2ab) + 5ab^2(1) - 5ab^2(3b)$$
$$= 5ab^2(2ab + 1 - 3b)$$

**43.** $9abc^2 + 6a^2bc - 6ab + 3bc$
$$= 3b(3ac^2) + 3b(2a^2c) + 3b(-2a) + 3b(c)$$
$$= 3b(3ac^2 + 2a^2c - 2a + c)$$

**45.** $4x(y - 2) - 3(y - 2) = (y - 2)(4x - 3)$

**47.** $6xy + 10x + 9y + 15$
$$= 2x(3y + 5) + 3(3y + 5)$$
$$= (2x + 3)(3y + 5)$$

**49.** $xy + 3y - 5x - 15 = y(x + 3) - 5(x + 3)$
$$= (x + 3)(y - 5)$$

**51.** $6ab - 2a - 9b + 3 = 2a(3b - 1) - 3(3b - 1)$
$$= (3b - 1)(2a - 3)$$

**53.** $12xy + 18x + 2y + 3$
$$= 6x(2y + 3) + 1(2y + 3)$$
$$= (6x + 1)(2y + 3)$$

**55.** $2m(n - 8) - (n - 8) = (2m - 1)(n - 8)$

**57.** $15x^3y^2 - 18x^2y^2 = 3x^2y^2 \cdot 5x - 3x^2y^2 \cdot 6$
$$= 3x^2y^2(5x - 6)$$

**59.** $2x^2 + 3xy + 4x + 6y$
$$= x(2x + 3y) + 2(2x + 3y)$$
$$= (2x + 3y)(x + 2)$$

**61.** $5x^2 + 5xy - 3x - 3y = 5x(x + y) - 3(x + y)$
$$= (x + y)(5x - 3)$$

**63.** $x^3 + 3x^2 + 4x + 12 = x^2(x + 3) + 4(x + 3)$
$$= (x + 3)(x^2 + 4)$$

**65.** $x^3 - x^2 - 2x + 2 = x^2(x - 1) - 2(x - 1)$
$$= (x - 1)(x^2 - 2)$$

**67.** $(5x^2)(11x^5) = 5(11)x^2x^5 = 55x^7$

**69.** $(5x^2)^3 = 5^3(x^2)^3 = 125x^6$

**71.** $(x + 2)(x - 5) = x^2 - 5x + 2x - 10$
$$= x^2 - 3x - 10$$

**73.** $(x + 3)(x + 2) = x^2 + 3x + 2x + 6$
$$= x^2 + 5x + 6$$

**75.** $(y - 3)(y - 1) = y^2 - 1y - 3y + 3$
$$= y^2 - 4y + 3$$

**77.** d

   **a.**   $2(5x^2 - x + 1) = 10x^2 - 2x + 2$

   **b.**   $2(5x^2 - x) = 10x^2 - 2x$

   **c.**   $2(5x^2 - x - 2) = 10x^2 - 2x - 4$

   **d.**   $2(5x^2 - x - 1) = 10x^2 - 2x - 2$

**79.** $2\pi r^2 + 2\pi rh = 2\pi r(r + h)$

**81.** $A = 5600 + 5600rt$
$A = 5600(1) + 5600(rt)$
$A = 5600(1 + rt)$

**83.** Answers may vary

**85.** None

    **a.** $(2-x)(3-y) = 6-2y-3x+xy$
$$= xy-3x-2y+6$$

    **b.** $(-2+x)(-3+y) = 6-2y-3x+xy$
$$= xy-3x-2y+6$$

    **c.** $(x-2)(y-3) = xy-3x-2y+6$

    **d.** $(-x+2)(-y+3) = xy-3x-2y+6$

**87.** a is correct

    **a.** $3(4x^2+3x+1) = 12x^2+9x+3$

    **b.** $3(4x^2+3x-1) = 12x^2+9x-3$

    **c.** $3(4x^2+3x-3) = 12x^2+9x-9$

    **d.** $3(4x^2+3x) = 12x^2+9x$

**89.** $A = P+PRT$
$$A = P(1+RT)$$

**91.** $3y^n+3y^{2n}+5y^{8n} = y^n \cdot 3 + y^n \cdot 3y^n + y^n \cdot 5y^{7n}$
$$= y^n(3+3y^n+5y^{7n})$$

**93.** $3x^{5a}-6x^{3a}+9x^{2a}$
$$= 3x^{2a} \cdot x^{3a} - 3x^{2a} \cdot 2x^a + 3x^{2a} \cdot 3$$
$$= 3x^{2a}(x^{3a}-2x^a+3)$$

**95.** $h(t) = -16t^2+224$

    **a.** $h(t) = -16(t^2-14)$

    **b.** $h(2) = -16(2)^2+224$
$$= -16(4)+224$$
$$= -64+224$$
$$= 160 \text{ feet}$$
$$h(2) = -16(2^2-14)$$
$$= -16(4-14)$$
$$= -16(-10)$$
$$= 160 \text{ feet}$$

    **c.** Answers may vary

## Section 5.6

### Practice Exercises

**1.** Find two integers whose product is 6 and whose sum is 5. Since our integers must have a positive product and a positive sum, look for positive factors.

| Positive Factors of 6 | Sum of Factors |
|---|---|
| 1, 6 | $1+6=7$ |
| 3, 2 | $3+2=5$ (correct) |

$$x^2+5x+6 = (x+3)(x+2)$$

**2.** Find two integers whose product is 24 and whose sum is $-11$. Since our integers must have a positive product and a negative sum, look for negative factors.

| Negative Factors of 24 | Sum of Factors |
|---|---|
| $-1, -24$ | $-1+(-24)=-25$ |
| $-2, -12$ | $-2+(-12)=-14$ |
| $-3, -8$ | $-3+(-8)=-11$ (correct) |
| $-4, -6$ | $-4+(-6)=-10$ |

$$x^2-11x+24 = (x-3)(x-8)$$

**3.** $3x^3-9x^2-30x = 3x(x^2-3x-10)$

Find two integers whose product is $-10$ and whose sum is $-3$. The numbers are $-5$ and 2.
$$3x^3-9x^2-30x = 3x(x^2-3x-10)$$
$$= 3x(x-5)(x+2)$$

**4.** $2b^2-18b-22 = 2(b^2-9b-11)$

Find two integers whose product is $-11$ and whose sum is $-9$.

| Factors | Sum |
|---|---|
| $-1, 11$ | 10 |
| $1, -11$ | $-10$ |

Neither of the pairs has a sum of $-9$, so no further factoring is possible.
$$2b^2-18b-22 = 2(b^2-9b-11)$$

**5.** Factors of $2x^2$: $2x \cdot x$

Factors of 6: $1 \cdot 6$ and $2 \cdot 3$

$(2x + 6)(x + 1) \Rightarrow 2x + 6x = 8x$ (incorrect middle term)

$(2x + 1)(x + 6) \Rightarrow 12x + x = 13x$ (correct middle term)

$(2x + 2)(x + 3) \Rightarrow 6x + 2x = 8x$ (incorrect middle term)

$(2x + 3)(x + 2) \Rightarrow 4x + 3x = 7x$ (incorrect middle term)

$2x^2 + 13x + 6 = (2x + 1)(x + 6)$

**6.** Factors of $4x^2$: $4x \cdot x$ and $2x \cdot 2x$

Factors of $-6$: $-6 \cdot 1, 6 \cdot -1, 2 \cdot -3, -2 \cdot 3$

$(4x - 6)(x + 1) \Rightarrow 4x - 6x = -2x$ (incorrect)

$(4x + 6)(x - 1) \Rightarrow -4x + 6x = 2x$ (incorrect)

$(4x + 2)(x - 3) \Rightarrow -12x + 2x = -10x$ (incorrect)

$(4x - 3)(x + 2) \Rightarrow 8x - 3x = 5x$ (correct)

$4x^2 + 5x - 6 = (4x - 3)(x + 2)$

**7.** $18b^4 - 57b^3 + 30b^2 = 3b^2(6b^2 - 19b + 10)$

Factors of $6b^2$: $2b \cdot 3b, 6b \cdot b$

Negative factors of 10: $-1 \cdot -10, -5 \cdot -2$

$(2b - 1)(3b - 10) \Rightarrow -20b - 3b = -23b$ (incorrect)

$(2b - 10)(3b - 1) \Rightarrow -2b - 30b = -32b$ (incorrect)

$(2b - 5)(3b - 2) \Rightarrow -4b - 15b = -19b$ (correct)

$18b^4 - 57b^3 + 30b^2 = 3b^2(6b^2 - 19b + 10)$
$$= 3b^2(2b - 5)(3b - 2)$$

**8.** No greatest common factor can be factored out.

Factors of $25x^2$: $25x \cdot x, 5x \cdot 5x$

Factors of $4y^2$: $4y \cdot y, 2y \cdot 2y$

Try possible combinations.

$25x^2 + 20xy + 4y^2 = (5x + 2y)(5x + 2y)$
$$= (5x + 2y)^2$$

**9.** $20x^2 + 23x + 6$

$a = 20, b = 23, c = 6$

Find two numbers whose product is $a \cdot c = 20 \cdot 6 = 120$, and whose sum is $b$, 23. The two numbers are 8 and 15.

$20x^2 + 23x + 6 = 20x^2 + 8x + 15x + 6$
$$= 4x(5x + 2) + 3(5x + 2)$$
$$= (5x + 2)(4x + 3)$$

**10.** $15x^2 + 4x - 3$

$a = 15, b = 4, c = -3$

Find two numbers whose product is $a \cdot c = 15(-3) = -45$ and whose sum is $b$, 4. The two numbers are 9 and $-5$.

$15x^2 + 4x - 3 = 15x^2 + 9x - 5x - 3$
$$= 3x(5x + 3) - 1(5x + 3)$$
$$= (5x + 3)(3x - 1)$$

**11.** Let $y = x + 1$,

$3(x + 1)^2 - 7(x + 1) - 20 = 3y^2 - 7y - 20$
$$= (3y + 5)(y - 4)$$

Replace $y$ with $x + 1$.

$(3y + 5)(y - 4) = [3(x + 1) + 5][(x + 1) - 4)]$
$$= (3x + 3 + 5)(x + 1 - 4)$$
$$= (3x + 8)(x - 3)$$

Thus, $3(x + 1)^2 - 7(x + 1) - 20 = (3x + 8)(x - 3)$.

**12.** Let $y = x^2$.

$6x^4 - 11x^2 - 10 = 6y^2 - 11y - 10$
$$= (3y + 2)(2y - 5)$$

Replace $y$ with $x^2$.

$(3y + 2)(2y - 5) = (3x^2 + 2)(2x^2 - 5)$

**Vocabulary and Readiness Check**

**1.** $10 = 2 \cdot 5$

$7 = 2 + 5$

2 and 5

**2.** $12 = 2 \cdot 2 \cdot 3 = 2 \cdot 6$

$8 = 2 + 6$

2 and 6

**3.** $24 = 2 \cdot 2 \cdot 2 \cdot 3 = 8 \cdot 3$

$11 = 8 + 3$

8 and 3

**4.** $30 = 2 \cdot 3 \cdot 5 = 10 \cdot 3$

$13 = 10 + 3$

10 and 3

**Exercise Set 5.6**

**1.** $x^2 + 9x + 18 = (x + 6)(x + 3)$

**3.** $x^2 - 12x + 32 = (x - 4)(x - 8)$

**5.** $x^2 + 10x - 24 = (x + 12)(x - 2)$

**7.** $x^2 - 2x - 24 = (x - 6)(x + 4)$

**9.** Note that the GCF is 3.
$$3x^2 - 18x + 24 = 3(x^2 - 6x + 8)$$
$$= 3(x - 2)(x - 4)$$

**11.** Note that the GCF is $4z$.
$$4x^2z + 28xz + 40z = 4z(x^2 + 7x + 10)$$
$$= 4z(x + 2)(x + 5)$$

**13.** Note that the GCF is 2.
$$2x^2 - 24x - 64 = 2(x^2 - 12x - 32)$$

**15.** $5x^2 + 16x + 3 = (5x + 1)(x + 3)$

**17.** $2x^2 - 11x + 12 = (2x - 3)(x - 4)$

**19.** $2x^2 + 25x - 20$ is prime.

**21.** $4x^2 - 12x + 9 = (2x - 3)(2x - 3)$
$$= (2x - 3)^2$$

**23.** Note that the GCF is 2.
$$12x^2 + 10x - 50 = 2(6x^2 + 5x - 25)$$
$$= 2(3x - 5)(2x + 5)$$

**25.** Note that the GCF is $y^2$.
$$3y^4 - y^3 - 10y^2 = y^2(3y^2 - y - 10)$$
$$= y^2(3y + 5)(y - 2)$$

**27.** Note that the GCF is $2x$.
$$6x^3 + 8x^2 + 24x = 2x(3x^2 + 4x + 12)$$

**29.** $2x^2 - 5xy - 3y^2 = (2x + y)(x - 3y)$

**31.** Note that the GCF is 2, so that
$$28y^2 + 22y + 4 = 2(14y^2 + 11y + 2).$$
$ac = 28$; the two numbers are 4 and 7.
$$14y^2 + 11y + 2 = 14y^2 + 7y + 4y + 2$$
$$= 7y(2y + 1) + 2(2y + 1)$$
$$= (7y + 2)(2y + 1)$$
So, $28y^2 + 22y + 4 = 2(7y + 2)(2y + 1)$.

**33.** $2x^2 + 15x - 27$; $ac = -54$ so the two numbers are 18 and $-3$.
$$2x^2 + 15x - 27 = 2x^2 + 18x - 3x - 27$$
$$= 2x(x + 9) - 3(x + 9)$$
$$= (2x - 3)(x + 9)$$

**35.** Let $y = x^2$. Then we have
$$x^4 + x^2 - 6 = y^2 + y - 6 = (y + 3)(y - 2).$$
This yields $(x^2 + 3)(x^2 - 2)$.

**37.** Let $y = 5x + 1$. Then we have
$$(5x + 1)^2 + 8(5x + 1) + 7 = y^2 + 8y + 7$$
$$= (y + 1)(y + 7).$$
This yields
$$[(5x + 1) + 1][(5x + 1) + 7] = (5x + 2)(5x + 8).$$

**39.** Let $y = x^3$. Then we have
$$x^6 - 7x^3 + 12 = y^2 - 7y + 12$$
$$= (y - 4)(y - 3).$$
This yields $(x^3 - 4)(x^3 - 3)$.

**41.** Let $y = a + 5$. Then we have
$$(a + 5)^2 - 5(a + 5) - 24 = y^2 - 5y - 24$$
$$= (y - 8)(y + 3).$$
This yields
$$[(a + 5) - 8][(a + 5) + 3] = (a - 3)(a + 8).$$

**43.** $x^2 - 24x - 81 = (x - 27)(x + 3)$

**45.** $x^2 - 15x - 54 = (x - 18)(x + 3)$

**47.** $3x^2 - 6x + 3 = 3(x^2 - 2x + 1)$
$$= 3(x - 1)(x - 1)$$
$$= 3(x - 1)^2$$

**49.** $3x^2 - 5x - 2 = (3x + 1)(x - 2)$

**51.** $8x^2 - 26x + 15 = (4x - 3)(2x - 5)$

**53.** $18x^4 + 21x^3 + 6x^2 = 3x^2(6x^2 + 7x + 2)$
$$= 3x^2(3x + 2)(2x + 1)$$

**55.** $x^2 + 8xz + 7z^2 = (x + z)(x + 7z)$

**57.** $x^2 - x - 12$; $ac = -12$ so the two numbers are $-4$ and $3$.
$$x^2 - x - 12 = x^2 - 4x + 3x - 12$$
$$= x(x-4) + 3(x-4)$$
$$= (x+3)(x-4)$$

**59.** $3a^2 + 12ab + 12b^2 = 3(a^2 + 4ab + 4b^2)$
$$= 3(a+2b)(a+2b)$$
$$= 3(a+2b)^2$$

**61.** $x^2 + 4x + 5$ is prime.

**63.** Let $y = x + 4$. Then
$$2(x+4)^2 + 3(x+4) - 5$$
$$= 2y^2 + 3y - 5$$
$$= (2y+5)(y-1)$$
$$= [2(x+4)+5][(x+4)-1]$$
$$= (2x+8+5)(x+3)$$
$$= (2x+13)(x+3)$$

**65.** $6x^2 - 49x + 30 = (3x-2)(2x-15)$

**67.** Let $y = x^2$. Then
$$x^4 - 5x^2 - 6 = y^2 - 5y - 6$$
$$= (y-6)(y+1)$$
$$= (x^2-6)(x^2+1)$$

**69.** $6x^3 - x^2 - x = x(6x^2 - x - 1)$
$$= x(3x+1)(2x-1)$$

**71.** $12a^2 - 29ab + 15b^2 = (4a-3b)(3a-5b)$

**73.** $9x^2 + 30x + 25 = (3x+5)(3x+5)$
$$= (3x+5)^2$$

**75.** $3x^2y - 11xy + 8y = y(3x^2 - 11x + 8)$
$$= y(3x-8)(x-1)$$

**77.** $2x^2 + 2x - 12 = 2(x^2 + x - 6)$
$$= 2(x+3)(x-2)$$

**79.** Let $y = x - 4$. Then
$$(x-4)^2 + 3(x-4) - 18$$
$$= y^2 + 3y - 18$$
$$= (y+6)(y-3)$$
$$= [(x-4)+6][(x-4)-3]$$
$$= (x+2)(x-7)$$

**81.** Let $y = x^3$. Then
$$2x^6 + 3x^3 - 9 = 2y^2 + 3y - 9$$
$$= (2y-3)(y+3)$$
$$= (2x^3-3)(x^3+3)$$

**83.** $72xy^4 - 24xy^2z + 2xz^2 = 2x(36y^4 - 12y^2z + z^2)$
$$= 2x(6y^2-z)(6y^2-z)$$
$$= 2x(6y^2-z)^2$$

**85.** $2x^3y + 2x^2y - 12xy = 2xy(x^2 + x - 6)$
$$= 2xy(x+3)(x-2)$$

**87.** $x^2 + 6xy + 5y^2 = (x+5y)(x+y)$

**89.** $(x-3)(x+3) = x^2 - 3^3 = x^2 - 9$

**91.** $(2x+1)^2 = (2x)^2 + 2(2x)(1) + 1^2$
$$= 4x^2 + 4x + 1$$

**93.**
$$\begin{array}{r} x^2 + 2x + 4 \\ x - 2 \\ \hline -2x^2 - 4x - 8 \\ x^3 + 2x^2 + 4x \\ \hline x^3 \qquad\qquad -8 \end{array}$$

**95.** $x^2 + bx + 6$
$6 = 2 \cdot 3$ or $6 = (-2)(-3)$
$6 = 1 \cdot 6$ or $6 = (-1)(-6)$
$(x+2)(x+3) = x^2 + 5x + 6$
$(x-2)(x-3) = x^2 - 5x + 6$
$(x+1)(x+6) = x^2 + 7x + 6$
$(x-1)(x-6) = x^2 - 7x + 6$
$b = \pm 5$ and $b = \pm 7$

**97.** $V(x) = x^3 + 2x^2 - 8x$
$$= x(x^2 + 2x - 8)$$
$$= x(x+4)(x-2)$$

**99.** $h(t) = -16t^2 + 80t + 576$

    **a.**  $h(0) = -16(0)^2 + 80(0) + 576 = 576$ ft

$$h(2) = -16(2)^2 + 80(2) + 576$$
$$= -16(4) + 160 + 576$$
$$= -64 + 160 + 576$$
$$= 672 \text{ ft}$$
$$h(4) = -16(4)^2 + 80(4) + 576$$
$$= -16(16) + 320 + 576$$
$$= -256 + 320 + 576$$
$$= 640 \text{ ft}$$
$$h(6) = -16(6)^2 + 80(6) + 576$$
$$= -16(36) + 480 + 576$$
$$= -576 + 480 + 576$$
$$= 480 \text{ ft}$$

    **b.**  Answers may vary

    **c.**  $h(t) = -16t^2 + 80t + 576$
$$= -16(t^2 - 5t - 36)$$
$$= -16(t - 9)(t + 4)$$

**101.** $x^{2n} + 10x^n + 16 = (x^n + 2)(x^n + 8)$

**103.** $x^{2n} - 3x^n - 18 = (x^n - 6)(x^n + 3)$

**105.** $2x^{2n} + 11x^n + 5 = (2x^n + 1)(x^n + 5)$

**107.** $4x^{2n} - 12x^n + 9 = (2x^n - 3)(2x^n - 3)$
$$= (2x^n - 3)^2$$

**109.** $x^4 + 6x^3 + 5x^2 = x^2(x^2 + 6x + 5)$
$$= x^2(x + 5)(x + 1)$$

**111.** $30x^3 + 9x^2 - 3x = 3x(10x^2 + 3x - 1)$
$$= 3x(5x - 1)(2x + 1)$$

**Section 5.7**

**Practice Exercises**

**1.** $b^2 + 16b + 64 = b^2 + 2(b)(8) + 8^2 = (b + 8)^2$

**2.** $45x^2b - 30xb + 5b = 5b(9x^2 - 6x + 1)$
$$= 5b[(3x)^2 - 2(3x)(1) + 1^2]$$
$$= 5b(3x - 1)^2$$

**3. a.** $x^2 - 16 = x^2 - 4^2 = (x + 4)(x - 4)$

    **b.**  $25b^2 - 49 = (5b)^2 - 7^2 = (5b - 7)(5b + 7)$

    **c.**  $45 - 20x^2 = 5(9 - 4x^2)$
$$= 5[3^2 - (2x)^2]$$
$$= 5(3 - 2x)(3 + 2x)$$

    **d.**  $y^2 - \dfrac{1}{81} = y^2 - \left(\dfrac{1}{9}\right)^2 = \left(y - \dfrac{1}{9}\right)\left(y + \dfrac{1}{9}\right)$

**4. a.** $x^4 - 10,000 = (x^2)^2 - 100^2$
$$= (x^2 + 100)(x^2 - 100)$$
$$= (x^2 + 100)(x + 10)(x - 10)$$

    **b.**  $(x + 2)^2 - 49 = (x + 2)^2 - 7^2$
$$= [(x + 2) + 7][(x + 2) - 7]$$
$$= (x + 2 + 7)(x + 2 - 7)$$
$$= (x + 9)(x - 5)$$

**5.** $m^2 + 6m + 9 - n^2 = (m^2 + 6m + 9) - n^2$
$$= (m + 3)^2 - n^2$$
$$= [(m + 3) + n][(m + 3) - n]$$
$$= (m + 3 + n)(m + 3 - n)$$

**6.** $x^3 + 64 = x^3 + 4^3$
$$= (x + 4)(x^2 - x \cdot 4 + 4^2)$$
$$= (x + 4)(x^2 - 4x + 16)$$

**7.** $a^3 + 8b^3 = a^3 + (2b)^3$
$$= (a + 2b)[a^2 - a(2b) + (2b)^2]$$
$$= (a + 2b)(a^2 - 2ab + 4b^2)$$

**8.** $27 - y^3 = 3^3 - y^3$
$= (3-y)(3^2 + 3 \cdot y + y^2)$
$= (3-y)(9 + 3y + y^2)$

**9.** $b^3 x^2 - 8x^2 = x^2(b^3 - 8)$
$= x^2(b^3 - 2^3)$
$= x^2(b-2)(b^2 + b \cdot 2 + 2^2)$
$= x^2(b-2)(b^2 + 2b + 4)$

**Vocabulary and Readiness Check**

**1.** $81y^2 = (9y)^2$

**2.** $4z^2 = (2z)^2$

**3.** $64x^6 = (8x^3)^2$

**4.** $49y^6 = (7y^3)^2$

**5.** $125 = 5^3$

**6.** $216 = 6^3$

**7.** $8x^3 = (2x)^3$

**8.** $27y^3 = (3y)^3$

**9.** $64y^6 = (4x^2)^3$

**10.** $x^3 y^6 = (xy^2)^3$

**Exercise Set 5.7**

**1.** $x^2 + 6x + 9 = x^2 + 2 \cdot x \cdot 3 + 3^2 = (x+3)^2$

**3.** $4x^2 - 12x + 9 = (2x)^2 - 2 \cdot 2x \cdot 3 + 3^2$
$= (2x-3)^2$

**5.** $3x^2 - 24x + 48 = 3(x^2 - 8x + 16)$
$= 3(x-4)^2$

**7.** $9y^2 x^2 + 12yx^2 + 4x^2 = x^2(9y^2 + 12y + 4)$
$= x^2(3y+2)^2$

**9.** $x^2 - 25 = x^2 - 5^2 = (x+5)(x-5)$

**11.** $9 - 4z^2 = 3^2 - (2z)^2 = (3+2z)(3-2z)$

**13.** $(y+2)^2 - 49 = (y+2)^2 - 7^2$
$= [(y+2) + 7][(y+2) - 7]$
$= (y+9)(y-5)$

**15.** $64x^2 - 100 = 4(16x^2 - 25)$
$= 4[(4x)^2 - 5^2]$
$= 4(4x+5)(4x-5)$

**17.** $x^2 + 27 = x^3 + 3^3 = (x+3)(x^2 - 3x + 9)$

**19.** $z^3 - 1 = z^3 - 1^3 = (z-1)(z^2 + z + 1)$

**21.** $m^3 + n^3 = (m+n)(m^2 - mn + n^2)$

**23.** $x^3 y^2 - 27y^2 = y^2(x^3 - 27)$
$= y^2(x^3 - 3^3)$
$= y^2(x-3)(x^2 + 3x + 9)$

**25.** $a^3 b + 8b^4 = b(a^3 + 8b^3)$
$= b[a^3 + (2b)^3]$
$= b(a+2b)(a^2 - 2ab + 4b^2)$

**27.** $125y^3 - 8x^3 = (5y)^3 - (2x)^3$
$= (5y-2x)(25y^2 + 10xy + 4x^2)$

**29.** $(x^2 + 6x + 9) - y^2 = (x+3)^2 - y^2$
$= (x+3+y)(x+3-y)$

**31.** $(x^2 - 10x + 25) - y^2 = (x-5)^2 - y^2$
$= (x-5+y)(x-5-y)$

**33.** $(4x^2 + 4x + 1) - z^2 = (2x+1)^2 - z^2$
$= (2x+1+z)(2x+1-z)$

**35.** $9x^2 - 49 = (3x)^2 - 7^2 = (3x+7)(3x-7)$

**37.** $x^2 - 12x + 36 = x^2 - 2 \cdot x \cdot 6 + 6^2 = (x-6)^2$

**39.** $x^4 - 81 = (x^2 + 9)(x^2 - 9)$
$= (x^2 + 9)(x+3)(x-3)$

**41.** $(x^2 + 8x + 16) - 4y^2 = (x+4)^2 - (2y)^2$
$$= (x + 4 + 2y)(x + 4 - 2y)$$

**43.** $(x + 2y)^2 - 9 = (x + 2y)^2 - 3^2$
$$= (x + 2y + 3)(x + 2y - 3)$$

**45.** $x^3 - 216 = x^3 - 6^3 = (x - 6)(x^2 + 6x + 36)$

**47.** $x^3 + 125 = x^3 + 5^3 = (x + 5)(x^2 - 5x + 25)$

**49.** $4x^2 + 25$ is prime.

**51.** $4a^2 + 12a + 9 = (2a)^2 + 2 \cdot 2a \cdot 3 + 3^2 = (2a + 3)^2$

**53.** $18x^2 y - 2y = 2y(9x^2 - 1)$
$$= 2y(3x + 1)(3x - 1)$$

**55.** $8x^3 + y^3 = (2x)^3 + y^3$
$$= (2x + y)(4x^2 - 2xy + y^2)$$

**57.** $x^6 - y^3 = (x^2)^3 - y^3$
$$= (x^2 - y)(x^4 + x^2 y + y^2)$$

**59.** $(x^2 + 16x + 64) - x^4 = (x + 8)^2 - (x^2)^2$
$$= (x + 8 + x^2)(x + 8 - x^2)$$

**61.** $3x^6 y^2 + 81y^2 = 3y^2(x^6 + 27)$
$$= 3y^2[(x^2)^3 + 3^3]$$
$$= 3y^2(x^2 + 3)(x^4 - 3x^2 + 9)$$

**63.** $(x + y)^3 + 125$
$$= (x + y)^3 + 5^3$$
$$= [(x + y) + 5][(x + y)^2 - 5(x + y) + 25]$$
$$= (x + y + 5)(x^2 + 2xy + y^2 - 5x - 5y + 25)$$

**65.** $(2x + 3)^3 - 64$
$$= (2x + 3)^3 - 4^3$$
$$= [(2x + 3) - 4][(2x + 3)^2 + 4(2x + 3) + 16]$$
$$= (2x - 1)(4x^2 + 12x + 9 + 8x + 12 + 16)$$
$$= (2x - 1)(4x^2 + 20x + 37)$$

**67.** $x - 5 = 0$
$$x = 5$$

**69.** $3x + 1 = 0$
$$3x = -1$$
$$x = -\frac{1}{3}$$

**71.** $-2x = 0$
$$x = 0$$

**73.** $-5x + 25 = 0$
$$-5x = -25$$
$$x = 5$$

**75.** No; $x^2 - 4$ can be factored further.
$$5x(x^2 - 4) = 5x(x^2 - 2^2) = 5x(x + 2)(x - 2)$$

**77.** Yes; $7y(a^2 + a + 1)$ is factored completely.

**79.** Area $= \pi R^2 - \pi r^2$
$$= \pi(R^2 - r^2)$$
$$= \pi(R + r)(R - r) \text{ sq units}$$

**81.** Volume $= x^3 - y^2 x$
$$= x(x^2 - y^2)$$
$$= x(x + y)(x - y) \text{ cubic units}$$

**83.** $\frac{1}{2} \cdot b = \frac{1}{2} \cdot 6 = 3$ so $c = 3^2 = 9$

**85.** $\frac{1}{2} \cdot b = \frac{1}{2}(-14) = -7$ so $c = (-7)^2 = 49$

**87.** $\frac{1}{2} \cdot c = \frac{c}{2}$ so $\left(\frac{c}{2}\right)^2 = 16$
$$\frac{c^2}{4} = 16$$
$$c^2 = 64$$
$$c = \pm 8$$

**89.** $x^6 - 1$

   **a.** $(x^3)^2 - 1^2$
$$= (x^3 + 1)(x^3 - 1)$$
$$= (x + 1)(x^2 - x + 1)(x - 1)(x^2 + x + 1)$$

   **b.** $(x^2)^3 - 1^3 = (x^2 - 1)(x^4 + x^2 + 1)$
$$= (x + 1)(x - 1)(x^4 + x^2 + 1)$$

**c.** No; answers may vary

**91.** $x^{2n} - 36 = (x^n)^2 - 6^2 = (x^n + 6)(x^n - 6)$

**93.** $25x^{2n} - 81 = (5x^n)^2 - 9^2$
$$= (5x^n + 9)(5x^n - 9)$$

**95.** $x^{4n} - 625 = (x^{2n})^2 - 25^2$
$$= (x^{2n} + 25)(x^{2n} - 25)$$
$$= (x^{2n} + 25)[(x^n)^2 - 5^2]$$
$$= (x^{2n} + 25)(x^n + 5)(x^n - 5)$$

**Integrated Review**

**Practice Exercises**

**1. a.** $12x^2y - 3xy = 3xy(4x) + 3xy(-1)$
$$= 3xy(4x - 1)$$

**b.** $49x^2 - 4 = (7x)^2 - 2^2 = (7x + 2)(7x - 2)$

**c.** $5x^2 + 2x - 3 = (5x - 3)(x + 1)$

**d.** $3x^2 + 6 + x^3 + 2x = 3(x^2 + 2) + x(x^2 + 2)$
$$= (x^2 + 2)(3 + x)$$

**e.** $4x^2 + 20x + 25 = (2x)^2 + 2 \cdot 2x \cdot 5 + 5^2$
$$= (2x + 5)^2$$

**f.** $b^2 + 100$ cannot be factored.

**2. a.** $64x^3 + y^3 = (4x)^3 + y^3$
$$= (4x + y)[(4x)^2 - 4x \cdot y + y^2]$$
$$= (4x + y)(16x^2 - 4xy + y^2)$$

**b.** $7x^2y^2 - 63y^4 = 7y^2(x^2 - 9y^2)$
$$= 7y^2[x^2 - (3y)^2]$$
$$= 7y^2(x - 3y)(x + 3y)$$

**c.** $3x^2 + 12x + 12 - 3b^2$
$$= 3(x^2 + 4x + 4 - b^2)$$
$$= 3[(x + 2)^2 - b^2]$$
$$= 3(x + 2 + b)(x + 2 - b)$$

**d.** $x^5y^4 + 27x^2y$
$$= x^2y(x^3y^3 + 27)$$
$$= x^2y[(xy)^3 + 3^3]$$
$$= x^2y(xy + 3)(x^2y^2 - 3xy + 9)$$

**e.** $(x + 7)^2 - 81y^2 = (x + 7)^2 - (9y)^2$
$$= (x + 7 + 9y)(x + 7 - 9y)$$

**Integrated Review Exercise Set**

**1.** $(-y^2 + 6y - 1) + (3y^2 - 4y - 10)$
$$= -y^2 + 6y - 1 + 3y^2 - 4y - 10$$
$$= 2y^2 + 2y - 11$$

**2.** $(5z^4 - 6z^2 + z + 1) - (7z^4 - 2z + 1)$
$$= 5z^4 - 6z^2 + z + 1 - 7z^4 + 2z - 1$$
$$= -2z^4 - 6z^2 + 3z$$

**3.** $(x^2 - 6x + 2) - (x - 5) = x^2 - 6x + 2 - x + 5$
$$= x^2 - 7x + 7$$

**4.** $(2x^2 + 6x - 5) + (5x^2 - 10x) = 7x^2 - 4x - 5$

**5.** $(5x - 3)^2 = (5x)^2 - 2(5x)(3) + 3^2$
$$= 25x^2 - 30x + 9$$

**6.** $\dfrac{5x^2 - 14x - 3}{5x + 1} = \dfrac{(x - 3)(5x + 1)}{5x + 1} = x - 3$

**7.**
$$\require{enclose}\begin{array}{r}2x^3 - 4x^2 + 5x - 3 \\ x+2 \enclose{longdiv}{2x^4 + 0x^3 - 3x^2 + 5x - 2} \\ \underline{2x^4 + 4x^3} \\ -4x^3 - 3x^2 \\ \underline{-4x^3 - 8x^2} \\ 5x^2 + 5x \\ \underline{5x^2 + 10x} \\ -5x - 2 \\ \underline{-5x - 10} \\ 8 \end{array}$$

$92x^4 - 3x^2 + 5x - 2) \div (x + 2)$
$$= 2x^3 - 4x^2 + 5x - 5 + \frac{8}{x + 2}$$

**8.**
$$x^2 - 3x - 2$$
$$\times \quad\quad 4x - 1$$
$$\overline{\quad -x^2 + 3x + 2}$$
$$\underline{4x^3 - 12x^2 - 8x}$$
$$4x^3 - 13x^2 - 5x + 2$$

**9.** $x^2 - 8x + 16 - y^2 = (x-4)^2 - y^2$
$$= (x-4+y)(x-4-y)$$

**10.** $12x^2 - 22x - 20 = 2(6x^2 - 11x - 10)$
$$= 2(3x+2)(2x-5)$$

**11.** $x^4 - x = x(x^3 - 1) = x(x-1)(x^2 + x + 1)$

**12.** Let $y = 2x + 1$. Then
$$(2x+1)^2 - 3(2x+1) + 2$$
$$= y^2 - 3y + 2$$
$$= (y-2)(y-1)$$
$$= [(2x+1)-2][(2x+1)-1]$$
$$= (2x-1)(2x)$$
$$= 2x(2x-1)$$

**13.** $14x^2y - 2xy = 2xy(7x - 1)$

**14.** $24ab^2 - 6ab = 6ab(4b - 1)$

**15.** $4x^2 - 16 = 4(x^2 - 4) = 4(x+2)(x-2)$

**16.** $9x^2 - 81 = 9(x^2 - 9) = 9(x+3)(x-3)$

**17.** $3x^2 - 8x - 11 = (3x-11)(x+1)$

**18.** $5x^2 - 2x - 3 = (5x+3)(x-1)$

**19.** $4x^2 + 8x - 12 = 4(x^2 + 2x - 3)$
$$= 4(x+3)(x-1)$$

**20.** $6x^2 - 6x - 12 = 6(x^2 - x - 2)$
$$= 6(x-2)(x+1)$$

**21.** $4x^2 + 36x + 81 = (2x)^2 + 2 \cdot 2x \cdot 9 + 9^2$
$$= (2x+9)^2$$

**22.** $25x^2 + 40x + 16 = (5x)^2 + 2 \cdot 5x \cdot 4 + 4^2$
$$= (5x+4)^2$$

**23.** $8x^3 + 125y^3 = (2x)^3 + (5y)^3$
$$= (2x+5y)(4x^2 - 10xy + 25y^2)$$

**24.** $27x^3 - 64y^3 = (3x)^3 - (4y)^3$
$$= (3x-4y)(9x^2 + 12xy + 16y^2)$$

**25.** $64x^2y^3 - 8x^2 = 8x^2(8y^3 - 1)$
$$= 8x^2[(2y)^3 - 1^3]$$
$$= 8x^2(2y-1)(4y^2 + 2y + 1)$$

**26.** $27x^5y^4 - 216x^2y$
$$= 27x^2y(x^3y^3 - 8)$$
$$= 27x^2y[(xy)^3 - 2^3]$$
$$= 27x^2y(xy-2)(x^2y^2 + 2xy + 4)$$

**27.** $(x+5)^3 + y^3$
$$= [(x+5)+y][(x+5)^2 - (x+5)y + y^2]$$
$$= (x+y+5)(x^2 + 10x + 25 - xy - 5y + y^2)$$
$$= (x+y+5)(x^2 + 10x - xy - 5y + y^2 + 25)$$

**28.** $(y-1)^3 + 27x^3$
$$= (y-1)^3 + (3x)^3$$
$$= [(y-1)+3x][(y-1)^2 - (y-1)(3x) + (3x)^2]$$
$$= (y-1+3x)(y^2 - 2y + 1 - 3xy + 3x + 9x^2)$$

**29.** Let $y = 5a - 3$. Then
$$(5a-3)^2 - 6(5a-3) + 9 = y^2 - 6y + 9$$
$$= (y-3)(y-3)$$
$$= (y-3)^2$$
$$= [(5a-3)-3]^2$$
$$= (5a-6)^2$$

**30.** Let $y = 4r + 1$. Then
$$(4r+1)^2 + 8(4r+1) + 16 = y^2 + 8y + 16$$
$$= (y+4)(y+4)$$
$$= (y+4)^2$$
$$= [(4r+1)+4]^2$$
$$= (4r+5)^2$$

**31.** $7x^2 - 63x = 7x(x-9)$

**32.** $20x^2 + 23x + 6 = (4x+3)(5x+2)$

33. $ab - 6a + 7b - 42 = a(b-6) + 7(b-6)$
$$= (a+7)(b-6)$$

34. $20x^2 - 220x + 600 = 20(x^2 - 11x + 30)$
$$= 20(x-6)(x-5)$$

35. $x^4 - 1 = (x^2)^2 - 1^2$
$$= (x^2+1)(x^2-1)$$
$$= (x^2+1)(x+1)(x-1)$$

36. $15x^2 - 20x = 5x(3x-4)$

37. $10x^2 - 7x - 33 = (5x-11)(2x+3)$

38. $45m^3n^3 - 27m^2n^2 = 9m^2n^2(5mn-3)$

39. $5a^3b^3 - 50a^3b = 5a^3b(b^2-10)$

40. $x^4 + x = x(x^3+1)$
$$= x(x^3+1^3)$$
$$= x(x+1)(x^2-x+1)$$

41. $16x^2 + 25$ is a prime polynomial.

42. $20x^3 + 20y^3 = 20(x^3+y^3)$
$$= 20(x+y)(x^2-xy+y^2)$$

43. $10x^3 - 210x^2 + 1100x = 10x(x^2-21x+110)$
$$= 10x(x-11)(x-10)$$

44. $9y^2 - 42y + 49 = (3y)^2 - 2 \cdot 3y \cdot 7 + 7^2$
$$= (3y-7)^2$$

45. $64a^3b^4 - 27a^3b$
$$= a^3b(64b^3-27)$$
$$= a^3b[(4b)^3 - 3^3]$$
$$= a^3b(4b-3)(16b^2+12b+9)$$

46. $y^4 - 16 = (y^2)^2 - 4^2$
$$= (y^2+4)(y^2-4)$$
$$= (y^2+4)(y+2)(y-2)$$

47. $2x^3 - 54 = 2(x^3-27)$
$$= 2(x^3-3^3)$$
$$= 2(x-3)(x^2+3x+9)$$

48. $2sr + 10s - r - 5 = 2s(r+5) - 1(r+5)$
$$= (2s-1)(r+5)$$

49. $3y^5 - 5y^4 + 6y - 10 = y^4(3y-5) + 2(3y-5)$
$$= (y^4+2)(3y-5)$$

50. $64a^2 + b^2$ is a prime polynomial.

51. $100z^3 + 100 = 100(z^3+1)$
$$= 100(z+1)(z^2-z+1)$$

52. $250x^4 - 16x = 2x(125x^3-8)$
$$= 2x[(5x)^3 - 2^3]$$
$$= 2x(5x-2)(25x^2+10x+4)$$

53. $4b^2 - 36b + 81 = (2b)^2 - 2 \cdot 2b \cdot 9 + 9^2$
$$= (2b-9)^2$$

54. $2a^5 - a^4 + 6a - 3 = a^4(2a-1) + 3(2a-1)$
$$= (a^4+3)(2a-1)$$

55. Let $x = y - 6$. Then
$$(y-6)^2 + 3(y-6) + 2 = x^2 + 3x + 2$$
$$= (x+2)(x+1)$$
$$= [(y-6)+2][(y-6)+1]$$
$$= (y-4)(y-5)$$

56. Let $x = c + 2$. Then
$$(c+2)^2 - 6(c+2) + 5 = x^2 - 6x + 5$$
$$= (x-5)(x-1)$$
$$= [(c+2)-5][(c+2)-1]$$
$$= (c-3)(c+1)$$

57. Area $= 3^2 - 4x^2 = 3^2 - (2x)^2 = (3+2x)(3-2x)$

### Section 5.8

### Practice Exercises

1. $(x+8)(x-5) = 0$
$$x+8 = 0 \quad \text{or} \quad x-5 = 0$$
$$x = -8 \quad \text{or} \quad x = 5$$
Both solutions check. The solution set is $\{-8, 5\}$.

**2.** $3x^2 + 10x - 8 = 0$

$(3x - 2)(x + 4) = 0$

$3x - 2 = 0$   or   $x + 4 = 0$

$3x = 2$

$x = \dfrac{2}{3}$   or     $x = -4$

Both solutions check. The solution set is

$\left\{ -4, \dfrac{2}{3} \right\}$.

**3.**      $x(3x + 14) = -8$

$3x^2 + 14x = -8$

$3x^2 + 14x + 8 = 0$

$(3x + 2)(x + 4) = 0$

$3x + 2 = 0$   or   $x + 4 = 0$

$3x = -2$

$x = -\dfrac{2}{3}$   or     $x = -4$

The solutions are $-\dfrac{2}{3}$ and $-4$.

**4.**     $8(x^2 + 3) + 4 = -8x(x + 3) + 19$

$8x^2 + 24 + 4 = -8x^2 - 24x + 19$

$16x^2 + 24x + 9 = 0$

$(4x + 3)(4x + 3) = 0$

$4x + 3 = 0$   or   $4x + 3 = 0$

$4x = -3$   or      $4x = -3$

$x = -\dfrac{3}{4}$   or      $x = -\dfrac{3}{4}$

The solution is $-\dfrac{3}{4}$.

**5.**         $4x^2 = \dfrac{15}{2}x + 1$

$2(4x^2) = 2\left( \dfrac{15}{2}x + 1 \right)$

$8x^2 = 15x + 2$

$8x^2 - 15x - 2 = 0$

$(8x + 1)(x - 2) = 0$

$8x + 1 = 0$   or   $x - 2 = 0$

$8x = -1$

$x = -\dfrac{1}{8}$   or     $x = 2$

The solutions are $-\dfrac{1}{8}$ and 2.

**6.**          $x^3 = 2x^2 + 3x$

$x^3 - 2x^2 - 3x = 0$

$x(x^2 - 2x - 3) = 0$

$x(x - 3)(x + 1) = 0$

$x = 0$   or   $x - 3 = 0$   or   $x + 1 = 0$

$x = 3$   or      $x = -1$

The solutions are 0, 3, and $-1$.

**7.**        $x^3 - 9x = 18 - 2x^2$

$x^3 + 2x^2 - 9x - 18 = 0$

$x^2(x + 2) - 9(x + 2) = 0$

$(x + 2)(x^2 - 9) = 0$

$(x + 2)(x + 3)(x - 3) = 0$

$x + 2 = 0$   or   $x + 3 = 0$   or   $x - 3 = 0$

$x = -2$   or     $x = -3$   or      $x = 3$

The solutions are 3, $-3$, and $-2$.

**8.** Let $h = 0$.

$-16t^2 + 96t = 0$

$-16t(t - 6) = 0$

$-16t = 0$   or   $t - 6 = 0$

$t = 0$   or      $t = 6$

The rocket will return to the ground in 6 seconds.

**9.** Let $x$ = first even integer, then
$x + 2$ = next even integer, and
$x + 4$ = third even integer.

$x^2 + (x + 2)^2 = (x + 4)^2$

$x^2 + x^2 + 4x + 4 = x^2 + 8x + 16$

$x^2 - 4x - 12 = 0$

$(x - 6)(x + 2) = 0$

$x - 6 = 0$   or   $x + 2 = 0$

$x = 6$   or      $x = -2$

Discard $x = -2$ since length cannot be negative. The legs are $x = 6$ units, $x + 2 = 8$ units, and $x + 4 = 10$ units.

**10.** The graph of $f(x) = (x - 1)(x + 3)$ has two $x$-intercepts, $(1, 0)$ and $(-3, 0)$, so the graph is C.
The graph of $g(x) = x(x + 3)(x - 2)$ has three $x$-intercepts, $(0, 0)$, $(-3, 0)$, and $(2, 0)$, so the graph is A.
The graph of $h(x) = (x - 3)(x + 2)(x - 2)$ has three $x$-intercepts, $(3, 0)$, $(-2, 0)$, and $(2, 0)$, so the graph is B.

## Graphing Calculator Explorations

**1.** $y = x^2 + 3x - 2$

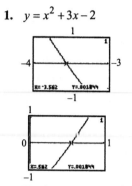

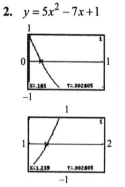

The intercepts are −3.562, 0.562.

**2.** $y = 5x^2 - 7x + 1$

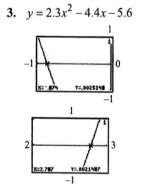

The intercepts are 0.161, 1.239.

**3.** $y = 2.3x^2 - 4.4x - 5.6$

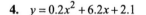

The intercepts are −0.874, 2.787.

**4.** $y = 0.2x^2 + 6.2x + 2.1$

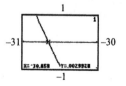

The intercepts are −30.658, −0.342.

**5.** $y = 0.09x^2 - 0.13x - 0.08$

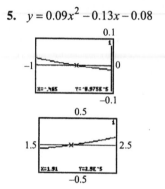

The intercepts are −0.465, 1.910.

**6.** $y = x^2 + 0.08x - 0.01$

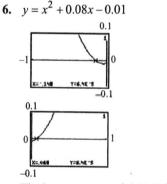

The intercepts are −0.148, 0.068.

## Vocabulary and Readiness Check

**1.** $(x - 3)(x + 5) = 0$
$x - 3 = 0$ or $x + 5 = 0$
$x = 3$ or $\quad x = -5$
The solutions are −5, 3.

**2.** $(y + 5)(y + 3) = 0$
$y + 5 = 0$ or $y + 3 = 0$
$y = -5$ or $\quad y = -3$
The solutions are −5, −3.

**3.** $(z - 3)(z + 7) = 0$
$z - 3 = 0$ or $z + 7 = 0$
$z = 3$ or $\quad z = -7$
The solutions are −7, 3.

**4.** $(c-2)(c-4)=0$
$c-2=0$ or $c-4=0$
$c=2$ or $\quad c=4$
The solutions are 2, 4.

**5.** $x(x-9)=0$
$x=0$ or $x-9=0$
$\qquad\qquad\quad x=9$
The solutions are 0, 9.

**6.** $w(w+7)=0$
$w=0$ or $w+7=0$
$\qquad\qquad\quad w=-7$
The solutions are $-7$, 0.

**Exercise Set 5.8**

**1.** $(x+3)(3x-4)=0$
$x+3=0$ or $3x-4=0$
$x=-3$ or $\quad 3x=4$
$\qquad\qquad\qquad x=\dfrac{4}{3}$
The solutions are $-3, \dfrac{4}{3}$.

**3.** $3(2x-5)(4x+3)=0$
$2x-5=0$ or $4x+3=0$
$2x=5$ or $\quad 4x=-3$
$x=\dfrac{5}{2}$ or $\quad x=-\dfrac{3}{4}$
The solutions are $-\dfrac{3}{4}, \dfrac{5}{2}$.

**5.** $x^2+11x+24=0$
$(x+8)(x+3)=0$
$x+8=0$ or $x+3=0$
$x=-8$ or $\quad x=-3$
The solutions are $-8, -3$.

**7.** $12x^2+5x-2=0$
$(4x-1)(3x+2)=0$
$4x-1=0$ or $3x+2=0$
$4x=1$ or $\quad 3x=-2$
$x=\dfrac{1}{4}$ or $\quad x=-\dfrac{2}{3}$
The solutions are $-\dfrac{2}{3}, \dfrac{1}{4}$.

**9.** $z^2+9=10z$
$z^2-10z+9=0$
$(z-9)(z-1)=0$
$z-9=0$ or $z-1=0$
$z=9$ or $\quad z=1$
The solutions are 1, 9.

**11.** $x(5x+2)=3$
$5x^2+2x-3=0$
$(5x-3)(x+1)=0$
$5x-3=0$ or $x+1=0$
$5x=3$ or $\quad x=-1$
$x=\dfrac{3}{5}$
The solutions are $-1, \dfrac{3}{5}$.

**13.** $x^2-6x=x(8+x)$
$x^2-6x=8x+x^2$
$-14x=0$
$x=0$
The solution is 0.

**15.** $\dfrac{z^2}{6}-\dfrac{z}{2}-3=0$
$z^2-3z-18=0$
$(z-6)(z+3)=0$
$z-6=0$ or $z+3=0$
$z=6$ or $\quad z=-3$
The solutions are $-3$, 6.

**17.** $\dfrac{x^2}{2}+\dfrac{x}{20}=\dfrac{1}{10}$
$10x^2+x=2$
$10x^2+x-2=0$
$(5x-2)(2x+1)=0$
$5x-2=0$ or $2x+1=0$
$5x=2$ or $\quad 2x=-1$
$x=\dfrac{2}{5}$ or $\quad x=-\dfrac{1}{2}$
The solutions are $-\dfrac{1}{2}, \dfrac{2}{5}$.

**19.**
$$\frac{4t^2}{5} = \frac{t}{5} + \frac{3}{10}$$
$$8t^2 = 2t + 3$$
$$8t^2 - 2t - 3 = 0$$
$$(4t - 3)(2t + 1) = 0$$
$$4t - 3 = 0 \text{ or } 2t + 1 = 0$$
$$4t = 3 \text{ or } \quad 2t = -1$$
$$t = \frac{3}{4} \text{ or } \quad t = -\frac{1}{2}$$
The solutions are $-\frac{1}{2}, \frac{3}{4}$.

**21.** $(x + 2)(x - 7)(3x - 8) = 0$
$$x + 2 = 0 \quad \text{or } x - 7 = 0 \text{ or } 3x - 8 = 0$$
$$x = -2 \text{ or } \quad x = 7 \text{ or } \quad 3x = 8$$
$$x = \frac{8}{3}$$
The solutions are $-2, 7, \frac{8}{3}$.

**23.**
$$y^3 = 9y$$
$$y^3 - 9y = 0$$
$$y(y^2 - 9) = 0$$
$$y(y + 3)(y - 3) = 0$$
$$y = 0 \text{ or } y + 3 = 0 \quad \text{or } y - 3 = 0$$
$$y = -3 \text{ or } \quad y = 3$$
The solutions are $-3, 0, 3$.

**25.**
$$x^3 - x = 2x^2 - 2$$
$$x^3 - 2x^2 - x + 2 = 0$$
$$x^2(x - 2) - 1(x - 2) = 0$$
$$(x^2 - 1)(x - 2) = 0$$
$$(x + 1)(x - 1)(x - 2) = 0$$
$$x + 1 = 0 \quad \text{or } x - 1 = 0 \text{ or } x - 2 = 0$$
$$x = -1 \text{ or } \quad x = 1 \text{ or } \quad x = 2$$
The solutions are $-1, 1, 2$.

**27.** Answers may vary

**29.** $(2x + 7)(x - 10) = 0$
$$2x + 7 = 0 \quad \text{or } x - 10 = 0$$
$$2x = -7 \text{ or } \quad x = 10$$
$$x = -\frac{7}{2}$$
The solutions are $-\frac{7}{2}, 10$.

**31.** $3x(x - 5) = 0$
$$3x = 0 \text{ or } x - 5 = 0$$
$$x = 0 \text{ or } \quad x = 5$$
The solutions are $0, 5$.

**33.** $x^2 - 2x - 15 = 0$
$$(x - 5)(x + 3) = 0$$
$$x - 5 = 0 \text{ or } x + 3 = 0$$
$$x = 5 \text{ or } \quad x = -3$$
The solutions are $3, 5$.

**35.**
$$12x^2 + 2x - 2 = 0$$
$$2(6x^2 + x - 1) = 0$$
$$2(3x - 1)(2x + 1) = 0$$
$$3x - 1 = 0 \text{ or } 2x + 1 = 0$$
$$3x = 1 \text{ or } \quad 2x = -1$$
$$x = \frac{1}{3} \text{ or } \quad x = -\frac{1}{2}$$
The solutions are $-\frac{1}{2}, \frac{1}{3}$.

**37.**
$$w^2 - 5w = 36$$
$$w^2 - 5w - 36 = 0$$
$$(w - 9)(w + 4) = 0$$
$$w - 9 = 0 \text{ or } w + 4 = 0$$
$$w = 9 \text{ or } \quad w = -4$$
The solutions are $-4, 9$.

**39.** $25x^2 - 40x + 16 = 0$
$$(5x - 4)^2 = 0$$
$$5x - 4 = 0$$
$$5x = 4$$
$$x = \frac{4}{5}$$
The solution is $\frac{4}{5}$.

**41.**
$$2r^3 + 6r^2 = 20r$$
$$2r^3 + 6r^2 - 20r = 0$$
$$2r(r^2 + 3r - 10) = 0$$
$$2r(r + 5)(r - 2) = 0$$
$$2r = 0 \text{ or } r + 5 = 0 \quad \text{or } r - 2 = 0$$
$$r = 0 \text{ or } \quad r = -5 \text{ or } \quad r = 2$$
The solutions are $-5, 0, 2$.

**43.** $z(5z-4)(z+3)=0$

$z=0$   or   $5z-4=0$   or   $z+3=0$

$5z=4$   or     $z=-3$

$z=\dfrac{4}{5}$

The solutions are $-3,\ 0,\ \dfrac{4}{5}$.

**45.** $2z(z+6)=2z^2+12z-8$

$2z^2+12z=2z^2+12z-8$

$0=-8$   False

No solutions exist; $\varnothing$.

**47.** $(x-1)(x+4)=24$

$x^2+3x-4=24$

$x^2+3x-28=0$

$(x+7)(x-4)=0$

$x+7=0$   or   $x-4=0$

$x=-7$   or     $x=4$

The solutions are $-7,\ 4$.

**49.** $\dfrac{x^2}{4}-\dfrac{5}{2}x+6=0$

$x^2-10x+24=0$

$(x-6)(x-4)=0$

$x-6=0$   or   $x-4=0$

$x=6$   or     $x=4$

The solutions are $4,\ 6$.

**51.** $y^2+\dfrac{1}{4}=-y$

$4y^2+1=-4y$

$4y^2+4y+1=0$

$(2y+1)^2=0$

$2y+1=0$

$2y=-1$

$y=-\dfrac{1}{2}$

The solution is $-\dfrac{1}{2}$.

**53.** $y^3+4y^2=9y+36$

$y^3+4y^2-9y-36=0$

$y^2(y+4)-9(y+4)=0$

$(y^2-9)(y+4)=0$

$(y+3)(y-3)(y+4)=0$

$y+3=0$   or   $y-3=0$   or   $y+4=0$

$y=-3$   or    $y=3$   or     $y=-4$

The solutions are $-4,\ -3,\ 3$.

**55.** $2x^3=50x$

$2x^3-50x=0$

$2x(x^2-25)=0$

$2x(x+5)(x-5)=0$

$2x=0$   or   $x+5=0$    or   $x-5=0$

$x=0$   or     $x=-5$   or     $x=5$

The solutions are $-5,\ 0,\ 5$.

**57.** $x^2+(x+1)^2=61$

$x^2+x^2+2x+1=61$

$2x^2+2x-60=0$

$2(x^2+x-30)=0$

$2(x+6)(x-5)=0$

$x+6=0$   or   $x-5=0$

$x=-6$   or     $x=5$

The solutions are $-6,\ 5$.

**59.** $m^2(3m-2)=m$

$3m^3-2m^2=m$

$3m^3-2m^2-m=0$

$m(3m^2-2m-1)=0$

$m(3m+1)(m-1)=0$

$m=0$   or   $3m+1=0$    or   $m-1=0$

$3m=-1$   or     $m=1$

$m=-\dfrac{1}{3}$

The solutions are $-\dfrac{1}{3},\ 0,\ 1$.

**61.**
$$3x^2 = -x$$
$$3x^2 + x = 0$$
$$x(3x+1) = 0$$
$$x = 0 \quad \text{or} \quad 3x+1 = 0$$
$$3x = -1$$
$$x = -\frac{1}{3}$$

The solutions are $-\frac{1}{3}, 0$.

**63.** $x(x-3) = x^2 + 5x + 7$
$$x^2 - 3x = x^2 + 5x + 7$$
$$-8x = 7$$
$$x = -\frac{7}{8}$$

The solution is $-\frac{7}{8}$.

**65.** $3(t-8) + 2t = 7 + t$
$$3t - 24 + 2t = 7 + t$$
$$5t - 24 = 7 + t$$
$$4t = 31$$
$$t = \frac{31}{4}$$

The solution is $\frac{31}{4}$.

**67.** $-3(x-4) + x = 5(3-x)$
$$-3x + 12 + x = 15 - 5x$$
$$-2x + 12 = 15 - 5x$$
$$3x = 3$$
$$x = 1$$
The solution is 1.

**69.** **a** and **d** are incorrect because the right side of the equation is not zero.

**71.** Let $n$ = the one number and $n + 5$ = the other number.
$$n(n+5) = 66$$
$$n^2 + 5n - 66 = 0$$
$$(n+11)(n-6) = 0$$
$$n+11 = 0 \quad \text{or} \quad n-6 = 0$$
$$n = -11 \quad \text{or} \quad n = 6$$
The two solutions are –11 and –6 and 6 and 11.

**73.** Let $d$ = amount of cable needed. Then from the Pythagorean theorem, $d^2 = 45^2 + 60^2 = 5625$ so $d = \sqrt{5625} = 75$ ft.

**75.** $C(x) = x^2 - 15x + 50$
$$9500 = x^2 - 15x + 50$$
$$0 = x^2 - 15x - 9450$$
$$0 = (x-105)(x+90)$$
$$x - 105 = 0 \quad \text{or} \quad x + 90 = 0$$
$$x = 105 \quad \text{or} \quad x = -90$$
Disregard the negative; 105 units.

**77.** Let $x$ = one leg of a right triangle and $x - 3$ = the other leg of the right triangle.
$$15^2 = x^2 + (x-3)^2$$
$$225 = x^2 + x^2 - 6x + 9$$
$$225 = 2x^2 - 6x + 9$$
$$0 = 2x^2 - 6x - 216$$
$$0 = 2(x^2 - 3x - 108)$$
$$0 = 2(x-12)(x+9)$$
$$x - 12 = 0 \quad \text{or} \quad x + 9 = 0$$
$$x = 12 \quad \text{or} \quad x = -9$$
Disregarding the negative solution, we find that one leg of the right triangle is 12 cm and the other leg is 9 cm.

**79.** Note that the outer rectangle has lengths of $2x + 12$ and $2x + 16$. Thus, the area of the border is $(2x + 12)(2x + 16) - 12 \cdot 16$. Set this equal to 128 and solve for $x$.
$$(2x+12)(2x+16) - 12 \cdot 16 = 128$$
$$4x^2 + 56x + 192 - 192 = 128$$
$$4x^2 + 56x = 128$$
$$4x^2 + 56x - 128 = 0$$
$$x^2 + 14x - 32 = 0$$
$$(x+16)(x-2) = 0$$
$$x + 16 = 0 \quad \text{or} \quad x - 2 = 0$$
$$x = -16 \quad \text{or} \quad x = 2$$
Since $x$ must be positive, we see that $x = 2$ inches.

**81.** The sunglasses will hit the ground when
$h(t)$ equals 0.

$$-16t^2 + 1600 = 0$$
$$-16(t^2 - 100) = 0$$
$$-16(t-10)(t+10) = 0$$
$$t - 10 = 0 \quad \text{or} \quad t + 10 = 0$$
$$t = 10 \quad \text{or} \quad t = -10$$

The sunglasses will hit the ground 10 seconds
after being dropped.

**83.** Let the width of the floor = $w$. Then the length is
$2w - 3$ and so the area is
$$(2w-3)w = 90$$
$$2w^2 - 3w - 90 = 0$$
$$(2w-15)(w+6) = 0$$
$$2w - 15 = 0 \qquad \text{or} \quad w + 6 = 0$$
$$2w = 15 \qquad \text{or} \qquad w = -6$$
$$w = \frac{15}{2} = 7.5$$

Disregard –6.
$$2w - 3 = 2(7.5) - 3 = 15 - 3 = 12$$
The width is 7.5 ft and the length is 12 ft.

**85.**
$$0.5x^2 = 50$$
$$0.5x^2 \;\; 50 = 0$$
$$5x^2 - 500 = 0$$
$$x^2 - 100 = 0$$
$$(x+10)(x-10) = 0$$
$$x + 10 = 0 \quad \text{or} \quad x - 10 = 0$$
$$x = -10 \quad \text{or} \qquad x = 10$$

Disregard the negative solution. A 10-inch
square tier is needed, provided each person has
one serving.

**87.** The object will hit the ground when $h(t)$ equals
0.
$$-16t^2 + 80t + 576 = 0$$
$$-16(t^2 - 5t - 36) = 0$$
$$-16(t-9)(t+4) = 0$$
$$t - 9 = 0 \quad \text{or} \quad t + 4 = 0$$
$$t = 9 \quad \text{or} \qquad t = -4$$

The object will hit the ground 9 seconds after
being dropped.

**89.** E; $x$-intercepts $(2, 0)$, $(-5, 0)$

**91.** F; $x$-intercepts $(0, 0)$, $(-3, 0)$, $(3, 0)$

**93.** B; $x$-intercepts $\left(-\frac{1}{2}, 0\right)$, $(-4, 0)$

**95.** $(-3, 0)$, $(0, 2)$; function, because any vertical line
will cross only once.

**97.** $(-4, 0)$, $(0, 2)$, $(4, 0)$, $(0, -2)$; not a function,
because a vertical line can be drawn that crosses
twice.

**99.** Answers may vary

**101.** $(x-5)(x+2) = 0$
$$x - 5 = 0 \quad \text{or} \quad x + 2 = 0$$
$$x = 5 \quad \text{or} \qquad x = -2$$

**103.** $$y(y-5) = -6$$
$$y^2 - 5y + 6 = 0$$
$$(y-2)(y-3) = 0$$
$$y - 2 = 0 \quad \text{or} \quad y - 3 = 0$$
$$y = 2 \quad \text{or} \qquad y = 3$$

**105.** $(x^2 + x - 6)(3x^2 - 14x - 5) = 0$
$$x^2 + x - 6 = 0 \quad \text{or} \quad 3x^2 - 14x - 5 = 0$$
$$(x+3)(x-2) = 0 \quad \text{or} \quad (3x+1)(x-5) = 0$$
$$x + 3 = 0 \quad \text{or } x - 2 = 0 \text{ or } 3x + 1 = 0$$
$$x = -3 \qquad x = 2 \qquad 3x = -1$$
$$x = -\frac{1}{3}$$
or $x - 5 = 0$
$$x = 5$$

The solutions are $-3$, $-\frac{1}{3}$, $2$, $5$.

**107.** No; answers may vary

**109.** Answers may vary
Ex.: $(x-6)(x-7) = x^2 - 13x + 42 = 0$

**111.** Answers may vary
Ex.: $(x-4)(x+3) = x^2 - x - 12 = 0$

**The Bigger Picture**

**1.** $|7x - 3| = |5x - 9|$
$$7x - 3 = 5x + 9 \quad \text{or} \quad 7x - 3 = -(5x+9)$$
$$2x = 12 \qquad\qquad 7x - 3 = -5x - 9$$
$$x = 6 \qquad\qquad 12x = -6$$
$$x = -\frac{1}{2}$$

**2.** $\left|\dfrac{x+2}{5}\right| < 1$

$-1 < \dfrac{x+2}{5} < 1$

$-5 < x+2 < 5$

$-7 < x < 3$

$(-7, 3)$

**3.** $3(x-6)+2 = 9+5(3x-1)$

$3x - 18 + 2 = 9 + 15x - 5$

$3x - 16 = 15x + 4$

$-12x = 20$

$x = -\dfrac{5}{3}$

**4.** $(x-6)(2x+3) = 0$

$x - 6 = 0$   or   $2x + 3 = 0$

$x = 6$   or        $x = -\dfrac{3}{2}$

**5.** $|-3x + 10| \geq -2$
The absolute value of any expression is always $\geq 0$. Therefore, the solution is $(-\infty, \infty)$.

**6.** $|-2x - 5| = 11$

$-2x - 5 = -11$   or   $-2x - 5 = 11$

$-2x = -6$   or        $-2x = 16$

$x = 3$   or        $x = -8$

**7.**      $x(x-7) = 30$

$x^2 - 7x = 30$

$x^2 - 7x - 30 = 0$

$(x+3)(x-10) = 0$

$x + 3 = 0$   or   $x - 10 = 0$

$x = -3$   or        $x = 10$

**8.** $8x - 4 \geq 15x - 4$

$-7x \geq 0$

$x \leq 0$

The solution set is $(-\infty, 0]$.

## Chapter 5 Vocabulary Check

**1.** A <u>polynomial</u> is a finite sum of terms in which all variables are raised to nonnegative integer powers and no variables appear in any denominator.

**2.** <u>Factoring</u> is the process of writing a polynomial as a product.

**3.** <u>Exponents</u> are used to write repeated factors in a more compact form.

**4.** The <u>degree of a term</u> is the sum of the exponents on the variables contained in the term.

**5.** A <u>monomial</u> is a polynomial with three terms.

**6.** If $a$ is not 0, $a^0 = \underline{1}$.

**7.** A <u>trinomial</u> is a polynomial with three terms.

**8.** A polynomial equation of degree 2 is also called a <u>quadratic equation</u>.

**9.** A positive number is written in <u>scientific notation</u> if it is written as the product of a number $a$, such that $1 \leq a < 10$ and a power of 10.

**10.** The <u>degree of a polynomial</u> is the largest degree of all of its terms.

**11.** A <u>binomial</u> is a polynomial with two terms.

**12.** If $a$ and $b$ are real numbers and $a \cdot b = \underline{0}$, then $a = 0$ and $b = 0$.

## Chapter 5 Review

**1.** $(-2)^2 = (-2)(-2) = 4$

**2.** $(-3)^4 = (-3)(-3)(-3)(-3) = 81$

**3.** $-2^2 = -(2 \cdot 2) = -4$

**4.** $-3^4 = -(3 \cdot 3 \cdot 3 \cdot 3) = -81$

**5.** $8^0 = 1$

**6.** $-9^0 = -1$

**7.** $-4^{-2} = -\dfrac{1}{4^2} = -\dfrac{1}{16}$

**8.** $(-4)^2 = \dfrac{1}{(-4)^2} = \dfrac{1}{16}$

**9.** $-xy^2 \cdot y^3 \cdot xy^2 z = -x^{1+1} y^{2+3+2} z = -x^2 y^7 z$

**10.** $(-4xy)(-3xy^2b) = (-4)(-3)x^{1+1}y^{1+2}b$
$= 12x^2y^3b$

**11.** $a^{-14}a^5 = a^{-14+5} = a^{-9} = \dfrac{1}{a^9}$

**12.** $\dfrac{a^{16}}{a^{17}} = a^{16-17} = a^{-1} = \dfrac{1}{a}$

**13.** $\dfrac{x^{-7}}{x^4} = x^{-7-4} = x^{-11} = \dfrac{1}{x^{11}}$

**14.** $\dfrac{9a(a^{-3})}{18a^{15}} = \dfrac{a^{1-3-15}}{2} = \dfrac{a^{-17}}{2} = \dfrac{1}{2a^{17}}$

**15.** $\dfrac{y^{6p-3}}{y^{6p+2}} = y^{(6p-3)-(6p+2)}$
$= y^{6p-3-6p-2}$
$= y^{-5}$
$= \dfrac{1}{y^5}$

**16.** $36,890,000 = 3.689 \times 10^7$

**17.** $-0.000362 = -3.62 \times 10^{-4}$

**18.** $1.678 \times 10^{-6} = 0.000001678$

**19.** $4.1 \times 10^5 = 410,000$

**20.** $(8^5)^3 = 8^{5\cdot3} = 8^{15}$

**21.** $\left(\dfrac{a}{4}\right)^2 = \dfrac{a^2}{4^2} = \dfrac{a^2}{16}$

**22.** $(3x)^3 = 3^3x^3 = 27x^3$

**23.** $(-4x)^{-2} = \dfrac{1}{(-4x)^2} = \dfrac{1}{(-4)^2x^2} = \dfrac{1}{16x^2}$

**24.** $\left(\dfrac{6x}{5}\right)^2 = \dfrac{(6x)^2}{5^2} = \dfrac{36x^2}{25}$

**25.** $(8^6)^{-3} = 8^{6(-3)} = 8^{-18} = \dfrac{1}{8^{18}}$

**26.** $\left(\dfrac{4}{3}\right)^{-2} = \dfrac{4^{-2}}{3^{-2}} = \dfrac{3^2}{4^2} = \dfrac{9}{16}$

**27.** $(-2x^3)^{-3} = \dfrac{1}{(-2x^3)^3}$
$= \dfrac{1}{(-2)^3(x^3)^3}$
$= \dfrac{1}{-8x^9}$
$= -\dfrac{1}{8x^9}$

**28.** $\left(\dfrac{8p^6}{4p^4}\right)^{-2} = (2p^2)^{-2} = 2^{-2}p^{-4} = \dfrac{1}{4p^4}$

**29.** $(-3x^{-2}y^2)^3 = (-3)^3(x^{-2})^3(y^2)^3$
$= -27x^{-6}y^6$
$= -\dfrac{27y^6}{x^6}$

**30.** $\left(\dfrac{x^{-5}y^{-3}}{z^3}\right)^{-5} = \dfrac{x^{25}y^{15}}{z^{-15}} = x^{25}y^{15}z^{15}$

**31.** $\dfrac{4^{-1}x^3yz}{x^{-2}yx^4} = \dfrac{x^{3-(-2)-4}z}{4} = \dfrac{x^{3+2-4}z}{4} = \dfrac{xz}{4}$

**32.** $(5xyz)^{-4}(x^{-2})^{-3} = \dfrac{1}{(5xyz)^4}x^6$
$= \dfrac{x^6}{5^4x^4y^4z^4}$
$= \dfrac{x^2}{625y^4z^4}$

**33.** $\dfrac{2(3yz)^{-3}}{y^{-3}} = \dfrac{2(3)^{-3}y^{-3}z^{-3}}{y^{-3}} = \dfrac{2}{3^3z^3} = \dfrac{2}{27z^3}$

**34.** $x^{4a}(3x^{5a})^3 = x^{4a}(3^3x^{15a})$
$= 27x^{4a+15a}$
$= 27x^{19a}$

**35.** $\dfrac{4y^{3x-3}}{2y^{2x+4}} = 2y^{(3x-3)-(2x+4)}$

$\qquad = 2y^{3x-3-2x-4}$

$\qquad = 2y^{x-7}$

**36.** $\dfrac{(0.00012)(144,000)}{0.0003} = \dfrac{(1.2\times10^{-4})(1.44\times10^{5})}{3\times10^{-4}}$

$\qquad\qquad = 0.576\times10^{5}$

$\qquad\qquad = 5.76\times10^{4}$

**37.** $\dfrac{(-0.00017)(0.00039)}{3000}$

$\qquad = \dfrac{(-1.7\times10^{-4})(3.9\times10^{-4})}{3\times10^{3}}$

$\qquad = -2.21\times10^{-4-4-3}$

$\qquad = -2.21\times10^{-11}$

**38.** $\dfrac{27x^{-5}y^{5}}{18x^{-6}y^{2}}\cdot\dfrac{x^{4}y^{-2}}{x^{-2}y^{3}} = \dfrac{3x^{-5+4}y^{5-2}}{2x^{-6-2}y^{2+3}}$

$\qquad = \dfrac{3x^{-1}y^{3}}{2x^{-8}y^{5}}$

$\qquad = \dfrac{3}{2}x^{-1-(-8)}y^{3-5}$

$\qquad = \dfrac{3}{2}x^{7}y^{-2}$

$\qquad = \dfrac{3x^{7}}{2y^{2}}$

**39.** $\dfrac{3x^{5}}{y^{-4}}\cdot\dfrac{(3xy^{-3})^{-2}}{(z^{-3})^{-4}} = \dfrac{3x^{5}\cdot3^{-2}x^{-2}y^{6}}{y^{-4}z^{12}}$

$\qquad = \dfrac{3^{1-2}x^{5-2}y^{6-(-4)}}{z^{12}}$

$\qquad = \dfrac{3^{-1}x^{3}y^{10}}{z^{12}}$

$\qquad = \dfrac{x^{3}y^{10}}{3z^{12}}$

**40.** $\dfrac{(x^{w})^{2}}{(x^{w-4})^{-2}} = \dfrac{x^{2w}}{x^{-2(w-4)}}$

$\qquad = \dfrac{x^{2w}}{x^{-2w+8}}$

$\qquad = x^{2w-(-2w+8)}$

$\qquad = x^{4w-8}$

**41.** The degree of the polynomial
$x^{2}y-3xy^{3}z+5x+7y$ is the degree of the term
$-3xy^{3}z$ which is 5.

**42.** $3x+2$ has degree 1.

**43.** $4x+8x-6x^{2}-6x^{2}y = (4+8)x-6x^{2}-6x^{2}y$

$\qquad = 12x-6x^{2}-6x^{2}y$

**44.** $-8xy^{3}+4xy^{3}-3x^{3}y = (-8+4)xy^{3}-3x^{3}y$

$\qquad = -4xy^{3}-3x^{3}y$

**45.** $(3x+7y)+(4x^{2}-3x+7)+(y-1)$

$\qquad = 3x+7y+4x^{2}-3x+7+y-1$

$\qquad = 4x^{2}+(3-3)x+(7+1)y+(7-1)$

$\qquad = 4x^{2}+8y+6$

**46.** $(4x^{2}-6xy+9y^{2})-(8x^{2}-6xy-y^{2})$

$\qquad = 4x^{2}-6xy+9y^{2}-8x^{2}+6xy+y^{2}$

$\qquad = (4-8)x^{2}+(9+1)y^{2}$

$\qquad = -4x^{2}+10y^{2}$

**47.** $(3x^{2}-4b+28)+(9x^{2}-30)-(4x^{2}-6b+20)$

$\qquad = 3x^{2}-4b+28+9x^{2}-30-4x^{2}+6b-20$

$\qquad = (3+9-4)x^{2}+(-4+6)b+(28-30-20)$

$\qquad = 8x^{2}+2b-22$

**48.** $(9xy+4x^{2}+18)+(7xy-4x^{3}-9x)$

$\qquad = 9xy+4x^{2}+18+7xy-4x^{3}-9x$

$\qquad = -4x^{3}+4x^{2}+(9+7)xy-9x+18$

$\qquad = -4x^{3}+4x^{2}+16xy-9x+18$

**49.** $(3x^{2}y-7xy-4)+(9x^{2}y+x)-(x-7)$

$\qquad = 3x^{2}y-7xy-4+9x^{2}y+x-x+7$

$\qquad = (3+9)x^{2}y-7xy+(-4+7)$

$\qquad = 12x^{2}y-7xy+3$

**50.** $\begin{array}{r} x^{2}-5x+7 \\ -\quad(x+4) \\ \hline x^{2}-6x+3 \end{array}$

**51.**
$$
\begin{array}{r}
x^3 \quad\; + 2xy^2 - y \\
+\;\; (x - 4xy^2 \quad - 7) \\
\hline
x^3 + x - 2xy^2 - y - 7
\end{array}
$$

**52.** $P(6) = 9(6)^2 - 7(6) + 8 = 290$

**53.** $P(-2) = 9(-2)^2 - 7(-2) + 8 = 58$

**54.** $P(-3) = 9(-3)^2 - 7(-3) + 8 = 110$

**55.** $P(x) + Q(x) = (2x - 1) + (x^2 + 2x - 5)$
$$= 2x - 1 + x^2 + 2x - 5$$
$$= x^2 + 4x - 6$$

**56.** $2[P(x)] - Q(x) = 2(2x - 1) - (x^2 + 2x - 5)$
$$= 4x - 2 - x^2 - 2x + 5$$
$$= -x^2 + 2x + 3$$

**57.** $2(2x^2 y - 6x + 1) + 2(x^2 y + 5)$
$$= 4x^2 y - 12x + 2 + 2x^2 y + 10$$
$$= (6x^2 y - 12x + 12) \text{ cm}$$

**58.** $-6x(4x^2 - 6x + 1) = -24x^3 + 36x^2 - 6x$

**59.** $-4ab^2(3ab^3 + 7ab + 1)$
$$= -4ab^2(3ab^3) - 4ab^2(7ab) - 4ab^2(1)$$
$$= -12a^2 b^5 - 28a^2 b^3 - 4ab^2$$

**60.** $(x - 4)(2x + 9) = 2x^2 + 9x - 8x - 36$
$$= 2x^2 + x - 36$$

**61.** $(-3xa + 4b)^2 = (-3xa)^2 + 2(-3xa)(4b) + (4b)^2$
$$= 9x^2 a^2 - 24xab + 16b^2$$

**62.**
$$
\begin{array}{r}
9x^2 + 4x + 1 \\
4x - 3 \\
\hline
-27x^2 - 12x - 3 \\
36x^3 + 16x^2 \;\; + 4x \\
\hline
36x^3 - 11x^2 \;\; - 8x - 3
\end{array}
$$

**63.** $(5x - 9y)(3x + 9y) = 15x^2 + 45xy - 27xy + 81y^2$
$$= 15x^2 + 18xy - 81y^2$$

**64.** $\left(x - \dfrac{1}{3}\right)\left(x + \dfrac{2}{3}\right) = x^2 + \dfrac{2}{3}x - \dfrac{1}{3}x - \dfrac{1}{3}\left(\dfrac{2}{3}\right)$
$$= x^2 + \frac{1}{3}x - \frac{2}{9}$$

**65.** $(x^2 + 9x + 1)^2$
$$= (x^2 + 9x + 1)(x^2 + 9x + 1)$$
$$= x^2(x^2 + 9x + 1) + 9x(x^2 + 9x + 1) + 1(x^2 + 9x + 1)$$
$$= x^4 + 9x^3 + x^2 + 9x^3 + 81x^2 + 9x + x^2 + 9x + 1$$
$$= x^4 + 18x^3 + 83x^2 + 18x + 1$$

**66.** $(3x - y)^2 = (3x)^2 - 2(3x)y + y^2$
$$= 9x^2 - 6xy + y^2$$

**67.** $(4x + 9)^2 = (4x)^2 + 2(4x)(9) + 9^2$
$$= 16x^2 + 72x + 81$$

**68.** $(x + 3y)(x - 3y) = x^2 - (3y)^2 = x^2 - 9y^2$

**69.** $[4 + (3a - b)][4 - (3a - b)]$
$$= 4^2 - (3a - b)^2$$
$$= 16 - [(3a)^2 - 2(3a)b + b^2]$$
$$= 16 - (9a^2 - 6ab + b^2)$$
$$= 16 - 9a^2 + 6ab - b^2$$

**70.** $P(x) \cdot Q(x)$
$$= (2x - 1)(x^2 + 2x - 5)$$
$$= 2x(x^2 + 2x - 5) - 1(x^2 + 2x - 5)$$
$$= 2x^3 + 4x^2 - 10x - x^2 - 2x + 5$$
$$= 2x^3 + 3x^2 - 12x + 5$$

**71.** Area $= lw$
$$= (3y + 7z)(3y - 7z)$$
$$= (3y)^2 - (7z)^2$$
$$= (9y^2 - 49z^2) \text{ square units}$$

**72.** $4a^b(3a^{b+2} - 7) = 4a^b(3a^{b+2}) + 4a^b(-7)$
$$= 12a^{b+b+2} - 28a^b$$
$$= 12a^{2b+2} - 28a^b$$

**73.** $(4xy^z - b)^2 = (4xy^z)^2 - 2(4xy^z)b + b^2$
$$= 4^2 x^2 (y^z)^2 - 8xy^z b + b^2$$
$$= 16x^2 y^{2z} - 8xy^z b + b^2$$

**74.** $(3x^a - 4)(3x^a + 4) = (3x^a)^2 - 4^2$
$\qquad\qquad\qquad\qquad = 3^2(x^a)^2 - 16$
$\qquad\qquad\qquad\qquad = 9x^{2a} - 16$

**75.** $16x^3 - 24x^2 = 8x^2(2x - 3)$

**76.** $36y - 24y^2 = 12y(3 - 2y)$

**77.** $6ah^2 + 8ah - 4a^2h^2 = 2ah(3h + 4 - 2ah)$

**78.** $14a^2b^2 - 21ab^2 + 7ab = 7ab(2ab - 3b + 1)$

**79.** $6a(a + 3b) - 5(a + 3b) = (6a - 5)(a + 3b)$

**80.** $4x(x - 2y) - 5(x - 2y) = (4x - 5)(x - 2y)$

**81.** $xy - 6y + 3x - 18 = y(x - 6) + 3(x - 6)$
$\qquad\qquad\qquad\qquad = (y + 3)(x - 6)$

**82.** $ab - 8b + 4a - 32 = b(a - 8) + 4(a - 8)$
$\qquad\qquad\qquad\qquad = (b + 4)(a - 8)$

**83.** $pq - 3p - 5q + 15 = p(q - 3) - 5(q - 3)$
$\qquad\qquad\qquad\qquad = (p - 5)(q - 3)$

**84.** $x^3 - x^2 - 2x + 2 = x^2(x - 1) - 2(x - 1)$
$\qquad\qquad\qquad\qquad = (x^2 - 2)(x - 1)$

**85.** Area $= 2xy - x^2 = x(2y - x)$ sq units

**86.** $x^2 - 14x - 72 = (x - 18)(x + 4)$

**87.** $x^2 + 16x - 80 = (x - 4)(x + 20)$

**88.** $2x^2 - 18x + 28 = 2(x^2 - 9x + 14)$
$\qquad\qquad\qquad\qquad = 2(x - 7)(x - 2)$

**89.** $3x^2 + 33x + 54 = 3(x^2 + 11x + 18)$
$\qquad\qquad\qquad\qquad = 3(x + 9)(x + 2)$

**90.** $2x^3 - 7x^2 - 9x = x(2x^2 - 7x - 9)$
$\qquad\qquad\qquad\qquad = x(2x - 9)(x + 1)$

**91.** $3x^2 + 2x - 16 = (3x + 8)(x - 2)$

**92.** $6x^2 + 17x + 10 = (6x + 5)(x + 2)$

**93.** $15x^2 - 91x + 6 = (15x - 1)(x - 6)$

**94.** $4x^2 + 2x - 12 = 2(2x^2 + x - 6)$
$\qquad\qquad\qquad\qquad = 2(2x - 3)(x + 2)$

**95.** $9x^2 - 12x - 12 = 3(3x^2 - 4x - 4)$
$\qquad\qquad\qquad\qquad = 3(3x + 2)(x - 2)$

**96.** $y^2(x + 6)^2 - 2y(x + 6)^2 - 3(x + 6)^2$
$\qquad = (x + 6)^2(y^2 - 2y - 3)$
$\qquad = (x + 6)^2(y - 3)(y + 1)$

**97.** Let $y = x + 5$. Then
$\qquad (x + 5)^2 + 6(x + 5) + 8 = y^2 + 6y + 8$
$\qquad\qquad\qquad\qquad\qquad = (y + 4)(y + 2)$
$\qquad\qquad\qquad\qquad\qquad = [(x + 5) + 4][(x + 5) + 2]$
$\qquad\qquad\qquad\qquad\qquad = (x + 9)(x + 7)$

**98.** $x^4 - 6x^2 - 16 = (x^2 - 8)(x^2 + 2)$

**99.** $x^4 + 8x^2 - 20 = (x^2 + 10)(x^2 - 2)$

**100.** $x^2 - 100 = x^2 - 10^2 = (x + 10)(x - 10)$

**101.** $x^2 - 81 = x^2 - 9^2 = (x + 9)(x - 9)$

**102.** $2x^2 - 32 = 2(x^2 - 16)$
$\qquad\qquad\quad = 2(x^2 - 4^2)$
$\qquad\qquad\quad = 2(x + 4)(x - 4)$

**103.** $6x^2 - 54 = 6(x^2 - 9)$
$\qquad\qquad\quad = 6(x^2 - 3^2)$
$\qquad\qquad\quad = 6(x + 3)(x - 3)$

**104.** $81 - x^4 = 9^2 - (x^2)^2$
$\qquad\qquad\quad = (9 + x^2)(9 - x^2)$
$\qquad\qquad\quad = (9 + x^2)(3 + x)(3 - x)$

**105.** $16 - y^4 = 4^2 - (y^2)^2$
$\qquad\qquad\quad = (4 + y^2)(4 - y^2)$
$\qquad\qquad\quad = (4 + y^2)(2 + y)(2 - y)$

**106.** $(y + 2)^2 - 25 = (y + 2)^2 - 5^2$
$\qquad\qquad\qquad = [(y + 2) + 5][(y + 2) - 5]$
$\qquad\qquad\qquad = (y + 7)(y - 3)$

**107.** $(x-3)^2 - 16 = (x-3)^2 - 4^2$
$$= [(x-3)+4][(x-3)-4]$$
$$= (x+1)(x-7)$$

**108.** $x^3 + 216 = x^3 + 6^3$
$$= (x+6)(x^2 - 6 \cdot x + 6^2)$$
$$= (x+6)(x^2 - 6x + 36)$$

**109.** $y^3 + 512 = y^3 + 8^3$
$$= (y+8)(y^2 - 8 \cdot y + 8^2)$$
$$= (y+8)(y^2 - 8y + 64)$$

**110.** $8 - 27y^3 = 2^3 - (3y)^3$
$$= (2-3y)(4 + 2 \cdot 3y + (3y)^2)$$
$$= (2-3y)(4 + 6y + 9y^2)$$

**111.** $1 - 64y^3 = 1^3 - (4y)^3$
$$= (1-4y)(1^2 + 1 \cdot 4y + (4y)^2)$$
$$= (1-4y)(1 + 4y + 16y^2)$$

**112.** $6x^4 y + 48xy = 6xy(x^3 + 8)$
$$= 6xy(x^3 + 2^3)$$
$$= 6xy(x+2)(x^2 - 2x + 2^2)$$
$$= 6xy(x+2)(x^2 - 2x + 4)$$

**113.** $2x^5 + 16x^2 y^3 = 2x^2(x^3 + 8y^3)$
$$= 2x^2(x^3 + (2y)^3)$$
$$= 2x^2(x+2y)(x^2 - x \cdot 2y + (2y)^2)$$
$$= 2x^2(x+2y)(x^2 - 2xy + 4y^2)$$

**114.** $x^2 - 2x + 1 - y^2 = (x^2 - 2x + 1) - y^2$
$$= (x-1)^2 - y^2$$
$$= [(x-1)+y][(x-1)-y]$$
$$= (x-1+y)(x-1-y)$$

**115.** $x^2 - 6x + 9 - 4y^2 = (x^2 - 6x + 9) - 4y^2$
$$= (x-3)^2 - (2y)^2$$
$$= [(x-3)+2y][(x-3)-2y]$$
$$= (x-3+2y)(x-3-2y)$$

**116.** $4x^2 + 12x + 9 = (2x+3)(2x+3)$
$$= (2x+3)^2$$

**117.** $16a^2 - 40ab + 25b^2 = (4a-5b)(4a-5b)$
$$= (4a-5b)^2$$

**118.** Volume $= \pi R^2 h - \pi r^2 h$
$$= \pi h(R^2 - r^2)$$
$$= \pi h(R+r)(R-r) \text{ cubic units}$$

**119.** $(3x-1)(x+7) = 0$
$3x - 1 = 0$ or $x + 7 = 0$
$x = \dfrac{1}{3}$ or $\quad x = -7$

The solutions are $-7, \dfrac{1}{3}$.

**120.** $3(x+5)(8x-3) = 0$
$x + 5 = 0$ or $8x - 3 = 0$
$x = -5$ or $\quad x = \dfrac{3}{8}$

The solutions are $-5, \dfrac{3}{8}$.

**121.** $5x(x-4)(2x-9) = 0$
$5x = 0$ or $x - 4 = 0$ or $2x - 9 = 0$
$x = 0$ or $\quad x = 4$ or $\quad x = \dfrac{9}{2}$

The solutions are $0, 4, \dfrac{9}{2}$.

**122.** $6(x+3)(x-4)(5x+1) = 0$
$x + 3 = 0$ or $x - 4 = 0$ or $5x + 1 = 0$
$x = -3$ or $\quad x = 4$ or $\quad 5x = -1$
$$x = -\dfrac{1}{5}$$

The solutions are $-\dfrac{1}{5}, -3, 4$.

**123.**
$$2x^2 = 12x$$
$$2x^2 - 12x = 0$$
$$2x(x-6) = 0$$
$2x = 0$ or $x - 6 = 0$
$x = 0$ or $\quad x = 6$
The solutions are $0, 6$.

**124.**
$$4x^3 - 36x = 0$$
$$4x(x^2 - 9) = 0$$
$$4x(x+3)(x-3) = 0$$
$$4x = 0 \text{ or } x+3 = 0 \quad \text{or } x-3 = 0$$
$$x = 0 \text{ or } \quad x = -3 \text{ or } \quad x = 3$$
The solutions are –3, 0, 3.

**125.**
$$(1-x)(3x+2) = -4x$$
$$3x+2-3x^2-2x = -4x$$
$$-3x^2 + x + 2 = -4x$$
$$-3x^2 + 5x + 2 = 0$$
$$3x^2 - 5x - 2 = 0$$
$$(3x+1)(x-2) = 0$$
$$3x+1 = 0 \quad \text{or } x-2 = 0$$
$$3x = -1 \text{ or } \quad x = 2$$
$$x = -\frac{1}{3}$$
The solutions are $-\frac{1}{3}$, 2.

**126.**
$$2x(x-12) = -40$$
$$2x^2 - 24x = -40$$
$$2x^2 - 24x + 40 = 0$$
$$2(x^2 - 12x + 20) = 0$$
$$2(x-10)(x-2) = 0$$
$$x-10 = 0 \quad \text{or } x-2 = 0$$
$$x = 10 \text{ or } \quad x = 2$$
The solutions are 2, 10.

**127.**
$$3x^2 + 2x = 12 - 7x$$
$$3x^2 + 9x - 12 = 0$$
$$3(x^2 + 3x - 4) = 0$$
$$3(x+4)(x-1) = 0$$
$$x+4 = 0 \quad \text{or } x-1 = 0$$
$$x = -4 \text{ or } \quad x = 1$$
The solutions are –4, 1.

**128.**
$$2x^2 + 3x = 35$$
$$2x^2 + 3x - 35 = 0$$
$$(2x-7)(x+5) = 0$$
$$2x-7 = 0 \text{ or } x+5 = 0$$
$$2x = 7 \text{ or } \quad x = -5$$
$$x = \frac{7}{2}$$
The solutions are $-5, \frac{7}{2}$.

**129.**
$$x^3 - 18x = 3x^2$$
$$x^3 - 3x^2 - 18x = 0$$
$$x(x^2 - 3x - 18) = 0$$
$$x(x-6)(x+3) = 0$$
$$x = 0 \text{ or } x-6 = 0 \text{ or } x+3 = 0$$
$$x = 6 \text{ or } \quad x = -3$$
The solutions are –3, 0, 6.

**130.**
$$19x^2 - 42x = -x^3$$
$$x^3 + 19x^2 - 42x = 0$$
$$x(x^2 + 19x - 42) = 0$$
$$x(x+21)(x-2) = 0$$
$$x = 0 \text{ or } x+21 = 0 \quad \text{or } x-2 = 0$$
$$x = -21 \text{ or } \quad x = 2$$
The solutions are –21, 0, 2.

**131.**
$$12x = 6x^3 + 6x^2$$
$$-6x^3 - 6x^2 + 12x = 0$$
$$-6x(x^2 + x - 2) = 0$$
$$-6x(x+2)(x-1) = 0$$
$$-6x = 0 \text{ or } x+2 = 0 \quad \text{or } x-1 = 0$$
$$x = 0 \text{ or } \quad x = -2 \text{ or } \quad x = 1$$
The solutions are –2, 0, 1.

**132.**
$$8x^3 + 10x^2 = 3x$$
$$8x^3 + 10x^2 - 3x = 0$$
$$x(8x^2 + 10x - 3) = 0$$
$$x(4x-1)(2x+3) = 0$$
$$x = 0 \text{ or } 4x-1 = 0 \text{ or } 2x+3 = 0$$
$$4x = 1 \text{ or } \quad 2x = -3$$
$$x = \frac{1}{4} \text{ or } \quad x = -\frac{3}{2}$$
The solutions are $-\frac{3}{2}, 0, \frac{1}{4}$.

**133.** Let $x$ = the number. Then
$$x + 2x^2 = 105$$
$$2x^2 + x - 105 = 0$$
$$(2x+15)(x-7) = 0$$
$$2x+15 = 0 \quad \text{or } x-7 = 0$$
$$2x = -15 \text{ or } \quad x = 7$$
$$x = -\frac{15}{2}$$
The number is $-\frac{15}{2}$ or 7.

**134.** Let $x$ = width; then $2x - 5$ = length.
$$x(2x - 5) = 33$$
$$2x^2 - 5x = 33$$
$$2x^2 - 5x - 33 = 0$$
$$(2x - 11)(x + 3) = 0$$
$$2x - 11 = 0 \quad \text{or} \quad x + 3 = 0$$
$$2x = 11 \text{ or} \quad x = -3$$
$$x = \frac{11}{2}$$

Disregard the negative.

Width = $\dfrac{11}{2} = 5\dfrac{1}{2}$ m

Length = $2\left(\dfrac{11}{2}\right) - 5 = 6$ m

**135.** $h(t) = -16t^2 + 400$
$$0 = -16t^2 + 400$$
$$0 = -16(t^2 - 25)$$
$$0 = -16(t + 5)(t - 5)$$
$$t + 5 = 0 \quad \text{or} \quad t - 5 = 0$$
$$t = -5 \text{ or} \quad t = 5$$

Disregard the negative. The stunt dummy will reach the ground after 5 seconds.

**136.** $P(t) = -16t^2 + 1053$

$$P(1) = -16(1)^2 + 1053 = -16 + 1053 = 1037$$

$$P(8) = -16(8)^2 + 1053 = -1024 + 1053 = 29$$

After 1 second, the object is at 1037 feet and after 8 seconds, the object is at 29 feet.

**137.** $(x + 5)(3x^2 - 2x + 1)$
$$= x(3x^2 - 2x + 1) + 5(3x^2 - 2x + 1)$$
$$= 3x^3 - 2x^2 + x + 15x^2 - 10x + 5$$
$$= 3x^3 + 13x^2 - 9x + 5$$

**138.** $(3x^2 + 4x - 1.2) - (5x^2 - x + 5.7)$
$$= 3x^2 + 4x - 1.2 - 5x^2 + x - 5.7$$
$$= -2x^2 + 5x - 6.9$$

**139.** $(3x^2 + 4x - 1.2) + (5x^2 - x + 5.7)$
$$= 3x^2 + 4x - 1.2 + 5x^2 - x + 5.7$$
$$= 8x^2 + 3x + 4.5$$

**140.** $\left(7ab - \dfrac{1}{2}\right)^2 = (7ab)^2 - 2(7ab)\left(\dfrac{1}{2}\right) + \left(\dfrac{1}{2}\right)^2$
$$= 49a^2b^2 - 7ab + \dfrac{1}{4}$$

**141.** $P(x) = -x^2 + x - 4$
$$P(5) = -5^2 + 5 - 4 = -25 + 5 - 4 = -24$$

**142.** $P(x) = -x^2 + x - 4$
$$P(-2) = -(-2)^2 + (-2) - 4 = -4 - 2 - 4 = -10$$

**143.** $12y^5 - 6y^4 = 6y^4(2y) + 6y^4(-1) = 6y^4(2y - 1)$

**144.** $x^2y + 4x^2 - 3y - 12 = x^2(y + 4) - 3(y + 4)$
$$= (y + 4)(x^2 - 3)$$

**145.** $6x^2 - 34x - 12 = 2(3x^2 - 17x - 6)$
$$= 2(3x + 1)(x - 6)$$

**146.** $y^2(4x + 3)^2 - 19y(4x + 3)^2 - 20(4x + 3)^2$
$$= (4x + 3)^2(y^2 - 19y - 20)$$
$$= (4x + 3)^2(y - 20)(y + 1)$$

**147.** $4z^7 - 49z^5 = z^5(4z^2 - 49)$
$$= z^5[(2z)^2 - 7^2]$$
$$= z^5(2z + 7)(2z - 7)$$

**148.** $5x^4 + 4x^2 - 9 = (x^2 - 1)(5x^2 + 9)$
$$= (x + 1)(x - 1)(5x^2 + 9)$$

**149.** $$8x^2 = 24x$$
$$8x^2 - 24x = 0$$
$$8x(x - 3) = 0$$
$$8x = 0 \quad \text{or} \quad x - 3 = 0$$
$$x = 0 \quad \text{or} \qquad x = 3$$

**150.** $$x(x - 11) = 26$$
$$x^2 - 11x = 26$$
$$x^2 - 11x - 26 = 0$$
$$(x + 2)(x - 13) = 0$$
$$x + 2 = 0 \quad \text{or} \quad x - 13 = 0$$
$$x = -2 \quad \text{or} \qquad x = 13$$

**Chapter 5 Test**

**1.** $(-9x)^{-2} = \dfrac{1}{(-9x)^2} = \dfrac{1}{81x^2}$

**2.** $-3xy^{-2}(4xy^2)z = -12x^{1+1}y^{-2+2}z = -12x^2z$

**3.** $\dfrac{6^{-1}a^2b^{-3}}{3^{-2}a^{-5}b^2} = \dfrac{3^2 a^{2+5}}{6^1 b^{2+3}} = \dfrac{9a^7}{6b^5} = \dfrac{3a^7}{2b^5}$

**4.** $\left(\dfrac{-xy^{-5}z}{xy^3}\right)^{-5} = \dfrac{-x^{-5}y^{25}z^{-5}}{x^{-5}y^{-15}}$

$\qquad = \dfrac{x^{-5+5}y^{25-(-15)}}{z^5}$

$\qquad = -\dfrac{y^{40}}{z^5}$

**5.** $630,000,000 = 6.3 \times 10^8$

**6.** $0.01200 = 1.2 \times 10^{-2}$

**7.** $5 \times 10^{-6} = 0.000005$

**8.** $\dfrac{(0.0024)(0.00012)}{0.00032} = \dfrac{(2.4 \times 10^{-3})(1.2 \times 10^{-4})}{3.2 \times 10^{-4}}$

$\qquad = \dfrac{(2.4)(1.2)}{3.2} \times 10^{-3+(-4)-(-4)}$

$\qquad = 0.9 \times 10^{-3}$

$\qquad = 0.0009$

**9.** $(4x^3y - 3x - 4) - (9x^3y + 8x + 5)$

$\qquad = 4x^3y - 3x - 4 - 9x^3y - 8x - 5$

$\qquad = -5x^3y - 11x - 9$

**10.** $-3xy(4x + y) = -3xy(4x) - 3xy(y)$

$\qquad = -12x^2y - 3xy^2$

**11.** $(3x + 4)(4x - 7) = 12x^2 - 21x + 16x - 28$

$\qquad = 12x^2 - 5x - 28$

**12.** $(5a - 2b)(5a + 2b) = (5a)^2 - (2b)^2 = 25a^2 - 4b^2$

**13.** $(6m + n)^2 = (6m)^2 + 2(6m)n + n^2$

$\qquad = 36m^2 + 12mn + n^2$

**14.**
$$\begin{array}{r} x^2 - 6x + 4 \\ \times \qquad 2x - 1 \\ \hline -x^2 + 6x - 4 \\ 2x^3 - 12x^2 + 8x \\ \hline 2x^3 - 13x^2 + 14x - 4 \end{array}$$

**15.** $16x^3y - 12x^2y^4 = 4x^2y(4x - 3y^3)$

**16.** $x^2 - 13x - 30 = (x - 15)(x + 2)$

**17.** $4y^2 + 20y + 25 = (2y + 5)(2y + 5)$

$\qquad = (2y + 5)^2$

**18.** $6x^2 - 15x - 9 = 3(2x^2 - 5x - 3)$

$\qquad = 3(2x + 1)(x - 3)$

**19.** $4x^2 - 25 = (2x)^2 - 5^2 = (2x + 5)(2x - 5)$

**20.** $x^3 + 64 = x^3 + 4^3 = (x + 4)(x^2 - 4x + 16)$

**21.** $3x^2y - 27y^3 = 3y(x^2 - 9y^2)$

$\qquad = 3y(x^2 - (3y)^2)$

$\qquad = 3y(x + 3y)(x - 3y)$

**22.** $6x^2 + 24 = 6(x^2 + 4)$

**23.** $16y^3 - 2 = 2(8y^3 - 1)$

$\qquad = 2((2y)^3 - 1^3)$

$\qquad = 2(2y - 1)(4y^2 + 2y + 1)$

**24.** $x^2y - 9y - 3x^2 + 27 = y(x^2 - 9) - 3(x^2 - 9)$

$\qquad = (x^2 - 9)(y - 3)$

$\qquad = (x + 3)(x - 3)(y - 3)$

**25.**
$\qquad 3n(7n - 20) = 96$

$\qquad 21n^2 - 60n = 96$

$\qquad 21n^2 - 60n - 96 = 0$

$\qquad 3(7n^2 - 20n - 32) = 0$

$\qquad 3(7n + 8)(n - 4) = 0$

$7n+8=0$  or  $n-4=0$

$7n=-8$ or   $n=4$

$n=-\dfrac{8}{7}$

The solutions are $-\dfrac{8}{7}$, 4.

**26.**  $(x+2)(x-2)=5(x+4)$

$x^2-4=5x+20$

$x^2-5x-24=0$

$(x-8)(x+3)=0$

$x-8=0$ or $x+3=0$

$x=8$ or   $x=-3$

The solutions are 8, –3.

**27.**   $2x^3+5x^2-8x-20=0$

$x^2(2x+5)-4(2x+5)=0$

$(2x+5)(x^2-4)=0$

$(2x+5)(x+2)(x-2)=0$

$2x+5=0$  or  $x+2=0$  or  $x-2=0$

$2x=-5$ or   $x=-2$ or   $x=2$

$x=-\dfrac{5}{2}$

The solutions are $-\dfrac{5}{2}$, $-2$, 2.

**28.**  Area $=x^2-(2y)^2$

$=(x+2y)(x-2y)$ square units

**29.**  $h(t)=-16t^2+96t+880$

**a.**  $-16(1)^2+96(1)+880=-16+96+880$

$=960$ feet

**b.**  $-16(5.1)^2+96(5.1)+880$

$=-416.16+489.6+880$

$=953.44$ feet

**c.**                     $0=-16t^2+96t+880$

$16t^2-96t-880=0$

$16(t^2-6t-55)=0$

$(t-11)(t+5)=0$

$t-11=0$  or  $t+5=0$

$t=11$ or    $t=-5$

Disregard the negative. The pebble will hit the ground in 11 seconds.

## Chapter 5 Cumulative Review

**1. a.**  $\sqrt[3]{27}=3$ since $3^3=27$.

**b.**  $\sqrt[5]{1}=1$ since $1^5=1$.

**c.**  $\sqrt[4]{16}=2$ since $2^4=16$.

**2. a.**  $\sqrt[3]{64}=4$ since $4^3=64$.

**b.**  $\sqrt[4]{81}=3$ since $3^4=81$.

**c.**  $\sqrt[5]{32}=2$ since $2^5=32$.

**3.**  $2(x-3)=5x-9$

$2x-6=5x-9$

$-3x=-3$

$x=1$

The solution is 1.

**4.**     $0.3y+2.4=0.1y+4$

$10(0.3y+2.4)=10(0.1y+4)$

$3y+24=y+40$

$2y=16$

$y=8$

The solution is 8.

**5.**  $A=10,000\left(1+\dfrac{0.05}{4}\right)^{4(3)}$

$=10,000(1.0125)^{12}$

$=10,000(1.160754518)$

$=11,607.54518$

There will be $11,607.55 in the account.

**6.**  The area of the room is

$2(14\cdot8)+2(18\cdot8)=512$ sq ft. Two coats means

$2\cdot512=1024$ sq ft of wall needs paint.

$\dfrac{1}{400}=\dfrac{x}{1024}$

$1024\left(\dfrac{1}{400}\right)=1024\left(\dfrac{x}{512}\right)$

$2.56=x$

$x\approx3$

3 gallons of paint are needed.

**7. a.**  $\dfrac{1}{4}x \le \dfrac{3}{8}$

$8\left(\dfrac{1}{4}x\right) \le 8\left(\dfrac{3}{8}\right)$

$2x \le 3$

$x \le \dfrac{3}{2}$

$\left\{x \,\middle|\, x \le \dfrac{3}{2}\right\}$ or $\left(-\infty, \dfrac{3}{2}\right]$

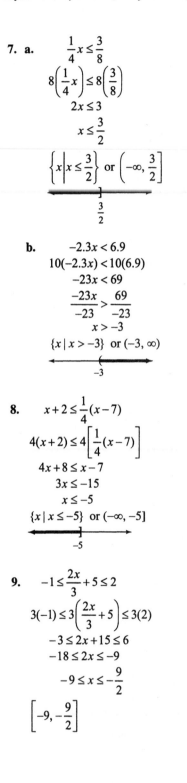

$\dfrac{3}{2}$

**b.**  $-2.3x < 6.9$

$10(-2.3x) < 10(6.9)$

$-23x < 69$

$\dfrac{-23x}{-23} > \dfrac{69}{-23}$

$x > -3$

$\{x \mid x > -3\}$ or $(-3, \infty)$

$-3$

**8.**  $x + 2 \le \dfrac{1}{4}(x - 7)$

$4(x + 2) \le 4\left[\dfrac{1}{4}(x - 7)\right]$

$4x + 8 \le x - 7$

$3x \le -15$

$x \le -5$

$\{x \mid x \le -5\}$ or $(-\infty, -5]$

$-5$

**9.**  $-1 \le \dfrac{2x}{3} + 5 \le 2$

$3(-1) \le 3\left(\dfrac{2x}{3} + 5\right) \le 3(2)$

$-3 \le 2x + 15 \le 6$

$-18 \le 2x \le -9$

$-9 \le x \le -\dfrac{9}{2}$

$\left[-9, -\dfrac{9}{2}\right]$

**10.**  $-\dfrac{1}{3} < \dfrac{3x+1}{6} \le \dfrac{1}{3}$

$6\left(-\dfrac{1}{3}\right) < 6\left(\dfrac{3x+1}{6}\right) \le 6\left(\dfrac{1}{3}\right)$

$-2 < 3x + 1 \le 2$

$-3 < 3x \le 1$

$-1 < x \le \dfrac{1}{3}$

$\left(-1, \dfrac{1}{3}\right]$

**11.**  $|y| = 0$

$y = 0$

The solution is 0.

**12.**  $8 + |4c| = 24$

$|4c| = 16$

$4c = 16$ or $4c = -16$

$c = 4$ or $c = -4$

The solutions are –4, 4.

**13.**  $\left|2x - \dfrac{1}{10}\right| < -13$ is impossible; $\varnothing$.

**14.**  $|5x - 1| + 9 > 5$

$|5x - 1| > -4$ is always true.

$(-\infty, \infty)$

**15.**  $y = \dfrac{1}{3}x$

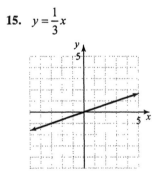

**16.**  $y = 3x$

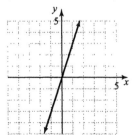

**17.** $f(x) = \begin{cases} 2x+3 & \text{if } x \le 0 \\ -x-1 & \text{if } x > 0 \end{cases}$

$f(2) = -2 - 1 = -3: (2, -3)$
$f(-6) = 2(-6) + 3 = -9: (-6, -9)$
$f(0) = 2(0) + 3 = 3: (0, 3)$

**18.** $f(x) = 3x^2 + 2x + 3$
$f(-3) = 3(-3)^2 + 2(-3) + 3$
$= 3(9) - 6 + 3$
$= 27 - 6 + 3$
$= 24$

**19.** $x = 2$

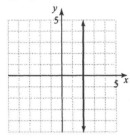

**20.** $y - 5 = 0$
$y = 5$

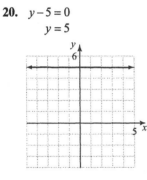

**21.** $y = 2$
This is a horizontal line.
$m = 0$

**22.** $f(x) = -2x - 3$
$m = -2$

**23.** $y = 3$

**24.** $x = -3$

**25.** $x + \frac{1}{2}y \ge -4 \qquad \text{or } y \le -2$
$\frac{1}{2}y \ge -x - 4 \quad \text{or } y \le -2$
$y \ge -2x - 8 \text{ or } y \le -2$

**26.** $y - 3 = 0[x - (-2)]$
$y - 3 = 0$
$y = 3$

**27.** $\begin{cases} 2x + 4y = -6 & (1) \\ x = 2y - 5 & (2) \end{cases}$
Substitute $2y - 5$ for $x$ in E1.
$2(2y - 5) + 4y = -6$
$4y - 10 + 4y = -6$
$8y = 4$
$y = \frac{1}{2}$
Substitute $\frac{1}{2}$ for $y$ in E2.
$x = 2\left(\frac{1}{2}\right) - 5 = 1 - 5 = -4$
The solution is $\left(-4, \frac{1}{2}\right)$.

**28.** $\begin{cases} 4x - 2y = 8 & (1) \\ y = 3x - 6 & (2) \end{cases}$
Substitute $3x - 6$ for $y$ in E1.
$4x - 2(3x - 6) = 8$
$4x - 6x + 12 = 8$
$-2x = -4$
$x = 2$
Substitute 2 for $x$ in E2.
$y = 3(2) - 6 = 6 - 6 = 0$
The solution is (2, 0).

**29.** $\begin{cases} 2x + 4y = 1 & (1) \\ 4x - 4z = -1 & (2) \\ y - 4z = -3 & (3) \end{cases}$
Multiply E2 by $-1$ and add to E3.

247

$$-4x \quad\;\; +4z = 1$$
$$\underline{\qquad\; y - 4z = -3}$$
$$-4x + y \qquad = -2 \;\; (4)$$

Muliply E1 by 2 and add to E4.

$$4x + 8y = 2$$
$$\underline{-4x \;\; + y = -2}$$
$$\qquad 9y = 0$$
$$\qquad\; y = 0$$

Replace $y$ with 0 in E1.

$$2x + 4(0) = 1$$
$$2x = 1$$
$$x = \frac{1}{2}$$

Replace $y$ with 0 in E3.

$$y - 4z = -3$$
$$-4z = -3$$
$$z = \frac{3}{4}$$

The solution is $\left(\dfrac{1}{2}, 0, \dfrac{3}{4}\right)$.

**30.** $\begin{cases} x + y - \dfrac{3}{2}z = \dfrac{1}{2} & (1) \\ \qquad -y - 2z = 14 & (2) \\ x - \dfrac{2}{3}y \qquad = -\dfrac{1}{3} & (3) \end{cases}$

Multiply E1 by 2 and E3 by 3 to clear fractions.

$$\begin{cases} 2x + 2y - 3z = 1 & (1) \\ \qquad -y - 2z = 14 & (2) \\ 3x - 2y \qquad = -1 & (3) \end{cases}$$

Add E1 and E3.

$$5x - 3z = 0 \;\; (4)$$

Multiply E2 by 2 and add to E1.

$$-2y - 4z = 28$$
$$\underline{2x + 2y - 3z = 1}$$
$$2x \qquad -7z = 29 \;\; (5)$$

Solve the new system $\begin{cases} 5x - 3z = 0 & (4) \\ 2x - 7z = 29 & (5) \end{cases}$.

Multiply E4 by −2, multiply E5 by 5, and add.

$$-10x + 6z = 0$$
$$\underline{10x - 35z = 145}$$
$$\qquad -29z = 145$$
$$\qquad\quad z = -5$$

Replace $z$ with −5 in E4.

$$5x - 3(-5) = 0$$
$$5x + 15 = 0$$
$$5x = -15$$
$$x = -3$$

Replace $z$ with −5 in E2.

$$-y - 2(-5) = 14$$
$$-y + 10 = 14$$
$$-y = 4$$
$$y = -4$$

The solution is (−3, −4, −5).

**31.** Let $x$ = the first number and
$y$ = the second number.

$$\begin{cases} x = y - 4 & (1) \\ 4x = 2y + 6 & (2) \end{cases}$$

Multiply E1 by −4 and add to E2.

$$-4x = -4y + 16$$
$$\underline{4x = \;\; 2y + 6}$$
$$0 = -2y + 22$$
$$2y = 22$$
$$y = 11$$

Replace $y$ with 11 in E1.

$$x = 11 - 4 = 7$$

The numbers are 7 and 11.

**32.** Let $x$ = ounces of 20% solution and
$y$ = ounces of 60% solution.

$$\begin{cases} x \qquad + y = 50 & (1) \\ 0.20x + 0.60y = 50(0.30) & (2) \end{cases}$$

Multiply E2 by 100 to clear decimals.

$$\begin{cases} x \quad + y = 50 & (1) \\ 20x + 60y = 1500 & (2) \end{cases}$$

Multiply E1 by −20 and add to E2.

$$-20x - 20y = -1000$$
$$\underline{20x + 60y = 1500}$$
$$\qquad 40y = 500$$
$$y = \frac{500}{40} = 12.5$$

Replace $y$ with 12.5 in E1.

$$x + 12.5 = 50$$
$$x = 37.5$$

You should mix 37.5 ounces of the 20% solution
and 12.5 ounces of the 60% solution.

**33.** $\begin{cases} 2x - y = 3 \\ 4x - 2y = 5 \end{cases}$

$$\begin{bmatrix} 2 & -1 & | & 3 \\ 4 & -2 & | & 5 \end{bmatrix}$$

Divide R1 by 2.

$$\begin{bmatrix} 1 & -\frac{1}{2} & | & \frac{3}{2} \\ 4 & -2 & | & 5 \end{bmatrix}$$

Multiply R1 by −4 and add to R2.

$$\begin{bmatrix} 1 & -\frac{1}{2} & \Big| & \frac{3}{2} \\ 0 & 0 & \Big| & -1 \end{bmatrix}$$

This corresponds to $\begin{cases} x - \dfrac{1}{2}y = \dfrac{3}{2} \\ \qquad\quad 0 = -1 \end{cases}$ . The last

equation is impossible. The system is inconsistent. The solution set is $\varnothing$.

**34.** $\begin{cases} 4y = 8 \\ x + y = 7 \end{cases}$

$$\begin{bmatrix} 0 & 4 & \big| & 8 \\ 1 & 1 & \big| & 7 \end{bmatrix}$$

Interchange R1 and R2.

$$\begin{bmatrix} 1 & 1 & \big| & 7 \\ 0 & 4 & \big| & 8 \end{bmatrix}$$

Divide R2 by 4.

$$\begin{bmatrix} 1 & 1 & \big| & 7 \\ 0 & 1 & \big| & 2 \end{bmatrix}$$

This corresponds to $\begin{cases} x + y = 7 \\ \quad\ \ y = 2 \end{cases}$.

Replace $y$ with 2 in the equation $x + y = 7$.

$x + 2 = 7$

$\quad x = 5$

The solution is (5, 2).

**35.** Let $x$ = measure of smallest angle, then
$x + 80$ = measure of largest angle, and
$x + 10$ = measure of remaining angle.
$x + (x + 80) + (x + 10) = 180$
$\qquad\qquad\quad 3x + 90 = 180$
$\qquad\qquad\qquad\ 3x = 90$
$\qquad\qquad\qquad\ \ x = 30$
$x + 80 = 110$
$x + 10 = 40$
The angles measure 30°, 110°, and 40°.

**36.** $m = \dfrac{1}{2}$, $y$-intercept (0, 5), $b = 5$

$\quad y = mx + b$

$\quad y = \dfrac{1}{2}x + 5$

$\quad f(x) = \dfrac{1}{2}x + 5$

**37. a.** $730,000 = 7.3 \times 10^5$

    **b.** $0.00000104 = 1.04 \times 10^{-6}$

**38. a.** $8,250,000 = 8.25 \times 10^6$

    **b.** $0.0000346 = 3.46 \times 10^{-5}$

**39. a.** $(2x^0 y^{-3})^{-2} = 2^{-2}(1)^{-2}(y^{-3})^{-2} = \dfrac{y^6}{2^2} = \dfrac{y^6}{4}$

    **b.** $\left(\dfrac{x^{-5}}{x^{-2}}\right)^{-3} = \dfrac{(x^{-5})^{-3}}{(x^{-2})^{-3}} = \dfrac{x^{15}}{x^6} = x^{15-6} = x^9$

    **c.** $\left(\dfrac{2}{7}\right)^{-2} = \dfrac{2^{-2}}{7^{-2}} = \dfrac{7^2}{2^2} = \dfrac{49}{4}$

    **d.** $\dfrac{5^{-2}x^{-3}y^{11}}{x^2 y^{-5}} = \dfrac{x^{-3-2}y^{11-(-5)}}{5^2}$

$\qquad\qquad\qquad\ = \dfrac{x^{-5}y^{16}}{25}$

$\qquad\qquad\qquad\ = \dfrac{y^{16}}{25x^5}$

**40. a.** $(4a^{-1}b^0)^{-3} = 4^{-3}(a^{-1})^{-3}(1)^{-3} = \dfrac{a^3}{4^3} = \dfrac{a^3}{64}$

    **b.** $\left(\dfrac{a^{-6}}{a^{-8}}\right)^{-2} = \dfrac{(a^{-6})^{-2}}{(a^{-8})^{-2}}$

$\qquad\qquad\qquad = \dfrac{a^{12}}{a^{16}}$

$\qquad\qquad\qquad = a^{12-16}$

$\qquad\qquad\qquad = a^{-4}$

$\qquad\qquad\qquad = \dfrac{1}{a^4}$

    **c.** $\left(\dfrac{2}{3}\right)^{-3} = \dfrac{2^{-3}}{3^{-3}} = \dfrac{3^3}{2^3} = \dfrac{27}{8}$

    **d.** $\dfrac{3^{-2}a^{-2}b^{12}}{a^4 b^{-5}} = \dfrac{a^{-2-4}b^{12-(-5)}}{3^2}$

$\qquad\qquad\qquad = \dfrac{a^{-6}b^{17}}{9}$

$\qquad\qquad\qquad = \dfrac{b^{17}}{9a^6}$

**41.** The degree is the degree of the term $x^2 y^2$, which is $2 + 2 = 4$.

**42.** $(3x^2 - 2x) - (5x^2 + 3x) = 3x^2 - 2x - 5x^2 - 3x$
$$= -2x^2 - 5x$$

**43. a.** $(2x^3)(5x^6) = 2(5)x^{3+6} = 10x^9$

   **b.** $(7y^4z^4)(-xy^{11}z^5) = -7xy^{4+11}z^{4+5}$
$$= -7xy^{15}z^9$$

**44. a.** $(3y^6)(4y^2) = 3(4)y^{6+2} = 12y^8$

   **b.** $(6a^3b^2)(-a^2bc^4) = -6a^{3+2}b^{2+1}c^4$
$$= -6a^5b^3c^4$$

**45.** $17x^3y^2 - 34x^4y^2 = 17x^3y^2(1 - 2x)$

**46.** $12x^3y - 3xy^3 = 3xy(4x^2 - y^2)$
$$= 3xy((2x)^2 - y^2)$$
$$= 3xy(2x + y)(2x - y)$$

**47.** $x^2 + 10x + 16 = (x + 8)(x + 2)$

**48.** $5a^2 + 14a - 3 = (5a - 1)(a + 3)$

**49.** $2x^2 + 9x - 5 = 0$
$(2x - 1)(x + 5) = 0$
$2x - 1 = 0$ or $x + 5 = 0$
$2x = 1$ or $x = -5$
$x = \dfrac{1}{2}$

The solution is $-5, \dfrac{1}{2}$.

**50.** $3x^2 - 10x - 8 = 0$
$(3x + 2)(x - 4) = 0$
$3x + 2 = 0$ or $x - 4 = 0$
$3x = -2$ or $x = 4$
$x = -\dfrac{2}{3}$

The solution is $-\dfrac{2}{3}, 4$.

# Chapter 6

## Section 6.1

### Practice Exercises

**1. a.** The denominator of $f(x)$ is never 0.
Domain: $\{x | x \text{ is a real number}\}$

**b.** Undefined values when
$x + 3 = 0$, or $x = -3$
Domain: $\{x | x \text{ is a real number and } x \neq -3\}$

**c.** Undefined values when
$$x^2 - 5x + 6 = 0$$
$$(x-3)(x-2) = 0$$
$$x - 3 = 0 \quad \text{or} \quad x - 2 = 0$$
$$x = 3 \quad \text{or} \quad x = 2$$
Domain:
$\{x | x \text{ is a real number and } x \neq 2, x \neq 3\}$

**2. a.** $\dfrac{5z^4}{10z^5 - 5z^4} = \dfrac{5z^4 \cdot 1}{5z^4(2z-1)}$
$$= 1 \cdot \dfrac{1}{2z-1} = \dfrac{1}{2z-1}$$

**b.** $\dfrac{5x^2 + 13x + 6}{6x^2 + 7x - 10} = \dfrac{(5x+3)(x+2)}{(6x-5)(x+2)}$
$$= \dfrac{5x+3}{6x-5} \cdot 1$$
$$= \dfrac{5x+3}{6x-5}$$

**3. a.** $\dfrac{x+3}{3+x} = \dfrac{x+3}{x+3} = 1$

**b.** $\dfrac{3-x}{x-3} = \dfrac{-1(-3+x)}{x-3} = \dfrac{-1(x-3)}{x-3} = \dfrac{-1}{1} = -1$

**4.** $\dfrac{20 - 5x^2}{x^2 + x - 6} = \dfrac{5(4 - x^2)}{(x+3)(x-2)}$
$$= \dfrac{5(2+x)(2-x)}{(x+3)(x-2)}$$
$$= \dfrac{5(2+x) \cdot (-1)(x-2)}{(x+3)(x-2)}$$
$$= -\dfrac{5(2+x)}{x+3}$$

**5. a.** $\dfrac{x^3 + 64}{4 + x} = \dfrac{(x+4)(x^2 - 4x + 16)}{x+4}$
$$= x^2 - 4x + 16$$

**b.** $\dfrac{5z^2 + 10}{z^3 - 3z^2 + 2z - 6} = \dfrac{5(z^2 + 2)}{(z^3 - 3z^2) + (2z - 6)}$
$$= \dfrac{5(z^2 + 2)}{z^2(z-3) + 2(z-3)}$$
$$= \dfrac{5(z^2 + 2)}{(z-3)(z^2 + 2)}$$
$$= \dfrac{5}{z-3}$$

**6. a.** $\dfrac{2 + 5n}{3n} \cdot \dfrac{6n + 3}{5n^2 - 3n - 2}$
$$= \dfrac{2 + 5n}{3n} \cdot \dfrac{3(2n+1)}{(5n+2)(n-1)}$$
$$= \dfrac{2n+1}{n(n-1)}$$

**b.** $\dfrac{x^3 - 8}{-6x + 12} \cdot \dfrac{6x^2}{x^2 + 2x + 4}$
$$= \dfrac{(x-2)(x^2 + 2x + 4)}{-6(x-2)} \cdot \dfrac{6x^2}{x^2 + 2x + 4}$$
$$= \dfrac{(x-2)(x^2 + 2x + 4) \cdot 6 \cdot x^2}{-1 \cdot 6(x-2)(x^2 + 2x + 4)}$$
$$= \dfrac{x^2}{-1}$$
$$= -x^2$$

**7. a.** $\dfrac{6y^3}{3y^2 - 27} \div \dfrac{42}{3 - y} = \dfrac{6y^3}{3y^2 - 27} \cdot \dfrac{3 - y}{42}$
$$= \dfrac{6y^3(3 - y)}{3(y+3)(y-3) \cdot 42}$$
$$= \dfrac{6y^3 \cdot (-1)(y-3)}{3(y+3)(y-3) \cdot 6 \cdot 7}$$
$$= -\dfrac{y^3}{21(y+3)}$$

**b.** $\dfrac{10x^2+23x-5}{5x^2-51x+10} \div \dfrac{2x^2+9x+10}{7x^2-68x-20}$

$= \dfrac{10x^2+23x-5}{5x^2-51x+10} \cdot \dfrac{7x^2-68x-20}{2x^2+9x+10}$

$= \dfrac{(5x-1)(2x+5)}{(5x-1)(x-10)} \cdot \dfrac{(7x+2)(x-10)}{(2x+5)(x+2)}$

$= \dfrac{7x+2}{x+2}$

**8.** $\dfrac{x^2-16}{(x-4)^2} \cdot \dfrac{5x-20}{3x} \div \dfrac{x^2+x-12}{x}$

$= \dfrac{x^2-16}{(x-4)^2} \cdot \dfrac{5x-20}{3x} \cdot \dfrac{x}{x^2+x-12}$

$= \dfrac{(x+4)(x-4)}{(x-4)(x-4)} \cdot \dfrac{5(x-4)}{3x} \cdot \dfrac{x}{(x+4)(x-3)}$

$= \dfrac{5}{3(x-3)}$

**9. a.** $C(100) = \dfrac{3.2(100)+400}{100} = \dfrac{720}{100} = 7.2$

$7.20$ per tee shirt

**b.** $C(1000) = \dfrac{3.2(1000)+400}{1000} = \dfrac{3600}{1000} = 3.6$

$3.60$ per tee shirt

**Graphing Calculator Explorations**

**1.** $x^2-4=0$

$(x+2)(x-2)=0$

$x+2=0 \quad$ or $\quad x-2=0$

$x=-2 \quad$ or $\quad x=2$

Domain: $\{x \mid x \text{ is a real number and } x \neq -2, x \neq 2\}$

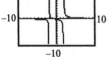

**2.** $x^2-9=0$

$(x+3)(x-3)=0$

$x+3=0 \quad$ or $\quad x-3=0$

$x=-3 \quad$ or $\quad x=3$

Domain: $\{x \mid x \text{ is a real number and } x \neq -3, x \neq 3\}$

**3.** $2x^2+7x-4=0$

$(2x-1)(x+4)=0$

$2x-1=0 \quad$ or $\quad x+4=0$

$2x=1 \quad$ or $\quad x=-4$

$x=\dfrac{1}{2}$

Domain:

$\left\{x \mid x \text{ is a real number and } x \neq -4, x \neq \dfrac{1}{2}\right\}$

**4.** $4x^2-19x-5=0$

$(4x+1)(x-5)=0$

$4x+1=0 \quad$ or $\quad x-5=0$

$4x=-1 \quad$ or $\quad x=5$

$x=-\dfrac{1}{4}$

Domain:

$\left\{x \mid x \text{ is a real number and } x \neq -\dfrac{1}{4}, x \neq 5\right\}$

**Vocabulary and Readiness Check**

**1.** A <u>rational</u> expression is an expression that can be written as the quotient $\dfrac{P}{Q}$ of two polynomials $P$ and $Q$ as long as $Q \neq 0$.

**2.** A rational expression is undefined if the denominator is <u>0</u>.

3. The <u>domain</u> of the rational function $f(x) = \dfrac{2}{x}$ is

   $\{x|x$ is a real number and $x \neq 0\}$.

4. A rational expression is <u>simplified</u> if the numerator and denominator have no common factors other than 1 or $-1$.

5. The expression $\dfrac{x^2 + 2}{2 + x^2}$ simplifies to <u>1</u>.

6. The expression $\dfrac{y-z}{z-y}$ simplifies to <u>$-1$</u>.

7. For a rational expression, $-\dfrac{a}{b} = \dfrac{-a}{\underline{b}} = \dfrac{a}{\underline{-b}}$.

8. The statement $\dfrac{a-6}{a+2} = \dfrac{-(a-6)}{-(a+2)} = \dfrac{-a+6}{-a-2}$ is true.

9. $\dfrac{x}{5} \cdot \dfrac{y}{2} = \dfrac{xy}{10}$

10. $\dfrac{y}{6} \cdot \dfrac{z}{5} = \dfrac{yz}{30}$

11. $\dfrac{2}{x} \cdot \dfrac{y}{3} = \dfrac{2y}{3x}$

12. $\dfrac{a}{5} \cdot \dfrac{7}{b} = \dfrac{7a}{5b}$

13. $\dfrac{m}{6} \cdot \dfrac{m}{6} = \dfrac{m^2}{36}$

14. $\dfrac{9}{x} \cdot \dfrac{8}{x} = \dfrac{72}{x^2}$

**Exercise Set 6.1**

1. 4 is never 0, so the domain of $f(x) = \dfrac{5x-7}{4}$ is

   $\{x|x$ is a real number$\}$.

3. $2t = 0$
   $t = 0$

   The domain of $s(t) = \dfrac{t^2+1}{2t}$ is

   $\{t|t$ is a real number and $t \neq 0\}$.

5. $7 - x = 0$
   $7 = x$

   The domain of $f(x) = \dfrac{3x}{7-x}$ is

   $\{x|x$ is a real number and $x \neq 7\}$.

7. $3x - 1 = 0$
   $3x = 1$
   $x = \dfrac{1}{3}$

   The domain of $f(x) = \dfrac{x}{3x-1}$ is

   $\left\{x \middle| x \text{ is a real number and } x \neq \dfrac{1}{3}\right\}$.

9. $x^3 + x^2 - 2x = 0$
   $x(x^2 + x - 2) = 0$
   $x(x+2)(x-1) = 0$
   $x = 0$ or $x + 2 = 0$ or $x - 1 = 0$
   $x = 0$ or $\phantom{x}x = -2$ or $\phantom{xx}x = 1$

   The domain of $R(x) = \dfrac{3+2x}{x^3+x^2-2x}$ is

   $\{x|x$ is a real number and $x \neq -2, x \neq 0,$
   $\phantom{xxxxxxxx}x \neq 1\}$.

11. $\phantom{xxx}x^2 - 4 = 0$
    $(x+2)(x-2) = 0$
    $x + 2 = 0$ or $x - 2 = 0$
    $\phantom{x}x = -2$ or $\phantom{xx}x = 2$

    The domain of $C(x) = \dfrac{x+3}{x^2-4}$ is

    $\{x|x$ is a real number and $x \neq 2, x \neq -2\}$.

13. $\dfrac{8x - 16x^2}{8x} = \dfrac{8x(1-2x)}{8x} = 1 - 2x$

15. $\dfrac{x^2-9}{3+x} = \dfrac{(x+3)(x-3)}{3+x}$
    $= \dfrac{(x+3)(x-3)}{x+3}$
    $= x - 3$

17. $\dfrac{9y-18}{7y-14} = \dfrac{9(y-2)}{7(y-2)} = \dfrac{9}{7}$

19. $\dfrac{x^2+6x-40}{x+10} = \dfrac{(x+10)(x-4)}{x+10} = x - 4$

**21.** $\dfrac{x-9}{9-x} = \dfrac{-1(9-x)}{9-x} = -1$

**23.** $\dfrac{x^2-49}{7-x} = \dfrac{(x+7)(x-7)}{7-x}$

$= \dfrac{(x+7)(x-7)}{-1(-7+x)}$

$= \dfrac{(x+7)(x-7)}{-1(x-7)}$

$= -(x+7)$

**25.** $\dfrac{2x^2-7x-4}{x^2-5x+4} = \dfrac{(2x+1)(x-4)}{(x-1)(x-4)} = \dfrac{2x+1}{x-1}$

**27.** $\dfrac{x^3-125}{2x-10} = \dfrac{(x-5)(x^2+5x+25)}{2(x-5)}$

$= \dfrac{x^2+5x+25}{2}$

**29.** $\dfrac{3x^2-5x-2}{6x^3+2x^2+3x+1} = \dfrac{(3x+1)(x-2)}{2x^2(3x+1)+1(3x+1)}$

$= \dfrac{(3x+1)(x-2)}{(3x+1)(2x^2+1)}$

$= \dfrac{x-2}{2x^2+1}$

**31.** $\dfrac{9x^2-15x+25}{27x^3+125} = \dfrac{9x^2-15x+25}{(3x+5)(9x^2-15x+25)}$

$= \dfrac{1}{3x+5}$

**33.** $\dfrac{2x-4}{15} \cdot \dfrac{6}{2-x} = \dfrac{2(x-2)}{3\cdot 5} \cdot \dfrac{2\cdot 3}{-(x-2)}$

$= \dfrac{2\cdot 2}{5(-1)}$

$= -\dfrac{4}{5}$

**35.** $\dfrac{18a-12a^2}{4a^2+4a+1} \cdot \dfrac{4a^2+8a+3}{4a^2-9}$

$= \dfrac{6a(3-2a)}{(2a+1)(2a+1)} \cdot \dfrac{(2a+3)(2a+1)}{(2a+3)(2a-3)}$

$= \dfrac{-6a(2a-3)}{(2a+1)(2a+1)} \cdot \dfrac{(2a+3)(2a+1)}{(2a+3)(2a-3)}$

$= -\dfrac{6a}{2a+1}$

**37.** $\dfrac{9x+9}{4x+8} \cdot \dfrac{2x+4}{3x^2-3} = \dfrac{9(x+1)}{4(x+2)} \cdot \dfrac{2(x+2)}{3(x^2-1)}$

$= \dfrac{3\cdot 3(x+1)}{2\cdot 2(x+2)} \cdot \dfrac{2(x+2)}{3(x+1)(x-1)}$

$= \dfrac{3}{2(x-1)}$

**39.** $\dfrac{2x^3-16}{6x^2+6x-36} \cdot \dfrac{9x+18}{3x^2+6x+12}$

$= \dfrac{2(x^3-8)}{6(x^2+x-6)} \cdot \dfrac{9(x+2)}{3(x^2+2x+4)}$

$= \dfrac{2(x-2)(x^2+2x+4)}{2\cdot 3(x-2)(x+3)} \cdot \dfrac{3\cdot 3(x+2)}{3(x^2+2x+4)}$

$= \dfrac{x+2}{x+3}$

**41.** $\dfrac{a^3+a^2b+a+b}{5a^3+5a} \cdot \dfrac{6a^2}{2a^2-2b^2}$

$= \dfrac{a^2(a+b)+1(a+b)}{5a(a^2+1)} \cdot \dfrac{6a^2}{2(a^2-b^2)}$

$= \dfrac{(a+b)(a^2+1)}{5a(a^2+1)} \cdot \dfrac{2\cdot 3\cdot a\cdot a}{2(a+b)(a-b)}$

$= \dfrac{3a}{5(a-b)}$

**43.** $\dfrac{x^2-6x-16}{2x^2-128} \cdot \dfrac{x^2+16x+64}{3x^2+30x+48}$

$= \dfrac{(x-8)(x+2)}{2(x^2-64)} \cdot \dfrac{(x+8)(x+8)}{3(x^2+10x+16)}$

$= \dfrac{(x-8)(x+2)}{2(x+8)(x-8)} \cdot \dfrac{(x+8)(x+8)}{3(x+2)(x+8)}$

$= \dfrac{1}{2\cdot 3}$

$= \dfrac{1}{6}$

**45.** $\dfrac{2x}{5} \div \dfrac{6x+12}{5x+10} = \dfrac{2x}{5} \cdot \dfrac{5x+10}{6x+12}$

$= \dfrac{2x}{5} \cdot \dfrac{5(x+2)}{6(x+2)}$

$= \dfrac{2x}{5} \cdot \dfrac{5(x+2)}{2\cdot 3(x+2)}$

$= \dfrac{x}{3}$

**47.** $\dfrac{a+b}{ab} \div \dfrac{a^2-b^2}{4a^3b} = \dfrac{a+b}{ab} \cdot \dfrac{4a^3b}{a^2-b^2}$

$\qquad = \dfrac{a+b}{ab} \cdot \dfrac{4a^3b}{(a+b)(a-b)}$

$\qquad = \dfrac{4a^2}{a-b}$

**49.** $\dfrac{x^2-6x+9}{x^2-x-6} \div \dfrac{x^2-9}{4}$

$\qquad = \dfrac{x^2-6x+9}{x^2-x-6} \cdot \dfrac{4}{x^2-9}$

$\qquad = \dfrac{(x-3)^2}{(x-3)(x+2)} \cdot \dfrac{4}{(x+3)(x-3)}$

$\qquad = \dfrac{4}{(x+2)(x+3)}$

**51.** $\dfrac{x^2-6x-16}{2x^2-128} \div \dfrac{x^2+10x+16}{x^2+16x+64}$

$\qquad = \dfrac{x^2-6x-16}{2x^2-128} \cdot \dfrac{x^2+16x+64}{x^2+10x+16}$

$\qquad = \dfrac{(x-8)(x+2)}{2(x^2-64)} \cdot \dfrac{(x+8)(x+8)}{(x+2)(x+8)}$

$\qquad = \dfrac{(x-8)(x+2)}{2(x-8)(x+8)} \cdot \dfrac{(x+8)(x+8)}{(x+2)(x+8)}$

$\qquad = \dfrac{1}{2}$

**53.** $\dfrac{3x-x^2}{x^3-27} \div \dfrac{x}{x^2+3x+9}$

$\qquad = \dfrac{3x-x^2}{x^3-27} \cdot \dfrac{x^2+3x+9}{x}$

$\qquad = \dfrac{x(3-x)}{(x-3)(x^2+3x+9)} \cdot \dfrac{x^2+3x+9}{x}$

$\qquad = \dfrac{-x(x-3)}{(x-3)(x^2+3x+9)} \cdot \dfrac{x^2+3x+9}{x}$

$\qquad = -1$

**55.** $\dfrac{8b+24}{3a+6} \div \dfrac{ab-2b+3a-6}{a^2-4a+4}$

$\qquad = \dfrac{8b+24}{3a+6} \cdot \dfrac{a^2-4a+4}{ab-2b+3a-6}$

$\qquad = \dfrac{8(b+3)}{3(a+2)} \cdot \dfrac{(a-2)(a-2)}{b(a-2)+3(a-2)}$

$\qquad = \dfrac{8(b+3)}{3(a+2)} \cdot \dfrac{(a-2)(a-2)}{(a-2)(b+3)}$

$\qquad = \dfrac{8(a-2)}{3(a+2)}$

**57.** $\dfrac{x^2-9}{4} \cdot \dfrac{x^2-x-6}{x^2-6x+9}$

$\qquad = \dfrac{(x+3)(x-3)}{4} \cdot \dfrac{(x+2)(x-3)}{(x-3)^2}$

$\qquad = \dfrac{(x+3)(x+2)}{4}$

**59.** $\dfrac{2x^2-4x-30}{5x^2-40x-75} \div \dfrac{x^2-8x+15}{x^2-6x+9}$

$\qquad = \dfrac{2x^2-4x-30}{5x^2-40x-75} \cdot \dfrac{x^2-6x+9}{x^2-8x+15}$

$\qquad = \dfrac{2(x^2-2x-15)}{5(x^2-8x-15)} \cdot \dfrac{(x-3)(x-3)}{(x-3)(x-5)}$

$\qquad = \dfrac{2(x-5)(x+3)}{5(x^2-8x-15)} \cdot \dfrac{(x-3)(x-3)}{(x-3)(x-5)}$

$\qquad = \dfrac{2(x+3)(x-3)}{5(x^2-8x-15)}$

**61.** $\dfrac{r^3+s^3}{r+s} = \dfrac{(r+s)(r^2-rs+s^2)}{r+s} = r^2-rs+s^2$

**63.** $\dfrac{4}{x} \div \dfrac{3xy}{x^2} \cdot \dfrac{6x^2}{x^4} = \dfrac{4}{x} \cdot \dfrac{x^2}{3xy} \cdot \dfrac{6x^2}{x^4} = \dfrac{8}{x^2y}$

**65.** $\dfrac{3x^2-5x-2}{y^2+y-2} \cdot \dfrac{y^2+4y-5}{12x^2+7x+1} \div \dfrac{5x^2-9x-2}{8x^2-2x-1}$

$\qquad = \dfrac{3x^2-5x-2}{y^2+y-2} \cdot \dfrac{y^2+4y-5}{12x^2+7x+1} \cdot \dfrac{8x^2-2x-1}{5x^2-9x-2}$

$\qquad = \dfrac{(3x+1)(x-2)(y+5)(y-1)(4x+1)(2x-1)}{(y+2)(y-1)(4x+1)(3x+1)(5x+1)(x-2)}$

$\qquad = \dfrac{(y+5)(2x-1)}{(y+2)(5x+1)}$

**67.** $\dfrac{5a^2-20}{3a^2-12a} \div \dfrac{a^3+2a^2}{2a^2-8a} \cdot \dfrac{9a^3+6a^2}{2a^2-4a}$

$= \dfrac{5a^2-20}{3a^2-12a} \cdot \dfrac{2a^2-8a}{a^3+2a^2} \cdot \dfrac{9a^3+6a^2}{2a^2-4a}$

$= \dfrac{5(a^2-4)}{3a(a-4)} \cdot \dfrac{2a(a-4)}{a^2(a+2)} \cdot \dfrac{3a^2(3a+2)}{2a(a-2)}$

$= \dfrac{5(a+2)(a-2)}{3a(a-4)} \cdot \dfrac{2a(a-4)}{a^2(a+2)} \cdot \dfrac{3a^2(3a+2)}{2a(a-2)}$

$= \dfrac{5(3a+2)}{a}$

**69.** $\dfrac{5x^4+3x^2-2}{x-1} \cdot \dfrac{x+1}{x^4-1}$

$= \dfrac{(5x^2-2)(x^2+1)}{x-1} \cdot \dfrac{x+1}{(x^2+1)(x^2-1)}$

$= \dfrac{(5x^2-2)(x^2+1)}{x-1} \cdot \dfrac{x+1}{(x^2+1)(x+1)(x-1)}$

$= \dfrac{5x^2-2}{(x-1)^2}$

**71.** $f(x)=\dfrac{x+8}{2x-1}$

$f(2)=\dfrac{2+8}{2(2)-1}=\dfrac{10}{4-1}=\dfrac{10}{3}$

$f(0)=\dfrac{0+8}{2(0)-1}=\dfrac{8}{0-1}=\dfrac{8}{-1}=-8$

$f(-1)=\dfrac{-1+8}{2(-1)-1}=\dfrac{7}{-2-1}=\dfrac{7}{-3}=-\dfrac{7}{3}$

**73.** $g(x)=\dfrac{x^2+8}{x^3-25x}$

$g(3)=\dfrac{3^2+8}{3^3-25(3)}=\dfrac{9+8}{27-75}=\dfrac{17}{-48}=-\dfrac{17}{48}$

$g(-2)=\dfrac{(-2)^2+8}{(-2)^3-25(-2)}=\dfrac{4+8}{-8+50}=\dfrac{12}{42}=\dfrac{2}{7}$

$g(1)=\dfrac{1^2+8}{1^3-25(1)}=\dfrac{1+8}{1-25}=\dfrac{9}{-24}=-\dfrac{3}{8}$

**75.** $R(x)=\dfrac{1000x^2}{x^2+4}$

**a.** $R(1)=\dfrac{1000 \cdot 1^2}{1^2+4}=\dfrac{1000}{5}=200$

The revenue at the end of the first year is $200 million.

**b.** $R(2)=\dfrac{1000 \cdot 2^2}{2^2+4}$

$=\dfrac{1000 \cdot 4}{4+4}$

$=\dfrac{4000}{8}$

$=500$

The revenue at the end of the second year is $500 million.

**c.** The revenue during the second year is equal to the revenue at the end of the second year minus the revenue at the end of the first year.

$500-200=300$

The revenue during the second year is $300 million.

**d.** $x^2+4=0$

$x^2=-4$

This equation has no solutions. Thus there are no values of $x$ that would make the denominator equal to zero and the function undefined. The domain of $R(x)$ is $\{x|x$ is a real number$\}$.

**77.** $\dfrac{4}{5}+\dfrac{3}{5}=\dfrac{7}{5}$

**79.** $\dfrac{5}{28}-\dfrac{2}{21}=\dfrac{15}{84}-\dfrac{8}{84}=\dfrac{7}{84}=\dfrac{1}{12}$

**81.** $\dfrac{3}{8}+\dfrac{1}{2}-\dfrac{3}{16}=\dfrac{6}{16}+\dfrac{8}{16}-\dfrac{3}{16}=\dfrac{11}{16}$

**83. a.** $\dfrac{-x}{5-x} \neq \dfrac{x}{5-x}$

**b.** $\dfrac{-x}{-5+x}=\dfrac{x}{-(-5+x)}=\dfrac{x}{5-x}$

**c.** $\dfrac{x}{x-5} = \dfrac{x}{-5+x} \neq \dfrac{x}{5-x}$

**d.** $\dfrac{-x}{x-5} = \dfrac{x}{-(x-5)} = \dfrac{x}{-x+5} = \dfrac{x}{5-x}$

**85.** No; answers may vary

**87.** $A = l \cdot w$

$= \left(\dfrac{x+2}{x}\right)\left(\dfrac{5x}{x^2-4}\right)$

$= \dfrac{x+2}{x} \cdot \dfrac{5x}{(x+2)(x-2)}$

$= \dfrac{5}{x-2}$

The area is $\dfrac{5}{x-2}$ square meters.

**89.** Since $A = b \cdot h$, $b = \dfrac{A}{h}$.

$b = \dfrac{\dfrac{x^2+x-2}{x^3}}{\dfrac{x^2}{x-1}}$

$= \dfrac{x^2+x-2}{x^3} \cdot \dfrac{x-1}{x^2}$

$= \dfrac{(x+2)(x-1)}{x^3} \cdot \dfrac{x-1}{x^2}$

$= \dfrac{(x+2)(x-1)^2}{x^5}$

The length of the base is $\dfrac{(x+2)(x-1)^2}{x^5}$ feet.

**91.** answers may vary

**93. a.** $\dfrac{x+5}{5+x} = \dfrac{x+5}{x+5} = 1$

**b.** $\dfrac{x-5}{5-x} = \dfrac{x-5}{-(x-5)} = -1$

**c.** $\dfrac{x+5}{x-5}$ neither

**d.** $\dfrac{-x-5}{x+5} = \dfrac{-(x+5)}{x+5} = -1$

**e.** $\dfrac{x-5}{-x+5} = \dfrac{x-5}{-(x-5)} = -1$

**f.** $\dfrac{-5+x}{x-5} = \dfrac{x-5}{x-5} = 1$

**95.** $\dfrac{x^2-4}{x^2-7x+10} \cdot \dfrac{?}{2x^2+11x+14} = 1$

$\dfrac{(x+2)(x-2)}{(x-2)(x-5)} \cdot \dfrac{?}{(2x+7)(x+2)} = 1$

$\dfrac{?}{(x-5)(2x+7)} = 1$

For the fraction to equal 1, the numerator needs to be $(x-5)(2x+7)$.

**97.** $f(x) = \dfrac{20x}{100-x}$

| $x$ | 0 | 10 | 30 | 50 | 70 | 90 | 95 | 99 |
|---|---|---|---|---|---|---|---|---|
| $y$ | 0 | $\dfrac{20}{9}$ | $\dfrac{60}{7}$ | 20 | $\dfrac{140}{3}$ | 180 | 380 | 1980 |

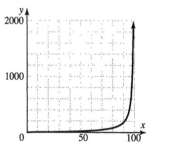

**99.** $\dfrac{x^{2n}-4}{7x} \cdot \dfrac{14x^3}{x^n-2} = \dfrac{(x^n+2)(x^n-2)}{7x} \cdot \dfrac{14x^3}{x^n-2}$

$\qquad = 2x^2(x^n+2)$

**101.** $\dfrac{y^{2n}+9}{10y} \cdot \dfrac{y^n-3}{y^{4n}-81}$

$= \dfrac{y^{2n}+9}{10y} \cdot \dfrac{y^n-3}{(y^{2n}+9)(y^{2n}-9)}$

$= \dfrac{y^{2n}+9}{10y} \cdot \dfrac{y^n-3}{(y^{2n}+9)(y^n+3)(y^n-3)}$

$= \dfrac{1}{10y(y^n+3)}$

**103.** $\dfrac{y^{2n}-y^n-2}{2y^n-4}\div\dfrac{y^{2n}-1}{1+y^n}$

$=\dfrac{y^{2n}-y^n-2}{2y^n-4}\cdot\dfrac{1+y^n}{y^{2n}-1}$

$=\dfrac{(y^n-2)(y^n+1)}{2(y^n-2)}\cdot\dfrac{1+y^n}{(y^n+1)(y^n-1)}$

$=\dfrac{1+y^n}{2(y^n-1)}$

## Section 6.2

**Practice Exercises**

**1. a.** $\dfrac{9}{11z^2}+\dfrac{x}{11z^2}=\dfrac{9+x}{11z^2}$

**b.** $\dfrac{x}{8}+\dfrac{5x}{8}=\dfrac{x+5x}{8}=\dfrac{6x}{8}=\dfrac{3x}{4}$

**c.** $\dfrac{x^2}{x+4}-\dfrac{16}{x+4}=\dfrac{x^2-16}{x+4}$

$=\dfrac{(x+4)(x-4)}{x+4}$

$=x-4$

**d.** $\dfrac{z}{2a^2}-\dfrac{z+3}{2a^2}=\dfrac{z-(z+3)}{2a^2}$

$=\dfrac{z-z-3}{2a^2}$

$=\dfrac{-3}{2a^2}$

**2. a.** $\dfrac{7}{6x^3y^5},\dfrac{2}{9x^2y^4}$

We factor each denominator.

$6x^3y^5=2\cdot3\cdot x^3\cdot y^5$

$9x^2y^4=3^2\cdot x^2\cdot y^4$

$\text{LCD}=2\cdot3^2\cdot x^3\cdot y^5=18x^3y^5$

**b.** $\dfrac{11}{x-2},\dfrac{x}{x-3}$

The denominators $x-2$ and $x-3$ do not factor further.

$\text{LCD}=(x-2)(x-3)$

**c.** $\dfrac{b+2}{b^2-16},\dfrac{8}{b^2-8b+16},\dfrac{5b}{2b^2-5b-12}$

We factor each denominator.

$b^2-16=(b-4)(b+4)$

$b^2-8b+16=(b-4)(b-4)$

$2b^2-5b-12=(2b+3)(b-4)$

$\text{LCD}=(b-4)^2(b+4)(2b+3)$

**d.** $\dfrac{y}{y^2-9},\dfrac{3}{12-4y}$

We factor each denominator.

$y^2-9=(y-3)(y+3)$

$12-4y=4(3-y)=4(-1)(y-3)$

$\text{LCD}=-4(y-3)(y+3)$

**3. a.** The LCD is $5p^4q$.

$\dfrac{4}{p^3q}+\dfrac{3}{5p^4q}=\dfrac{4\cdot5p}{p^3q\cdot5p}+\dfrac{3}{5p^4q}$

$=\dfrac{20p}{5p^4q}+\dfrac{3}{5p^4q}$

$=\dfrac{20p+3}{5p^4q}$

**b.** The LCD is the product of the two denominators: $(y+3)(y-3)$.

$\dfrac{4}{y+3}+\dfrac{5y}{y-3}$

$=\dfrac{4\cdot(y-3)}{(y+3)\cdot(y-3)}+\dfrac{5y\cdot(y+3)}{(y-3)\cdot(y+3)}$

$=\dfrac{4y-12}{(y+3)(y-3)}+\dfrac{5y^2+15y}{(y+3)(y-3)}$

$=\dfrac{4y-12+5y^2+15y}{(y+3)(y-3)}$

$=\dfrac{5y^2+19y-12}{(y+3)(y-3)}$

**c.** The LCD is either $z - 5$ or $5 - z$.

$$\frac{3z-18}{z-5} - \frac{3}{5-z} = \frac{3z-18}{z-5} - \frac{3}{-1(z-5)}$$

$$= \frac{3z-18}{z-5} - \frac{-1\cdot 3}{z-5}$$

$$= \frac{3z-18-(-3)}{z-5}$$

$$= \frac{3z-18+3}{z-5}$$

$$= \frac{3z-15}{z-5}$$

$$= \frac{3(z-5)}{z-5}$$

$$= 3$$

**4.** $\dfrac{t}{t^2-25} - \dfrac{3}{t^2-3t-10}$

$$= \frac{t}{(t+5)(t-5)} - \frac{3}{(t-5)(t+2)}$$

The LCD is $(t + 5)(t - 5)(t + 2)$.

$$\frac{t}{(t+5)(t-5)} - \frac{3}{(t-5)(t+2)}$$

$$= \frac{t\cdot(t+2)}{(t+5)(t-5)\cdot(t+2)} - \frac{3\cdot(t+5)}{(t-5)(t+2)\cdot(t+5)}$$

$$= \frac{t^2+2t}{(t+5)(t-5)(t+2)} - \frac{3t+15}{(t+5)(t-5)(t+2)}$$

$$= \frac{t^2+2t-3t-15}{(t+5)(t-5)(t+2)}$$

$$= \frac{t^2-t-15}{(t+5)(t-5)(t+2)}$$

**5.** $\dfrac{2x+3}{3x^2-5x-2} + \dfrac{x-6}{6x^2-13x-5}$

$$= \frac{2x+3}{(3x+1)(x-2)} + \frac{x-6}{(3x+1)(2x-5)}$$

The LCD is $(3x + 1)(x - 2)(2x - 5)$.

$$= \frac{(2x+3)\cdot(2x-5)}{(3x+1)(x-2)\cdot(2x-5)} + \frac{(x-6)\cdot(x-2)}{(3x+1)(2x-5)\cdot(x-2)}$$

$$= \frac{4x^2-4x-15}{(3x+1)(x-2)(2x-5)} + \frac{x^2-8x+12}{(3x+1)(x-2)(2x-5)}$$

$$= \frac{4x^2-4x-15+x^2-8x+12}{(3x+1)(x-2)(2x-5)}$$

$$= \frac{5x^2-12x-3}{(3x+1)(x-2)(2x-5)}$$

**6.** $\dfrac{2}{x-2} + \dfrac{3x}{x^2-x-2} - \dfrac{1}{x+1}$

$$= \frac{2}{x-2} + \frac{3x}{(x-2)(x+1)} - \frac{1}{x+1}$$

The LCD is $(x - 2)(x - 1)$.

$$= \frac{2\cdot(x+1)}{(x-2)\cdot(x+1)} + \frac{3x}{(x-2)(x+1)} - \frac{1\cdot(x-2)}{(x+1)\cdot(x-2)}$$

$$= \frac{2x+2}{(x-2)(x+1)} + \frac{3x}{(x-2)(x+1)} - \frac{x-2}{(x-2)(x+1)}$$

$$= \frac{2x+2+3x-x+2}{(x-2)(x+1)}$$

$$= \frac{4x+4}{(x-2)(x+1)}$$

$$= \frac{4(x+1)}{(x-2)(x+1)}$$

$$= \frac{4}{x-2}$$

**Vocabulary and Readiness Check**

1. The denominators must be the same before performing the operations of addition and subtraction (<u>a, b</u>).

2. To perform the operation of division (<u>d</u>), you multiply the first rational expression by the reciprocal of the second rational expression.

3. Numerator times numerator all over denominator times denominator is multiplication (<u>c</u>).

4. The operations of addition and multiplication (<u>a, c</u>) are commutative (order doesn't matter).

5. Addition: $\dfrac{5}{y} + \dfrac{7}{y} = \dfrac{12}{y}$

6. Subtraction: $\dfrac{5}{y} - \dfrac{7}{y} = -\dfrac{2}{y}$

7. Multiplication: $\dfrac{5}{y}\cdot\dfrac{7}{y} = \dfrac{35}{y^2}$

8. Division: $\dfrac{5}{y} \div \dfrac{7}{y} = \dfrac{5}{y}\cdot\dfrac{y}{7} = \dfrac{5}{7}$

**9.** $\dfrac{5}{2x} - \dfrac{x+1}{2x} = \dfrac{5-(x+1)}{2x} = \dfrac{-x+4}{2x}$

**10.** $\dfrac{9}{5x} - \dfrac{6-x}{5x} = \dfrac{9-(6-x)}{5x} = \dfrac{x+3}{5x}$

**11.** $\dfrac{y+11}{y-2} - \dfrac{y-5}{y-2} = \dfrac{y+11-(y-5)}{y-2} = \dfrac{16}{y-2}$

**12.** $\dfrac{z-1}{z+6} - \dfrac{z+4}{z+6} = \dfrac{z-1-(z+4)}{z+6} = \dfrac{-5}{z+6}$

**Exercise Set 6.2**

**1.** $\dfrac{2}{xz^2} - \dfrac{5}{xz^2} = \dfrac{2-5}{xz^2} = \dfrac{-3}{xz^2} = -\dfrac{3}{xz^2}$

**3.** $\dfrac{2}{x-2} + \dfrac{x}{x-2} = \dfrac{2+x}{x-2} = \dfrac{x+2}{x-2}$

**5.** $\dfrac{x^2}{x+2} - \dfrac{4}{x+2} = \dfrac{x^2-4}{x+2}$
$$= \dfrac{(x+2)(x-2)}{x+2}$$
$$= x-2$$

**7.** $\dfrac{2x-6}{x^2+x-6} + \dfrac{3-3x}{x^2+x-6} = \dfrac{2x-6+3-3x}{x^2+x-6}$
$$= \dfrac{-x-3}{x^2+x-6}$$
$$= \dfrac{-1(x+3)}{(x+3)(x-2)}$$
$$= \dfrac{-1}{x-2} \text{ or } \dfrac{1}{-(x-2)}$$
$$= \dfrac{-1}{x-2} \text{ or } \dfrac{1}{2-x}$$

**9.** $\dfrac{x-5}{2x} - \dfrac{x+5}{2x} = \dfrac{x-5-x-5}{2x} = \dfrac{-10}{2x} = -\dfrac{5}{x}$

**11.** $7 = 7$
$5x = 5x$
$\text{LCD} = 7 \cdot 5x = 35x$

**13.** $x = x$
$x + 1 = x + 1$
$\text{LCD} = x(x + 1)$

**15.** $x + 7 = x + 7$
$x - 7 = x - 7$
$\text{LCD} = (x + 7)(x - 7)$

**17.** $3x + 6 = 3(x + 2)$
$2x - 4 = 2(x - 2)$
$\text{LCD} = 3 \cdot 2(x + 2)(x - 2) = 6(x + 2)(x - 2)$

**19.** $a^2 - b^2 = (a+b)(a-b)$
$a^2 - 2ab + b^2 = (a-b)^2$
$\text{LCD} = (a+b)(a-b)^2$

**21.** $x^2 - 9 = (x+3)(x-3)$
$x = x$
$12 - 4x = -4(x - 3)$
$\text{LCD} = -4x(x + 3)(x - 3)$

**23.** $\dfrac{4}{3x} + \dfrac{3}{2x} = \dfrac{4\cdot2}{3x(2)} + \dfrac{3\cdot3}{2x(3)} = \dfrac{8}{6x} + \dfrac{9}{6x} = \dfrac{17}{6x}$

**25.** $\dfrac{5}{2y^2} - \dfrac{2}{7y} = \dfrac{5\cdot7}{2y^2\cdot7} - \dfrac{2\cdot2y}{7y\cdot2y}$
$$= \dfrac{35}{14y^2} - \dfrac{4y}{14y^2}$$
$$= \dfrac{35-4y}{14y^2}$$

**27.** $\dfrac{x-3}{x+4} - \dfrac{x+2}{x-4}$
$$= \dfrac{(x-3)(x-4)}{(x+4)(x-4)} - \dfrac{(x+2)(x+4)}{(x-4)(x+4)}$$
$$= \dfrac{x^2-7x+12}{(x+4)(x-4)} - \dfrac{x^2+6x+8}{(x+4)(x-4)}$$
$$= \dfrac{x^2-7x+12-x^2-6x-8}{(x+4)(x-4)}$$
$$= \dfrac{-13x+4}{(x+4)(x-4)}$$

**29.** $\dfrac{1}{x-5} - \dfrac{19-2x}{(x-5)(x+4)} = \dfrac{1 \cdot (x+4)}{(x-5) \cdot (x+4)} - \dfrac{19-2x}{(x-5)(x+4)}$

$\qquad\qquad = \dfrac{x+4+19-2x}{(x-5)(x+4)}$

$\qquad\qquad = \dfrac{3x-15}{(x-5)(x+4)}$

$\qquad\qquad = \dfrac{3(x-5)}{(x-5)(x+4)}$

$\qquad\qquad = \dfrac{3}{x+4}$

**31.** $\dfrac{1}{a-b} + \dfrac{1}{b-a} = \dfrac{1}{a-b} + \dfrac{1}{-1(-b+a)}$

$\qquad\qquad = \dfrac{1}{a-b} + \dfrac{-1}{a-b}$

$\qquad\qquad = \dfrac{0}{a-b}$

$\qquad\qquad = 0$

**33.** $\dfrac{x+1}{1-x} + \dfrac{1}{x-1} = \dfrac{x+1}{-(x-1)} + \dfrac{1}{x-1}$

$\qquad\qquad = \dfrac{-(x+1)}{x-1} + \dfrac{1}{x-1}$

$\qquad\qquad = \dfrac{-x-1+1}{x-1}$

$\qquad\qquad = \dfrac{-x}{x-1}$

$\qquad\qquad = -\dfrac{x}{x-1}$

**35.** $\dfrac{5}{x-2} + \dfrac{x+4}{2-x} = \dfrac{5}{x-2} + \dfrac{x+4}{-(-2+x)}$

$\qquad\qquad = \dfrac{5}{x-2} + \dfrac{-(x+4)}{x-2}$

$\qquad\qquad = \dfrac{5-x-4}{x-2}$

$\qquad\qquad = \dfrac{-x+1}{x-2}$

**37.** $\dfrac{y+1}{y^2-6y+8} - \dfrac{3}{y^2-16} = \dfrac{y+1}{(y-2)(y-4)} - \dfrac{3}{(y+4)(y-4)}$

$$= \dfrac{(y+1)(y+4)}{(y-2)(y-4)(y+4)} - \dfrac{3(y-2)}{(y-2)(y+4)(y-4)}$$

$$= \dfrac{(y+1)(y+4)-3(y-2)}{(y-2)(y-4)(y+4)}$$

$$= \dfrac{y^2+5y+4-3y+6}{(y-2)(y-4)(y+4)}$$

$$= \dfrac{y^2+2y+10}{(y-2)(y-4)(y+4)}$$

**39.** $\dfrac{x+4}{3x^2+11x+6} + \dfrac{x}{2x^2+x-15} = \dfrac{x+4}{(3x+2)(x+3)} + \dfrac{x}{(2x-5)(x+3)}$

$$= \dfrac{(x+4)(2x-5)}{(3x+2)(x+3)(2x-5)} + \dfrac{x(3x+2)}{(2x-5)(x+3)(3x+2)}$$

$$= \dfrac{2x^2+3x-20}{(3x+2)(x+3)(2x-5)} + \dfrac{3x^2+2x}{(3x+2)(x+3)(2x-5)}$$

$$= \dfrac{2x^2+3x-20+3x^2+2x}{(3x+2)(x+3)(2x-5)}$$

$$= \dfrac{5x^2+5x-20}{(3x+2)(x+3)(2x-5)}$$

$$= \dfrac{5(x^2+x-4)}{(3x+2)(x+3)(2x-5)}$$

**41.** $\dfrac{7}{x^2-x-2} - \dfrac{x-1}{x^2+4x+3} = \dfrac{7}{(x-2)(x+1)} - \dfrac{x-1}{(x+3)(x+1)}$

$$= \dfrac{7(x+3)}{(x-2)(x+1)(x+3)} - \dfrac{(x-1)(x-2)}{(x+3)(x+1)(x-2)}$$

$$= \dfrac{7(x+3)-(x-1)(x-2)}{(x-2)(x+1)(x+3)}$$

$$= \dfrac{7x+21-x^2+3x-2}{(x-2)(x+1)(x+3)}$$

$$= \dfrac{-x^2+10x+19}{(x-2)(x+1)(x+3)}$$

**43.** $\dfrac{x}{x^2-8x+7}-\dfrac{x+2}{2x^2-9x-35}$

$=\dfrac{x}{(x-1)(x-7)}-\dfrac{x+2}{(2x+5)(x-7)}$

$=\dfrac{x(2x+5)}{(x-1)(x-7)(2x+5)}-\dfrac{(x+2)(x-1)}{(2x+5)(x-7)(x-1)}$

$=\dfrac{x(2x+5)-(x+2)(x-1)}{(2x+5)(x-7)(x-1)}$

$=\dfrac{2x^2+5x-(x^2+x-2)}{(2x+5)(x-7)(x-1)}$

$=\dfrac{2x^2+5x-x^2-x+2}{(2x+5)(x-7)(x-1)}$

$=\dfrac{x^2+4x+2}{(2x+5)(x-7)(x-1)}$

**45.** $\dfrac{2}{a^2+2a+1}+\dfrac{3}{a^2-1}$

$=\dfrac{2}{(a+1)^2}+\dfrac{3}{(a+1)(a-1)}$

$=\dfrac{2(a-1)}{(a+1)^2(a-1)}+\dfrac{3(a+1)}{(a+1)(a-1)(a+1)}$

$=\dfrac{2(a-1)+3(a+1)}{(a+1)^2(a-1)}$

$=\dfrac{2a-2+3a+3}{(a+1)^2(a-1)}$

$=\dfrac{5a+1}{(a+1)^2(a-1)}$

**47.** $\dfrac{4}{3x^2y^3}+\dfrac{5}{3x^2y^3}=\dfrac{9}{3x^2y^3}=\dfrac{3}{x^2y^3}$

**49.** $\dfrac{13x-5}{2x}-\dfrac{13x+5}{2x}=\dfrac{13x-5-13x-5}{2x}$

$=\dfrac{-10}{2x}$

$=-\dfrac{5}{x}$

**51.** $\dfrac{3}{2x+10}+\dfrac{8}{3x+15}=\dfrac{3}{2(x+5)}+\dfrac{8}{3(x+5)}$

$=\dfrac{3\cdot3}{2(x+5)\cdot3}+\dfrac{8\cdot2}{3(x+5)\cdot2}$

$=\dfrac{9}{6(x+5)}+\dfrac{16}{6(x+5)}$

$=\dfrac{25}{6(x+5)}$

**53.** $\dfrac{-2}{x^2-3x}-\dfrac{1}{x^3-3x^2}=\dfrac{-2}{x(x-3)}-\dfrac{1}{x^2(x-3)}$

$=\dfrac{-2x}{x^2(x-3)}-\dfrac{1}{x^2(x-3)}$

$=\dfrac{-2x-1}{x^2(x-3)}$

**55.** $\dfrac{ab}{a^2-b^2}+\dfrac{b}{a+b}$

$=\dfrac{ab}{(a+b)(a-b)}+\dfrac{b}{a+b}$

$=\dfrac{ab}{(a+b)(a-b)}+\dfrac{b(a-b)}{(a+b)(a-b)}$

$=\dfrac{ab}{(a+b)(a-b)}+\dfrac{ab-b^2}{(a+b)(a-b)}$

$=\dfrac{ab+ab-b^2}{(a+b)(a-b)}$

$=\dfrac{2ab-b^2}{(a+b)(a-b)}$

$=\dfrac{b(2a-b)}{(a+b)(a-b)}$

**57.** $\dfrac{5}{x^2-4}-\dfrac{3}{x^2+4x+4}$

$=\dfrac{5}{(x+2)(x-2)}-\dfrac{3}{(x+2)^2}$

$=\dfrac{5(x+2)}{(x+2)(x-2)(x+2)}-\dfrac{3(x-2)}{(x+2)^2(x-2)}$

$=\dfrac{5(x+2)-3(x-2)}{(x+2)^2(x-2)}$

$=\dfrac{5x+10-3x+6}{(x+2)^2(x-2)}$

$=\dfrac{2x+16}{(x+2)^2(x-2)}$

$=\dfrac{2(x+8)}{(x+2)^2(x-2)}$

**59.**
$$\frac{3x}{2x^2-11x+5}+\frac{7}{x^2-2x-15}=\frac{3x}{(2x-1)(x-5)}+\frac{7}{(x-5)(x+3)}$$

$$=\frac{3x(x+3)}{(2x-1)(x-5)(x+3)}+\frac{7(2x-1)}{(x-5)(x+3)(2x-1)}$$

$$=\frac{3x^2+9x}{(2x-1)(x-5)(x+3)}+\frac{14x-7}{(2x-1)(x-5)(x+3)}$$

$$=\frac{3x^2+9x+14x-7}{(2x-1)(x-5)(x+3)}$$

$$=\frac{3x^2+23x-7}{(2x-1)(x-5)(x+3)}$$

**61.**
$$\frac{2}{x+1}-\frac{3x}{3x+3}+\frac{1}{2x+2}=\frac{2}{x+1}-\frac{3x}{3(x+1)}+\frac{1}{2(x+1)}$$

$$=\frac{2}{x+1}-\frac{x}{x+1}+\frac{1}{2(x+1)}$$

$$=\frac{2\cdot 2}{2(x+1)}-\frac{2\cdot x}{2(x+1)}+\frac{1}{2(x+1)}$$

$$=\frac{4-2x+1}{2(x+1)}$$

$$=\frac{5-2x}{2(x+1)}$$

**63.**
$$\frac{3}{x+3}+\frac{5}{x^2+6x+9}-\frac{x}{x^2-9}=\frac{3}{x+3}+\frac{5}{(x+3)^2}-\frac{x}{(x+3)(x-3)}$$

$$=\frac{3(x+3)(x-3)}{(x+3)(x+3)(x-3)}+\frac{5(x-3)}{(x+3)^2(x-3)}-\frac{x(x+3)}{(x+3)(x-3)(x+3)}$$

$$=\frac{3x^2-27}{(x+3)^2(x-3)}+\frac{5x-15}{(x+3)^2(x-3)}-\frac{x^2+3x}{(x+3)^2(x-3)}$$

$$=\frac{3x^2-27+5x-15-x^2-3x}{(x+3)^2(x-3)}$$

$$=\frac{2x^2+2x-42}{(x+3)^2(x-3)}$$

$$=\frac{2(x^2+x-21)}{(x+3)^2(x-3)}$$

**65.** $\dfrac{x}{x^2-9}+\dfrac{3}{x^2-6x+9}-\dfrac{1}{x+3}=\dfrac{x}{(x+3)(x-3)}+\dfrac{3}{(x-3)^2}-\dfrac{1}{x+3}$

$$=\frac{x(x-3)}{(x+3)(x-3)^2}+\frac{3(x+3)}{(x-3)^2(x+3)}-\frac{1(x-3)^2}{(x+3)(x-3)^2}$$

$$=\frac{x(x-3)+3(x+3)-(x-3)^2}{(x+3)(x-3)^2}$$

$$=\frac{x^2-3x+3x+9-(x^2-6x+9)}{(x+3)(x-3)^2}$$

$$=\frac{x^2+9-x^2+6x-9}{(x+3)(x-3)^2}$$

$$=\frac{6x}{(x+3)(x-3)^2}$$

**67.** $\left(\dfrac{1}{x}+\dfrac{2}{3}\right)-\left(\dfrac{1}{x}-\dfrac{2}{3}\right)=\left(\dfrac{3}{3x}+\dfrac{2x}{3x}\right)-\left(\dfrac{3}{3x}-\dfrac{2x}{3x}\right)$

$$=\left(\frac{3+2x}{3x}\right)-\left(\frac{3-2x}{3x}\right)$$

$$=\frac{3+2x-3+2x}{3x}$$

$$=\frac{4x}{3x}$$

$$=\frac{4}{3}$$

**69.** $\left(\dfrac{2}{3}-\dfrac{1}{x}\right)\cdot\left(\dfrac{3}{x}+\dfrac{1}{2}\right)=\left(\dfrac{2x}{3x}-\dfrac{3}{3x}\right)\cdot\left(\dfrac{3\cdot2}{2x}+\dfrac{x}{2x}\right)$

$$=\left(\frac{2x-3}{3x}\right)\cdot\left(\frac{6+x}{2x}\right)$$

$$=\frac{(2x-3)(x+6)}{6x^2}\text{ or }\frac{2x^2+9x-18}{6x^2}$$

**71.** $\left(\dfrac{2a}{3}\right)^2\div\left(\dfrac{a^2}{a+1}-\dfrac{1}{a+1}\right)=\dfrac{4a^2}{9}\div\dfrac{a^2-1}{a+1}$

$$=\frac{4a^2}{9}\div\frac{(a+1)(a-1)}{a+1}$$

$$=\frac{4a^2}{9}\div(a-1)$$

$$=\frac{4a^2}{9}\cdot\frac{1}{a-1}$$

$$=\frac{4a^2}{9(a-1)}$$

**73.** $\left(\dfrac{2x}{3}\right)^2 \div \left(\dfrac{x}{3}\right)^2 = \left(\dfrac{2^2 x^2}{3^2}\right) \div \left(\dfrac{x^2}{3^2}\right)$

$= \dfrac{2^2 x^2}{3^2} \cdot \dfrac{3^2}{x^2}$

$= 2^2$

$= 4$

**75.** $\left(\dfrac{x}{x+1} - \dfrac{x}{x-1}\right) \div \dfrac{x}{2x+2}$

$= \left(\dfrac{x \cdot (x-1)}{(x+1)(x-1)} - \dfrac{x \cdot (x+1)}{(x-1)(x+1)}\right) \div \dfrac{x}{2(x+1)}$

$= \dfrac{x(x-1) - x(x+1)}{(x+1)(x-1)} \div \dfrac{x}{2(x+1)}$

$= \dfrac{x^2 - x - x^2 - x}{(x+1)(x-1)} \div \dfrac{x}{2(x+1)}$

$= \dfrac{-2x}{(x+1)(x-1)} \cdot \dfrac{2(x+1)}{x}$

$= -\dfrac{4}{x-1}$

**77.** $\dfrac{4}{x} \cdot \left(\dfrac{2}{x+2} - \dfrac{2}{x-2}\right)$

$= \dfrac{4}{x} \cdot \left(\dfrac{2(x-2)}{(x+2)(x-2)} - \dfrac{2(x+2)}{(x-2)(x+2)}\right)$

$= \dfrac{4}{x} \cdot \left(\dfrac{2x-4}{(x+2)(x-2)} - \dfrac{2x+4}{(x+2)(x-2)}\right)$

$= \dfrac{4}{x} \cdot \left(\dfrac{2x-4-2x-4}{(x+2)(x-2)}\right)$

$= \dfrac{4}{x}\left(\dfrac{-8}{(x+2)(x-2)}\right)$

$= -\dfrac{32}{x(x+2)(x-2)}$

**79.** $12\left(\dfrac{2}{3} + \dfrac{1}{6}\right) = 12 \cdot \dfrac{2}{3} + 12 \cdot \dfrac{1}{6} = \dfrac{24}{3} + \dfrac{12}{6} = 8 + 2 = 10$

**81.** $x^2\left(\dfrac{4}{x^2} + 1\right) = x^2 \cdot \dfrac{4}{x^2} + x^2 \cdot 1 = 4 + x^2$

**83.** $\sqrt{100} = 10$ because $10^2 = 100$.

**85.** $\sqrt[3]{8} = 2$ because $2^3 = 8$.

**87.** $\sqrt[4]{81} = 3$ because $3^4 = 81$.

**89.** $a^2 + b^2 = c^2$

$3^2 + 4^2 = c^2$

$9 + 16 = c^2$

$25 = c^2$

$c = 5$ meters

**91.** $\dfrac{2x-3}{x^2+1} - \dfrac{x-6}{x^2+1} = \dfrac{2x-3-(x-6)}{x^2+1}$

$= \dfrac{2x-3-x+6}{x^2+1}$

$= \dfrac{x+3}{x^2+1}$

**93.** $P = 4s$

$P = 4 \cdot \left(\dfrac{x}{x+5}\right) = \dfrac{4x}{x+5}$

$A = s^2$

$A = \left(\dfrac{x}{x+5}\right)^2$

$A = \left(\dfrac{x}{x+5}\right)\left(\dfrac{x}{x+5}\right) = \dfrac{x^2}{(x+5)^2}$

The perimeter is $\dfrac{4x}{x+5}$ feet, and the area is

$\dfrac{x^2}{(x+5)^2}$ square feet.

**95.** Answers may vary

**97.** Answers may vary

**99.** Answers may vary

**101.** $x^{-1} + (2x)^{-1} = \dfrac{1}{x} + \dfrac{1}{2x}$

$= \dfrac{1 \cdot 2}{x \cdot 2} + \dfrac{1}{2x}$

$= \dfrac{2+1}{2x}$

$= \dfrac{3}{2x}$

**103.** $4x^{-2} - 3x^{-1} = \dfrac{4}{x^2} - \dfrac{3}{x} = \dfrac{4}{x^2} - \dfrac{3x}{x^2} = \dfrac{4-3x}{x^2}$

**105.**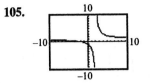

**Section 6.3**

**Practice Exercises**

**1. a.** $\dfrac{\frac{5k}{36m}}{\frac{15k}{9}} = \dfrac{5k}{36m} \div \dfrac{15k}{9}$

$= \dfrac{5k}{36m} \cdot \dfrac{9}{15k}$

$= \dfrac{5k \cdot 9}{36m \cdot 15k}$

$= \dfrac{1}{12m}$

**b.** $\dfrac{\frac{8x}{x-4}}{\frac{3}{x+4}} = \dfrac{8x}{x-4} \div \dfrac{3}{x+4}$

$= \dfrac{8x}{x-4} \cdot \dfrac{x+4}{3}$

$= \dfrac{8x(x+4)}{3(x-4)}$

**c.** $\dfrac{\frac{5}{a}+\frac{b}{a^2}}{\frac{5a}{b^2}+\frac{1}{b}} = \dfrac{\frac{5 \cdot a}{a \cdot a}+\frac{b}{a^2}}{\frac{5a}{b^2}+\frac{1 \cdot b}{b \cdot b}}$

$= \dfrac{\frac{5a+b}{a^2}}{\frac{5a+b}{b^2}}$

$= \dfrac{5a+b}{a^2} \cdot \dfrac{b^2}{5a+b}$

$= \dfrac{b^2(5a+b)}{a^2(5a+b)}$

$= \dfrac{b^2}{a^2}$

**2. a.** The LCD is $(x-4)(x+4)$.

$\dfrac{\frac{8x}{x-4}}{\frac{3}{x+4}} = \dfrac{\left(\frac{8x}{x-4}\right) \cdot (x-4)(x+4)}{\left(\frac{3}{x+4}\right) \cdot (x-4)(x+4)}$

$= \dfrac{8x(x+4)}{3(x-4)}$

**b.** The LCD is $a^2b^2$.

$\dfrac{\frac{b}{a^2}+\frac{1}{a}}{\frac{a}{b^2}+\frac{1}{b}} = \dfrac{\left(\frac{b}{a^2}+\frac{1}{a}\right) \cdot a^2b^2}{\left(\frac{a}{b^2}+\frac{1}{b}\right) \cdot a^2b^2}$

$= \dfrac{\frac{b}{a^2} \cdot a^2b^2 + \frac{1}{a} \cdot a^2b^2}{\frac{a}{b^2} \cdot a^2b^2 + \frac{1}{b} \cdot a^2b^2}$

$= \dfrac{b^3 + ab^2}{a^3 + a^2b}$

$= \dfrac{b^2(b+a)}{a^2(a+b)}$

$= \dfrac{b^2}{a^2}$

**3.** $\dfrac{3x^{-1}+x^{-2}y^{-1}}{y^{-2}+xy^{-1}} = \dfrac{\frac{3}{x}+\frac{1}{x^2y}}{\frac{1}{y^2}+\frac{x}{y}}$

The LCD is $x^2y^2$.

$= \dfrac{\left(\frac{3}{x}+\frac{1}{x^2y}\right) \cdot x^2y^2}{\left(\frac{1}{y^2}+\frac{x}{y}\right) \cdot x^2y^2}$

$= \dfrac{\frac{3}{x} \cdot x^2y^2 + \frac{1}{x^2y} \cdot x^2y^2}{\frac{1}{y^2} \cdot x^2y^2 + \frac{x}{y} \cdot x^2y^2}$

$= \dfrac{3xy^2 + y}{x^2 + x^3y}$ or $\dfrac{y(3xy+1)}{x^2(1+xy)}$

**4.** $\dfrac{(3x)^{-1}-2}{5x^{-1}+2} = \dfrac{\frac{1}{3x}-2}{\frac{5}{x}+2}$

$= \dfrac{\left(\frac{1}{3x}-2\right) \cdot 3x}{\left(\frac{5}{x}+2\right) \cdot 3x}$

$= \dfrac{\frac{1}{3x} \cdot 3x - 2 \cdot 3x}{\frac{5}{x} \cdot 3x + 2 \cdot 3x}$

$= \dfrac{1-6x}{15+6x}$

**Vocabulary and Readiness Check**

**1.** $\dfrac{\frac{7}{x}}{\frac{1}{x}+\frac{z}{x}} = \dfrac{x\left(\frac{7}{x}\right)}{x\left(\frac{1}{x}\right)+x\left(\frac{z}{x}\right)} = \dfrac{7}{1+z}$

**2.** $\dfrac{\frac{x}{4}}{\frac{x^2}{2}+\frac{1}{4}}=\dfrac{4\left(\frac{x}{4}\right)}{4\left(\frac{x^2}{2}\right)+4\left(\frac{1}{4}\right)}=\dfrac{x}{2x^2+1}$

**3.** $x^{-2}=\dfrac{1}{x^2}$

**4.** $y^{-3}=\dfrac{1}{y^3}$

**5.** $2x^{-1}=\dfrac{2}{x}$

**6.** $(2x)^{-1}=\dfrac{1}{2x}$

**7.** $(9y)^{-1}=\dfrac{1}{9y}$

**8.** $9y^{-2}=\dfrac{9}{y^2}$

**Exercise Set 6.3**

**1.** $\dfrac{\frac{10}{3x}}{\frac{5}{6x}}=\dfrac{10}{3x}\cdot\dfrac{6x}{5}=\dfrac{60x}{15x}=4$

**3.** $\dfrac{1+\frac{2}{5}}{2+\frac{3}{5}}=\dfrac{5\left(1+\frac{2}{5}\right)}{5\left(2+\frac{3}{5}\right)}=\dfrac{5+2}{10+3}=\dfrac{7}{13}$

**5.** $\dfrac{\frac{4}{x-1}}{\frac{x}{x-1}}=\dfrac{4}{x-1}\cdot\dfrac{x-1}{x}=\dfrac{4}{x}$

**7.** $\dfrac{1-\frac{2}{x}}{x+\frac{4}{9x}}=\dfrac{9x\left(1-\frac{2}{x}\right)}{9x\left(x+\frac{4}{9x}\right)}=\dfrac{9x-18}{9x^2+4}=\dfrac{9(x-2)}{9x^2+4}$

**9.** $\dfrac{\frac{4x^2-y^2}{xy}}{\frac{2}{y}-\frac{1}{x}}=\dfrac{\left(\frac{4x^2-y^2}{xy}\right)\cdot xy}{\left(\frac{2}{y}-\frac{1}{x}\right)\cdot xy}$

$=\dfrac{4x^2-y^2}{2x-y}$

$=\dfrac{(2x-y)(2x+y)}{2x-y}$

$=2x+y$

**11.** $\dfrac{\frac{x+1}{3}}{\frac{2x-1}{6}}=\dfrac{x+1}{3}\cdot\dfrac{6}{2x-1}=\dfrac{2(x+1)}{2x-1}$

**13.** $\dfrac{\frac{2}{x}+\frac{3}{x^2}}{\frac{4}{x^2}-\frac{9}{x}}=\dfrac{\left(\frac{2}{x}+\frac{3}{x^2}\right)x^2}{\left(\frac{4}{x^2}-\frac{9}{x}\right)x^2}=\dfrac{2x+3}{4-9x}$

**15.** $\dfrac{\frac{1}{x}+\frac{2}{x^2}}{x+\frac{8}{x^2}}=\dfrac{x^2\left(\frac{1}{x}+\frac{2}{x^2}\right)}{x^2\left(x+\frac{8}{x^2}\right)}$

$=\dfrac{x+2}{x^3+8}$

$=\dfrac{x+2}{(x+2)(x^2-2x+4)}$

$=\dfrac{1}{x^2-2x+4}$

**17.** $\dfrac{\frac{4}{5-x}+\frac{5}{x-5}}{\frac{2}{x}+\frac{3}{x-5}}=\dfrac{-\frac{4}{x-5}+\frac{5}{x-5}}{\frac{2(x-5)+3x}{x(x-5)}}$

$=\dfrac{\frac{1}{x-5}}{\frac{2x-10+3x}{x(x-5)}}$

$=\dfrac{1}{x-5}\cdot\dfrac{x(x-5)}{5x-10}$

$=\dfrac{x}{5x-10}$ or $\dfrac{x}{5(x-2)}$

**19.**
$$\frac{\frac{x+2}{x}-\frac{2}{x-1}}{\frac{x+1}{x}+\frac{x+1}{x-1}}=\frac{\frac{(x+2)(x-1)-2x}{x(x-1)}}{\frac{(x+1)(x-1)+(x+1)(x)}{x(x-1)}}$$

$$=\frac{\frac{x^2+x-2-2x}{x(x-1)}}{\frac{x^2-1+x^2+x}{x(x-1)}}$$

$$=\frac{x^2-x-2}{x(x-1)}\cdot\frac{x(x-1)}{2x^2+x-1}$$

$$=\frac{(x-2)(x+1)}{x(x-1)}\cdot\frac{x(x-1)}{(2x-1)(x+1)}$$

$$=\frac{x-2}{2x-1}$$

**21.**
$$\frac{\frac{2}{x}+3}{\frac{4}{x^2}-9}=\frac{\left(\frac{2}{x}+3\right)\cdot x^2}{\left(\frac{4}{x^2}-9\right)\cdot x^2}$$

$$=\frac{2x+3x^2}{4-9x^2}$$

$$=\frac{x(2+3x)}{(2+3x)(2-3x)}$$

$$=\frac{x}{2-3x}$$

**23.**
$$\frac{1-\frac{x}{y}}{\frac{x^2}{y^2}-1}=\frac{\left(1-\frac{x}{y}\right)\cdot y^2}{\left(\frac{x^2}{y^2}-1\right)\cdot y^2}$$

$$=\frac{y^2-xy}{x^2-y^2}$$

$$=\frac{y(y-x)}{(x+y)(x-y)}$$

$$=\frac{-y(x-y)}{(x+y)(x-y)}$$

$$=-\frac{y}{x+y}$$

**25.**
$$\frac{\frac{-2x}{x-y}}{\frac{y}{x^2}}=\frac{-2x}{x-y}\cdot\frac{x^2}{y}=-\frac{2x^3}{y(x-y)}$$

**27.**
$$\frac{\frac{2}{x}+\frac{1}{x^2}}{\frac{y}{x^2}}=\frac{\left(\frac{2}{x}+\frac{1}{x^2}\right)x^2}{\left(\frac{y}{x^2}\right)x^2}=\frac{2x+1}{y}$$

**29.**
$$\frac{\frac{x}{9}-\frac{1}{x}}{1+\frac{3}{x}}=\frac{\left(\frac{x}{9}-\frac{1}{x}\right)\cdot 9x}{\left(1+\frac{3}{x}\right)\cdot 9x}$$

$$=\frac{x^2-9}{9x+27}$$

$$=\frac{(x+3)(x-3)}{9(x+3)}$$

$$=\frac{x-3}{9}$$

**31.**
$$\frac{\frac{x-1}{x^2-4}}{1+\frac{1}{x-2}}=\frac{\frac{x-1}{x^2-4}}{\frac{x-2+1}{x-2}}=\frac{\frac{x-1}{x^2-4}}{\frac{x-1}{x-2}}$$

$$=\frac{x-1}{x^2-4}\cdot\frac{x-2}{x-1}$$

$$=\frac{x-1}{(x+2)(x-2)}\cdot\frac{x-2}{x-1}$$

$$=\frac{1}{x+2}$$

**33.**
$$\frac{\frac{2}{x+5}+\frac{4}{x+3}}{\frac{3x+13}{x^2+8x+15}}=\frac{\frac{2}{x+5}+\frac{4}{x+3}}{\frac{3x+13}{(x+5)(x+3)}}$$

$$=\frac{\left(\frac{2}{x+5}+\frac{4}{x+3}\right)(x+5)(x+3)}{\frac{3x+13}{(x+5)(x+3)}(x+5)(x+3)}$$

$$=\frac{2(x+3)+4(x+5)}{3x+13}$$

$$=\frac{2x+6+4x+20}{3x+13}$$

$$=\frac{6x+26}{3x+13}$$

$$=\frac{2(3x+13)}{3x+13}$$

$$=2$$

**35.**
$$\frac{x^{-1}}{x^{-2}+y^{-2}}=\frac{\frac{1}{x}}{\frac{1}{x^2}+\frac{1}{y^2}}$$

$$=\frac{x^2y^2\left(\frac{1}{x}\right)}{x^2y^2\left(\frac{1}{x^2}+\frac{1}{y^2}\right)}$$

$$=\frac{xy^2}{y^2+x^2}$$

$$=\frac{xy^2}{x^2+y^2}$$

**37.** $\dfrac{2a^{-1}+3b^{-2}}{a^{-1}-b^{-1}} = \dfrac{\frac{2}{a}+\frac{3}{b^2}}{\frac{1}{a}-\frac{1}{b}}$

$= \dfrac{ab^2\left(\frac{2}{a}+\frac{3}{b^2}\right)}{ab^2\left(\frac{1}{a}-\frac{1}{b}\right)}$

$= \dfrac{2b^2+3a}{b^2-ab}$

$= \dfrac{2b^2+3a}{b(b-a)}$

**39.** $\dfrac{1}{x-x^{-1}} = \dfrac{1}{x-\frac{1}{x}}$

$= \dfrac{x(1)}{x\left(x-\frac{1}{x}\right)}$

$= \dfrac{x}{x^2-1}$

$= \dfrac{x}{(x+1)(x-1)}$

**41.** $\dfrac{a^{-1}+1}{a^{-1}-1} = \dfrac{\frac{1}{a}+1}{\frac{1}{a}-1} = \dfrac{a\left(\frac{1}{a}+1\right)}{a\left(\frac{1}{a}-1\right)} = \dfrac{1+a}{1-a}$

**43.** $\dfrac{3x^{-1}+(2y)^{-1}}{x^{-2}} = \dfrac{\frac{3}{x}+\frac{1}{2y}}{\frac{1}{x^2}}$

$= \dfrac{2x^2y\left(\frac{3}{x}+\frac{1}{2y}\right)}{2x^2y\left(\frac{1}{x^2}\right)}$

$= \dfrac{6xy+x^2}{2y}$

$= \dfrac{x(x+6y)}{2y}$

**45.** $\dfrac{2a^{-1}+(2a)^{-1}}{a^{-1}+2a^{-2}} = \dfrac{\frac{2}{a}+\frac{1}{2a}}{\frac{1}{a}+\frac{2}{a^2}}$

$= \dfrac{2a^2\left(\frac{2}{a}+\frac{1}{2a}\right)}{2a^2\left(\frac{1}{a}+\frac{2}{a^2}\right)}$

$= \dfrac{4a+a}{2a+4}$

$= \dfrac{5a}{2(a+2)}$

**47.** $\dfrac{5x^{-1}+2y^{-1}}{x^{-2}y^{-2}} = \dfrac{\frac{5}{x}+\frac{2}{y}}{\frac{1}{x^2y^2}}$

$= \dfrac{x^2y^2\left(\frac{5}{x}+\frac{2}{y}\right)}{x^2y^2\left(\frac{1}{x^2y^2}\right)}$

$= 5xy^2+2x^2y$

$= xy(5y+2x)$

**49.** $\dfrac{5x^{-1}-2y^{-1}}{25x^{-2}-4y^{-2}} = \dfrac{\frac{5}{x}-\frac{2}{y}}{\frac{25}{x^2}-\frac{4}{y^2}}$

$= \dfrac{x^2y^2\left(\frac{5}{x}-\frac{2}{y}\right)}{x^2y^2\left(\frac{25}{x^2}-\frac{4}{y^2}\right)}$

$= \dfrac{5xy^2-2x^2y}{25y^2-4x^2}$

$= \dfrac{xy(5y-2x)}{(5y+2x)(5y-2x)}$

$= \dfrac{xy}{5y+2x}$ or $\dfrac{xy}{2x+5y}$

**51.** $\dfrac{3x^3y^2}{12x} = \dfrac{3x\cdot x^2y^2}{3x\cdot 4} = \dfrac{x^2y^2}{4}$

**53.** $\dfrac{144x^5y^5}{-16x^2y} = \dfrac{16x^2y\cdot 9x^3y^4}{16x^2y\cdot(-1)} = -9x^3y^4$

**55.** $|x-5| = 9$

$x-5 = -9$   or   $x-5 = 9$

$x = -4$   or        $x = 14$

The solution set is $\{-4,\ 14\}$.

**57.** $\dfrac{\frac{x+1}{9}}{\frac{y-2}{5}} = \dfrac{x+1}{9} \div \dfrac{y-2}{5} = \dfrac{x+1}{9}\cdot\dfrac{5}{y-2}$

Both a and c are equivalent to the original expression.

**59.** $\dfrac{a}{1-\frac{s}{770}} = \dfrac{770(a)}{770\left(1-\frac{s}{770}\right)} = \dfrac{770a}{770-s}$

**61.** $\dfrac{\frac{1}{x}}{\frac{3}{y}} = \dfrac{1}{x} \div \dfrac{3}{y} = \dfrac{1}{x} \cdot \dfrac{y}{3}$

Both a and b are equivalent to the original expression.

**63.** $\dfrac{1}{1+(1+x)^{-1}} = \dfrac{1}{1+\frac{1}{1+x}}$

$\qquad = \dfrac{(1+x)\cdot 1}{(1+x)\left(1+\frac{1}{1+x}\right)}$

$\qquad = \dfrac{1+x}{1+x+1}$

$\qquad = \dfrac{1+x}{2+x}$

**65.** $\dfrac{x}{1-\frac{1}{1+\frac{1}{x}}} = \dfrac{x}{1-\frac{1}{\frac{x+1}{x}}}$

$\qquad = \dfrac{x}{1-\frac{x}{x+1}}$

$\qquad = \dfrac{(x+1)(x)}{(x+1)\left(1-\frac{x}{x+1}\right)}$

$\qquad = \dfrac{x(x+1)}{x+1-x}$

$\qquad = \dfrac{x(x+1)}{1}$

$\qquad = x(x+1)$

**67.** $\dfrac{\frac{2}{y^2}-\frac{5}{xy}-\frac{3}{x^2}}{\frac{2}{y^2}+\frac{7}{xy}+\frac{3}{x^2}} = \dfrac{x^2 y^2 \left(\frac{2}{y^2}-\frac{5}{xy}-\frac{3}{x^2}\right)}{x^2 y^2 \left(\frac{2}{y^2}+\frac{7}{xy}+\frac{3}{x^2}\right)}$

$\qquad = \dfrac{2x^2 - 5xy - 3y^2}{2x^2 + 7xy + 3y^2}$

$\qquad = \dfrac{(2x+y)(x-3y)}{(2x+y)(x+3y)}$

$\qquad = \dfrac{x-3y}{x+3y}$

**69.** $\dfrac{3(a+1)^{-1}+4a^{-2}}{(a^3+a^2)^{-1}} = \dfrac{\frac{3}{a+1}+\frac{4}{a^2}}{\frac{1}{a^3+a^2}}$

$\qquad = \dfrac{\frac{3a^2+4(a+1)}{a^2(a+1)}}{\frac{1}{a^2(a+1)}}$

$\qquad = \dfrac{3a^2+4a+4}{a^2(a+1)} \cdot \dfrac{a^2(a+1)}{1}$

$\qquad = 3a^2 + 4a + 4$

**71.** $f(x) = \dfrac{1}{x}$

    **a.** $f(a+h) = \dfrac{1}{a+h}$

    **b.** $f(a) = \dfrac{1}{a}$

    **c.** $\dfrac{f(a+h)-f(a)}{h} = \dfrac{\frac{1}{a+h}-\frac{1}{a}}{h}$

    **d.** $\dfrac{\frac{1}{a+h}-\frac{1}{a}}{h} = \dfrac{a(a+h)\left(\frac{1}{a+h}-\frac{1}{a}\right)}{a(a+h)\cdot h}$

$\qquad\qquad = \dfrac{a-(a+h)}{ah(a+h)}$

$\qquad\qquad = \dfrac{-h}{ah(a+h)}$

$\qquad\qquad = \dfrac{-1}{a(a+h)}$

**73.** $f(x) = \dfrac{3}{x+1}$

    **a.** $f(a+h) = \dfrac{3}{a+h+1}$

    **b.** $f(a) = \dfrac{3}{a+1}$

    **c.** $\dfrac{f(a+h)-f(a)}{h} = \dfrac{\frac{3}{a+h+1}-\frac{3}{a+1}}{h}$

**d.** $\dfrac{\frac{3}{a+h+1} - \frac{3}{a+1}}{h}$

$= \dfrac{\left(\frac{3}{a+h+1} - \frac{3}{a+1}\right) \cdot (a+h+1)(a+1)}{h \cdot (a+h+1)(a+1)}$

$= \dfrac{3(a+1) - 3(a+h+1)}{h(a+h+1)(a+1)}$

$= \dfrac{3a+3-3a-3h-3}{h(a+h+1)(a+1)}$

$= \dfrac{-3h}{h(a+h+1)(a+1)}$

$= \dfrac{-3}{(a+h+1)(a+1)}$

## Section 6.4

### Practice Exercises

**1.** $\dfrac{18a^3 - 12a^2 + 30a}{6a} = \dfrac{18a^3}{6a} - \dfrac{12a^2}{6a} + \dfrac{30a}{6a}$

$= 3a^2 - 2a + 5$

**2.** $\dfrac{5a^3b^4 - 8a^2b^3 + ab^2 - 8b}{ab^2}$

$= \dfrac{5a^3b^4}{ab^2} - \dfrac{8a^2b^3}{ab^2} + \dfrac{ab^2}{ab^2} - \dfrac{8b}{ab^2}$

$= 5a^2b^2 - 8ab + 1 - \dfrac{8}{ab}$

**3.**
$$\begin{array}{r} 3x - 2 \\ x+3 \overline{)\, 3x^2 + 7x - 6} \\ \underline{3x^2 + 9x} \\ -2x - 6 \\ \underline{-2x - 6} \\ 0 \end{array}$$

Answer: $3x - 2$

**4.**
$$\begin{array}{r} 3x - 2 \\ 2x-1 \overline{)\, 6x^2 - 7x + 2} \\ \underline{6x^2 - 3x} \\ -4x + 2 \\ \underline{-4x + 2} \\ 0 \end{array}$$

Answer: $3x - 2$

**5.**
$$\begin{array}{r} 5x^2 - 6x + 8 \\ x+3 \overline{)\, 5x^3 + 9x^2 - 10x + 30} \\ \underline{5x^3 + 15x^2} \\ -6x^2 - 10x \\ \underline{-6x^2 - 18x} \\ 8x + 30 \\ \underline{8x + 24} \\ 6 \end{array}$$

Answer: $5x^2 - 6x + 8 + \dfrac{6}{x+3}$

**6.**
$$\begin{array}{r} 2x^2 + 3x - 2 \\ x^2+0x+1 \overline{)\, 2x^4 + 3x^3 + 0x^2 - 5x + 2} \\ \underline{2x^4 + 0x^3 + 2x^2} \\ 3x^3 - 2x^2 - 5x \\ \underline{3x^3 + 0x^2 + 3x} \\ -2x^2 - 8x + 2 \\ \underline{-2x^2 + 0x - 2} \\ -8x + 4 \end{array}$$

Answer: $2x^2 + 3x - 2 + \dfrac{-8x+4}{x^2+1}$

**7.**
$$\begin{array}{r} 16x^2 + 20x + 25 \\ 4x-5 \overline{)\, 64x^3 + 0x^2 + 0x - 125} \\ \underline{64x^3 - 80x^2} \\ 80x^2 + 0x \\ \underline{80x^2 - 100x} \\ 100x - 125 \\ \underline{100x - 125} \\ 0 \end{array}$$

Answer: $16x^2 + 20x + 25$

**8.** Since $x - c = x - 1$, $c$ is 1.

$$\begin{array}{r|rrrr} 1 & 4 & -3 & 6 & 5 \\ & & 4 & 1 & 7 \\ \hline & 4 & 1 & 7 & 12 \end{array}$$

$4x^2 + x + 7 + \dfrac{12}{x-1}$

**9.** Since $x - c = x + 3 = x - (-3)$, $c$ is $-3$.

$$\begin{array}{r|rrrrr} -3 & 1 & 3 & -5 & 6 & 12 \\ & & -3 & 0 & 15 & -63 \\ \hline & 1 & 0 & -5 & 21 & -51 \end{array}$$

$$x^3 - 5x + 21 - \frac{51}{x+3}$$

**10. a.** $P(x) = x^3 - 5x - 2$

$$\begin{aligned} P(2) &= 2^3 - 5(2) - 2 \\ &= 8 - 10 - 2 \\ &= -4 \end{aligned}$$

**b.** Since $x - c = x - 2$, $c$ is 2.

$$\begin{array}{r|rrrr} 2 & 1 & 0 & -5 & -2 \\ & & 2 & 4 & -2 \\ \hline & 1 & 2 & -1 & -4 \end{array}$$

The remainder is $-4$.

**11.**
$$\begin{array}{r|rrrrrr} 3 & 2 & -18 & 0 & 90 & 59 & 0 \\ & & 6 & -36 & -108 & -54 & 15 \\ \hline & 2 & -12 & -36 & -18 & 5 & 15 \end{array}$$

$$P(3) = 15$$

## Exercise Set 6.4

**1.** $\dfrac{4a^2 + 8a}{2a} = \dfrac{4a^2}{2a} + \dfrac{8a}{2a} = 2a + 4$

**3.** $\dfrac{12a^5b^2 + 16a^4b}{4a^4b} = \dfrac{12a^5b^2}{4a^4b} + \dfrac{16a^4b}{4a^4b}$
$$= 3ab + 4$$

**5.** $\dfrac{4x^2y^2 + 6xy^2 - 4y^2}{2x^2y}$
$$= \dfrac{4x^2y^2}{2x^2y} + \dfrac{6xy^2}{2x^2y} - \dfrac{4y^2}{2x^2y}$$
$$= 2y + \dfrac{3y}{x} - \dfrac{2y}{x^2}$$

**7.**
$$\begin{array}{r} x+1 \phantom{xxxx} \\ x+2\overline{)x^2 + 3x + 2} \\ \underline{x^2 + 2x} \phantom{xxx} \\ x + 2 \\ \underline{x + 2} \\ 0 \end{array}$$

$$\frac{x^2 + 3x + 2}{x+2} = x + 1$$

**9.**
$$\begin{array}{r} 2x - 8 \phantom{xxx} \\ x+1\overline{)2x^2 - 6x - 8} \\ \underline{2x^2 + 2x} \phantom{xxx} \\ -8x - 8 \\ \underline{-8x - 8} \\ 0 \end{array}$$

$$\frac{2x^2 - 6x - 8}{x+1} = 2x - 8$$

**11.**
$$\begin{array}{r} x - \dfrac{1}{2} \phantom{xxx} \\ 2x+4\overline{)2x^2 + 3x - 2} \\ \underline{2x^2 + 4x} \phantom{xxx} \\ -x - 2 \\ \underline{-x - 2} \\ 0 \end{array}$$

$$\frac{2x^2 + 3x - 2}{2x+4} = x - \frac{1}{2}$$

**13.**
$$\begin{array}{r} 2x^2 - \dfrac{1}{2}x + 5 \phantom{xxx} \\ 2x+4\overline{)4x^3 + 7x^2 + 8x + 20} \\ \underline{4x^3 + 8x^2} \phantom{xxxxxxx} \\ x^2 + 8x \\ \underline{-x^2 - 2x} \\ 10x + 20 \\ \underline{10x + 20} \\ 0 \end{array}$$

$$\frac{4x^3 + 7x^2 + 8x + 20}{2x+4} = 2x^2 - \frac{1}{2}x + 5$$

**15.**
$$\begin{array}{r} 2x^2 \phantom{xxxx} - 6 \phantom{x} \\ 3x+1\overline{)6x^3 + 2x^2 - 18x - 6} \\ \underline{6x^3 + 2x^2} \phantom{xxxxxxx} \\ -18x - 6 \\ \underline{-18x - 6} \\ 0 \end{array}$$

$$\frac{2x^2 + 6x^3 - 18x - 6}{3x+1} = 2x^2 - 6$$

**17.**

$$
\begin{array}{r}
3x^3 + 5x + 4 \\
x^2 + 0x - 2 \overline{)\, 3x^5 + 0x^4 \; -x^3 + 4x^2 -12x - 8} \\
\underline{3x^5 + 0x^4 - 6x^3} \\
5x^3 + 4x^2 - 12x \\
\underline{5x^3 + 0x^2 - 10x} \\
4x^2 \; - 2x - 8 \\
\underline{4x^2 + 0x - 8} \\
-2x
\end{array}
$$

$$\frac{3x^5 - x^3 + 4x^2 - 12x - 8}{x^2 - 2} = 3x^3 + 5x + 4 - \frac{2x}{x^2 - 2}$$

**19.**

$$
\begin{array}{r}
2x^3 + \dfrac{9}{2}x^2 + 10x + 21 \\
x - 2 \overline{)\, 2x^4 + \dfrac{1}{2}x^3 \; + x^2 \; + x \; + 0} \\
\underline{2x^4 - 4x^3} \\
\dfrac{9}{2}x^3 \; + x^2 \\
\underline{\dfrac{9}{2}x^3 - 9x^2} \\
10x^2 \; + x \\
\underline{10x^2 - 20x} \\
21x \; + 0 \\
\underline{21x - 42} \\
42
\end{array}
$$

$$\frac{2x^4 + \frac{1}{2}x^3 + x^2 + x}{x - 2}$$
$$= 2x^3 + \frac{9}{2}x^2 + 10x + 21 + \frac{42}{x - 2}$$

**21.** $x - 5 = x - c$ where $c = 5$.

$$
\begin{array}{r|rrr}
5 & 1 & 3 & -40 \\
  &   & 5 & 40 \\
\hline
  & 1 & 8 & 0
\end{array}
$$

$$\frac{x^2 + 3x - 40}{x - 5} = x + 8$$

**23.** $x + 6 = x - c$ where $c = -6$.

$$
\begin{array}{r|rrr}
-6 & 1 & 5 & -6 \\
   &   & -6 & 6 \\
\hline
   & 1 & -1 & 0
\end{array}
$$

$$\frac{x^2 + 5x - 6}{x + 6} = x - 1$$

**25.** $x - 2 = x - c$ where $c = 2$.

$$
\begin{array}{r|rrrr}
2 & 1 & -7 & -13 & 5 \\
  &   & 2 & -10 & -46 \\
\hline
  & 1 & -5 & -23 & -41
\end{array}
$$

$$\frac{x^3 - 7x^2 - 13x + 5}{x - 2} = x^2 - 5x - 23 - \frac{41}{x - 2}$$

**27.** $x - 2 = x - c$ where $c = 2$.

$$
\begin{array}{r|rrr}
2 & 4 & 0 & -9 \\
  &   & 8 & 16 \\
\hline
  & 4 & 8 & 7
\end{array}
$$

$$\frac{4x^2 - 9}{x - 2} = 4x + 8 + \frac{7}{x - 2}$$

**29.** $\dfrac{4x^7 y^4 + 8xy^2 + 4xy^3}{4xy^3}$

$$= \frac{4x^7 y^4}{4xy^3} + \frac{8xy^2}{4xy^3} + \frac{4xy^3}{4xy^3}$$

$$= x^6 y + \frac{2}{y} + 1$$

**31.**

$$
\begin{array}{r}
5x^2 \qquad\;\; - 6 \\
2x - 1 \overline{)\, 10x^3 - 5x^2 - 12x + 1} \\
\underline{10x^3 - 5x^2} \\
-12x + 1 \\
\underline{-12x + 6} \\
-5
\end{array}
$$

$$\frac{10x^3 - 5x^2 - 12x + 1}{2x - 1} = 5x^2 - 6 - \frac{5}{2x - 1}$$

**33.** $x - 4$ has the form $x - c$, where $c = 4$, so synthetic division can be used.

$$2x^3 - 6x^2 - 4 = 2x^3 - 6x^2 + 0x - 4$$

$$\begin{array}{r|rrrr} 4 & 2 & -6 & 0 & -4 \\ & & 8 & 8 & 32 \\ \hline & 2 & 2 & 8 & 28 \end{array}$$

$$\frac{2x^3 - 6x^2 - 4}{x - 4} = 2x^2 + 2x + 8 + \frac{28}{x - 4}$$

**35.** $x - 5$ has the form $x - c$, where $c = 5$, so synthetic division can be used.

$$\begin{array}{r|rrrrr} 5 & 2 & -13 & 16 & -9 & 20 \\ & & 10 & -15 & 5 & -20 \\ \hline & 2 & -3 & 1 & -4 & 0 \end{array}$$

$$\frac{2x^4 - 13x^3 + 16x^2 - 9x + 20}{x - 5}$$
$$= 2x^3 - 3x^2 + x - 4$$

**37.** $x + 1$ has the form $x - c$, where $c = -1$, so synthetic division can be used.

$$7x^2 - 4x + 12 + 3x^3 = 3x^3 + 7x^2 - 4x + 12$$

$$\begin{array}{r|rrrr} -1 & 3 & 7 & -4 & 12 \\ & & -3 & -4 & 8 \\ \hline & 3 & 4 & -8 & 20 \end{array}$$

$$\frac{7x^2 - 4x + 12 + 3x^3}{x + 1} = 3x^2 + 4x - 8 + \frac{20}{x + 1}$$

**39.** $x - \dfrac{1}{3}$ has the form $x - c$, where $c = \dfrac{1}{3}$, so synthetic division can be used.

$$\begin{array}{r|rrrr} \frac{1}{3} & 3 & 2 & -4 & 1 \\ & & 1 & 1 & -1 \\ \hline & 3 & 3 & -3 & 0 \end{array}$$

$$\frac{3x^3 + 2x^2 - 4x + 1}{x - \frac{1}{3}} = 3x^2 + 3x - 3$$

**41.** $x - 1$ has the form $x - c$, where $c = 1$, so synthetic division can be used.

$$x^3 - 1 = x^3 + 0x^2 + 0x - 1$$

$$\begin{array}{r|rrrr} 1 & 1 & 0 & 0 & -1 \\ & & 1 & 1 & 1 \\ \hline & 1 & 1 & 1 & 0 \end{array}$$

$$\frac{x^3 - 1}{x - 1} = x^2 + x + 1$$

**43.** $\dfrac{25xy^2 + 75xyz + 125x^2yz}{-5x^2y}$

$$= \frac{25xy^2}{-5x^2y} + \frac{75xyz}{-5x^2y} + \frac{125x^2yz}{-5x^2y}$$

$$= -\frac{5y}{x} - \frac{15z}{x} - 25z$$

**45.** $9x^5 + 6x^4 - 6x^2 - 4x$
$$= 9x^5 + 6x^4 + 0x^3 - 6x^2 - 4x + 0$$

$$\require{enclose}\begin{array}{r} 3x^4 - 2x \phantom{+0} \\ 3x + 2 \enclose{longdiv}{9x^5 + 6x^4 + 0x^3 - 6x^2 - 4x + 0} \\ \underline{9x^5 + 6x^4 \phantom{+0x^3-6x^2-4x+0}} \\ 0 + 0x^3 - 6x^2 - 4x \phantom{+0} \\ \underline{-6x^2 - 4x \phantom{+0}} \\ 0 \end{array}$$

$$(9x^5 + 6x^4 - 6x^2 - 4x) \div (3x + 2) = 3x^4 - 2x$$

**47.** $\begin{array}{r|rrrr} 1 & 1 & 3 & -7 & 4 \\ & & 1 & 4 & -3 \\ \hline & 1 & 4 & -3 & 1 \end{array}$

Thus, $P(1) = 1$.

**49.** $\begin{array}{r|rrrr} -3 & 3 & -7 & -2 & 5 \\ & & -9 & 48 & -138 \\ \hline & 3 & -16 & 46 & -133 \end{array}$

Thus, $P(-3) = -133$.

**51.** $\begin{array}{r|rrrrr} -1 & 4 & 0 & 1 & 0 & -2 \\ & & -4 & 4 & -5 & 5 \\ \hline & 4 & -4 & 5 & -5 & 3 \end{array}$

Thus, $P(-1) = 3$.

**53.** $\begin{array}{r|rrrrr} \frac{1}{3} & 2 & 0 & -3 & 0 & -2 \\ & & \frac{2}{3} & \frac{2}{9} & -\frac{25}{27} & -\frac{25}{81} \\ \hline & 2 & \frac{2}{3} & -\frac{25}{9} & -\frac{25}{27} & -\frac{187}{181} \end{array}$

Thus, $P\!\left(\dfrac{1}{3}\right) = -\dfrac{187}{81}$.

**55.**

$$\frac{1}{2}\bigg|\begin{array}{cccccc} 1 & 1 & -1 & 0 & 0 & 3 \end{array}$$

$$\begin{array}{cccccc} & \frac{1}{2} & \frac{3}{4} & -\frac{1}{8} & -\frac{1}{16} & -\frac{1}{32} \end{array}$$

$$\begin{array}{cccccc} 1 & \frac{3}{2} & -\frac{1}{4} & -\frac{1}{8} & -\frac{1}{16} & \frac{95}{32} \end{array}$$

Thus, $P\left(\dfrac{1}{2}\right)=\dfrac{95}{32}$.

**57.** $7x+2=x-3$
$7x-x=-3-2$
$6x=-5$
$x=-\dfrac{5}{6}$

The solution is $-\dfrac{5}{6}$.

**59.** $\quad x^2=4x-4$
$x^2-4x+4=0$
$(x-2)^2=0$
$x-2=0$
$x=2$
The solution is 2.

**61.** $\quad\dfrac{x}{3}-5=13$
$3\left(\dfrac{x}{3}-5\right)-(13)\cdot 3$
$x-15=39$
$x=54$
The solution is 54.

**63.** $x^3-1=x^3-1^3=(x-1)(x^2+x+1)$

**65.** $125z^3+8=(5z)^3+2^3$
$\quad\quad\quad\quad=(5z+2)(25z^2-10z+4)$

**67.** $xy+2x+3y+6=(xy+2x)+(3y+6)$
$\quad\quad\quad\quad\quad\quad\quad=x(y+2)+3(y+2)$
$\quad\quad\quad\quad\quad\quad\quad=(y+2)(x+3)$

**69.** $x^3-9x=x(x^2-9)=x(x+3)(x-3)$

**71.** $(5x^2-3x+2)\div(x+2)$ is a candidate for synthetic division since $x+2$ is in the form $x-c$, where $c=-2$.

**73.** $(x^7-2)\div(x^5+1)$ is not a candidate for synthetic division since $x^5+1$ does not have the form $x-c$.

**75.** The degree of the remainder must be less than that of the divisor, or 3 in this case. The choices are a or d.

**77.** $\dfrac{3x^4+6x^2-18}{3}=\dfrac{3x^4}{3}+\dfrac{6x^2}{3}-\dfrac{18}{3}$
$\quad\quad\quad\quad\quad\quad=x^4+2x^2-6$
The length of each piece is $(x^4+2x^2-6)$ meters.

**79.**

$$\begin{array}{r} 3x-7 \\ 5x+2\overline{)15x^2-29x-14} \\ \underline{15x^2+6x} \\ -35x-14 \\ \underline{-35x-14} \\ 0 \end{array}$$

The width is $(3x-7)$ inches.

**81.** $A=bh$ so $h=\dfrac{A}{b}=\dfrac{x^4-23x^2+9x-5}{x+5}$

$$-5\big|\begin{array}{ccccc} 1 & 0 & -23 & 9 & -5 \end{array}$$

$$\begin{array}{ccccc} & -5 & 25 & -10 & 5 \end{array}$$

$$\begin{array}{ccccc} 1 & -5 & 2 & -1 & 0 \end{array}$$

The height is $(x^3-5x^2+2x-1)$ cm.

**83.**

$$x-1\overline{)x^4+\frac{2}{3}x^3+0x^2+\ x+\ 0}$$

quotient: $x^3+\frac{5}{3}x^2+\frac{5}{3}x\ +\frac{8}{3}$

$$\underline{x^4-\ x^3}$$
$$\frac{5}{3}x^3-0x^2$$
$$\underline{\frac{5}{3}x^3-\frac{5}{3}x^2}$$
$$\frac{5}{3}x^2+\ x$$
$$\underline{\frac{5}{3}x^2-\frac{5}{3}x}$$
$$\frac{8}{3}x+0$$
$$\underline{\frac{8}{3}x-\frac{8}{3}}$$
$$\frac{8}{3}$$

Answer: $x^3+\dfrac{5}{3}x^2+\dfrac{5}{3}x+\dfrac{8}{3}+\dfrac{8}{3(x-1)}$

**85.**

$$2x-1\overline{)3x^4-\ x^3+0x^2-\ x+\ \frac{1}{2}}$$

quotient: $\frac{3}{2}x^3+\frac{1}{4}x^2+\frac{1}{8}x\ -\frac{7}{16}$

$$\underline{3x^4-\frac{3}{2}\ x^3}$$
$$\frac{1}{2}x^3+0x^2$$
$$\underline{\frac{1}{2}x^3-\frac{1}{4}x^2}$$
$$\frac{1}{4}x^2-\ x$$
$$\underline{\frac{1}{4}x^2-\frac{1}{8}x}$$
$$-\frac{7}{8}x+\frac{1}{2}$$
$$\underline{-\frac{7}{8}x+\frac{7}{16}}$$
$$\frac{1}{16}$$

Answer: $\dfrac{3}{2}x^3+\dfrac{1}{4}x^2+\dfrac{1}{8}x-\dfrac{7}{16}+\dfrac{1}{16(2x-1)}$

**87.**

$$5x+10\overline{)5x^4+10x^3-2x^2-4x+\ 0}$$

quotient: $x^3\ \ \ \ \ \ \ -\frac{2}{5}x$

$$\underline{5x^4+10x^3}$$
$$-2x^2-4x$$
$$\underline{-2x^2-4x}$$
$$0$$

Answer: $x^3-\dfrac{2}{5}x$

**89.** $\dfrac{f(x)}{g(x)}=\dfrac{25x^2-5x+30}{5x}$

$$=\frac{25x^2}{5x}-\frac{5x}{5x}+\frac{30}{5x}$$

$$=5x-1+\frac{6}{x}$$

Setting the denominator equal to 0, we get
$5x=0$
$\ x=0.$

Thus, $x=0$ is not in the domain of $\dfrac{f(x)}{g(x)}$.

**91.** $\dfrac{f(x)}{g(x)}=\dfrac{7x^4-3x^2+2}{x-2}$

$$x-2\overline{)7x^4+0x^3-\ 3x^2+\ 0x+\ 2}$$

quotient: $7x^3+14x^2+\ 25x+50$

$$\underline{7x^4-14x^3}$$
$$14x^3-\ 3x^2$$
$$\underline{14x^3-28x^2}$$
$$25x^2+\ 0x$$
$$\underline{25x^2-50x}$$
$$50x+\ 2$$
$$\underline{50x-100}$$
$$102$$

Therefore, $\dfrac{f(x)}{g(x)}=\dfrac{7x^4-3x^2+2}{x-2}$

$$=7x^3+14x^2+25x+50+\frac{102}{x-2}$$

Setting the denominator equal to 0, we get
$x-2=0$, or $x=2$. Thus, $x=2$ is not in the
domain of $\dfrac{f(x)}{g(x)}$.

**93.** Answers may vary

**95.** Answers may vary

**97.**  $\underline{-3|}$  1    3    4    12

$\phantom{xxxxx}$ $\underline{\phantom{xx}-3\phantom{xx}0\phantom{x}-12}$

$\phantom{xxxxx}$ 1    0    4    0

Remainder = 0 and

$(x+3)(x^2+4)=x^3+3x^2+4x+12$

**99.** $P(c)$ is equal to the remainder when $P(x)$ is divided by $x - c$. Therefore, $P(0) = 0$.

**101.** Multiply $(x^2-x+10)$ by $(x+3)$ and add the remainder, $-2$.

$(x^2-x+10)(x+3)-2$

$=(x^3+3x^2-x^2-3x+10x+30)-2$

$=x^3+2x^2+7x+28$

**Section 6.5**

**Practice Exercises**

**1.** The LCD is 8.

$$\frac{5x}{4}-\frac{3}{2}=\frac{7x}{8}$$

$$8\left(\frac{5x}{4}-\frac{3}{2}\right)=8\left(\frac{7x}{8}\right)$$

$$8\cdot\frac{5x}{4}-8\cdot\frac{3}{2}=8\cdot\frac{7x}{8}$$

$$10x-12=7x$$

$$3x=12$$

$$x=4$$

**2.** The LCD of the denominators $x$, $5x$, and 5 is $5x$.

$$\frac{6}{x}-\frac{x+9}{5x}=\frac{2}{5}$$

$$5x\left(\frac{6}{x}-\frac{x+9}{5x}\right)=5x\left(\frac{2}{5}\right)$$

$$5x\cdot\frac{6}{x}-5x\cdot\frac{x+9}{5x}=5x\cdot\frac{2}{5}$$

$$30-(x+9)=2x$$

$$30-x-9=2x$$

$$21=3x$$

$$7=x$$

**3.** The LCD is $x+3$.

$$\frac{x-5}{x+3}=\frac{2(x-1)}{x+3}$$

$$(x+3)\cdot\frac{x-5}{x+3}=(x+3)\cdot\frac{2(x-1)}{x+3}$$

$$x-5=2(x-1)$$

$$x-5=2x-2$$

$$-3=x$$

The number $-3$ makes the denominator $x+3$ equal to 0, so it is not a solution. The solution set is { } or $\varnothing$.

**4.** The LCD is $x(5x-1)$.

$$\frac{5x}{5x-1}+\frac{1}{x}=\frac{1}{5x-1}$$

$$x(5x-1)\cdot\frac{5x}{5x-1}+x(5x-1)\cdot\frac{1}{x}=x(5x-1)\cdot\frac{1}{5x-1}$$

$$x(5x)+(5x-1)=x$$

$$5x^2+5x-1-x=0$$

$$5x^2+4x-1=0$$

$$(5x-1)(x+1)=0$$

$$5x-1=0 \text{ or } x+1=0$$

$$x=\frac{1}{5} \text{ or } x=-1$$

The number $\frac{1}{5}$ makes the denominator $5x-1$ equal 0, so it is not a solution. The solution is $-1$.

**5.** $x^2-4=(x+2)(x-2)$

The LCD is $(x+2)(x-2)$.

$$\frac{2}{x-2}-\frac{5+2x}{x^2-4}=\frac{x}{x+2}$$

$$(x+2)(x-2)\cdot\frac{2}{x-2}-(x+2)(x-2)\cdot\frac{5+2x}{(x+2)(x-2)}$$

$$=(x+2)(x-2)\cdot\frac{x}{x+2}$$

$$2(x+2)-(5+2x)=x(x-2)$$

$$2x+4-5-2x=x^2-2x$$

$$x^2-2x+1=0$$

$$(x-1)(x-1)=0$$

$$x-1=0$$

$$x=1$$

Since 1 does not make any denominator 0, the solution is 1.

**6.** $2z^2 - z - 6 = (2z+3)(z-2)$

$z^2 - 2z = z(z-2)$

The LCD is $3z(2z+3)(z-2)$.

$$\frac{z}{2z^2-z-6} - \frac{1}{3z} = \frac{2}{z^2-2z}$$

$$\frac{z}{(2z+3)(z-2)} - \frac{1}{3z} = \frac{2}{z(z-2)}$$

$$3z(2z+3)(z-2)\cdot\frac{z}{(2z+3)(z-2)} - 3z(2z+3)(z-2)\cdot\frac{1}{3z} = 3z(2z+3)(z-2)\cdot\frac{2}{z(z-2)}$$

$$3z(z) - (2z+3)(z-2) = 2\cdot3(2z+3)$$

$$3z^2 - (2z^2 - z - 6) = 12z+18$$

$$3z^2 - 2z^2 + z + 6 = 12z+18$$

$$z^2 + z + 6 = 12z+18$$

$$z^2 - 11z - 12 = 0$$

$$(z-12)(z+1) = 0$$

$z - 12 = 0$ or $z + 1 = 0$

$z = 12$ or $z = -1$

Neither 12 nor –1 makes any denominator 0, so they are both solutions. The solutions are 12 and –1.

**Vocabulary and Readiness Check**

**1.** The LCD of $\frac{x}{7}, \frac{x}{2},$ and $\frac{1}{2}$ is <u>14</u>.

**2.** The LCD of $\frac{9}{x+1}, \frac{5}{(x+1)^2},$ and $\frac{x}{x+1}$ is <u>$(x+1)^2$</u>.

**3.** The LCD of $\frac{7}{x-4}, \frac{x}{x^2-16} = \frac{x}{(x+4)(x-4)},$ and $\frac{1}{x+4}$ is <u>$(x+4)(x-4)$</u>.

**4.** The LCD of $3 = \frac{3}{1}, \frac{1}{x-5},$ and $\frac{2}{x^2-5x} = \frac{2}{x(x-5)}$ is <u>$x(x-5)$</u>.

**Exercise Set 6.5**

**1.** $\frac{x}{2} - \frac{x}{3} = 12$

$6\left(\frac{x}{2} - \frac{x}{3}\right) = 6(12)$

$3x - 2x = 72$

$x = 72$

**3.** $\frac{x}{3} = \frac{1}{6} + \frac{x}{4}$

$12\left(\frac{x}{3}\right) = 12\left(\frac{1}{6} + \frac{x}{4}\right)$

$4x = 2 + 3x$

$x = 2$

**5.**  $\dfrac{2}{x} + \dfrac{1}{2} = \dfrac{5}{x}$

$2x\left(\dfrac{2}{x} + \dfrac{1}{2}\right) = 2x\left(\dfrac{5}{x}\right)$

$4 + x = 10$

$x = 6$

**7.**  $\dfrac{x^2 + 1}{x} = \dfrac{5}{x}$

$x\left(\dfrac{x^2 + 1}{x}\right) = x\left(\dfrac{5}{x}\right)$

$x^2 + 1 = 5$

$x^2 - 4 = 0$

$x + 2 = 0$  or  $x - 2 = 0$

$x = -2$  or    $x = 2$

**9.**  $\dfrac{x+5}{x+3} = \dfrac{2}{x+3}$

$(x+3) \cdot \dfrac{x+5}{x+3} = (x+3) \cdot \dfrac{2}{x+3}$

$x + 5 = 2$

$x = -3$

which we disregard as extraneous. No solution, or $\varnothing$.

**11.**  $\dfrac{5}{x-2} - \dfrac{2}{x+4} = \dfrac{4}{x^2 + 2x - 8}$

$\dfrac{5}{x-2} - \dfrac{2}{x+4} = -\dfrac{4}{(x+4)(x-2)}$

$(x-4)(x+2)\left(\dfrac{5}{x-2} - \dfrac{2}{x+4}\right) = (x-4)(x+2)\left(-\dfrac{4}{(x+4)(x-2)}\right)$

$5(x+4) - 2(x-2) = -4$

$5x + 20 - 2x + 4 = -4$

$3x + 24 = -4$

$3x = -28$

$x = -\dfrac{28}{3}$

**13.**  $\dfrac{1}{x-1} = \dfrac{2}{x+1}$

$(x+1)(x-1) \cdot \dfrac{1}{x-1} = (x+1)(x-1) \cdot \dfrac{2}{x+1}$

$1(x+1) = 2(x-1)$

$x + 1 = 2x - 2$

$-x = -3$

$x = 3$

**15.**

$$\frac{x^2-23}{2x^2-5x-3}+\frac{2}{x-3}=\frac{-1}{2x+1}$$

$$\frac{x^2-23}{(2x+1)(x-3)}+\frac{2}{x-3}=\frac{-1}{2x+1}$$

$$(2x+1)(x-3)\left(\frac{x^2-23}{(2x+1)(x-3)}+\frac{2}{x-3}\right)=(2x+1)(x-3)\left(\frac{-1}{2x+1}\right)$$

$$(x^2-23)+2(2x+1)=-1(x-3)$$

$$x^2-23+4x+2=-x+3$$

$$x^2+5x-24=0$$

$$(x+8)(x-3)=0$$

$$x+8=0 \quad \text{or} \quad x-3=0$$

$$x=-8 \quad \text{or} \qquad x=3$$

We discard 3 as extraneous.

$$x=-8$$

**17.**

$$\frac{1}{x-4}-\frac{3x}{x^2-16}=\frac{2}{x+4}$$

$$\frac{1}{x-4}-\frac{3x}{(x+4)(x-4)}=\frac{2}{x+4}$$

$$(x+4)(x-4)\left[\frac{1}{x-4}-\frac{3x}{(x+4)(x-4)}\right]=(x+4)(x-4)\left(\frac{2}{x+4}\right)$$

$$1(x+4)-3x=2(x-4)$$

$$x+4-3x=2x-8$$

$$-2x+4=2x-8$$

$$-4x=-12$$

$$x=3$$

**19.**

$$\frac{1}{x-4}=\frac{8}{x^2-16}$$

$$\frac{1}{x-4}=\frac{8}{(x+4)(x-4)}$$

$$(x+4)(x-4)\left(\frac{1}{x-4}\right)=(x+4)(x-4)\left(\frac{8}{(x+4)(x-4)}\right)$$

$$1(x+4)=8$$

$$x+4=8$$

$$x=-4$$

which we discard as extraneous. No solution, or $\varnothing$.

**21.**
$$\frac{1}{x-2} - \frac{2}{x^2 - 2x} = 1$$
$$\frac{1}{x-2} - \frac{2}{x(x-2)} = 1$$
$$x(x-2)\left[\frac{1}{x-2} - \frac{2}{x(x-2)}\right] = x(x-2) \cdot 1$$
$$x - 2 = x(x-2)$$
$$x - 2 = x^2 - 2x$$
$$0 = x^2 - 3x + 2$$
$$0 = (x-2)(x-1)$$
$$x - 2 = 0 \text{ or } x - 1 = 1$$
$$x = 2 \text{ or } \quad x = 1$$

We discard 2 as extraneous.
$$x = 1$$

**23.**
$$\frac{5}{x} = \frac{20}{12}$$
$$12x\left(\frac{5}{x}\right) = 12x\left(\frac{20}{12}\right)$$
$$60 = 20x$$
$$3 = x$$

**25.**
$$1 - \frac{4}{a} = 5$$
$$a\left(1 - \frac{4}{a}\right) = a(5)$$
$$a - 4 = 5a$$
$$-4 = 4a$$
$$-1 = a$$

**27.**
$$\frac{x^2 + 5}{x} - 1 = \frac{5(x+1)}{x}$$
$$x\left(\frac{x^2 + 5}{x} - 1\right) = x\left[\frac{5(x+1)}{x}\right]$$
$$x^2 + 5 - x = 5x + 5$$
$$x^2 - 6x = 0$$
$$x(x-6) = 0$$
$$x = 0 \text{ or } x - 6 = 0$$
$$x = 6$$

We discard 0 as extraneous.
$$x = 6$$

**29.**
$$\frac{1}{2x} - \frac{1}{x+1} = \frac{1}{3x^2 + 3x}$$
$$\frac{1}{2x} - \frac{1}{x+1} = \frac{1}{3x(x+1)}$$
$$6x(x+1)\left(\frac{1}{2x} - \frac{1}{x+1}\right) = 6x(x+1)\left(\frac{1}{3x(x+1)}\right)$$
$$3(x+1) - 6x = 2$$
$$3x + 3 - 6x = 2$$
$$-3x + 3 = 2$$
$$-3x = -1$$
$$x = \frac{1}{3}$$

**31.**
$$\frac{1}{x} - \frac{x}{25} = 0$$
$$25x\left(\frac{1}{x} - \frac{x}{25}\right) = 25x(0)$$
$$25 - x^2 = 0$$
$$-(x^2 - 25) = 0$$
$$-(x+5)(x-5) = 0$$
$$x + 5 = 0 \quad \text{or } x - 5 = 0$$
$$x = -5 \text{ or } \quad x = 5$$

**33.**
$$5 - \frac{2}{2y-5} = \frac{3}{2y-5}$$
$$(2y-5)\left(5 - \frac{2}{2y-5}\right) = (2y-5) \cdot \frac{3}{2y-5}$$
$$5(2y-5) - 2 = 3$$
$$10y - 25 - 2 = 3$$
$$10y - 27 = 3$$
$$10y = 30$$
$$y = 3$$

**35.**
$$\frac{x-1}{x+2} = \frac{2}{3}$$
$$3(x+2)\left(\frac{x-1}{x+2}\right) = 3(x+2)\left(\frac{2}{3}\right)$$
$$3(x-1) = 2(x+2)$$
$$3x - 3 = 2x + 4$$
$$x = 7$$

**37.**
$$\frac{x+3}{x+2} = \frac{1}{x+2}$$
$$(x+2) \cdot \frac{x+3}{x+2} = (x+2) \cdot \frac{1}{x+2}$$
$$x+3 = 1$$
$$x = -2$$

which we discard as extraneous. No solution, or $\varnothing$.

**39.**
$$\frac{1}{a-3} + \frac{2}{a+3} = \frac{1}{a^2-9}$$
$$\frac{1}{a-3} + \frac{2}{a+3} = \frac{1}{(a+3)(a-3)}$$
$$(a+3)(a-3)\left(\frac{1}{a-3} + \frac{2}{a+3}\right) = (a+3)(a-3) \cdot \frac{1}{(a+3)(a-3)}$$
$$1(a+3) + 2(a-3) = 1$$
$$a+3+2a-6 = 1$$
$$3a-3 = 1$$
$$3a = 4$$
$$a = \frac{4}{3}$$

**41.**
$$\frac{64}{x^2-16} + 1 = \frac{2x}{x-4}$$
$$\frac{64}{(x+4)(x-4)} + 1 = \frac{2x}{x-4}$$
$$(x+4)(x-4)\left[\frac{64}{(x+4)(x-4)} + 1\right] = (x+4)(x-4) \cdot \frac{2x}{x-4}$$
$$64 + 1(x+4)(x-4) = 2x(x+4)$$
$$64 + (x^2-16) = 2x^2 + 8x$$
$$x^2 + 48 = 2x^2 + 8x$$
$$0 = x^2 + 8x - 48$$
$$0 = (x+12)(x-4)$$

$$x+12 = 0 \quad \text{or} \quad x-4 = 0$$
$$x = -12 \quad \text{or} \quad x = 4$$

We discard 4 as extraneous.
$$x = -12$$

**43.**
$$\frac{-15}{4y+1}+4=y$$

$$(4y+1)\left(\frac{-15}{4y+1}+4\right)=(4y+1)y$$

$$-15+4(4y+1)=4y^2+y$$

$$-15+16y+4=4y^2+y$$

$$-11+16y=4y^2+y$$

$$0=4y^2-15y+11$$

$$0=(4y-11)(y-1)$$

$$4y-11=0 \quad \text{or} \quad y-1=0$$

$$4y=11 \quad \text{or} \quad y=1$$

$$y=\frac{11}{4}$$

**45.**
$$\frac{28}{x^2-9}+\frac{2x}{x-3}+\frac{6}{x+3}=0$$

$$\frac{28}{(x+3)(x-3)}+\frac{2x}{x-3}+\frac{6}{x+3}=0$$

$$(x+3)(x-3)\left[\frac{28}{(x+3)(x-3)}+\frac{2x}{x-3}+\frac{6}{x+3}\right]=(x+3)(x-3)\cdot 0$$

$$28+2x(x+3)+6(x-3)=0$$

$$28+2x^2+6x+6x-18=0$$

$$2x^2+12x+10=0$$

$$2(x^2+6x+5)=0$$

$$2(x+5)(x+1)=0$$

$$x+5=0 \quad \text{or} \quad x+1=0$$

$$x=-5 \quad \text{or} \quad x=-1$$

**47.**
$$\frac{x+2}{x^2+7x+10}=\frac{1}{3x+6}-\frac{1}{x+5}$$

$$\frac{x+2}{(x+5)(x+2)}=\frac{1}{3(x+2)}-\frac{1}{x+5}$$

$$3(x+5)(x+2)\cdot\frac{x+2}{(x+5)(x+2)}=3(x+5)(x+2)\left[\frac{1}{3(x+2)}-\frac{1}{x+5}\right]$$

$$3(x+2)=1(x+5)-1\cdot 3(x+2)$$

$$3x+6=x+5-3x-6$$

$$3x+6=-2x-1$$

$$5x=-7$$

$$x=-\frac{7}{5}$$

**49.** Let $x$ = the number.
$$3x+4=19$$
$$3x=15$$
$$x=5$$
The number is 5.

**51.** Let $w$ = width. Then $w + 5$ = length.
$$2l + 2w = 50$$
$$2(w+5) + 2w = 50$$
$$2w + 10 + 2w = 50$$
$$4w + 10 = 50$$
$$4w = 40$$
$$w = 10;$$
$$w + 5 = 10 + 5 = 15$$
The length is 15 inches and the width is 10 inches.

**53.** 36% (reading from the graph)

**55.** The shortest bar is for the category 12-19 years old.

**57.** 14% of 284,000
$$0.14(284{,}000) = 39{,}760$$
We would expect approximately 40,000 students to eat breakfast regularly.

**59.** Answers may vary

**61.** $f(x) = 20 + \dfrac{4000}{x}$
$$25 = 20 + \frac{4000}{x}$$
$$x \cdot 5 = x \cdot \frac{4000}{x}$$
$$5 - \frac{4000}{x}$$
$$5x = 4000$$
$$x = 800$$
800 pencil sharpeners

**63.** $x^{-2} - 5x^{-1} - 36 = 0$
$$\frac{1}{x^2} - \frac{5}{x} - 36 = 0$$
$$x^2\left(\frac{1}{x^2} - \frac{5}{x} - 36\right) = x^2 \cdot 0$$
$$1 - 5x - 36x^2 = 0$$
$$36x^2 + 5x - 1 = 0$$
$$(9x - 1)(4x + 1) = 0$$
$$9x - 1 = 0 \text{ or } 4x + 1 = 0$$
$$9x = 1 \text{ or } \quad 4x = -1$$
$$x = \frac{1}{9} \text{ or } \quad x = -\frac{1}{4}$$

**65.**  $6p^{-2} - 5p^{-1} + 1 = 0$

$$\frac{6}{p^2} - \frac{5}{p} + 1 = 0$$

$$p^2\left(\frac{6}{p^2} - \frac{5}{p} + 1\right) = p^2 \cdot 0$$

$$6 - 5p + p^2 = 0$$

$$p^2 - 5p + 6 = 0$$

$$(p - 2)(p - 3) = 0$$

$$p - 2 = 0 \text{ or } p - 3 = 0$$

$$p = 2 \text{ or } \quad p = 3$$

**67.**
$$\frac{-8.5}{x + 1.9} = \frac{5.7}{x - 3.6}$$

$$(x + 1.9)(x - 3.6) \cdot \frac{-8.5}{x + 1.9} = (x + 1.9)(x - 3.6) \cdot \frac{5.7}{x - 3.6}$$

$$-8.5(x - 3.6) = 5.7(x + 1.9)$$

$$-8.5x + 30.6 = 5.7x + 10.83$$

$$-14.2x = -19.77$$

$$x \approx 1.39$$

**69.**
$$\frac{12.2}{x} + 17.3 = \frac{9.6}{x} - 14.7$$

$$x\left(\frac{12.2}{x} + 17.3\right) = x\left(\frac{9.6}{x} - 14.7\right)$$

$$12.2 + 17.3x = 9.6 - 14.7x$$

$$32x = -2.6$$

$$x \approx -0.08$$

**71.**  $(4 - x)^2 - 5(4 - x) + 6 = 0$

Let $u = 4 - x$. Then $u^2 = (4 - x)^2$ and

$$u^2 - 5u + 6 = 0$$

$$(u - 3)(u - 2) = 0$$

$$u = 3 \text{ or } \quad u = 2$$

$$4 - x = 3 \text{ or } 4 - x = 2$$

$$-x = -1 \text{ or } \quad -x = -2$$

$$x = 1 \text{ or } \quad x = 2$$

**73.** $\left(\dfrac{5}{2+x}\right)^2 + \left(\dfrac{5}{2+x}\right) - 20 = 0$

Let $u = \dfrac{5}{2+x}$. Then $u^2 = \left(\dfrac{5}{2+x}\right)^2$ and

$u^2 + u - 20 = 0$

$(u+5)(u-4) = 0$

$\quad u = -5 \qquad\qquad \text{or} \qquad u = 4$

$\quad \dfrac{5}{2+x} = -5 \qquad \text{or} \qquad \dfrac{5}{2+x} = 4$

$\qquad\quad 5 = -5(2+x) \quad \text{or} \qquad 5 = 4(2+x)$

$\qquad\quad 5 = -10 - 5x \quad \text{or} \qquad 5 = 8 + 4x$

$\qquad\quad 5x = -15 \qquad \text{or} \qquad -3 = 4x$

$\qquad\quad x = -3 \qquad\quad \text{or} \qquad -\dfrac{3}{4} = x$

**75.**

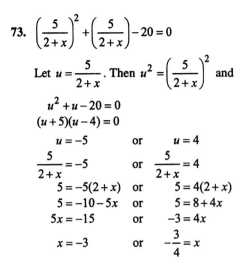

**77.**

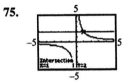

**The Bigger Picture**

**1.** $|-7x + 1| < 15$

$\quad -15 < -7x + 1 < 15$

$\quad -16 < -7x < 14$

$\quad \dfrac{16}{7} > x > -2$

The solution set is $\left(-2, \dfrac{16}{7}\right)$.

**2.** $|-7x + 1| = 15$

$\quad -7x + 1 = 15 \quad \text{or} \quad -7x + 1 = -15$

$\quad -7x = 14 \qquad\qquad -7x = -16$

$\quad\quad x = -2 \qquad\qquad\quad x = \dfrac{16}{7}$

The solution set is $\left\{-2, \dfrac{16}{7}\right\}$.

**3.**     $x^2 - 121 = 0$

$(x - 11)(x + 11) = 0$

$x - 11 = 0$   or   $x + 11 = 0$

$x = 11$   or       $x = -11$

The solution set is $\{11, -11\}$.

**4.** $x^2 + x - 2 = (x + 2)(x - 1)$

The LCD is $(x + 2)(x - 1)$.

$$\frac{8}{x+2} - \frac{3}{x-1} - \frac{x+6}{x^2+x-2}$$

$$(x+2)(x-1) \cdot \frac{8}{x+2} - (x+2)(x-1) \cdot \frac{3}{x-1} = (x+2)(x-1) \cdot \frac{x+6}{(x+2)(x-1)}$$

$$8(x-1) - 3(x+2) = x+6$$

$$8x - 8 - 3x - 6 = x + 6$$

$$5x - 14 = x + 6$$

$$4x - 14 = 6$$

$$4x = 20$$

$$x = 5$$

The solution set is $\{5\}$.

**5.**  $9x + 6 = 4x - 2$

$9x = 4x - 8$

$5x = -8$

$x = -\dfrac{8}{5}$

The solution set is $\left\{ -\dfrac{8}{5} \right\}$.

**6.**  $3x \le 6$   or   $-x \ge 5$

$x \le 2$   or    $x \le -5$

$(-\infty, 2] \cup (-\infty, -5] = (-\infty, 2]$

The solution set is $(-\infty, 2]$.

**7.**  $3x \le 6$   and   $-x \ge 5$

$x \le 2$   and    $x \le -5$

$(-\infty, 2] \cap (-\infty, -5] = (-\infty, -5]$

The solution set is $(-\infty, -5]$.

**8.**  $-9 \le -3x + 21 < 0$

$-30 \le -3x < -21$

$10 \ge x > 7$

The solution set is $(7, 10]$.

**9.** $\left|\dfrac{2x-1}{5}\right| > 7$

$\dfrac{2x-1}{5} > 7$   or   $\dfrac{2x-1}{5} < -7$

$2x - 1 > 35$   or   $2x - 1 < -35$

$2x > 36$   or   $2x < -34$

$x > 18$   or   $x < -17$

$(18, \infty) \cup (-\infty, -17)$

The solution set is $(-\infty, -17) \cup (18, \infty)$.

**10.**    $15x^3 - 16x^2 = 7x$

$15x^3 - 16x^2 - 7x = 0$

$x(15x^2 - 16x - 7) = 0$

$x(3x + 1)(5x - 7) = 0$

$x = 0$  or  $3x + 1 = 0$  or  $5x - 7 = 0$

$x = 0$  or  $3x = -1$  or  $5x = 7$

$x = 0$  or  $x = -\dfrac{1}{3}$  or  $x = \dfrac{7}{5}$

The solution set is $\left\{ 0, -\dfrac{1}{3}, \dfrac{7}{5} \right\}$.

**Integrated Review**

**1.**  $\dfrac{x}{2} = \dfrac{1}{8} + \dfrac{x}{4}$

The LCD is 8.

$8 \cdot \dfrac{x}{2} = 8 \cdot \dfrac{1}{8} + 8 \cdot \dfrac{x}{4}$

$4x = 1 + 2x$

$2x = 1$

$x = \dfrac{1}{2}$

The solution set is $\left\{ \dfrac{1}{2} \right\}$.

**2.**  $\dfrac{x}{4} = \dfrac{3}{2} + \dfrac{x}{10}$

The LCD is 20.

$20 \cdot \dfrac{x}{4} = 20 \cdot \dfrac{3}{2} + 20 \cdot \dfrac{x}{10}$

$5x = 30 + 2x$

$3x = 30$

$x = 10$

The solution set is $\{10\}$.

**3.**  $\dfrac{1}{8} + \dfrac{x}{4} = \dfrac{1}{8} + \dfrac{x}{4} \cdot \dfrac{2}{2} = \dfrac{1}{8} + \dfrac{2x}{8} = \dfrac{1 + 2x}{8}$

**4.**  $\dfrac{3}{2} + \dfrac{x}{10} = \dfrac{5}{5} \cdot \dfrac{3}{2} + \dfrac{x}{10} = \dfrac{15}{10} + \dfrac{x}{10} = \dfrac{15 + x}{10}$

**5.**  $\dfrac{4}{x+2} - \dfrac{2}{x-1} = \dfrac{4}{x+2} \cdot \dfrac{x-1}{x-1} - \dfrac{2}{x-1} \cdot \dfrac{x+2}{x+2}$

$= \dfrac{4(x-1)}{(x+2)(x-1)} - \dfrac{2(x+2)}{(x+2)(x+1)}$

$= \dfrac{4x - 4 - 2x - 4}{(x+2)(x-1)}$

$= \dfrac{2x - 8}{(x+2)(x-1)}$

$= \dfrac{2(x-4)}{(x+2)(x-1)}$

**6.**  $\dfrac{5}{x-2} - \dfrac{10}{x+4} = \dfrac{5}{x-2} \cdot \dfrac{x+4}{x+4} - \dfrac{10}{x+4} \cdot \dfrac{x-2}{x-2}$

$= \dfrac{5(x+4)}{(x-2)(x+4)} - \dfrac{10(x-2)}{(x-2)(x+4)}$

$= \dfrac{5x + 20 - 10x + 20}{(x-2)(x+4)}$

$= \dfrac{-5x + 40}{(x-2)(x+4)}$

$= \dfrac{-5(x-8)}{(x-2)(x+4)}$  or  $-\dfrac{5(x-8)}{(x-2)(x+4)}$

**7.**  $\dfrac{4}{x+2} = \dfrac{2}{x-1}$

The LCD is $(x + 2)(x - 1)$.

$(x+2)(x-1) \cdot \dfrac{4}{x+2} = (x+2)(x-1) \cdot \dfrac{2}{x-1}$

$4(x-1) = 2(x+2)$

$4x - 4 = 2x + 4$

$4x = 2x + 8$

$2x = 8$

$x = 4$

The solution set is $\{4\}$.

**8.**  $\dfrac{5}{x-2} = \dfrac{10}{x+4}$

The LCD is $(x - 2)(x + 4)$.

$(x-2)(x+4) \cdot \dfrac{5}{x-2} = (x-2)(x+4) \cdot \dfrac{10}{x+4}$

$5(x+4) = 10(x-2)$

$5x + 20 = 10x - 20$

$5x = 10x - 40$

$-5x = -40$

$x = 8$

The solution set is $\{8\}$.

**9.** $x^2 - 4 = (x+2)(x-2)$

The LCD is $(x+2)(x-2)$.

$$\frac{2}{x^2-4} = \frac{1}{x+2} - \frac{3}{x-2}$$

$$(x+2)(x-2)\cdot\frac{2}{x^2-4} = (x+2)(x-2)\cdot\frac{1}{x+2} - (x+2)(x-2)\cdot\frac{3}{x-2}$$

$$2 = (x-2) - 3(x+2)$$
$$2 = x-2-3x-6$$
$$2 = -2x-8$$
$$2x = -10$$
$$x = -5$$

The solution set is $\{-5\}$.

**10.** $x^2 - 25 = (x+5)(x-5)$

The LCD is $(x+5)(x-5)$.

$$\frac{3}{x^2-25} = \frac{1}{x+5} + \frac{2}{x-5}$$

$$(x+5)(x-5)\cdot\frac{3}{(x+5)(x-5)} = (x+5)(x-5)\cdot\frac{1}{x+5} + (x+5)(x-5)\cdot\frac{2}{x-5}$$

$$3 = (x-5) + 2(x+5)$$
$$3 = x-5+2x+10$$
$$3 = 3x+5$$
$$-2 = 3x$$
$$-\frac{2}{3} = x$$

The solution set is $\left\{-\frac{2}{3}\right\}$.

**11.**
$$\frac{5}{x^2-3x} + \frac{4}{2x-6} = \frac{5}{x(x-3)} + \frac{4}{2(x-3)}$$
$$= \frac{5}{x(x-3)}\cdot\frac{2}{2} + \frac{4}{2(x-3)}\cdot\frac{x}{x}$$
$$= \frac{10}{2x(x-3)} + \frac{4x}{2x(x-3)}$$
$$= \frac{4x+10}{2x(x-3)}$$
$$= \frac{2(2x+5)}{2x(x-3)}$$
$$= \frac{2x+5}{x(x-3)}$$

**12.**
$$\frac{5}{x^2-3x} \div \frac{4}{2x-6} = \frac{5}{x^2-3x}\cdot\frac{2x-6}{4}$$
$$= \frac{5}{x(x-3)}\cdot\frac{2(x-3)}{4}$$
$$= \frac{5}{2x}$$

13.  $x^2 - 1 = (x-1)(x+1)$

The LCD is $(x-1)(x+1)$.

$$\frac{x-1}{x+1} + \frac{x+7}{x-1} = \frac{4}{x^2-1}$$

$$(x-1)(x+1) \cdot \frac{x-1}{x+1} + (x-1)(x+1) \cdot \frac{x+7}{x-1} = (x-1)(x+1) \cdot \frac{4}{(x-1)(x+1)}$$

$$(x-1)(x-1) + (x+1)(x+7) = 4$$

$$x^2 - 2x + 1 + x^2 + 8x + 7 = 4$$

$$2x^2 + 6x + 8 = 4$$

$$2x^2 + 6x + 4 = 0$$

$$2(x^2 + 3x + 2) = 0$$

$$2(x+1)(x+2) = 0$$

$x+1 = 0$    or    $x+2 = 0$
   $x = -1$  or       $x = -2$

The number $-1$ makes the denominator $x+1$ equal to 0, so it is not a solution. The solution set is $\{-2\}$.

14.  $$\left(1 - \frac{y}{x}\right) \div \left(1 - \frac{x}{y}\right) = \left(\frac{x}{x} - \frac{y}{x}\right) \div \left(\frac{y}{y} - \frac{x}{y}\right)$$

$$= \left(\frac{x-y}{x}\right) \div \left(\frac{y-x}{y}\right)$$

$$= \frac{x-y}{x} \cdot \frac{y}{y-x}$$

$$= \frac{x-y}{x} \cdot \frac{y}{-(x-y)}$$

$$= -\frac{y}{x}$$

15.  $$\frac{a^2-9}{a-6} \cdot \frac{a^2-5a-6}{a^2-a-6} = \frac{(a+3)(a-3)}{a-6} \cdot \frac{(a-6)(a+1)}{(a-3)(a+2)}$$

$$= \frac{(a+3)(a+1)}{a+2}$$

16.  $$\frac{2}{a-6} + \frac{3a}{a^2-5a-6} - \frac{a}{5a+5} = \frac{2}{a-6} + \frac{3a}{(a-6)(a+1)} - \frac{a}{5(a+1)}$$

$$= \frac{2}{a-6} \cdot \frac{5(a+1)}{5(a+1)} + \frac{3a}{(a-6)(a+1)} \cdot \frac{5}{5} - \frac{a}{5(a+1)} \cdot \frac{a-6}{a-6}$$

$$= \frac{10a+10}{5(a+1)(a-6)} + \frac{15a}{5(a+1)(a-6)} - \frac{a^2-6a}{5(a+1)(a-6)}$$

$$= \frac{10a+10+15a-a^2+6a}{5(a+1)(a-6)}$$

$$= \frac{-a^2+31a+10}{5(a+1)(a-6)}$$

**17.** $\dfrac{2x+3}{3x-2} = \dfrac{4x+1}{6x+1}$

The LCD is $(3x-2)(6x+1)$.

$$(3x-2)(6x+1) \cdot \dfrac{2x+3}{3x-2} = (3x-2)(6x+1) \cdot \dfrac{4x+1}{6x+1}$$

$$(6x+1)(2x+3) = (3x-2)(4x+1)$$

$$12x^2 + 18x + 2x + 3 = 12x^2 + 3x - 8x - 2$$

$$12x^2 + 20x + 3 = 12x^2 - 5x - 2$$

$$20x + 3 = -5x - 2$$

$$25x + 3 = -2$$

$$25x = -5$$

$$x = -\dfrac{5}{25}$$

$$x = -\dfrac{1}{5}$$

The solution set is $\left\{ -\dfrac{1}{5} \right\}$.

**18.** The LCD is $2x(4x+1)$.

$$\dfrac{5x-3}{2x} = \dfrac{10x+3}{4x+1}$$

$$2x(4x+1) \cdot \dfrac{5x-3}{2x} = 2x(4x+1) \cdot \dfrac{10x+3}{4x+1}$$

$$(4x+1)(5x-3) = 2x(10x+3)$$

$$20x^2 - 12x + 5x - 3 = 20x^2 + 6x$$

$$20x^2 - 7x - 3 = 20x^2 + 6x$$

$$-7x - 3 = 6x$$

$$-3 = 13x$$

$$-\dfrac{3}{13} = x$$

The solution set is $\left\{ -\dfrac{3}{13} \right\}$.

**19.** $\dfrac{a}{9a^2-1} + \dfrac{2}{6a-2} = \dfrac{a}{(3a-1)(3a+1)} + \dfrac{2}{2(3a-1)}$

$$= \dfrac{a}{(3a-1)(3a+1)} \cdot \dfrac{2}{2} + \dfrac{2}{2(3a-1)} \cdot \dfrac{(3a+1)}{(3a+1)}$$

$$= \dfrac{2a}{2(3a-1)(3a+1)} + \dfrac{6a+2}{2(3a-1)(3a+1)}$$

$$= \dfrac{8a+2}{2(3a-1)(3a+1)}$$

$$= \dfrac{2(4a+1)}{2(3a-1)(3a+1)}$$

$$= \dfrac{4a+1}{(3a-1)(3a+1)}$$

**20.** $\dfrac{3}{4a-8} - \dfrac{a+2}{a^2-2a} = \dfrac{3}{4(a-2)} - \dfrac{a+2}{a(a-2)}$

$\qquad = \dfrac{3}{4(a-2)} \cdot \dfrac{a}{a} - \dfrac{a+2}{a(a-2)} \cdot \dfrac{4}{4}$

$\qquad = \dfrac{3a}{4a(a-2)} - \dfrac{4(a+2)}{4a(a-2)}$

$\qquad = \dfrac{3a}{4a(a-2)} - \dfrac{4a+8}{4a(a-2)}$

$\qquad = \dfrac{3a-4a-8}{4a(a-2)}$

$\qquad = \dfrac{-a-8}{4a(a-2)}$

$\qquad = -\dfrac{a+8}{4a(a-2)}$

**21.** The LCD is $x^2$.

$$-\dfrac{3}{x^2} - \dfrac{1}{x} + 2 = 0$$

$$x^2 \cdot -\dfrac{3}{x^2} - x^2 \cdot \dfrac{1}{x} + x^2 \cdot 2 = 0$$

$$-3 - x + 2x^2 = 0$$

$$2x^2 - x - 3 = 0$$

$$(2x-3)(x+1) = 0$$

$2x - 3 = 0 \quad$ or $\quad x + 1 = 0$

$\quad 2x = 3 \quad$ or $\qquad x = -1$

$\qquad x = \dfrac{3}{2} \quad$ or $\qquad x = -1$

The solution set is $\left\{-1, \dfrac{3}{2}\right\}$.

**22.** $\dfrac{x}{2x+6} + \dfrac{5}{x^2-9}$

$\qquad = \dfrac{x}{2(x+3)} + \dfrac{5}{(x-3)(x+3)}$

$\qquad = \dfrac{x}{2(x+3)} \cdot \dfrac{x-3}{x-3} + \dfrac{5}{(x-3)(x+3)} \cdot \dfrac{2}{2}$

$\qquad = \dfrac{x(x-3)}{2(x+3)(x-3)} + \dfrac{10}{2(x+3)(x-3)}$

$\qquad = \dfrac{x^2-3x}{2(x+3)(x-3)} + \dfrac{10}{2(x+3)(x-3)}$

$\qquad = \dfrac{x^2-3x+10}{2(x+3)(x-3)}$

**23.** $\dfrac{x-8}{x^2-x-2}+\dfrac{2}{x-2}=\dfrac{x-8}{(x-2)(x+1)}+\dfrac{2}{x-2}$

$\qquad = \dfrac{x-8}{(x-2)(x+1)}+\dfrac{2}{x-2}\cdot\dfrac{x+1}{x+1}$

$\qquad = \dfrac{x-8}{(x-2)(x+1)}+\dfrac{2x+2}{(x-2)(x+1)}$

$\qquad = \dfrac{x-8+2x+2}{(x-2)(x+1)}$

$\qquad = \dfrac{3x-6}{(x-2)(x+1)}$

$\qquad = \dfrac{3(x-2)}{(x-2)(x+1)}$

$\qquad = \dfrac{3}{x+1}$

**24.** $x^2-x-2=(x-2)(x+1)$

The LCD is $(x-2)(x+1)$.

$$\dfrac{x-8}{x^2-x-2}+\dfrac{2}{x-2}=\dfrac{3}{x+1}$$

$$(x-2)(x+1)\cdot\dfrac{x-8}{(x-2)(x+1)}+(x-2)(x+1)\cdot\dfrac{2}{x-2}=(x-2)(x+1)\cdot\dfrac{3}{x+1}$$

$$(x-8)+2(x+1)=3(x-2)$$
$$x-8+2x+2=3x-6$$
$$3x-6=3x-6$$
$$-6=-6\quad\text{True}$$

The solution set is
$\{x|x \text{ is a real number and } x\neq 2, x\neq -1\}$.

**25.** The LCD is $a$.

$$\dfrac{3}{a}-5=\dfrac{7}{a}-1$$
$$a\cdot\dfrac{3}{a}-a\cdot5=a\cdot\dfrac{7}{a}-a\cdot1$$
$$3-5a=7-a$$
$$3=7+4a$$
$$-4=4a$$
$$-1=a$$

The solution set is $\{-1\}$.

**26.**
$$\frac{7}{3z-9}+\frac{5}{z}=\frac{7}{3(z-3)}+\frac{5}{z}$$
$$=\frac{7}{3(z-3)}\cdot\frac{z}{z}+\frac{5}{z}\cdot\frac{3(z-3)}{3(z-3)}$$
$$=\frac{7z}{3z(z-3)}+\frac{15(z-3)}{3z(z-3)}$$
$$=\frac{7z+15z-45}{3z(z-3)}$$
$$=\frac{22z-45}{3z(z-3)}$$

**27. a.** $\dfrac{x}{5}-\dfrac{x}{4}+\dfrac{1}{10}$ is an expression.

**b.** The first step to simplify this expression is to write each rational expression term so that the denominator is the LCD, 20.

**c.**
$$\frac{x}{5}-\frac{x}{4}+\frac{1}{10}=\frac{x}{5}\cdot\frac{4}{4}-\frac{x}{4}\cdot\frac{5}{5}+\frac{1}{10}\cdot\frac{2}{2}$$
$$=\frac{4x}{20}-\frac{5x}{20}+\frac{2}{20}$$
$$=\frac{4x-5x+2}{20}$$
$$-\frac{-x+2}{20}$$

**28. a.** $\dfrac{x}{5}-\dfrac{x}{4}=\dfrac{1}{10}$ is an equation.

**b.** The first step to solve this equation is to clear the equation of fractions by multiplying each term by the LCD, 20.

**c.**
$$\frac{x}{5}-\frac{x}{4}=\frac{1}{10}$$
$$20\cdot\frac{x}{5}-20\cdot\frac{x}{4}=20\cdot\frac{1}{10}$$
$$4x-5x=2$$
$$-x=2$$
$$x=-2$$
The solution set is $\{-2\}$.

**29.** $\dfrac{\triangle+\square}{\triangle}=\dfrac{\triangle}{\triangle}+\dfrac{\square}{\triangle}=1+\dfrac{\square}{\triangle}$

b is the correct answer.

**30.** $\dfrac{\triangle}{\square}+\dfrac{\square}{\triangle}=\dfrac{\triangle}{\square}\cdot\dfrac{\triangle}{\triangle}+\dfrac{\square}{\triangle}\cdot\dfrac{\square}{\square}$
$$=\frac{\triangle\triangle}{\square\triangle}+\frac{\square\square}{\square\triangle}$$
$$=\frac{\triangle\triangle+\square\square}{\square\triangle}$$

d is the correct answer.

**31.** $\dfrac{\triangle}{\square}\cdot\dfrac{\bigcirc}{\square}=\dfrac{\triangle\bigcirc}{\square\square}$

d is the correct answer.

**32.** $\dfrac{\triangle}{\square}\div\dfrac{\bigcirc}{\triangle}=\dfrac{\triangle}{\square}\cdot\dfrac{\triangle}{\bigcirc}=\dfrac{\triangle\triangle}{\square\bigcirc}$

a is the correct answer.

**33.** $\dfrac{\frac{\triangle+\square}{\bigcirc}}{\frac{\triangle}{\bigcirc}}=\dfrac{\triangle+\square}{\bigcirc}\div\dfrac{\triangle}{\bigcirc}=\dfrac{\triangle+\square}{\bigcirc}\cdot\dfrac{\bigcirc}{\triangle}=\dfrac{\triangle+\square}{\triangle}$

d is the correct answer.

**Section 6.6**

**Practice Exercises**

**1.** *abc* is the LCD.
$$\frac{1}{a}-\frac{1}{b}=\frac{1}{c}$$
$$abc\left(\frac{1}{a}-\frac{1}{b}\right)=abc\left(\frac{1}{c}\right)$$
$$abc\left(\frac{1}{a}\right)-abc\left(\frac{1}{b}\right)=abc\left(\frac{1}{c}\right)$$
$$bc-ac=ab$$
$$bc=ab+ac$$
$$bc=a(b+c)$$
$$\frac{bc}{b+c}=a$$

**2.** Let $n$ = the number.
$$\frac{3+n}{11-n}=\frac{5}{2}$$
$$2(11-n)\cdot\frac{3+n}{11-n}=2(11-n)\cdot\frac{5}{2}$$
$$2(3+n)=5(11-n)$$
$$6+2n=55-5n$$
$$7n=49$$
$$n=7$$
The number is 7.

**3.** Let $x$ = the number of homes heated by fuel oil.

$$\frac{1}{12} = \frac{x}{36,000}$$

$$12x = 1 \cdot 36,000$$

$$x = \frac{36,000}{12}$$

$$x = 3000$$

3000 homes in the community are heated by fuel oil.

**4.** Let $t$ = the time it takes them to clean the cages together.

|          | Time | Part done in one hour |
|----------|------|-----------------------|
| Elissa   | 3    | $\frac{1}{3}$         |
| Bill     | 2    | $\frac{1}{2}$         |
| Together | $t$  | $\frac{1}{t}$         |

$$\frac{1}{3} + \frac{1}{2} = \frac{1}{t}$$

$$6t\left(\frac{1}{3} + \frac{1}{2}\right) = 6t\left(\frac{1}{t}\right)$$

$$2t + 3t = 6$$

$$5t = 6$$

$$t = \frac{6}{5} \text{ or } 1\frac{1}{5}$$

Elissa and Bill can clean the cages in $1\frac{1}{5}$ hours if they work together.

**5.** Let $x$ = the speed of the wind.

|          | Distance $(r \cdot t)$ | Rate      | Time                        |
|----------|------------------------|-----------|-----------------------------|
| Tailwind | $450 + x$              | $450 + x$ | 1                           |
| Headwind | $\frac{5}{4}(450 - x)$ | $450 - x$ | $1\frac{1}{4} = \frac{5}{4}$ |

$$450 + x = \frac{5}{4}(450 - x)$$

$$4 \cdot (450 + x) = 4 \cdot \frac{5}{4}(450 - x)$$

$$1800 + 4x = 5(450 - x)$$

$$1800 + 4x = 2250 - 5x$$

$$9x = 450$$

$$x = 50$$

The wind speed is 50 mph.

**Exercise Set 6.6**

**1.** $F = \frac{9}{5}C + 32$

$$F - 32 = \frac{9}{5}C$$

$$C = \frac{5}{9}(F - 32)$$

**3.** $Q = \frac{A - I}{L}$

$$QL = L\left(\frac{A - I}{L}\right)$$

$$QL = A - I$$

$$I = A - QL$$

**5.** $\frac{1}{R} = \frac{1}{R_1} + \frac{1}{R_2}$

$$RR_1R_2 \cdot \frac{1}{R} = RR_1R_2\left(\frac{1}{R_1} + \frac{1}{R_2}\right)$$

$$R_1R_2 = RR_2 + RR_1$$

$$R_1R_2 = R(R_2 + R_1)$$

$$R = \frac{R_1R_2}{R_1 + R_2}$$

**7.** $S = \frac{n(a + L)}{2}$

$$2S = n(a + L)$$

$$n = \frac{2S}{a + L}$$

**9.** $A = \frac{h(a + b)}{2}$

$$2A = h(a + b)$$

$$2A = ah + bh$$

$$2A - ah = bh$$

$$b = \frac{2A - ah}{h}$$

**11.**
$$\frac{P_1 V_1}{T_1} = \frac{P_2 V_2}{T_2}$$
$$T_1 T_2 \cdot \frac{P_1 V_1}{T_1} = T_1 T_2 \cdot \frac{P_2 V_2}{T_2}$$
$$P_1 V_1 T_2 = P_2 V_2 T_1$$
$$T_2 = \frac{P_2 V_2 T_1}{P_1 V_1}$$

**13.**
$$f = \frac{f_1 f_2}{f_1 + f_2}$$
$$(f_1 + f_2) f = f_1 f_2$$
$$f_1 f + f_2 f = f_1 f_2$$
$$f_1 f = f_1 f_2 - f_2 f$$
$$f_1 f = f_2 (f_1 - f)$$
$$\frac{f_1 f}{f_1 - f} = f_2$$

**15.**
$$\lambda = \frac{2L}{n}$$
$$n\lambda = 2L$$
$$\frac{n\lambda}{2} = L$$

**17.**
$$\frac{\theta}{\omega} = \frac{2L}{c}$$
$$c\omega \cdot \frac{\theta}{\omega} = c\omega \cdot \frac{2L}{c}$$
$$c\theta = 2L\omega$$
$$c = \frac{2L\omega}{\theta}$$

**19.** Let $n$ = the number. Then
$$\frac{1}{n} = \text{the reciprocal of the number.}$$
$$n + 5\left(\frac{1}{n}\right) = 6$$
$$n + \frac{5}{n} = 6$$
$$n\left(n + \frac{5}{n}\right) = 6n$$
$$n^2 + 5 = 6n$$
$$n^2 - 6n + 5 = 0$$
$$(n-5)(n-1) = 0$$
$$n - 5 = 0 \text{ or } n - 1 = 0$$
$$n = 5 \text{ or } \quad n = 1$$
The numbers are 1 and 5.

**21.** Let $x$ = the number.
$$\frac{12 + x}{41 + 2x} = \frac{1}{3}$$
$$3(12 + x) = 1(41 + 2x)$$
$$36 + 3x = 41 + 2x$$
$$x = 5$$
The number is 5.

**23.** Let $a$ = amount of water in 3 minutes.
$$\frac{15}{10} = \frac{a}{3}$$
$$10a = 15(3)$$
$$10a = 45$$
$$a = 4.5$$
The camel can drink 4.5 gallons.

**25.** Let $w$ = the number of women.
$$\frac{5.5}{50} = \frac{w}{40,639}$$
$$50w = 5.5(40,639)$$
$$50w = 223,514.5$$
$$w = 4470.29$$
There are 4470 women.

**27.** Let $x$ = number of hours needed working together.
$$\frac{1}{26} + \frac{1}{39} = \frac{1}{x}$$
$$78x\left(\frac{1}{26} + \frac{1}{39}\right) = 78x\left(\frac{1}{x}\right)$$
$$3x + 2x = 78$$
$$5x = 78$$
$$x = \frac{78}{5} = 15.6$$

The roofers together would take 15.6 hours.

**29.** Let $x$ = time to sort the stack working together.
$$\frac{1}{20} + \frac{1}{30} + \frac{1}{60} = \frac{1}{x}$$
$$60x\left(\frac{1}{20} + \frac{1}{30} + \frac{1}{60}\right) = 60x \cdot \frac{1}{x}$$
$$3x + 2x + x = 60$$
$$6x = 60$$
$$x = 10$$

It takes them 10 minutes to sort the mail when all three work together.

**31.** Let $r$ = speed of the car. Then
$r+150$ = speed of the plane.

$$t_{\text{plane}} = t_{\text{car}}$$

$$\frac{600}{r+150} = \frac{150}{r}$$

$$600r = 150(r+150)$$
$$600r = 150r + 22{,}500$$
$$450r = 22{,}500$$
$$r = \frac{22{,}500}{450} = 50$$

$$r+150 = 50+150 = 200$$

The speed of the plane was 200 mph.

**33.** Let $r$ = speed of the boat in still water.

$$t_{\text{downstream}} = t_{\text{upstream}}$$

$$\frac{20}{r+5} = \frac{10}{r-5}$$

$$20(r-5) = 10(r+5)$$
$$20r-100 = 10r+50$$
$$10r = 150$$
$$r = 15$$

The speed of the boat in still water is 15 mph.

**35.** Let $x$ = the first integer. Then
$x+1$ = the next integer.

$$\frac{1}{x} + \frac{1}{x+1} = -\frac{15}{56}$$

$$56x(x+1)\left[\frac{1}{x} + \frac{1}{x+1}\right] = 56x(x+1)\left(-\frac{15}{56}\right)$$

$$56(x+1) + 56x = -15x(x+1)$$

$$56x+56+56x = -15x^2 - 15x$$

$$112x+56 = -15x^2 - 15x$$

$$15x^2 + 127x + 56 = 0$$

$$(15x+7)(x+8) = 0$$

$$15x+7 = 0 \quad \text{or} \quad x+8 = 0$$
$$15x = -7 \quad \text{or} \qquad x = -8$$
$$x = -\frac{7}{15} \qquad x+1 = -8+1 = -7$$

$-\dfrac{7}{15}$ is not an integer.

The integers are –8 and –7.

**37.** Let $t$ = time for 2nd hose to fill the pond.

$$\frac{1}{45} + \frac{1}{t} = \frac{1}{20}$$

$$180t\left(\frac{1}{45} + \frac{1}{t}\right) = 180t \cdot \frac{1}{20}$$

$$4t + 180 = 9t$$
$$180 = 5t$$
$$36 = t$$

The second hose will take 36 minutes to fill the pond alone.

**39.** Let $r$ = the speed of the first train. Then
$r+15$ = the speed of the 2nd train.

$$d_{\text{train 1}} + d_{\text{train 2}} = 630$$
$$6r + 6(r+15) = 630$$
$$6r + 6r + 90 = 630$$
$$12r = 540$$
$$r = 45$$

$$r+15 = 45+15 = 60$$

The speed of the trains were 45 mph and 60 mph.

**41.** Let $t$ = time to travel 1 mile.

$$\frac{0.17}{1} = \frac{1}{t}$$

$$0.17t = 1$$
$$100(0.17t) = 100(1)$$
$$17t = 100$$
$$t = \frac{100}{17} \approx 5.882352941$$

It would take 5.9 hours.

**43.** Let $t$ = time to fill quota working together.

$$\frac{1}{5} + \frac{1}{6} + \frac{1}{7.5} = \frac{1}{t}$$

$$225t\left(\frac{1}{5} + \frac{1}{6} + \frac{1}{7.5}\right) = 225t \cdot \frac{1}{t}$$

$$45t + 37.5t + 30t = 225$$
$$112.5t = 225$$
$$t = 2$$

It would take 2 hours using all three machines.

**45.** Let $r$ = the speed of plane in still air.

$$t_{\text{with}} = t_{\text{against}}$$

$$\frac{465}{r+20} = \frac{345}{r-20}$$

$$465(r-20) = 345(r+20)$$
$$465r - 9300 = 345r + 6900$$
$$120r = 16{,}200$$
$$r = 135$$

The planes speed in still air is 135 mph.

**47.** Let $d$ = the distance of the run.

$$t_{\text{jogger 2}} = \frac{1}{2} + t_{\text{jogger 1}}$$

$$\frac{d}{6} = \frac{1}{2} + \frac{d}{8}$$

$$24\left(\frac{d}{6}\right) = 24\left(\frac{1}{2} + \frac{d}{8}\right)$$

$$4d = 12 + 3d$$

$$d = 12$$

The run was 12 miles.

**49.** Let $n$ = numerator. Then
$n+1$ = the denominator, and

$\dfrac{n}{n+1}$ = the fraction. Now

$$\frac{n-3}{(n+1)-3} = \frac{4}{5}$$

$$\frac{n-3}{n-2} = \frac{4}{5}$$

$$5(n-3) = 4(n-2)$$

$$5n-15 = 4n-8$$

$$n = 7$$

Thus, $\dfrac{n}{n+1} = \dfrac{7}{7+1} = \dfrac{7}{8}$ is the fraction.

**51.** Let $t$ = time to move the cans working together.

$$\frac{1}{2} + \frac{1}{6} = \frac{1}{t}$$

$$6t\left(\frac{1}{2} + \frac{1}{6}\right) = 6t \cdot \frac{1}{t}$$

$$3t + t = 6$$

$$4t = 6$$

$$t = \frac{6}{4} = 1\frac{1}{2}$$

It would take them $1\frac{1}{2}$ minutes.

**53.** Let $t$ = time to complete the job working together.

$$\frac{1}{4} + \frac{1}{5} = \frac{1}{t}$$

$$20t\left(\frac{1}{4} + \frac{1}{5}\right) = 20t \cdot \frac{1}{t}$$

$$5t + 4t = 20$$

$$9t = 20$$

$$t = \frac{20}{9} = 2\frac{2}{9}$$

It would take them $2\frac{2}{9}$ hours.

**55.** Let $r$ = the rate for the 1st portion. Then
$r-2$ = the rate for the cooldown portion.

$$t_{\text{first portion}} = t_{\text{cooldown}}$$

$$\frac{20}{r} = \frac{16}{r-2}$$

$$20(r-2) = 16r$$

$$20r - 40 = 16r$$

$$4r = 40$$

$$r = 10;\ r-2 = 10-2 = 8$$

His rate was 10 mph during the first portion and 8 mph for the cool-down portion.

**57.** Let $t$ = time if they worked together.

$$\frac{1}{3} + \frac{1}{6} = \frac{1}{t}$$

$$6t\left(\frac{1}{3} + \frac{1}{6}\right) = 6t \cdot \frac{1}{t}$$

$$2t + t = 6$$

$$3t = 6$$

$$t = 2$$

It would take them 2 hours.

**59.** Let $r$ = the speed of the car. Then
$6r$ = speed of the jet.

$$t_{\text{car}} = t_{\text{jet}} + 1$$

$$\frac{240}{r} = \frac{1080}{6r} + 1$$

$$6r \cdot \frac{240}{r} = 6r\left(\frac{1080}{6r} + 1\right)$$

$$1440 = 1080 + 6r$$

$$360 = 6r$$

$$60 = r$$

Thus, $t_{\text{jet}} = \dfrac{1080}{6(60)} = 3;\ t_{\text{car}} = \dfrac{240}{6} = 4.$

She travels 3 hours by jet and 4 hours by car.

**61.** Let $m$ = the number of movies that cost between $50 and $99 million to make.

$$\frac{5}{7} = \frac{m}{599}$$

$$7m = 5 \cdot 599$$

$$7m = 2995$$

$$m = \frac{2995}{7} \approx 427.86$$

Approximately 428 movies cost between $50 and $99 million to make.

**63.** $\dfrac{x}{4} = \dfrac{x+3}{6}$

$6x = 4(x+3)$

$6x = 4x + 12$

$2x = 12$

$x = 6$

**65.** $\dfrac{x-6}{4} = \dfrac{x-2}{5}$

$5(x-6) = 4(x-2)$

$5x - 30 = 4x - 8$

$x = 22$

**67.** Answers may vary

$\dfrac{705w}{h^2} = 47$

$\dfrac{705(240)}{h^2} = 47$

$169,200 = 47h^2$

$3600 = h^2$

$0 = h^2 - 3600$

$0 = (h+60)(h-60)$

$h + 60 = 0 \quad$ or $\quad h - 60 = 0$

$h = -60 \quad$ or $\quad h = 60$

Discard the –60. The patient is 60 inches, or 5 feet tall.

**69.** $\dfrac{1}{R} = \dfrac{1}{R_1} + \dfrac{1}{R_2}$

$\dfrac{1}{2} = \dfrac{1}{3} + \dfrac{1}{R_2}$

$6R_2\left(\dfrac{1}{2}\right) = 6R_2\left(\dfrac{1}{3} + \dfrac{1}{R_2}\right)$

$3R_2 = 2R_2 + 6$

$R_2 = 6$

6 ohms

**71.** $\dfrac{1}{R} = \dfrac{1}{R_1} + \dfrac{1}{R_2} + \dfrac{1}{R_3}$

$\dfrac{1}{R} = \dfrac{1}{5} + \dfrac{1}{6} + \dfrac{1}{2}$

$30R\left(\dfrac{1}{R}\right) = 30R\left(\dfrac{1}{5} + \dfrac{1}{6} + \dfrac{1}{2}\right)$

$30 = 6R + 5R + 15R$

$30 = 26R$

$R = \dfrac{30}{26} = \dfrac{15}{13}$

$\dfrac{15}{13}$ ohms

**Section 6.7**

**Practice Exercises**

**1.** $y = kx$

$20 = k(15)$

$\dfrac{4}{3} = k$

$k = \dfrac{4}{3}; \ y = \dfrac{4}{3}x$

**2.** $d = kw$

$9 = k(36)$

$\dfrac{1}{4} = k$

$d = \dfrac{1}{4}w$

$d = \dfrac{1}{4}(75)$

$d = \dfrac{75}{4}$ inches or $18\dfrac{3}{4}$ inches

**3.** $b = \dfrac{k}{a}$

$5 = \dfrac{k}{9}$

$k = 45; \ b = \dfrac{45}{a}$

**4.**    $P = \dfrac{k}{V}$

       $350 = \dfrac{k}{2.8}$

       $980 = k$

       $P = \dfrac{980}{V}$

       $P = \dfrac{980}{1.5}$

       $P = 653\dfrac{1}{3}$ kilopascals

**5.**    $A = kap$

**6.**    $y = \dfrac{k}{x^3}$

       $\dfrac{1}{2} = \dfrac{k}{2^3}$

       $\dfrac{1}{2} = \dfrac{k}{8}$

       $4 = k$

       $k = 4; \; y = \dfrac{4}{x^3}$

**7.**    $y = \dfrac{kz}{x^3}$

       $15 = \dfrac{k \cdot 5}{3^3}$

       $81 = k$

       $k = 81; \; y = \dfrac{81z}{x^3}$

## Vocabulary and Readiness Check

**1.** $y = 5x$ represents direct variation.

**2.** $y = \dfrac{700}{x}$ represents inverse variation.

**3.** $y = 5xz$ represents joint variation.

**4.** $y = \dfrac{1}{2}abc$ represents joint variation.

**5.** $y = \dfrac{9.1}{x}$ represents inverse variation.

**6.** $y = 2.3x$ represents direct variation.

**7.** $y = \dfrac{2}{3}x$ represents direct variation.

**8.** $y = 3.1st$ represents joint variation.

## Exercise Set 6.7

**1.**    $y = kx$

       $4 = k(20)$

       $k = \dfrac{1}{5}$

       $y = \dfrac{1}{5}x$

**3.**    $y = kx$

       $6 = k(4)$

       $k = \dfrac{3}{2}$

       $y = \dfrac{3}{2}x$

**5.**    $y = kx$

       $7 = k\left(\dfrac{1}{2}\right)$

       $k = 14$

       $y = 14x$

**7.**    $y = kx$

       $0.2 = k(0.8)$

       $k = 0.25$

       $y = 0.25x$

**9.**    $W = kr^3$

       $1.2 = k \cdot 2^3$

       $k = \dfrac{1.2}{8} = 0.15$

       $W = 0.15r^3$

         $= 0.15(3)^3$

         $= 0.15(27)$

         $= 4.05$

The ball weighs 4.05 pounds.

**11.**        $P = kN$

     $260,000 = k(442,000)$

           $k = \dfrac{10}{17}$

      $P = \dfrac{10}{17}N$

      $P = \dfrac{10}{17}(348,000) \approx 204,706$

St. Louis produces 204,706 tons.

**13.** $y = \dfrac{k}{x}$

$6 = \dfrac{k}{5}$

$k = 30$

$y = \dfrac{30}{x}$

**15.** $y = \dfrac{k}{x}$

$100 = \dfrac{k}{7}$

$k = 700$

$y = \dfrac{700}{x}$

**17.** $y = \dfrac{k}{x}$

$\dfrac{1}{8} = \dfrac{k}{16}$

$k = 2$

$y = \dfrac{2}{x}$

**19.** $y = \dfrac{k}{x}$

$0.2 = \dfrac{k}{0.7}$

$k = 0.14$

$y = \dfrac{0.14}{x}$

**21.** $R = \dfrac{k}{T}$

$45 = \dfrac{k}{6}$

$k = 270$

$R = \dfrac{270}{5} = 54$

The car's speed is 54 mph.

**23.** $I = \dfrac{k}{R}$

$40 = \dfrac{k}{270}$

$k = 10,800$

$I = \dfrac{10,800}{R} = \dfrac{10,800}{150} = 72$

The current is 72 amps.

**25.** $I_1 = \dfrac{k}{d^2}$

Replace $d$ by $2d$.

$I_2 = \dfrac{k}{(2d)^2} = \dfrac{k}{4d^2} = \dfrac{1}{4}I_1$

Thus, the intensity is divided by 4.

**27.** $x = kyz$

**29.** $r = kst^3$

**31.** $y = kx^3$

$9 = k(3)^3$

$9 = 27k$

$k = \dfrac{1}{3}$

$y = \dfrac{1}{3}x^3$

**33.** $y = k\sqrt{x}$

$0.4 = k\sqrt{4}$

$0.4 = 2k$

$\dfrac{0.4}{2} = k$

$0.2 = k$

$y = 0.2\sqrt{x}$

**35.** $y = \dfrac{k}{x^2}$

$0.052 = \dfrac{k}{5^2}$

$k = 1.3$

$y = \dfrac{1.3}{x^2}$

**37.** $y = kxz^3$

$120 = k(5)(2^3)$

$120 = k(5)(8)$

$120 = 40k$

$3 = k$

$y = 3xz^3$

**39.** $\text{Weight} = \dfrac{kwh^2}{l}$

$$12 = \dfrac{k\left(\frac{1}{2}\right)\left(\frac{1}{3}\right)^2}{10}$$

$$120 = k \cdot \dfrac{1}{2} \cdot \dfrac{1}{9}$$

$$k = 2160$$

$\text{Weight} = \dfrac{2160wh^2}{l} = \dfrac{2160\left(\frac{2}{3}\right)\left(\frac{1}{2}\right)^2}{16} = 22.5$

The beam can support 22.5 tons.

**41.** $V = kr^2h$

$$32\pi = k(4)^2(6)$$

$$32\pi = k(16)(6)$$

$$32\pi = 96k$$

$$\dfrac{32\pi}{96} = k$$

$$\dfrac{\pi}{3} = k$$

$$V = \dfrac{\pi}{3}r^2h$$

$$V = \dfrac{\pi}{3}(3)^2(5)$$

$$V = 15\pi$$

The volume is $15\pi$ cubic inches.

**43.** $I = \dfrac{k}{x^2}$

$$80 = \dfrac{k}{2^2}$$

$$k = 320$$

$$I = \dfrac{320}{x^2}$$

$$5 = \dfrac{320}{x^2}$$

$$5x^2 = 320$$

$$x^2 = 64$$

$$x = 8$$

The source is 8 feet from the light source.

**45.** $y$ varies directly as $x$ is written as $y = kx$.

**47.** $a$ varies inversely as $b$ is written as $a = \dfrac{k}{b}$.

**49.** $y$ varies jointly as $x$ and $z$ is written as $y = kxz$.

**51.** $y$ varies inversely as $x^3$ is written as $y = \dfrac{k}{x^3}$.

**53.** $y$ varies directly as $x$ and inversely as $p^2$ is written as $y = \dfrac{kx}{p^2}$.

**55.** $r = 4$ in.
$C = 2\pi r = 2\pi(4) = 8\pi$ in.
$A = \pi r^2 = \pi(4)^2 = 16\pi$ sq in.

**57.** $r = 9$ cm
$C = 2\pi r = 2\pi(9) = 18\pi$ cm
$A = \pi r^2 = \pi(9)^2 = 81\pi$ sq cm

**59.** $\sqrt{81} = 9$

**61.** $\sqrt{1} = 1$

**63.** $\sqrt{\dfrac{1}{4}} = \dfrac{1}{2}$

**65.** $\sqrt{\dfrac{4}{9}} = \dfrac{2}{3}$

**67.** $y = \dfrac{2}{3}x$ is an example of direct variation; a.

**69.** $y = 9ab$ is an example of joint variation; c.

**71.** $H_1 = ks^3$
$H_2 = k(2s)^3 = 8(ks^3) = 8H_1$
It is multiplied by 8.

**73.** $y_1 = kx$
$y_2 = k(2x) = 2(kx) = 2y_1$
It is multiplied by 2.

**75.**

| $x$ | $\frac{1}{4}$ | $\frac{1}{2}$ | 1 | 2 | 4 |
|---|---|---|---|---|---|
| $y = \frac{3}{x}$ | 12 | 6 | 3 | $\frac{3}{2}$ | $\frac{3}{4}$ |

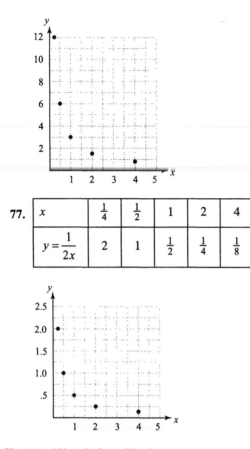

| $x$ | $\frac{1}{4}$ | $\frac{1}{2}$ | 1 | 2 | 4 |
|---|---|---|---|---|---|
| $y = \dfrac{1}{2x}$ | 2 | 1 | $\frac{1}{2}$ | $\frac{1}{4}$ | $\frac{1}{8}$ |

**77.**

## Chapter 6 Vocabulary Check

1. A rational expression whose numerator, denominator, or both contain one or more rational expressions is called a <u>complex fraction</u>.

2. To divide a polynomial by a polynomial other than a monomial, we use <u>long division</u>.

3. In the equation $y = kx$, $y$ varies <u>directly</u> as $x$.

4. In the equation $y = \dfrac{k}{x}$, $y$ varies <u>inversely</u> as $x$.

5. The <u>least common denominator</u> of a list of rational expressions is a polynomial of least degree whose factors include the denominator factors in the list.

6. When a polynomial is to be divided by a binomial of the form $x - c$, a shortcut process called <u>synthetic division</u> may be used.

7. In the equation $y = kxz$, $y$ varies <u>jointly</u> as $x$ and $z$.

8. The expressions $(x - 5)$ and $(5 - x)$ are called <u>opposites</u>.

9. A <u>rational expression</u> is an expression that can be written as the quotient $\dfrac{P}{Q}$ of two polynomials $P$ and $Q$ as long as $Q$ is not 0.

10. Which is an expression and which is an equation? An example of an <u>equation</u> is $\dfrac{2}{x} + \dfrac{2}{x^2} = 7$ and an example of an <u>expression</u> is $\dfrac{2}{x} + \dfrac{5}{x^2}$.

## Chapter 6 Review

1. 7 is never 0 so the domain of $f(x) = \dfrac{3 - 5x}{7}$ is $\{x | x$ is a real number$\}$.

2. 11 is never 0 so the domain of $g(x) = \dfrac{2x + 4}{11}$ is $\{x | x$ is a real number$\}$.

3. $x - 5 = 0$
   $x = 5$

   The domain of $F(x) = \dfrac{-3x^2}{x - 5}$ is $\{x | x$ is a real number and $x \neq 5\}$.

4. $3x - 12 = 0$
   $3x = 12$
   $x = 4$

   The domain of $h(x) = \dfrac{4x}{3x - 12}$ is $\{x | x$ is a real number and $x \neq 4\}$.

5. $x^2 + 8x = 0$
   $x(x + 8) = 0$
   $x = 0$   or   $x + 8 = 0$
   $x = 0$   or        $x = -8$

   The domain of $f(x) = \dfrac{x^3 + 2}{x^2 + 8x}$ is $\{x | x$ is a real number and $x \neq 0, x \neq -8\}$.

**6.**    $3x^2 - 48 = 0$

$3(x^2 - 16) = 0$

$3(x+4)(x-4) = 0$

$x+4 = 0 \quad$ or $\quad x-4 = 0$

$\qquad x = -4 \quad$ or $\qquad x = 4$

The domain of $G(x) = \dfrac{20}{3x^2 - 48}$ is

$\{x | x$ is a real number and $x \neq -4, \, x \neq 4\}$.

**7.**    $\dfrac{x-12}{12-x} = \dfrac{x-12}{-(x-12)} = -1$

**8.**    $\dfrac{5x-15}{25x-75} = \dfrac{5(x-3)}{25(x-3)} = \dfrac{5}{25} = \dfrac{1}{5}$

**9.**    $\dfrac{2x}{2x^2-2x} = \dfrac{2x}{2x(x-1)} = \dfrac{1}{x-1}$

**10.**   $\dfrac{x+7}{x^2-49} = \dfrac{x+7}{(x-7)(x+7)} = \dfrac{1}{x-7}$

**11.**   $\dfrac{2x^2+4x-30}{x^2+x-20} = \dfrac{2(x^2+2x-15)}{(x+5)(x-4)}$

$= \dfrac{2(x+5)(x-3)}{(x+5)(x-4)}$

$= \dfrac{2(x-3)}{x-4}$

**12.**   $C(x) = \dfrac{35x+4200}{x}$

     **a.**    $C(50) = \dfrac{35(50)+4200}{50}$

$= \dfrac{1750+4200}{50}$

$= \dfrac{5950}{50}$

$= 119$

The average cost is \$119.

     **b.**    $C(100) = \dfrac{35(100)+4200}{100}$

$= \dfrac{3500+4200}{100}$

$= \dfrac{7700}{100}$

$= 77$

The average cost is \$77.

     **c.**   It will decrease.

**13.**   $\dfrac{4-x}{5} \cdot \dfrac{15}{2x-8} = \dfrac{4-x}{5} \cdot \dfrac{5 \cdot 3}{2(x-4)}$

$= \dfrac{-1(x-4)}{5} \cdot \dfrac{5 \cdot 3}{2(x-4)}$

$= -\dfrac{3}{2}$

**14.**   $\dfrac{x^2-6x+9}{2x^2-18} \cdot \dfrac{4x+12}{5x-15}$

$= \dfrac{(x-3)(x-3)}{2(x^2-9)} \cdot \dfrac{4(x+3)}{5(x-3)}$

$= \dfrac{(x-3)(x-3)}{2(x-3)(x+3)} \cdot \dfrac{4(x+3)}{5(x-3)}$

$= \dfrac{4}{10}$

$= \dfrac{2}{5}$

**15.**   $\dfrac{a-4b}{a^2+ab} \cdot \dfrac{b^2-a^2}{8b-2a}$

$= \dfrac{a-4b}{a(a+b)} \cdot \dfrac{(b-a)(b+a)}{2(4b-a)}$

$= \dfrac{-(4b-a)}{a(a+b)} \cdot \dfrac{(a-b)(a+b)}{2(4b-a)}$

$= \dfrac{a-b}{2a}$

**16.**   $\dfrac{x^2-x-12}{2x^2-32} \cdot \dfrac{x^2+8x+16}{3x^2+21x+36}$

$= \dfrac{(x-4)(x+3)}{2(x^2-16)} \cdot \dfrac{(x+4)(x+4)}{3(x^2+7x+12)}$

$= \dfrac{(x-4)(x+3)}{2(x-4)(x+4)} \cdot \dfrac{(x+4)(x+4)}{3(x+4)(x+3)}$

$= \dfrac{1}{2 \cdot 3}$

$= \dfrac{1}{6}$

**17.**   $\dfrac{4x+8y}{3} \div \dfrac{5x+10y}{9} = \dfrac{4x+8y}{3} \cdot \dfrac{9}{5x+10y}$

$= \dfrac{4(x+2y)}{3} \cdot \dfrac{3 \cdot 3}{5(x+2y)}$

$= \dfrac{12}{5}$

**18.** $\dfrac{x^2-25}{3} \div \dfrac{x^2-10x+25}{x^2-x-20}$

$= \dfrac{x^2-25}{3} \cdot \dfrac{x^2-x-20}{x^2-10x+25}$

$= \dfrac{(x+5)(x-5)}{3} \cdot \dfrac{(x-5)(x+4)}{(x-5)(x-5)}$

$= \dfrac{(x+5)(x+4)}{3}$

**19.** $\dfrac{a-4b}{a^2+ab} \div \dfrac{20b-5a}{b^2-a^2}$

$= \dfrac{a-4b}{a^2+ab} \cdot \dfrac{b^2-a^2}{20b-5a}$

$= \dfrac{a-4b}{a(a+b)} \cdot \dfrac{(b+a)(b-a)}{5(4b-a)}$

$= \dfrac{a-4b}{a(a+b)} \cdot \dfrac{-(a+b)(a-b)}{-5(a-4b)}$

$= \dfrac{a-b}{5a}$

**20.** $\dfrac{3x+3}{x-1} \div \dfrac{x^2-6x-7}{x^2-1} = \dfrac{3x+3}{x-1} \cdot \dfrac{x^2-1}{x^2-6x-7}$

$= \dfrac{3(x+1)}{x-1} \cdot \dfrac{(x+1)(x-1)}{(x-7)(x+1)}$

$= \dfrac{3(x+1)}{x-7}$

**21.** $\dfrac{2x-x^2}{x^3-8} \div \dfrac{x^2}{x^2+2x+4}$

$= \dfrac{2x-x^2}{x^3-8} \cdot \dfrac{x^2+2x+4}{x^2}$

$= \dfrac{x(2-x)}{(x-2)(x^2+2x+4)} \cdot \dfrac{x^2+2x+4}{x^2}$

$= \dfrac{-x(x-2)}{(x-2)(x^2+2x+4)} \cdot \dfrac{x^2+2x+4}{x^2}$

$= -\dfrac{1}{x}$

**22.** $\dfrac{5x-15}{3-x} \cdot \dfrac{x+2}{10x+20} \cdot \dfrac{x^2-9}{x^2-x-6}$

$= \dfrac{5(x-3)}{-(x-3)} \cdot \dfrac{x+2}{10(x+2)} \cdot \dfrac{(x+3)(x-3)}{(x-3)(x+2)}$

$= -\dfrac{x+3}{2(x+2)}$

**23.** $4x^2y^5 = 2 \cdot 2x^2y^5$

$10x^2y^4 = 2 \cdot 5x^2y^4$

$6y^4 = 2 \cdot 3y^4$

The LCD is $2 \cdot 2 \cdot 5 \cdot 3x^2y^5 = 60x^2y^5$.

**24.** The LCD is $2x(x-2)$.

**25.** The LCD is $5x(x-5)$.

**26.** $5x^3 = 5 \cdot x^3$

$x^2+3x-28 = (x+7)(x-4)$

$10x^2-30x = 10x(x-3) = 2 \cdot 5 \cdot x \cdot (x-3)$

The LCD is

$2 \cdot 5 \cdot x^3 \cdot (x-4)(x+7)(x-3)$

$= 10x^3(x-4)(x+7)(x-3)$.

**27.** $\dfrac{4}{x-4} + \dfrac{x}{x-4} = \dfrac{4+x}{x-4}$

**28.** $\dfrac{4}{3x^2} + \dfrac{2}{3x^2} = \dfrac{4+2}{3x^2} = \dfrac{6}{3x^2} = \dfrac{2}{x^2}$

**29.** $\dfrac{1}{x-2} - \dfrac{1}{4-2x} = \dfrac{1}{x-2} - \dfrac{1}{2(2-x)}$

$= \dfrac{1}{x-2} - \dfrac{-1}{2(x-2)}$

$= \dfrac{1}{x-2} \cdot \dfrac{2}{2} - \dfrac{-1}{2(x-2)}$

$= \dfrac{2}{2(x-2)} - \dfrac{-1}{2(x-2)}$

$= \dfrac{2+1}{2(x-2)}$

$= \dfrac{3}{2(x-2)}$

**30.** $\dfrac{1}{10-x} + \dfrac{x-1}{x-10} = \dfrac{-1}{x-10} + \dfrac{x-1}{x-10}$

$= \dfrac{-1+x-1}{x-10}$

$= \dfrac{x-2}{x-10}$

**31.** $\dfrac{x}{9-x^2} - \dfrac{2}{5x-15} = \dfrac{-x}{x^2-9} - \dfrac{2}{5x-15}$

$\qquad = \dfrac{-x}{(x-3)(x+3)} - \dfrac{2}{5(x-3)}$

$\qquad = \dfrac{-x}{(x-3)(x+3)} \cdot \dfrac{5}{5} - \dfrac{2}{5(x-3)} \cdot \dfrac{x+3}{x+3}$

$\qquad = \dfrac{-5x}{5(x-3)(x+3)} - \dfrac{2(x+3)}{5(x-3)(x+3)}$

$\qquad = \dfrac{-5x - 2(x+3)}{5(x-3)(x+3)}$

$\qquad = \dfrac{-5x - 2x - 6}{5(x-3)(x+3)}$

$\qquad = \dfrac{-7x - 6}{5(x-3)(x+3)}$

**32.** $2x+1 - \dfrac{1}{x-3} = 2x \cdot \dfrac{x-3}{x-3} + 1 \cdot \dfrac{x-3}{x-3} - \dfrac{1}{x-3}$

$\qquad = \dfrac{2x^2 - 6x}{x-3} + \dfrac{x-3}{x-3} - \dfrac{1}{x-3}$

$\qquad = \dfrac{2x^2 - 6x + x - 3 - 1}{x-3}$

$\qquad = \dfrac{2x^2 - 5x - 4}{x-3}$

**33.** $\dfrac{2}{a^2 - 2a + 1} + \dfrac{3}{a^2 - 1} = \dfrac{2}{(a-1)(a-1)} + \dfrac{3}{(a+1)(a-1)}$

$\qquad = \dfrac{2}{(a-1)(a-1)} \cdot \dfrac{a+1}{a+1} + \dfrac{3}{(a+1)(a-1)} \cdot \dfrac{(a-1)}{(a-1)}$

$\qquad = \dfrac{2(a+1)}{(a-1)^2(a+1)} + \dfrac{3(a-1)}{(a-1)^2(a+1)}$

$\qquad = \dfrac{2a+2}{(a-1)^2(a+1)} + \dfrac{3a-3}{(a-1)^2(a+1)}$

$\qquad = \dfrac{2a+2+3a-3}{(a-1)^2(a+1)}$

$\qquad = \dfrac{5a-1}{(a-1)^2(a+1)}$

**34.** $\dfrac{x}{9x^2+12x+16} - \dfrac{3x+4}{27x^3-64} = \dfrac{x}{9x^2+12x+16} - \dfrac{3x+4}{(3x-4)(9x^2+12x+16)}$

$\qquad = \dfrac{x}{9x^2+12x+16} \cdot \dfrac{3x-4}{3x-4} - \dfrac{3x+4}{(3x-4)(9x^2+12x+16)}$

$\qquad = \dfrac{3x^2 - 4x - 3x - 4}{(3x-4)(9x^2+12x+16)}$

$\qquad = \dfrac{3x^2 - 7x - 4}{(3x-4)(9x^2+12x+16)}$

**35.**
$$\frac{2}{x-1} - \frac{3x}{3x-3} + \frac{1}{2x-2}$$
$$= \frac{2}{x-1} - \frac{3x}{3(x-1)} + \frac{1}{2(x-1)}$$
$$= \frac{2}{x-1} \cdot \frac{6}{6} - \frac{3x}{3(x-1)} \cdot \frac{2}{2} + \frac{1}{2(x-1)} \cdot \frac{3}{3}$$
$$= \frac{12}{6(x-1)} - \frac{6x}{6(x-1)} + \frac{3}{6(x-1)}$$
$$= \frac{12 - 6x + 3}{6(x-1)}$$
$$= \frac{15 - 6x}{6(x-1)}$$
$$= \frac{3(5 - 2x)}{6(x-1)}$$
$$= \frac{5 - 2x}{2(x-1)}$$

**36.** Perimeter $= \dfrac{1}{x} + \dfrac{1}{x} + \dfrac{1}{x} + \dfrac{2}{x} + \dfrac{2}{x} + \dfrac{3}{2x} + \dfrac{5}{2x}$
$$= \frac{7}{x} + \frac{8}{2x}$$
$$= \frac{7}{x} \cdot \frac{2}{2} + \frac{8}{2x}$$
$$= \frac{14}{2x} + \frac{8}{2x}$$
$$= \frac{14 + 8}{2x}$$
$$= \frac{22}{2x}$$
$$= \frac{11}{x}$$

**37.** $\dfrac{1 - \frac{3x}{4}}{2 + \frac{x}{4}} = \dfrac{4\left(1 - \frac{3x}{4}\right)}{4\left(2 + \frac{x}{4}\right)} = \dfrac{4 - 3x}{8 + x}$

**38.** $\dfrac{\frac{x^2}{15}}{\frac{x+1}{5x}} = \dfrac{x^2}{15} \div \dfrac{x+1}{5x} = \dfrac{x^2}{15} \cdot \dfrac{5x}{x+1} = \dfrac{x^3}{3(x+1)}$

**39.** $\dfrac{2 - \frac{3}{2x}}{x - \frac{2}{5x}} = \dfrac{10x\left(2 - \frac{3}{2x}\right)}{10x\left(x - \frac{2}{5x}\right)}$
$$= \frac{20x - 15}{10x^2 - 4}$$
$$= \frac{5(4x - 3)}{2(5x^2 - 2)}$$

**40.** $\dfrac{1 + \frac{x}{y}}{\frac{x^2}{y^2} - 1} = \dfrac{y^2\left(1 + \frac{x}{y}\right)}{y^2\left(\frac{x^2}{y^2} - 1\right)}$
$$= \frac{y^2 + xy}{x^2 - y^2}$$
$$= \frac{y(y + x)}{(x + y)(x - y)}$$
$$= \frac{y}{x - y}$$

**41.** $\dfrac{\frac{5}{x} + \frac{1}{xy}}{\frac{3}{x^2}} = \dfrac{x^2 y\left(\frac{5}{x} + \frac{1}{xy}\right)}{x^2 y\left(\frac{3}{x^2}\right)} = \dfrac{5xy + x}{3y} = \dfrac{x(5y + 1)}{3y}$

**42.** $\dfrac{\frac{x}{3} - \frac{3}{x}}{1 + \frac{3}{x}} = \dfrac{3x\left(\frac{x}{3} - \frac{3}{x}\right)}{3x\left(1 + \frac{3}{x}\right)}$
$$= \frac{x^2 - 9}{3x + 9}$$
$$= \frac{(x + 3)(x - 3)}{3(x + 3)}$$
$$= \frac{x - 3}{3}$$

**43.** $\dfrac{\frac{1}{x-1} + 1}{\frac{1}{x+1} - 1} = \dfrac{(x+1)(x-1)\left(\frac{1}{x-1} + 1\right)}{(x+1)(x-1)\left(\frac{1}{x+1} - 1\right)}$
$$= \frac{x + 1 + (x+1)(x-1)}{x - 1 - (x+1)(x-1)}$$
$$= \frac{x + 1 + x^2 - 1}{x - 1 - x^2 + 1}$$
$$= \frac{x + x^2}{x - x^2}$$
$$= \frac{x(1 + x)}{x(1 - x)}$$
$$= \frac{1 + x}{1 - x}$$

**44.**
$$\frac{\frac{x-3}{x+3}+\frac{x+3}{x-3}}{\frac{x-3}{x+3}-\frac{x+3}{x-3}}=\frac{(x-3)(x+3)\left(\frac{x-3}{x+3}+\frac{x+3}{x-3}\right)}{(x-3)(x+3)\left(\frac{x-3}{x+3}-\frac{x+3}{x-3}\right)}$$

$$=\frac{(x-3)^2+(x+3)^2}{(x-3)^2-(x+3)^2}$$

$$=\frac{x^2-6x+9+x^2+6x+9}{x^2-6x+9-(x^2+6x+9)}$$

$$=\frac{2x^2+18}{x^2-6x+9-x^2-6x-9}$$

$$=\frac{2(x^2+9)}{-12x}$$

$$=-\frac{x^2+9}{6x}$$

**45.** $f(a+h)=\dfrac{3}{a+h}$

**46.** $f(a)=\dfrac{3}{a}$

**47.** $\dfrac{f(a+h)-f(a)}{h}=\dfrac{\frac{3}{a+h}-\frac{3}{a}}{h}$

**48.** $\dfrac{f(a+h)-f(a)}{h}=\dfrac{\frac{3}{a+h}-\frac{3}{a}}{h}$

$$=\frac{\left(\frac{3}{a+h}-\frac{3}{a}\right)\cdot a(a+h)}{h\cdot a(a+h)}$$

$$=\frac{3a-3(a+h)}{h\cdot a(a+h)}$$

$$=\frac{3a-3a-3h}{h\cdot a(a+h)}$$

$$=\frac{-3h}{h\cdot a(a+h)}$$

$$=\frac{-3}{a(a+h)}$$

**49.** $\dfrac{4xy+2x^2-9}{4xy}=\dfrac{4xy}{4xy}+\dfrac{2x^2}{4xy}-\dfrac{9}{4xy}$

$$=1+\frac{x}{2y}-\frac{9}{4xy}$$

**50.** $\dfrac{12xb^2+16xb^4}{4xb^3}=\dfrac{12xb^2}{4xb^3}+\dfrac{16xb^4}{4xb^3}$

$$=\frac{3}{b}+4b$$

**51.**
$$
\require{enclose}
\begin{array}{r}
3x^3+9x^2+2x+6 \\
x-3\,\enclose{longdiv}{3x^4+0x^3-25x^2+0x-20} \\
\underline{3x^4-9x^3}\phantom{} \\
9x^3-25x^2 \\
\underline{9x^3-27x^2} \\
2x^2+0x \\
\underline{2x^2-6x} \\
6x-20 \\
\underline{6x-18} \\
-2
\end{array}
$$

Answer: $3x^3+9x^2+2x+6-\dfrac{2}{x-3}$

**52.**
$$
\begin{array}{r}
2x^3-4x^2+7x-9 \\
x+2\,\enclose{longdiv}{2x^4+0x^3-x^2+5x-12} \\
\underline{2x^4+4x^3}\phantom{} \\
-4x^3-x^2 \\
\underline{-4x^3-8x^2} \\
7x^2+5x \\
\underline{7x^2+14x} \\
-9x-12 \\
\underline{-9x-18} \\
6
\end{array}
$$

Answer: $2x^3-4x^2+7x-9+\dfrac{6}{x+2}$

**53.**
$$
\begin{array}{r}
x^2-1 \\
2x+3\,\enclose{longdiv}{2x^3+3x^2-2x+2} \\
\underline{2x^3+3x^2}\phantom{} \\
-2x+2 \\
\underline{-2x-3} \\
5
\end{array}
$$

Answer: $x^2-1+\dfrac{5}{2x+3}$

**54.**
$$x^2 + x + 2 \overline{\smash{\big)}\, 3x^4 + 5x^3 + 7x^2 + 3x - 2}$$

quotient: $3x^2 + 2x - 1$

$$\underline{3x^4 + 3x^3 + 6x^2}$$
$$2x^3 + \;\;x^2 + 3x$$
$$\underline{2x^3 + 2x^2 + 4x}$$
$$-x^2 - x - 2$$
$$\underline{-x^2 - x - 2}$$
$$0$$

Answer: $3x^2 + 2x - 1$

**55.** 
$$2\underline{\big|\,3 \quad 0 \quad 12 \quad -4}$$
$$\phantom{2\big|\,3\;}\; 6 \quad 12 \quad 48$$
$$\overline{\phantom{2\big|}\;3 \quad 6 \quad 24 \quad 44}$$

Answer: $3x^2 + 6x + 24 + \dfrac{44}{x-2}$

**56.** 
$$-1\underline{\big|\,1 \quad 0 \quad 0 \quad 0 \quad 0 \quad -1}$$
$$\phantom{-1\big|\,1\;}\; -1 \quad 1 \quad -1 \quad 1 \quad -1$$
$$\overline{\phantom{-1\big|}\;1 \;-1 \quad 1 \;-1 \quad 1 \;-2}$$

Answer: $x^4 - x^3 + x^2 - x + 1 - \dfrac{2}{x+1}$

**57.** 
$$3\underline{\big|\,1 \quad 0 \quad 0 \quad -81}$$
$$\phantom{3\big|\,1\;}\; 3 \quad 9 \quad 27$$
$$\overline{\phantom{3\big|}\;1 \quad 3 \quad 9 \;-54}$$

Answer: $x^2 + 3x + 9 - \dfrac{54}{x-3}$

**58.** 
$$-2\underline{\big|\,3 \quad 0 \quad -2 \quad 0 \quad 10}$$
$$\phantom{-2\big|\,3\;}\; -6 \quad 12 \;-20 \quad 40$$
$$\overline{\phantom{-2\big|}\;3 \;-6 \quad 10 \;-20 \quad 50}$$

Answer: $3x^3 - 6x^2 + 10x - 20 + \dfrac{50}{x+2}$

**59.** 
$$4\underline{\big|\,3 \quad 0 \quad 0 \quad 0 \quad -9 \quad 7}$$
$$\phantom{4\big|\,3\;}\; 12 \quad 48 \quad 192 \quad 768 \quad 3036$$
$$\overline{\phantom{4\big|}\;3 \quad 12 \quad 48 \quad 192 \quad 759 \quad 3043}$$

Thus, $P(4) = 3043$.

**60.** 
$$-5\underline{\big|\,3 \quad 0 \quad 0 \quad 0 \quad -9 \quad 7}$$
$$\phantom{-5\big|\,3\;}\; -15 \quad 75 \;-375 \quad 1875 \;-9330$$
$$\overline{\phantom{-5\big|}\;3 \;-15 \quad 75 \;-375 \quad 1866 \;-9323}$$

Thus, $P(-5) = -9323$.

**61.** 
$$-\tfrac{1}{2}\underline{\big|\,3 \quad 0 \quad 0 \quad 0 \quad -9 \quad 7}$$
$$\phantom{-\tfrac{1}{2}\big|\,3\;}\; -\tfrac{3}{2} \quad \tfrac{3}{4} \quad -\tfrac{3}{8} \quad \tfrac{3}{16} \quad \tfrac{141}{32}$$
$$\overline{\phantom{-\tfrac{1}{2}\big|}\;3 \;-\tfrac{3}{2} \quad \tfrac{3}{4} \;-\tfrac{3}{8} \;-\tfrac{141}{16} \quad \tfrac{365}{32}}$$

Thus, $P\left(-\dfrac{1}{2}\right) = \dfrac{365}{32}$.

**62.** 
$$3\underline{\big|\,1 \quad -1 \quad -6 \quad -6 \quad 18}$$
$$\phantom{3\big|\,1\;}\; 3 \quad 6 \quad 0 \;-18$$
$$\overline{\phantom{3\big|}\;1 \quad 2 \quad 0 \;-6 \quad 0}$$

length $= (x^3 + 2x^2 - 6)$ miles

**63.** The LCD is $3x$.
$$\frac{3}{x} + \frac{1}{3} = \frac{5}{x}$$
$$3x\left(\frac{3}{x} + \frac{1}{3}\right) = 3x\left(\frac{5}{x}\right)$$
$$3x\left(\frac{3}{x}\right) + 3x\left(\frac{1}{3}\right) = 3x\left(\frac{5}{x}\right)$$
$$9 + x = 15$$
$$x = 6$$
The solution set is $\{6\}$.

**64.** The LCD is $2(5x - 9)$.
$$\frac{2x+3}{5x-9} = \frac{3}{2}$$
$$2(5x-9) \cdot \frac{2x+3}{5x-9} = 2(5x-9) \cdot \frac{3}{2}$$
$$2(2x+3) = (5x-9) \cdot 3$$
$$4x + 6 = 15x - 27$$
$$6 = 11x - 27$$
$$33 = 11x$$
$$3 = x$$
The solution set is $\{3\}$.

**65.** The LCD is $(x-2)(x+2)$.

$$\frac{1}{x-2}-\frac{3x}{x^2-4}=\frac{2}{x+2}$$

$$(x-2)(x+2)\left(\frac{1}{x-2}-\frac{3x}{x^2-4}\right)=(x-2)(x+2)\left(\frac{2}{x+2}\right)$$

$$(x-2)(x+2)\cdot\frac{1}{x-2}-(x-2)(x+2)\cdot\frac{3x}{(x+2)(x-2)}=(x-2)(x+2)\cdot\frac{2}{x+2}$$

$$(x+2)-3x=2(x-2)$$

$$-2x+2=2x-4$$

$$-4x+2=-4$$

$$-4x=-6$$

$$x=\frac{-6}{-4}=\frac{3}{2}$$

The solution set is $\left\{\dfrac{3}{2}\right\}$.

**66.** The LCD is $7x$.

$$\frac{7}{x}-\frac{x}{7}=0$$

$$7x\left(\frac{7}{x}-\frac{x}{7}\right)=7x(0)$$

$$7x\left(\frac{7}{x}\right)-7x\left(\frac{x}{7}\right)=0$$

$$49-x^2=0$$

$$(7-x)(7+x)=0$$

$$7-x=0 \quad\text{or}\quad 7+x=0$$

$$7=x \quad\text{or}\qquad x=-7$$

The solution set is $\{-7, 7\}$.

**67.**

$$\frac{5}{x^2-7x}+\frac{4}{2x-14}$$

$$=\frac{5}{x(x-7)}+\frac{4}{2(x-7)}$$

$$=\frac{5}{x(x-7)}\cdot\frac{2}{2}+\frac{4}{2(x-7)}\cdot\frac{x}{x}$$

$$=\frac{10}{2x(x-7)}+\frac{4x}{2x(x-7)}$$

$$=\frac{10+4x}{2x(x-7)}$$

$$=\frac{2(5+2x)}{2x(x-7)}$$

$$=\frac{5+2x}{x(x-7)}$$

**68.** The LCD is $x^2$.

$$3 - \frac{5}{x} - \frac{2}{x^2} = 0$$

$$x^2\left(3 - \frac{5}{x} - \frac{2}{x^2}\right) = x^2(0)$$

$$x^2 \cdot 3 - x^2\left(\frac{5}{x}\right) - x^2\left(\frac{2}{x^2}\right) = 0$$

$$3x^2 - 5x - 2 = 0$$

$$(3x+1)(x-2) = 0$$

$$3x+1 = 0 \quad \text{or} \quad x-2 = 0$$

$$3x = -1 \quad \text{or} \quad x = 2$$

$$x = -\frac{1}{3} \quad \text{or} \quad x = 2$$

The solution set is $\left\{-\frac{1}{3}, 2\right\}$.

**69.**

$$\frac{4}{3-x} - \frac{7}{2x-6} + \frac{5}{x}$$

$$= \frac{-4}{x-3} - \frac{7}{2(x-3)} + \frac{5}{x}$$

$$= \frac{-4}{x-3} \cdot \frac{2x}{2x} - \frac{7}{2(x-3)} \cdot \frac{x}{x} + \frac{5}{x} \cdot \frac{2(x-3)}{2(x-3)}$$

$$= \frac{-8x}{2x(x-3)} - \frac{7x}{2x(x-3)} + \frac{10x-30}{2x(x-3)}$$

$$= \frac{-8x - 7x + 10x - 30}{2x(x-3)}$$

$$= \frac{-5x - 30}{2x(x-3)}$$

$$= \frac{-5(x+6)}{2x(x-3)}$$

**70.**

$$A = \frac{h(a+b)}{2}$$

$$2A = h(a+b)$$

$$\frac{2A}{h} = a+b$$

$$a = \frac{2A}{h} - b$$

**71.**

$$\frac{1}{R} = \frac{1}{R_1} + \frac{1}{R_2}$$

$$RR_1R_2\left(\frac{1}{R}\right) = RR_1R_2\left(\frac{1}{R_1}\right) + RR_1R_2\left(\frac{1}{R_2}\right)$$

$$R_1R_2 = RR_2 + RR_1$$

$$R_1R_2 - RR_2 = RR_1$$

$$R_2(R_1 - R) = RR_1$$

$$R_2 = \frac{RR_1}{R_1 - R}$$

**72.**

$$I = \frac{E}{R+r}$$

$$I(R+r) = E$$

$$R+r = \frac{E}{I}$$

$$R = \frac{E}{I} - r$$

**73.**

$$A = P + Prt$$

$$A - P = Prt$$

$$\frac{A-P}{Pt} = r \text{ or } r = \frac{A-P}{Pt}$$

**74.**

$$H = \frac{kA(T_1 - T_2)}{L}$$

$$HL = kA(T_1 - T_2)$$

$$\frac{HL}{k(T_1 - T_2)} = A \text{ or } A = \frac{HL}{k(T_1 - T_2)}$$

**75.** Let $x$ = the number.

$$x + 2\left(\frac{1}{x}\right) = 3$$

$$x\left[x + 2\left(\frac{1}{x}\right)\right] = x \cdot 3$$

$$x^2 + 2 = 3x$$

$$x^2 - 3x + 2 = 0$$

$$(x-1)(x-2) = 0$$

$$x-1 = 0 \quad \text{or} \quad x-2 = 0$$

$$x = 1 \quad \text{or} \quad x = 2$$

The numbers are 1 and 2.

**76.** Let $x$ = the number.
$$\frac{3+x}{7+2x}=\frac{10}{21}$$
$$21(3+x)=10(7+2x)$$
$$63+21x=70+20x$$
$$63+1x=70$$
$$x=7$$
The number is 7.

**77.** Let $x$ = amount of time required for all three boys to paint the fence together.
$$\frac{1}{4}+\frac{1}{5}+\frac{1}{6}=\frac{1}{x}$$
$$60x\cdot\frac{1}{4}+60x\cdot\frac{1}{5}+60x\cdot\frac{1}{6}=60x\cdot\frac{1}{x}$$
$$15x+12x+10x=60$$
$$37x=60$$
$$x=\frac{60}{37}=1\frac{23}{37}$$
It will take $1\frac{23}{37}$ hours for all three boys to paint the fence together.

**78.** Let $x$ = amount of time it takes Tom to type the mailing labels when working alone.
$$\frac{1}{6}+\frac{1}{x}=\frac{1}{4}$$
$$12x\cdot\frac{1}{6}+12x\cdot\frac{1}{x}=12x\cdot\frac{1}{4}$$
$$2x+12=3x$$
$$12=x$$
It takes Tom 12 hours to complete the task alone.

**79.** Let $x$ = the speed of the current.

| | distance | = | rate | · | time |
|---|---|---|---|---|---|
| Upstream | 72 | | $32-x$ | | $\frac{72}{32-x}$ |
| Downstream | 120 | | $32+x$ | | $\frac{120}{32+x}$ |

$$\frac{72}{32-x}=\frac{120}{32+x}$$
$$72(32+x)=120(32-x)$$
$$2304+72x=3840-120x$$
$$72x=1536-120x$$
$$192x=1536$$
$$x=8$$
The speed of the current is 8 mph.

**80.** Let $x$ = the speed of the walker.

| | distance | = | rate | · | time |
|---|---|---|---|---|---|
| Jogger | 14 | | $x+3$ | | $\frac{14}{x+3}$ |
| Walker | 8 | | $x$ | | $\frac{8}{x}$ |

$$\frac{14}{x+3}=\frac{8}{x}$$
$$14x=8(x+3)$$
$$14x=8x+24$$
$$6x=24$$
$$x=4$$
The speed of the walker is 4 mph.

**81.** $A=kB$
$$6=k(14)$$
$$k=\frac{6}{14}=\frac{3}{7}$$
$$A=\frac{3}{7}B=\frac{3}{7}(21)=9$$

**82.** $P=\dfrac{K}{V}$
$$1250=\frac{K}{2}$$
$$K=2500$$
$$P=\frac{2500}{V}$$
$$800=\frac{2500}{V}$$
$$800V=2500$$
$$V=3.125$$
When the pressure is 800 kilopascals, the volume is 3.125 cubic meters.

**83.** $\dfrac{22x+8}{11x+4}=\dfrac{2(11x+4)}{11x+4}=2$

**84.** $\dfrac{xy-3x+2y-6}{x^2+4x+4}=\dfrac{x(y-3)+2(y-3)}{(x+2)(x+2)}$
$$=\frac{(x+2)(y-3)}{(x+2)(x+2)}$$
$$=\frac{y-3}{x+2}$$

**85.** $\dfrac{2}{5x} \div \dfrac{4-18x}{6-27x} = \dfrac{2}{5x} \cdot \dfrac{6-27x}{4-18x}$

$= \dfrac{2}{5x} \cdot \dfrac{3(2-9x)}{2(2-9x)}$

$= \dfrac{3}{5x}$

**86.** $\dfrac{7x+28}{2x+4} \div \dfrac{x^2+2x-8}{x^2-2x-8}$

$= \dfrac{7x+28}{2x+4} \cdot \dfrac{x^2-2x-8}{x^2+2x-8}$

$= \dfrac{7(x+4)}{2(x+2)} \cdot \dfrac{(x-4)(x+2)}{(x+4)(x-2)}$

$= \dfrac{7(x-4)}{2(x-2)}$

**87.** $\dfrac{5a^2-20}{a^3+2a^2+a+2} \div \dfrac{7a}{a^3+a}$

$= \dfrac{5a^2-20}{a^3+2a^2+a+2} \cdot \dfrac{a^3+a}{7a}$

$= \dfrac{5(a^2-4)}{a^2(a+2)+1(a+2)} \cdot \dfrac{a(a^2+1)}{7a}$

$= \dfrac{5(a+2)(a-2)}{(a+2)(a^2+1)} \cdot \dfrac{a(a^2+1)}{7a}$

$= \dfrac{5(a-2)}{7}$

**88.** $\dfrac{4a+8}{5a^2-20} \cdot \dfrac{3a^2-6a}{a+3} \div \dfrac{2a^2}{5a+15}$

$= \dfrac{4a+8}{5a^2-20} \cdot \dfrac{3a^2-6a}{a+3} \cdot \dfrac{5a+15}{2a^2}$

$= \dfrac{4(a+2)}{5(a^2-4)} \cdot \dfrac{3a(a-2)}{a+3} \cdot \dfrac{5(a+3)}{2a^2}$

$= \dfrac{4(a+2)}{5(a-2)(a+2)} \cdot \dfrac{3a(a-2)}{a+3} \cdot \dfrac{5(a+3)}{2a^2}$

$= \dfrac{6}{a}$

**89.** $\dfrac{7}{2x} + \dfrac{5}{6x} = \dfrac{7}{2x} \cdot \dfrac{3}{3} + \dfrac{5}{6x}$

$= \dfrac{21}{6x} + \dfrac{5}{6x}$

$= \dfrac{21+5}{6x}$

$= \dfrac{26}{6x}$

$= \dfrac{13}{3x}$

**90.** $\dfrac{x-2}{x+1} - \dfrac{x-3}{x-1} = \dfrac{x-2}{x+1} \cdot \dfrac{x-1}{x-1} - \dfrac{x-3}{x-1} \cdot \dfrac{x+1}{x+1}$

$= \dfrac{(x-2)(x-1)}{(x+1)(x-1)} - \dfrac{(x-3)(x+1)}{(x+1)(x-1)}$

$= \dfrac{x^2-3x+2}{(x+1)(x-1)} - \dfrac{x^2-2x-3}{(x+1)(x-1)}$

$= \dfrac{x^2-3x+2-x^2+2x+3}{(x+1)(x-1)}$

$= \dfrac{-x+5}{(x+1)(x-1)}$

**91.** $\dfrac{2x+1}{x^2+x-6} + \dfrac{2-x}{x^2+x-6} = \dfrac{2x+1+2-x}{x^2+x-6}$

$- \dfrac{x+3}{x^2+x-6}$

$= \dfrac{x+3}{(x+3)(x-2)}$

$= \dfrac{1}{x-2}$

**92.** 
$$\frac{2}{x^2-16}-\frac{3x}{x^2+8x+16}+\frac{3}{x+4}=\frac{2}{(x+4)(x-4)}-\frac{3x}{(x+4)^2}+\frac{3}{x+4}$$

$$=\frac{2}{(x+4)(x-4)}\cdot\frac{x+4}{x+4}-\frac{3x}{(x+4)^2}\cdot\frac{x-4}{x-4}+\frac{3}{x+4}\cdot\frac{(x+4)(x-4)}{(x+4)(x-4)}$$

$$=\frac{2x+8}{(x+4)^2(x-4)}-\frac{3x^2-12x}{(x+4)^2(x-4)}+\frac{3x^2-48}{(x+4)^2(x-4)}$$

$$=\frac{2x+8-3x^2+12x+3x^2-48}{(x+4)^2(x-4)}$$

$$=\frac{14x-40}{(x+4)^2(x-4)}$$

$$=\frac{2(7x-20)}{(x+4)^2(x-4)}$$

**93.** 
$$\frac{\frac{1}{x}-\frac{2}{3x}}{\frac{5}{2x}-\frac{1}{3}}=\frac{6x\left(\frac{1}{x}-\frac{2}{3x}\right)}{6x\left(\frac{5}{2x}-\frac{1}{3}\right)}=\frac{6-4}{15-2x}=\frac{2}{15-2x}$$

**94.** 
$$\frac{2}{1-\frac{2}{x}}=\frac{x(2)}{x\left(1-\frac{2}{x}\right)}=\frac{2x}{x-2}$$

**95.** 
$$\frac{\frac{x^2+5x-6}{4x+3}}{\frac{(x+6)^2}{8x+6}}=\frac{x^2+5x-6}{4x+3}\div\frac{(x+6)^2}{8x+6}$$

$$=\frac{x^2+5x-6}{4x+3}\cdot\frac{8x+6}{(x+6)^2}$$

$$=\frac{(x+6)(x-1)}{4x+3}\cdot\frac{2(4x+3)}{(x+6)^2}$$

$$=\frac{2(x-1)}{x+6}$$

**96.** 
$$\frac{\frac{3}{x-1}-\frac{2}{1-x}}{\frac{2}{x-1}-\frac{2}{x}}=\frac{\frac{3}{x-1}-\frac{-2}{x-1}}{\frac{2}{x-1}-\frac{2}{x}}$$

$$=\frac{(x)(x-1)\left(\frac{3}{x-1}-\frac{-2}{x-1}\right)}{(x)(x-1)\left(\frac{2}{x-1}-\frac{2}{x}\right)}$$

$$=\frac{3x+2x}{2x-2(x-1)}$$

$$=\frac{5x}{2x-2x+2}$$

$$=\frac{5x}{2}$$

**97.** $4 + \dfrac{8}{x} = 8$

The LCD is $x$.

$$x(4) + x\left(\dfrac{8}{x}\right) = x(8)$$
$$4x + 8 = 8x$$
$$8 = 4x$$
$$x = 2$$

The solution set is $\{2\}$.

**98.** $\dfrac{x-2}{x^2 - 7x + 10} = \dfrac{1}{5x - 10} - \dfrac{1}{x - 5}$

$$\dfrac{x-2}{(x-2)(x-5)} = \dfrac{1}{5(x-2)} - \dfrac{1}{x-5}$$

The LCD is $5(x-2)(x-5)$.

$$5(x-2)(x-5) \cdot \dfrac{x-2}{(x-2)(x-5)} = 5(x-2)(x-5) \cdot \dfrac{1}{5(x-2)} - 5(x-2)(x-5) \cdot \dfrac{1}{x-5}$$
$$5(x-2) = (x-5) - 5(x-2)$$
$$5x - 10 = x - 5 - 5x + 10$$
$$5x - 10 = -4x + 5$$
$$9x - 10 = 5$$
$$9x = 15$$
$$x = \dfrac{15}{9} = \dfrac{5}{3}$$

The solution set is $\left\{\dfrac{5}{3}\right\}$.

**99.** Let $x$ be the numerator of a fraction. Then $x + 2$ is the denominator.

$$\dfrac{x-3}{x+2+5} = \dfrac{2}{3}$$
$$\dfrac{x-3}{x+7} = \dfrac{2}{3}$$
$$3(x-3) = 2(x+7)$$
$$3x - 9 = 2x + 14$$
$$x - 9 = 14$$
$$x = 23$$
$$x + 2 = 23 + 2 = 25$$

The fraction is $\dfrac{23}{25}$.

**100.** Let $x$ be the first even integer and $x + 2$ be the next consecutive even integer.

$$\frac{1}{x} + \frac{1}{x+2} = -\frac{9}{40}$$

$$40x(x+2) \cdot \frac{1}{x} + 40x(x+2) \cdot \frac{1}{x+2} = 40x(x+2) \cdot \frac{-9}{40}$$

$$40(x+2) + 40x = -9x(x+2)$$

$$40x + 80 + 40x = -9x^2 - 18x$$

$$80x + 80 = -9x^2 - 18x$$

$$9x^2 + 98x + 80 = 0$$

$$(9x+8)(x+10) = 0$$

$$9x + 8 = 0 \quad \text{or} \quad x + 10 = 0$$

$$9x = -8 \quad \text{or} \quad x = -10$$

$$x = -\frac{8}{9} \quad \text{or} \quad x = -10$$

$-\frac{8}{9}$ is not an integer.

$x + 2 = -10 + 2 = -8$

The two integers are $-10$ and $-8$.

**101.** Let $x$ = time it takes to empty a full tank if both pipes are open.

$$-\frac{1}{2.5} + \frac{1}{2} = \frac{1}{x}$$

$$(2.5)(2x) \cdot -\frac{1}{2.5} + (2.5)(2x) \cdot \frac{1}{2} = (2.5)(2x) \cdot \frac{1}{x}$$

$$-2x + 2.5x = 5$$

$$0.5x - 5$$

$$x = 10$$

It takes 10 hours to empty a full tank if both pipes are open.

**102.** Let $x$ = the speed of the car and
$x + 430$ = the speed of the jet.

| | distance = | rate | · time |
|---|---|---|---|
| Car | 210 | $x$ | $\frac{210}{x}$ |
| Jet | 1715 | $x + 430$ | $\frac{1715}{x+430}$ |

$$\frac{210}{x} = \frac{1715}{x+430}$$

$$210(x+430) = 1715x$$

$$210x + 90,300 = 1715x$$

$$90,300 = 1505x$$

$$60 = x$$

$x + 430 = 60 + 430 = 490$

The speed of the jet is 490 mph.

**103.** One train traveled 382 miles in 6 hours and the second train traveled $382 - 112 = 270$ miles in 6 hours.

Recall $D = rt$ or $r = \dfrac{D}{t}$.

$$r = \frac{382}{6} = 63\frac{2}{3} \qquad r = \frac{270}{6} = 45$$

The speeds of the trains are $63\frac{2}{3}$ mph and 45 mph.

**104.** $C = \dfrac{k}{D}$

$12 = \dfrac{k}{8}$

$96 = k$

$C = \dfrac{96}{D} = \dfrac{96}{24} = 4$

**105.** $A = kr^2$

$36\pi = k(3)^2$

$36\pi = 9k$

$k = 4\pi$

$A = 4\pi r^2$

$A = 4\pi(4)^2 = 4\pi \cdot 16 = 64\pi$

The surface area is $64\pi$ square inches.

**106.**

$$
\require{enclose}
\begin{array}{r}
3x^3 + 13x^2 + 51x + 204 \\
x-4 \enclose{longdiv}{3x^4 + x^3 - x^2 + 0x - 2} \\
\underline{3x^4 - 12x^3} \phantom{............................} \\
13x^3 - x^2 \phantom{..................} \\
\underline{13x^3 - 52x^2} \phantom{...............} \\
51x^2 + 0x \phantom{..........} \\
\underline{51x^2 - 204x} \phantom{.......} \\
204x - 2 \phantom{..} \\
\underline{204x - 816} \\
814
\end{array}
$$

$$3x^3 + 13x^2 + 51x + 204 + \frac{814}{x-4}$$

**Chapter 6 Test**

**1.** $1 - x = 0$

$1 = x$

The domain of $f(x) = \dfrac{5x^2}{1-x}$ is

$\{x | x \text{ is a real number and } x \neq 1\}$.

**2.** $x^2 + 4x + 3 = 0$

$(x+3)(x+1) = 0$

$x + 3 = 0 \quad$ or $\quad x + 1 = 0$

$\phantom{x}x = -3 \quad$ or $\phantom{..........} x = -1$

The domain of $g(x) = \dfrac{9x^2 - 9}{x^2 + 4x + 3}$ is

$\{x | x \text{ is a real number and } x \neq -3,\ x \neq -1\}$.

**3.** $\dfrac{7x - 21}{24 - 8x} = \dfrac{7(x-3)}{8(3-x)} = \dfrac{7(x-3)}{-8(x-3)} = -\dfrac{7}{8}$

**4.** $\dfrac{x^2 - 4x}{x^2 + 5x - 36} = \dfrac{x(x-4)}{(x+9)(x-4)} = \dfrac{x}{x+9}$

**5.** $\dfrac{x^3 - 8}{x - 2} = \dfrac{x^3 - 2^3}{x - 2}$

$= \dfrac{(x-2)(x^2 + 2x + 4)}{x - 2}$

$= x^2 + 2x + 4$

**6.** $\dfrac{2x^3 + 16}{6x^2 + 12x} \cdot \dfrac{5}{x^2 - 2x + 4}$

$= \dfrac{2(x^3 + 8)}{6x(x+2)} \cdot \dfrac{5}{x^2 - 2x + 4}$

$= \dfrac{2(x+2)(x^2 - 2x + 4)}{6x(x+2)} \cdot \dfrac{5}{x^2 - 2x + 4}$

$= \dfrac{5}{3x}$

**7.** $\dfrac{5}{4x^3} + \dfrac{7}{4x^3} = \dfrac{5+7}{4x^3} = \dfrac{12}{4x^3} = \dfrac{3}{x^3}$

**8.** $\dfrac{3x^2 - 12}{x^2 + 2x - 8} \div \dfrac{6x + 18}{x + 4}$

$= \dfrac{3x^2 - 12}{x^2 + 2x - 8} \cdot \dfrac{x + 4}{6x + 18}$

$= \dfrac{3(x^2 - 4)}{(x+4)(x-2)} \cdot \dfrac{x + 4}{6(x+3)}$

$= \dfrac{3(x+2)(x-2)}{(x+4)(x-2)} \cdot \dfrac{(x+4)}{6(x+3)}$

$= \dfrac{x + 2}{2(x+3)}$

**9.**
$$\frac{4x-12}{2x-9} \div \frac{3-x}{4x^2-81} \cdot \frac{x+3}{5x+15} = \frac{4x-12}{2x-9} \cdot \frac{4x^2-81}{3-x} \cdot \frac{x+3}{5x+15}$$
$$= \frac{4(x-3)}{2x-9} \cdot \frac{(2x+9)(2x-9)}{-(x-3)} \cdot \frac{x+3}{5(x+3)}$$
$$= \frac{4(2x+9)}{-5}$$
$$= -\frac{4(2x+9)}{5}$$

**10.**
$$\frac{3+2x}{10-x} + \frac{13+x}{x-10} = \frac{-(3+2x)}{x-10} + \frac{13+x}{x-10}$$
$$= \frac{-3-2x+13+x}{x-10}$$
$$= \frac{-x+10}{x-10}$$
$$= -\frac{x-10}{x-10}$$
$$= -1$$

**11.**
$$\frac{2x^2+7}{2x^4-18x^2} - \frac{6x+7}{2x^4-18x^2} = \frac{2x^2+7-6x-7}{2x^4-18x^2}$$
$$= \frac{2x^2-6x}{2x^4-18x^2}$$
$$= \frac{2x(x-3)}{2x^2(x^2-9)}$$
$$= \frac{2x(x-3)}{2x^2(x-3)(x+3)}$$
$$= \frac{1}{x(x+3)}$$

**12.**
$$\frac{3}{x^2-x-6} + \frac{2}{x^2-5x+6} = \frac{3}{(x-3)(x+2)} + \frac{2}{(x-3)(x-2)}$$
$$= \frac{3}{(x-3)(x+2)} \cdot \frac{x-2}{x-2} + \frac{2}{(x-3)(x-2)} \cdot \frac{x+2}{x+2}$$
$$= \frac{3(x-2)}{(x-3)(x+2)(x-2)} + \frac{2(x+2)}{(x-3)(x+2)(x-2)}$$
$$= \frac{3x-6}{(x-3)(x+2)(x-2)} + \frac{2x+4}{(x-3)(x+2)(x-2)}$$
$$= \frac{3x-6+2x+4}{(x-3)(x+2)(x-2)}$$
$$= \frac{5x-2}{(x-3)(x+2)(x-2)}$$

**13.** $3x - 21 = 3(x - 7)$

$2x - 14 = 2(x - 7)$

The LCD is $3 \cdot 2(x - 7) = 6(x - 7)$.

$$\frac{5}{x-7} - \frac{2x}{3x-21} + \frac{x}{2x-14} = \frac{5}{x-7} \cdot \frac{6}{6} - \frac{2x}{3(x-7)} \cdot \frac{2}{2} + \frac{x}{2(x-7)} \cdot \frac{3}{3}$$

$$= \frac{30}{6(x-7)} - \frac{4x}{6(x-7)} + \frac{3x}{6(x-7)}$$

$$= \frac{30 - 4x + 3x}{6(x-7)}$$

$$= \frac{30 \quad x}{6(x-7)}$$

**14.** $\dfrac{3x}{5} \cdot \left( \dfrac{5}{x} - \dfrac{5}{2x} \right) = \dfrac{3x}{5} \cdot \left( \dfrac{5}{x} \cdot \dfrac{2}{2} - \dfrac{5}{2x} \right)$

$$= \frac{3x}{5} \left( \frac{10}{2x} - \frac{5}{2x} \right)$$

$$= \frac{3x}{5} \left( \frac{10 - 5}{2x} \right)$$

$$= \frac{3x}{5} \left( \frac{5}{2x} \right)$$

$$= \frac{3}{2}$$

**15.** $\dfrac{\frac{5}{x} - \frac{7}{3x}}{\frac{9}{8x} - \frac{1}{x}} = \dfrac{24x\left( \frac{5}{x} - \frac{7}{3x} \right)}{24x\left( \frac{9}{8x} - \frac{1}{x} \right)} = \dfrac{120 - 56}{27 - 24} = \dfrac{64}{3}$

**16.** $\dfrac{\frac{x^2 - 5x + 6}{x+3}}{\frac{x^2 - 4x + 4}{x^2 - 9}} = \dfrac{x^2 - 5x + 6}{x + 3} \div \dfrac{x^2 - 4x + 4}{x^2 - 9}$

$$= \frac{x^2 - 5x + 6}{x + 3} \cdot \frac{x^2 - 9}{x^2 - 4x + 4}$$

$$= \frac{(x-3)(x-2)}{x+3} \cdot \frac{(x+3)(x-3)}{(x-2)(x-2)}$$

$$= \frac{(x-3)^2}{x-2}$$

**17.** $\dfrac{4x^2 y + 9x + 3xz}{3xz} = \dfrac{4x^2 y}{3xz} + \dfrac{9x}{3xz} + \dfrac{3xz}{3xz}$

$$= \frac{4xy}{3z} + \frac{3}{z} + 1$$

**18.**
$$2x+1 \overline{\smash{\big)}\ 4x^3 + 0x^2 - 5x + 0}$$

quotient: $2x^2 - x - 2$

$$\underline{4x^3 + 2x^2}$$
$$-2x^2 - 5x$$
$$\underline{-2x^2 - x}$$
$$-4x + 0$$
$$\underline{-4x - 2}$$
$$2$$

Answer: $2x^2 - x - 2 + \dfrac{2}{2x+1}$

**19.**
$$-3 \,\underline{|\ \ 4 \quad -3 \quad\ \ 0 \quad\ \ -1 \quad\ \ -1}$$
$$\quad\quad\quad -12 \quad 45 \quad -135 \quad 408$$
$$\overline{\quad\ 4 \quad -15 \quad 45 \quad -136 \quad 407}$$

Answer: $4x^3 - 15x^2 + 45x - 136 + \dfrac{407}{x+3}$

**20.**
$$-2 \,\underline{|\ \ 4 \quad\ \ 0 \quad\ \ 7 \quad -2 \quad\ \ -5}$$
$$\quad\quad\quad -8 \quad 16 \quad -46 \quad 96$$
$$\overline{\quad\ 4 \quad -8 \quad 23 \quad -48 \quad 91}$$

Thus, $P(-2) = 91$.

**21.** The LCD is $x - 4$.

$$\frac{x}{x-4} - 3 = \frac{4}{x-4}$$
$$(x-4)\frac{x}{x-4} = (x-4)\cdot 3 - (x-4)\cdot\frac{4}{x-4}$$
$$x = 3(x-4) - 4$$
$$x = 3x - 12 - 4$$
$$x = 3x - 16$$
$$-2x = -16$$
$$x = 8$$

The solution set is $\{8\}$.

**22.**
$$\frac{3}{x+2} - \frac{1}{5x} = \frac{2}{5x^2 + 10x}$$
$$\frac{3}{x+2} - \frac{1}{5x} = \frac{2}{5x(x+2)}$$
$$5x(x+2)\left(\frac{3}{x+2} - \frac{1}{5x}\right) = 5x(x+2)\cdot\frac{2}{5x(x+2)}$$
$$3(5x) - 1(x+2) = 2$$
$$15x - x - 2 = 2$$
$$14x = 4$$
$$x = \frac{4}{14} = \frac{2}{7}$$

The solution set is $\left\{\dfrac{2}{7}\right\}$.

**23.**
$$\frac{x^2 + 8}{x} - 1 = \frac{2(x+4)}{x}$$
$$x\left(\frac{x^2 + 8}{x} - 1\right) = x\left(\frac{2(x+4)}{x}\right)$$
$$(x^2 + 8) - x = 2(x+4)$$
$$x^2 - x + 8 = 2x + 8$$
$$x^2 - 3x = 0$$
$$x(x-3) = 0$$
$$x = 0 \ \text{ or } \ x - 3 = 0$$
$$x = 3$$

Discard the answer 0 as extraneous.
The solution set is $\{3\}$.

**24.**
$$\frac{x+b}{a} = \frac{4x - 7a}{b}$$
$$ab\left(\frac{x+b}{a}\right) = ab\left(\frac{4x - 7a}{b}\right)$$
$$b(x+b) = a(4x - 7a)$$
$$xb + b^2 = 4ax - 7a^2$$
$$b^2 + 7a^2 = 4ax - xb$$
$$b^2 + 7a^2 = x(4a - b)$$
$$x = \frac{b^2 + 7a^2}{4a - b}$$

**25.** Let $x$ = the number.
$$(x+1)\cdot\frac{2}{x} = \frac{12}{5}$$
$$\frac{2(x+1)}{x} = \frac{12}{5}$$
$$\frac{2x+2}{x} = \frac{12}{5}$$
$$5(2x+2) = 12x$$
$$10x + 10 = 12x$$
$$10 = 2x$$
$$5 = x$$

The number is 5.

**26.** Let $t$ = time to weed garden together.

Note that 1 hr and 30 min = $\dfrac{3}{2}$ hours.

$$\frac{\frac{1}{2}+\frac{1}{3}=\frac{1}{t}}{\frac{3}{2}}$$

$$\frac{1}{2}+\frac{2}{3}=\frac{1}{t}$$

$$6t\left(\frac{1}{2}+\frac{2}{3}\right)=6t\left(\frac{1}{t}\right)$$

$$3t+4t=6$$

$$7t=6$$

$$t=\frac{6}{7}$$

It takes them $\dfrac{6}{7}$ hour.

**27.**  $W=\dfrac{k}{V}$

$20=\dfrac{k}{12}$

$k=20(12)=240$

$W=\dfrac{240}{V}=\dfrac{240}{15}=16$

**28.**  $Q=kRS^2$

$24=k(3)(4)^2$

$24=48k$

$k=\dfrac{24}{48}=\dfrac{1}{2}$

$Q=\dfrac{1}{2}RS^2=\dfrac{1}{2}(2)(3)^2=9$

**29.**  $S=k\sqrt{d}$

$160=k\sqrt{400}$

$160=20k$

$k=\dfrac{160}{20}=8$

$S=8\sqrt{d}$

$128=8\sqrt{d}$

$\sqrt{d}=\dfrac{128}{8}$

$\sqrt{d}=16$

$d=256$

The height of the cliff is 256 feet.

**Chapter 6 Cumulative Review**

**1. a.**  $8x$

**b.**  $8x+3$

**c.**  $x\div(-7)$ or $\dfrac{x}{-7}$

**d.**  $2x-1\dfrac{6}{10}=2x-1.6$

**e.**  $x-6$

**f.**  $2(4+x)$

**2. a.**  $x-\dfrac{1}{3}$

**b.**  $5x-6$

**c.**  $8x+3$

**d.**  $\dfrac{7}{2-x}$

**3.**  $\dfrac{y}{3}-\dfrac{y}{4}=\dfrac{1}{6}$

$12\left(\dfrac{y}{3}-\dfrac{y}{4}\right)=12\left(\dfrac{1}{6}\right)$

$4y-3y=2$

$y=2$

**4.**  $\dfrac{x}{7}+\dfrac{x}{5}=\dfrac{12}{5}$

$35\left(\dfrac{x}{7}+\dfrac{x}{5}\right)=35\left(\dfrac{12}{5}\right)$

$5x+7x=84$

$12x=84$

$x=7$

**5.**  $c<200$

$-9.2t+527.33<200$

$-9.2t<-327.33$

$t>35.58\approx36$

$1990+36=2026$

The consumption of cigarettes will be less than 200 billion per year in 2026 and after.

**6.** Let $x$ = score on final exam.
$$\frac{78+65+82+79+2x}{6} \geq 78$$
$$\frac{304+2x}{6} \geq 78$$
$$6\left(\frac{304+2x}{6}\right) \geq 6(78)$$
$$304+2x \geq 468$$
$$2x \geq 164$$
$$x \geq 82$$
The minimum score she can make on her final is 82.

**7.** $\left|\dfrac{3x+1}{2}\right| = -2$ is impossible. The solution set is $\varnothing$.

**8.** $\left|\dfrac{2x-1}{3}\right| + 6 = 3$
$$\left|\dfrac{2x-1}{3}\right| = -3, \text{ which is impossible.}$$
The solution set is $\varnothing$.

**9.** $\left|\dfrac{2(x+1)}{3}\right| \leq 0$
$$\frac{2(x+1)}{3} = 0$$
$$2(x+1) = 0$$
$$2x+2 = 0$$
$$2x = -2$$
$$x = -1$$
The solution is $-1$.

**10.** $\left|\dfrac{3(x-1)}{4}\right| \geq 2$
$$\frac{3(x-1)}{4} \leq -2 \quad \text{or} \quad \frac{3(x-1)}{4} \geq 2$$
$$\frac{3x-3}{4} \leq -2 \quad \text{or} \quad \frac{3x-3}{4} \geq 2$$
$$3x-3 \leq -8 \quad \text{or} \quad 3x-3 \geq 8$$
$$3x \leq -5 \quad \text{or} \quad 3x \geq 11$$
$$x \leq -\frac{5}{3} \quad \text{or} \quad x \geq \frac{11}{3}$$
$$\left(-\infty, -\frac{5}{3}\right] \cup \left[\frac{11}{3}, \infty\right)$$

**11.** $y = -2x+3$

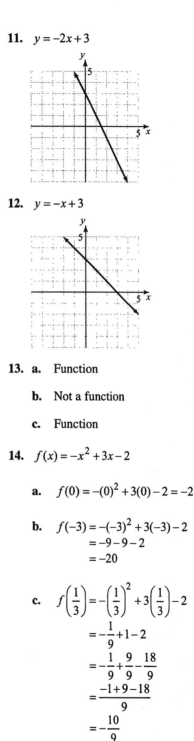

**12.** $y = -x+3$

**13. a.** Function

    **b.** Not a function

    **c.** Function

**14.** $f(x) = -x^2 + 3x - 2$

    **a.** $f(0) = -(0)^2 + 3(0) - 2 = -2$

    **b.** $f(-3) = -(-3)^2 + 3(-3) - 2$
$$= -9 - 9 - 2$$
$$= -20$$

    **c.** $f\left(\dfrac{1}{3}\right) = -\left(\dfrac{1}{3}\right)^2 + 3\left(\dfrac{1}{3}\right) - 2$
$$= -\frac{1}{9} + 1 - 2$$
$$= -\frac{1}{9} + \frac{9}{9} - \frac{18}{9}$$
$$= \frac{-1+9-18}{9}$$
$$= -\frac{10}{9}$$

**15.** $x - 3y = 6$
Let $y = 0$.
$x - 3(0) = 6$
$x = 6$
Plot (6, 0).
Let $x = 0$.
$0 - 3y = 6$
$-3y = 6$
$y = -2$
Plot (0, −2).

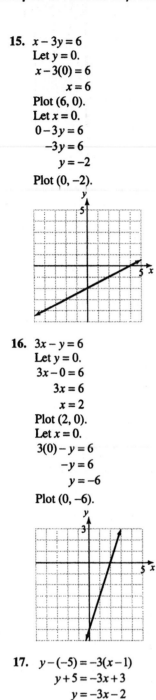

**16.** $3x - y = 6$
Let $y = 0$.
$3x - 0 = 6$
$3x = 6$
$x = 2$
Plot (2, 0).
Let $x = 0$.
$3(0) - y = 6$
$-y = 6$
$y = -6$
Plot (0, −6).

**17.** $y - (-5) = -3(x - 1)$
$y + 5 = -3x + 3$
$y = -3x - 2$

**18.** $y - 3 = \frac{1}{2}(x - (-1))$
$y - 3 = \frac{1}{2}(x + 1)$
$y - 3 = \frac{1}{2}x + \frac{1}{2}$
$y = \frac{1}{2}x + \frac{1}{2} + 3$
$y = \frac{1}{2}x + \frac{7}{2}$
$f(x) = \frac{1}{2}x + \frac{7}{2}$

**19.** $x \geq 1$ and $y \geq 2x - 1$

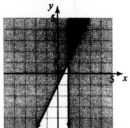

The solution region is the overlap, which has darker shading, along with its boundary.

**20.** $2x + y \leq 4$ or $y > 2$

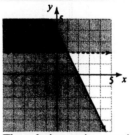

The solution region consists of all shaded regions and the boundary where the boundary line is solid.

**21.** $\begin{cases} 3x - 2y = 10 & (1) \\ 4x - 3y = 15 & (2) \end{cases}$
Multiply E1 by −4 and E2 by 3, and add.
$-12x + 8y = -40$
$\underline{12x - 9y = 45}$
$-y = 5$
$y = -5$
Replace $y$ with −5 in E1.

$3x - 2(-5) = 10$
$3x + 10 = 10$
$3x = 0$
$x = 0$
The solution is (0, –5).

**22.** $\begin{cases} -2x + 3y = 6 & (1) \\ 3x - y = 5 & (2) \end{cases}$

Solve E2 for $y$:
$y = 3x - 5$
Replace $y$ with $3x - 5$ in E1.
$-2x + 3(3x - 5) = 6$
$-2x + 9x - 15 = 6$
$7x = 21$
$x = 3$
Replace $x$ with 3 in the equation $y = 3x - 5$.
$y = 3(3) - 5 = 9 - 5 = 4$
The solution is (3, 4).

**23.** $\begin{cases} 2x - 4y + 8z = 2 & (1) \\ -x - 3y + z = 11 & (2) \\ x - 2y + 4z = 0 & (3) \end{cases}$

Add E2 and E3.
$-5y + 5z = 11$ (4)
Multiply E2 by 2 and add to E1.
$-2x - 6y + 2z = 22$
$\underline{2x - 4y + 8z = 2}$
$-10y + 10z = 24$ (5)
Solve the new system.
$\begin{cases} -5y + 5z = 11 & (4) \\ -10y + 10z = 24 & (5) \end{cases}$
Multiply E4 by –2 and add to E5.
$10y - 10z = -22$
$\underline{-10y + 10z = 24}$
$\qquad 0 = 2$, which is impossible.
The solution is $\varnothing$.

**24.** $\begin{cases} 2x - 2y + 4z = 6 & (1) \\ -4x - y + z = -8 & (2) \\ 3x - y + z = 6 & (3) \end{cases}$

Multiply E2 by –1 and add to E3.
$4x + y - z = 8$
$\underline{3x - y + z = 6}$
$7x \qquad = 14$
$x = 2$
Multiply E2 by –2 and add to E1.
$8x + 2y - 2z = 16$
$\underline{2x - 2y + 4z = 6}$
$10x \qquad + 2z = 22$ or $5x + z = 11$

Replace $x$ with 2 in the equation $5x + z = 11$.
$5(2) + z = 11$
$10 + z = 11$
$z = 1$
Replace $x$ with 2 and $z$ with 1 in E3.
$3(2) - y + 1 = 6$
$7 - y = 6$
$-y = -1$
$y = 1$
The solution is (2, 1, 1).

**25.** Let $x$ = measure of the smallest angle,
$y$ = measure of the largest angle and,
$z$ = measure of the remaining angle.
$\begin{cases} x + y + z = 180 & (1) \\ y = x + 80 & (2) \\ z = x + 10 & (3) \end{cases}$
Substitute $x + 80$ for $y$ and $x + 10$ for $z$ in E1.
$x + (x + 80) + (x + 10) = 180$
$3x + 90 = 180$
$3x = 90$
$x = 30$
Replace $x$ with 30 in E2 and E3.
$y = 30 + 80 = 110$
$z = 30 + 10 = 40$
The angles measure 30°, 110°, and 40°.

**26.** Let $x$ = the price of a ream of paper and
$y$ = the price of a box of manila folders.
$\begin{cases} 3x + 2y = 21.90 & (1) \\ 5x + y = 24.25 & (2) \end{cases}$
Multiply E2 by – 2 and add to E1.
$-10x - 2y = -48.50$
$\underline{3x + 2y = 21.90}$
$-7x \qquad = -26.60$
$x = 3.80$
Replace $x$ with 3.80 in E2.
$5(3.80) + y = 24.25$
$19 + y = 24.25$
$y = 5.25$
A ream of paper cost \$3.80 and a box of manila folders cost \$5.25.

**27.** $\begin{cases} x + 2y + z = 2 \\ -2x - y + 2z = 5 \\ x + 3y - 2z = -8 \end{cases}$

$\begin{bmatrix} 1 & 2 & 1 & | & 2 \\ -2 & -1 & 2 & | & 5 \\ 1 & 3 & -2 & | & -8 \end{bmatrix}$

Multiply R1 by 2 and add to R2.
Multiply R1 by –1 and add to R3.

$$\begin{bmatrix} 1 & 2 & 1 & | & 2 \\ 0 & 3 & 4 & | & 9 \\ 0 & 1 & -3 & | & -10 \end{bmatrix}$$

Interchange R2 and R3.

$$\begin{bmatrix} 1 & 2 & 1 & | & 2 \\ 0 & 1 & -3 & | & -10 \\ 0 & 3 & 4 & | & 9 \end{bmatrix}$$

Multiply R2 by $-3$ and add to R3.

$$\begin{bmatrix} 1 & 2 & 1 & | & 2 \\ 0 & 1 & 3 & | & 10 \\ 0 & 0 & 13 & | & 39 \end{bmatrix}$$

Divide R3 by 13.

$$\begin{bmatrix} 1 & 2 & 1 & | & 2 \\ 0 & 1 & -3 & | & -10 \\ 0 & 0 & 1 & | & 3 \end{bmatrix}$$

This corresponds to $\begin{cases} x+2y+ z = 2 \\ \quad y-3z = -10 \\ \qquad\quad z = 3. \end{cases}$

$y-3z = -10$ and so $x+2(-1)+(3) = 2$
$y-3(3) = -10 \qquad\qquad x-2+3 = 2$
$y-9 = -10 \qquad\qquad\quad x+1 = 2$
$y = -1 \qquad\qquad\qquad\quad x = 1$

The solution is $(1, -1, 3)$.

**28.** $\begin{cases} x+ y+ z = 9 \\ 2x-2y+3z = 2 \\ -3x+ y- z = 1 \end{cases}$

$$\begin{bmatrix} 1 & 1 & 1 & | & 9 \\ 2 & -2 & 3 & | & 2 \\ -3 & 1 & -1 & | & 1 \end{bmatrix}$$

Multiply R1 by $-2$ and add to R2.
Multiply R1 by 3 and add to R3.

$$\begin{bmatrix} 1 & 1 & 1 & | & 9 \\ 0 & -4 & 1 & | & -16 \\ 0 & 4 & 2 & | & 28 \end{bmatrix}$$

Divide R2 by $-4$.

$$\begin{bmatrix} 1 & 1 & 1 & | & 9 \\ 0 & 1 & -\frac{1}{4} & | & 4 \\ 0 & 4 & 2 & | & 28 \end{bmatrix}$$

Multiply R2 by $-4$ and add to R3.

$$\begin{bmatrix} 1 & 1 & 1 & | & 9 \\ 0 & 1 & -\frac{1}{4} & | & 4 \\ 0 & 0 & 3 & | & 12 \end{bmatrix}$$

Divide R3 by 3.

$$\begin{bmatrix} 1 & 1 & 1 & | & 9 \\ 0 & 1 & -\frac{1}{4} & | & 4 \\ 0 & 0 & 1 & | & 4 \end{bmatrix}$$

This corresponds to $\begin{cases} x+y+ z = 9 \\ \quad y-\frac{1}{4}z = 4 \\ \qquad\quad z = 4 \end{cases}$

$y-\frac{1}{4}(4) = 4$
$\qquad\qquad\qquad x+5+4 = 9$
$y-1 = 4$ and so $\quad x+9 = 9$
$\quad y = 5 \qquad\qquad\qquad x = 0$

The solution is $(0, 5, 4)$.

**29. a.** $7^0 = 1$

**b.** $-7^0 = -1 \cdot 7^0 = -1 \cdot 1 = -1$

**c.** $(2x+5)^0 = 1$

**d.** $2x^0 = 2 \cdot x^0 = 2 \cdot 1 = 2$

**30. a.** $2^{-2} + 3^{-1} = \dfrac{1}{2^2} + \dfrac{1}{3}$
$= \dfrac{1}{4} + \dfrac{1}{3}$
$= \dfrac{3}{12} + \dfrac{4}{12}$
$= \dfrac{7}{12}$

**b.** $-6a^0 = -6 \cdot a^0 = -6 \cdot 1 = -6$

**c.** $\dfrac{x^{-5}}{x^{-2}} = x^{-5-(-2)} = x^{-3} = \dfrac{1}{x^3}$

**31. a.** $x^{-b}(2x^b)^2 = \dfrac{2^2(x^b)^2}{x^b}$
$= \dfrac{4x^{2b}}{x^b}$
$= 4x^{2b-b}$
$= 4x^b$

**b.** $\dfrac{(y^{3a})^2}{y^{a-6}} = \dfrac{y^{6a}}{y^{a-6}} = y^{6a-(a-6)} = y^{5a+6}$

**32. a.** $3x^{4a}(4x^{-a})^2 = 3x^{4a} \cdot 16x^{-2a}$
$= 48x^{4a+(-2a)}$
$= 48x^{2a}$

**b.** $\dfrac{(y^{4b})^3}{y^{2b-3}} = \dfrac{y^{12b}}{y^{2b-3}}$

$= y^{12b-(2b-3)}$

$= y^{12b-2b+3}$

$= y^{10b+3}$

**33. a.** $3x^2$ has degree = 2.

**b.** $-2^3 x^5 = -8x^5$ has degree = 5.

**c.** $y$ has degree = 1.

**d.** $12x^2 yz^3$ has degree = 2 + 1 + 3 = 6.

**e.** 5 has degree = 0.

**34.** $(2x^2 + 8x - 3) - (2x - 7)$

$= 2x^2 + 8x - 3 - 2x + 7$

$= 2x^2 + 6x + 4$

**35.** $[3 + (2a + b)]^2$

$= 3^2 + 2(3)(2a + b) + (2a + b)^2$

$= 9 + 6(2a + b) + (4a^2 + 2(2a)b + b^2)$

$= 9 + 12a + 6b + 4a^2 + 4ab + b^2$

**36.** $[4 + (3x - y)]^2$

$= 4^2 + 2(4)(3x - y) + (3x - y)^2$

$= 16 + 8(3x - y) + (9x^2 - 2(3x)y + y^2)$

$= 16 + 24x - 8y + 9x^2 - 6xy + y^2$

**37.** $ab - 6a + 2b - 12 = a(b - 6) + 2(b - 6)$

$= (b - 6)(a + 2)$

**38.** $xy + 2x - 5y - 10 = x(y + 2) - 5(y + 2)$

$= (y + 2)(x - 5)$

**39.** $2n^2 - 38n + 80 = 2(n^2 - 19n + 40)$

**40.** $6x^2 - x - 35 = (2x - 5)(3x + 7)$

**41.** $x^2 + 4x + 4 - y^2 = (x^2 + 4x + 4) - y^2$

$= (x + 2)^2 - y^2$

$= [(x + 2) + y][(x + 2) - y]$

$= (x + 2 + y)(x + 2 - y)$

**42.** $4x^2 - 4x + 1 - 9y^2$

$= (4x^2 - 4x + 1) - 9y^2$

$= (2x - 1)^2 - (3y)^2$

$= [(2x - 1) + 3y][(2x - 1) - 3y]$

$= (2x - 1 + 3y)(2x - 1 - 3y)$

**43.** $(x + 2)(x - 6) = 0$

$x + 2 = 0$ or $x - 6 = 0$

$x = -2$ or $x = 6$

The solutions are –2 and 6.

**44.** $2x(3x + 1)(x - 3) = 0$

$x = 0$ or $3x + 1 = 0$ or $x - 3 = 0$

$3x = -1$ or $x = 3$

$x = -\dfrac{1}{3}$

The solutions are $-\dfrac{1}{3}, 0, 3$.

**45. a.** $\dfrac{2x^2}{10x^3 - 2x^2} = \dfrac{2x^2}{2x^2(5x - 1)} = \dfrac{1}{5x - 1}$

**b.** $\dfrac{9x^2 + 13x + 4}{8x^2 + x - 7} = \dfrac{(9x + 4)(x + 1)}{(8x - 7)(x + 1)} = \dfrac{9x + 4}{8x - 7}$

**46. a.** Domain: $(-\infty, \infty)$; Range: $[-4, \infty)$

**b.** $x$-intercepts: (–2, 0), (2, 0)
$y$-intercept: (0, –4)

**c.** There is no such point.

**d.** The point with the least $y$-value is (0, –4).

**e.** –2, 2

**f.** $x$-values between $x = -2$ and $x = 2$

**g.** The solutions are –2 and 2.

**47.** $\dfrac{5k}{k^2-4} - \dfrac{2}{k^2+k-2}$

$= \dfrac{5k}{(k+2)(k-2)} - \dfrac{2}{(k+2)(k-1)}$

$= \dfrac{5k(k-1)-2(k-2)}{(k+2)(k-2)(k-1)}$

$= \dfrac{5k^2-5k-2k+4}{(k+2)(k-2)(k-1)}$

$= \dfrac{5k^2-7k+4}{(k+2)(k-2)(k-1)}$

**48.** $\dfrac{5a}{a^2-4} - \dfrac{3}{2-a} = \dfrac{5a}{(a+2)(a-2)} + \dfrac{3}{a-2}$

$= \dfrac{5a+3(a+2)}{(a+2)(a-2)}$

$= \dfrac{5a+3a+6}{(a+2)(a-2)}$

$= \dfrac{8a+6}{(a+2)(a-2)}$

**49.** $\dfrac{3}{x} - \dfrac{x+21}{3x} = \dfrac{5}{3}$

$3x\left(\dfrac{3}{x} - \dfrac{x+21}{3x}\right) = 3x\left(\dfrac{5}{3}\right)$

$9-(x+21) = 5x$

$9-x-21 = 5x$

$-x-12 = 5x$

$-12 = 6x$

$-2 = x$

The solution is $-2$.

**50.** $\dfrac{3x-4}{2x} = -\dfrac{8}{x}$

$x(3x-4) = -8(2x)$

$3x^2-4x = -16x$

$3x^2+12x = 0$

$3x(x+4) = 0$

$3x = 0 \text{ or } x+4 = 0$

$x = 0 \text{ or } \quad x = -4$

Discard the answer 0 as extraneous. The solution is $-4$.

# Chapter 7

1. a. $\sqrt{49} = 7$ because $7^2 = 49$ and 7 is not negative.

   b. $\sqrt{\dfrac{0}{1}} = \sqrt{0} = 0$ because $0^2 = 0$ and 0 is not negative.

   c. $\sqrt{\dfrac{16}{81}} = \dfrac{4}{9}$ because $\left(\dfrac{4}{9}\right)^2 = \dfrac{16}{81}$ and $\dfrac{4}{9}$ is not negative.

   d. $\sqrt{0.64} = 0.8$ because $(0.8)^2 = 0.64$.

   e. $\sqrt{z^8} = z^4$ because $(z^4)^2 = z^8$.

   f. $\sqrt{16b^4} = 4b^2$ because $(4b^2)^2 = 16b^4$.

   g. $-\sqrt{36} = -6$. The negative in front of the radical indicates the negative square root of 36.

   h. $\sqrt{-36}$ is not a real number.

2. $\sqrt{45} \approx 6.708$
   Since $36 < 45 < 49$, then $\sqrt{36} < \sqrt{45} < \sqrt{49}$, or $6 < \sqrt{45} < 7$. The approximation is between 6 and 7 and thus is reasonable.

3. a. $\sqrt[3]{-1} = -1$ because $(-1)^3 = -1$.

   b. $\sqrt[3]{27} = 3$ because $3^3 = 27$.

   c. $\sqrt[3]{\dfrac{27}{64}} = \dfrac{3}{4}$ because $\left(\dfrac{3}{4}\right)^3 = \dfrac{27}{64}$.

   d. $\sqrt[3]{x^{12}} = x^4$ because $(x^4)^3 = x^{12}$.

   e. $\sqrt[3]{-8x^3} = -2x$ because $(-2x)^3 = -8x^3$.

4. a. $\sqrt[4]{10,000} = 10$ because $10^4 = 10,000$ and 10 is positive.

   b. $\sqrt[5]{-1} = -1$ because $(-1)^5 = -1$.

   c. $-\sqrt{81} = -9$ because $-9$ is the opposite of $\sqrt{81}$.

   d. $\sqrt[4]{-625}$ is not a real number. There is no real number that, when raised to the fourth power, is $-625$.

   e. $\sqrt[3]{27x^9} = 3x^3$ because $(3x^3)^3 = 27x^9$.

5. a. $\sqrt{(-4)^2} = |-4| = 4$

   b. $\sqrt{x^{14}} = |x^7|$

   c. $\sqrt[4]{(x+7)^4} = |x+7|$

   d. $\sqrt[3]{(-7)^3} = -7$

   e. $\sqrt[5]{(3x-5)^5} = 3x-5$

   f. $\sqrt{49x^2} = 7|x|$

   g. $\sqrt{x^2+4x+4} = \sqrt{(x+2)^2} = |x+2|$

6. $f(x) = \sqrt{x+5}$, $g(x) = \sqrt[3]{x-3}$

   a. $f(11) = \sqrt{11+5} = \sqrt{16} = 4$

   b. $f(-1) = \sqrt{-1+5} = \sqrt{4} = 2$

   c. $g(11) = \sqrt[3]{11-3} = \sqrt[3]{8} = 2$

   d. $g(-5) = \sqrt[3]{-5-3} = \sqrt[3]{-8} = -2$

7. $h(x) = \sqrt{x+2}$
   Find the domain.
   $x+2 \geq 0$
   $\quad x \geq -2$
   The domain of $h(x)$ is $\{x \mid x \geq -2\}$.

| $x$ | $h(x) = \sqrt{x+2}$ |
|-----|---------------------|
| $-2$ | 0 |
| $-1$ | 1 |
| 1 | $\sqrt{1+2} = \sqrt{3} \approx 1.7$ |
| 2 | 2 |
| 7 | 3 |

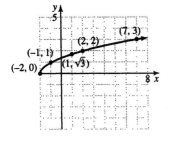

**8.** $f(x) = \sqrt[3]{x} - 4$

The domain is the set of all real numbers.

| $x$ | $f(x) = \sqrt[3]{x} - 4$ |
|-----|--------------------------|
| 0 | $-4$ |
| 1 | $-3$ |
| $-1$ | $-5$ |
| 6 | $\sqrt[3]{6} - 4 \approx 1.8 - 4 = -2.2$ |
| $-6$ | $\sqrt[3]{-6} - 4 \approx -1.8 - 4 = -5.8$ |
| 8 | $-2$ |
| $-8$ | $-6$ |

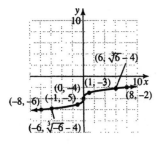

**Vocabulary and Readiness Check**

1. In the expression $\sqrt[n]{a}$, the $n$ is called the <u>index</u>, the $\sqrt{\ }$ is called the <u>radical sign</u>, and $a$ is called the <u>radicand</u>.

2. If $\sqrt{a}$ is the positive square root of $a$, $a \neq 0$, then $-\sqrt{a}$ is the negative square root of $a$.

3. The square root of a negative number <u>is not</u> a real number.

4. Numbers such as 1, 4, 9, and 25 are called perfect <u>squares</u> where numbers such as 1, 8, 27, and 125 are called perfect <u>cubes</u>.

5. The domain of the function $f(x) = \sqrt{x}$ is $[0, \infty)$.

6. The domain of the function $f(x) = \sqrt[3]{x}$ is <u>$(-\infty, \infty)$</u>.

7. If $f(16) = 4$, the corresponding ordered pair is <u>(16, 4)</u>.

8. If $g(-8) = -2$, the corresponding ordered pair is <u>$(-8, -2)$</u>.

9. The radical that is not a real number is $\sqrt{-10}$, choice d.

10. The radicals that simplify to 3 are $\sqrt{9}$ and $\sqrt[3]{27}$, choices a and c.

11. The radical that simplifies to $-3$ is $\sqrt[3]{-27}$, choice d.

12. The radical that does not simplify to a whole number is $\sqrt{8}$, choice c.

**Exercise Set 7.1**

1. $\sqrt{100} = 10$ because $10^2 = 100$.

3. $\sqrt{\dfrac{1}{4}} = \dfrac{1}{2}$ because $\left(\dfrac{1}{2}\right)^2 = \dfrac{1}{4}$.

5. $\sqrt{0.0001} = 0.01$ because $(0.01)^2 = 0.0001$.

7. $-\sqrt{36} = -1 \cdot \sqrt{36} = -1 \cdot 6 = -6$

9. $\sqrt{x^{10}} = x^5$ because $(x^5)^2 = x^{10}$.

11. $\sqrt{16y^6} = 4y^3$ because $(4y^3)^2 = 16y^6$.

**13.** $\sqrt{7} \approx 2.646$

Since $4 < 7 < 9$, then $\sqrt{4} < \sqrt{7} < \sqrt{9}$, or

$2 < \sqrt{7} < 3$. The approximation is between 2 and 3 and thus is reasonable.

**15.** $\sqrt{38} \approx 6.164$

Since $36 < 38 < 49$, then $\sqrt{36} < \sqrt{38} < \sqrt{49}$, or

$6 < \sqrt{38} < 7$. The approximation is between 6 and 7 and thus is reasonable.

**17.** $\sqrt{200} \approx 14.142$

Since $196 < 200 < 225$, then

$\sqrt{196} < \sqrt{200} < \sqrt{225}$, or $14 < \sqrt{200} < 15$. The approximation is between 14 and 15 and thus is reasonable.

**19.** $\sqrt[3]{64} = 4$ because $4^3 = 64$.

**21.** $\sqrt[3]{\dfrac{1}{8}} = \dfrac{1}{2}$ because $\left(\dfrac{1}{2}\right)^3 = \dfrac{1}{8}$.

**23.** $\sqrt[3]{-1} = -1$ because $(-1)^3 = -1$.

**25.** $\sqrt[3]{x^{12}} = x^4$ because $(x^4)^3 = x^{12}$.

**27.** $\sqrt[3]{-27x^9} = -3x^3$ because $(-3x^3)^3 = -27x^9$.

**29.** $-\sqrt[4]{16} = -2$ because $2^4 = 16$.

**31.** $\sqrt[4]{-16}$ is not a real number. There is no real number that, when raised to the fourth power, is $-16$.

**33.** $\sqrt[5]{-32} = -2$ because $(-2)^5 = -32$.

**35.** $\sqrt[5]{x^{20}} = x^4$ because $(x^4)^5 = x^{20}$.

**37.** $\sqrt[6]{64x^{12}} = 2x^2$ because $(2x^2)^6 = 64x^{12}$.

**39.** $\sqrt{81x^4} = 9x^2$ because $(9x^2)^2 = 81x^4$.

**41.** $\sqrt[4]{256x^8} = 4x^2$ because $(4x^2)^4 = 256x^8$.

**43.** $\sqrt{(-8)^2} = |-8| = 8$

**45.** $\sqrt[3]{(-8)^3} = -8$

**47.** $\sqrt{4x^2} = 2|x|$

**49.** $\sqrt[3]{x^3} = x$

**51.** $\sqrt{(x-5)^2} = |x-5|$

**53.** $\sqrt{x^2 + 4x + 4} = \sqrt{(x+2)^2} = |x+2|$

**55.** $-\sqrt{121} = -11$

**57.** $\sqrt[3]{8x^3} = 2x$

**59.** $\sqrt{y^{12}} = y^6$

**61.** $\sqrt{25a^2b^{20}} = 5ab^{10}$

**63.** $\sqrt[3]{-27x^{12}y^9} = -3x^4y^3$

**65.** $\sqrt[4]{a^{16}b^4} = a^4b$

**67.** $\sqrt[3]{-32x^{10}y^5} = -2x^2y$

**69.** $\sqrt{\dfrac{25}{49}} = \dfrac{5}{7}$

**71.** $\sqrt{\dfrac{x^2}{4y^2}} = \dfrac{x}{2y}$

**73.** $-\sqrt[3]{\dfrac{z^{21}}{27x^3}} = -\dfrac{z^7}{3x}$

**75.** $\sqrt[4]{\dfrac{x^4}{16}} = \dfrac{x}{2}$

**77.** $f(x) = \sqrt{2x+3}$

$f(0) = \sqrt{2(0)+3} = \sqrt{3}$

**79.** $g(x) = \sqrt[3]{x-8}$

$g(7) = \sqrt[3]{7-8} = \sqrt[3]{-1} = -1$

**81.** $g(x) = \sqrt[3]{x-8}$

$g(-19) = \sqrt[3]{-19-8} = \sqrt[3]{-27} = -3$

**83.** $f(x) = \sqrt{2x+3}$

$f(2) = \sqrt{2(2)+3} = \sqrt{7}$

**85.** $f(x) = \sqrt{x} + 2$

$x \geq 0$

Domain: $[0, \infty)$

| $x$ | $f(x) = \sqrt{x} + 2$ |
|-----|------------------------|
| 0   | $\sqrt{0} + 2 = 2$     |
| 1   | $\sqrt{1} + 2 = 3$     |
| 3   | $\sqrt{3} + 2 \approx 3.7$ |
| 4   | $\sqrt{4} + 2 = 4$     |

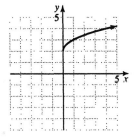

**87.** $f(x) = \sqrt{x-3}$

$x - 3 \geq 0$

$x \geq 3$

Domain: $[3, \infty)$

| $x$ | $f(x) = \sqrt{x-3}$ |
|-----|----------------------|
| 3   | $\sqrt{3-3} = \sqrt{0} = 0$ |
| 4   | $\sqrt{4-3} = \sqrt{1} = 1$ |
| 7   | $\sqrt{7-3} = \sqrt{4} = 2$ |
| 12  | $\sqrt{12-3} = \sqrt{9} = 3$ |

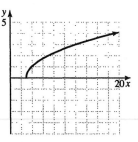

**89.** $f(x) = \sqrt[3]{x} + 1$

Domain: $(-\infty, \infty)$

| $x$ | $f(x) = \sqrt[3]{x} + 1$ |
|-----|---------------------------|
| $-4$ | $\sqrt[3]{-4} + 1 \approx -0.6$ |
| $-1$ | $\sqrt[3]{-1} + 1 = 0$ |
| 0   | $\sqrt[3]{0} + 1 = 1$ |
| 1   | $\sqrt[3]{1} + 1 = 2$ |
| 4   | $\sqrt[3]{4} + 1 \approx 2.6$ |

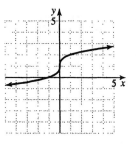

**91.** $g(x) = \sqrt[3]{x-1}$

Domain: $(-\infty, \infty)$

| $x$ | $g(x) = \sqrt[3]{x-1}$ |
|-----|-------------------------|
| 1   | $\sqrt[3]{1-1} = \sqrt[3]{0} = 0$ |
| 2   | $\sqrt[3]{2-1} = \sqrt[3]{1} = 1$ |
| 0   | $\sqrt[3]{0-1} = \sqrt[3]{-1} = -1$ |
| 9   | $\sqrt[3]{9-1} = \sqrt[3]{8} = 2$ |
| $-7$ | $\sqrt[3]{-7-1} = \sqrt[3]{-8} = -2$ |

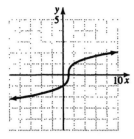

**93.** $(-2x^3y^2)^5 = (-2)^5 x^{3\cdot5} y^{2\cdot5} = -32x^{15}y^{10}$

**95.** $(-3x^2y^3z^5)(20x^5y^7) = -3(20)x^{2+5}y^{3+7}z^5$
$$= -60x^7y^{10}z^5$$

**97.** $\dfrac{7x^{-1}y}{14(x^5y^2)^{-2}} = \dfrac{7x^{-1}y}{14x^{-10}y^{-4}} = \dfrac{x^9y^5}{2}$

**99.** $\sqrt{-17}$ is not a real number.

**101.** $\sqrt[10]{-17}$ is not a real number.

**103.** Answers may vary

**105.** $144 < 160 < 169$ so $\sqrt{144} < \sqrt{160} < \sqrt{169}$, or $12 < \sqrt{160} < 13$. Thus $\sqrt{160}$ is between 12 and 13. Therefore, the answer is **b**.

**107.** $\sqrt{30} \approx 5, \sqrt{10} \approx 3,$ and $\sqrt{90} \approx 10$ so
$P = \sqrt{30} + \sqrt{10} + \sqrt{90} \approx 5 + 3 + 10 = 18.$
Therefore, the answer is **b**.

**109.** $B = \sqrt{\dfrac{hw}{3131}} = \sqrt{\dfrac{66\cdot135}{3131}}$
$$= \sqrt{\dfrac{8910}{3131}}$$
$$\approx 1.69 \text{ sq meters}$$

**111.** Answers may vary

**113.** $f(x) = \sqrt{x} + 2$

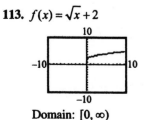

Domain: $[0, \infty)$

**115.** $f(x) = \sqrt[3]{x} + 1$

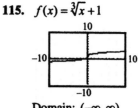

Domain: $(-\infty, \infty)$

## Section 7.2

### Practice Exercises

**1. a.** $36^{1/2} = \sqrt{36} = 6$

   **b.** $1000^{1/3} = \sqrt[3]{1000} = 10$

   **c.** $x^{1/5} = \sqrt[5]{x}$

   **d.** $1^{1/4} = \sqrt[4]{1} = 1$

   **e.** $-64^{1/2} = -\sqrt{64} = -8$

   **f.** $(125x^9)^{1/3} = \sqrt[3]{125x^9} = 5x^3$

   **g.** $(3x)^{1/4} = \sqrt[4]{3x}$

**2. a.** $16^{3/2} = \left(\sqrt{16}\right)^3 = 4^3 = 64$

   **b.** $-1^{3/5} = -\left(\sqrt[5]{1}\right)^3 = -(1)^3 = -1$

   **c.** $-(81)^{3/4} = -\left(\sqrt[4]{81}\right)^3 = -(3)^3 = -27$

   **d.** $\left(\dfrac{1}{25}\right)^{3/2} = \left(\sqrt{\dfrac{1}{25}}\right)^3 = \left(\dfrac{1}{5}\right)^3 = \dfrac{1}{125}$

   **e.** $(3x+2)^{5/9} = \sqrt[9]{(3x+2)^5}$

**3. a.** $9^{-3/2} = \dfrac{1}{9^{3/2}} = \dfrac{1}{\left(\sqrt{9}\right)^3} = \dfrac{1}{3^3} = \dfrac{1}{27}$

   **b.** $(-64)^{-2/3} = \dfrac{1}{(-64)^{2/3}} = \dfrac{1}{\left(\sqrt[3]{-64}\right)^2} = \dfrac{1}{(-4)^2} = \dfrac{1}{16}$

**4. a.** $y^{2/3} \cdot y^{8/3} = y^{(2/3+8/3)} = y^{10/3}$

**b.** $x^{3/5} \cdot x^{1/4} = x^{3/5+1/4} = x^{12/20+5/20} = x^{17/20}$

**c.** $\dfrac{9^{2/7}}{9^{9/7}} = 9^{2/7-9/7} = 9^{-7/7} = 9^{-1} = \dfrac{1}{9}$

**d.** $b^{4/9} \cdot b^{-2/9} = b^{4/9+(-2/9)} = b^{2/9}$

**e.** $\dfrac{\left(3x^{1/4}y^{-2/3}\right)^4}{x^4 y} = \dfrac{3^4 (x^{1/4})^4 (y^{-2/3})^4}{x^4 y}$

$= \dfrac{81xy^{-8/3}}{x^4 y}$

$= 81x^{1-4}y^{-8/3-3/3}$

$= 81x^{-3}y^{-11/3}$

$= \dfrac{81}{x^3 y^{11/3}}$

**5. a.** $x^{3/5}(x^{1/3} - x^2) = x^{3/5}x^{1/3} - x^{3/5}x^2$

$= x^{(3/5+1/3)} - x^{(3/5+2)}$

$= x^{(9/15+5/15)} - x^{(3/5+10/5)}$

$= x^{14/15} - x^{13/5}$

**b.** $(x^{1/2}+6)(x^{1/2}-2)$

$= x^{2/2} - 2x^{1/2} + 6x^{1/2} - 12$

$= x + 4x^{1/2} - 12$

**6.** $2x^{-1/5} - 7x^{4/5} = (x^{-1/5})(2) - (x^{-1/5})(7x^{5/5})$

$= x^{-1/5}(2-7x)$

**7. a.** $\sqrt[9]{x^3} = x^{3/9} = x^{1/3} = \sqrt[3]{x}$

**b.** $\sqrt[4]{36} = 36^{1/4} = (6^2)^{1/4} = 6^{2/4} = 6^{1/2} = \sqrt{6}$

**c.** $\sqrt[8]{a^4 b^2} = (a^4 b^2)^{1/8}$

$= a^{4/8}b^{2/8}$

$= a^{2/4}b^{1/4}$

$= (a^2 b)^{1/4}$

$= \sqrt[4]{a^2 b}$

**8. a.** $\sqrt[3]{x} \cdot \sqrt[4]{x} = x^{1/3} \cdot x^{1/4}$

$= x^{1/3+1/4}$

$= x^{4/12+3/12}$

$= x^{7/12}$

$= \sqrt[12]{x^7}$

**b.** $\dfrac{\sqrt[3]{y}}{\sqrt[5]{y}} = \dfrac{y^{1/3}}{y^{1/5}}$

$= y^{1/3-1/5}$

$= y^{5/15-3/15}$

$= y^{2/15}$

$= \sqrt[15]{y^2}$

**c.** $\sqrt[3]{5} \cdot \sqrt{3} = 5^{1/3} \cdot 3^{1/2}$

$= 5^{2/6} \cdot 3^{3/6}$

$= (5^2 \cdot 3^3)^{1/6}$

$= \sqrt[6]{5^2 \cdot 3^3}$

$= \sqrt[6]{675}$

**Vocabulary and Readiness Check**

**1.** It is true that $9^{-1/2}$ is a positive number.

**2.** It is false that $9^{-1/2}$ is a whole number.

**3.** It is true that $\dfrac{1}{a^{-m/n}} = a^{m/n}$ (where $a^{m/n}$ is a nonzero real number).

**4.** To simplify $x^{2/3} \cdot x^{1/5}$, <u>add</u> the exponents.

**5.** To simplify $(x^{2/3})^{1/5}$, <u>multiply</u> the exponents.

**6.** To simplify $\dfrac{x^{2/3}}{x^{1/5}}$, <u>subtract</u> the exponents.

**7.** $4^{1/2} = 2$, A

**8.** $-4^{1/2} = -2$, B

**9.** $(-4)^{1/2}$ is not a real number, C

**10.** $8^{1/3} = 2$, A

**11.** $-8^{1/3} = -2$, B

**12.** $(-8)^{1/3} = -2$ , **B**

**Exercise Set 7.2**

**1.** $49^{1/2} = \sqrt{49} = 7$

**3.** $27^{1/3} = \sqrt[3]{27} = 3$

**5.** $\left(\dfrac{1}{16}\right)^{1/4} = \sqrt[4]{\dfrac{1}{16}} = \dfrac{1}{2}$

**7.** $169^{1/2} = \sqrt{169} = 13$

**9.** $2m^{1/3} = 2\sqrt[3]{m}$

**11.** $(9x^4)^{1/2} = \sqrt{9x^4} = 3x^2$

**13.** $(-27)^{1/3} = \sqrt[3]{-27} = -3$

**15.** $-16^{1/4} = -\sqrt[4]{16} = -2$

**17.** $16^{3/4} = \left(\sqrt[4]{16}\right)^3 = 2^3 = 8$

**19.** $(-64)^{2/3} = \left(\sqrt[3]{-64}\right)^2 = (-4)^2 = 16$

**21.** $(-16)^{3/4} = \left(\sqrt[4]{-16}\right)^3$ is not a real number.

**23.** $(2x)^{3/5} = \sqrt[5]{(2x)^3}$ or $\left(\sqrt[5]{2x}\right)^3$

**25.** $(7x+2)^{2/3} = \sqrt[3]{(7x+2)^2}$ or $\left(\sqrt[3]{7x+2}\right)^2$

**27.** $\left(\dfrac{16}{9}\right)^{3/2} = \left(\sqrt{\dfrac{16}{9}}\right)^3 = \left(\dfrac{4}{3}\right)^3 = \dfrac{64}{27}$

**29.** $8^{-4/3} = \dfrac{1}{8^{4/3}} = \dfrac{1}{\left(\sqrt[3]{8}\right)^4} = \dfrac{1}{2^4} = \dfrac{1}{16}$

**31.** $(-64)^{-2/3} = \dfrac{1}{(-64)^{2/3}} = \dfrac{1}{\left(\sqrt[3]{-64}\right)^2} = \dfrac{1}{(-4)^2} = \dfrac{1}{16}$

**33.** $(-4)^{-3/2} = \dfrac{1}{(-4)^{3/2}} = \dfrac{1}{\left(\sqrt{-4}\right)^3}$ is not a real number.

**35.** $x^{-1/4} = \dfrac{1}{x^{1/4}}$

**37.** $\dfrac{1}{a^{-2/3}} = a^{2/3}$

**39.** $\dfrac{5}{7x^{-3/4}} = \dfrac{5x^{3/4}}{7}$

**41.** $a^{2/3}a^{5/3} = a^{2/3+5/3} = a^{7/3}$

**43.** $x^{-2/5} \cdot x^{7/5} = x^{-\frac{2}{5}+\frac{7}{5}} = x^{5/5} = x$

**45.** $3^{1/4} \cdot 3^{3/8} = 3^{\frac{1}{4}+\frac{3}{8}} = 3^{\frac{2}{8}+\frac{3}{8}} = 3^{5/8}$

**47.** $\dfrac{y^{1/3}}{y^{1/6}} = y^{\frac{1}{3}-\frac{1}{6}} = y^{\frac{2}{6}-\frac{1}{6}} = y^{1/6}$

**49.** $(4u^2)^{3/2} = 4^{3/2}u^{2(3/2)}$
$\phantom{(4u^2)^{3/2}} = \left(\sqrt{4}\right)^3 u^3$
$\phantom{(4u^2)^{3/2}} = 2^3 u^3$
$\phantom{(4u^2)^{3/2}} = 8u^3$

**51.** $\dfrac{b^{1/2}b^{3/4}}{-b^{1/4}} = -b^{\frac{1}{2}+\frac{3}{4}-\frac{1}{4}} = -b^{\frac{2}{4}+\frac{3}{4}-\frac{1}{4}} = -b^1 = -b$

**53.** $\dfrac{(x^3)^{1/2}}{x^{7/2}} = \dfrac{x^{3/2}}{x^{7/2}}$
$\phantom{\dfrac{(x^3)^{1/2}}{x^{7/2}}} = x^{3/2-7/2}$
$\phantom{\dfrac{(x^3)^{1/2}}{x^{7/2}}} = x^{-2}$
$\phantom{\dfrac{(x^3)^{1/2}}{x^{7/2}}} = \dfrac{1}{x^2}$

**55.** $\dfrac{(3x^{1/4})^3}{x^{1/12}} = \dfrac{3^3 x^{3/4}}{x^{1/12}}$

$= 27x^{\frac{3}{4}-\frac{1}{12}}$

$= 27x^{\frac{9}{12}-\frac{1}{12}}$

$= 27x^{8/12}$

$= 27x^{2/3}$

**57.** $\dfrac{(y^3 z)^{1/6}}{y^{-1/2} z^{1/3}} = \dfrac{y^{3/6} z^{1/6}}{y^{-1/2} z^{1/3}}$

$= y^{3/6-(-1/2)} z^{1/6-1/3}$

$= y^{1/2+1/2} z^{1/6-2/6}$

$= y^1 z^{-1/6}$

$= \dfrac{y}{z^{1/6}}$

**59.** $\dfrac{(x^3 y^2)^{1/4}}{(x^{-5} y^{-1})^{-1/2}} = \dfrac{x^{3/4} y^{2/4}}{x^{5/2} y^{1/2}}$

$= x^{\frac{3}{4}-\frac{5}{2}} y^{\frac{2}{4}-\frac{1}{2}}$

$= x^{\frac{3}{4}-\frac{10}{4}} y^{\frac{1}{2}-\frac{1}{2}}$

$= x^{-7/4}$

$= \dfrac{1}{x^{7/4}}$

**61.** $y^{1/2}(y^{1/2} - y^{2/3}) = y^{1/2} y^{1/2} - y^{1/2} y^{2/3}$

$= y^{1/2+1/2} - y^{1/2+2/3}$

$= y^1 - y^{7/6}$

$= y - y^{7/6}$

**63.** $x^{2/3}(x - 2) = x \cdot x^{2/3} - 2x^{2/3}$

$= x^{1+2/3} - 2x^{2/3}$

$= x^{5/3} - 2x^{2/3}$

**65.** $(2x^{1/3} + 3)(2x^{1/3} - 3) = (2x^{1/3})^2 - 3^2$

$= 2^2(x^{1/3})^2 - 9$

$= 4x^{2/3} - 9$

**67.** $x^{8/3} + x^{10/3} = x^{8/3}(1) + x^{8/3}(x^{2/3})$

$= x^{8/3}(1 + x^{2/3})$

**69.** $x^{2/5} - 3x^{1/5} = x^{1/5}(x^{1/5}) - x^{1/5}(3)$

$= x^{1/5}(x^{1/5} - 3)$

**71.** $5x^{-1/3} + x^{2/3} = x^{-1/3}(5) + x^{-1/3}(x^{3/3})$

$= x^{-1/3}(5 + x)$

**73.** $\sqrt[6]{x^3} = x^{3/6} = x^{1/2} = \sqrt{x}$

**75.** $\sqrt[6]{4} = 4^{1/6} = (2^2)^{1/6} = 2^{1/3} = \sqrt[3]{2}$

**77.** $\sqrt[4]{16x^2} = (16x^2)^{1/4}$

$= 16^{1/4} x^{2/4} = 2x^{1/2} = 2\sqrt{x}$

**79.** $\sqrt[8]{x^4 y^4} = (x^4 y^4)^{1/8}$

$= x^{4/8} y^{4/8}$

$= x^{1/2} y^{1/2}$

$= (xy)^{1/2}$

$= \sqrt{xy}$

**81.** $\sqrt[12]{a^8 b^4} = a^{8/12} b^{4/12}$

$= a^{2/3} b^{1/3}$

$= (a^2 b)^{1/3}$

$= \sqrt[3]{a^2 b}$

**83.** $\sqrt[4]{(x+3)^2} = (x+3)^{2/4} = (x+3)^{1/2} = \sqrt{x+3}$

**85.** $\sqrt[3]{y} \cdot \sqrt[5]{y^2} = y^{1/3} \cdot y^{2/5}$

$= y^{\frac{1}{3}+\frac{2}{5}}$

$= y^{\frac{5}{15}+\frac{6}{15}}$

$= y^{11/15}$

$= \sqrt[15]{y^{11}}$

**87.** $\dfrac{\sqrt[3]{b^2}}{\sqrt[4]{b}} = \dfrac{b^{2/3}}{b^{1/4}} = b^{\frac{2}{3}-\frac{1}{4}} = b^{\frac{8}{12}-\frac{3}{12}} = b^{5/12} = \sqrt[12]{b^5}$

**89.** $\sqrt[3]{x} \cdot \sqrt[4]{x} \cdot \sqrt[8]{x^3} = x^{1/3} \cdot x^{1/4} \cdot x^{3/8}$

$= x^{8/24} \cdot x^{6/24} \cdot x^{9/24}$

$= x^{23/24}$

$= \sqrt[24]{x^{23}}$

**91.** $\dfrac{\sqrt[3]{a^2}}{\sqrt[6]{a}} = \dfrac{a^{2/3}}{a^{1/6}}$

$= a^{\frac{2}{3}-\frac{1}{6}} = a^{\frac{4}{6}-\frac{1}{6}} = a^{3/6} = a^{1/2} = \sqrt{a}$

**93.** $\sqrt{3}\cdot\sqrt[3]{4}=3^{1/2}\cdot4^{1/3}$
$\qquad =3^{3/6}\cdot4^{2/6}$
$\qquad =\left(3^3\cdot4^2\right)^{1/6}$
$\qquad =(27\cdot16)^{1/6}$
$\qquad =(432)^{1/6}$
$\qquad =\sqrt[6]{432}$

**95.** $\sqrt[5]{7}\cdot\sqrt[3]{y}=7^{1/5}\cdot y^{1/3}$
$\qquad =7^{3/15}\cdot y^{5/15}$
$\qquad =\left(7^3\cdot y^5\right)^{1/15}$
$\qquad =\left(343y^5\right)^{1/15}$
$\qquad =\sqrt[15]{343y^5}$

**97.** $\sqrt{5r}\cdot\sqrt[3]{s}=(5r)^{1/2}\cdot s^{1/3}$
$\qquad =(5r)^{3/6}\cdot s^{2/6}$
$\qquad =\left[(5r)^3\cdot s^2\right]^{1/6}$
$\qquad =\left(125r^3s^2\right)^{1/6}$
$\qquad =\sqrt[6]{125r^3s^2}$

**99.** $75 = 25\cdot3$ where 25 is a perfect square.

**101.** $48 = 4\cdot12$ or $16\cdot3$ where both 4 and 16 are perfect squares.

**103.** $16 = 8\cdot2$ where 8 is a perfect cube.

**105.** $54 = 27\cdot2$ where 27 is a perfect cube.

**107.** $B(w)=70w^{3/4}$
$\qquad B(60)=70(60)^{3/4}$
$\qquad\qquad \approx1509$ calories

**109.** $f(x)=33.3x^{4/5}$
$\qquad f(10)=33.3(10)^{4/5}$
$\qquad\qquad \approx210.1$ million subscriptions

**111.** $\square\cdot a^{2/3}=a^{3/3}$
$\qquad \square=\dfrac{a^{3/3}}{a^{2/3}}$
$\qquad \square=a^{3/3-2/3}$
$\qquad \square=a^{1/3}$

**113.** $\qquad \dfrac{\square}{x^{-2/5}}=x^{3/5}$
$\qquad x^{-2/5}\left(\dfrac{\square}{x^{-2/5}}\right)=x^{3/5}\cdot x^{-2/5}$
$\qquad\qquad \square=x^{3/5-2/5}$
$\qquad\qquad \square=x^{1/5}$

**115.** $8^{1/4}\approx1.6818$

**117.** $18^{3/5}\approx5.6645$

**119.** $\dfrac{\sqrt{t}}{\sqrt{u}}=\dfrac{t^{1/2}}{u^{1/2}}$

**Section 7.3**

**Practice Exercises**

**1. a.** $\sqrt{5}\cdot\sqrt{7}=\sqrt{5\cdot7}=\sqrt{35}$

    **b.** $\sqrt{13}\cdot\sqrt{z}=\sqrt{13z}$

    **c.** $\sqrt[4]{125}\cdot\sqrt[4]{5}=\sqrt[4]{125\cdot5}=\sqrt[4]{625}=5$

    **d.** $\sqrt[3]{5y}\ \sqrt[3]{3x^2}=\sqrt[3]{5y\ 3x^2}=\sqrt[3]{15x^2y}$

    **e.** $\sqrt{\dfrac{5}{m}}\cdot\sqrt{\dfrac{t}{2}}=\sqrt{\dfrac{5}{m}\cdot\dfrac{t}{2}}=\sqrt{\dfrac{5t}{2m}}$

**2. a.** $\sqrt{\dfrac{36}{49}}=\dfrac{\sqrt{36}}{\sqrt{49}}=\dfrac{6}{7}$

    **b.** $\sqrt{\dfrac{z}{16}}=\dfrac{\sqrt{z}}{\sqrt{16}}=\dfrac{\sqrt{z}}{4}$

    **c.** $\sqrt[3]{\dfrac{125}{8}}=\dfrac{\sqrt[3]{125}}{\sqrt[3]{8}}=\dfrac{5}{2}$

    **d.** $\sqrt[4]{\dfrac{5}{81x^8}}=\dfrac{\sqrt[4]{5}}{\sqrt[4]{81x^8}}=\dfrac{\sqrt[4]{5}}{3x^2}$

**3. a.** $\sqrt{98}=\sqrt{49\cdot2}=\sqrt{49}\cdot\sqrt{2}=7\sqrt{2}$

    **b.** $\sqrt[3]{54}=\sqrt[3]{27\cdot2}=\sqrt[3]{27}\cdot\sqrt[3]{2}=3\sqrt[3]{2}$

    **c.** The largest perfect square factor of 35 is 1, so $\sqrt{35}$ cannot be simplified further.

**d.** $\sqrt[4]{243} = \sqrt[4]{81 \cdot 3} = \sqrt[4]{81} \cdot \sqrt[4]{3} = 3\sqrt[4]{3}$

**4. a.** $\sqrt{36z^7} = \sqrt{36z^6 \cdot z} = \sqrt{36z^6} \cdot \sqrt{z} = 6z^3\sqrt{z}$

**b.** $\sqrt[3]{32p^4q^7} = \sqrt[3]{8 \cdot 4 \cdot p^3 \cdot p \cdot q^6 \cdot q}$

$\qquad = \sqrt[3]{8p^3q^6 \cdot 4pq}$

$\qquad = \sqrt[3]{8p^3q^6} \cdot \sqrt[3]{4pq}$

$\qquad = 2pq^2\sqrt[3]{4pq}$

**c.** $\sqrt[4]{16x^{15}} = \sqrt[4]{16 \cdot x^{12} \cdot x^3}$

$\qquad = \sqrt[4]{16x^{12}} \cdot \sqrt[4]{x^3}$

$\qquad = 2x^3\sqrt[4]{x^3}$

**5. a.** $\dfrac{\sqrt{80}}{\sqrt{5}} = \sqrt{\dfrac{80}{5}} = \sqrt{16} = 4$

**b.** $\dfrac{\sqrt{98z}}{3\sqrt{2}} = \dfrac{1}{3} \cdot \sqrt{\dfrac{98z}{2}}$

$\qquad = \dfrac{1}{3} \cdot \sqrt{49z}$

$\qquad = \dfrac{1}{3} \cdot \sqrt{49} \cdot \sqrt{z}$

$\qquad = \dfrac{1}{3} \cdot 7 \cdot \sqrt{z}$

$\qquad = \dfrac{7}{3}\sqrt{z}$

**c.** $\dfrac{5\sqrt[3]{40x^5y^7}}{\sqrt[3]{5y}} = 5 \cdot \sqrt[3]{\dfrac{40x^5y^7}{5y}}$

$\qquad = 5 \cdot \sqrt[3]{8x^5y^6}$

$\qquad = 5 \cdot \sqrt[3]{8x^3y^6 \cdot x^2}$

$\qquad = 5 \cdot \sqrt[3]{8x^3y^6} \cdot \sqrt[3]{x^2}$

$\qquad = 5 \cdot 2xy^2 \cdot \sqrt[3]{x^2}$

$\qquad = 10xy^2\sqrt[3]{x^2}$

**d.** $\dfrac{3\sqrt[5]{64x^9y^8}}{\sqrt[5]{x^{-1}y^2}} = 3 \cdot \sqrt[5]{\dfrac{64x^9y^8}{x^{-1}y^2}}$

$\qquad = 3 \cdot \sqrt[5]{64x^{10}y^6}$

$\qquad = 3 \cdot \sqrt[5]{32 \cdot x^{10} \cdot y^5 \cdot 2 \cdot y}$

$\qquad = 3 \cdot \sqrt[5]{32x^{10}y^5} \cdot \sqrt[5]{2y}$

$\qquad = 3 \cdot 2x^2y \cdot \sqrt[5]{2y}$

$\qquad = 6x^2y\sqrt[5]{2y}$

**6.** Let $(x_1, y_1) = (-3, 7)$ and $(x_2, y_2) = (-2, 3)$.

$d = \sqrt{(x_2 - x_1)^2 + (y_2 - y_1)^2}$

$\quad = \sqrt{[-2 - (-3)]^2 + (3 - 7)^2}$

$\quad = \sqrt{(1)^2 + (-4)^2}$

$\quad = \sqrt{1 + 16}$

$\quad = \sqrt{17} \approx 4.123$

The distance between the two points is exactly $\sqrt{17}$ units, or approximately 4.123 units.

**7.** Let $(x_1, y_1) = (5, -2)$ and $(x_2, y_2) = (8, -6)$.

$\text{midpoint} = \left( \dfrac{x_1 + x_2}{2}, \dfrac{y_1 + y_2}{2} \right)$

$\qquad = \left( \dfrac{5 + 8}{2}, \dfrac{-2 + (-6)}{2} \right)$

$\qquad = \left( \dfrac{13}{2}, \dfrac{-8}{2} \right)$

$\qquad = \left( \dfrac{13}{2}, -4 \right)$

The midpoint of the segment is $\left( \dfrac{13}{2}, -4 \right)$.

**Vocabulary and Readiness Check**

1. The <u>midpoint</u> of a line segment is a <u>point</u> exactly halfway between the two endpoints of the line segment.

2. The <u>distance</u> formula is
$d = \sqrt{(x_2 - x_1)^2 + (y_2 - y_1)^2}$.

3. The <u>midpoint</u> formula is $\left( \dfrac{x_1 + x_2}{2}, \dfrac{y_1 + y_2}{2} \right)$.

4. The statement $\sqrt[n]{a} \cdot \sqrt[n]{b} = \sqrt[n]{ab}$ is <u>true</u>.

5. The statement $\sqrt[3]{7} \cdot \sqrt[3]{11} = \sqrt[3]{18}$ is <u>false</u>.

**6.** The statement $\sqrt[3]{7}\cdot\sqrt{11}=\sqrt{77}$ is <u>false</u>.

**7.** The statement $\sqrt{x^7 y^8}=\sqrt{x^7}\cdot\sqrt{y^8}$ is <u>true</u>.

**8.** The statement $\dfrac{\sqrt[n]{a}}{\sqrt[n]{b}}=\sqrt[n]{\dfrac{a}{b}}$ is <u>true</u>.

**9.** The statement $\dfrac{\sqrt[3]{12}}{\sqrt[3]{4}}=\sqrt[3]{8}$ is <u>false</u>.

**10.** The statement $\dfrac{\sqrt[n]{x^7}}{\sqrt[n]{x}}=\sqrt[n]{x^6}$ is <u>true</u>.

**Exercise Set 7.3**

**1.** $\sqrt{7}\cdot\sqrt{2}=\sqrt{7\cdot2}=\sqrt{14}$

**3.** $\sqrt[4]{8}\cdot\sqrt[4]{2}=\sqrt[4]{8\cdot2}=\sqrt[4]{16}=2$

**5.** $\sqrt[3]{4}\cdot\sqrt[3]{9}=\sqrt[3]{4\cdot9}=\sqrt[3]{36}$

**7.** $\sqrt{2}\cdot\sqrt{3x}=\sqrt{2\cdot3x}=\sqrt{6x}$

**9.** $\sqrt{\dfrac{7}{x}}\cdot\sqrt{\dfrac{2}{y}}=\sqrt{\dfrac{7}{x}\cdot\dfrac{2}{y}}=\sqrt{\dfrac{14}{xy}}$

**11.** $\sqrt[4]{4x^3}\cdot\sqrt[4]{5}=\sqrt[4]{4x^3\cdot5}=\sqrt[4]{20x^3}$

**13.** $\sqrt{\dfrac{6}{49}}=\dfrac{\sqrt{6}}{\sqrt{49}}=\dfrac{\sqrt{6}}{7}$

**15.** $\sqrt{\dfrac{2}{49}}=\dfrac{\sqrt{2}}{\sqrt{49}}=\dfrac{\sqrt{2}}{7}$

**17.** $\sqrt[4]{\dfrac{x^3}{16}}=\dfrac{\sqrt[4]{x^3}}{\sqrt[4]{16}}=\dfrac{\sqrt[4]{x^3}}{2}$

**19.** $\sqrt[3]{\dfrac{4}{27}}=\dfrac{\sqrt[3]{4}}{\sqrt[3]{27}}=\dfrac{\sqrt[3]{4}}{3}$

**21.** $\sqrt[4]{\dfrac{8}{x^8}}=\dfrac{\sqrt[4]{8}}{\sqrt[4]{x^8}}=\dfrac{\sqrt[4]{8}}{x^2}$

**23.** $\sqrt[3]{\dfrac{2x}{81y^{12}}}=\dfrac{\sqrt[3]{2x}}{\sqrt[3]{81y^{12}}}$
$=\dfrac{\sqrt[3]{2x}}{\sqrt[3]{27y^{12}}\cdot\sqrt[3]{3}}$
$=\dfrac{\sqrt[3]{2x}}{3y^4\sqrt[3]{3}}$

**25.** $\sqrt{\dfrac{x^2y}{100}}=\dfrac{\sqrt{x^2y}}{\sqrt{100}}=\dfrac{\sqrt{x^2}\sqrt{y}}{10}=\dfrac{x\sqrt{y}}{10}$

**27.** $\sqrt{\dfrac{5x^2}{4y^2}}=\dfrac{\sqrt{5x^2}}{\sqrt{4y^2}}=\dfrac{\sqrt{5}\sqrt{x^2}}{2y}=\dfrac{x\sqrt{5}}{2y}$

**29.** $-\sqrt[3]{\dfrac{z^7}{27x^3}}=-\dfrac{\sqrt[3]{z^7}}{\sqrt[3]{27x^3}}=-\dfrac{\sqrt[3]{z^6\cdot z}}{3x}=-\dfrac{z^2\sqrt[3]{z}}{3x}$

**31.** $\sqrt{32}=\sqrt{16\cdot2}=\sqrt{16}\cdot\sqrt{2}=4\sqrt{2}$

**33.** $\sqrt[3]{192}=\sqrt[3]{64\cdot3}=\sqrt[3]{64}\cdot\sqrt[3]{3}=4\sqrt[3]{3}$

**35.** $5\sqrt{75}=5\sqrt{25\cdot3}=5\sqrt{25}\cdot\sqrt{3}=5(5)\sqrt{3}=25\sqrt{3}$

**37.** $\sqrt{24}=\sqrt{4\cdot6}=\sqrt{4}\cdot\sqrt{6}=2\sqrt{6}$

**39.** $\sqrt{100x^5}=\sqrt{100x^4\cdot x}=\sqrt{100x^4}\cdot\sqrt{x}=10x^2\sqrt{x}$

**41.** $\sqrt[3]{16y^7}=\sqrt[3]{8y^6\cdot2y}=\sqrt[3]{8y^6}\cdot\sqrt[3]{2y}=2y^2\sqrt[3]{2y}$

**43.** $\sqrt[4]{a^8b^7}=\sqrt[4]{a^8b^4\cdot b^3}=\sqrt[4]{a^8b^4}\cdot\sqrt[4]{b^3}=a^2b\sqrt[4]{b^3}$

**45.** $\sqrt{y^5}=\sqrt{y^4\cdot y}=\sqrt{y^4}\cdot\sqrt{y}=y^2\sqrt{y}$

**47.** $\sqrt{25a^2b^3}=\sqrt{25a^2b^2\cdot b}$
$=\sqrt{25a^2b^2}\cdot\sqrt{b}$
$=5ab\sqrt{b}$

**49.** $\sqrt[5]{-32x^{10}y}=\sqrt[5]{-32x^{10}\cdot y}$
$=\sqrt[5]{-32x^{10}}\cdot\sqrt[5]{y}$
$=-2x^2\sqrt[5]{y}$

**51.** $\sqrt[3]{50x^{14}} = \sqrt[3]{x^{12} \cdot 50x^2}$

$= \sqrt[3]{x^{12}} \cdot \sqrt[3]{50x^2}$

$= x^4 \sqrt[3]{50x^2}$

**53.** $-\sqrt{32a^8b^7} = -\sqrt{16a^8b^6 \cdot 2b}$

$= -\sqrt{16a^8b^6} \cdot \sqrt{2b}$

$= -4a^4b^3 \sqrt{2b}$

**55.** $\sqrt{9x^7y^9} = \sqrt{9x^6y^8 \cdot xy}$

$= \sqrt{9x^6y^8} \cdot \sqrt{xy}$

$= 3x^3y^4 \sqrt{xy}$

**57.** $\sqrt[3]{125r^9s^{12}} = 5r^3s^4$

**59.** $\dfrac{\sqrt{14}}{\sqrt{7}} = \sqrt{\dfrac{14}{7}} = \sqrt{2}$

**61.** $\dfrac{\sqrt[3]{24}}{\sqrt[3]{3}} = \sqrt[3]{\dfrac{24}{3}} = \sqrt[3]{8} = 2$

**63.** $\dfrac{5\sqrt[4]{48}}{\sqrt[4]{3}} = 5\sqrt[4]{\dfrac{48}{3}} = 5\sqrt[4]{16} = 5(2) = 10$

**65.** $\dfrac{\sqrt{x^5y^3}}{\sqrt{xy}} = \sqrt{\dfrac{x^5y^3}{xy}} = \sqrt{x^4y^2} = x^2y$

**67.** $\dfrac{8\sqrt[3]{54m^7}}{\sqrt[3]{2m}} = 8\sqrt[3]{\dfrac{54m^7}{2m}}$

$= 8\sqrt[3]{27m^6}$

$= 8(3m^2)$

$= 24m^2$

**69.** $\dfrac{3\sqrt{100x^2}}{2\sqrt{2x^{-1}}} = \dfrac{3}{2}\sqrt{\dfrac{100x^2}{2x^{-1}}}$

$= \dfrac{3}{2}\sqrt{50x^3}$

$= \dfrac{3}{2}\sqrt{25x^2 \cdot 2x}$

$= \dfrac{3}{2}(5x)\sqrt{2x}$

$= \dfrac{15x}{2}\sqrt{2x}$

**71.** $\dfrac{\sqrt[4]{96a^{10}b^3}}{\sqrt[4]{3a^2b^3}} = \sqrt[4]{\dfrac{96a^{10}b^3}{3a^2b^3}}$

$= \sqrt[4]{32a^8}$

$= \sqrt[4]{16a^8 \cdot 2}$

$= 2a^2\sqrt[4]{2}$

**73.** $(5, 1), (8, 5)$

$d = \sqrt{(8-5)^2 + (5-1)^2}$

$= \sqrt{3^2 + 4^2}$

$= \sqrt{9+16}$

$= \sqrt{25}$

$= 5$ units

**75.** $(-3, 2), (1, -3)$

$d = \sqrt{[1-(-3)]^2 + (-3-2)^2}$

$= \sqrt{4^2 + (-5)^2}$

$= \sqrt{16+25}$

$= \sqrt{41} \approx 6.403$ units

**77.** $(-9, 4), (-8, 1)$

$d = \sqrt{[-8-(-9)]^2 + (1-4)^2}$

$= \sqrt{1^2 + (-3)^2}$

$= \sqrt{1+9}$

$= \sqrt{10} \approx 3.162$ units

**79.** $\left(0, -\sqrt{2}\right), \left(\sqrt{3}, 0\right)$

$d = \sqrt{\left(\sqrt{3}-0\right)^2 + \left[0-\left(-\sqrt{2}\right)\right]^2}$

$= \sqrt{\left(\sqrt{3}\right)^2 + \left(\sqrt{2}\right)^2}$

$= \sqrt{3+2}$

$= \sqrt{5} \approx 2.236$ units

**81.** $(1.7, -3.6), (-8.6, 5.7)$

$d = \sqrt{(-8.6-1.7)^2 + [5.7-(-3.6)]^2}$

$= \sqrt{(-10.3)^2 + (9.3)^2}$

$= \sqrt{192.58} \approx 13.877$ units

**83.** $(6, -8), (2, 4)$

$\left(\dfrac{6+2}{2}, \dfrac{-8+4}{2}\right) = \left(\dfrac{8}{2}, \dfrac{-4}{2}\right) = (4, -2)$

The midpoint of the segment is $(4, -2)$.

**85.** $(-2, -1), (-8, 6)$

$$\left(\frac{-2+(-8)}{2}, \frac{-1+6}{2}\right) = \left(\frac{-10}{2}, \frac{5}{2}\right) = \left(-5, \frac{5}{2}\right)$$

The midpoint of the segment is $\left(-5, \frac{5}{2}\right)$.

**87.** $(7, 3), (-1, -3)$

$$\left(\frac{7+(-1)}{2}, \frac{3+(-3)}{2}\right) = \left(\frac{6}{2}, \frac{0}{2}\right) = (3, 0)$$

The midpoint of the segment is $(3, 0)$.

**89.** $\left(\frac{1}{2}, \frac{3}{8}\right), \left(-\frac{3}{2}, \frac{5}{8}\right)$

$$\left(\frac{\frac{1}{2}+\left(-\frac{3}{2}\right)}{2}, \frac{\frac{3}{8}+\frac{5}{8}}{2}\right) = \left(\frac{-1}{2}, \frac{1}{2}\right)$$

The midpoint of the segment is $\left(-\frac{1}{2}, \frac{1}{2}\right)$.

**91.** $\left(\sqrt{2}, 3\sqrt{5}\right), \left(\sqrt{2}, -2\sqrt{5}\right)$

$$\left(\frac{\sqrt{2}+\sqrt{2}}{2}, \frac{3\sqrt{5}+\left(-2\sqrt{5}\right)}{2}\right) = \left(\frac{2\sqrt{2}}{2}, \frac{\sqrt{5}}{2}\right)$$

$$= \left(\sqrt{2}, \frac{\sqrt{5}}{2}\right)$$

The midpoint of the segment is $\left(\sqrt{2}, \frac{\sqrt{5}}{2}\right)$.

**93.** $(4.6, -3.5), (7.8, -9.8)$

$$\left(\frac{4.6+7.8}{2}, \frac{-3.5+(-9.8)}{2}\right) = \left(\frac{12.4}{2}, \frac{-13.3}{2}\right)$$

$$= (6.2, -6.65)$$

The midpoint of the segment is $(6.2, -6.65)$.

**95.** $6x + 8x = (6+8)x = 14x$

**97.** $(2x+3)(x-5) = 2x^2 - 10x + 3x - 15$
$$= 2x^2 - 7x - 15$$

**99.** $9y^2 - 8y^2 = (9-8)y^2 = 1y^2 = y^2$

**101.** $-3(x+5) = -3x - 3(5) = -3x - 15$

**103.** $(x-4)^2 = x^2 - 2(x)(4) + 4^2$
$$= x^2 - 8x + 16$$

**105.** $\dfrac{\sqrt[3]{64}}{\sqrt{64}} = \dfrac{4}{8} = \dfrac{1}{2}$

**107.** $\sqrt[5]{x^{35}} = x^7$

**109.** $\sqrt[4]{a^{12}b^4c^{20}} = a^3bc^5$

**111.** $\sqrt[3]{z^{32}} = \sqrt[3]{z^{30} \cdot z^2} = \sqrt[3]{z^{30}} \cdot \sqrt[3]{z^2} = z^{10}\sqrt[3]{z^2}$

**113.** $\sqrt[7]{q^{17}r^{40}s^7} = \sqrt[7]{q^{14} \cdot q^3 \cdot r^{35} \cdot r^5 \cdot s^7}$
$$= \sqrt[7]{q^{14}r^{35}s^7 \cdot q^3 r^5}$$
$$= q^2 r^5 s\sqrt[7]{q^3 r^5}$$

**115.** $r = \sqrt{\dfrac{A}{4\pi}} = \sqrt{\dfrac{32.17}{4\pi}} \approx \sqrt{2.56} = 1.6$

The radius of a standard zorb is 1.6 meters.

**117.** $F(x) = 0.6\sqrt{49 - x^2}$

**a.** $F(3) = 0.6\sqrt{49 - 3^2}$
$$= 0.6\sqrt{49 - 9}$$
$$= 0.6\sqrt{40} \approx 3.8 \text{ times}$$

**b.** $F(5) = 0.6\sqrt{49 - 5^2}$
$$= 0.6\sqrt{49 - 25}$$
$$= 0.6\sqrt{24} \approx 2.9 \text{ times}$$

**c.** Answers may vary

## Section 7.4

### Practice Exercises

**1. a.** $3\sqrt{17} + 5\sqrt{17} = (3+5)\sqrt{17} = 8\sqrt{17}$

**b.** $7\sqrt[3]{5z} - 12\sqrt[3]{5z} = (7-12)\sqrt[3]{5z} = -5\sqrt[3]{5z}$

**c.** $3\sqrt{2} + 5\sqrt[3]{2}$
This expression cannot be simplified since $3\sqrt{2}$ and $5\sqrt[3]{2}$ do not contain like radicals.

**2. a.** 
$$\sqrt{24}+3\sqrt{54}=\sqrt{4\cdot6}+3\sqrt{9\cdot6}$$
$$=\sqrt{4}\cdot\sqrt{6}+3\cdot\sqrt{9}\cdot\sqrt{6}$$
$$=2\cdot\sqrt{6}+3\cdot3\cdot\sqrt{6}$$
$$=2\sqrt{6}+9\sqrt{6}$$
$$=11\sqrt{6}$$

**b.** 
$$\sqrt[3]{24}-4\sqrt[3]{81}+\sqrt[3]{3}$$
$$=\sqrt[3]{8}\cdot\sqrt[3]{3}-4\cdot\sqrt[3]{27}\cdot\sqrt[3]{3}+\sqrt[3]{3}$$
$$=2\sqrt[3]{3}-4\cdot3\cdot\sqrt[3]{3}+\sqrt[3]{3}$$
$$=2\sqrt[3]{3}-12\sqrt[3]{3}+\sqrt[3]{3}$$
$$=-9\sqrt[3]{3}$$

**c.** 
$$\sqrt{75x}-3\sqrt{27x}+\sqrt{12x}$$
$$=\sqrt{25}\cdot\sqrt{3x}-3\cdot\sqrt{9}\cdot\sqrt{3x}+\sqrt{4}\cdot\sqrt{3x}$$
$$=5\cdot\sqrt{3x}-3\cdot3\cdot\sqrt{3x}+2\cdot\sqrt{3x}$$
$$=5\sqrt{3x}-9\sqrt{3x}+2\sqrt{3x}$$
$$=-2\sqrt{3x}$$

**d.** 
$$\sqrt{40}+\sqrt[3]{40}=\sqrt{4}\cdot\sqrt{10}+\sqrt[3]{8}\cdot\sqrt[3]{5}$$
$$=2\sqrt{10}+2\sqrt[3]{5}$$

**e.** 
$$\sqrt[3]{81x^4}+\sqrt[3]{3x^4}=\sqrt[3]{27x^3}\cdot\sqrt[3]{3x}+\sqrt[3]{x^3}\cdot\sqrt[3]{3x}$$
$$=3x\sqrt[3]{3x}+x\sqrt[3]{3x}$$
$$=4x\sqrt[3]{3x}$$

**3. a.** 
$$\frac{\sqrt{28}}{3}-\frac{\sqrt7}{4}=\frac{2\sqrt7}{3}-\frac{\sqrt7}{4}$$
$$=\frac{2\sqrt7\cdot4}{3\cdot4}-\frac{\sqrt7\cdot3}{4\cdot3}$$
$$=\frac{8\sqrt7}{12}-\frac{3\sqrt7}{12}$$
$$=\frac{5\sqrt7}{12}$$

**b.** 
$$\sqrt[3]{\frac{6y}{64}}+3\sqrt[3]{6y}=\frac{\sqrt[3]{6y}}{\sqrt[3]{64}}+3\sqrt[3]{6y}$$
$$=\frac{\sqrt[3]{6y}}{4}+3\sqrt[3]{6y}$$
$$=\frac{\sqrt[3]{6y}}{4}+\frac{3\sqrt[3]{6y}\cdot4}{4}$$
$$=\frac{\sqrt[3]{6y}}{4}+\frac{12\sqrt[3]{6y}}{4}$$
$$=\frac{13\sqrt[3]{6y}}{4}$$

**4. a.** 
$$\sqrt5(2+\sqrt{15})=\sqrt5(2)+\sqrt5(\sqrt{15})$$
$$=2\sqrt5+\sqrt{5\cdot15}$$
$$=2\sqrt5+\sqrt{5\cdot5\cdot3}$$
$$=2\sqrt5+5\sqrt3$$

**b.** 
$$(\sqrt2-\sqrt5)(\sqrt6+2)$$
$$=\sqrt2\cdot\sqrt6+\sqrt2\cdot2-\sqrt5\cdot\sqrt6-\sqrt5\cdot2$$
$$=\sqrt{2\cdot2\cdot3}+2\sqrt2-\sqrt{30}-2\sqrt5$$
$$=2\sqrt3+2\sqrt2-\sqrt{30}-2\sqrt5$$

**c.** 
$$(3\sqrt z-4)(2\sqrt z+3)$$
$$=3\sqrt z(2\sqrt z)+3\sqrt z(3)-4(2\sqrt z)-4(3)$$
$$=6\cdot z+9\sqrt z-8\sqrt z-12$$
$$=6z+\sqrt z-12$$

**d.** 
$$(\sqrt6-3)^2=(\sqrt6-3)(\sqrt6-3)$$
$$=\sqrt6(\sqrt6)-\sqrt6(3)-3(\sqrt6)-3(-3)$$
$$=6-3\sqrt6-3\sqrt6+9$$
$$=6-6\sqrt6+9$$
$$=15-6\sqrt6$$

**e.** 
$$(\sqrt{5x}+3)(\sqrt{5x}-3)$$
$$=\sqrt{5x}\cdot\sqrt{5x}-3\sqrt{5x}+3\sqrt{5x}-3\cdot3$$
$$=5x-9$$

**f.** 
$$(\sqrt{x+2}+3)^2=(\sqrt{x+2})^2+2\cdot\sqrt{x+2}\cdot3+3^2$$
$$=x+2+6\sqrt{x+2}+9$$
$$=x+11+6\sqrt{x+2}$$

**Vocabulary and Readiness Check**

**1.** The terms $\sqrt7$ and $\sqrt[3]7$ are <u>unlike</u> terms.

**2.** The terms $\sqrt[3]{x^2y}$ and $\sqrt[3]{yx^2}$ are <u>like</u> terms.

**3.** The terms $\sqrt[3]{abc}$ and $\sqrt[3]{cba}$ are <u>like</u> terms.

**4.** The terms $2x\sqrt5$ and $2x\sqrt{10}$ are <u>unlike</u> terms.

**5.** $2\sqrt3+4\sqrt3=\underline{6\sqrt3}$

**6.** $5\sqrt7+3\sqrt7=\underline{8\sqrt7}$

**7.** $8\sqrt x-\sqrt x=\underline{7\sqrt x}$

**8.** $3\sqrt y-\sqrt y=\underline{2\sqrt y}$

**9.** $7\sqrt[3]{x} + \sqrt[3]{x} = \underline{8\sqrt[3]{x}}$

**10.** $8\sqrt[3]{z} + \sqrt[3]{z} = \underline{9\sqrt[3]{z}}$

**11.** $\sqrt{11} + \sqrt[3]{11} = \underline{\sqrt{11} + \sqrt[3]{11}}$

**12.** $9\sqrt{13} - \sqrt[4]{13} = \underline{9\sqrt{13} - \sqrt[4]{13}}$

**13.** $8\sqrt[3]{2x} + 3\sqrt[3]{2x} - \sqrt[3]{2x} = \underline{10\sqrt[3]{2x}}$

**14.** $8\sqrt[3]{2x} + 3\sqrt[3]{2x^2} - \sqrt[3]{2x} = \underline{7\sqrt[3]{2x} + 3\sqrt[3]{2x^2}}$

**Exercise Set 7.4**

**1.** $\sqrt{8} - \sqrt{32} = \sqrt{4 \cdot 2} - \sqrt{16 \cdot 2}$
$= \sqrt{4} \cdot \sqrt{2} - \sqrt{16} \cdot \sqrt{2}$
$= 2\sqrt{2} - 4\sqrt{2}$
$= -2\sqrt{2}$

**3.** $2\sqrt{2x^3} + 4x\sqrt{8x} = 2\sqrt{x^2 \cdot 2x} + 4x\sqrt{4 \cdot 2x}$
$= 2\sqrt{x^2} \cdot \sqrt{2x} + 4x\sqrt{4} \cdot \sqrt{2x}$
$= 2x\sqrt{2x} + 4x(2)\sqrt{2x}$
$= 2x\sqrt{2x} + 8x\sqrt{2x}$
$= 10x\sqrt{2x}$

**5.** $2\sqrt{50} - 3\sqrt{125} + \sqrt{98}$
$= 2\sqrt{25 \cdot 2} - 3\sqrt{25 \cdot 5} + \sqrt{49 \cdot 2}$
$= 2\sqrt{25} \cdot \sqrt{2} - 3\sqrt{25} \cdot \sqrt{5} + \sqrt{49} \cdot \sqrt{2}$
$= 2(5)\sqrt{2} - 3(5)\sqrt{5} + 7\sqrt{2}$
$= 10\sqrt{2} - 15\sqrt{5} + 7\sqrt{2}$
$= 17\sqrt{2} - 15\sqrt{5}$

**7.** $\sqrt[3]{16x} - \sqrt[3]{54x} = \sqrt[3]{8 \cdot 2x} - \sqrt[3]{27 \cdot 2x}$
$= \sqrt[3]{8} \cdot \sqrt[3]{2x} - \sqrt[3]{27} \cdot \sqrt[3]{2x}$
$= 2\sqrt[3]{2x} - 3\sqrt[3]{2x}$
$= -\sqrt[3]{2x}$

**9.** $\sqrt{9b^3} - \sqrt{25b^3} + \sqrt{49b^3}$
$= \sqrt{9b^2 \cdot b} - \sqrt{25b^2 \cdot b} + \sqrt{49b^2 \cdot b}$
$= \sqrt{9b^2} \cdot \sqrt{b} - \sqrt{25b^2} \cdot \sqrt{b} + \sqrt{49b^2} \cdot \sqrt{b}$
$= 3b\sqrt{b} - 5b\sqrt{b} + 7b\sqrt{b}$
$= 5b\sqrt{b}$

**11.** $\dfrac{5\sqrt{2}}{3} + \dfrac{2\sqrt{2}}{5} = \dfrac{5(5\sqrt{2}) + 3(2\sqrt{2})}{3(5)}$
$= \dfrac{25\sqrt{2} + 6\sqrt{2}}{15}$
$= \dfrac{31\sqrt{2}}{15}$

**13.** $\sqrt[3]{\dfrac{11}{8}} - \dfrac{\sqrt[3]{11}}{6} = \dfrac{\sqrt[3]{11}}{\sqrt[3]{8}} - \dfrac{\sqrt[3]{11}}{6}$
$= \dfrac{\sqrt[3]{11}}{2} - \dfrac{\sqrt[3]{11}}{6}$
$= \dfrac{3\sqrt[3]{11} - \sqrt[3]{11}}{6}$
$= \dfrac{2\sqrt[3]{11}}{6}$
$= \dfrac{\sqrt[3]{11}}{3}$

**15.** $\dfrac{\sqrt{20x}}{9} + \sqrt{\dfrac{5x}{9}} = \dfrac{\sqrt{4 \cdot 5x}}{9} + \dfrac{\sqrt{5x}}{\sqrt{9}}$
$= \dfrac{2\sqrt{5x}}{9} + \dfrac{\sqrt{5x}}{3}$
$= \dfrac{2\sqrt{5x} + 3\sqrt{5x}}{9}$
$= \dfrac{5\sqrt{5x}}{9}$

**17.** $7\sqrt{9} - 7 + \sqrt{3} = 7(3) - 7 + \sqrt{3}$
$= 21 - 7 + \sqrt{3}$
$= 14 + \sqrt{3}$

**19.** $2 + 3\sqrt{y^2} - 6\sqrt{y^2} + 5 = 2 + 3y - 6y + 5$
$= 7 - 3y$

**21.** $3\sqrt{108} - 2\sqrt{18} - 3\sqrt{48}$
$= 3\sqrt{36 \cdot 3} - 2\sqrt{9 \cdot 2} - 3\sqrt{16 \cdot 3}$
$= 3\sqrt{36} \cdot \sqrt{3} - 2\sqrt{9} \cdot \sqrt{2} - 3\sqrt{16} \cdot \sqrt{3}$
$= 3(6)\sqrt{3} - 2(3)\sqrt{2} - 3(4)\sqrt{3}$
$= 18\sqrt{3} - 6\sqrt{2} - 12\sqrt{3}$
$= 6\sqrt{3} - 6\sqrt{2}$

**23.** $-5\sqrt[3]{625} + \sqrt[3]{40} = -5\sqrt[3]{125 \cdot 5} + \sqrt[3]{8 \cdot 5}$
$$= -5(5)\sqrt[3]{5} + 2\sqrt[3]{5}$$
$$= -25\sqrt[3]{5} + 2\sqrt[3]{5}$$
$$= -23\sqrt[3]{5}$$

**25.** $\sqrt{9b^3} - \sqrt{25b^3} + \sqrt{16b^3}$
$$= \sqrt{9b^2 \cdot b} - \sqrt{25b^2 \cdot b} + \sqrt{16b^2 \cdot b}$$
$$= 3b\sqrt{b} - 5b\sqrt{b} + 4b\sqrt{b}$$
$$= 2b\sqrt{b}$$

**27.** $5y\sqrt{8y} + 2\sqrt{50y^3} = 5y\sqrt{4 \cdot 2y} + 2\sqrt{25y^2 \cdot 2y}$
$$= 5y(2)\sqrt{2y} + 2(5y)\sqrt{2y}$$
$$= 10y\sqrt{2y} + 10y\sqrt{2y}$$
$$= 20y\sqrt{2y}$$

**29.** $\sqrt[3]{54xy^3} - 5\sqrt[3]{2xy^3} + y\sqrt[3]{128x}$
$$= \sqrt[3]{27y^3 \cdot 2x} - 5\sqrt[3]{y^3 \cdot 2x} + y\sqrt[3]{64 \cdot 2x}$$
$$= 3y\sqrt[3]{2x} - 5y\sqrt[3]{2x} + 4y\sqrt[3]{2x}$$
$$= 2y\sqrt[3]{2x}$$

**31.** $6\sqrt[3]{11} + 8\sqrt{11} - 12\sqrt{11} = 6\sqrt[3]{11} - 4\sqrt{11}$

**33.** $-2\sqrt[4]{x^7} + 3\sqrt[4]{16x^7} = -2\sqrt[4]{x^4 \cdot x^3} + 3\sqrt[4]{16x^4 \cdot x^3}$
$$= -2x\sqrt[4]{x^3} + 3(2x)\sqrt[4]{x^3}$$
$$= -2x\sqrt[4]{x^3} + 6x\sqrt[4]{x^3}$$
$$= 4x\sqrt[4]{x^3}$$

**35.** $\dfrac{4\sqrt{3}}{3} - \dfrac{\sqrt{12}}{3} = \dfrac{4\sqrt{3}}{3} - \dfrac{\sqrt{4 \cdot 3}}{3}$
$$= \dfrac{4\sqrt{3} - 2\sqrt{3}}{3}$$
$$= \dfrac{2\sqrt{3}}{3}$$

**37.** $\dfrac{\sqrt[3]{8x^4}}{7} + \dfrac{3x\sqrt[3]{x}}{7} = \dfrac{\sqrt[3]{8x^3 \cdot x}}{7} + \dfrac{3x\sqrt[3]{x}}{7}$
$$= \dfrac{2x\sqrt[3]{x} + 3x\sqrt[3]{x}}{7}$$
$$= \dfrac{5x\sqrt[3]{x}}{7}$$

**39.** $\sqrt{\dfrac{28}{x^2}} + \sqrt{\dfrac{7}{4x^2}} = \dfrac{\sqrt{28}}{\sqrt{x^2}} + \dfrac{\sqrt{7}}{\sqrt{4x^2}}$
$$= \dfrac{\sqrt{4 \cdot 7}}{x} + \dfrac{\sqrt{7}}{2x}$$
$$= \dfrac{2\sqrt{7}}{x} + \dfrac{\sqrt{7}}{2x}$$
$$= \dfrac{2(2\sqrt{7}) + \sqrt{7}}{2x}$$
$$= \dfrac{4\sqrt{7} + \sqrt{7}}{2x}$$
$$= \dfrac{5\sqrt{7}}{2x}$$

**41.** $\sqrt[3]{\dfrac{16}{27}} - \dfrac{\sqrt[3]{54}}{6} = \dfrac{\sqrt[3]{8 \cdot 2}}{\sqrt[3]{27}} - \dfrac{\sqrt[3]{27 \cdot 2}}{6}$
$$= \dfrac{2\sqrt[3]{2}}{3} - \dfrac{3\sqrt[3]{2}}{6}$$
$$= \dfrac{2(2\sqrt[3]{2}) - 3\sqrt[3]{2}}{6}$$
$$= \dfrac{4\sqrt[3]{2} - 3\sqrt[3]{2}}{6}$$
$$= \dfrac{\sqrt[3]{2}}{6}$$

**43.** $-\dfrac{\sqrt[3]{2x^4}}{9} + \sqrt[3]{\dfrac{250x^4}{27}} = -\dfrac{\sqrt[3]{x^3 \cdot 2x}}{9} + \dfrac{\sqrt[3]{125x^3 \cdot 2x}}{\sqrt[3]{27}}$
$$= \dfrac{-x\sqrt[3]{2x}}{9} + \dfrac{5x\sqrt[3]{2x}}{3}$$
$$= \dfrac{-x\sqrt[3]{2x} + 3\left(5x\sqrt[3]{2x}\right)}{9}$$
$$= \dfrac{-x\sqrt[3]{2x} + 15x\sqrt[3]{2x}}{9}$$
$$= \dfrac{14x\sqrt[3]{2x}}{9}$$

**45.** $P = 2\sqrt{12} + \sqrt{12} + 2\sqrt{27} + 3\sqrt{3}$
$$= 2\sqrt{4 \cdot 3} + \sqrt{4 \cdot 3} + 2\sqrt{9 \cdot 3} + 3\sqrt{3}$$
$$= 2(2)\sqrt{3} + 2\sqrt{3} + 2(3)\sqrt{3} + 3\sqrt{3}$$
$$= 4\sqrt{3} + 2\sqrt{3} + 6\sqrt{3} + 3\sqrt{3}$$
$$= 15\sqrt{3} \text{ inches}$$

**47.** $\sqrt{7}\left(\sqrt{5} + \sqrt{3}\right) = \sqrt{7}\sqrt{5} + \sqrt{7}\sqrt{3}$
$$= \sqrt{35} + \sqrt{21}$$

**49.** $\left(\sqrt{5}-\sqrt{2}\right)^2 = \left(\sqrt{5}\right)^2 - 2\sqrt{5}\sqrt{2} + \left(\sqrt{2}\right)^2$
$\qquad\qquad\qquad = 5 - 2\sqrt{10} + 2$
$\qquad\qquad\qquad = 7 - 2\sqrt{10}$

**51.** $\sqrt{3x}\left(\sqrt{3}-\sqrt{x}\right) = \sqrt{3x}\sqrt{3} - \sqrt{3x}\sqrt{x}$
$\qquad\qquad\qquad = \sqrt{9x} - \sqrt{3x^2}$
$\qquad\qquad\qquad = 3\sqrt{x} - x\sqrt{3}$

**53.** $\left(2\sqrt{x}-5\right)\left(3\sqrt{x}+1\right)$
$\qquad = 2\sqrt{x}\left(3\sqrt{x}\right) + 2\sqrt{x}\cdot 1 - 5\left(3\sqrt{x}\right) - 5(1)$
$\qquad = 6x + 2\sqrt{x} - 15\sqrt{x} - 5$
$\qquad = 6x - 13\sqrt{x} - 5$

**55.** $\left(\sqrt[3]{a}-4\right)\left(\sqrt[3]{a}+5\right)$
$\qquad = \sqrt[3]{a}\left(\sqrt[3]{a}\right) + \sqrt[3]{a}\cdot 5 - 4\sqrt[3]{a} - 4(5)$
$\qquad = \sqrt[3]{a^2} + 5\sqrt[3]{a} - 4\sqrt[3]{a} - 20$
$\qquad = \sqrt[3]{a^2} + \sqrt[3]{a} - 20$

**57.** $6\left(\sqrt{2}-2\right) = 6\sqrt{2} - 6(2) = 6\sqrt{2} - 12$

**59.** $\sqrt{2}\left(\sqrt{2}+x\sqrt{6}\right) = \sqrt{2}\sqrt{2} + \sqrt{2}\left(x\sqrt{6}\right)$
$\qquad\qquad\qquad = 2 + x\sqrt{12}$
$\qquad\qquad\qquad = 2 + x\sqrt{4\cdot 3}$
$\qquad\qquad\qquad = 2 + 2x\sqrt{3}$

**61.** $\left(2\sqrt{7}+3\sqrt{5}\right)\left(\sqrt{7}-2\sqrt{5}\right)$
$\qquad = 2\sqrt{7}\sqrt{7} + 2\sqrt{7}\left(-2\sqrt{5}\right) + 3\sqrt{5}\sqrt{7} + 3\sqrt{5}\left(-2\sqrt{5}\right)$
$\qquad = 2(7) - 4\sqrt{35} + 3\sqrt{35} - 6(5)$
$\qquad = 14 - \sqrt{35} - 30$
$\qquad = -16 - \sqrt{35}$

**63.** $\left(\sqrt{x}-y\right)\left(\sqrt{x}+y\right) = \left(\sqrt{x}\right)^2 - y^2 = x - y^2$

**65.** $\left(\sqrt{3}+x\right)^2 = \left(\sqrt{3}\right)^2 + 2\sqrt{3}\cdot x + x^2$
$\qquad\qquad\qquad = 3 + 2x\sqrt{3} + x^2$

**67.** $\left(\sqrt{5x}-2\sqrt{3x}\right)\left(\sqrt{5x}-3\sqrt{3x}\right)$
$\qquad = \left(\sqrt{5x}\right)^2 - \sqrt{5x}\left(3\sqrt{3x}\right) - 2\sqrt{3x}\left(\sqrt{5x}\right)$
$\qquad\qquad\qquad\qquad - 2\sqrt{3x}\left(-3\sqrt{3x}\right)$
$\qquad = 5x - 3x\sqrt{15} - 2x\sqrt{15} + 6\cdot 3x$
$\qquad = 23x - 5x\sqrt{15}$

**69.** $\left(\sqrt[3]{4}+2\right)\left(\sqrt[3]{2}-1\right)$
$\qquad = \sqrt[3]{4}\left(\sqrt[3]{2}\right) + \sqrt[3]{4}\cdot(-1) + 2\sqrt[3]{2} + 2(-1)$
$\qquad = \sqrt[3]{8} - \sqrt[3]{4} + 2\sqrt[3]{2} - 2$
$\qquad = 2 - \sqrt[3]{4} + 2\sqrt[3]{2} - 2$
$\qquad = 2\sqrt[3]{2} - \sqrt[3]{4}$

**71.** $\left(\sqrt[3]{x}+1\right)\left(\sqrt[3]{x^2}-\sqrt[3]{x}+1\right)$
$\qquad = \sqrt[3]{x}\left(\sqrt[3]{x^2}\right) - \sqrt[3]{x}\left(\sqrt[3]{x}\right) + \sqrt[3]{x}(1)$
$\qquad\qquad + 1\left(\sqrt[3]{x^2}\right) - 1\left(\sqrt[3]{x}\right) + 1(1)$
$\qquad = \sqrt[3]{x^3} - \sqrt[3]{x^2} + \sqrt[3]{x} + \sqrt[3]{x^2} - \sqrt[3]{x} + 1$
$\qquad = x + 1$

**73.** $\left(\sqrt{x-1}+5\right)^2 = \left(\sqrt{x-1}\right)^2 + 2\sqrt{x-1}\cdot 5 + 5^2$
$\qquad\qquad\qquad = (x-1) + 10\sqrt{x-1} + 25$
$\qquad\qquad\qquad = x + 10\sqrt{x-1} + 24$

**75.** $\left(\sqrt{2x+5}-1\right)^2 = \left(\sqrt{2x+5}\right)^2 - 2\sqrt{2x+5}\cdot 1 + 1^2$
$\qquad\qquad\qquad = (2x+5) - 2\sqrt{2x+5} + 1$
$\qquad\qquad\qquad = 2x - 2\sqrt{2x+5} + 6$

**77.** $\dfrac{2x-14}{2} = \dfrac{2(x-7)}{2} = x - 7$

**79.** $\dfrac{7x-7y}{x^2-y^2} = \dfrac{7(x-y)}{(x+y)(x-y)} = \dfrac{7}{x+y}$

**81.** $\dfrac{6a^2b-9ab}{3ab} = \dfrac{3ab(2a-3)}{3ab} = 2a - 3$

**83.** $\dfrac{-4+2\sqrt{3}}{6} = \dfrac{2\left(-2+\sqrt{3}\right)}{6} = \dfrac{-2+\sqrt{3}}{3}$

**85.**  $P = 2l + 2w$

$\qquad = 2\left(3\sqrt{20}\right) + 2\left(\sqrt{125}\right)$

$\qquad = 6\sqrt{4 \cdot 5} + 2\sqrt{25 \cdot 5}$

$\qquad = 6(2)\sqrt{5} + 2(5)\sqrt{5}$

$\qquad = 12\sqrt{5} + 10\sqrt{5}$

$\qquad = 22\sqrt{5}$ feet

$\quad A = lw$

$\qquad = \left(3\sqrt{20}\right)\left(\sqrt{125}\right)$

$\qquad = 3\sqrt{4 \cdot 5}\sqrt{25 \cdot 5}$

$\qquad = 3(2)\sqrt{5} \cdot 5\sqrt{5}$

$\qquad = 30 \cdot 5$

$\qquad = 150$ square feet

**87. a.**  $\sqrt{3} + \sqrt{3} = 2\sqrt{3}$

**b.**  $\sqrt{3} \cdot \sqrt{3} = \sqrt{9} = 3$

**c.**  Answers may vary

**89.**  Answer may vary

## Section 7.5

### Practice Exercises

**1. a.**  $\dfrac{5}{\sqrt{3}} = \dfrac{5 \cdot \sqrt{3}}{\sqrt{3} \cdot \sqrt{3}} = \dfrac{5\sqrt{3}}{3}$

**b.**  $\dfrac{3\sqrt{25}}{\sqrt{4x}} = \dfrac{3(5)}{2\sqrt{x}} = \dfrac{15}{2\sqrt{x}} = \dfrac{15 \cdot \sqrt{x}}{2\sqrt{x} \cdot \sqrt{x}} = \dfrac{15\sqrt{x}}{2x}$

**c.**  $\sqrt[3]{\dfrac{2}{9}} = \dfrac{\sqrt[3]{2}}{\sqrt[3]{9}} = \dfrac{\sqrt[3]{2} \cdot \sqrt[3]{3}}{\sqrt[3]{3^2} \cdot \sqrt[3]{3}} = \dfrac{\sqrt[3]{6}}{3}$

**2.**  $\sqrt{\dfrac{3z}{5y}} = \dfrac{\sqrt{3z}}{\sqrt{5y}} = \dfrac{\sqrt{3z} \cdot \sqrt{5y}}{\sqrt{5y} \cdot \sqrt{5y}} = \dfrac{\sqrt{15yz}}{5y}$

**3.**  $\dfrac{\sqrt[3]{z^2}}{\sqrt[3]{27x^4}} = \dfrac{\sqrt[3]{z^2}}{\sqrt[3]{27x^3} \cdot \sqrt[3]{x}}$

$\qquad = \dfrac{\sqrt[3]{z^2}}{3x\sqrt[3]{x}}$

$\qquad = \dfrac{\sqrt[3]{z^2} \cdot \sqrt[3]{x^2}}{3x\sqrt[3]{x} \cdot \sqrt[3]{x^2}}$

$\qquad = \dfrac{\sqrt[3]{z^2 x^2}}{3x\sqrt[3]{x^3}}$

$\qquad = \dfrac{\sqrt[3]{x^2 z^2}}{3x^2}$

**4. a.**  $\dfrac{5}{3\sqrt{5} + 2} = \dfrac{5\left(3\sqrt{5} - 2\right)}{\left(3\sqrt{5} + 2\right)\left(3\sqrt{5} - 2\right)}$

$\qquad = \dfrac{5\left(3\sqrt{5} - 2\right)}{\left(3\sqrt{5}\right)^2 - 2^2}$

$\qquad = \dfrac{5\left(3\sqrt{5} - 2\right)}{45 - 4}$

$\qquad = \dfrac{5\left(3\sqrt{5} - 2\right)}{41}$

**b.**  $\dfrac{\sqrt{2} + 5}{\sqrt{3} - \sqrt{5}} = \dfrac{\left(\sqrt{2} + 5\right)\left(\sqrt{3} + \sqrt{5}\right)}{\left(\sqrt{3} - \sqrt{5}\right)\left(\sqrt{3} + \sqrt{5}\right)}$

$\qquad = \dfrac{\sqrt{2}\sqrt{3} + \sqrt{2}\sqrt{5} + 5\sqrt{3} + 5\sqrt{5}}{\left(\sqrt{3}\right)^2 - \left(\sqrt{5}\right)^2}$

$\qquad = \dfrac{\sqrt{6} + \sqrt{10} + 5\sqrt{3} + 5\sqrt{5}}{3 - 5}$

$\qquad = \dfrac{\sqrt{6} + \sqrt{10} + 5\sqrt{3} + 5\sqrt{5}}{-2}$

**c.**  $\dfrac{3\sqrt{x}}{2\sqrt{x} + \sqrt{y}} = \dfrac{3\sqrt{x}\left(2\sqrt{x} - \sqrt{y}\right)}{\left(2\sqrt{x} + \sqrt{y}\right)\left(2\sqrt{x} - \sqrt{y}\right)}$

$\qquad = \dfrac{6\sqrt{x^2} - 3\sqrt{xy}}{\left(2\sqrt{x}\right)^2 - \left(\sqrt{y}\right)^2}$

$\qquad = \dfrac{6x - 3\sqrt{xy}}{4x - y}$

**5.**  $\dfrac{\sqrt{32}}{\sqrt{80}} = \dfrac{\sqrt{16 \cdot 2}}{\sqrt{16 \cdot 5}} = \dfrac{4\sqrt{2}}{4\sqrt{5}} = \dfrac{\sqrt{2}}{\sqrt{5}} = \dfrac{\sqrt{2} \cdot \sqrt{2}}{\sqrt{5} \cdot \sqrt{2}} = \dfrac{2}{\sqrt{10}}$

**6.** $\dfrac{\sqrt[3]{5b}}{\sqrt[3]{2a}} = \dfrac{\sqrt[3]{5b}\cdot\sqrt[3]{25b^2}}{\sqrt[3]{2a}\cdot\sqrt[3]{25b^2}} = \dfrac{\sqrt[3]{125b^3}}{\sqrt[3]{50ab^2}} = \dfrac{5b}{\sqrt[3]{50ab^2}}$

**7.** $\dfrac{\sqrt{x}-3}{4} = \dfrac{\left(\sqrt{x}-3\right)\left(\sqrt{x}+3\right)}{4\left(\sqrt{x}+3\right)}$

$\qquad\quad = \dfrac{\left(\sqrt{x}\right)^2 - (3)^2}{4\left(\sqrt{x}+3\right)}$

$\qquad\quad = \dfrac{x-9}{4\left(\sqrt{x}+3\right)}$

**Vocabulary and Readiness Check**

**1.** The <u>conjugate</u> of $a+b$ is $a-b$.

**2.** The process of writing an equivalent expression, but without a radical in the denominator is called <u>rationalizing the denominator</u>.

**3.** The process of writing an equivalent expression, but without a radical in the numerator is called <u>rationalizing the numerator</u>.

**4.** To rationalize the denominator of $\dfrac{5}{\sqrt{3}}$, we multiply by $\dfrac{\sqrt{3}}{\sqrt{3}}$.

**5.** The conjugate of $\sqrt{2}+x$ is $\sqrt{2}-x$.

**6.** The conjugate of $\sqrt{3}+y$ is $\sqrt{3}-y$.

**7.** The conjugate of $5-\sqrt{a}$ is $5+\sqrt{a}$.

**8.** The conjugate of $6-\sqrt{b}$ is $6+\sqrt{b}$.

**9.** The conjugate of $-7\sqrt{5}+8\sqrt{x}$ is $-7\sqrt{5}-8\sqrt{x}$.

**10.** The conjugate of $-9\sqrt{2}-6\sqrt{y}$ is $-9\sqrt{2}+6\sqrt{y}$.

**Exercise Set 7.5**

**1.** $\dfrac{\sqrt{2}}{\sqrt{7}} = \dfrac{\sqrt{2}\cdot\sqrt{7}}{\sqrt{7}\cdot\sqrt{7}} = \dfrac{\sqrt{14}}{\sqrt{49}} = \dfrac{\sqrt{14}}{7}$

**3.** $\sqrt{\dfrac{1}{5}} = \dfrac{\sqrt{1}}{\sqrt{5}} = \dfrac{1\cdot\sqrt{5}}{\sqrt{5}\cdot\sqrt{5}} = \dfrac{\sqrt{5}}{5}$

**5.** $\sqrt{\dfrac{4}{x}} = \dfrac{\sqrt{4}}{\sqrt{x}} = \dfrac{2\cdot\sqrt{x}}{\sqrt{x}\cdot\sqrt{x}} = \dfrac{2\sqrt{x}}{\sqrt{x^2}} = \dfrac{2\sqrt{x}}{x}$

**7.** $\dfrac{4}{\sqrt[3]{3}} = \dfrac{4\cdot\sqrt[3]{9}}{\sqrt[3]{3}\cdot\sqrt[3]{9}} = \dfrac{4\sqrt[3]{9}}{\sqrt[3]{27}} = \dfrac{4\sqrt[3]{9}}{3}$

**9.** $\dfrac{3}{\sqrt{8x}} = \dfrac{3\cdot\sqrt{2x}}{\sqrt{8x}\cdot\sqrt{2x}} = \dfrac{3\sqrt{2x}}{\sqrt{16x^2}} = \dfrac{3\sqrt{2x}}{4x}$

**11.** $\dfrac{3}{\sqrt[3]{4x^2}} = \dfrac{3\cdot\sqrt[3]{2x}}{\sqrt[3]{4x^2}\cdot\sqrt[3]{2x}} = \dfrac{3\sqrt[3]{2x}}{\sqrt[3]{8x^3}} = \dfrac{3\sqrt[3]{2x}}{2x}$

**13.** $\dfrac{9}{\sqrt{3a}} = \dfrac{9\cdot\sqrt{3a}}{\sqrt{3a}\cdot\sqrt{3a}} = \dfrac{9\sqrt{3a}}{3a} = \dfrac{3\sqrt{3a}}{a}$

**15.** $\dfrac{3}{\sqrt[3]{2}} = \dfrac{3\cdot\sqrt[3]{4}}{\sqrt[3]{2}\cdot\sqrt[3]{4}} = \dfrac{3\sqrt[3]{4}}{\sqrt[3]{8}} = \dfrac{3\sqrt[3]{4}}{2}$

**17.** $\dfrac{2\sqrt{3}}{\sqrt{7}} = \dfrac{2\sqrt{3}\cdot\sqrt{7}}{\sqrt{7}\cdot\sqrt{7}} = \dfrac{2\sqrt{21}}{\sqrt{49}} = \dfrac{2\sqrt{21}}{7}$

**19.** $\sqrt{\dfrac{2x}{5y}} = \dfrac{\sqrt{2x}}{\sqrt{5y}} = \dfrac{\sqrt{2x}\cdot\sqrt{5y}}{\sqrt{5y}\cdot\sqrt{5y}} = \dfrac{\sqrt{10xy}}{5y}$

**21.** $\sqrt[3]{\dfrac{3}{5}} = \dfrac{\sqrt[3]{3}}{\sqrt[3]{5}}\cdot\dfrac{\sqrt[3]{25}}{\sqrt[3]{25}} = \dfrac{\sqrt[3]{75}}{5}$

**23.** $\sqrt{\dfrac{3x}{50}} = \dfrac{\sqrt{3x}}{\sqrt{50}}$

$\qquad\quad = \dfrac{\sqrt{3x}}{5\sqrt{2}}$

$\qquad\quad = \dfrac{\sqrt{3x}\cdot\sqrt{2}}{5\sqrt{2}\cdot\sqrt{2}}$

$\qquad\quad = \dfrac{\sqrt{6x}}{5\cdot2}$

$\qquad\quad = \dfrac{\sqrt{6x}}{10}$

**25.** $\dfrac{1}{\sqrt{12z}} = \dfrac{1}{\sqrt{4\cdot3z}} = \dfrac{1}{2\sqrt{3z}}\cdot\dfrac{\sqrt{3z}}{\sqrt{3z}} = \dfrac{\sqrt{3z}}{6z}$

**27.** $\dfrac{\sqrt[3]{2y^2}}{\sqrt[3]{9x^2}} = \dfrac{\sqrt[3]{2y^2}\cdot\sqrt[3]{3x}}{\sqrt[3]{9x^2}\cdot\sqrt[3]{3x}} = \dfrac{\sqrt[3]{6xy^2}}{3x}$

**29.** $\sqrt[4]{\dfrac{81}{8}} = \dfrac{\sqrt[4]{81}}{\sqrt[4]{8}} = \dfrac{3 \cdot \sqrt[4]{2}}{\sqrt[4]{8} \cdot \sqrt[4]{2}} = \dfrac{3\sqrt[4]{2}}{\sqrt[4]{16}} = \dfrac{3\sqrt[4]{2}}{2}$

**31.** $\sqrt[4]{\dfrac{16}{9x^7}} = \dfrac{\sqrt[4]{16}}{\sqrt[4]{9x^7}} = \dfrac{2 \cdot \sqrt[4]{9x}}{\sqrt[4]{9x^7} \cdot \sqrt[4]{9x}} = \dfrac{2\sqrt[4]{9x}}{\sqrt[4]{81x^8}} = \dfrac{2\sqrt[4]{9x}}{3x^2}$

**33.** $\dfrac{5a}{\sqrt[5]{8a^9b^{11}}} = \dfrac{5a \cdot \sqrt[5]{4ab^4}}{\sqrt[5]{8a^9b^{11}} \cdot \sqrt[5]{4ab^4}}$

$= \dfrac{5a\sqrt[5]{4ab^4}}{\sqrt[5]{32a^{10}b^{15}}}$

$= \dfrac{5a\sqrt[5]{4ab^4}}{2a^2b^3}$

**35.** $\dfrac{6}{2-\sqrt{7}} = \dfrac{6\left(2+\sqrt{7}\right)}{\left(2-\sqrt{7}\right)\left(2+\sqrt{7}\right)}$

$= \dfrac{6\left(2+\sqrt{7}\right)}{2^2 - \left(\sqrt{7}\right)^2}$

$= \dfrac{6\left(2+\sqrt{7}\right)}{4-7}$

$= \dfrac{6\left(2+\sqrt{7}\right)}{-3}$

$= -2\left(2+\sqrt{7}\right)$

**37.** $\dfrac{-7}{\sqrt{x}-3} = \dfrac{-7\left(\sqrt{x}+3\right)}{\left(\sqrt{x}-3\right)\left(\sqrt{x}+3\right)}$

$= \dfrac{-7\left(\sqrt{x}+3\right)}{\left(\sqrt{x}\right)^2 - (3)^2}$

$= \dfrac{-7\left(\sqrt{x}+3\right)}{x-9}$ or $\dfrac{7\left(\sqrt{x}+3\right)}{9-x}$

**39.** $\dfrac{\sqrt{2}-\sqrt{3}}{\sqrt{2}+\sqrt{3}} = \dfrac{\left(\sqrt{2}-\sqrt{3}\right)\left(\sqrt{2}-\sqrt{3}\right)}{\left(\sqrt{2}+\sqrt{3}\right)\left(\sqrt{2}-\sqrt{3}\right)}$

$= \dfrac{\left(\sqrt{2}\right)^2 - 2\sqrt{2}\sqrt{3} + \left(\sqrt{3}\right)^2}{\left(\sqrt{2}\right)^2 - \left(\sqrt{3}\right)^2}$

$= \dfrac{2 - 2\sqrt{6} + 3}{2-3}$

$= \dfrac{5 - 2\sqrt{6}}{-1}$

$= -5 + 2\sqrt{6}$

**41.** $\dfrac{\sqrt{a}+1}{2\sqrt{a}-\sqrt{b}}$

$= \dfrac{\left(\sqrt{a}+1\right)\left(2\sqrt{a}+\sqrt{b}\right)}{\left(2\sqrt{a}-\sqrt{b}\right)\left(2\sqrt{a}+\sqrt{b}\right)}$

$= \dfrac{\sqrt{a} \cdot 2\sqrt{a} + \sqrt{a}\sqrt{b} + 1 \cdot 2\sqrt{a} + 1 \cdot \sqrt{b}}{\left(2\sqrt{a}\right)^2 - \left(\sqrt{b}\right)^2}$

$= \dfrac{2a + \sqrt{ab} + 2\sqrt{a} + \sqrt{b}}{4a-b}$

**43.** $\dfrac{8}{1+\sqrt{10}} = \dfrac{8\left(1-\sqrt{10}\right)}{\left(1+\sqrt{10}\right)\left(1-\sqrt{10}\right)}$

$= \dfrac{8\left(1-\sqrt{10}\right)}{1^2 - \left(\sqrt{10}\right)^2}$

$= \dfrac{8\left(1-\sqrt{10}\right)}{1-10}$

$= -\dfrac{8\left(1-\sqrt{10}\right)}{9}$

**45.**
$$\frac{\sqrt{x}}{\sqrt{x}+\sqrt{y}} = \frac{\sqrt{x}\left(\sqrt{x}-\sqrt{y}\right)}{\left(\sqrt{x}+\sqrt{y}\right)\left(\sqrt{x}-\sqrt{y}\right)}$$
$$= \frac{\sqrt{x}\left(\sqrt{x}-\sqrt{y}\right)}{\left(\sqrt{x}\right)^2 - \left(\sqrt{y}\right)^2}$$
$$= \frac{\sqrt{x}\left(\sqrt{x}-\sqrt{y}\right)}{x-y}$$
$$= \frac{\sqrt{x}\sqrt{x} - \sqrt{x}\sqrt{y}}{x-y}$$
$$= \frac{x - \sqrt{xy}}{x-y}$$

**47.**
$$\frac{2\sqrt{3}+\sqrt{6}}{4\sqrt{3}-\sqrt{6}} = \frac{\left(2\sqrt{3}+\sqrt{6}\right)\left(4\sqrt{3}+\sqrt{6}\right)}{\left(4\sqrt{3}-\sqrt{6}\right)\left(4\sqrt{3}+\sqrt{6}\right)}$$
$$= \frac{8\cdot3 + 2\sqrt{18} + 4\sqrt{18} + 6}{\left(4\sqrt{3}\right)^2 - \left(\sqrt{6}\right)^2}$$
$$= \frac{30 + 6\sqrt{18}}{16\cdot3 - 6}$$
$$= \frac{30 + 6(3)\sqrt{2}}{42}$$
$$= \frac{30 + 18\sqrt{2}}{42}$$
$$= \frac{6\left(5 + 3\sqrt{2}\right)}{42}$$
$$= \frac{5 + 3\sqrt{2}}{7}$$

**49.**
$$\sqrt{\frac{5}{3}} = \frac{\sqrt{5}}{\sqrt{3}} = \frac{\sqrt{5}\cdot\sqrt{5}}{\sqrt{3}\cdot\sqrt{5}} = \frac{\sqrt{25}}{\sqrt{15}} = \frac{5}{\sqrt{15}}$$

**51.**
$$\sqrt{\frac{18}{5}} = \frac{\sqrt{18}}{\sqrt{5}}$$
$$= \frac{\sqrt{9}\cdot\sqrt{2}}{\sqrt{5}}$$
$$= \frac{3\sqrt{2}}{\sqrt{5}}$$
$$= \frac{3\sqrt{2}\cdot\sqrt{2}}{\sqrt{5}\cdot\sqrt{2}}$$
$$= \frac{3\cdot2}{\sqrt{10}}$$
$$= \frac{6}{\sqrt{10}}$$

**53.**
$$\frac{\sqrt{4x}}{7} = \frac{2\sqrt{x}}{7} = \frac{2\sqrt{x}\cdot\sqrt{x}}{7\cdot\sqrt{x}} = \frac{2\sqrt{x^2}}{7\sqrt{x}} = \frac{2x}{7\sqrt{x}}$$

**55.**
$$\frac{\sqrt[3]{5y^2}}{\sqrt[3]{4x}} = \frac{\sqrt[3]{5y^2}\cdot\sqrt[3]{5^2 y}}{\sqrt[3]{4x}\cdot\sqrt[3]{5^2 y}} = \frac{\sqrt[3]{5^3 y^3}}{\sqrt[3]{100xy}} = \frac{5y}{\sqrt[3]{100xy}}$$

**57.**
$$\sqrt{\frac{2}{5}} = \frac{\sqrt{2}}{\sqrt{5}} = \frac{\sqrt{2}\cdot\sqrt{2}}{\sqrt{5}\cdot\sqrt{2}} = \frac{\sqrt{4}}{\sqrt{10}} = \frac{2}{\sqrt{10}}$$

**59.**
$$\frac{\sqrt{2x}}{11} = \frac{\sqrt{2x}\cdot\sqrt{2x}}{11\cdot\sqrt{2x}} = \frac{\sqrt{4x^2}}{11\sqrt{2x}} = \frac{2x}{11\sqrt{2x}}$$

**61.**
$$\sqrt[3]{\frac{7}{8}} = \frac{\sqrt[3]{7}}{\sqrt[3]{8}}$$
$$= \frac{\sqrt[3]{7}}{2}$$
$$= \frac{\sqrt[3]{7}\cdot\sqrt[3]{7^2}}{2\cdot\sqrt[3]{7^2}}$$
$$= \frac{\sqrt[3]{7^3}}{2\sqrt[3]{49}}$$
$$= \frac{7}{2\sqrt[3]{49}}$$

**63.**
$$\frac{\sqrt[3]{3x^5}}{10} = \frac{\sqrt[3]{x^3\cdot3x^2}}{10}$$
$$= \frac{x\sqrt[3]{3x^2}}{10}$$
$$= \frac{x\sqrt[3]{3x^2}\cdot\sqrt[3]{3^2 x}}{10\cdot\sqrt[3]{3^2 x}}$$
$$= \frac{x\sqrt[3]{3^3 x^3}}{10\sqrt[3]{9x}}$$
$$= \frac{x\cdot3x}{10\sqrt[3]{9x}}$$
$$= \frac{3x^2}{10\sqrt[3]{9x}}$$

**65.** $\sqrt{\dfrac{18x^4y^6}{3z}} = \dfrac{\sqrt{18x^4y^6}}{\sqrt{3z}}$

$\qquad = \dfrac{\sqrt{9x^4y^6 \cdot 2}}{\sqrt{3z}}$

$\qquad = \dfrac{3x^2y^3\sqrt{2}}{\sqrt{3z}}$

$\qquad = \dfrac{3x^2y^3\sqrt{2} \cdot \sqrt{2}}{\sqrt{3z} \cdot \sqrt{2}}$

$\qquad = \dfrac{3x^2y^3 \cdot 2}{\sqrt{6z}}$

$\qquad = \dfrac{6x^2y^3}{\sqrt{6z}}$

**67.** Answers may vary

**69.** $\dfrac{2-\sqrt{11}}{6} = \dfrac{\left(2-\sqrt{11}\right)\left(2+\sqrt{11}\right)}{6\left(2+\sqrt{11}\right)}$

$\qquad = \dfrac{4-11}{12+6\sqrt{11}}$

$\qquad = \dfrac{-7}{12+6\sqrt{11}}$

**71.** $\dfrac{2-\sqrt{7}}{-5} = \dfrac{\left(2-\sqrt{7}\right)\left(2+\sqrt{7}\right)}{-5\left(2+\sqrt{7}\right)}$

$\qquad = \dfrac{4-7}{-5\left(2+\sqrt{7}\right)}$

$\qquad = \dfrac{-3}{-5\left(2+\sqrt{7}\right)}$

$\qquad = \dfrac{3}{5\left(2+\sqrt{7}\right)}$

$\qquad = \dfrac{3}{10+5\sqrt{7}}$

**73.** $\dfrac{\sqrt{x}+3}{\sqrt{x}} = \dfrac{\left(\sqrt{x}+3\right)\left(\sqrt{x}-3\right)}{\sqrt{x}\left(\sqrt{x}-3\right)}$

$\qquad = \dfrac{\sqrt{x^2}-9}{\sqrt{x^2}-3\sqrt{x}}$

$\qquad = \dfrac{x-9}{x-3\sqrt{x}}$

**75.** $\dfrac{\sqrt{2}-1}{\sqrt{2}+1} = \dfrac{\left(\sqrt{2}-1\right)\left(\sqrt{2}+1\right)}{\left(\sqrt{2}+1\right)\left(\sqrt{2}+1\right)}$

$\qquad = \dfrac{\sqrt{4}-1}{\sqrt{4}+2\sqrt{2}+1}$

$\qquad = \dfrac{2-1}{2+2\sqrt{2}+1}$

$\qquad = \dfrac{1}{3+2\sqrt{2}}$

**77.** $\dfrac{\sqrt{x}+1}{\sqrt{x}-1} = \dfrac{\left(\sqrt{x}+1\right)\left(\sqrt{x}-1\right)}{\left(\sqrt{x}-1\right)\left(\sqrt{x}-1\right)}$

$\qquad = \dfrac{\sqrt{x^2}-1}{\sqrt{x^2}-2\sqrt{x}+1}$

$\qquad = \dfrac{x-1}{x-2\sqrt{x}+1}$

**79.** $2x-7 = 3(x-4)$

$\qquad 2x-7 = 3x-12$

$\qquad -x-7 = -12$

$\qquad -x = -5$

$\qquad x = 5$

The solution is 5.

**81.** $(x-6)(2x+1) = 0$

$\qquad x-6 = 0$ or $2x+1 = 0$

$\qquad x = 6$ or $\quad 2x = -1$

$\qquad\qquad\qquad\qquad x = -\dfrac{1}{2}$

The solutions are $-\dfrac{1}{2}, 6$.

**83.** $\qquad x^2 - 8x = -12$

$\qquad x^2 - 8x + 12 = 0$

$\qquad (x-6)(x-2) = 0$

$\qquad x-6 = 0$ or $x-2 = 0$

$\qquad x = 6$ or $\quad x = 2$

The solutions are 2, 6.

**85.** $\dfrac{9}{\sqrt[3]{5}} = \dfrac{9}{\sqrt[3]{5}} \cdot \dfrac{\sqrt[3]{25}}{\sqrt[3]{25}} = \dfrac{9\sqrt[3]{25}}{\sqrt[3]{125}} = \dfrac{9\sqrt[3]{25}}{5}$

The smallest number is $\sqrt[3]{25}$.

**87.** $r = \sqrt{\dfrac{A}{4\pi}}$

$= \dfrac{\sqrt{A}}{\sqrt{4\pi}}$

$= \dfrac{\sqrt{A}}{2\sqrt{\pi}}$

$= \dfrac{\sqrt{A}\cdot\sqrt{\pi}}{2\sqrt{\pi}\cdot\sqrt{\pi}}$

$= \dfrac{\sqrt{A\pi}}{2\pi}$

**89.** Answers may vary

**Integrated Review**

**1.** $\sqrt{81} = 9$ because $9^2 = 81$.

**2.** $\sqrt[3]{-8} = -2$ because $(-2)^3 = -8$.

**3.** $\sqrt[4]{\dfrac{1}{16}} = \dfrac{1}{2}$ because $\left(\dfrac{1}{2}\right)^4 = \dfrac{1}{16}$.

**4.** $\sqrt{x^6} = x^3$ because $(x^3)^2 = x^6$.

**5.** $\sqrt[3]{y^9} = y^3$ because $(y^3)^3 = y^9$.

**6.** $\sqrt{4y^{10}} = 2y^5$ because $(2y^5)^2 = 4y^{10}$.

**7.** $\sqrt[5]{-32y^5} = -2y$ because $(-2y)^5 = -32y^5$.

**8.** $\sqrt[4]{81b^{12}} = 3b^3$ because $(3b^3)^4 = 81b^{12}$.

**9.** $36^{1/2} = \sqrt{36} = 6$

**10.** $(3y)^{1/4} = \sqrt[4]{3y}$

**11.** $64^{-2/3} = \dfrac{1}{\left(\sqrt[3]{64}\right)^2} = \dfrac{1}{4^2} = \dfrac{1}{16}$

**12.** $(x+1)^{3/5} = \sqrt[5]{(x+1)^3}$

**13.** $y^{-1/6}\cdot y^{7/6} = y^{-\frac{1}{6}+\frac{7}{6}} = y^{6/6} = y$

**14.** $\dfrac{(2x^{1/3})^4}{x^{5/6}} = 16x^{4/3}x^{-5/6}$

$= 16x^{\frac{8}{6}-\frac{5}{6}}$

$= 16x^{3/6}$

$= 16x^{1/2}$

**15.** $\dfrac{x^{1/4}x^{3/4}}{x^{-1/4}} = x^{\frac{1}{4}+\frac{3}{4}+\frac{1}{4}} = x^{5/4}$

**16.** $4^{1/3}\cdot 4^{2/5} = 4^{\frac{1}{3}+\frac{2}{5}} = 4^{\frac{5}{15}+\frac{6}{15}} = 4^{11/15}$

**17.** $\sqrt[3]{8x^6} = (8x^6)^{1/3} = (2^3x^6)^{1/3} = 2^{3/3}x^{6/3} = 2x^2$

**18.** $\sqrt[12]{a^9b^6} = (a^9b^6)^{1/12}$

$= a^{9/12}b^{6/12}$

$= a^{3/4}b^{1/2}$

$= a^{3/4}b^{2/4}$

$= (a^3b^2)^{1/4}$

$= \sqrt[4]{a^3b^2}$

**19.** $\sqrt[4]{x}\cdot\sqrt{x} = x^{1/4}\cdot x^{1/2} = x^{\frac{1}{4}+\frac{2}{4}} = x^{3/4} = \sqrt[4]{x^3}$

**20.** $\sqrt{5}\cdot\sqrt[3]{2} = 5^{1/2}\cdot 2^{1/3}$

$= 5^{3/6}\cdot 2^{2/6}$

$= (5^3\cdot 2^2)^{1/6}$

$= \sqrt[6]{5^3\cdot 2^2}$

$= \sqrt[6]{500}$

**21.** $\sqrt{40} = \sqrt{4}\sqrt{10} = 2\sqrt{10}$

**22.** $\sqrt[4]{16x^7y^{10}} = \sqrt[4]{16x^4y^8}\sqrt[4]{x^3y^2} = 2xy^2\sqrt[4]{x^3y^2}$

**23.** $\sqrt[3]{54x^4} = \sqrt[3]{27x^3}\sqrt[3]{2x} = 3x\sqrt[3]{2x}$

**24.** $\sqrt[5]{-64b^{10}} = \sqrt[5]{-32b^{10}}\sqrt[5]{2} = -2b^2\sqrt[5]{2}$

**25.** $\sqrt{5}\cdot\sqrt{x} = \sqrt{5x}$

**26.** $\sqrt[3]{8x}\cdot\sqrt[3]{8x^2} = \sqrt[3]{64x^3} = 4x$

**27.** $\dfrac{\sqrt{98y^6}}{\sqrt{2y}} = \sqrt{\dfrac{98y^6}{2y}}$

$= \sqrt{49y^5}$

$= \sqrt{49y^4} \cdot \sqrt{y}$

$= 7y^2\sqrt{y}$

**28.** $\dfrac{\sqrt[4]{48a^9b^3}}{\sqrt[4]{ab^3}} = \sqrt[4]{\dfrac{48a^9b^3}{ab^3}}$

$= \sqrt[4]{48a^8}$

$= \sqrt[4]{16a^8} \cdot \sqrt[4]{3}$

$= 2a^2\sqrt[4]{3}$

**29.** $\sqrt{20} - \sqrt{75} + 5\sqrt{7} = \sqrt{4}\sqrt{5} - \sqrt{25}\sqrt{3} + 5\sqrt{7}$

$= 2\sqrt{5} - 5\sqrt{3} + 5\sqrt{7}$

**30.** $\sqrt[3]{54y^4} - y\sqrt[3]{16y} = \sqrt[3]{27y^3}\sqrt[3]{2y} - y\sqrt[3]{8}\sqrt[3]{2y}$

$= 3y\sqrt[3]{2y} - 2y\sqrt[3]{2y}$

$= y\sqrt[3]{2y}$

**31.** $\sqrt{3}\left(\sqrt{5} - \sqrt{2}\right) = \sqrt{3}\sqrt{5} - \sqrt{3}\sqrt{2} = \sqrt{15} - \sqrt{6}$

**32.** $\left(\sqrt{7} + \sqrt{3}\right)^2 = \left(\sqrt{7}\right)^2 + 2\sqrt{7}\sqrt{3} + \left(\sqrt{3}\right)^2$

$= 7 + 2\sqrt{21} + 3$

$= 10 + 2\sqrt{21}$

**33.** $\left(2x - \sqrt{5}\right)\left(2x + \sqrt{5}\right) = (2x)^2 - \left(\sqrt{5}\right)^2$

$= 4x^2 - 5$

**34.** $\left(\sqrt{x+1} - 1\right)^2 = \left(\sqrt{x+1}\right)^2 - 2\left(\sqrt{x+1}\right) + 1^2$

$= x + 1 - 2\sqrt{x+1} + 1$

$= x + 2 - 2\sqrt{x+1}$

**35.** $\sqrt{\dfrac{7}{3}} = \dfrac{\sqrt{7}}{\sqrt{3}} = \dfrac{\sqrt{7}}{\sqrt{3}} \cdot \dfrac{\sqrt{3}}{\sqrt{3}} = \dfrac{\sqrt{21}}{3}$

**36.** $\dfrac{5}{\sqrt[3]{2x^2}} = \dfrac{5}{\sqrt[3]{2x^2}} \cdot \dfrac{\sqrt[3]{4x}}{\sqrt[3]{4x}} = \dfrac{5\sqrt[3]{4x}}{\sqrt[3]{8x^3}} = \dfrac{5\sqrt[3]{4x}}{2x}$

**37.** $\dfrac{\sqrt{3} - \sqrt{7}}{2\sqrt{3} + \sqrt{7}}$

$= \dfrac{\sqrt{3} - \sqrt{7}}{2\sqrt{3} + \sqrt{7}} \cdot \dfrac{\left(2\sqrt{3} - \sqrt{7}\right)}{\left(2\sqrt{3} - \sqrt{7}\right)}$

$= \dfrac{\sqrt{3}\left(2\sqrt{3}\right) - \sqrt{3}\sqrt{7} - \sqrt{7}\left(2\sqrt{3}\right) + \sqrt{7}\sqrt{7}}{\left(2\sqrt{3}\right)^2 - \left(\sqrt{7}\right)^2}$

$\dfrac{6 - \sqrt{21} - 2\sqrt{21} + 7}{12 - 7}$

$= \dfrac{13 - 3\sqrt{21}}{5}$

**38.** $\sqrt{\dfrac{7}{3}} = \dfrac{\sqrt{7}}{\sqrt{3}} = \dfrac{\sqrt{7}}{\sqrt{3}} \cdot \dfrac{\sqrt{7}}{\sqrt{7}} = \dfrac{7}{\sqrt{21}}$

**39.** $\sqrt[3]{\dfrac{9y}{11}} = \dfrac{\sqrt[3]{9y}}{\sqrt[3]{11}} = \dfrac{\sqrt[3]{9y}}{\sqrt[3]{11}} \cdot \dfrac{\sqrt[3]{3y^2}}{\sqrt[3]{3y^2}} = \dfrac{\sqrt[3]{27y^3}}{\sqrt[3]{31y^2}} = \dfrac{3y}{\sqrt[3]{33y^2}}$

**40.** $\dfrac{\sqrt{x} - 2}{\sqrt{x}} = \dfrac{\sqrt{x} - 2}{\sqrt{x}} \cdot \dfrac{\sqrt{x} + 2}{\sqrt{x} + 2}$

$= \dfrac{\left(\sqrt{x}\right)^2 - 2^2}{\sqrt{x}\sqrt{x} + 2\sqrt{x}}$

$= \dfrac{x - 4}{x + 2\sqrt{x}}$

## Section 7.6

### Practice Exercises

**1.** $\sqrt{3x - 5} = 7$

$\left(\sqrt{3x - 5}\right)^2 = 7^2$

$3x - 5 = 49$

$3x = 54$

$x = 18$

Check:

$\sqrt{3x - 5} = 7$

$\sqrt{3(18) - 5} \stackrel{?}{=} 7$

$\sqrt{54 - 5} \stackrel{?}{=} 7$

$\sqrt{49} \stackrel{?}{=} 7$

$7 = 7$

The solution is 18.

**2.**
$$\sqrt{3-2x}-4x=0$$
$$\sqrt{3-2x}-4x+4x=0+4x$$
$$\sqrt{3-2x}=4x$$
$$\left(\sqrt{3-2x}\right)^2=(4x)^2$$
$$3-2x=16x^2$$
$$16x^2+2x-3=0$$
$$(8x-3)(2x+1)=0$$
$$8x-3=0 \text{ or } 2x+1=0$$
$$x=\frac{3}{8} \text{ or } x=-\frac{1}{2}$$

Check $\frac{3}{8}$:
$$\sqrt{3-2x}-4x=0$$
$$\sqrt{3-2\left(\frac{3}{8}\right)}-4\left(\frac{3}{8}\right)\overset{?}{=}0$$
$$\sqrt{\frac{24}{8}-\frac{6}{8}}-\frac{3}{2}\overset{?}{=}0$$
$$\sqrt{\frac{9}{4}}-\frac{3}{2}\overset{?}{=}0$$
$$\frac{3}{2}-\frac{3}{2}=0$$

Check $-\frac{1}{2}$:
$$\sqrt{3-2x}-4x=0$$
$$\sqrt{3-2\left(-\frac{1}{2}\right)}-4\left(-\frac{1}{2}\right)\overset{?}{=}0$$
$$\sqrt{3+1}+2\overset{?}{=}0$$
$$2+2\overset{?}{=}0$$
$$4\neq0$$

$-\frac{1}{2}$ does not check, so the only solution is $\frac{3}{8}$.

**3.**
$$\sqrt[3]{x-2}+1=3$$
$$\sqrt[3]{x-2}=2$$
$$\left(\sqrt[3]{x-2}\right)^3=2^3$$
$$x-2=8$$
$$x=10$$

Check:
$$\sqrt[3]{x-2}+1=3$$
$$\sqrt[3]{10-2}+1\overset{?}{=}3$$
$$\sqrt[3]{8}+1\overset{?}{=}3$$
$$2+1=3$$

The solution is 10.

**4.**
$$\sqrt{16+x}=x-4$$
$$\left(\sqrt{16+x}\right)^2=(x-4)^2$$
$$16+x=x^2-8x+16$$
$$x^2-9x=0$$
$$x(x-9)=0$$
$$x=0 \text{ or } x-9=0$$
$$x=9$$

Check 0:
$$\sqrt{16+x}=x-4$$
$$\sqrt{16+0}\overset{?}{=}0-4$$
$$\sqrt{16}\overset{?}{=}-4$$
$$4\neq-4$$

Check 9:
$$\sqrt{16+x}=x-4$$
$$\sqrt{16+9}\overset{?}{=}9-4$$
$$\sqrt{25}\overset{?}{=}5$$
$$5=5$$

0 does not check, so the only solution is 9.

**5.**
$$\sqrt{8x+1}+\sqrt{3x}=2$$
$$\sqrt{8x+1}=2-\sqrt{3x}$$
$$\left(\sqrt{8x+1}\right)^2=\left(2-\sqrt{3x}\right)^2$$
$$8x+1=4-4\sqrt{3x}+3x$$
$$4\sqrt{3x}=3-5x$$
$$\left(4\sqrt{3x}\right)^2=(3-5x)^2$$
$$16(3x)=9-30x+25x^2$$
$$25x^2-78x+9=0$$
$$(25x-3)(x-3)=0$$
$$25x-3=0 \text{ or } x-3=0$$
$$x=\frac{3}{25} \text{ or } x=3$$

Check $\frac{3}{25}$:
$$\sqrt{8x+1}+\sqrt{3x}=2$$
$$\sqrt{8\left(\frac{3}{25}\right)+1}+\sqrt{3\left(\frac{3}{25}\right)}\overset{?}{=}2$$
$$\sqrt{\frac{24}{25}+\frac{25}{25}}+\sqrt{\frac{9}{25}}\overset{?}{=}2$$
$$\sqrt{\frac{49}{25}}+\sqrt{\frac{9}{25}}\overset{?}{=}2$$
$$\frac{7}{5}+\frac{3}{5}\overset{?}{=}2$$
$$\frac{10}{5}=2$$

Check 3:
$$\sqrt{8x+1}+\sqrt{3x}=2$$
$$\sqrt{8(3)+1}+\sqrt{3(3)} \overset{?}{=} 2$$
$$\sqrt{25}+\sqrt{9} \overset{?}{=} 2$$
$$5+3 \neq 2$$

3 does not check, so the only solution is $\dfrac{3}{25}$.

6. $a^2 + b^2 = c^2$
$a^2 + 6^2 = 12^2$
$a^2 + 36 = 144$
$a^2 = 108$
$a = \pm\sqrt{108} = \pm\sqrt{36 \cdot 3} = \pm 6\sqrt{3}$

Since $a$ is a length, we will use the positive value only. The unknown leg is $6\sqrt{3}$ meters long.

7. Consider the base of the tank, and the plastic divider in the diagonal. Use the Pythagorean theorem to find $l$.

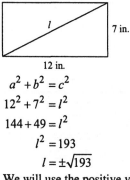

$a^2 + b^2 = c^2$
$12^2 + 7^2 = l^2$
$144 + 49 = l^2$
$l^2 = 193$
$l = \pm\sqrt{193}$

We will use the positive value because $l$ represents length. The divider must be $\sqrt{193} \approx 13.89$ inches long.

**Graphing Calculator Explorations**

1.
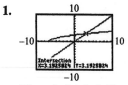
The solution is 3.19.

2.
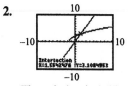
The solution is 1.55.

3.
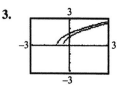
There is no solution. The solution set is ∅.

4.
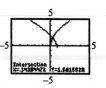
The solution is 0.34.

5.
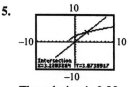
The solution is 3.23.

6.
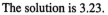
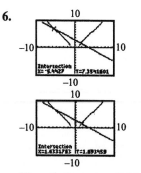
The solutions are −5.44 and 7.35.

**Vocabulary and Readiness Check**

1. A proposed solution that is not a solution of the original equation is called an <u>extraneous solution</u>.

2. The Pythagorean Theorem states that $a^2 + b^2 = c^2$ where $a$ and $b$ are the lengths of the <u>legs</u> of a <u>right</u> triangle and $c$ is the length of the <u>hypotenuse</u>.

3. The square of $x - 5$, or $(x-5)^2 = \underline{x^2 - 10x + 25}$.

4. The square of $4 - \sqrt{7x}$, or
$$\left(4-\sqrt{7x}\right)^2 = \underline{16 - 8\sqrt{7x} + 7x}.$$

**Exercise Set 7.6**

**1.**　$\sqrt{2x} = 4$

$\left(\sqrt{2x}\right)^2 = 4^2$

$2x = 16$

$x = 8$

The solution is 8.

**3.**　$\sqrt{x-3} = 2$

$\left(\sqrt{x-3}\right)^2 = 2^2$

$x - 3 = 4$

$x = 7$

The solution is 7.

**5.**　$\sqrt{2x} = -4$

No solution since a principle square root does not yield a negative number.

**7.**　$\sqrt{4x-3} - 5 = 0$

$\sqrt{4x-3} = 5$

$\left(\sqrt{4x-3}\right)^2 = 5^2$

$4x - 3 = 25$

$4x = 28$

$x = 7$

The solution is 7.

**9.**　$\sqrt{2x-3} - 2 = 1$

$\sqrt{2x-3} = 3$

$\left(\sqrt{2x-3}\right)^2 = 3^2$

$2x - 3 = 9$

$2x = 12$

$x = 6$

The solution is 6.

**11.**　$\sqrt[3]{6x} = -3$

$\left(\sqrt[3]{6x}\right)^3 = (-3)^3$

$6x = -27$

$x = -\dfrac{27}{6} = -\dfrac{9}{2}$

The solution is $-\dfrac{9}{2}$.

**13.**　$\sqrt[3]{x-2} - 3 = 0$

$\sqrt[3]{x-2} = 3$

$\left(\sqrt[3]{x-2}\right)^3 = 3^3$

$x - 2 = 27$

$x = 29$

The solution is 29.

**15.**　$\sqrt{13-x} = x - 1$

$\left(\sqrt{13-x}\right)^2 = (x-1)^2$

$13 - x = x^2 - 2x + 1$

$0 = x^2 - x - 12$

$0 = (x-4)(x+3)$

$x - 4 = 0$　or　$x + 3 = 0$

$x = 4$　or　　$x = -3$

We discard $-3$ as extraneous. The solution is 4.

**17.**　$x - \sqrt{4-3x} = -8$

$x + 8 = \sqrt{4-3x}$

$(x+8)^2 = \left(\sqrt{4-3x}\right)^2$

$x^2 + 16x + 64 = 4 - 3x$

$x^2 + 19x + 60 = 0$

$(x+4)(x+15) = 0$

$x + 4 = 0$　　or　$x + 15 = 0$

$x = -4$　or　　　$x = -15$

We discard $-15$ as extraneous. The solution is $-4$.

**19.**　$\sqrt{y+5} = 2 - \sqrt{y-4}$

$\left(\sqrt{y+5}\right)^2 = \left(2 - \sqrt{y-4}\right)^2$

$y + 5 = 4 - 4\sqrt{y-4} + (y-4)$

$y + 5 = y - 4\sqrt{y-4}$

$5 = -4\sqrt{y-4}$

$5^2 = \left(-4\sqrt{y-4}\right)^2$

$25 = 16(y-4)$

$25 = 16y - 64$

$89 = 16y$

$\dfrac{89}{16} = y$

We discard $\dfrac{89}{16}$ as extraneous. There is no solution.

**21.**
$$\sqrt{x-3}+\sqrt{x+2}=5$$
$$\sqrt{x-3}=5-\sqrt{x+2}$$
$$\left(\sqrt{x-3}\right)^2=\left(5-\sqrt{x+2}\right)^2$$
$$x-3=25-10\sqrt{x+2}+(x+2)$$
$$x-3=27-10\sqrt{x+2}+x$$
$$-30=-10\sqrt{x+2}$$
$$3=\sqrt{x+2}$$
$$3^2=\left(\sqrt{x+2}\right)^2$$
$$9=x+2$$
$$7=x$$
The solution is 7.

**23.**
$$\sqrt{3x-2}=5$$
$$\left(\sqrt{3x-2}\right)^2=5^2$$
$$3x-2=25$$
$$3x=27$$
$$x=9$$
The solution is 9.

**25.**
$$-\sqrt{2x}+4=-6$$
$$10=\sqrt{2x}$$
$$10^2=\left(\sqrt{2x}\right)^2$$
$$100=2x$$
$$50=x$$
The solution is 50.

**27.**
$$\sqrt{3x+1}+2=0$$
$$\sqrt{3x+1}=-2$$
No solution since a principle square root does not yield a negative number.

**29.**
$$\sqrt[4]{4x+1}-2=0$$
$$\sqrt[4]{4x+1}=2$$
$$\left(\sqrt[4]{4x+1}\right)^4=2^4$$
$$4x+1=16$$
$$4x=15$$
$$x=\frac{15}{4}$$
The solution is $\frac{15}{4}$.

**31.**
$$\sqrt{4x-3}=7$$
$$\left(\sqrt{4x-3}\right)^2=7^2$$
$$4x-3=49$$
$$4x=52$$
$$x=13$$
The solution is 13.

**33.**
$$\sqrt[3]{6x-3}-3=0$$
$$\sqrt[3]{6x-3}=3$$
$$\left(\sqrt[3]{6x-3}\right)^3=3^3$$
$$6x-3=27$$
$$6x=30$$
$$x=5$$
The solution is 5.

**35.**
$$\sqrt[3]{2x-3}-2=-5$$
$$\sqrt[3]{2x-3}=-3$$
$$\left(\sqrt[3]{2x-3}\right)^3=(-3)^3$$
$$2x-3=-27$$
$$2x=-24$$
$$x=-12$$
The solution is $-12$.

**37.**
$$\sqrt{x+4}=\sqrt{2x-5}$$
$$\left(\sqrt{x+4}\right)^2=\left(\sqrt{2x-5}\right)^2$$
$$x+4=2x-5$$
$$-x=-9$$
$$x=9$$
The solution is 9.

**39.**
$$x-\sqrt{1-x}=-5$$
$$x+5=\sqrt{1-x}$$
$$(x+5)^2=\left(\sqrt{1-x}\right)^2$$
$$x^2+10x+25=1-x$$
$$x^2+11x+24=0$$
$$(x+8)(x+3)=0$$
$$x+8=0\quad\text{or}\quad x+3=0$$
$$x=-8\quad\text{or}\qquad x=-3$$
We discard $-8$ as extraneous. The solution is $-3$.

**41.** $\sqrt[3]{-6x-1} = \sqrt[3]{-2x-5}$

$\left(\sqrt[3]{-6x-1}\right)^3 = \left(\sqrt[3]{-2x-5}\right)^3$

$-6x-1 = -2x-5$

$-4x = -4$

$x = 1$

The solution is 1.

**43.** $\sqrt{5x-1} - \sqrt{x+2} = 3$

$\sqrt{5x-1} = \sqrt{x}+1$

$\left(\sqrt{5x-1}\right)^2 = \left(\sqrt{x}+1\right)^2$

$5x-1 = x+2\sqrt{x}+1$

$4x-2 = 2\sqrt{x}$

$2x-1 = \sqrt{x}$

$(2x-1)^2 = \left(\sqrt{x}\right)^2$

$4x^2 - 4x + 1 = x$

$4x^2 - 5x + 1 = 0$

$(4x-1)(x-1) = 0$

$4x-1 = 0$ or $x-1 = 0$

$4x = 1$ or $\quad x = 1$

$x = \dfrac{1}{4}$

We discard $\dfrac{1}{4}$ as extraneous. The solution is 1.

**45.** $\sqrt{2x-1} = \sqrt{1-2x}$

$\left(\sqrt{2x-1}\right)^2 = \left(\sqrt{1-2x}\right)^2$

$2x-1 = 1-2x$

$4x = 2$

$x = \dfrac{2}{4} = \dfrac{1}{2}$

The solution is $\dfrac{1}{2}$.

**47.** $\sqrt{3x+4} - 1 = \sqrt{2x+1}$

$\sqrt{3x+4} = \sqrt{2x+1} + 1$

$\left(\sqrt{3x+4}\right)^2 = \left(\sqrt{2x+1}+1\right)^2$

$3x+4 = (2x+1) + 2\sqrt{2x+1} + 1$

$3x+4 = 2x+2+2\sqrt{2x+1}$

$x+2 = 2\sqrt{2x+1}$

$(x+2)^2 = \left(2\sqrt{2x+1}\right)^2$

$x^2 + 4x + 4 = 4(2x+1)$

$x^2 + 4x + 4 = 8x+4$

$x^2 - 4x = 0$

$x(x-4) = 0$

$x = 0$ or $x-4 = 0$

$\quad\quad x = 4$

The solutions are 0 and 4.

**49.** $\sqrt{y+3} - \sqrt{y-3} = 1$

$\sqrt{y+3} = 1 + \sqrt{y-3}$

$\left(\sqrt{y+3}\right)^2 = \left(1+\sqrt{y-3}\right)^2$

$y+3 = 1 + 2\sqrt{y-3} + (y-3)$

$y+3 = -2 + 2\sqrt{y-3} + y$

$5 = 2\sqrt{y-3}$

$(5)^2 = \left(2\sqrt{y-3}\right)^2$

$25 = 4(y-3)$

$25 = 4y - 12$

$37 = 4y$

$\dfrac{37}{4} = y$

The solution is $\dfrac{37}{4}$.

**51.** Let $c$ = length of the hypotenuse.

$6^2 + 3^2 = c^2$

$36 + 9 = c^2$

$45 = c^2$

$\sqrt{45} = \sqrt{c^2}$

$\sqrt{9 \cdot 5} = c$

$3\sqrt{5} = c$ so $c = 3\sqrt{5}$ feet

**53.** Let $b$ = length of the unknown leg.
$$3^2 + b^2 = 7^2$$
$$9 + b^2 = 49$$
$$b^2 = 40$$
$$\sqrt{b^2} = \sqrt{40}$$
$$b = \sqrt{4 \cdot 10}$$
$$b = 2\sqrt{10} \text{ meters}$$

**55.** Let $b$ = length of the unknown leg.
$$9^2 + b^2 = \left(11\sqrt{5}\right)^2$$
$$81 + b^2 = 121 \cdot 5$$
$$81 + b^2 = 605$$
$$b^2 = 524$$
$$\sqrt{b^2} = \sqrt{524}$$
$$b = \sqrt{4 \cdot 131}$$
$$b = 2\sqrt{131} \approx 22.9 \text{ meters}$$

**57.** Let $c$ = length of the hypotenuse.
$$7^2 + (7.2)^2 = c^2$$
$$49 + 51.84 = c^2$$
$$100.84 = c^2$$
$$\sqrt{100.84} = \sqrt{c^2}$$
$$c = \sqrt{100.84} \approx 10.0 \text{ mm}$$

**59.** Let $c$ = amount of cable needed.
$$15^2 + 8^2 = c^2$$
$$225 + 64 = c^2$$
$$289 = c^2$$
$$\sqrt{289} = \sqrt{c^2}$$
$$17 = c$$
Thus, 17 feet of cable is needed.

**61.** Let $c$ = length of the ladder.
$$12^2 + 5^2 = c^2$$
$$144 + 25 = c^2$$
$$169 = c^2$$
$$\sqrt{169} = \sqrt{c^2}$$
$$13 = c$$
A 13-foot ladder is needed.

**63.**
$$r = \sqrt{\frac{A}{4\pi}}$$
$$1080 = \sqrt{\frac{A}{4\pi}}$$
$$(1080)^2 = \left(\sqrt{\frac{A}{4\pi}}\right)^2$$
$$1,166,400 = \frac{A}{4\pi}$$
$$14,657,415 \approx A$$
The surface area is approximately 14,657,415 square miles.

**65.**
$$v = \sqrt{2gh}$$
$$80 = \sqrt{2(32)h}$$
$$(80)^2 = \left(\sqrt{64h}\right)^2$$
$$6400 = 64h$$
$$100 = h$$
The object fell 100 feet.

**67.**
$$S = 2\sqrt{I} - 9$$
$$11 = 2\sqrt{I} - 9$$
$$20 = 2\sqrt{I}$$
$$10 = \sqrt{I}$$
$$10^2 = \left(\sqrt{I}\right)^2$$
$$100 = I$$
The estimated IQ is 100.

**69.** $P = 2\pi\sqrt{\dfrac{l}{32}}$
$$= 2\pi\sqrt{\frac{2}{32}}$$
$$= 2\pi\sqrt{\frac{1}{16}}$$
$$= 2\pi\left(\frac{1}{4}\right)$$
$$= \frac{\pi}{2} \text{ sec} \approx 1.57 \text{ sec}$$

**71.**
$$P = 2\pi\sqrt{\frac{l}{32}}$$
$$4 = 2\pi\sqrt{\frac{l}{32}}$$
$$\frac{4}{2\pi} = \sqrt{\frac{l}{32}}$$
$$\left(\frac{2}{\pi}\right)^2 = \left(\sqrt{\frac{l}{32}}\right)^2$$
$$\frac{4}{\pi^2} = \frac{l}{32}$$
$$l = 32\left(\frac{4}{\pi^2}\right) \approx 12.97 \text{ feet}$$

**73.** Answers may vary

**75.**
$$s = \frac{1}{2}(6+10+14) = \frac{1}{2}(30) = 15$$
$$A = \sqrt{s(s-a)(s-b)(s-c)}$$
$$= \sqrt{15(15-6)(15-10)(15-14)}$$
$$= \sqrt{15(9)(5)(1)}$$
$$= \sqrt{675}$$
$$= \sqrt{225 \cdot 3}$$
$$= 15\sqrt{3} \text{ sq mi} \approx 25.98 \text{ sq mi.}$$

**77.** Answers may vary

**79.**
$$D(h) = 111.7\sqrt{h}$$
$$80 = 111.7\sqrt{h}$$
$$\frac{80}{111.7} = \sqrt{h}$$
$$\left(\frac{80}{111.7}\right)^2 = \left(\sqrt{h}\right)^2$$
$$0.5129483389 \approx h$$
$$h \approx 0.51 \text{ km}$$

**81.** Function; no vertical line intersects the graph more than one time.

**83.** Function; no vertical line intersects the graph more than one time.

**85.** Not a function; the *y*-axis is an example of a vertical line that intersects the graph more than one time.

**87.** $\dfrac{\frac{x}{6}}{\frac{2x}{3}+\frac{1}{2}} = \dfrac{\left(\frac{x}{6}\right)6}{\left(\frac{2x}{3}+\frac{1}{2}\right)6} = \dfrac{x}{4x+3}$

**89.**
$$\frac{\frac{z}{5}+\frac{1}{10}}{\frac{z}{20}-\frac{z}{5}} = \frac{\left(\frac{z}{5}+\frac{1}{10}\right)20}{\left(\frac{z}{20}-\frac{z}{5}\right)20}$$
$$= \frac{4z+2}{z-4z}$$
$$= \frac{4z+2}{-3z}$$
$$= -\frac{4z+2}{3z}$$

**91.**
$$\sqrt{5x-1}+4 = 7$$
$$\sqrt{5x-1} = 3$$
$$\left(\sqrt{5x-1}\right)^2 = 3^2$$
$$5x-1 = 9$$
$$5x = 10$$
$$x = 2$$

**93.**
$$\sqrt{\sqrt{x+3}+\sqrt{x}} = \sqrt{3}$$
$$\left(\sqrt{\sqrt{x+3}+\sqrt{x}}\right)^2 = \left(\sqrt{3}\right)^2$$
$$\sqrt{x+3}+\sqrt{x} = 3$$
$$\sqrt{x+3} = 3-\sqrt{x}$$
$$\left(\sqrt{x+3}\right)^2 = \left(3-\sqrt{x}\right)^2$$
$$x+3 = 9-6\sqrt{x}+x$$
$$-6 = -6\sqrt{x}$$
$$(-6)^2 = \left(-6\sqrt{x}\right)^2$$
$$36 = 36x$$
$$1 = x$$

**95. a.** Answers may vary

  **b.** Answers may vary

**97.**
$$\sqrt{(x^2-x)+7} = 2(x^2-x)-1$$
Let $t = x^2-x$. Then
$$\sqrt{t+7} = 2t-1$$
$$\left(\sqrt{t+7}\right)^2 = (2t-1)^2$$
$$t+7 = 4t^2-4t+1$$
$$0 = 4t^2-5t-6$$
$$0 = (4t+3)(t-2)$$
$$t = -\frac{3}{4} \text{ or } t = 2$$

Replace *t* with $x^2-x$.

$$x^2 - x = -\frac{3}{4} \quad \text{or} \quad x^2 - x = 2$$

$4x^2 - 4x + 3 = 0$      $x^2 - x - 2 = 0$

which has no real     $(x-2)(x+1) = 0$

solutions           $x = 2 \text{ or } x = -1$

The solutions are −1 and 2.

**99.** $x^2 + 6x = 4\sqrt{x^2 + 6x}$

Let $t = x^2 + 6x.$ Then

$$t = 4\sqrt{t}$$
$$t^2 = \left(4\sqrt{t}\right)^2$$
$$t^2 = 16t$$
$$t^2 - 16t = 0$$
$$t(t - 16) = 0$$
$$t = 0 \quad \text{or} \quad t = 16$$

Replace $t$ with $x^2 + 6x.$

$$x^2 + 6x = 0$$
$$x(x + 6) = 0$$
$$x = 0 \quad \text{or} \quad x = -6$$

or

$$x^2 + 6x = 16$$
$$x^2 + 6x - 16 = 0$$
$$(x + 8)(x - 2) = 0$$
$$x = -8 \quad \text{or} \quad x = 2$$

The solutions are −8, −6, 0, and 2.

**The Bigger Picture**

**1.**
$$\frac{x}{4} + \frac{x+18}{20} = \frac{x-5}{5}$$
$$20\left(\frac{x}{4}\right) + 20\left(\frac{x+18}{20}\right) = 20\left(\frac{x-5}{5}\right)$$
$$5x + (x + 18) = 4(x - 5)$$
$$6x + 18 = 4x - 20$$
$$2x = -38$$
$$x = -19$$

The solution set is {−19}.

**2.** $|3x - 5| = 10$

$3x - 5 = -10 \quad \text{or} \quad 3x - 5 = 10$

$3x = -5 \qquad\qquad 3x = 15$

$x = -\dfrac{5}{3} \qquad\qquad x = 5$

The solution set is $\left\{-\dfrac{5}{3}, 5\right\}.$

**3.**
$$2x^2 - x = 45$$
$$2x^2 - x - 45 = 0$$
$$(2x + 9)(x - 5) = 0$$
$$2x + 9 = 0 \quad \text{or} \quad x - 5 = 0$$
$$x = -\frac{9}{2} \qquad\qquad x = 5$$

The solution set is $\left\{-\dfrac{9}{2}, 5\right\}.$

**4.** $-6 \le -5x - 1 \le 10$

$-5 \le -5x \le 11$

$1 \ge x \ge -\dfrac{11}{5}$

$-\dfrac{11}{5} \le x \le 1$

The solution is $\left[-\dfrac{11}{5}, 1\right].$

**5.** $4(x - 1) + 3x > 1 + 2(x - 6)$

$4x - 4 + 3x > 1 + 2x - 12$

$7x - 4 > 2x - 11$

$5x > -7$

$x > -\dfrac{7}{5}$

The solution is $\left(-\dfrac{7}{5}, \infty\right).$

**6.** $\sqrt{x} + 14 = x - 6$

$\sqrt{x} = x - 20$

$\left(\sqrt{x}\right)^2 = (x - 20)^2$

$x = x^2 - 40x + 400$

$0 = x^2 - 41x + 400$

$0 = (x - 25)(x - 16)$

$x - 25 = 0 \quad \text{or} \quad x - 16 = 0$

$x = 25 \qquad\qquad x = 16$

Discard 16 as an extraneous solution. The solution set is {25}.

**7.** $x \ge 10 \quad \text{or} \quad -x < 5$

$x \ge 10 \quad \text{or} \quad x > -5$

The solution is (−5, ∞).

**8.** $\sqrt{3x - 1} + 4 = 1$

$\sqrt{3x - 1} = -3$

There is no real number whose square root is negative. The solution set is ∅.

**9.** $|x - 2| > 15$

$\quad x - 2 < -15 \quad$ or $\quad x - 2 > 15$

$\quad\quad x < -13 \quad$ or $\quad\quad x > 17$

$\quad$ The solution is $(-\infty, -13) \cup (17, \infty)$.

**10.** $5x - 4[x - 2(3x + 1)] = 25$

$\quad\quad 5x - 4(x - 6x - 2) = 25$

$\quad\quad\quad 5x - 4(-5x - 2) = 25$

$\quad\quad\quad\quad 5x + 20x + 8 = 25$

$\quad\quad\quad\quad\quad\quad\quad 25x = 17$

$\quad\quad\quad\quad\quad\quad\quad\quad x = \dfrac{17}{25}$

$\quad$ The solution set is $\left\{\dfrac{17}{25}\right\}$.

## Section 7.7

**Practice Exercises**

**1. a.** $\sqrt{-4} = \sqrt{-1 \cdot 4} = \sqrt{-1} \cdot \sqrt{4} = i \cdot 2,$ or $2i$

   **b.** $\sqrt{-7} = \sqrt{-1(7)} = \sqrt{-1} \cdot \sqrt{7} = i\sqrt{7}$

   **c.** $-\sqrt{-18} = -\sqrt{-1 \cdot 18}$

$\quad\quad\quad\quad\quad = -\sqrt{-1} \cdot \sqrt{9 \cdot 2}$

$\quad\quad\quad\quad\quad = -i \cdot 3\sqrt{2}$

$\quad\quad\quad\quad\quad = -3i\sqrt{2}$

**2. a.** $\sqrt{-5} \cdot \sqrt{-6} = i\sqrt{5}\left(i\sqrt{6}\right)$

$\quad\quad\quad\quad\quad = i^2\sqrt{30}$

$\quad\quad\quad\quad\quad = -1\sqrt{30}$

$\quad\quad\quad\quad\quad = -\sqrt{30}$

   **b.** $\sqrt{-9} \cdot \sqrt{-1} = 3i \cdot i = 3i^2 = 3(-1) = -3$

   **c.** $\sqrt{125} \cdot \sqrt{-5} = 5\sqrt{5}\left(i\sqrt{5}\right)$

$\quad\quad\quad\quad\quad = 5i\left(\sqrt{5}\sqrt{5}\right)$

$\quad\quad\quad\quad\quad = 5i(5)$

$\quad\quad\quad\quad\quad = 25i$

   **d.** $\dfrac{\sqrt{-27}}{\sqrt{3}} = \dfrac{i\sqrt{27}}{\sqrt{3}} = i\sqrt{9} = 3i$

**3. a.** $(3 - 5i) + (-4 + i) = (3 - 4) + (-5 + 1)i$

$\quad\quad\quad\quad\quad\quad\quad\quad\quad = -1 - 4i$

   **b.** $4i - (3 - i) = 4i - 3 + i$

$\quad\quad\quad\quad\quad = -3 + (4 + 1)i$

$\quad\quad\quad\quad\quad = -3 + 5i$

   **c.** $(-5 - 2i) - (-8) = -5 - 2i + 8$

$\quad\quad\quad\quad\quad\quad = (-5 + 8) - 2i$

$\quad\quad\quad\quad\quad\quad = 3 - 2i$

**4. a.** $-4i \cdot 5i = -20i^2 = -20(-1) = 20$

   **b.** $5i(2 + i) = 5i \cdot 2 + 5i \cdot i$

$\quad\quad\quad\quad\quad = 10i + 5i^2$

$\quad\quad\quad\quad\quad = 10i + 5(-1)$

$\quad\quad\quad\quad\quad = 10i - 5$

$\quad\quad\quad\quad\quad = -5 + 10i$

   **c.** $(2 + 3i)(6 - i) = 2(6) - 2(i) + 3i(6) - 3i(i)$

$\quad\quad\quad\quad\quad\quad\quad = 12 - 2i + 18i - 3i^2$

$\quad\quad\quad\quad\quad\quad\quad = 12 + 16i - 3(-1)$

$\quad\quad\quad\quad\quad\quad\quad = 12 + 16i + 3$

$\quad\quad\quad\quad\quad\quad\quad = 15 + 16i$

   **d.** $(3 - i)^2 = (3 - i)(3 - i)$

$\quad\quad\quad\quad\quad = 3(3) - 3(i) - 3(i) + i^2$

$\quad\quad\quad\quad\quad = 9 - 6i + (-1)$

$\quad\quad\quad\quad\quad\; - 8 - 6i$

   **e.** $(9 + 2i)(9 - 2i) = 9(9) - 9(2i) + 2i(9) - 2i(2i)$

$\quad\quad\quad\quad\quad\quad\quad = 81 - 18i + 18i - 4i^2$

$\quad\quad\quad\quad\quad\quad\quad = 81 - 4(-1)$

$\quad\quad\quad\quad\quad\quad\quad = 81 + 4$

$\quad\quad\quad\quad\quad\quad\quad = 85$

**5. a.** $\dfrac{4 - i}{3 + i} = \dfrac{(4 - i)(3 - i)}{(3 + i)(3 - i)}$

$\quad\quad\quad\quad = \dfrac{4(3) - 4(i) - 3(i) + i^2}{3^2 - i^2}$

$\quad\quad\quad\quad = \dfrac{12 - 7i - 1}{9 + 1}$

$\quad\quad\quad\quad = \dfrac{11 - 7i}{10}$

$\quad\quad\quad\quad = \dfrac{11}{10} - \dfrac{7i}{10}$ or $\dfrac{11}{10} - \dfrac{7}{10}i$

**b.**  $\dfrac{5}{2i} = \dfrac{5(-2i)}{2i(-2i)}$

$= \dfrac{-10i}{-4i^2}$

$= \dfrac{-10i}{-4(-1)}$

$= \dfrac{-10i}{4}$

$= \dfrac{-5i}{2}$

$= 0 - \dfrac{5i}{2}$ or $0 - \dfrac{5}{2}i$

**6. a.**  $i^9 = i^4 \cdot i^4 \cdot i = 1 \cdot 1 \cdot i = i$

**b.**  $i^{16} = (i^4)^4 = 1^4 = 1$

**c.**  $i^{34} = i^{32} \cdot i^2 = (i^4)^8 \cdot i^2 = 1^8(-1) = -1$

**d.**  $i^{-24} = \dfrac{1}{i^{24}} = \dfrac{1}{(i^4)^6} = \dfrac{1}{(1)^6} = \dfrac{1}{1} = 1$

**Vocabulary and Readiness Check**

1. A <u>complex</u> number is one that can be written in the form $a + bi$ where $a$ and $b$ are real numbers.

2. In the complex number system, $i$ denotes the <u>imaginary unit</u>.

3. $i^2 = \underline{-1}$

4. $i = \underline{\sqrt{-1}}$

5. A complex number, $a + bi$, is a <u>real</u> number if $b = 0$.

6. A complex number, $a + bi$, is a <u>pure imaginary</u> number if $a = 0$ and $b \neq 0$.

7. $\sqrt{-81} = 9i$

8. $\sqrt{-49} = 7i$

9. $\sqrt{-7} = i\sqrt{7}$

10. $\sqrt{-3} = i\sqrt{3}$

11. $-\sqrt{16} = -4$

12. $-\sqrt{4} = -2$

13. $\sqrt{-64} = 8i$

14. $\sqrt{-100} = 10i$

**Exercise Set 7.7**

1. $\sqrt{-24} = \sqrt{-1 \cdot 24} = \sqrt{-1}\sqrt{4 \cdot 6} = i \cdot 2\sqrt{6} = 2i\sqrt{6}$

3. $-\sqrt{-36} = -\sqrt{-1 \cdot 36} = -\sqrt{-1}\sqrt{36} = -i \cdot 6 = -6i$

5. $8\sqrt{-63} = 8\sqrt{-1 \cdot 63}$
$= 8\sqrt{-1}\sqrt{9 \cdot 7}$
$= 8i \cdot 3\sqrt{7}$
$= 24i\sqrt{7}$

7. $-\sqrt{54} = -\sqrt{9 \cdot 6} = -3\sqrt{6}$

9. $\sqrt{-2} \cdot \sqrt{-7} = i\sqrt{2} \cdot i\sqrt{7}$
$= i^2\sqrt{14}$
$= (-1)\sqrt{14}$
$= -\sqrt{14}$

11. $\sqrt{-5} \cdot \sqrt{-10} = i\sqrt{5} \cdot i\sqrt{10}$
$= i^2\sqrt{50}$
$= (-1)\sqrt{25 \cdot 2}$
$= -5\sqrt{2}$

13. $\sqrt{16} \cdot \sqrt{-1} = 4i$

15. $\dfrac{\sqrt{-9}}{\sqrt{3}} = \dfrac{i\sqrt{9}}{\sqrt{3}} = i\sqrt{\dfrac{9}{3}} = i\sqrt{3}$

17. $\dfrac{\sqrt{-80}}{\sqrt{-10}} = \dfrac{i\sqrt{80}}{i\sqrt{10}} = \sqrt{\dfrac{80}{10}} = \sqrt{8} = \sqrt{4 \cdot 2} = 2\sqrt{2}$

19. $(4 - 7i) + (2 + 3i) = (4 + 2) + (-7 + 3)i$
$= 6 + (-4)i$
$= 6 - 4i$

21. $(6 + 5i) - (8 - i) = 6 + 5i - 8 + i$
$= (6 - 8) + (5 + 1)i$
$= -2 + 6i$

23. $6 - (8 + 4i) = 6 - 8 - 4i$
$= (6 - 8) - 4i$
$= -2 - 4i$

**25.** $-10i \cdot -4i = 40i^2 = 40(-1) = -40$

**27.** $6i(2-3i) = 12i - 18i^2$
$$= 12i - 18(-1)$$
$$= 18 + 12i$$

**29.** $\left(\sqrt{3} + 2i\right)\left(\sqrt{3} - 2i\right)$
$$= \sqrt{3} \cdot \sqrt{3} - \sqrt{3} \cdot 2i + \sqrt{3} \cdot 2i - 4i^2$$
$$= 3 - 4(-1)$$
$$= 3 + 4$$
$$= 7$$

**31.** $\left(4 - 2i\right)^2 = (4-2i)(4-2i)$
$$= 16 - 4 \cdot 2i - 4 \cdot 2i + 4i^2$$
$$= 16 - 8i - 8i + 4(-1)$$
$$= 16 - 16i - 4$$
$$= 12 - 16i$$

**33.** $\dfrac{4}{i} = \dfrac{4(-i)}{i(-i)} = \dfrac{-4i}{-i^2} = \dfrac{-4i}{-(-1)} = -4i$

**35.** $\dfrac{7}{4+3i} = \dfrac{7(4-3i)}{(4+3i)(4-3i)}$
$$= \dfrac{28 - 21i}{4^2 - 9i^2}$$
$$= \dfrac{28 - 21i}{16 + 9}$$
$$= \dfrac{28 - 21i}{25}$$
$$= \dfrac{28}{25} - \dfrac{21}{25}i$$

**37.** $\dfrac{3+5i}{1+i} = \dfrac{(3+5i)(1-i)}{(1+i)(1-i)}$
$$= \dfrac{3 - 3i + 5i - 5i^2}{1^2 - i^2}$$
$$= \dfrac{3 + 2i + 5}{1 + 1}$$
$$= \dfrac{8 + 2i}{2}$$
$$= \dfrac{8}{2} + \dfrac{2}{2}i$$
$$= 4 + i$$

**39.** $\dfrac{5-i}{3-2i} = \dfrac{(5-i)(3+2i)}{(3-2i)(3+2i)}$
$$= \dfrac{15 + 10i - 3i - 2i^2}{3^2 - 4i^2}$$
$$= \dfrac{15 + 7i + 2}{9 + 4}$$
$$= \dfrac{17 + 7i}{13}$$
$$= \dfrac{17}{13} + \dfrac{7}{13}i$$

**41.** $(7i)(-9i) = -63i^2 = -63(-1) = 63$

**43.** $(6 - 3i) - (4 - 2i) = 6 - 3i - 4 + 2i = 2 - i$

**45.** $-3i(-1 + 9i) = 3i - 27i^2$
$$= 3i - 27(-1)$$
$$= 27 + 3i$$

**47.** $\dfrac{4-5i}{2i} = \dfrac{4-5i}{2i} \cdot \dfrac{-2i}{-2i}$
$$= \dfrac{-8i + 10i^2}{-4i^2}$$
$$= \dfrac{-10 - 8i}{4}$$
$$= \dfrac{-10}{4} - \dfrac{8}{4}i$$
$$= -\dfrac{5}{2} - 2i$$

**49.** $(4+i)(5+2i) = 20 + 8i + 5i + 2i^2$
$$= 20 + 13i + 2(-1)$$
$$= 20 + 13i - 2$$
$$= 18 + 13i$$

**51.** $(6-2i)(3+i) = 18 + 6i - 6i - 2i^2$
$$= 18 + 2$$
$$= 20$$

**53.** $(8 - 3i) + (2 + 3i) = 8 - 3i + 2 + 3i = 10$

**55.** $(1-i)(1+i) = 1 + i - i - i^2 = 1 + 1 = 2$

**57.** $\dfrac{16+15i}{-3i} = \dfrac{(16+15i)(3i)}{-3i(3i)}$

$= \dfrac{48i+45i^2}{-9i^2}$

$= \dfrac{-45+48i}{9}$

$= \dfrac{-45}{9} + \dfrac{48}{9}i$

$= -5 + \dfrac{16}{3}i$

**59.** $(9+8i)^2 = 9^2 + 2(9)(8i) + (8i)^2$

$= 81 + 144i + 64i^2$

$= 81 + 144i - 64$

$= 17 + 144i$

**61.** $\dfrac{2}{3+i} = \dfrac{2(3-i)}{(3+i)(3-i)}$

$= \dfrac{6-2i}{3^2 - i^2}$

$= \dfrac{6-2i}{9+1}$

$= \dfrac{6-2i}{10}$

$= \dfrac{6}{10} - \dfrac{2}{10}i$

$= \dfrac{3}{5} - \dfrac{1}{5}i$

**63.** $(5-6i) - 4i = 5 - 6i - 4i = 5 - 10i$

**65.** $\dfrac{2-3i}{2+i} = \dfrac{(2-3i)(2-i)}{(2+i)(2-i)}$

$= \dfrac{4 - 2i - 6i + 3i^2}{2^2 - i^2}$

$= \dfrac{4 - 8i - 3}{4 + 1}$

$= \dfrac{1 - 8i}{5}$

$= \dfrac{1}{5} - \dfrac{8}{5}i$

**67.** $(2+4i) + (6-5i) = 2 + 4i + 6 - 5i = 8 - i$

**69.** $\left(\sqrt{3}+2i\right)\left(\sqrt{3}-2i\right) = \left(\sqrt{3}\right)^2 - (2i)^2$

$= 3 - 4i^2$

$= 3 - 4(-1)$

$= 7$

**71.** $(4-2i)^2 = 16 - 2 \cdot 4 \cdot 2i + 4i^2$

$= 16 - 16i + 4(-1)$

$= 16 - 4 - 16i$

$= 12 - 16i$

**73.** $i^8 = (i^4)^2 = 1^2 = 1$

**75.** $i^{21} = i^{20} \cdot i = (i^4)^5 \cdot i = 1^5 \cdot i = i$

**77.** $i^{11} = i^8 \cdot i^3 = (i^4)^2 \cdot i^3 = 1^2 \cdot (-i) = -i$

**79.** $i^{-6} = \dfrac{1}{i^6} = \dfrac{1}{i^4 \cdot i^2} = \dfrac{1}{1 \cdot (-1)} = -1$

**81.** $(2i)^6 = 2^6 i^6 = 64 i^4 \cdot i^2 = 64(1)(-1) = -64$

**83.** $(-3i)^5 = (-3)^5 i^5 = -243 i^4 \cdot i = -243(1)i = -243i$

**85.** $x + 50° + 90° = 180°$

$x + 140° = 180°$

$x = 40°$

**87.** 

$$\begin{array}{r|rrrr} 1 & 1 & -6 & 3 & -4 \\ & & 1 & -5 & -2 \\ \hline & 1 & -5 & -2 & -6 \end{array}$$

Answer: $x^2 - 5x - 2 - \dfrac{6}{x-1}$

**89.** 5 people

**91.** $5 + 9 = 14$ people

**93.** $\dfrac{5 \text{ people}}{30 \text{ people}} = \dfrac{1}{6} \approx 0.1666$

About 16.7% of the people reported an average checking balance of $201 to $300.

**95.** $i^3 - i^4 = -i - 1 = -1 - i$

**97.** $i^6 + i^8 = i^4 \cdot i^2 + (i^4)^2 = 1(-1) + 1^2 = -1 + 1 = 0$

**99.** $2 + \sqrt{-9} = 2 + i\sqrt{9} = 2 + 3i$

**101.** $\dfrac{6+\sqrt{-18}}{3} = \dfrac{6+i\sqrt{9\cdot 2}}{3}$

$\qquad = \dfrac{6+3i\sqrt{2}}{3}$

$\qquad = \dfrac{6}{3} + \dfrac{3\sqrt{2}}{3}i$

$\qquad = 2 + i\sqrt{2}$

**103.** $\dfrac{5-\sqrt{-75}}{10} = \dfrac{5-i\sqrt{25\cdot 3}}{10}$

$\qquad = \dfrac{5-5i\sqrt{3}}{10}$

$\qquad = \dfrac{5}{10} - \dfrac{5\sqrt{3}}{10}i$

$\qquad = \dfrac{1}{2} - \dfrac{\sqrt{3}}{2}i$

**105.** Answers may vary

**107.** $\left(8-\sqrt{-4}\right) - \left(2+\sqrt{-16}\right) = (8-2i) - (2+4i)$

$\qquad = 8 - 2i - 2 - 4i$

$\qquad = 6 - 6i$

**109.**  $\qquad x^2 + 2x = -2$

$(-1+i)^2 + 2(-1+i) = -2$

$(1 - 2i + i^2) - 2 + 2i = -2$

$1 - 1 - 2 = -2$

$\qquad\qquad -2 = -2$, which is true.

Yes, $-1+i$ is a solution.

## Chapter 7 Vocabulary Check

1. The conjugate of $\sqrt{3}+2$ is $\sqrt{3}-2$.

2. The principal square root of a nonnegative number $a$ is written as $\sqrt{a}$.

3. The process of writing a radical expression as an equivalent expression but without a radical in the denominator is called rationalizing the denominator.

4. The imaginary unit written $i$, is the number whose square is $-1$.

5. The cube root of a number is written as $\sqrt[3]{a}$.

6. In the notation $\sqrt[n]{a}$, $n$ is called the index and $a$ is called the radicand.

7. Radicals with the same index and the same radicand are called like radicals.

8. A complex number is a number that can be written in the form $a + bi$, where $a$ and $b$ are real numbers.

9. The distance formula is
$$d = \sqrt{(x_2 - x_1)^2 + (y_2 - y_1)^2}.$$

10. The midpoint formula is $\left( \dfrac{x_1 + x_2}{2}, \dfrac{y_1 + y_2}{2} \right)$.

## Chapter 7 Review

1. $\sqrt{81} = 9$ because $9^2 = 81$.

2. $\sqrt[4]{81} = 3$ because $3^4 = 81$.

3. $\sqrt[3]{-8} = -2$ because $(-2)^3 = -8$.

4. $\sqrt[4]{-16}$ is not a real number.

5. $-\sqrt{\dfrac{1}{49}} = -\dfrac{1}{7}$ because $\left(\dfrac{1}{7}\right)^2 = \dfrac{1}{49}$.

6. $\sqrt{x^{64}} = x^{32}$ because $(x^{32})^2 = x^{32\cdot 2} = x^{64}$.

7. $-\sqrt{36} = -6$ because $6^2 = 36$.

8. $\sqrt[3]{64} = 4$ because $4^3 = 64$.

9. $\sqrt[3]{-a^6 b^9} = \sqrt[3]{-1}\sqrt[3]{a^6}\sqrt[3]{b^9}$

$\qquad = -1a^2 b^3$

$\qquad = -a^2 b^3$

10. $\sqrt{16a^4 b^{12}} = \sqrt{16}\sqrt{a^4}\sqrt{b^{12}} = 4a^2 b^6$

11. $\sqrt[5]{32a^5 b^{10}} = \sqrt[5]{32}\sqrt[5]{a^5}\sqrt[5]{b^{10}} = 2ab^2$

12. $\sqrt[5]{-32x^{15} y^{20}} = \sqrt[5]{-32}\sqrt[5]{x^{15}}\sqrt[5]{y^{20}} = -2x^3 y^4$

13. $\sqrt{\dfrac{x^{12}}{36y^2}} = \dfrac{\sqrt{x^{12}}}{\sqrt{36y^2}} = \dfrac{x^6}{6y}$

14. $\sqrt[3]{\dfrac{27y^3}{z^{12}}} = \dfrac{\sqrt[3]{27y^3}}{\sqrt[3]{z^{12}}} = \dfrac{3y}{z^4}$

15. $\sqrt{(-x)^2} = |-x|$

16. $\sqrt[4]{(x^2-4)^4} = |x^2-4|$

17. $\sqrt[3]{(\ 27)^3} = 27$

18. $\sqrt[5]{(-5)^5} = -5$

19. $-\sqrt[5]{x^5} = -x$

20. $\sqrt[4]{16(2y+z)^{12}} = \sqrt[4]{16}\sqrt[4]{(2y+z)^{12}} = 2\left|(2y+z)^3\right|$

21. $\sqrt{25(x-y)^{10}} = \sqrt{25}\sqrt{(x-y)^{10}}$
    $= 5\left|(x-y)^5\right|$

22. $\sqrt[5]{-y^5} = \sqrt[5]{-1}\sqrt[5]{y^5} = -1y = -y$

23. $\sqrt[9]{-x^9} = \sqrt[9]{-1}\sqrt[9]{x^9} = -1x = -x$

24. $f(x) = \sqrt{x} + 3$
    $x \ge 0$
    Domain: $[0, \infty)$

| $x$ | 0 | 1 | 4 | 9 |
|-----|---|---|---|---|
| $f(x)$ | 3 | 4 | 5 | 6 |

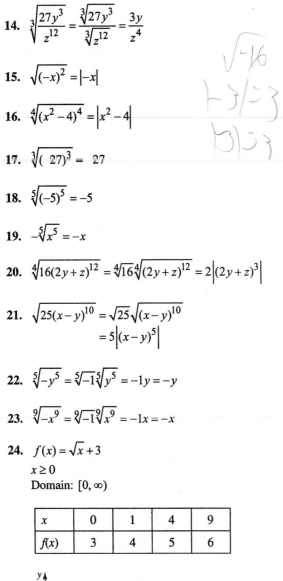

25. $g(x) = \sqrt[3]{x} - 3$
    Domain: $(-\infty, \infty)$

| $x$ | –5 | 2 | 3 | 4 | 11 |
|-----|----|----|----|----|----|
| $g(x)$ | –2 | –1 | 0 | 1 | 2 |

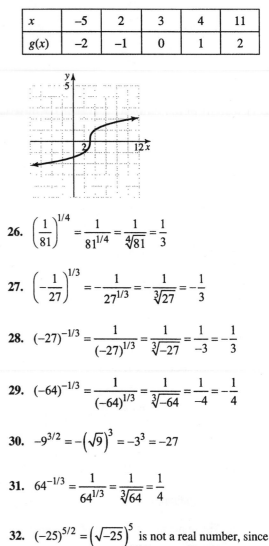

26. $\left(\dfrac{1}{81}\right)^{1/4} = \dfrac{1}{81^{1/4}} = \dfrac{1}{\sqrt[4]{81}} = \dfrac{1}{3}$

27. $\left(-\dfrac{1}{27}\right)^{1/3} = -\dfrac{1}{27^{1/3}} = -\dfrac{1}{\sqrt[3]{27}} = -\dfrac{1}{3}$

28. $(-27)^{-1/3} = \dfrac{1}{(-27)^{1/3}} = \dfrac{1}{\sqrt[3]{-27}} = \dfrac{1}{-3} = -\dfrac{1}{3}$

29. $(-64)^{-1/3} = \dfrac{1}{(-64)^{1/3}} = \dfrac{1}{\sqrt[3]{-64}} = \dfrac{1}{-4} = -\dfrac{1}{4}$

30. $-9^{3/2} = -\left(\sqrt{9}\right)^3 = -3^3 = -27$

31. $64^{-1/3} = \dfrac{1}{64^{1/3}} = \dfrac{1}{\sqrt[3]{64}} = \dfrac{1}{4}$

32. $(-25)^{5/2} = \left(\sqrt{-25}\right)^5$ is not a real number, since there is no real number whose square is –25.

**33.** $\left(\dfrac{25}{49}\right)^{-3/2} = \dfrac{1}{\left(\frac{25}{49}\right)^{3/2}}$

$= \dfrac{1}{\left(\sqrt{\frac{25}{49}}\right)^3}$

$= \dfrac{1}{\left(\frac{5}{7}\right)^3}$

$= \dfrac{1}{\frac{125}{343}}$

$= \dfrac{343}{125}$

**34.** $\left(\dfrac{8}{27}\right)^{-2/3} = \dfrac{1}{\left(\frac{8}{27}\right)^{2/3}} = \dfrac{1}{\left(\sqrt[3]{\frac{8}{27}}\right)^2} = \dfrac{1}{\left(\frac{2}{3}\right)^2} = \dfrac{1}{\frac{4}{9}} = \dfrac{9}{4}$

**35.** $\left(-\dfrac{1}{36}\right)^{-1/4} = \dfrac{1}{\left(-\frac{1}{36}\right)^{1/4}} = \dfrac{1}{\sqrt[4]{-\frac{1}{36}}}$ is not a real

number, since there is no real number whose 4th

power is $-\dfrac{1}{36}$.

**36.** $\sqrt[3]{x^2} = (x^2)^{1/3} = x^{2/3}$

**37.** $\sqrt[5]{5x^2y^3} = (5x^2y^3)^{1/5}$

$= 5^{1/5}(x^2)^{1/5}(y^3)^{1/5}$

$= 5^{1/5}x^{2/5}y^{3/5}$

**38.** $y^{4/5} = (y^4)^{1/5} = \sqrt[5]{y^4}$

**39.** $5(xy^2z^5)^{1/3} = 5\sqrt[3]{xy^2z^5}$

**40.** $(x+2y)^{-1/2} = \dfrac{1}{(x+2y)^{1/2}} = \dfrac{1}{\sqrt{x+2y}}$

**41.** $a^{1/3}a^{4/3}a^{1/2} = a^{\frac{1}{3}+\frac{4}{3}+\frac{1}{2}} = a^{\frac{2}{6}+\frac{8}{6}+\frac{3}{6}} = a^{13/6}$

**42.** $\dfrac{b^{1/3}}{b^{4/3}} = b^{1/3-4/3} = b^{-3/3} = b^{-1} = \dfrac{1}{b}$

**43.** $(a^{1/2}a^{-2})^3 = (a^{1/2-2})^3$

$= (a^{1/2-4/2})^3$

$= (a^{-3/2})^3$

$= a^{-9/2}$

$= \dfrac{1}{a^{9/2}}$

**44.** $(x^{-3}y^6)^{1/3} = (x^{-3})^{1/3}(y^6)^{1/3} = x^{-1}y^2 = \dfrac{y^2}{x}$

**45.** $\left(\dfrac{b^{3/4}}{a^{-1/2}}\right)^8 = (a^{1/2}b^{3/4})^8$

$= (a^{1/2})^8(b^{3/4})^8$

$= a^4b^6$

**46.** $\dfrac{x^{1/4}x^{-1/2}}{x^{2/3}} = x^{1/4+(-1/2)-2/3}$

$= x^{\frac{3}{12}-\frac{6}{12}-\frac{8}{12}}$

$= x^{-11/12}$

$= \dfrac{1}{x^{11/12}}$

**47.** $\left(\dfrac{49c^{5/3}}{a^{-1/4}b^{5/6}}\right)^1 = \dfrac{49^{-1}c^{-5/3}}{a^{1/4}b^{-5/6}} = \dfrac{b^{5/6}}{49a^{1/4}c^{5/3}}$

**48.** $a^{-1/4}(a^{5/4} - a^{9/4}) = a^{-1/4}(a^{5/4}) - a^{-1/4}(a^{9/4})$

$= a^{-1/4+5/4} - a^{-1/4+9/4}$

$= a^{4/4} - a^{8/4}$

$= a - a^2$

**49.** $\sqrt{20} \approx 4.472$

**50.** $\sqrt[3]{-39} \approx -3.391$

**51.** $\sqrt[4]{726} \approx 5.191$

**52.** $56^{1/3} \approx 3.826$

**53.** $-78^{3/4} \approx -26.246$

**54.** $105^{-2/3} \approx 0.045$

**55.**  $\sqrt[3]{2} \cdot \sqrt{7} = 2^{1/3} \cdot 7^{1/2}$
$= 2^{2/6} \cdot 7^{3/6}$
$= (2^2 \cdot 7^3)^{1/6}$
$= \sqrt[6]{4 \cdot 343}$
$= \sqrt[6]{1372}$

**56.**  $\sqrt[3]{3} \cdot \sqrt[4]{x} = 3^{1/3} \cdot x^{1/4}$
$= 3^{4/12} \cdot x^{3/12}$
$= (3^4 \cdot x^3)^{1/12}$
$= \sqrt[12]{81x^3}$

**57.**  $\sqrt{3} \cdot \sqrt{8} = \sqrt{24} = \sqrt{4 \cdot 6} = 2\sqrt{6}$

**58.**  $\sqrt[3]{7y} \cdot \sqrt[3]{x^2 z} = \sqrt[3]{7y \cdot x^2 z} = \sqrt[3]{7x^2 yz}$

**59.**  $\dfrac{\sqrt{44x^3}}{\sqrt{11x}} = \sqrt{\dfrac{44x^3}{11x}} = \sqrt{4x^2} = 2x$

**60.**  $\dfrac{\sqrt[4]{a^6 b^{13}}}{\sqrt[4]{a^2 b}} = \sqrt[4]{\dfrac{a^6 b^{13}}{a^2 b}} = \sqrt[4]{a^4 b^{12}} = ab^3$

**61.**  $\sqrt{60} = \sqrt{4 \cdot 15} = 2\sqrt{15}$

**62.**  $-\sqrt{75} = -\sqrt{25 \cdot 3} = -5\sqrt{3}$

**63.**  $\sqrt[3]{162} = \sqrt[3]{27 \cdot 6} = 3\sqrt[3]{6}$

**64.**  $\sqrt[3]{-32} = \sqrt[3]{-8 \cdot 4} = -2\sqrt[3]{4}$

**65.**  $\sqrt{36x^7} = \sqrt{36x^6 \cdot x} = 6x^3\sqrt{x}$

**66.**  $\sqrt[3]{24a^5 b^7} = \sqrt[3]{8a^3 b^6 \cdot 3a^2 b} = 2ab^2\sqrt[3]{3a^2 b}$

**67.**  $\sqrt{\dfrac{p^{17}}{121}} = \dfrac{\sqrt{p^{17}}}{\sqrt{121}} = \dfrac{\sqrt{p^{16} \cdot p}}{11} = \dfrac{p^8\sqrt{p}}{11}$

**68.**  $\sqrt[3]{\dfrac{y^5}{27x^6}} = \dfrac{\sqrt[3]{y^5}}{\sqrt[3]{27x^6}} = \dfrac{\sqrt[3]{y^3 y^2}}{\sqrt[3]{27x^6}} = \dfrac{y\sqrt[3]{y^2}}{3x^2}$

**69.**  $\sqrt[4]{\dfrac{xy^6}{81}} = \dfrac{\sqrt[4]{xy^6}}{\sqrt[4]{81}} = \dfrac{\sqrt[4]{y^4 \cdot xy^2}}{3} = \dfrac{y\sqrt[4]{xy^2}}{3}$

**70.**  $\sqrt{\dfrac{2x^3}{49y^4}} = \dfrac{\sqrt{2x^3}}{\sqrt{49y^4}} = \dfrac{\sqrt{x^2 \cdot 2x}}{7y^2} = \dfrac{x\sqrt{2x}}{7y^2}$

**71.**  $r = \sqrt{\dfrac{A}{\pi}}$

**a.**  $r = \sqrt{\dfrac{25}{\pi}} = \dfrac{\sqrt{25}}{\sqrt{\pi}} = \dfrac{5}{\sqrt{\pi}}$ meters, or
$r = \dfrac{5}{\sqrt{\pi}} = \dfrac{5\sqrt{\pi}}{\sqrt{\pi}\sqrt{\pi}} = \dfrac{5\sqrt{\pi}}{\pi}$ meters

**b.**  $r = \sqrt{\dfrac{104}{\pi}} \approx 5.75$ inches

**72.**  $(x_1, y_1) = (-6, 3), (x_2, y_2) = (8, 4)$
$d = \sqrt{(x_2 - x_1)^2 + (y_2 - y_1)^2}$
$= \sqrt{(8+6)^2 + (4-3)^2}$
$= \sqrt{196+1}$
$= \sqrt{197} \approx 14.036$ units

**73.**  $(x_1, y_1) = (-4, -6), (x_2, y_2) = (-1, 5)$
$d = \sqrt{(x_2 - x_1)^2 + (y_2 - y_1)^2}$
$= \sqrt{(-1+4)^2 + (5+6)^2}$
$= \sqrt{9+121}$
$= \sqrt{130} \approx 11.402$ units

**74.**  $(x_1, y_1) = (-1, 5), (x_2, y_2) = (2, -3)$
$d = \sqrt{(x_2 - x_1)^2 + (y_2 - y_1)^2}$
$= \sqrt{(2+1)^2 + (-3-5)^2}$
$= \sqrt{9+64}$
$= \sqrt{73} \approx 8.544$ units

**75.**  $(x_1, y_1) = \left(-\sqrt{2}, 0\right), (x_2, y_2) = \left(0, -4\sqrt{6}\right)$
$d = \sqrt{(x_2 - x_1)^2 + (y_2 - y_1)^2}$
$= \sqrt{\left(0+\sqrt{2}\right)^2 + \left(-4\sqrt{6}-0\right)^2}$
$= \sqrt{2+96}$
$= \sqrt{98}$
$= 7\sqrt{2} \approx 9.899$ units

**76.** $(x_1,\ y_1) = \left(-\sqrt{5},\ -\sqrt{11}\right),$

$(x_2,\ y_2) = \left(-\sqrt{5},\ -3\sqrt{11}\right)$

$d = \sqrt{(x_2 - x_1)^2 + (y_2 - y_1)^2}$

$= \sqrt{\left(-\sqrt{5} + \sqrt{5}\right)^2 + \left(-3\sqrt{11} + \sqrt{11}\right)^2}$

$= \sqrt{0 + 44}$

$= \sqrt{44}$

$= 2\sqrt{11} \approx 6.633$ units

**77.** $(x_1,\ y_1) = (7.4,\ -8.6),\ (x_2,\ y_2) = (-1.2,\ 5.6)$

$d = \sqrt{(-1.2 - 7.4)^2 + (5.6 + 8.6)^2}$

$= \sqrt{(-8.6)^2 + (14.2)^2}$

$= \sqrt{73.96 + 201.64}$

$= \sqrt{275.6} \approx 16.601$ units

**78.** $(x_1,\ y_1) = (2,\ 6),\ (x_2,\ y_2) = (-12,\ 4)$

midpoint $= \left(\dfrac{x_1 + x_2}{2},\ \dfrac{y_1 + y_2}{2}\right)$

$= \left(\dfrac{2 - 12}{2},\ \dfrac{6 + 4}{2}\right)$

$= \left(\dfrac{-10}{2},\ \dfrac{10}{2}\right)$

$= (-5,\ 5)$

**79.** $(x_1,\ y_1) = (-6,\ -5),\ (x_2,\ y_2) = (-9,\ 7)$

midpoint $= \left(\dfrac{x_1 + x_2}{2},\ \dfrac{y_1 + y_2}{2}\right)$

$= \left(\dfrac{-6 - 9}{2},\ \dfrac{-5 + 7}{2}\right)$

$= \left(\dfrac{-15}{2},\ \dfrac{2}{2}\right)$

$= \left(-\dfrac{15}{2},\ 1\right)$

**80.** $(x_1,\ y_1) = (4,\ -6),\ (x_2,\ y_2) = (-15,\ 2)$

midpoint $= \left(\dfrac{x_1 + x_2}{2},\ \dfrac{y_1 + y_2}{2}\right)$

$= \left(\dfrac{4 - 15}{2},\ \dfrac{-6 + 2}{2}\right)$

$= \left(\dfrac{-11}{2},\ \dfrac{-4}{2}\right)$

$= \left(-\dfrac{11}{2},\ -2\right)$

**81.** $(x_1,\ y_1) = \left(0,\ -\dfrac{3}{8}\right),\ (x_2,\ y_2) = \left(\dfrac{1}{10},\ 0\right)$

midpoint $= \left(\dfrac{x_1 + x_2}{2},\ \dfrac{y_1 + y_2}{2}\right)$

$= \left(\dfrac{0 + \frac{1}{10}}{2},\ \dfrac{-\frac{3}{8} + 0}{2}\right)$

$= \left(\dfrac{1}{20},\ -\dfrac{3}{16}\right)$

**82.** $(x_1,\ y_1) = \left(\dfrac{3}{4},\ -\dfrac{1}{7}\right),\ (x_2,\ y_2) = \left(-\dfrac{1}{4},\ -\dfrac{3}{7}\right)$

midpoint $= \left(\dfrac{x_1 + x_2}{2},\ \dfrac{y_1 + y_2}{2}\right)$

$= \left(\dfrac{\frac{3}{4} - \frac{1}{4}}{2},\ \dfrac{-\frac{1}{7} - \frac{3}{7}}{2}\right)$

$= \left(\dfrac{\frac{1}{2}}{2},\ \dfrac{-\frac{4}{7}}{2}\right)$

$= \left(\dfrac{1}{4},\ -\dfrac{2}{7}\right)$

**83.** $(x_1,\ y_1) = \left(\sqrt{3},\ -2\sqrt{6}\right),\ (x_2,\ y_2) = \left(\sqrt{3},\ -4\sqrt{6}\right)$

midpoint $= \left(\dfrac{x_1 + x_2}{2},\ \dfrac{y_1 + y_2}{2}\right)$

$= \left(\dfrac{\sqrt{3} + \sqrt{3}}{2},\ \dfrac{-2\sqrt{6} - 4\sqrt{6}}{2}\right)$

$= \left(\dfrac{2\sqrt{3}}{2},\ \dfrac{-6\sqrt{6}}{2}\right)$

$= \left(\sqrt{3},\ -3\sqrt{6}\right)$

**84.** $2\sqrt{50} - 3\sqrt{125} + \sqrt{98}$

$= 2\sqrt{25 \cdot 2} - 3\sqrt{25 \cdot 5} + \sqrt{49 \cdot 2}$

$= 2 \cdot 5\sqrt{2} - 3 \cdot 5\sqrt{5} + 7\sqrt{2}$

$= 10\sqrt{2} - 15\sqrt{5} + 7\sqrt{2}$

$= 17\sqrt{2} - 15\sqrt{5}$

**85.** $x\sqrt{75xy} - \sqrt{27x^3 y} = x\sqrt{25 \cdot 3xy} - \sqrt{9x^2 \cdot 3xy}$

$= x \cdot 5\sqrt{3xy} - 3x\sqrt{3xy}$

$= 2x\sqrt{3xy}$

**86.** $\sqrt[3]{128}+\sqrt[3]{250}=\sqrt[3]{64\cdot2}+\sqrt[3]{125\cdot2}$
$$=4\sqrt[3]{2}+5\sqrt[3]{2}$$
$$=9\sqrt[3]{2}$$

**87.** $3\sqrt[4]{32a^5}-a\sqrt[4]{162a}=3\sqrt[4]{16a^4\cdot2a}-a\sqrt[4]{81\cdot2a}$
$$=3\cdot2a\sqrt[4]{2a}-3a\sqrt[4]{2a}$$
$$=6a\sqrt[4]{2a}-3a\sqrt[4]{2a}$$
$$=3a\sqrt[4]{2a}$$

**88.** $\dfrac{5}{\sqrt{4}}+\dfrac{\sqrt{3}}{3}=\dfrac{5}{2}+\dfrac{\sqrt{3}}{3}=\dfrac{5\cdot3+2\sqrt{3}}{6}=\dfrac{15+2\sqrt{3}}{6}$

**89.** $\sqrt{\dfrac{8}{x^2}}-\sqrt{\dfrac{50}{16x^2}}=\dfrac{\sqrt{8}}{\sqrt{x^2}}-\dfrac{\sqrt{50}}{\sqrt{16x^2}}$
$$=\dfrac{\sqrt{4\cdot2}}{x}-\dfrac{\sqrt{25\cdot2}}{4x}$$
$$=\dfrac{2\sqrt{2}\cdot4}{x\cdot4}-\dfrac{5\sqrt{2}}{4x}$$
$$=\dfrac{8\sqrt{2}-5\sqrt{2}}{4x}$$
$$=\dfrac{3\sqrt{2}}{4x}$$

**90.** $2\sqrt{32x^2y^3}-xy\sqrt{98y}$
$$=2\sqrt{16x^2y^2\cdot2y}-xy\sqrt{49\cdot2y}$$
$$=2\cdot4xy\sqrt{2y}-xy\cdot7\sqrt{2y}$$
$$=8xy\sqrt{2y}-7xy\sqrt{2y}$$
$$=xy\sqrt{2y}$$

**91.** $2a\sqrt[4]{32b^5}-3b\sqrt[4]{162a^4b}+\sqrt[4]{2a^4b^5}$
$$=2a\sqrt[4]{16b^4\cdot2b}-3b\sqrt[4]{81a^4\cdot2b}+\sqrt[4]{a^4b^4\cdot2b}$$
$$=2a\cdot2b\sqrt[4]{2b}-3b\cdot3a\sqrt[4]{2b}+ab\sqrt[4]{2b}$$
$$=4ab\sqrt[4]{2b}-9ab\sqrt[4]{2b}+ab\sqrt[4]{2b}$$
$$=-4ab\sqrt[4]{2b}$$

**92.** $\sqrt{3}\left(\sqrt{27}-\sqrt{3}\right)=\sqrt{3}\left(\sqrt{9\cdot3}-\sqrt{3}\right)$
$$=\sqrt{3}\left(3\sqrt{3}-\sqrt{3}\right)$$
$$=\sqrt{3}\left(2\sqrt{3}\right)$$
$$=2\sqrt{9}$$
$$=2(3)$$
$$=6$$

**93.** $\left(\sqrt{x}-3\right)^2=\left(\sqrt{x}\right)^2-2\cdot\sqrt{x}\cdot3+3^2=x-6\sqrt{x}+9$

**94.** $\left(\sqrt{5}-5\right)\left(2\sqrt{5}+2\right)=2\sqrt{25}+2\sqrt{5}-10\sqrt{5}-10$
$$=2(5)-8\sqrt{5}-10$$
$$=10-8\sqrt{5}-10$$
$$=-8\sqrt{5}$$

**95.** $\left(2\sqrt{x}-3\sqrt{y}\right)\left(2\sqrt{x}+3\sqrt{y}\right)$
$$=\left(2\sqrt{x}\right)^2-\left(3\sqrt{y}\right)^2$$
$$=2^2\left(\sqrt{x}\right)^2-3^2\left(\sqrt{y}\right)^2$$
$$=4x-9y$$

**96.** $\left(\sqrt{a}+3\right)\left(\sqrt{a}-3\right)=\left(\sqrt{a}\right)^2-(3)^2=a-9$

**97.** $\left(\sqrt[3]{a}+2\right)^2=\left(\sqrt[3]{a}\right)^2+2\cdot\sqrt[3]{a}\cdot2+2^2$
$$=\sqrt[3]{a^2}+4\sqrt[3]{a}+4$$

**98.** $\left(\sqrt[3]{5x}+9\right)\left(\sqrt[3]{5x}-9\right)=\left(\sqrt[3]{5x}\right)^2-9^2$
$$=\sqrt[3]{(5x)^2}-81$$
$$=\sqrt[3]{25x^2}-81$$

**99.** $\left(\sqrt[3]{a}+4\right)\left(\sqrt[3]{a^2}-4\sqrt[3]{a}+16\right)$
$$=\left(\sqrt[3]{a}\right)\left(\sqrt[3]{a^2}\right)-4\cdot\left(\sqrt[3]{a}\right)^2+16\sqrt[3]{a}+4\sqrt[3]{a^2}$$
$$-16\sqrt[3]{a}+64$$
$$=\sqrt[3]{a^3}-4\sqrt[3]{a^2}+4\sqrt[3]{a^2}+64$$
$$=a+64$$

**100.** $\dfrac{3}{\sqrt{7}}=\dfrac{3\cdot\sqrt{7}}{\sqrt{7}\cdot\sqrt{7}}=\dfrac{3\sqrt{7}}{7}$

**101.**
$$\sqrt{\frac{x}{12}} = \frac{\sqrt{x}}{\sqrt{12}}$$
$$= \frac{\sqrt{x}}{\sqrt{4 \cdot 3}}$$
$$= \frac{\sqrt{x}}{2\sqrt{3}}$$
$$= \frac{\sqrt{x} \cdot \sqrt{3}}{2\sqrt{3} \cdot \sqrt{3}}$$
$$= \frac{\sqrt{3x}}{2 \cdot 3}$$
$$= \frac{\sqrt{3x}}{6}$$

**102.** $\dfrac{5}{\sqrt[3]{4}} = \dfrac{5 \cdot \sqrt[3]{2}}{\sqrt[3]{4} \cdot \sqrt[3]{2}} = \dfrac{5\sqrt[3]{2}}{\sqrt[3]{8}} = \dfrac{5\sqrt[3]{2}}{2}$

**103.**
$$\sqrt{\frac{24x^5}{3y^2}} = \sqrt{\frac{8x^5}{y^2}}$$
$$= \frac{\sqrt{8x^5}}{\sqrt{y^2}}$$
$$= \frac{\sqrt{4x^4 \cdot 2x}}{y}$$
$$= \frac{2x^2\sqrt{2x}}{y}$$

**104.**
$$\sqrt[3]{\frac{15x^6y^7}{z^2}} = \frac{\sqrt[3]{15x^6y^7}}{\sqrt[3]{z^2}}$$
$$= \frac{\sqrt[3]{15x^6y^7} \cdot \sqrt[3]{z}}{\sqrt[3]{z^2} \cdot \sqrt[3]{z}}$$
$$= \frac{\sqrt[3]{15x^6y^7z}}{\sqrt[3]{z^3}}$$
$$= \frac{\sqrt[3]{15x^6y^6 \cdot yz}}{z}$$
$$= \frac{x^2y^2\sqrt[3]{15yz}}{z}$$

**105.**
$$\frac{5}{2-\sqrt{7}} = \frac{5\left(2+\sqrt{7}\right)}{\left(2-\sqrt{7}\right)\left(2+\sqrt{7}\right)}$$
$$= \frac{5\left(2+\sqrt{7}\right)}{2^2 - \left(\sqrt{7}\right)^2}$$
$$= \frac{10+5\sqrt{7}}{4-7}$$
$$= \frac{10+5\sqrt{7}}{-3}$$
$$= -\frac{10+5\sqrt{7}}{3}$$

**106.**
$$\frac{3}{\sqrt{y}-2} = \frac{3\left(\sqrt{y}+2\right)}{\left(\sqrt{y}-2\right)\left(\sqrt{y}+2\right)}$$
$$= \frac{3\left(\sqrt{y}+2\right)}{\left(\sqrt{y}\right)^2 - 2^2}$$
$$= \frac{3\sqrt{y}+6}{y-4}$$

**107.**
$$\frac{\sqrt{2}-\sqrt{3}}{\sqrt{2}+\sqrt{3}} = \frac{\left(\sqrt{2}-\sqrt{3}\right)\left(\sqrt{2}-\sqrt{3}\right)}{\left(\sqrt{2}+\sqrt{3}\right)\left(\sqrt{2}-\sqrt{3}\right)}$$
$$= \frac{2-\sqrt{2}\sqrt{3}-\sqrt{3}\sqrt{2}+3}{\left(\sqrt{2}\right)^2 - \left(\sqrt{3}\right)^2}$$
$$= \frac{5-\sqrt{6}-\sqrt{6}}{2-3}$$
$$= \frac{5-2\sqrt{6}}{-1}$$
$$= -5+2\sqrt{6}$$

**108.** $\dfrac{\sqrt{11}}{3} = \dfrac{\sqrt{11} \cdot \sqrt{11}}{3 \cdot \sqrt{11}} = \dfrac{11}{3\sqrt{11}}$

**109.** $\sqrt{\dfrac{18}{y}} = \dfrac{\sqrt{18}}{\sqrt{y}} = \dfrac{3\sqrt{2}}{\sqrt{y}} = \dfrac{3\sqrt{2} \cdot \sqrt{2}}{\sqrt{y} \cdot \sqrt{2}} = \dfrac{3 \cdot 2}{\sqrt{2y}} = \dfrac{6}{\sqrt{2y}}$

**110.** $\dfrac{\sqrt[3]{9}}{7} = \dfrac{\sqrt[3]{9} \cdot \sqrt[3]{3}}{7 \cdot \sqrt[3]{3}} = \dfrac{\sqrt[3]{27}}{7\sqrt[3]{3}} = \dfrac{3}{7\sqrt[3]{3}}$

**111.** $\sqrt{\dfrac{24x^5}{3y^2}} = \sqrt{\dfrac{8x^5}{y^2}}$

$= \dfrac{\sqrt{4x^4 \cdot 2x}}{\sqrt{y^2}}$

$= \dfrac{2x^2\sqrt{2x}}{y}$

$= \dfrac{2x^2\sqrt{2x} \cdot \sqrt{2x}}{y \;\; \sqrt{2x}}$

$= \dfrac{2x^2 \cdot 2x}{y\sqrt{2x}} = \dfrac{4x^3}{y\sqrt{2x}}$

**112.** $\sqrt[3]{\dfrac{xy^2}{10z}} = \dfrac{\sqrt[3]{xy^2}}{\sqrt[3]{10z}}$

$= \dfrac{\sqrt[3]{xy^2} \cdot \sqrt[3]{x^2y}}{\sqrt[3]{10z} \cdot \sqrt[3]{x^2y}}$

$= \dfrac{\sqrt[3]{x^3y^3}}{\sqrt[3]{10x^2yz}}$

$= \dfrac{xy}{\sqrt[3]{10x^2yz}}$

**113.** $\dfrac{\sqrt{x}+5}{-3} = \dfrac{\left(\sqrt{x}+5\right)\left(\sqrt{x}-5\right)}{-3\left(\sqrt{x}-5\right)}$

$= \dfrac{\left(\sqrt{x}\right)^2 - 5^2}{-3\sqrt{x}+15}$

$= \dfrac{x-25}{-3\sqrt{x}+15}$

**114.** $\sqrt{y-7} = 5$

$\left(\sqrt{y-7}\right)^2 = 5^2$

$y - 7 = 25$

$y = 32$

The solution is 32.

**115.** $\sqrt{2x} + 10 = 4$

$\sqrt{2x} = -6$

No solution exists since the principle square root of a number is not negative.

**116.** $\sqrt[3]{2x-6} = 4$

$\left(\sqrt[3]{2x-6}\right)^3 = 4^3$

$2x - 6 = 64$

$2x = 70$

$x = 35$

The solution is 35.

**117.** $\sqrt{x+6} = \sqrt{x+2}$

$\left(\sqrt{x+6}\right)^2 \;\; \left(\sqrt{x+2}\right)^2$

$x + 6 = x + 2$

$6 = 2$, which is false.

There is no solution.

**118.** $2x - 5\sqrt{x} = 3$

$2x - 3 = 5\sqrt{x}$

$(2x-3)^2 = \left(5\sqrt{x}\right)^2$

$4x^2 - 12x + 9 = 25x$

$4x^2 - 37x + 9 = 0$

$(4x-1)(x-9) = 0$

$4x - 1 = 0$  or  $x - 9 = 0$

$4x = 1$  or  $\quad x = 9$

$x = \dfrac{1}{4}$

Discard the solution $\dfrac{1}{4}$ as extraneous. The solution is 9.

**119.** $\sqrt{x+9} = 2 + \sqrt{x-7}$

$\left(\sqrt{x+9}\right)^2 = \left(2+\sqrt{x-7}\right)^2$

$x + 9 = 4 + 4\sqrt{x-7} + (x-7)$

$x + 9 = x - 3 + 4\sqrt{x-7}$

$12 = 4\sqrt{x-7}$

$3 = \sqrt{x-7}$

$3^2 = \left(\sqrt{x-7}\right)^2$

$9 = x - 7$

$16 = x$

The solution is 16.

**120.** Let $c$ = length of the hypotenuse.
$$3^2 + 3^2 = c^2$$
$$18 = c^2$$
$$\sqrt{18} = \sqrt{c^2}$$
$$3\sqrt{2} = c$$
The length is $3\sqrt{2}$ centimeters.

**121.** Let $c$ = length of the hypotenuse.
$$7^2 + \left(8\sqrt{3}\right)^2 = c^2$$
$$49 + 64 \cdot 3 = c^2$$
$$241 = c^2$$
$$\sqrt{241} = \sqrt{c^2}$$
$$\sqrt{241} = c$$
The length is $\sqrt{241}$ feet.

**122.** Let $b$ = width of the lake.
$$a^2 + b^2 = c^2$$
$$40^2 + b^2 = 65^2$$
$$1600 + b^2 = 4225$$
$$b^2 = 2625$$
$$\sqrt{b^2} = \sqrt{2625}$$
$$b \approx 51.23475$$
The width is about 51.2 feet.

**123.** Let $c$ = length of the shortest pipe.
$$a^2 + b^2 = c^2$$
$$3^2 + 3^2 = c^2$$
$$18 = c^2$$
$$\sqrt{18} = \sqrt{c^2}$$
$$4.24264 = c$$
The shortest possible pipe is 4.24 feet.

**124.** $\sqrt{-8} = i\sqrt{4 \cdot 2} = 2i\sqrt{2}$

**125.** $-\sqrt{-6} = -i\sqrt{6}$

**126.** $\sqrt{-4} + \sqrt{-16} = 2i + 4i = 6i$

**127.** $\sqrt{-2} \cdot \sqrt{-5} = i\sqrt{2} \cdot i\sqrt{5}$
$$= i^2\sqrt{10}$$
$$= -1 \cdot \sqrt{10}$$
$$= -\sqrt{10}$$

**128.** $(12 - 6i) + (3 + 2i) = (12 + 3) + (-6 + 2)i$
$$= 15 + (-4)i$$
$$= 15 - 4i$$

**129.** $(-8 - 7i) - (5 - 4i) = -8 - 7i - 5 + 4i$
$$= -13 - 3i$$

**130.** $(2i)^6 = 2^6 i^6 = 64i^4 \cdot i^2 = 64(1)(-1) = -64$

**131.** $-3i(6 - 4i) = -18i + 12i^2$
$$= -18i + 12(-1)$$
$$= -12 - 18i$$

**132.** $(3 + 2i)(1 + i) = 3 + 3i + 2i + 2i^2$
$$= 3 + 5i + 2(-1)$$
$$= 1 + 5i$$

**133.** $(2 - 3i)^2 = 2^2 + 2 \cdot 2 \cdot (-3i) + (3i)^2$
$$= 4 - 12i + 9i^2$$
$$= 4 - 12i + 9(-1)$$
$$= -5 - 12i$$

**134.** $\left(\sqrt{6} - 9i\right)\left(\sqrt{6} + 9i\right) = \left(\sqrt{6}\right)^2 - (9i)^2$
$$= 6 - 81i^2$$
$$= 6 + 81$$
$$= 87$$

**135.** $\dfrac{2 + 3i}{2i} = \dfrac{(2 + 3i) \cdot (-2i)}{2i \cdot (-2i)}$
$$= \dfrac{-4i - 6i^2}{-4i^2}$$
$$= \dfrac{-4i + 6}{4}$$
$$= \dfrac{6}{4} - \dfrac{4}{4}i$$
$$= \dfrac{3}{2} - i$$

**136.** $\dfrac{1 + i}{-3i} = \dfrac{(1 + i) \cdot (3i)}{-3i \cdot (3i)}$
$$= \dfrac{3i + 3i^2}{-9i^2}$$
$$= \dfrac{3i - 3}{9}$$
$$= \dfrac{-3}{9} - \dfrac{3}{9}i$$
$$= -\dfrac{1}{3} + \dfrac{1}{3}i$$

**137.** $\sqrt[3]{x^3} = x$

**138.** $\sqrt{(x+2)^2} = |x+2|$

**139.** $-\sqrt{100} = -10$

**140.** $\sqrt[3]{-x^{12}y^3} = -x^4 y$

**141.** $\sqrt[4]{\dfrac{y^{20}}{16x^{12}}} = \dfrac{\sqrt[4]{y^{20}}}{\sqrt[4]{16x^{12}}} = \dfrac{y^5}{2x^3}$

**142.** $9^{1/2} = \sqrt{9} = 3$

**143.** $64^{-1/2} = \dfrac{1}{64^{1/2}} = \dfrac{1}{\sqrt{64}} = \dfrac{1}{8}$

**144.** $\left(\dfrac{27}{64}\right)^{-2/3} = \left(\dfrac{64}{27}\right)^{2/3}$
$= \left(\sqrt[3]{\dfrac{64}{27}}\right)^2$
$= \left(\dfrac{4}{3}\right)^2$
$= \dfrac{16}{9}$

**145.** $\dfrac{(x^{2/3}x^{-3})^3}{x^{-1/2}} = \dfrac{x^{6/3}x^{-9}}{x^{-1/2}}$
$= x^{2-9+\frac{1}{2}}$
$= x^{-13/2}$
$= \dfrac{1}{x^{13/2}}$

**146.** $\sqrt{200x^9} = \sqrt{100x^8 \cdot 2x} = 10x^4\sqrt{2x}$

**147.** $\sqrt{\dfrac{3n^3}{121m^{10}}} = \dfrac{\sqrt{3n^3}}{\sqrt{121m^{10}}} = \dfrac{\sqrt{n^2 \cdot 3n}}{\sqrt{121m^{10}}} = \dfrac{n\sqrt{3n}}{11m^5}$

**148.** $3\sqrt{20} - 7x\sqrt[3]{40} + 3\sqrt[3]{5x^3}$
$= 3\sqrt{4}\sqrt{5} - 7x\sqrt[3]{8}\sqrt[3]{5} + 3\sqrt[3]{x^3}\sqrt[3]{5}$
$= 6\sqrt{5} - 14x\sqrt[3]{5} + 3x\sqrt[3]{5}$
$= 6\sqrt{5} - 11x\sqrt[3]{5}$

**149.** $\left(2\sqrt{x}-5\right)^2 = \left(2\sqrt{x}\right)^2 - 2(5)\left(2\sqrt{x}\right) + 5^2$
$= 4x - 20\sqrt{x} + 25$

**150.** $(x_1, y_1) = (-3, 5), (x_2, y_2) = (-8, 9)$
$d = \sqrt{(x_2 - x_1)^2 + (y_2 - y_1)^2}$
$= \sqrt{(-8+3)^2 + (9-5)^2}$
$= \sqrt{(-5)^2 + (4)^2}$
$= \sqrt{25 + 16}$
$= \sqrt{41}$
The distance is $\sqrt{41}$ units.

**151.** $(x_1, y_1) = (-3, 8), (x_2, y_2) = (11, 24)$
$\text{midpoint} = \left(\dfrac{x_1 + x_2}{2}, \dfrac{y_1 + y_2}{2}\right)$
$= \left(\dfrac{-3+11}{2}, \dfrac{8+24}{2}\right)$
$= \left(\dfrac{8}{2}, \dfrac{32}{2}\right)$
$= (4, 16)$

**152.** $\dfrac{7}{\sqrt{13}} = \dfrac{7}{\sqrt{13}} \cdot \dfrac{\sqrt{13}}{\sqrt{13}} = \dfrac{7\sqrt{13}}{13}$

**153.** $\dfrac{2}{\sqrt{x}+3} = \dfrac{2}{\sqrt{x}+3} \cdot \dfrac{\sqrt{x}-3}{\sqrt{x}-3} = \dfrac{2\sqrt{x}-6}{x-9}$

**154.** $\sqrt{x}+2 = x$
$\sqrt{x} = x-2$
$\left(\sqrt{x}\right)^2 = (x-2)^2$
$x = x^2 - 4x + 4$
$0 = x^2 - 5x + 4$
$0 = (x-4)(x-1)$
$x - 4 = 0 \quad \text{or} \quad x - 1 = 0$
$x = 4 \qquad\qquad x = 1$
Discard the extraneous solution 1. The solution set is {4}.

**Chapter 7 Test**

**1.** $\sqrt{216} = \sqrt{36 \cdot 6} = 6\sqrt{6}$

**2.** $-\sqrt[4]{x^{64}} = -x^{16}$

**3.** $\left(\dfrac{1}{125}\right)^{1/3} = \dfrac{1}{125^{1/3}} = \dfrac{1}{\sqrt[3]{125}} = \dfrac{1}{5}$

**4.** $\left(\dfrac{1}{125}\right)^{-1/3} = \dfrac{1}{\left(\frac{1}{125}\right)^{1/3}} = \dfrac{1}{\frac{1}{5}} = 5$

**5.** $\left(\dfrac{8x^3}{27}\right)^{2/3} = \dfrac{(8x^3)^{2/3}}{27^{2/3}}$

$\qquad = \dfrac{\left(\sqrt[3]{8x^3}\right)^2}{\left(\sqrt[3]{27}\right)^2}$

$\qquad = \dfrac{(2x)^2}{3^2}$

$\qquad = \dfrac{4x^2}{9}$

**6.** $\sqrt[3]{-a^{18}b^9} = \sqrt[3]{-1a^{18}b^9} = (-1)a^6b^3 = -a^6b^3$

**7.** $\left(\dfrac{64c^{4/3}}{a^{-2/3}b^{5/6}}\right)^{1/2} = \left(\dfrac{64a^{2/3}c^{4/3}}{b^{5/6}}\right)^{1/2}$

$\qquad = \dfrac{64^{1/2}(a^{2/3})^{1/2}(c^{4/3})^{1/2}}{(b^{5/6})^{1/2}}$

$\qquad = \dfrac{\sqrt{64}\,a^{1/3}c^{2/3}}{b^{5/12}}$

$\qquad = \dfrac{8a^{1/3}c^{2/3}}{b^{5/12}}$

**8.** $a^{-2/3}(a^{5/4} - a^3) = a^{-2/3}a^{5/4} - a^{-2/3}a^3$

$\qquad = a^{-\frac{2}{3}+\frac{5}{4}} - a^{-\frac{2}{3}+3}$

$\qquad = a^{-\frac{8}{12}+\frac{15}{12}} - a^{-\frac{2}{3}+\frac{9}{3}}$

$\qquad = a^{7/12} - a^{7/3}$

**9.** $\sqrt[4]{(4xy)^4} = |4xy| = 4|xy|$

**10.** $\sqrt[3]{(-27)^3} = -27$

**11.** $\sqrt{\dfrac{9}{y}} = \dfrac{\sqrt{9}}{\sqrt{y}} = \dfrac{3}{\sqrt{y}} = \dfrac{3 \cdot \sqrt{y}}{\sqrt{y} \cdot \sqrt{y}} = \dfrac{3\sqrt{y}}{y}$

**12.** $\dfrac{4 - \sqrt{x}}{4 + 2\sqrt{x}} = \dfrac{4 - \sqrt{x}}{2(2 + \sqrt{x})}$

$\qquad = \dfrac{\left(4 - \sqrt{x}\right)\left(2 - \sqrt{x}\right)}{2\left(2 + \sqrt{x}\right)\left(2 - \sqrt{x}\right)}$

$\qquad = \dfrac{8 - 4\sqrt{x} - 2\sqrt{x} + x}{2\left[2^2 - \left(\sqrt{x}\right)^2\right]}$

$\qquad = \dfrac{8 - 6\sqrt{x} + x}{2(4 - x)}$ or $\dfrac{8 - 6\sqrt{x} + x}{8 - 2x}$

**13.** $\dfrac{\sqrt[3]{ab}}{\sqrt[3]{ab^2}} = \sqrt[3]{\dfrac{ab}{ab^2}}$

$\qquad = \sqrt[3]{\dfrac{1}{b}}$

$\qquad = \dfrac{1}{\sqrt[3]{b}}$

$\qquad = \dfrac{1 \cdot \sqrt[3]{b^2}}{\sqrt[3]{b} \cdot \sqrt[3]{b^2}}$

$\qquad = \dfrac{\sqrt[3]{b^2}}{b}$

**14.** $\dfrac{\sqrt{6} + x}{8} = \dfrac{\left(\sqrt{6} + x\right)\left(\sqrt{6} - x\right)}{8\left(\sqrt{6} - x\right)}$

$\qquad = \dfrac{\left(\sqrt{6}\right)^2 - x^2}{8\left(\sqrt{6} - x\right)}$

$\qquad = \dfrac{6 - x^2}{8\left(\sqrt{6} - x\right)}$

**15.** $\sqrt{125x^3} - 3\sqrt{20x^3} = \sqrt{25x^2 \cdot 5x} - 3\sqrt{4x^2 \cdot 5x}$

$\qquad = 5x\sqrt{5x} - 3 \cdot 2x\sqrt{5x}$

$\qquad = 5x\sqrt{5x} - 6x\sqrt{5x}$

$\qquad = -x\sqrt{5x}$

**16.** $\sqrt{3}\left(\sqrt{16} - \sqrt{2}\right) = \sqrt{3}\left(4 - \sqrt{2}\right)$

$\qquad = 4\sqrt{3} - \sqrt{3}\sqrt{2}$

$\qquad = 4\sqrt{3} - \sqrt{6}$

**17.** $\left(\sqrt{x} + 1\right)^2 = \left(\sqrt{x}\right)^2 + 2\sqrt{x} + 1^2$

$\qquad = x + 2\sqrt{x} + 1$

**18.** $\left(\sqrt{2}-4\right)\left(\sqrt{3}+1\right) = \sqrt{2}\sqrt{3}+1\cdot\sqrt{2}-4\sqrt{3}-4$
$$= \sqrt{6}+\sqrt{2}-4\sqrt{3}-4$$

**19.** $\left(\sqrt{5}+5\right)\left(\sqrt{5}-5\right) = \left(\sqrt{5}\right)^2-5^2$
$$= 5-25$$
$$= -20$$

**20.** $\sqrt{561} \approx 23.685$

**21.** $386^{-2/3} \approx 0.019$

**22.**
$$x = \sqrt{x-2}+2$$
$$x-2 = \sqrt{x-2}$$
$$(x-2)^2 = \left(\sqrt{x-2}\right)^2$$
$$x^2-4x+4 = x-2$$
$$x^2-5x+6 = 0$$
$$(x-2)(x-3) = 0$$
$$x = 2 \text{ or } x = 3$$
The solutions are 2 and 3.

**23.** $\sqrt{x^2-7}+3 = 0$
$$\sqrt{x^2-7} = -3$$
No solution exists since the principle square root of a number is not negative.

**24.**
$$\sqrt[3]{x+5} = \sqrt[3]{2x-1}$$
$$\left(\sqrt[3]{x+5}\right)^3 = \left(\sqrt[3]{2x-1}\right)^3$$
$$x+5 = 2x-1$$
$$-x = -6$$
$$x = 6$$
The solution is 6.

**25.** $\sqrt{-2} = i\sqrt{2}$

**26.** $-\sqrt{-8} = -i\sqrt{4\cdot2} = -2i\sqrt{2}$

**27.** $(12-6i)-(12-3i) = 12-6i-12+3i = -3i$

**28.** $(6-2i)(6+2i) = 6^2-(2i)^2$
$$= 36-4i^2$$
$$= 36+4$$
$$= 40$$

**29.** $(4+3i)^2 = 4^2+2\cdot4\cdot3i+(3i)^2$
$$= 16+24i+9i^2$$
$$= 16+24i-9$$
$$= 7+24i$$

**30.** $\dfrac{1+4i}{1-i} = \dfrac{(1+4i)(1+i)}{(1-i)(1+i)}$
$$= \frac{1+i+4i+4i^2}{1^2-i^2}$$
$$= \frac{1+5i-4}{1-(-1)}$$
$$= \frac{-3+5i}{2}$$
$$= -\frac{3}{2}+\frac{5}{2}i$$

**31.** $x^2+x^2 = 5^2$
$$2x^2 = 25$$
$$x^2 = \frac{25}{2}$$
$$\sqrt{x^2} = \sqrt{\frac{25}{2}}$$
$$x = \frac{5}{\sqrt{2}} = \frac{5\cdot\sqrt{2}}{\sqrt{2}\cdot\sqrt{2}} = \frac{5\sqrt{2}}{2}$$

**32.** $g(x) = \sqrt{x+2}$
$$x+2 \geq 0$$
$$x \geq -2$$
Domain: $[-2, \infty)$

| $x$ | $-2$ | $-1$ | 2 | 7 |
|------|------|------|---|---|
| $g(x)$ | 0 | 1 | 2 | 3 |

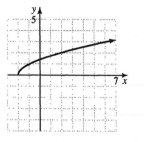

**33.** $(x_1, y_1) = (-6, 3), (x_2, y_2) = (-8, -7)$

$$d = \sqrt{(-8-(-6))^2 + (-7-3)^2}$$
$$= \sqrt{(-2)^2 + (-10)^2}$$
$$= \sqrt{4+100}$$
$$= \sqrt{104}$$
$$= \sqrt{4 \cdot 26}$$
$$= 2\sqrt{26}$$

The distance is $2\sqrt{26}$ units.

**34.** $(x_1, y_1) = \left(-2\sqrt{5}, \sqrt{10}\right),$

$(x_2, y_2) = \left(-\sqrt{5}, 4\sqrt{10}\right)$

$$d = \sqrt{(x_2 - x_1)^2 + (y_2 - y_1)^2}$$
$$= \sqrt{\left(-\sqrt{5} + 2\sqrt{5}\right)^2 + \left(4\sqrt{10} - \sqrt{10}\right)^2}$$
$$= \sqrt{\left(\sqrt{5}\right)^2 + \left(3\sqrt{10}\right)^2}$$
$$= \sqrt{5 + 90}$$
$$= \sqrt{95}$$

The distance is $\sqrt{95}$ units.

**35.** $(x_1, y_1) = (-2, -5), (x_2, y_2) = (-6, 12)$

$$\text{midpoint} = \left(\frac{x_1 + x_2}{2}, \frac{y_1 + y_2}{2}\right)$$
$$= \left(\frac{-2-6}{2}, \frac{-5+12}{2}\right)$$
$$= \left(-\frac{8}{2}, \frac{7}{2}\right)$$
$$= \left(-4, \frac{7}{2}\right)$$

**36.** $(x_1, y_1) = \left(-\frac{2}{3}, -\frac{1}{5}\right), (x_2, y_2) = \left(-\frac{1}{3}, \frac{4}{5}\right)$

$$\text{midpoint} = \left(\frac{x_1 + x_2}{2}, \frac{y_1 + y_2}{2}\right)$$
$$= \left(\frac{-\frac{2}{3} - \frac{1}{3}}{2}, \frac{-\frac{1}{5} + \frac{4}{5}}{2}\right)$$
$$= \left(\frac{-\frac{3}{3}}{2}, \frac{\frac{3}{5}}{2}\right)$$
$$= \left(-\frac{1}{2}, \frac{3}{10}\right)$$

**37.** $V(r) = \sqrt{2.5r}$

$$V(300) = \sqrt{2.5(300)} = \sqrt{750} \approx 27 \text{ mph}$$

**38.** $V(r) = \sqrt{2.5r}$

$$30 = \sqrt{2.5r}$$
$$30^2 = \left(\sqrt{2.5r}\right)^2$$
$$900 = 2.5r$$
$$r = \frac{900}{2.5} = 360 \text{ feet}$$

## Chapter 7 Cumulative Review

**1. a.** $3xy - 2xy + 5 - 7 + xy = 2xy - 2$

   **b.** $7x^2 + 3 - 5(x^2 - 4) = 7x^2 + 3 - 5x^2 + 20$
$$= 2x^2 + 23$$

   **c.** $(2.1x - 5.6) - (-x - 5.3) = 2.1x - 5.6 + x + 5.3$
$$= 3.1x - 0.3$$

   **d.** $\frac{1}{2}(4a - 6b) - \frac{1}{3}(9a + 12b - 1) + \frac{1}{4}$
$$= 2a - 3b - 3a - 4b + \frac{1}{3} + \frac{1}{4}$$
$$= -a - 7b + \frac{4}{12} + \frac{3}{12}$$
$$= -a - 7b + \frac{7}{12}$$

**2. a.** $2(x - 3) + (5x + 3) = 2x - 6 + 5x + 3$
$$= 7x - 3$$

   **b.** $4(3x + 2) - 3(5x - 1) = 12x + 8 - 15x + 3$
$$= -3x + 11$$

   **c.** $7x + 2(x - 7) - 3x = 7x + 2x - 14 - 3x$
$$= 6x - 14$$

**3.** $\frac{x+5}{2} + \frac{1}{2} = 2x - \frac{x-3}{8}$
$$8\left(\frac{x+5}{2} + \frac{1}{2}\right) = 8\left(2x - \frac{x-3}{8}\right)$$
$$4(x + 5) + 4 = 16x - (x - 3)$$
$$4x + 20 + 4 = 16x - x + 3$$
$$4x + 24 = 15x + 3$$
$$-11x = -21$$
$$x = \frac{21}{11}$$

**4.**   $\dfrac{a-1}{2}+a=2-\dfrac{2a+7}{8}$

$8\left(\dfrac{a-1}{2}+a\right)=8\left(2-\dfrac{2a+7}{8}\right)$

$4(a-1)+8a=16-(2a+7)$

$4a-4+8a=16-2a-7$

$12a-4=9-2a$

$14a=13$

$a=\dfrac{13}{14}$

**5.** Let $x=$ the sales needed.

$600+0.20x>1500$

$0.20x>900$

$x>\dfrac{900}{0.20}$

$x>4500$

The salesperson needs sales of at least $4500.

**6.** Let $r=$ their average speed.

$t_{\text{going}}+t_{\text{returning}}=4.5$ hrs

$\dfrac{121.5}{r}+\dfrac{121.5}{r}=4.5$

$\dfrac{243}{r}=4.5$

$243=4.5r$

$r=\dfrac{243}{4.5}=54$

Their average speed was 54 mph.

**7.**   $2|x|+25=23$

$2|x|=-2$

$|x|=-1$, which is impossible.

There is no solution, or the solution set is $\varnothing$.

**8.**   $|3x-2|+5=5$

$|3x-2|=0$

$3x-2=0$

$3x=2$

$x=\dfrac{2}{3}$

**9.**   $\left|\dfrac{x}{3}-1\right|-7\ge-5$

$\left|\dfrac{x}{3}-1\right|\ge2$

$\dfrac{x}{3}-1\le-2$  or  $\dfrac{x}{3}-1\ge2$

$\dfrac{x}{3}\le-1$  or   $\dfrac{x}{3}\ge3$

$x\le-3$  or    $x\ge9$

$(-\infty,\ -3]\cup[9,\ \infty)$

**10.**   $\left|\dfrac{x}{2}-1\right|\le0$

$\dfrac{x}{2}-1=0$

$\dfrac{x}{2}=1$

$x=2$

**11.**   $y=|x|$

**12.**   $y=|x-2|$

**13. a.** Domain: $\{2, 0, 3\}$
Range: $\{3, 4, -1\}$

**b.** Domain: $\{-4, -3, -2, -1, 0, 1, 2, 3\}$
Range: $\{1\}$

**c.** Domain: {Lubbock, Colorado Springs, Omaha, Yonkers, Sacramento}
Range: $\{307, 404, 445, 206, 197\}$

**14. a.** Domain: $(-\infty, 0]$, Range: $(-\infty, \infty)$
not a function

**b.** Domain: $(-\infty, \infty)$, Range: $(-\infty, \infty)$
function

**c.** Domain: $(-\infty, -2]\cup[2, \infty)$
Range: $(-\infty, \infty)$
not a function

**15.** $y = -3$
This is a horizontal line passing through $(0, -3)$.

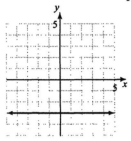

**16.** $f(x) = -2$
This is a horizontal line passing through $(0, -2)$.

**17.** $x = -5$ is a vertical line. The slope is undefined.

**18.** $y = -3$ is a horizontal line. The slope is 0.

**19.** $\begin{cases} -\dfrac{x}{6}+\dfrac{y}{2}=\dfrac{1}{2} \\ \dfrac{x}{3}-\dfrac{y}{6}=-\dfrac{3}{4} \end{cases}$ or $\begin{cases} -x+3y=3 & (1) \\ 4x-2y=-9 & (2) \end{cases}$

Solve equation (1) for $x$.
$-x+3y=3$
$3y-3=x$
Replace $x$ with $3y - 3$ in equation (2).
$4(3y-3)-2y=-9$
$12y-12-2y=-9$
$10y-12=-9$
$10y=3$
$y=\dfrac{3}{10}$

Substitute $\dfrac{3}{10}$ for $y$ in $x = 3y - 3$.

$x=3\left(\dfrac{3}{10}\right)-3=\dfrac{9}{10}-\dfrac{30}{10}=-\dfrac{21}{10}$

The solution is $\left(-\dfrac{21}{10}, \dfrac{3}{10}\right)$.

**20.** $\begin{cases} \dfrac{x}{6}-\dfrac{y}{2}=1 \\ \dfrac{x}{3}-\dfrac{y}{4}=2 \end{cases}$ or $\begin{cases} x-3y=6 & (1) \\ 4x-3y=24 & (2) \end{cases}$

Solve equation (1) for $x$.
$x-3y=6$
$x=3y+6$
Replace $x$ with $3y + 6$ in equation (2).
$4(3y+6)-3y=24$
$12y+24-3y=24$
$9y+24=24$
$9y=0$
$y=0$
Substitute 0 for $y$ in $x = 3y + 6$.
$x=3(0)+6=0+6=6$
The solution is $(6, 0)$.

**21. a.** $2^2 \cdot 2^5 = 2^{2+5} = 2^7$

**b.** $x^7 x^3 = x^{7+3} = x^{10}$

**c.** $y \cdot y^2 \cdot y^4 = y^{1+2+4} = y^7$

**22.** Let $x$ = number of tee-shirts and $y$ = number of shorts.
$\begin{cases} x+y=9 & (1) \\ 3.50x+4.25y=33.75 & (2) \end{cases}$
Solve equation (1) for $y$.
$x+y=9$
$y=9-x$
Substitute $9 - x$ for $y$ in equation (2).
$3.50x+4.25(9-x)=33.75$
$3.50x+38.25-4.25x=33.75$
$-0.75x+38.25=33.75$
$-0.75x=-4.5$
$x=\dfrac{-4.5}{-0.75}=6$
Replace $x$ with 6 in $y = 9 - x$.
$y=9-6=3$
Nana bought 6 shirts and 3 shorts.

**23.** $\dfrac{2000 \times 0.000021}{700} = \dfrac{(2 \times 10^3) \times (2.1 \times 10^{-5})}{7 \times 10^2}$

$\qquad = \dfrac{2(2.1)}{7} \times 10^{3+(-5)-2}$

$\qquad = 0.6 \times 10^{-4}$

$\qquad = (6 \times 10^{-1}) \times 10^{-4}$

$\qquad = 6 \times 10^{-5}$

**24.** $\dfrac{0.0000035 \times 4000}{0.28} \quad \dfrac{(3.5 \times 10^{-6}) \times (4 \times 10^3)}{2.8 \times 10^{-1}}$

$\qquad = \dfrac{3.5 \times 4}{2.8} \times 10^{-6+3-(-1)}$

$\qquad = 5 \times 10^{-2}$

**25.** $P(x) = 3x^2 - 2x - 5$

    **a.** $P(1) = 3(1)^2 - 2(1) - 5$

$\qquad = 3(1) - 2(1) - 5$

$\qquad = 3 - 2 - 5$

$\qquad = -4$

    **b.** $P(-2) = 3(-2)^2 - 2(-2) - 5$

$\qquad = 3(4) - (-4) - 5$

$\qquad = 12 + 4 - 5$

$\qquad = 11$

**26.** $(5x^2 - 3x + 6) + (4x^2 + 5x - 3) - (2x - 5)$

$\qquad = 5x^2 - 3x + 6 + 4x^2 + 5x - 3 - 2x + 5$

$\qquad = 9x^2 + 8$

**27.**  **a.** $(x+3)(2x+5) = 2x^2 + 5x + 6x + 15$

$\qquad\qquad\qquad\qquad = 2x^2 + 11x + 15$

    **b.** $(2x-3)(5x^2 - 6x + 7)$

$\qquad = 10x^3 - 12x^2 + 14x - 15x^2 + 18x - 21$

$\qquad = 10x^3 - 27x^2 + 32x - 21$

**28.**  **a.** $(y-2)(3y+4) = 3y^2 + 4y - 6y - 8$

$\qquad\qquad\qquad\qquad = 3y^2 - 2y - 8$

    **b.** $(3y-1)(2y^2 + 3y - 1)$

$\qquad = 6y^3 + 9y^2 - 3y - 2y^2 - 3y + 1$

$\qquad = 6y^3 + 7y^2 - 6y + 1$

**29.** $20x^3 y = 2^2 \cdot 5x^3 y$

$\qquad 10x^2 y^2 = 2 \cdot 5x^2 y^2$

$\qquad 35x^3 = 5 \cdot 7x^3$

$\qquad \text{GCF} = 5x^2$

**30.** $x^3 - x^2 + 4x - 4 = (x^3 - x^2) + (4x - 4)$

$\qquad\qquad\qquad\qquad = x^2(x-1) + 4(x-1)$

$\qquad\qquad\qquad\qquad = (x-1)(x^2 + 4)$

**31.**  **a.** $\dfrac{x^3 + 8}{2 + x} = \dfrac{x^3 + 2^3}{x + 2}$

$\qquad\qquad = \dfrac{(x+2)(x^2 - 2x + 4)}{x + 2}$

$\qquad\qquad = x^2 - 2x + 4$

    **b.** $\dfrac{2y^2 + 2}{y^3 - 5y^2 + y - 5} = \dfrac{2(y^2 + 1)}{y^2(y-5) + 1(y-5)}$

$\qquad\qquad = \dfrac{2(y^2 + 1)}{(y-5)(y^2 + 1)}$

$\qquad\qquad = \dfrac{2}{y - 5}$

**32.**  **a.** $\dfrac{a^3 - 8}{2 - a} = \dfrac{a^3 - 2^3}{2 - a}$

$\qquad\qquad = \dfrac{(a-2)(a^2 + 2a + 4)}{-1(a-2)}$

$\qquad\qquad = -1(a^2 + 2a + 4)$

$\qquad\qquad = -a^2 - 2a - 4$

    **b.** $\dfrac{3a^2 - 3}{a^3 + 5a^2 - a - 5} = \dfrac{3(a^2 - 1)}{a^2(a+5) - 1(a+5)}$

$\qquad\qquad = \dfrac{3(a^2 - 1)}{(a+5)(a^2 - 1)}$

$\qquad\qquad = \dfrac{3}{a + 5}$

**33.**  **a.** $\dfrac{2}{x^2 y} + \dfrac{5}{3x^3 y} = \dfrac{2 \cdot 3x}{x^2 y \cdot 3x} + \dfrac{5}{3x^3 y}$

$\qquad\qquad = \dfrac{6x + 5}{3x^3 y}$

b. $\dfrac{3}{x+2}+\dfrac{2x}{x-2}=\dfrac{3(x-2)+2x(x+2)}{(x+2)(x-2)}$

$=\dfrac{3x-6+2x^2+4x}{(x+2)(x-2)}$

$=\dfrac{2x^2+7x-6}{(x+2)(x-2)}$

c. $\dfrac{2x-6}{x-1}-\dfrac{4}{1-x}=\dfrac{2x-6}{x-1}+\dfrac{4}{x-1}$

$=\dfrac{2x-2}{x-1}$

$=\dfrac{2(x-1)}{x-1}$

$=2$

34. a. $\dfrac{3}{xy^2}-\dfrac{2}{3x^2y}=\dfrac{3\cdot 3x}{xy^2\cdot 3x}-\dfrac{2\cdot y}{3x^2y\cdot y}$

$=\dfrac{9x-2y}{3x^2y^2}$

b. $\dfrac{5x}{x+3}-\dfrac{2x}{x-3}=\dfrac{5x(x-3)-2x(x+3)}{(x+3)(x-3)}$

$=\dfrac{5x^2-15x-2x^2-6x}{(x+3)(x-3)}$

$=\dfrac{3x^2-21x}{(x+3)(x-3)}$

or $\dfrac{3x(x-7)}{(x+3)(x-3)}$

c. $\dfrac{x}{x-2}-\dfrac{5}{2-x}=\dfrac{x}{x-2}+\dfrac{5}{x-2}=\dfrac{x+5}{x-2}$

35. a. $\dfrac{\frac{5x}{x+2}}{\frac{10}{x-2}}=\dfrac{5x}{x+2}\cdot\dfrac{x-2}{10}=\dfrac{x(x-2)}{2(x+2)}$

b. $\dfrac{\frac{x}{y^2}+\frac{1}{y}}{\frac{y}{x^2}+\frac{1}{x}}=\dfrac{\left(\frac{x}{y^2}+\frac{1}{y}\right)x^2y^2}{\left(\frac{y}{x^2}+\frac{1}{x}\right)x^2y^2}$

$=\dfrac{x^3+x^2y}{y^3+xy^2}$

$=\dfrac{x^2(x+y)}{y^2(y+x)}$

$=\dfrac{x^2}{y^2}$

36. a. $\dfrac{\frac{y-2}{16}}{\frac{2y+3}{12}}=\dfrac{y-2}{16}\cdot\dfrac{12}{2y+3}=\dfrac{3(y-2)}{4(2y+3)}$

b. $\dfrac{\frac{x}{16}-\frac{1}{x}}{1-\frac{4}{x}}=\dfrac{\left(\frac{x}{16}-\frac{1}{x}\right)16x}{\left(1-\frac{4}{x}\right)16x}$

$=\dfrac{x^2-16}{16x-64}$

$=\dfrac{(x+4)(x-4)}{16(x-4)}$

$=\dfrac{x+4}{16}$

37. $\dfrac{10x^3-5x^2+20x}{5x}=\dfrac{10x^3}{5x}-\dfrac{5x^2}{5x}+\dfrac{20x}{5x}$

$=2x^2-x+4$

38. 
$$\begin{array}{r} x^2\phantom{xxx}+3\phantom{x} \\ x-2\overline{\smash{\big)}\,x^3-2x^2+3x-6\phantom{x}} \\ \underline{x^3-2x^2\phantom{xxxxxxxxx}} \\ 3x-6 \\ \underline{3x-6} \\ 0 \end{array}$$

Answer: $x^2+3$

39. 
$$\begin{array}{r} 3\,|\phantom{x}2\phantom{xx}-1\phantom{xx}-13\phantom{xxx}1\phantom{x} \\ \phantom{3|xxxx}6\phantom{xxx}15\phantom{xxx}6\phantom{x} \\ \hline \phantom{3|x}2\phantom{xxx}5\phantom{xxx}2\phantom{xxx}7\phantom{x} \end{array}$$

Answer: $2x^2+5x+2+\dfrac{7}{x-3}$

40. 
$$\begin{array}{r} 3\,|\phantom{x}4\phantom{xx}-12\phantom{xx}-1\phantom{xxx}12\phantom{x} \\ \phantom{3|xxxx}12\phantom{xxx}0\phantom{xx}-3\phantom{x} \\ \hline \phantom{3|x}4\phantom{xxx}0\phantom{xx}-1\phantom{xxx}9\phantom{x} \end{array}$$

Answer: $4y^2-1+\dfrac{9}{y-3}$

41. $\dfrac{x+6}{x-2}=\dfrac{2(x+2)}{x-2}$

$(x-2)\left(\dfrac{x+6}{x-2}\right)=(x-2)\left[\dfrac{2(x+2)}{x-2}\right]$

$x+6=2(x+2)$

$x+6=2x+4$

$-x=-2$

$x=2$

which we discard as extraneous. There is no solution.

**42.**
$$\frac{28}{9-a^2} = \frac{2a}{a-3} + \frac{6}{a+3}$$

$$\frac{28}{-(a^2-9)} = \frac{2a}{a-3} + \frac{6}{a+3}$$

$$\frac{-28}{(a+3)(a-3)} = \frac{2a}{a-3} + \frac{6}{a+3}$$

$$(a+3)(a-3) \cdot \frac{-28}{(a+3)(a-3)} = (a+3)(a-3) \cdot \left( \frac{2a}{a-3} + \frac{6}{a+3} \right)$$

$$-28 = 2a(a+3) + 6(a-3)$$

$$-28 = 2a^2 + 6a + 6a - 18$$

$$0 = 2a^2 + 12a + 10$$

$$0 = 2(a^2 + 6a + 5)$$

$$0 = 2(a+5)(a+1)$$

$a = -5$ or $a = -1$

The solutions are $-5$ and $-1$.

**43.**
$$\frac{1}{x} + \frac{1}{y} = \frac{1}{z}$$

$$xyz \left( \frac{1}{x} + \frac{1}{y} \right) = xyz \left( \frac{1}{z} \right)$$

$$yz + xz = xy$$

$$yz = xy - xz$$

$$yz = x(y-z)$$

$$x = \frac{yz}{y-z}$$

**44.**
$$A = \frac{h(a+b)}{2}$$

$$2A = h(a+b)$$

$$2A = ah + bh$$

$$2A - bh = ah$$

$$\frac{2A-bh}{h} = a$$

**45.** $u = \dfrac{k}{w}$

$$3 = \frac{k}{5}$$

$$k = 3(5) = 15$$

$$u = \frac{15}{w}$$

**46.** $y = kx$

$$0.51 = k(3)$$

$$k = \frac{0.51}{3} = 0.17$$

$$y = 0.17x$$

**47. a.** $16^{-3/4} = \dfrac{1}{16^{3/4}} = \dfrac{1}{\left(\sqrt[4]{16}\right)^3} = \dfrac{1}{(2)^3} = \dfrac{1}{8}$

   **b.** $(-27)^{-2/3} = \dfrac{1}{(-27)^{2/3}}$

   $= \dfrac{1}{\left(\sqrt[3]{-27}\right)^2}$

   $= \dfrac{1}{(-3)^2}$

   $= \dfrac{1}{9}$

**48. a.** $81^{-3/4} = \dfrac{1}{81^{3/4}} = \dfrac{1}{\left(\sqrt[4]{81}\right)^3} = \dfrac{1}{(3)^3} = \dfrac{1}{27}$

   **b.** $(-125)^{-2/3} = \dfrac{1}{(-125)^{2/3}}$

   $= \dfrac{1}{\left(\sqrt[3]{-125}\right)^2}$

   $= \dfrac{1}{(-5)^2}$

   $= \dfrac{1}{25}$

**49.** $\dfrac{\sqrt{x}+2}{5} = \dfrac{\left(\sqrt{x}+2\right)\left(\sqrt{x}-2\right)}{5\left(\sqrt{x}-2\right)}$

   $= \dfrac{\left(\sqrt{x}\right)^2 - 2^2}{5\left(\sqrt{x}-2\right)}$

   $= \dfrac{x-4}{5\left(\sqrt{x}-2\right)}$

**50. a.** $\sqrt{36a^3} - \sqrt{144a^3} + \sqrt{4a^3}$

   $= \sqrt{36a^2 \cdot a} - \sqrt{144a^2 \cdot a} + \sqrt{4a^2 \cdot a}$

   $= 6a\sqrt{a} - 12a\sqrt{a} + 2a\sqrt{a}$

   $= -4a\sqrt{a}$

   **b.** $\sqrt[3]{128ab^3} - 3\sqrt[3]{2ab^3} + b\sqrt[3]{16a}$

   $= \sqrt[3]{64b^3 \cdot 2a} - 3\sqrt[3]{b^3 \cdot 2a} + b\sqrt[3]{8 \cdot 2a}$

   $= 4b\sqrt[3]{2a} - 3b\sqrt[3]{2a} + 2b\sqrt[3]{2a}$

   $= 3b\sqrt[3]{2a}$

   **c.** $\dfrac{\sqrt[3]{81}}{10} + \sqrt[3]{\dfrac{192}{125}} = \dfrac{\sqrt[3]{27 \cdot 3}}{10} + \dfrac{\sqrt[3]{192}}{\sqrt[3]{125}}$

   $= \dfrac{3\sqrt[3]{3}}{10} + \dfrac{\sqrt[3]{64 \cdot 3}}{5}$

   $= \dfrac{3\sqrt[3]{3}}{10} + \dfrac{4\sqrt[3]{3}}{5}$

   $= \dfrac{3\sqrt[3]{3}}{10} + \dfrac{4\sqrt[3]{3} \cdot 2}{5 \cdot 2} = \dfrac{11\sqrt[3]{3}}{10}$

# Chapter 8

**Practice Exercises**

1. $x^2 = 18$

   $x = \pm\sqrt{18}$

   $x = \pm 3\sqrt{2}$

   Check.

   Let $x = 3\sqrt{2}$.      Let $x = -3\sqrt{2}$.

      $x^2 = 18$          $x^2 = 18$

   $\left(3\sqrt{2}\right)^2 \stackrel{?}{=} 18$    $\left(-3\sqrt{2}\right)^2 \stackrel{?}{=} 18$

      $9 \cdot 2 \stackrel{?}{=} 18$       $9 \cdot 2 \stackrel{?}{=} 18$

       $18 = 18$   True     $18 = 18$   True

   The solutions are $3\sqrt{2}$ and $-3\sqrt{2}$, or the solution set is $\left\{-3\sqrt{2}, 3\sqrt{2}\right\}$.

2. First we get the squared variable alone on one side of the equation.

   $3x^2 - 30 = 0$

   $3x^2 = 30$

   $x^2 = 10$

   $x = \pm\sqrt{10}$

   The solutions are $\sqrt{10}$ and $-\sqrt{10}$, or the solution set is $\left\{-\sqrt{10}, \sqrt{10}\right\}$.

3. $(x+3)^2 = 20$

   $x+3 = \pm\sqrt{20}$

   $x+3 = \pm 2\sqrt{5}$

   $x = -3 \pm 2\sqrt{5}$

   Check:

   $(x+3)^2 = 20$

   $\left(-3 + 2\sqrt{5} + 3\right)^2 \stackrel{?}{=} 20$

   $\left(2\sqrt{5}\right)^2 \stackrel{?}{=} 20$

   $4 \cdot 5 \stackrel{?}{=} 20$

   $20 = 20$   True

   $(x+3)^2 = 20$

   $\left(-3 - 2\sqrt{5} + 3\right)^2 \stackrel{?}{=} 20$

   $\left(-2\sqrt{5}\right)^2 \stackrel{?}{=} 20$

   $4 \cdot 5 \stackrel{?}{=} 20$

   $20 = 20$   True

   The solutions are $-3 + 2\sqrt{5}$ and $-3 - 2\sqrt{5}$.

4. $(5x-2)^2 = -9$

   $5x - 2 = \pm\sqrt{-9}$

   $5x - 2 = \pm 3i$

   $5x = 2 \pm 3i$

   $x = \dfrac{2 \pm 3i}{5}$

   The solutions are $\dfrac{2+3i}{5}$ and $\dfrac{2-3i}{5}$.

5. $b^2 + 4b = 3$

   Add the square of half the coefficient of $b$ to both sides.

   $b^2 + 4b + \left(\dfrac{4}{2}\right)^2 = 3 + \left(\dfrac{4}{2}\right)^2$

   $b^2 + 4b + 4 = 7$

   $(b+2)^2 = 7$

   $b + 2 = \pm\sqrt{7}$

   $b = -2 \pm \sqrt{7}$

   The solutions are $-2 + \sqrt{7}$ and $-2 - \sqrt{7}$.

6. $p^2 - 3p + 1 = 0$

   Subtract 1 from both sides.

   $p^2 - 3p = -1$

   Add the square of half the coefficient of $p$ to both sides.

$$p^2 - 3p + \left(\frac{-3}{2}\right)^2 = -1 + \left(\frac{-3}{2}\right)^2$$

$$p^2 - 3p + \frac{9}{4} = -1 + \frac{9}{4} = \frac{5}{4}$$

$$\left(p - \frac{3}{2}\right)^2 = \frac{5}{4}$$

$$p - \frac{3}{2} = \pm\frac{\sqrt{5}}{2}$$

$$p = \frac{3 \pm \sqrt{5}}{2}$$

The solutions are $\dfrac{3+\sqrt{5}}{2}$ and $\dfrac{3-\sqrt{5}}{2}$.

**7.** $3x^2 - 12x + 1 = 0$

Divide both sides by 3.

$$3x^2 - 12x + 1 = 0$$

$$x^2 - 4x + \frac{1}{3} = 0$$

$$x^2 - 4x = -\frac{1}{3}$$

Find the square of half of $-4$.

$$\left(\frac{-4}{2}\right)^2 = (-2)^2 = 4$$

Add 4 to both sides of the equation.

$$x^2 - 4x + 4 = -\frac{1}{3} + 4$$

$$(x-2)^2 = -\frac{1}{3} + \frac{12}{3} = \frac{11}{3}$$

$$x - 2 = \pm\sqrt{\frac{11}{3}} = \pm\frac{\sqrt{33}}{3}$$

$$x = \frac{6}{3} \pm \frac{\sqrt{33}}{3} = \frac{6 \pm \sqrt{33}}{3}$$

The solutions are $\dfrac{6+\sqrt{33}}{3}$ and $\dfrac{6-\sqrt{33}}{3}$.

**8.** $2x^2 - 5x + 7 = 0$

$$2x^2 - 5x = -7$$

$$x^2 - \frac{5}{2}x = -\frac{7}{2}$$

Since $\dfrac{1}{2}\left(-\dfrac{5}{2}\right) = -\dfrac{5}{4}$ and $\left(-\dfrac{5}{4}\right)^2 = \dfrac{25}{16}$, we add

$\dfrac{25}{16}$ to both sides of the equation.

$$x^2 - \frac{5}{2}x + \frac{25}{16} = -\frac{7}{2} + \frac{25}{16}$$

$$\left(x - \frac{5}{4}\right)^2 = -\frac{56}{16} + \frac{25}{16} = -\frac{31}{16}$$

$$x - \frac{5}{4} = \pm\sqrt{-\frac{31}{16}}$$

$$x = \frac{5}{4} \pm \frac{i\sqrt{31}}{4} = \frac{5 \pm i\sqrt{31}}{4}$$

The solutions are $\dfrac{5+i\sqrt{31}}{4}$ and $\dfrac{5-i\sqrt{31}}{4}$.

**9.** $A = P(1+r)^t$; $A = 5618$, $P = 5000$, $t = 2$

$$A = P(1+r)^t$$

$$5618 = 5000(1+r)^2$$

$$1.1236 = (1+r)^2$$

$$\pm\sqrt{1.1236} = 1 + r$$

$$-1 \pm 1.06 = r$$

$$0.06 = r \text{ or } -2.06 = r$$

The rate cannot be negative, so we reject $-2.06$.

Check: $A = 5000(1 + 0.06)^2$

$$= 5000(1.06)^2$$

$$= 5000 \cdot 1.1236$$

$$= 5618$$

The interest rate is 6% compounded annually.

**Graphing Calculator Explorations**

**1.** $-1.27, 6.27$

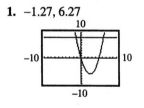

**2.** $-3.45, 1.45$

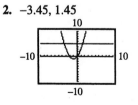

**3.** $-1.10, 0.90$

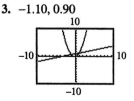

**4.** −1.54, 1.94

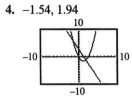

**5.** No real solutions, or ∅

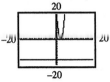

**6.** Answers may vary

**Vocabulary and Readiness Check**

**1.** By the square root property, if $b$ is a real number, and $a^2 = b$, then $a = \underline{\pm\sqrt{b}}$.

**2.** A <u>quadratic</u> equation can be written in the form $ax^2 + bx + c = 0$, $a \neq 0$.

**3.** The process of writing a quadratic equation so that one side is a perfect square trinomial is called <u>completing the square</u>.

**4.** A perfect square trinomial is one that can be factored as a <u>binomial</u> squared.

**5.** To solve $x^2 + 6x = 10$ by completing the square, add $\underline{9}$ to both sides.

**6.** To solve $x^2 + bx = c$ by completing the square, add $\underline{\left(\dfrac{b}{2}\right)^2}$ to both sides.

**7.** $m^2 + 2m + \underline{1}$

**8.** $m^2 - 2m + \underline{1}$

**9.** $y^2 - 14y + \underline{49}$

**10.** $z^2 + z + \underline{\dfrac{1}{4}}$

**Exercise Set 8.1**

**1.** $x^2 = 16$
$x = \pm\sqrt{16}$
$x = \pm 4$

**3.** $x^2 - 7 = 0$
$x^2 = 7$
$x = \pm\sqrt{7}$

**5.** $x^2 = 18$
$x = \pm\sqrt{18}$
$x = \pm\sqrt{9 \cdot 2}$
$x = \pm 3\sqrt{2}$

**7.** $3z^2 - 30 = 0$
$3z^2 = 30$
$z^2 = 10$
$z = \pm\sqrt{10}$

**9.** $(x+5)^2 = 9$
$x + 5 = \pm\sqrt{9}$
$x + 5 = \pm 3$
$x = -5 \pm 3$
$x = -8$ or $x = -2$

**11.** $(z-6)^2 = 18$
$z - 6 = \pm\sqrt{18}$
$z - 6 = \pm 3\sqrt{2}$
$z = 6 \pm 3\sqrt{2}$

**13.** $(2x-3)^2 = 8$
$2x - 3 = \pm\sqrt{8}$
$2x - 3 = \pm 2\sqrt{2}$
$2x = 3 \pm 2\sqrt{2}$
$x = \dfrac{3 \pm 2\sqrt{2}}{2}$

**15.** $x^2 + 9 = 0$
$x^2 = -9$
$x = \pm\sqrt{-9}$
$x = \pm 3i$

**17.** $x^2 - 6 = 0$

$\quad x^2 = 6$

$\quad\quad x = \pm\sqrt{6}$

**19.** $2z^2 + 16 = 0$

$\quad 2z^2 = -16$

$\quad\quad z^2 = -8$

$\quad\quad z = \pm\sqrt{-8}$

$\quad\quad z = \pm i\sqrt{8}$

$\quad\quad z = \pm 2i\sqrt{2}$

**21.** $(x-1)^2 = -16$

$\quad x - 1 = \pm\sqrt{-16}$

$\quad x - 1 = \pm 4i$

$\quad\quad x = 1 \pm 4i$

**23.** $(z+7)^2 = 5$

$\quad z + 7 = \pm\sqrt{5}$

$\quad\quad z = -7 \pm\sqrt{5}$

**25.** $(x+3)^2 = -8$

$\quad x + 3 = \pm\sqrt{-8}$

$\quad x + 3 = \pm i\sqrt{8}$

$\quad x + 3 = \pm 2i\sqrt{2}$

$\quad\quad x = -3 \pm 2i\sqrt{2}$

**27.** $x^2 + 16x + \left(\dfrac{16}{2}\right)^2 = x^2 + 16x + 64$

$\quad\quad\quad\quad\quad\quad = (x+8)^2$

**29.** $z^2 - 12z + \left(\dfrac{-12}{2}\right)^2 = z^2 - 12z + 36$

$\quad\quad\quad\quad\quad\quad\quad = (z-6)^2$

**31.** $p^2 + 9p + \left(\dfrac{9}{2}\right)^2 = p^2 + 9p + \dfrac{81}{4}$

$\quad\quad\quad\quad\quad\quad = \left(p + \dfrac{9}{2}\right)^2$

**33.** $x^2 + x + \left(\dfrac{1}{2}\right)^2 = x^2 + 16x + \dfrac{1}{4}$

$\quad\quad\quad\quad\quad\quad = \left(x + \dfrac{1}{2}\right)^2$

**35.** $\quad\quad x^2 + 8x = -15$

$\quad x^2 + 8x + \left(\dfrac{8}{2}\right)^2 = -15 + 16$

$\quad\quad x^2 + 8x + 16 = 1$

$\quad\quad\quad (x+4)^2 = 1$

$\quad\quad\quad\quad x + 4 = \pm\sqrt{1}$

$\quad\quad\quad\quad\quad x = -4 \pm 1$

$\quad\quad\quad\quad\quad x = -5 \text{ or } x = -3$

**37.** $\quad\quad x^2 + 6x + 2 = 0$

$\quad\quad\quad x^2 + 6x = -2$

$\quad x^2 + 6x + \left(\dfrac{6}{2}\right)^2 = -2 + 9$

$\quad\quad x^2 + 6x + 9 = 7$

$\quad\quad\quad (x+3)^2 = 7$

$\quad\quad\quad\quad x + 3 = \pm\sqrt{7}$

$\quad\quad\quad\quad\quad x = -3 \pm\sqrt{7}$

**39.** $\quad\quad x^2 + x - 1 = 0$

$\quad\quad\quad x^2 + x = 1$

$\quad x^2 + x + \left(\dfrac{1}{2}\right)^2 = 1 + \dfrac{1}{4}$

$\quad\quad x^2 + x + \dfrac{1}{4} = \dfrac{5}{4}$

$\quad\quad\quad \left(x + \dfrac{1}{2}\right)^2 = \dfrac{5}{4}$

$\quad\quad\quad\quad x + \dfrac{1}{2} = \pm\sqrt{\dfrac{5}{4}}$

$\quad\quad\quad\quad\quad x = -\dfrac{1}{2} \pm \dfrac{\sqrt{5}}{2} = \dfrac{-1\pm\sqrt{5}}{2}$

**41.** $\quad\quad x^2 + 2x - 5 = 0$

$\quad\quad\quad x^2 + 2x = 5$

$\quad x^2 + 2x + \left(\dfrac{2}{2}\right)^2 = 5 + 1$

$\quad\quad x^2 + 2x + 1 = 6$

$\quad\quad\quad (x+1)^2 = 6$

$\quad\quad\quad\quad x + 1 = \pm\sqrt{6}$

$\quad\quad\quad\quad\quad x = -1 \pm\sqrt{6}$

**43.**
$$3p^2 - 12p + 2 = 0$$
$$3p^2 - 12p = -2$$
$$p^2 - 4p = -\frac{2}{3}$$
$$p^2 - 4p + \left(\frac{-4}{2}\right)^2 = -\frac{2}{3} + 4$$
$$(p-2)^2 = \frac{10}{3}$$
$$p - 2 = \pm\sqrt{\frac{10}{3}}$$
$$p - 2 = \pm\frac{\sqrt{10}\cdot\sqrt{3}}{\sqrt{3}\cdot\sqrt{3}}$$
$$p - 2 = \pm\frac{\sqrt{30}}{3}$$
$$p = 2 \pm \frac{\sqrt{30}}{3} = \frac{6 \pm \sqrt{30}}{3}$$

**45.**
$$4y^2 - 12y - 2 = 0$$
$$4y^2 - 12y = 2$$
$$y^2 - 3y = \frac{1}{2}$$
$$y^2 - 3y + \left(\frac{-3}{2}\right)^2 = \frac{1}{2} + \frac{9}{4}$$
$$y^2 - 3y + \frac{9}{4} = \frac{11}{4}$$
$$\left(y - \frac{3}{2}\right)^2 = \frac{11}{4}$$
$$y - \frac{3}{2} = \pm\sqrt{\frac{11}{4}}$$
$$y = \frac{3}{2} \pm \frac{\sqrt{11}}{2} = \frac{3 \pm \sqrt{11}}{2}$$

**47.**
$$2x^2 + 7x = 4$$
$$x^2 + \frac{7}{2}x = 2$$
$$x^2 + \frac{7}{2}x + \left(\frac{\frac{7}{2}}{2}\right)^2 = 2 + \frac{49}{16}$$
$$x^2 + \frac{7}{2}x + \frac{49}{16} = \frac{81}{16}$$
$$\left(x + \frac{7}{4}\right)^2 = \frac{81}{16}$$
$$x + \frac{7}{4} = \pm\sqrt{\frac{81}{16}}$$
$$x = -\frac{7}{4} \pm \frac{9}{4} = \frac{-7 \pm 9}{4}$$
$$x = -4, \frac{1}{2}$$

**49.**
$$x^2 - 4x - 5 = 0$$
$$x^2 - 4x = 5$$
$$x^2 - 4x + \left(\frac{-4}{2}\right)^2 = 5 + 4$$
$$x^2 - 4x + 4 = 9$$
$$(x-2)^2 = 9$$
$$x - 2 = \pm\sqrt{9}$$
$$x = 2 \pm 3$$
$$x = -1, 5$$

**51.**
$$x^2 + 8x + 1 = 0$$
$$x^2 + 8x = -1$$
$$x^2 + 8x + \left(\frac{8}{2}\right)^2 = -1 + 16$$
$$x^2 + 8x + 16 = 15$$
$$(x+4)^2 = 15$$
$$x + 4 = \pm\sqrt{15}$$
$$x = -4 \pm \sqrt{15}$$

**53.**
$$3y^2 + 6y - 4 = 0$$
$$3y^2 + 6y = 4$$
$$y^2 + 2y = \frac{4}{3}$$
$$y^2 + 2y + \left(\frac{2}{2}\right)^2 = \frac{4}{3} + 1$$
$$y^2 + 2y + 1 = \frac{7}{3}$$
$$(y+1)^2 = \frac{7}{3}$$
$$y + 1 = \pm\sqrt{\frac{7}{3}}$$
$$y + 1 = \pm\frac{\sqrt{7} \cdot \sqrt{3}}{\sqrt{3} \cdot \sqrt{3}}$$
$$y + 1 = \pm\frac{\sqrt{21}}{3}$$
$$y = -1 \pm \frac{\sqrt{21}}{3} = \frac{-3 \pm \sqrt{21}}{3}$$

**55.**
$$2x^2 - 3x - 5 = 0$$
$$2x^2 - 3x = 5$$
$$x^2 - \frac{3}{2}x = \frac{5}{2}$$
$$x^2 - \frac{3}{2}x + \left(\frac{\frac{3}{2}}{2}\right)^2 = \frac{5}{2} + \frac{9}{16}$$
$$x^2 - \frac{3}{2}x + \frac{9}{16} = \frac{49}{16}$$
$$\left(x - \frac{3}{4}\right)^2 = \frac{49}{16}$$
$$x - \frac{3}{4} = \pm\sqrt{\frac{49}{16}}$$
$$x = \frac{3}{4} \pm \frac{7}{4} = \frac{3 \pm 7}{4}$$
$$x = -1, \frac{5}{2}$$

**57.**
$$y^2 + 2y + 2 = 0$$
$$y^2 + 2y = -2$$
$$y^2 + 2y + \left(\frac{2}{2}\right)^2 = -2 + 1$$
$$y^2 + 2y + 1 = -1$$
$$(y+1)^2 = -1$$
$$y + 1 = \pm\sqrt{-1}$$
$$y = -1 \pm i$$

**59.**
$$x^2 - 6x + 3 = 0$$
$$x^2 - 6x = -3$$
$$x^2 - 6x + \left(\frac{-6}{2}\right)^2 = -3 + 9$$
$$x^2 - 6x + 9 = 6$$
$$(x - 3)^2 = 6$$
$$x - 3 = \pm\sqrt{6}$$
$$x = 3 \pm \sqrt{6}$$

**61.**
$$2a^2 + 8a = -12$$
$$a^2 + 4a = -6$$
$$a^2 + 4a + \left(\frac{4}{2}\right)^2 = -6 + 4$$
$$a^2 + 4a + 4 = -2$$
$$(a + 2)^2 = -2$$
$$a + 2 = \pm\sqrt{-2}$$
$$a + 2 = \pm i\sqrt{2}$$
$$a = -2 \pm i\sqrt{2}$$

**63.**
$$5x^2 + 15x - 1 = 0$$
$$5x^2 + 15x = 1$$
$$x^2 + 3x = \frac{1}{5}$$
$$x^2 + 3x + \left(\frac{3}{2}\right)^2 = \frac{1}{5} + \frac{9}{4}$$
$$x^2 + 3x + \frac{9}{4} = \frac{49}{20}$$
$$\left(x + \frac{3}{2}\right)^2 = \frac{49}{20}$$
$$x + \frac{3}{2} = \pm\sqrt{\frac{49}{20}}$$
$$x + \frac{3}{2} = \pm\frac{7}{\sqrt{20}}$$
$$x + \frac{3}{2} = \pm\frac{7}{2\sqrt{5}}$$
$$x + \frac{3}{2} = \pm\frac{7 \cdot \sqrt{5}}{2\sqrt{5} \cdot \sqrt{5}}$$
$$x + \frac{3}{2} = \pm\frac{7\sqrt{5}}{10}$$
$$x = -\frac{3}{2} \pm \frac{7\sqrt{5}}{10} = \frac{-15 \pm 7\sqrt{5}}{10}$$

**65.**
$$2x^2 - x + 6 = 0$$
$$2x^2 - x = -6$$
$$x^2 - \frac{1}{2}x = -3$$
$$x^2 - \frac{1}{2}x + \left(\frac{-\frac{1}{2}}{2}\right)^2 = -3 + \frac{1}{16}$$
$$x^2 - \frac{1}{2}x + \frac{1}{16} = -\frac{47}{16}$$
$$\left(x - \frac{1}{4}\right)^2 = -\frac{47}{16}$$
$$x - \frac{1}{4} = \pm\sqrt{-\frac{47}{16}}$$
$$x - \frac{1}{4} = \pm i\frac{\sqrt{47}}{4}$$
$$x = \frac{1}{4} \pm i\frac{\sqrt{47}}{4} = \frac{1 \pm i\sqrt{47}}{4}$$

**67.**
$$x^2 + 10x + 28 = 0$$
$$x^2 + 10x = -28$$
$$x^2 + 10x + \left(\frac{10}{2}\right)^2 = -28 + 25$$
$$(x + 5)^2 = -3$$
$$x + 5 = \pm\sqrt{-3}$$
$$x = -5 \pm i\sqrt{3}$$

**69.**
$$z^2 + 3z - 4 = 0$$
$$z^2 + 3z = 4$$
$$z^2 + 3z + \left(\frac{3}{2}\right)^2 = 4 + \frac{9}{4}$$
$$z^2 + 3z + \frac{9}{4} = \frac{25}{4}$$
$$\left(z + \frac{3}{2}\right)^2 = \frac{25}{4}$$
$$z + \frac{3}{2} = \pm\sqrt{\frac{25}{4}}$$
$$z = -\frac{3}{2} \pm \frac{5}{2} = \frac{-3 \pm 5}{2}$$
$$z = -4, 1$$

**71.**
$$2x^2 - 4x = -3$$
$$x^2 - 2x = -\frac{3}{2}$$
$$x^2 - 2x + \left(\frac{-2}{2}\right)^2 = -\frac{3}{2} + 1$$
$$x^2 - 2x + 1 = -\frac{1}{2}$$
$$(x - 1)^2 = -\frac{1}{2}$$
$$x - 1 = \pm\sqrt{-\frac{1}{2}}$$
$$x - 1 = \pm i\frac{1}{\sqrt{2}}$$
$$x - 1 = \pm i\frac{1 \cdot \sqrt{2}}{\sqrt{2} \cdot \sqrt{2}}$$
$$x - 1 = \pm i\frac{\sqrt{2}}{2}$$
$$x = 1 \pm i\frac{\sqrt{2}}{2} = \frac{2 \pm i\sqrt{2}}{2}$$

**73.**
$$3x^2 + 3x = 5$$
$$x^2 + x = \frac{5}{3}$$
$$x^2 + x + \left(\frac{1}{2}\right)^2 = \frac{5}{3} + \frac{1}{4}$$
$$x^2 + x + \frac{1}{4} = \frac{23}{12}$$
$$\left(x + \frac{1}{2}\right)^2 = \frac{23}{12}$$
$$x + \frac{1}{2} = \pm\sqrt{\frac{23}{12}}$$
$$x + \frac{1}{2} = \pm\frac{\sqrt{23}}{2\sqrt{3}}$$
$$x + \frac{1}{2} = \pm\frac{\sqrt{23}\cdot\sqrt{3}}{2\sqrt{3}\cdot\sqrt{3}}$$
$$x + \frac{1}{2} = \pm\frac{\sqrt{69}}{6}$$
$$x = -\frac{1}{2} \pm \frac{\sqrt{69}}{6} = \frac{-3 \pm \sqrt{69}}{6}$$

**75.**
$$A = P(1+r)^t$$
$$4320 = 3000(1+r)^2$$
$$\frac{4320}{3000} = (1+r)^2$$
$$1.44 = (1+r)^2$$
$$\pm\sqrt{1.44} = 1+r$$
$$\pm 1.2 = 1+r$$
$$-1 \pm 1.2 = r$$
$$-2.2 = r \text{ or } 0.2 = r$$
Rate cannot be negative, so the rate is $r = 0.2 = 20\%$.

**77.**
$$A = P(1+r)^t$$
$$16,224 = 15,000(1+r)^2$$
$$\frac{16,224}{15,000} = (1+r)^2$$
$$\pm\sqrt{1.0816} = 1+r$$
$$\pm 1.04 = 1+r$$
$$-1 \pm 1.04 = r$$
$$0.04 = r \text{ or } -2.04 = r$$
Rate cannot be negative, so the rate is $r = 0.04$, or 4%.

**79.** Answers may vary

**81.**
$$s(t) = 16t^2$$
$$1053 = 16t^2$$
$$t^2 = \frac{1053}{16}$$
$$t = \pm\sqrt{\frac{1053}{16}}$$
$$t \approx 8.11 \text{ or } -8.11 \text{ (disregard)}$$
It would take 8.11 seconds.

**83.**
$$s(t) = 16t^2$$
$$725 = 16t^2$$
$$t^2 = \frac{725}{16}$$
$$t = \pm\sqrt{\frac{725}{16}}$$
$$t \approx 6.73 \text{ or } -6.73 \text{ (disregard)}$$
It would take 6.73 seconds.

**85.** Simple; answers may vary

**87.** $\dfrac{3}{5} + \sqrt{\dfrac{16}{25}} = \dfrac{3}{5} + \dfrac{4}{5} = \dfrac{7}{5}$

**89.** $\dfrac{9}{10} - \sqrt{\dfrac{49}{100}} = \dfrac{9}{10} - \dfrac{7}{10} = \dfrac{2}{10} = \dfrac{1}{5}$

**91.** $\dfrac{10 - 20\sqrt{3}}{2} = \dfrac{10}{2} - \dfrac{20\sqrt{3}}{2} = 5 - 10\sqrt{3}$

**93.**
$$\frac{12 - 8\sqrt{7}}{16} = \frac{12}{16} - \frac{8\sqrt{7}}{16}$$
$$= \frac{3}{4} - \frac{\sqrt{7}}{2}$$
$$= \frac{3}{4} - \frac{2\sqrt{7}}{4}$$
$$= \frac{3 - 2\sqrt{7}}{4}$$

**95.** $\sqrt{b^2 - 4ac} = \sqrt{(6)^2 - 4(1)(2)}$
$$= \sqrt{36 - 8}$$
$$= \sqrt{28}$$
$$= \sqrt{4 \cdot 7}$$
$$= 2\sqrt{7}$$

**97.** $\sqrt{b^2 - 4ac} = \sqrt{(-3)^2 - 4(1)(-1)}$

$\qquad\qquad = \sqrt{9 + 4}$

$\qquad\qquad = \sqrt{13}$

**99.** The solutions of $(y-5)^2 = -9$ are complex, but not real numbers; answers may vary

**101.** The solutions of $4x^2 = 17$ are real; answers may vary

**103.** The solutions of $(3m+2)^2 + 4 = 1$ are complex, but not real numbers; answers may vary

**105.** $y^2 + \underline{\quad} + 9$

$\left(\dfrac{b}{2}\right)^2 = 9$

$\dfrac{b}{2} = \pm\sqrt{9}$

$\dfrac{b}{2} = \pm 3$

$b = \pm 6$

Answer: $\pm 6y$

**107.** $x^2 + \underline{\quad} + \dfrac{1}{4}$

$\left(\dfrac{b}{2}\right)^2 = \dfrac{1}{4}$

$\dfrac{b}{2} = \pm\sqrt{\dfrac{1}{4}}$

$\dfrac{b}{2} = \pm\dfrac{1}{2}$

$b = \pm 1$

Answer: $\pm x$

**109.** $A = \pi r^2$

$36\pi = \pi r^2$

$r^2 = \dfrac{36\pi}{\pi}$

$r^2 = 36$

$r = \pm\sqrt{36}$

$r = 6$ or $-6$ (disregard)

The radius is 6 inches.

**111.** $a^2 + b^2 = c^2$

$(4x)^2 + (3x)^2 = 27^2$

$16x^2 + 9x^2 = 729$

$25x^2 = 729$

$x^2 = \dfrac{729}{25}$

$x = \pm\sqrt{\dfrac{729}{25}} = \pm\dfrac{27}{5}$

$x = 5.4$ or $-5.4$ (disregard)

$3x = 3(5.4) = 16.2$

$4x = 4(5.4) = 21.6$

The sides are 16.2 in. and 21.6 in.

**113.** $p = -x^2 + 15$

$7 = -x^2 + 15$

$x^2 = 8$

$x = \pm\sqrt{8}$

$x \approx \pm 2.828$

Demand cannot be negative. Therefore, the demand is approximately 2.828 thousand (or 2828) units.

**Section 8.2**

**Practice Exercises**

**1.** $3x^2 - 5x - 2 = 0$

$a = 3, b = -5, c = -2$

$x = \dfrac{-b \pm \sqrt{b^2 - 4ac}}{2a}$

$\quad = \dfrac{-(-5) \pm \sqrt{(-5)^2 - 4(3)(-2)}}{2(3)}$

$\quad = \dfrac{5 \pm \sqrt{25 + 24}}{6}$

$\quad = \dfrac{5 \pm \sqrt{49}}{6}$

$\quad = \dfrac{5 \pm 7}{6}$

$x = \dfrac{5+7}{6} = \dfrac{12}{6} = 2$ or $x = \dfrac{5-7}{6} = \dfrac{-2}{6} = -\dfrac{1}{3}$

The solutions are $-\dfrac{1}{3}$ and 2, or the solution set is $\left\{-\dfrac{1}{3}, 2\right\}$.

**2.** $3x^2 - 8x = 2$

Write in standard form.

$3x^2 - 8x - 2 = 0$

$a = 3,\ b = -8,\ c = -2$

$x = \dfrac{-b \pm \sqrt{b^2 - 4ac}}{2a}$

$= \dfrac{-(-8) \pm \sqrt{(-8)^2 - 4(3)(-2)}}{2(3)}$

$= \dfrac{8 \pm \sqrt{64 + 24}}{6}$

$= \dfrac{8 \pm \sqrt{88}}{6}$

$= \dfrac{8 \pm 2\sqrt{22}}{6}$

$= \dfrac{4 \pm \sqrt{22}}{3}$

The solutions are $\dfrac{4 + \sqrt{22}}{3}$ and $\dfrac{4 - \sqrt{22}}{3}$, or the

solution set is $\left\{ \dfrac{4 + \sqrt{22}}{3}, \dfrac{4 - \sqrt{22}}{3} \right\}$.

**3.** $\dfrac{1}{8}x^2 - \dfrac{1}{4}x - 2 = 0$

Multiply both sides of the equation by 8.

$8\left( \dfrac{1}{8}x^2 - \dfrac{1}{4}x - 2 \right) = 8 \cdot 0$

$x^2 - 2x - 16 = 0$

Substitute $a = 1$, $b = -2$, and $c = -16$ into the quadratic formula and simplify.

$x = \dfrac{-(-2) \pm \sqrt{(-2)^2 - 4(1)(-16)}}{2(1)}$

$= \dfrac{2 \pm \sqrt{4 + 64}}{2}$

$= \dfrac{2 \pm \sqrt{68}}{2}$

$= \dfrac{2 \pm 2\sqrt{17}}{2}$

$= 1 \pm \sqrt{17}$

The solutions are $1 + \sqrt{17}$ or $1 - \sqrt{17}$.

**4.** $x = -2x^2 - 2$

The equation in standard form is

$2x^2 + x + 2 = 0$. Thus, let $a = 2$, $b = 1$, and $c = 2$ in the quadratic formula.

$x = \dfrac{-1 \pm \sqrt{1^2 - 4(2)(2)}}{2(2)}$

$= \dfrac{-1 \pm \sqrt{1 - 16}}{4}$

$= \dfrac{-1 \pm \sqrt{-15}}{4}$

$= \dfrac{-1 \pm i\sqrt{15}}{4}$

The solutions are $\dfrac{-1 + i\sqrt{15}}{4}$ and $\dfrac{-1 - i\sqrt{15}}{4}$.

**5. a.** $x^2 - 6x + 9 = 0$

In $x^2 - 6x + 9$, $a = 1$, $b = -6$, and $c = 9$. Thus,

$b^2 - 4ac = (-6)^2 - 4(1)(9) = 36 - 36 = 0$

Since $b^2 - 4ac = 0$, this equation has one real solution.

**b.** $x^2 - 3x - 1 = 0$

In this equation, $a = 1$, $b = -3$, and $c = -1$.

$b^2 - 4ac = (-3)^2 - 4(1)(-1) = 9 + 4 = 13 > 0$

Since $b^2 - 4ac$ is positive, this equation has two real solutions.

**c.** $7x^2 + 11 = 0$

In this equation, $a = 7$, $b = 0$, and $c = 11$.

$b^2 - 4ac = 0^2 - 4(7)(11) = -308 < 0$

Since $b^2 - 4ac$ is negative, this equation has two complex but not real solutions.

**6.** By the Pythagorean theorem, we have

$x^2 + (x + 3)^2 = 15^2$

$x^2 + x^2 + 6x + 9 = 225$

$2x^2 + 6x - 216 = 0$

$x^2 + 3x - 108 = 0$

Here, $a = 1$, $b = 3$, and $c = -108$. By the quadratic formula,

$$x = \frac{-3 \pm \sqrt{3^2 - 4(1)(-108)}}{2(1)}$$

$$= \frac{-3 \pm \sqrt{9 + 432}}{2}$$

$$= \frac{-3 \pm \sqrt{441}}{2}$$

$$= \frac{-3 \pm 21}{2}$$

$$x = \frac{-3 + 21}{2} = \frac{18}{2} = 9 \text{ or}$$

$$x = \frac{-3 - 21}{2} = \frac{-24}{2} = -12$$

The length can't be negative, so reject −12. The distance along the sidewalk is
$x + (x + 3) = 2x + 3 = 2(9) + 3 = 18 + 3 = 21$ feet
A person can save $21 − 15 = 6$ feet by cutting across the lawn.

7.  $h = -16t^2 + 20t + 45$
    At the ground, $h = 0$.
    $0 = -16t^2 + 20t + 45$
    Here, $a = -16$, $b = 20$, and $c = 45$. By the quadratic formula,

$$t = \frac{-20 \pm \sqrt{20^2 - 4(-16)(45)}}{2(-16)}$$

$$= \frac{-20 \pm \sqrt{400 + 2880}}{-32}$$

$$= \frac{-20 \pm \sqrt{3280}}{-32}$$

$$= \frac{20 \pm \sqrt{16 \cdot 205}}{32}$$

$$= \frac{20 \pm 4\sqrt{205}}{32}$$

$$= \frac{5 \pm \sqrt{205}}{8}$$

$$t = \frac{5 + \sqrt{205}}{8} \approx 2.4 \text{ or } t = \frac{5 - \sqrt{205}}{8} \approx -1.2$$

Since the time won't be negative, we reject −1.2. The rocket will strike the ground 2.4 seconds after launch.

**Vocabulary and Readiness Check**

1.  The quadratic formula is $x = \dfrac{-b \pm \sqrt{b^2 - 4ac}}{2a}$.

2.  For $2x^2 + x + 1 = 0$, if $a = 2$, then $b = \underline{1}$ and $c = \underline{1}$.

3.  For $5x^2 - 5x - 7 = 0$, if $a = 5$, then $b = \underline{-5}$ and $c = \underline{-7}$.

4.  For $7x^2 - 4 = 0$, if $a = 7$, then $b = \underline{0}$ and $c = \underline{-4}$.

5.  For $x^2 + 9 = 0$, if $c = 9$, then $a = \underline{1}$ and $b = \underline{0}$.

6.  The correct simplified form of $\dfrac{5 \pm 10\sqrt{2}}{5}$ is $1 \pm 2\sqrt{2}$. The answer is **c**.

**Exercise Set 8.2**

1.  $m^2 + 5m - 6 = 0$
    $a = 1, b = 5, c = -6$

$$m = \frac{-5 \pm \sqrt{(5)^2 - 4(1)(-6)}}{2(1)}$$

$$= \frac{-5 \pm \sqrt{25 + 24}}{2}$$

$$= \frac{-5 \pm \sqrt{49}}{2}$$

$$= \frac{-5 \pm 7}{2}$$

$$= -6 \text{ or } 1$$

The solutions are −6 and 1.

3.          $2y = 5y^2 - 3$
    $5y^2 - 2y - 3 = 0$
    $a = 5, b = -2, c = -3$

$$y = \frac{2 \pm \sqrt{(-2)^2 - 4(5)(-3)}}{2(5)}$$

$$= \frac{2 \pm \sqrt{4 + 60}}{10}$$

$$= \frac{2 \pm \sqrt{64}}{10}$$

$$= \frac{2 \pm 8}{10}$$

$$= -\frac{3}{5} \text{ or } 1$$

The solutions are $-\dfrac{3}{5}$ and 1.

**5.** $x^2 - 6x + 9 = 0$
$a = 1, b = -6, c = 9$

$$x = \frac{6 \pm \sqrt{(-6)^2 - 4(1)(9)}}{2(1)}$$

$$= \frac{6 \pm \sqrt{36 - 36}}{2}$$

$$= \frac{6 \pm \sqrt{0}}{2}$$

$$= \frac{6}{2}$$

$$= 3$$

The solution is 3.

**7.** $x^2 + 7x + 4 = 0$
$a = 1, b = 7, c = 4$

$$x = \frac{-7 \pm \sqrt{(7)^2 - 4(1)(4)}}{2(1)}$$

$$= \frac{-7 \pm \sqrt{49 - 16}}{2}$$

$$= \frac{-7 \pm \sqrt{33}}{2}$$

The solutions are $\dfrac{-7 + \sqrt{33}}{2}$ and $\dfrac{-7 - \sqrt{33}}{2}$.

**9.** $8m^2 - 2m = 7$
$8m^2 - 2m - 7 = 0$
$a = 8, b = -2, c = -7$

$$m = \frac{2 \pm \sqrt{(-2)^2 - 4(8)(-7)}}{2(8)}$$

$$= \frac{2 \pm \sqrt{4 + 224}}{16}$$

$$= \frac{2 \pm \sqrt{228}}{16}$$

$$= \frac{2 \pm \sqrt{4 \cdot 57}}{16}$$

$$= \frac{2 \pm 2\sqrt{57}}{16}$$

$$= \frac{1 \pm \sqrt{57}}{8}$$

The solutions are $\dfrac{1 + \sqrt{57}}{8}$ and $\dfrac{1 - \sqrt{57}}{8}$.

**11.** $3m^2 - 7m = 3$
$3m^2 - 7m - 3 = 0$
$a = 3, b = -7, c = -3$

$$m = \frac{7 \pm \sqrt{(-7)^2 - 4(3)(-3)}}{2(3)}$$

$$= \frac{7 \pm \sqrt{49 + 36}}{6}$$

$$= \frac{7 \pm \sqrt{85}}{6}$$

The solutions are $\dfrac{7 + \sqrt{85}}{6}$ and $\dfrac{7 - \sqrt{85}}{6}$.

**13.** $\dfrac{1}{2}x^2 - x - 1 = 0$
$x^2 - 2x - 2 = 0$
$a = 1, b = -2, c = -2$

$$x = \frac{2 \pm \sqrt{(-2)^2 - 4(1)(-2)}}{2(1)}$$

$$= \frac{2 \pm \sqrt{4 + 8}}{2}$$

$$= \frac{2 \pm \sqrt{12}}{2}$$

$$= \frac{2 \pm 2\sqrt{3}}{2}$$

$$= 1 \pm \sqrt{3}$$

The solutions are $1 + \sqrt{3}$ and $1 - \sqrt{3}$.

**15.** $\dfrac{2}{5}y^2 + \dfrac{1}{5}y = \dfrac{3}{5}$
$2y^2 + y - 3 = 0$
$a = 2, b = 1, c = -3$

$$y = \frac{-1 \pm \sqrt{(1)^2 - 4(2)(-3)}}{2(2)}$$

$$= \frac{-1 \pm \sqrt{1 + 24}}{4}$$

$$= \frac{-1 \pm \sqrt{25}}{4}$$

$$= \frac{-1 \pm 5}{4}$$

$$= -\frac{3}{2} \text{ or } 1$$

The solutions are $-\dfrac{3}{2}$ and 1.

**17.**
$$\frac{1}{3}y^2 = y + \frac{1}{6}$$
$$\frac{1}{3}y^2 - y - \frac{1}{6} = 0$$
$$2y^2 - 6y - 1 = 0$$
$$a = 2, b = -6, c = -1$$
$$y = \frac{6 \pm \sqrt{(-6)^2 - 4(2)(-1)}}{2(2)}$$
$$= \frac{6 \pm \sqrt{36 + 8}}{4}$$
$$= \frac{6 \pm \sqrt{44}}{4}$$
$$= \frac{6 \pm 2\sqrt{11}}{4}$$
$$= \frac{3 \pm \sqrt{11}}{2}$$

The solutions are $\dfrac{3 + \sqrt{11}}{2}$ and $\dfrac{3 - \sqrt{11}}{2}$.

**19.**
$$x^2 + 5x = -2$$
$$x^2 + 5x + 2 = 0$$
$$a = 1, b = 5, c = 2$$
$$x = \frac{-5 \pm \sqrt{(5)^2 - 4(1)(2)}}{2(1)}$$
$$= \frac{-5 \pm \sqrt{25 - 8}}{2}$$
$$= \frac{-5 \pm \sqrt{17}}{2}$$

The solutions are $\dfrac{-5 + \sqrt{17}}{2}$ and $\dfrac{-5 - \sqrt{17}}{2}$.

**21.**
$$(m+2)(2m-6) = 5(m-1) - 12$$
$$2m^2 - 6m + 4m - 12 = 5m - 5 - 12$$
$$2m^2 - 7m + 5 = 0$$
$$a = 2, b = -7, c = 5$$
$$m = \frac{7 \pm \sqrt{(-7)^2 - 4(2)(5)}}{2(2)}$$
$$= \frac{7 \pm \sqrt{49 - 40}}{4}$$
$$= \frac{7 \pm \sqrt{9}}{4}$$
$$= \frac{7 \pm 3}{4}$$
$$= 1 \text{ or } \frac{5}{2}$$

The solutions are 1 and $\dfrac{5}{2}$.

**23.** $x^2 + 6x + 13 = 0$
$$a = 1, b = 6, c = 13$$
$$x = \frac{-6 \pm \sqrt{(6)^2 - 4(1)(13)}}{2(1)}$$
$$= \frac{-6 \pm \sqrt{36 - 52}}{2}$$
$$= \frac{-6 \pm \sqrt{-16}}{2}$$
$$= \frac{-6 \pm 4i}{2}$$
$$= -3 \pm 2i$$

The solutions are $-3 + 2i$ and $-3 - 2i$.

**25.** $(x+5)(x-1) = 2$
$$x^2 + 4x - 5 = 2$$
$$x^2 + 4x - 7 = 0$$
$$a = 1, b = 4, c = -7$$
$$x = \frac{-4 \pm \sqrt{(4)^2 - 4(1)(-7)}}{2(1)}$$
$$= \frac{-4 \pm \sqrt{16 + 28}}{2}$$
$$= \frac{-4 \pm \sqrt{44}}{2}$$
$$= \frac{-4 \pm 2\sqrt{11}}{2}$$
$$= -2 \pm \sqrt{11}$$

The solutions are $-2 + \sqrt{11}$ and $-2 - \sqrt{11}$.

**27.**
$$6 = -4x^2 + 3x$$
$$4x^2 - 3x + 6 = 0$$
$$a = 4, b = -3, c = 6$$
$$x = \frac{3 \pm \sqrt{(-3)^2 - 4(4)(6)}}{2(4)}$$
$$= \frac{3 \pm \sqrt{9 - 96}}{8}$$
$$= \frac{3 \pm \sqrt{-87}}{8}$$
$$= \frac{3 \pm i\sqrt{87}}{8}$$

The solutions are $\dfrac{3 + i\sqrt{87}}{8}$ and $\dfrac{3 - i\sqrt{87}}{8}$.

**29.**
$$\frac{x^2}{3} - x = \frac{5}{3}$$
$$x^2 - 3x = 5$$
$$x^2 - 3x - 5 = 0$$
$$a = 1, b = -3, c = -5$$
$$x = \frac{3 \pm \sqrt{(-3)^2 - 4(1)(-5)}}{2(1)}$$
$$= \frac{3 \pm \sqrt{9 + 20}}{2}$$
$$= \frac{3 \pm \sqrt{29}}{2}$$

The solutions are $\dfrac{3 + \sqrt{29}}{2}$ and $\dfrac{3 - \sqrt{29}}{2}$.

**31.** $10y^2 + 10y + 3 = 0$
$$a = 10, b = 10, c = 3$$
$$y = \frac{-10 \pm \sqrt{(10)^2 - 4(10)(3)}}{2(10)}$$
$$= \frac{-10 \pm \sqrt{100 - 120}}{20}$$
$$= \frac{-10 \pm \sqrt{-20}}{20}$$
$$= \frac{-10 \pm i\sqrt{4 \cdot 5}}{20}$$
$$= \frac{-10 \pm 2i\sqrt{5}}{20}$$
$$= \frac{-5 \pm i\sqrt{5}}{10}$$

The solutions are $\dfrac{-5 + i\sqrt{5}}{10}$ and $\dfrac{-5 - i\sqrt{5}}{10}$.

**33.**
$$x(6x + 2) = 3$$
$$x(6x + 2) - 3 = 0$$
$$6x^2 + 2x - 3 = 0$$
$$a = 6, b = 2, c = -3$$
$$x = \frac{-2 \pm \sqrt{(2)^2 - 4(6)(-3)}}{2(6)}$$
$$= \frac{-2 \pm \sqrt{4 + 72}}{12}$$
$$= \frac{-2 \pm \sqrt{76}}{12}$$
$$= \frac{-2 \pm \sqrt{4 \cdot 19}}{12}$$
$$= \frac{-2 \pm 2\sqrt{19}}{12}$$
$$= \frac{-1 \pm \sqrt{19}}{6}$$

The solutions are $\dfrac{-1 + \sqrt{19}}{6}$ and $\dfrac{-1 - \sqrt{19}}{6}$.

**35.** $\dfrac{2}{5}y^2 + \dfrac{1}{5}y + \dfrac{3}{5} = 0$
$$2y^2 + y + 3 = 0$$
$$a = 2, b = 1, c = 3$$
$$y = \frac{-1 \pm \sqrt{(1)^2 - 4(2)(3)}}{2(2)}$$
$$= \frac{-1 \pm \sqrt{1 - 24}}{4}$$
$$= \frac{-1 \pm \sqrt{-23}}{4}$$
$$= \frac{-1 \pm i\sqrt{23}}{4}$$

The solutions are $\dfrac{-1 + i\sqrt{23}}{4}$ and $\dfrac{-1 - i\sqrt{23}}{4}$.

**37.**
$$\frac{1}{2}y^2 = y - \frac{1}{2}$$
$$y^2 = 2y - 1$$
$$y^2 - 2y + 1 = 0$$
$$a = 1, b = -2, c = 1$$
$$y = \frac{2 \pm \sqrt{(-2)^2 - 4(1)(1)}}{2(1)}$$
$$= \frac{2 \pm \sqrt{4-4}}{2}$$
$$= \frac{2 \pm \sqrt{0}}{2}$$
$$= \frac{2}{2}$$
$$= 1$$
The solution is 1.

**39.**
$$(n-2)^2 = 2n$$
$$n^2 - 4n + 4 = 2n$$
$$n^2 - 6n + 4 = 0$$
$$a = 1, b = -6, c = 4$$
$$n = \frac{6 \pm \sqrt{(-6)^2 - 4(1)(4)}}{2(1)}$$
$$= \frac{6 \pm \sqrt{36-16}}{2}$$
$$= \frac{6 \pm \sqrt{20}}{2}$$
$$= \frac{6 \pm 2\sqrt{5}}{2}$$
$$= 3 \pm \sqrt{5}$$
The solutions are $3 + \sqrt{5}$ and $3 - \sqrt{5}$.

**41.** $x^2 - 5 = 0$
$$a = 1, b = 0, c = -5$$
$$b^2 - 4ac = 0^2 - 4(1)(-5) = 20 > 0$$
Therefore, there are two real solutions.

**43.**
$$4x^2 + 12x = -9$$
$$4x^2 - 12x + 9 = 0$$
$$a = 4, b = -12, c = 9$$
$$b^2 - 4ac = (-12)^2 - 4(4)(9)$$
$$= 144 - 144$$
$$= 0$$
Therefore, there is one real solution.

**45.**
$$3x = -2x^2 + 7$$
$$2x^2 + 3x - 7 = 0$$
$$a = 2, b = 3, c = -7$$
$$b^2 - 4ac = 3^2 - 4(2)(-7)$$
$$= 9 + 56$$
$$= 65 > 0$$
Therefore, there are two real solutions.

**47.**
$$6 = 4x - 5x^2$$
$$5x^2 - 4x + 6 = 0$$
$$a = 5, b = -4, c = 6$$
$$b^2 - 4ac = (-4)^2 - 4(5)(6)$$
$$= 16 - 120$$
$$= -104 < 0$$
Therefore, there are two complex but not real solutions.

**49.** $9x - 2x^2 + 5 = 0$
$$-2x^2 + 9x + 5 = 0$$
$$a = -2, b = 9, c = 5$$
$$b^2 - 4ac = 9^2 - 4(-2)(5)$$
$$= 81 + 40$$
$$= 121 > 0$$
Therefore, there are two real solutions.

**51.**
$$(x+8)^2 + x^2 = 36^2$$
$$(x^2 + 16x + 64) + x^2 = 1296$$
$$2x^2 + 16x - 1232 = 0$$
$$a = 2, b = 16, c = -1232$$
$$x = \frac{-16 \pm \sqrt{(16)^2 - 4(2)(-1232)}}{2(2)}$$
$$= \frac{-16 \pm \sqrt{10,112}}{4}$$
$$x \approx 21 \text{ or } x \approx -29 \text{ (disregard)}$$
$$x + (x+8) = 21 + 21 + 8 = 50$$
$$50 - 36 = 14$$
They save about 14 feet of walking distance.

**53.** Let $x$ = length of leg. Then
$x + 2$ = length of hypotenuse.
$$x^2 + x^2 = (x+2)^2$$
$$2x^2 = x^2 + 4x + 4$$
$$x^2 - 4x - 4 = 0$$
$$a = 1, b = -4, c = -4$$

$$x = \frac{4 \pm \sqrt{(-4)^2 - 4(1)(-4)}}{2(1)}$$

$$= \frac{4 \pm \sqrt{32}}{2}$$

$$= \frac{4 \pm 4\sqrt{2}}{2}$$

$$= 2 \pm 2\sqrt{2} \text{ (disregard the negative)}$$

$$= 2 + 2\sqrt{2}$$

The sides measure $2 + 2\sqrt{2}$ cm, $2 + 2\sqrt{2}$ cm, and $4 + 2\sqrt{2}$ cm.

**55.** Let $x$ = width; then $x + 10$ = length.
Area = length · width
$$400 = (x + 10)x$$
$$0 = x^2 + 10x - 400$$
$$a = 1, b = 10, c = -400$$
$$x = \frac{-10 \pm \sqrt{(10)^2 - 4(1)(-400)}}{2(1)}$$
$$= \frac{-10 \pm \sqrt{1700}}{2}$$
$$= \frac{-10 \pm 10\sqrt{17}}{2}$$
$$= -5 \pm 5\sqrt{17}$$

Disregard the negative length. The width is $-5 + 5\sqrt{17}$ ft and the length is $5 + 5\sqrt{17}$ ft.

**57. a.** Let $x$ = length.
$$x^2 + x^2 = 100^2$$
$$2x^2 - 10,000 = 0$$
$$a = 2, b = 0, c = -10,000$$
$$x = \frac{0 \pm \sqrt{(0)^2 - 4(2)(-10,000)}}{2(2)}$$
$$= \frac{\pm\sqrt{80,000}}{4}$$
$$= \frac{\pm 200\sqrt{2}}{4}$$
$$= \pm 50\sqrt{2}$$

Disregard the negative length. The side measures $50\sqrt{2}$ meters.

**b.** Area = $s^2$
$$= \left(50\sqrt{2}\right)^2$$
$$= 2500(2)$$
$$= 5000$$
The area is 5000 square meters.

**59.** Let $w$ = width; then $w + 1.1$ = height.
Area = length · width
$$1439.9 = (w + 1.1)w$$
$$0 = w^2 + 1.1w - 1439.9$$
$$a = 1, b = 1.1, c = -1439.9$$
$$w = \frac{-1.1 \pm \sqrt{(1.1)^2 - 4(1)(-1439.9)}}{2(1)}$$
$$= \frac{-1.1 \pm \sqrt{5760.81}}{2}$$
$$= 37.4 \text{ or } -38.5 \text{ (disregard)}$$
Its width is 37.4 ft and its height is 38.5 ft.

**61.** Let $h$ = height. Then $2h + 4$ = base.
$$\text{Area} = \frac{1}{2} \text{base} \cdot \text{height}$$
$$42 = \frac{1}{2}(2h + 4)h$$
$$42 = h^2 + 2h$$
$$0 = h^2 + 2h - 42$$
$$a = 1, b = 2, c = -42$$
$$h = \frac{-2 \pm \sqrt{(2)^2 - 4(1)(-42)}}{2(1)}$$
$$= \frac{-2 \pm \sqrt{172}}{2}$$
$$= \frac{-2 \pm 2\sqrt{43}}{2}$$
$$= -1 \pm \sqrt{43} \text{ (disregard the negative)}$$
$$\text{base} = 2\left(-1 + \sqrt{43}\right) + 4 = 2 + 2\sqrt{43}$$

Height: $-1 + \sqrt{43}$ cm
Base: $2 + 2\sqrt{43}$ cm

**63.** $h = -16t^2 + 20t + 1100$
$$0 = -16t^2 + 20t + 1100$$
$$a = -16, b = 20, c = 1100$$
$$t = \frac{-20 \pm \sqrt{(20)^2 - 4(-16)(1100)}}{2(-16)}$$
$$= \frac{-20 \pm \sqrt{70,800}}{-32}$$
$$\approx 8.9 \text{ or } -7.7 \text{ (disregard)}$$
It will take about 8.9 seconds.

**65.** $h = -16t^2 - 20t + 180$

$0 = -16t^2 - 20t + 180$

$a = -16, b = -20, c = 180$

$t = \dfrac{20 \pm \sqrt{(-20)^2 - 4(-16)(180)}}{2(-16)}$

$= \dfrac{20 \pm \sqrt{11,920}}{-32}$

$\approx 2.8$ or $-4.0$ (disregard)

It will take about 2.8 seconds.

**67.** $\sqrt{5x-2} = 3$

$\left(\sqrt{5x-2}\right)^2 = 3^2$

$5x - 2 = 9$

$5x = 11$

$x = \dfrac{11}{5}$

**69.** $\dfrac{1}{x} + \dfrac{2}{5} = \dfrac{7}{x}$

$5x\left(\dfrac{1}{x} + \dfrac{2}{5}\right) = 5x\left(\dfrac{7}{x}\right)$

$5 + 2x = 35$

$2x = 30$

$x = 15$

**71.** $x^4 + x^2 - 20 = (x^2 + 5)(x^2 - 4)$

$\qquad\qquad\quad = (x^2 + 5)(x + 2)(x - 2)$

**73.** $z^4 - 13z^2 + 36 = (z^2 - 9)(z^2 - 4)$

$\qquad\qquad\qquad = (z + 3)(z - 3)(z + 2)(z - 2)$

**75.** $x^2 = -10$

$x^2 + 10 = 0$

$a = 1, b = 0, c = 10$

The correct substitution is **b**.

**77.** $m^2 + 5m - 6 = 0$

$(m + 6)(m - 1) = 0$

$m + 6 = 0$    or    $m - 1 = 0$

$m = -6$   or     $m = 1$

The results are the same. Answers may vary.

**79.** $2x^2 - 6x + 3 = 0$

$a = 2, b = -6, c = 3$

$x = \dfrac{6 \pm \sqrt{(-6)^2 - 4(2)(3)}}{2(2)}$

$= \dfrac{6 \pm \sqrt{12}}{4}$

$\approx 0.6$ or $2.4$

**81.** From Sunday to Monday

**83.** Wednesday

**85.** $f(x) = 3x^2 - 18x + 56$

$f(4) = 3(4)^2 - 18(4) + 56 = 32$

This answers appears to agree with the graph.

**87.** $f(x) = 115x^2 + 711x + 3946$

  **a.**   $x = 2004 - 2000 = 4$

$f(4) = 115(4)^2 + 711(4) + 3946 = 8630$

There were 8630 stores.

  **b.**   Let $f(x) = 25{,}000$.

$25{,}000 = 115x^2 + 711x + 3946$

$0 = 115x^2 + 711x - 21{,}054$

$a = 115, b = 711, c = -21{,}054$

$x = \dfrac{-711 \pm \sqrt{711^2 - 4(115)(-21{,}054)}}{2(115)}$

$= \dfrac{-711 \pm \sqrt{10{,}190{,}361}}{230}$

$\approx -3.0913 \pm 13.8793$

$x \approx 10.788 \approx 11$ or $x \approx -16.9706 \approx -17$

We are not concerned with the past, so we reject $-17$. There will be 25,000 Starbucks in 2011.

**89.** $\dfrac{-b + \sqrt{b^2 - 4ac}}{2a} + \dfrac{-b - \sqrt{b^2 - 4ac}}{2a}$

$= \dfrac{-b + \sqrt{b^2 - 4ac} - b - \sqrt{b^2 - 4ac}}{2a}$

$= \dfrac{-2b}{2a}$

$= -\dfrac{b}{a}$

**91.** $3x^2 - \sqrt{12}x + 1 = 0$

$a = 3, b = -\sqrt{12}, c = 1$

$$x = \frac{\sqrt{12} \pm \sqrt{\left(-\sqrt{12}\right)^2 - 4(3)(1)}}{2(3)}$$

$$= \frac{\sqrt{12} \pm \sqrt{12 - 12}}{6}$$

$$= \frac{\sqrt{4 \cdot 3} \pm \sqrt{0}}{6}$$

$$= \frac{2\sqrt{3}}{6}$$

$$= \frac{\sqrt{3}}{3}$$

The solution is $\dfrac{\sqrt{3}}{3}$.

**93.** $x^2 + \sqrt{2}x + 1 = 0$

$a = 1, b = \sqrt{2}, c = 1$

$$x = \frac{-\sqrt{2} \pm \sqrt{\left(\sqrt{2}\right)^2 - 4(1)(1)}}{2(1)}$$

$$= \frac{-\sqrt{2} \pm \sqrt{2 - 4}}{2}$$

$$= \frac{-\sqrt{2} \pm \sqrt{-2}}{2}$$

$$= \frac{-\sqrt{2} \pm i\sqrt{2}}{2}$$

The solutions are $\dfrac{-\sqrt{2} + i\sqrt{2}}{2}$ and $\dfrac{-\sqrt{2} - i\sqrt{2}}{2}$.

**95.** $2x^2 - \sqrt{3}x - 1 = 0$

$a = 2, b = -\sqrt{3}, c = -1$

$$x = \frac{\sqrt{3} \pm \sqrt{\left(-\sqrt{3}\right)^2 - 4(2)(-1)}}{2(2)}$$

$$= \frac{\sqrt{3} \pm \sqrt{3 + 8}}{4}$$

$$= \frac{\sqrt{3} \pm \sqrt{11}}{4}$$

The solutions are $\dfrac{\sqrt{3} + \sqrt{11}}{4}$ and $\dfrac{\sqrt{3} - \sqrt{11}}{4}$.

**97.** Exercise 63:

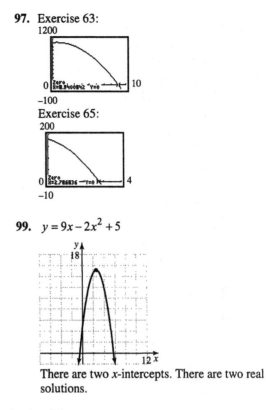

Exercise 65:

**99.** $y = 9x - 2x^2 + 5$

There are two $x$-intercepts. There are two real solutions.

## Section 8.3

### Practice Exercises

**1.** $x - \sqrt{x+1} - 5 = 0$

Get the radical alone on one side of the equation. Then square both sides.

$$x - \sqrt{x+1} - 5 = 0$$

$$x - 5 = \sqrt{x+1}$$

$$(x-5)^2 = x+1$$

$$x^2 - 10x + 25 = x+1$$

$$x^2 - 11x + 24 = 0$$

$$(x-8)(x-3) = 0$$

$$x - 8 = 0 \quad \text{or} \quad x - 3 = 0$$

$$x = 8 \quad \text{or} \quad x = 3$$

Check:

Let $x = 3$.

$$x - \sqrt{x+1} - 5 = 0$$

$$3 - \sqrt{3+1} - 5 \stackrel{?}{=} 0$$

$$-2 - \sqrt{4} \stackrel{?}{=} 0$$

$$-2 - 2 \stackrel{?}{=} 0$$

$$-4 = 0 \quad \text{False}$$

Let $x = 8$.

$$x - \sqrt{x+1} - 5 = 0$$
$$8 - \sqrt{8+1} - 5 \stackrel{?}{=} 0$$
$$3 - \sqrt{9} \stackrel{?}{=} 0$$
$$3 - 3 \stackrel{?}{=} 0$$
$$0 = 0 \quad \text{True}$$

The solution is 8 or the solution set is {8}.

**2.** $$\dfrac{5x}{x+1} - \dfrac{x+4}{x} = \dfrac{3}{x(x+1)}$$

$x$ cannot be either −1 or 0, because these values cause denominators to equal zero. Multiply both sides of the equation by $x(x+1)$.

$$x(x+1)\left(\dfrac{5x}{x+1}\right) - x(x+1)\left(\dfrac{x+4}{x}\right) = x(x+1)\left[\dfrac{3}{x(x+1)}\right]$$
$$5x^2 - (x+1)(x+4) = 3$$
$$5x^2 - x^2 - 5x - 4 = 3$$
$$4x^2 - 5x - 7 = 0$$

Use the quadratic formula with $a = 4$, $b = -5$, and $c = -7$.

$$x = \dfrac{-(-5) \pm \sqrt{(-5)^2 - 4(4)(-7)}}{2(4)} = \dfrac{5 \pm \sqrt{25 + 112}}{8} = \dfrac{5 \pm \sqrt{137}}{8}$$

Neither proposed solution will make denominators 0. The solutions are $\dfrac{5 + \sqrt{137}}{8}$ and $\dfrac{5 - \sqrt{137}}{8}$ or the

solution set is $\left\{ \dfrac{5 + \sqrt{137}}{8}, \dfrac{5 - \sqrt{137}}{8} \right\}$.

**3.** $$p^4 - 7p^2 - 144 = 0$$
$$(p^2 + 9)(p^2 - 16) = 0$$
$$(p^2 + 9)(p + 4)(p - 4) = 0$$

$$p^2 + 9 = 0 \qquad \text{or} \quad p + 4 = 0 \quad \text{or} \quad p - 4 = 0$$
$$p^2 = -9 \qquad\qquad\quad p = -4 \qquad\qquad p = 4$$
$$p = \pm\sqrt{-9}$$
$$p = \pm 3i$$

The solutions are 4, −4, $3i$, and $-3i$.

**4.** $$(x+2)^2 - 2(x+2) - 3 = 0$$

Let $y = x + 2$.
$$y^2 - 2y - 3 = 0$$
$$(y-3)(y+1) = 0$$
$$y - 3 = 0 \quad \text{or} \quad y + 1 = 0$$
$$y = 3 \qquad\qquad y = -1$$

Substitute $x + 2$ for $y$.
$$x + 2 = 3 \quad \text{or} \quad x + 2 = -1$$
$$x = 1 \qquad\qquad x = -3$$

Both 1 and −3 check. The solutions are 1 and −3.

**5.** $x^{2/3} - 5x^{1/3} + 4 = 0$

Let $m = x^{1/3}$.

$m^2 - 5m + 4 = 0$

$(m - 4)(m - 1) = 0$

$m - 4 = 0$  or  $m - 1 = 0$

$m = 4$          $m = 1$

Since $m = x^{1/3}$, we have

$x^{1/3} = 4$          or  $x^{1/3} = 1$

$x = 4^3 = 64$          $x = 1^3 = 1$

Both 64 and 1 check. The solutions are 64 and 1.

**6.** Let $x =$ the time in hours it takes Steve to groom all the dogs. Then,
$x - 1 =$ the time it takes Katy to groom all the dogs.

The part of the job completed in one hour by Steve is $\dfrac{1}{x}$, and the part completed by Katy in one hour is

$\dfrac{1}{x-1}$. In one hour, $\dfrac{1}{4}$ of the job is completed. We have,

$$\frac{1}{x} + \frac{1}{x-1} = \frac{1}{4}$$

$$4x(x-1)\left(\frac{1}{x}\right) + 4x(x-1)\left(\frac{1}{x-1}\right) = 4x(x-1)\left(\frac{1}{4}\right)$$

$$4(x-1) + 4x = x(x-1)$$

$$4x - 4 + 4x = x^2 - x$$

$$0 = x^2 - 9x + 4$$

Use the quadratic formula with $a = 1$, $b = -9$, and $c = 4$.

$$x = \frac{-(-9) \pm \sqrt{(-9)^2 - 4(1)(4)}}{2(1)}$$

$$x = \frac{9 \pm \sqrt{81 - 16}}{2} = \frac{9 \pm \sqrt{65}}{2}$$

$x \approx 8.53$  or  $x \approx 0.47$

Since $x - 1 = 0.47 - 1 = -0.53 < 0$, representing negative time worked, we reject 0.47. It takes Steve

$\dfrac{9 + \sqrt{65}}{2} \approx 8.5$ hours  and Katy $\dfrac{9 + \sqrt{65}}{2} - 1 = \dfrac{7 + \sqrt{65}}{2} \approx 7.5$ hours  to groom all the dogs when working

alone.

**7.** Let $x =$ the speed driven to Shanghai. Then
$x + 50 =$ the speed driven to Ningbo.

|  | distance = | rate | · | time |
|---|---|---|---|---|
| To Shanghai | 36 | $x$ | | $\dfrac{36}{x}$ |
| To Ningbo | 36 | $x + 50$ | | $\dfrac{36}{x+50}$ |

The total travel time was 1.3 hours, so

$$\frac{36}{x}+\frac{36}{x+50}=1.3$$

$$x(x+50)\left(\frac{36}{x}\right)+x(x+50)\left(\frac{36}{x+50}\right)=1.3x(x+50)$$

$$36(x+50)+36x=1.3x^2+65x$$

$$36x+1800+36x=1.3x^2+65x$$

$$0=1.3x^2-7x-1800$$

Use the quadratic formula with $a=1.3$, $b=-7$, and $c=-1800$.

$$x=\frac{-(-7)\pm\sqrt{(-7)^2-4(1.3)(-1800)}}{2(1.3)}=\frac{7\pm\sqrt{9409}}{2.6}$$

$$x=\frac{7+\sqrt{9409}}{2.6}=40 \quad\text{or}\quad x=\frac{7-\sqrt{9409}}{2.6}\approx-34.6$$

The speed is not negative, so reject −34.6. The speed to Shanghai was 40 km/hr and to Ningbo it was 40 + 50 = 90 km/hr.

**Exercise Set 8.3**

1.
$$2x=\sqrt{10+3x}$$
$$4x^2=10+3x$$
$$4x^2-3x-10=0$$
$$(4x+5)(x-2)=0$$
$$4x+5=0 \quad\text{or}\quad x-2=0$$
$$x=-\frac{5}{4} \quad\text{or}\quad x=2$$

Discard $-\frac{5}{4}$. The solution is 2.

3.
$$x-2\sqrt{x}=8$$
$$x-8=2\sqrt{x}$$
$$(x-8)^2=\left(2\sqrt{x}\right)^2$$
$$x^2-16x+64=4x$$
$$x^2-20x+64=0$$
$$(x-16)(x-4)=0$$
$$x-16=0 \quad\text{or}\quad x-4=0$$
$$x=16 \quad\text{or}\quad x=4 \text{ (discard)}$$

The solution is 16.

**5.** $\sqrt{9x} = x + 2$

$\left(\sqrt{9x}\right)^2 = (x+2)^2$

$9x = x^2 + 4x + 4$

$0 = x^2 - 5x + 4$

$0 = (x-4)(x-1)$

$x - 4 = 0$ or $x - 1 = 0$

$x = 4$ or $x = 1$

The solutions are 1 and 4.

**7.** $\dfrac{2}{x} + \dfrac{3}{x-1} = 1$

Multiply each term by $x(x-1)$.

$2(x-1) + 3x = x(x-1)$

$2x - 2 + 3x = x^2 - x$

$0 = x^2 - 6x + 2$

$x = \dfrac{6 \pm \sqrt{(-6)^2 - 4(1)(2)}}{2(1)}$

$= \dfrac{6 \pm \sqrt{28}}{2}$

$= \dfrac{6 \pm 2\sqrt{7}}{2} = 3 \pm \sqrt{7}$

The solutions are $3 + \sqrt{7}$ and $3 - \sqrt{7}$.

**9.** $\dfrac{3}{x} + \dfrac{4}{x+2} = 2$

Multiply each term by $x(x+2)$.

$3(x+2) + 4x = 2x(x+2)$

$3x + 6 + 4x = 2x^2 + 4x$

$0 = 2x^2 - 3x - 6$

$x = \dfrac{3 \pm \sqrt{(-3)^2 - 4(2)(-6)}}{2(2)}$

$= \dfrac{3 \pm \sqrt{57}}{4}$

The solutions are $\dfrac{3 + \sqrt{57}}{4}$ and $\dfrac{3 - \sqrt{57}}{4}$.

**11.** $\dfrac{7}{x^2 - 5x + 6} = \dfrac{2x}{x-3} - \dfrac{x}{x-2}$

$\dfrac{7}{(x-3)(x-2)} = \dfrac{2x}{x-3} - \dfrac{x}{x-2}$

Multiply each term by $(x-3)(x-2)$.

$7 = 2x(x-2) - x(x-3)$

$7 = 2x^2 - 4x - x^2 + 3x$

$0 = x^2 - x - 7$

$x = \dfrac{1 \pm \sqrt{(-1)^2 - 4(1)(-7)}}{2(1)}$

$= \dfrac{1 \pm \sqrt{29}}{2}$

The solutions are $\dfrac{1 + \sqrt{29}}{2}$ and $\dfrac{2 - \sqrt{29}}{2}$.

**13.** $p^4 - 16 = 0$

$(p^2 - 4)(p^2 + 4) = 0$

$(p+2)(p-2)(p^2 + 4) = 0$

$p + 2 = 0$ or $p - 2 = 0$ or $p^2 + 4 = 0$

$p = -2$ or $p = 2$ or $p^2 = -4$

$p = \pm\sqrt{-4}$

$p = \pm 2i$

The solutions are $-2$, $2$, $-2i$, and $2i$.

**15.** $4x^4 + 11x^2 = 3$

$4x^4 + 11x^2 - 3 = 0$

$(4x^2 - 1)(x^2 + 3) = 0$

$(2x+1)(2x-1)(x^2 + 3) = 0$

$2x + 1 = 0$ or $2x - 1 = 0$ or $x^2 + 3 = 0$

$x = -\dfrac{1}{2}$ or $x = \dfrac{1}{2}$ or $x^2 = -3$

$x = \pm\sqrt{-3}$

$x = \pm i\sqrt{3}$

The solutions are $-\dfrac{1}{2}, \dfrac{1}{2}, -i\sqrt{3}$, and $i\sqrt{3}$.

**17.** $z^4 - 13z^2 + 36 = 0$

$(z^2 - 9)(z^2 - 4) = 0$

$(z+3)(z-3)(z+2)(z-2) = 0$

$z = -3, z = 3, z = -2, z = 2$

The solutions are $-3$, $3$, $-2$, and $2$.

**19.** $x^{2/3} - 3x^{1/3} - 10 = 0$

Let $y = x^{1/3}$. Then $y^2 = x^{2/3}$ and

$y^2 - 3y - 10 = 0$

$(y-5)(y+2) = 0$

$y - 5 = 0$ or $y + 2 = 0$

$y = 5$ or $y = -2$

$x^{1/3} = 5$ or $x^{1/3} = -2$

$x = 125$ or $x = -8$

The solutions are $-8$ and $125$.

**21.** $(5n+1)^2 + 2(5n+1) - 3 = 0$

Let $y = 5n + 1$. Then $y^2 = (5n+1)^2$ and

$y^2 + 2y - 3 = 0$
$(y+3)(y-1) = 0$
$y + 3 = 0$ or $y - 1 = 0$
$y = -3$ or $y = 1$
$5n + 1 = -3$ or $5n + 1 = 1$
$5n = -4$ or $5n = 0$
$n = -\dfrac{4}{5}$ or $n = 0$

The solutions are $-\dfrac{4}{5}$ and 0.

**23.** $2x^{2/3} - 5x^{1/3} = 3$

Let $y = x^{1/3}$. Then $y^2 = x^{2/3}$ and

$2y^2 - 5y = 3$
$2y^2 - 5y - 3 = 0$
$(2y+1)(y-3) = 0$
$2y + 1 = 0$ or $y - 3 = 0$
$y = -\dfrac{1}{2}$ or $y = 3$
$x^{1/3} = -\dfrac{1}{2}$ or $x^{1/3} = 3$
$x = -\dfrac{1}{8}$ or $x = 27$

The solutions are $-\dfrac{1}{8}$ and 27.

**25.**
$$1 + \frac{2}{3t-2} = \frac{8}{(3t-2)^2}$$

$(3t-2)^2 + 2(3t-2) = 8$
$(3t-2)^2 + 2(3t-2) - 8 = 0$

Let $y = 3t - 2$. Then $y^2 = (3t-2)^2$ and

$y^2 + 2y - 8 = 0$
$(y+4)(y-2) = 0$
$y + 4 = 0$ or $y - 2 = 0$
$y = -4$ or $y = 2$
$3t - 2 = -4$ or $3t - 2 = 2$
$3t = -2$ or $3t = 4$
$t = -\dfrac{2}{3}$ or $t = \dfrac{4}{3}$

The solutions are $-\dfrac{2}{3}$ and $\dfrac{4}{3}$.

**27.** $20x^{2/3} - 6x^{1/3} - 2 = 0$

Let $y = x^{1/3}$. Then $y^2 = x^{2/3}$ and

$20y^2 - 6y - 2 = 0$
$2(10y^2 - 3y - 1) = 0$
$2(5y+1)(2y-1) = 0$
$5y + 1 = 0$ or $2y - 1 = 0$
$y = -\dfrac{1}{5}$ or $y = \dfrac{1}{2}$
$x^{1/3} = -\dfrac{1}{5}$ or $x^{1/3} = \dfrac{1}{2}$
$x = -\dfrac{1}{125}$ or $x = \dfrac{1}{8}$

The solutions are $\dfrac{1}{8}$ and $-\dfrac{1}{125}$.

**29.** $a^4 - 5a^2 + 6 = 0$

$(a^2 - 3)(a^2 - 2) = 0$
$a^2 - 3 = 0$ or $a^2 - 2 = 0$
$a^2 = 3$ or $a^2 = 2$
$a = \pm\sqrt{3}$ or $a = \pm\sqrt{2}$

The solutions are $-\sqrt{3}, \sqrt{3}, -\sqrt{2},$ and $\sqrt{2}$.

**31.** $\dfrac{2x}{x-2} + \dfrac{x}{x+3} = \dfrac{5}{x+3}$

Multiply each term by $(x+3)(x-2)$.

$2x(x+3) + x(x-2) = -5(x-2)$
$2x^2 + 6x + x^2 - 2x = -5x + 10$
$3x^2 + 9x - 10 = 0$
$$x = \frac{-9 \pm \sqrt{(9)^2 - 4(3)(-10)}}{2(3)}$$
$$= \frac{-9 \pm \sqrt{201}}{6}$$

The solutions are $\dfrac{-9 + \sqrt{201}}{6}$ and $\dfrac{-9 - \sqrt{201}}{6}$.

**33.** $(p+2)^2 = 9(p+2) - 20$

$(p+2)^2 - 9(p+2) + 20 = 0$

Let $x = p + 2$. Then $x^2 = (p+2)^2$ and

$x^2 - 9x + 20 = 0$
$(x-5)(x-4) = 0$
$x = 5$ or $x = 4$
$p + 2 = 5$ or $p + 2 = 4$
$p = 3$ or $p = 2$

The solutions are 2 and 3.

**35.**
$$2x = \sqrt{11x+3}$$
$$(2x)^2 = \left(\sqrt{11x+3}\right)^2$$
$$4x^2 = 11x+3$$
$$4x^2 - 11x - 3 = 0$$
$$(4x+1)(x-3) = 0$$
$$x = -\frac{1}{4} \text{ (discard) or } x = 3$$
The solution is 3.

**37.** $x^{2/3} - 8x^{1/3} + 15 = 0$
Let $y = x^{1/3}$. Then $y^2 = x^{2/3}$ and
$$y^2 - 8y + 15 = 0$$
$$(y-5)(y-3) = 0$$
$$y = 5 \quad \text{or} \quad y = 3$$
$$x^{1/3} = 5 \quad \text{or} \quad x^{1/3} = 3$$
$$x = 125 \text{ or} \quad x = 27$$
The solutions are 27 and 125.

**39.**
$$y^3 + 9y - y^2 - 9 = 0$$
$$y(y^2+9) - 1(y^2+9) = 0$$
$$(y^2+9)(y-1) = 0$$
$$y^2 + 9 = 0 \quad \text{or } y - 1 = 0$$
$$y^2 = -9 \quad \text{or} \quad y = 1$$
$$y = \pm\sqrt{-9}$$
$$y = \pm 3i$$
The solutions are 1, $-3i$, and $3i$.

**41.** $2x^{2/3} + 3x^{1/3} - 2 = 0$
Let $y = x^{1/3}$. Then $y^2 = x^{2/3}$ and
$$2y^2 + 3y - 2 = 0$$
$$(2y-1)(y+2) = 0$$
$$y = \frac{1}{2} \quad \text{or} \quad y = -2$$
$$x^{1/3} = \frac{1}{2} \quad \text{or } x^{1/3} = -2$$
$$x = \frac{1}{8} \quad \text{or} \quad x = -8$$
The solutions are $-8$ and $\frac{1}{8}$.

**43.** $x^{-2} - x^{-1} - 6 = 0$
Let $y = x^{-1}$. Then $y^2 = x^{-2}$ and
$$y^2 - y - 6 = 0$$
$$(y-3)(y+2) = 0$$
$$y = 3 \quad \text{or} \quad y = -2$$
$$x^{-1} = 3 \quad \text{or} \quad x^{-1} = -2$$
$$\frac{1}{x} = 3 \quad \text{or} \quad \frac{1}{x} = -2$$
$$x = \frac{1}{3} \quad \text{or} \quad x = -\frac{1}{2}$$
The solutions are $-\frac{1}{2}$ and $\frac{1}{3}$.

**45.**
$$x - \sqrt{x} = 2$$
$$x - 2 = \sqrt{x}$$
$$(x-2)^2 = x$$
$$x^2 - 4x + 4 = x$$
$$x^2 - 5x + 4 = 0$$
$$(x-4)(x-1) = 0$$
$$x = 4 \text{ or } x = 1 \text{ (discard)}$$
The solution is 4.

**47.**
$$\frac{x}{x-1} + \frac{1}{x+1} = \frac{2}{x^2-1}$$
$$\frac{x}{x-1} + \frac{1}{x+1} = \frac{2}{(x+1)(x-1)}$$
$$x(x+1) + (x-1) = 2$$
$$x^2 + x + x - 1 = 2$$
$$x^2 + 2x - 3 = 0$$
$$(x+3)(x-1) = 0$$
$$x = -3 \text{ or } x = 1 \text{ (discard)}$$
The solution is $-3$.

**49.**
$$p^4 - p^2 - 20 = 0$$
$$(p^2 - 5)(p^2 + 4) = 0$$
$$p^2 - 5 = 0 \quad \text{or } p^2 + 4 = 0$$
$$p^2 = 5 \quad \text{or} \quad p^2 = -4$$
$$p = \pm\sqrt{5} \quad \text{or} \quad p = \pm 2i$$
The solutions are $-\sqrt{5}, \sqrt{5}, -2i$, and $2i$.

**51.** $(x+3)(x^2-3x+9)=0$

$x+3=0 \quad$ or $\quad x^2-3x+9=0$

$x=-3 \quad$ or

$x=\dfrac{3\pm\sqrt{(-3)^2-4(1)(9)}}{2(1)}$

$=\dfrac{3\pm\sqrt{-27}}{2}$

$=\dfrac{3\pm 3i\sqrt{3}}{2}$

The solutions are $-3$, $\dfrac{3+3i\sqrt{3}}{2}$, and

$\dfrac{3-3i\sqrt{3}}{2}$.

**53.** $\qquad\qquad 1=\dfrac{4}{x-7}+\dfrac{5}{(x-7)^2}$

$(x-7)^2-4(x-7)-5=0$

Let $y=x-7$. Then $y^2=(x-7)^2$ and

$y^2-4y-5=0$

$(y-5)(y+1)=0$

$y=5 \quad$ or $\quad y=-1$

$x-7=5 \quad$ or $\quad x-7=-1$

$x=12 \quad$ or $\quad x=6$

The solutions are 6 and 12.

**55.** $\qquad\qquad 27y^4+15y^2=2$

$27y^4+15y^2-2=0$

$(9y^2-1)(3y^2+2)=0$

$(3y+1)(3y-1)(3y^2+2)=0$

$y=-\dfrac{1}{3} \quad$ or $\quad y=\dfrac{1}{3} \quad$ or $\quad y^2=-\dfrac{2}{3}$

$y=\pm\sqrt{-\dfrac{2}{3}}$

$y=\pm\dfrac{i\sqrt{6}}{3}$

The solutions are $-\dfrac{1}{3}, \dfrac{1}{3}, -\dfrac{i\sqrt{6}}{3}$, and $\dfrac{i\sqrt{6}}{3}$.

**57.** Let $x$ = speed on the first part. Then
$x-1$ = speed on the second part.

$d=rt \Rightarrow t=\dfrac{d}{r}$

$t_{\text{on first part}}+t_{\text{on second part}}=1\dfrac{3}{5}$

$\dfrac{3}{x}+\dfrac{4}{x-1}=\dfrac{8}{5}$

$3\cdot 5(x-1)+4\cdot 5x=8x(x-1)$

$15x-15+20x=8x^2-8x$

$0=8x^2-43x+15$

$0=(8x-3)(x-5)$

$8x-3=0 \quad$ or $\quad x-5=0$

$x=\dfrac{3}{8} \quad$ or $\quad x=5$

$\qquad\qquad x-1=4$

Discard $\dfrac{3}{8}$. Her speeds were 5 mph and 4 mph.

**59.** Let $x$ = time for hose alone. Then
$x-1$ = time for the inlet pipe alone.

$\dfrac{1}{x}+\dfrac{1}{x-1}=\dfrac{1}{8}$

$8(x-1)+8x=x(x-1)$

$8x-8+8x=x^2-x$

$0=x^2-17x+8$

$x=\dfrac{17\pm\sqrt{(-17)^2-4(1)(8)}}{2(1)}$

$=\dfrac{17\pm\sqrt{257}}{2}$

$x\approx 0.5$ (discard) $\quad$ or $\quad x\approx 16.5$

$\qquad\qquad\qquad\qquad x-1\approx 15.5$

Hose: 16.5 hrs; Inlet pipe: 15.5 hrs

**61.** Let $x$ = original speed. Then
$x+11$ = return speed.

$d=rt \Rightarrow t=\dfrac{d}{r}$

$t_{\text{return}}=t_{\text{original}}-1$

$\dfrac{330}{x+11}=\dfrac{330}{x}-1$

$330x=330(x+11)-x(x+11)$

$330x=330x+3630-x^2-11x$

$x^2+11x-3630=0$

$$x = \frac{-11 \pm \sqrt{(11)^2 - 4(1)(-3630)}}{2(1)}$$

$$= \frac{-11 \pm \sqrt{14,641}}{2}$$

$$= \frac{-11 \pm 121}{2} = 55 \text{ or } -66 \text{ (disregard)}$$

$x + 11 = 55 + 11 = 66$

Original speed: 55 mph

Return speed: 66 mph

**63.** Let $x$ = time for son alone. Then
$x - 1$ = time for dad alone.

$$\frac{1}{x} + \frac{1}{x-1} = \frac{1}{4}$$

$$4(x-1) + 4x = x(x-1)$$

$$4x - 4 + 4x = x^2 - x$$

$$0 = x^2 - 9x + 4$$

$$x = \frac{9 \pm \sqrt{(-9)^2 - 4(1)(4)}}{2(1)}$$

$$= \frac{9 \pm \sqrt{65}}{2}$$

$\approx 0.5$ (discard) or $8.5$

It takes his son about 8.5 hours.

**65.** Let $x$ = the number.

$$x(x-4) = 96$$

$$x^2 - 4x - 96 = 0$$

$$(x-12)(x+8) = 0$$

$$x = 12 \text{ or } x = -8$$

The number is 12 or –8.

**67. a.** length $= x - 3 - 3 = x - 6 = (x - 6)$ cm

    **b.**    $V = lwh$

         $300 = (x-6)(x-6) \cdot 3$

    **c.**    $300 = 3(x-6)^2$

         $100 = x^2 - 12x + 36$

         $0 = x^2 - 12x - 64$

         $0 = (x-16)(x+4)$

         $x = 16$ or $x = -4$ (discard)

         The sheet is 16 cm by 16 cm.

         Check: $V = 3(x-6)(x-6)$

                 $= 3(16-6)(16-6)$

                 $= 3(10)(10)$

                 $= 300$ cubic cm

**69.** Let $x$ = length of the side of the square.

    Area $= x^2$

    $920 = x^2$

    $\sqrt{920} = x$

Adding another radial line to a different corner would yield a right triangle with legs $r$ and hypotenuse $x$.

$$r^2 + r^2 = x^2$$

$$2r^2 = \left(\sqrt{920}\right)^2$$

$$2r^2 = 920$$

$$r^2 = 460$$

$$r = \pm\sqrt{460} = \pm 21.4476$$

Disregard the negative. The smallest radius would be 22 feet.

**71.**   $\dfrac{5x}{3} + 2 \le 7$

        $\dfrac{5x}{3} \le 5$

        $5x \le 15$

        $x \le 3$

   $(-\infty, 3]$

**73.**       $\dfrac{y-1}{15} > -\dfrac{2}{5}$

   $15\left(\dfrac{y-1}{15}\right) > 15\left(-\dfrac{2}{5}\right)$

         $y - 1 > -6$

            $y > -5$

   $(-5, \infty)$

**75.** Domain: $\{x \mid x \text{ is a real number}\}$ or $(-\infty, \infty)$

     Range: $\{y \mid y \text{ is a real number}\}$ or $(-\infty, \infty)$

     It is a function.

**77.** Domain: $\{x \mid x \text{ is a real number}\}$ or $(-\infty, \infty)$

     Range: $\{y \mid y \ge -1\}$ or $[-1, \infty)$

     It is a function.

**79.**
$$y^3 + 9y - y^2 - 9 = 0$$
$$y(y^2 + 9) - (y^2 + 9) = 0$$
$$(y-1)(y^2 + 9) = 0$$
$$y - 1 = 0 \quad \text{or} \quad y^2 + 9 = 0$$
$$y = 1 \qquad\qquad y^2 = -9$$
$$y = \pm\sqrt{-9} = \pm 3i$$

The solutions are 1, $3i$, and $-3i$.

**81.**
$$x^{-2} - x^{-1} - 6 = 0$$
$$1 - x - 6x^2 = 0$$
$$(1 - 3x)(1 + 2x) = 0$$
$$1 - 3x = 0 \quad \text{or} \quad 1 + 2x = 0$$
$$1 = 3x \qquad\qquad 2x = -1$$
$$\frac{1}{3} = x \qquad\qquad x = -\frac{1}{2}$$

The solutions are $\frac{1}{3}$ and $-\frac{1}{2}$.

**83.**
$$2x^3 = -54$$
$$x^3 = -27$$
$$x^3 + 27 = 0$$
$$(x+3)(x^2 - 3x + 9) = 0$$
$$x + 3 = 0 \quad \text{or} \quad x^2 - 3x + 9 = 0$$
$$x = -3$$
$$x = \frac{-(-3) \pm \sqrt{(-3)^2 - 4(1)(9)}}{2(1)}$$
$$x = \frac{3 \pm \sqrt{9 - 36}}{2} = \frac{3 \pm \sqrt{-27}}{2}$$
$$x = \frac{3 \pm 3i\sqrt{3}}{2}$$

The solutions are $-3$, $\frac{3 + 3i\sqrt{3}}{2}$, and $\frac{3 - 3i\sqrt{3}}{2}$.

**85.** Answers may vary

**87. a.** Let $x$ = Bourdais's fastest lap speed and $x + 0.55$ = Pagenaud's fastest lap speed.

Using $t = \dfrac{d}{r}$, we have
$$t_{\text{Bourdais}} = t_{\text{Pagenaud}} + 0.25$$
$$\frac{10,391}{x} = \frac{10,391}{x + 0.55} + 0.25$$
$$10,391(x + 0.55) = 10,391x + 0.25x(x + 0.55)$$
$$10,391x + 5715.05 = 10,391x + 0.25x^2 + 0.1375x$$
$$0 = 0.25x^2 + 0.1375x - 5715.05$$

$$x = \frac{-0.1375 \pm \sqrt{(0.1375)^2 - 4(0.25)(-5715.05)}}{2(0.25)}$$

Using the positive square root, $x \approx 150.92$ feet per second.

**b.**  $x + 0.55 = 150.92 + 0.55$
$\quad\quad\quad\quad\quad = 151.47$ feet per second

**c.**  5280 ft = 1 mile, and 3600 sec = 1 hr.

Bourdais: $\dfrac{150.92 \text{ ft}}{\text{sec}} \cdot \dfrac{3600 \text{ sec}}{\text{hr}} \cdot \dfrac{1 \text{ mile}}{5280 \text{ ft}} \approx 102.9$ mph

Fernandez: $\dfrac{151.47 \text{ ft}}{\text{sec}} \cdot \dfrac{3600 \text{ sec}}{\text{hr}} \cdot \dfrac{1 \text{ mile}}{5280 \text{ ft}} \approx 103.3$ mph

## Integrated Review

**1.**  $x^2 - 10 = 0$
$\quad\quad x^2 = 10$
$\quad\quad x = \pm\sqrt{10}$

**2.**  $x^2 - 14 = 0$
$\quad\quad x^2 = 14$
$\quad\quad x = \pm\sqrt{14}$

**3.**  $(x-1)^2 = 8$
$\quad\quad x - 1 = \pm\sqrt{8}$
$\quad\quad x - 1 = \pm 2\sqrt{2}$
$\quad\quad\quad x = 1 \pm 2\sqrt{2}$

**4.**  $(x+5)^2 = 12$
$\quad\quad x + 5 = \pm\sqrt{12}$
$\quad\quad x + 5 = \pm 2\sqrt{3}$
$\quad\quad\quad x = -5 \pm 2\sqrt{3}$

**5.**  $x^2 + 2x - 12 = 0$
$\quad\quad x^2 + 2x + \left(\dfrac{2}{2}\right)^2 = 12 + 1$
$\quad\quad\quad x^2 + 2x + 1 = 13$
$\quad\quad\quad\quad (x+1)^2 = 13$
$\quad\quad\quad\quad\quad x + 1 = \pm\sqrt{13}$
$\quad\quad\quad\quad\quad\quad x = -1 \pm \sqrt{13}$

**6.** $x^2 - 12x + 11 = 0$

$$x^2 - 12x + \left(\frac{-12}{2}\right)^2 = -11 + 36$$

$$x^2 - 12x + 36 = 25$$

$$(x-6)^2 = \pm\sqrt{25}$$

$$x - 6 = \pm 5$$

$$x = 6 \pm 5$$

$$x = 1 \text{ or } x = 11$$

**7.** $3x^2 + 3x = 5$

$$x^2 + x = \frac{5}{3}$$

$$x^2 + x + \left(\frac{1}{2}\right)^2 = \frac{5}{3} + \frac{1}{4}$$

$$x^2 + x + \frac{1}{4} = \frac{23}{12}$$

$$\left(x + \frac{1}{2}\right)^2 = \frac{23}{12}$$

$$x + \frac{1}{2} = \pm\sqrt{\frac{23}{12}}$$

$$x + \frac{1}{2} = \pm\frac{\sqrt{23}}{2\sqrt{3}}$$

$$x + \frac{1}{2} = \pm\frac{\sqrt{23} \cdot \sqrt{3}}{2\sqrt{3} \cdot \sqrt{3}}$$

$$x + \frac{1}{2} = \pm\frac{\sqrt{69}}{6}$$

$$x = -\frac{1}{2} \pm \frac{\sqrt{69}}{6} = \frac{-3 \pm \sqrt{69}}{6}$$

**8.** $16y^2 + 16y = 1$

$$y^2 + y = \frac{1}{16}$$

$$y^2 + y + \left(\frac{1}{2}\right)^2 = \frac{1}{16} + \frac{1}{4}$$

$$y^2 + y + \frac{1}{4} = \frac{5}{16}$$

$$\left(y + \frac{1}{2}\right)^2 = \frac{5}{16}$$

$$y + \frac{1}{2} = \pm\sqrt{\frac{5}{16}}$$

$$y + \frac{1}{2} = \pm\frac{\sqrt{5}}{4}$$

$$y = -\frac{1}{2} \pm \frac{\sqrt{5}}{4} = \frac{-2 \pm \sqrt{5}}{4}$$

**9.** $2x^2 - 4x + 1 = 0$

$a = 2, b = -4, c = 1$

$$x = \frac{4 \pm \sqrt{(-4)^2 - 4(2)(1)}}{2(2)}$$

$$= \frac{4 \pm \sqrt{8}}{4}$$

$$= \frac{4 \pm 2\sqrt{2}}{4} = \frac{2 \pm \sqrt{2}}{2}$$

**10.** $\frac{1}{2}x^2 + 3x + 2 = 0$

$$x^2 + 6x + 4 = 0$$

$a = 1, b = 6, c = 4$

$$x = \frac{-6 \pm \sqrt{(6)^2 - 4(1)(4)}}{2(1)}$$

$$= \frac{-6 \pm \sqrt{20}}{2}$$

$$= \frac{-6 \pm 2\sqrt{5}}{2} = -3 \pm \sqrt{5}$$

**11.** $x^2 + 4x = -7$

$$x^2 + 4x + 7 = 0$$

$a = 1, b = 4, c = 7$

$$x = \frac{-4 \pm \sqrt{(4)^2 - 4(1)(7)}}{2(1)}$$

$$= \frac{-4 \pm \sqrt{-12}}{2}$$

$$= \frac{-4 \pm i\sqrt{4 \cdot 3}}{2}$$

$$= \frac{-4 \pm 2i\sqrt{3}}{2} = -2 \pm i\sqrt{3}$$

**12.** $x^2 + x = -3$

$$x^2 + x + 3 = 0$$

$a = 1, b = 1, c = 3$

$$x = \frac{-1 \pm \sqrt{(1)^2 - 4(1)(3)}}{2(1)}$$

$$= \frac{-1 \pm \sqrt{-11}}{2}$$

$$= \frac{-1 \pm i\sqrt{11}}{2}$$

**13.** $x^2 + 3x + 6 = 0$

$a = 1, b = 3, c = 6$

$x = \dfrac{-3 \pm \sqrt{(3)^2 - 4(1)(6)}}{2(1)}$

$\quad = \dfrac{-3 \pm \sqrt{-15}}{2}$

$\quad = \dfrac{-3 \pm i\sqrt{15}}{2}$

**14.** $2x^2 + 18 = 0$

$2x^2 = -18$

$x^2 = -9$

$x = \pm\sqrt{-9}$

$x = \pm 3i$

**15.** $x^2 + 17x = 0$

$x(x + 17) = 0$

$x = 0 \ \text{ or } \ x + 17 = 0$

$\qquad\qquad\qquad x = -17$

$x = 0, -17$

**16.** $4x^2 - 2x - 3 = 0$

$a = 4, b = -2, c = -3$

$x = \dfrac{2 + \sqrt{(-2)^2 - 4(4)(-3)}}{2(4)}$

$\quad = \dfrac{2 \pm \sqrt{52}}{8}$

$\quad = \dfrac{2 \pm 2\sqrt{13}}{8}$

$\quad = \dfrac{1 \pm \sqrt{13}}{4}$

**17.** $(x - 2)^2 = 27$

$x - 2 = \pm\sqrt{27}$

$x - 2 = \pm 3\sqrt{3}$

$\qquad x = 2 \pm 3\sqrt{3}$

**18.** $\dfrac{1}{2}x^2 - 2x + \dfrac{1}{2} = 0$

$x^2 - 4x + 1 = 0$

$x^2 - 4x + \left(\dfrac{-4}{2}\right)^2 = -1 + 4$

$x^2 - 4x + 4 = 3$

$(x - 2)^2 = 3$

$x - 2 = \pm\sqrt{3}$

$x = 2 \pm \sqrt{3}$

**19.** $3x^2 + 2x = 8$

$3x^2 + 2x - 8 = 0$

$(3x - 4)(x + 2) = 0$

$3x - 4 = 0 \ \text{ or } \ x + 2 = 0$

$x = \dfrac{4}{3} \ \text{ or } \quad x = -2$

**20.** $2x^2 = -5x - 1$

$2x^2 + 5x + 1 = 0$

$a = 2, b = 5, c = 1$

$x = \dfrac{-5 \pm \sqrt{(5)^2 - 4(2)(1)}}{2(2)}$

$\quad = \dfrac{-5 \pm \sqrt{17}}{4}$

**21.** $x(x - 2) = 5$

$x^2 - 2x = 5$

$x^2 - 2x + \left(\dfrac{-2}{2}\right)^2 = 5 + 1$

$x^2 - 2x + 1 = 6$

$(x - 1)^2 = 6$

$x - 1 = \pm\sqrt{6}$

$x = 1 \pm \sqrt{6}$

**22.** $x^2 - 31 = 0$

$x^2 = 31$

$x = \pm\sqrt{31}$

**23.** $5x^2 - 55 = 0$

$5x^2 = 55$

$x^2 = 11$

$x = \pm\sqrt{11}$

**24.** $5x^2 + 55 = 0$

$$5x^2 = -55$$
$$x^2 = -11$$
$$x = \pm\sqrt{-11}$$
$$x = \pm i\sqrt{11}$$

**25.** $\phantom{x}$ $x(x+5) = 66$

$$x^2 + 5x = 66$$
$$x^2 + 5x - 66 = 0$$
$$(x+11)(x-6) = 0$$
$$x + 11 = 0 \quad \text{or} \quad x - 6 = 0$$
$$x = -11 \text{ or} \quad x = 6$$

**26.** $5x^2 + 6x - 2 = 0$

$a = 5, b = 6, c = -2$

$$x = \frac{-6 \pm \sqrt{(6)^2 - 4(5)(-2)}}{2(5)}$$
$$= \frac{-6 \pm \sqrt{76}}{10}$$
$$= \frac{-6 \pm \sqrt{4 \cdot 19}}{10}$$
$$= \frac{-6 \pm 2\sqrt{19}}{10}$$
$$= \frac{-3 \pm \sqrt{19}}{5}$$

**27.** $\phantom{x}$ $2x^2 + 3x = 1$

$$2x^2 + 3x - 1 = 0$$
$a = 2, b = 3, c = -1$

$$x = \frac{-3 \pm \sqrt{(3)^2 - 4(2)(-1)}}{2(2)}$$
$$= \frac{-3 \pm \sqrt{17}}{4}$$

**28.** $a^2 + b^2 = c^2$

$$x^2 + x^2 = 20^2$$
$$2x^2 = 400$$
$$x^2 = 200$$
$$x = \pm\sqrt{200}$$
$$= \pm 10\sqrt{2} \approx 14.1421$$

Disregard the negative. A side of the room is $10\sqrt{2}$ feet $\approx 14.1$ feet.

**29.** Let $x$ = time for Jack alone. Then
$x - 2$ = time for Lucy alone.

$$\frac{1}{x} + \frac{1}{x-2} = \frac{1}{4}$$
$$4(x-2) + 4x = x(x-2)$$
$$4x - 8 + 4x = x^2 - 2x$$
$$0 = x^2 - 10x + 8$$

$$x = \frac{10 \pm \sqrt{(-10)^2 - 4(1)(8)}}{2(1)}$$
$$= \frac{10 \pm \sqrt{68}}{2}$$
$$\approx 9.1 \text{ or } 0.9 \text{ (disregard)}$$
$$x - 2 = 9.1 - 2 = 7.1$$

It would take Jack 9.1 hours and Lucy 7.1 hours.

**30.** Let $x$ = initial speed on treadmill. Then
$x + 1$ = speed increased.

$$t_{initial} + t_{increased} = \frac{4}{3}$$
$$\frac{5}{x} + \frac{2}{x+1} = \frac{4}{3}$$
$$5 \cdot 3(x+1) + 2 \cdot 3x = 4x(x+1)$$
$$15x + 15 + 6x = 4x^2 + 4x$$
$$0 = 4x^2 - 17x - 15$$
$$0 = (4x+3)(x-5)$$

$$x = -\frac{4}{3} \text{ (disregard) or } x = 5$$
$$x + 1 = 5 + 1 = 6$$

Initial speed: 5 mph
Increased speed: 6 mph

## Section 8.4

### Practice Exercises

**1.** $(x-4)(x+3) > 0$

Solve the related equation, $(x-4)(x+3) = 0$.

$$(x-4)(x+3) = 0$$
$$x - 4 = 0 \quad \text{or} \quad x + 3 = 0$$
$$x = 4 \qquad\qquad x = -3$$

Test points in the three regions separated by $x = 4$ and $x = -3$.

| Region | Test Point | $(x-4)(x+3) > 0$ Result |
|---|---|---|
| $A$: $(-\infty, -3)$ | $-4$ | $(-8)(-1) > 0$ True |
| $B$: $(-3, 4)$ | $0$ | $(-4)(3) > 0$ False |
| $C$: $(4, \infty)$ | $5$ | $(1)(8) > 0$ True |

The points in regions $A$ and $C$ satisfy the inequality. The numbers 4 and $-3$ are not included in the solution since the inequality symbol is >. The solution set is $(-\infty, -3) \cup (4, \infty)$.

2.  $x^2 - 8x \le 0$

Solve the related equation, $x^2 - 8x = 0$.

$x^2 - 8x = 0$
$x(x-8) = 0$
$x = 0 \quad$ or $\quad x - 8 = 0$
$\qquad\qquad\qquad x = 8$

The numbers 0 and 8 separate the number line into three regions, $A$, $B$, and $C$. Test a point in each region.

| Region | Test Point | $x^2 - 8x \le 0$ Result |
|---|---|---|
| $A$: $(-\infty, 0]$ | $-1$ | $1 + 8 \le 0$ False |
| $B$: $[0, 8]$ | $1$ | $1 - 8 \le 0$ True |
| $C$: $[8, \infty)$ | $9$ | $81 - 72 \le 0$ False |

Values in region $B$ satisfy the inequality. The numbers 0 and 8 are included in the solution since the inequality symbol is $\le$. The solution set is $[0, 8]$.

3.  $(x+3)(x-2)(x+1) \le 0$

Solve $(x+3)(x-2)(x+1) = 0$ by inspection.
$x = -3 \quad$ or $\quad x = 2 \quad$ or $\quad x = -1$
These separate the number line into four regions. Test points in each region.

| Region | Test Point | $(x+3)(x-2)(x+1) \le 0$ Result |
|---|---|---|
| $A$: $(-\infty, -3]$ | $-4$ | $(-1)(-6)(-3) \le 0$ True |
| $B$: $[-3, -1]$ | $-2$ | $(1)(-4)(-1) \le 0$ False |
| $C$: $[-1, 2]$ | $0$ | $(3)(-2)(1) \le 0$ True |
| $D$: $[2, \infty)$ | $3$ | $(6)(1)(4) \le 0$ False |

The solution set is $(-\infty, -3] \cup [-1, 2]$. We include the numbers $-3$, $-1$, and 2 because the inequality symbol is $\le$.

4.  $\dfrac{x-5}{x+4} \le 0$

$x + 4 = 0$
$\quad x = -4$

$x = -4$ makes the denominator zero. Solve the related equation $\dfrac{x-5}{x+4} = 0$.

$\dfrac{x-5}{x+4} = 0$
$x - 5 = 0$
$\quad x = 5$

Test points in the three regions separated by $x = -4$ and $x = 5$.

| Region | Test Point | $\dfrac{x-5}{x+4} \le 0$ Result |
|---|---|---|
| $A$: $(-\infty, -4)$ | $-5$ | $\dfrac{-10}{-1} \le 0$ False |
| $B$: $(-4, 5]$ | $0$ | $\dfrac{-5}{4} \le 0$ True |
| $C$: $[5, \infty)$ | $6$ | $\dfrac{1}{10} \le 0$ False |

The solution set is $(-4, 5]$. The interval includes 5 because 5 satisfies the original inequality. This interval does not include $-4$, because $-4$ would make the denominator zero.

**5.** $\dfrac{7}{x+3} < 5$

$x+3=0$

$x=-3$

$x=-3$ makes the denominator zero.

Solve $\dfrac{7}{x+3}=5$.

$(x+3)\left(\dfrac{7}{x+3}\right)=5(x+3)$

$7=5x+15$

$-8=5x$

$-\dfrac{8}{5}=x$

We use these two solutions to divide the number line into three regions and choose test points.

| Region | Test Point | $\dfrac{7}{x+3}<5$ Result |
|---|---|---|
| $A$: $(-\infty,-3)$ | $-4$ | $\dfrac{7}{-1}<5$ True |
| $B$: $\left(-3,-\dfrac{8}{5}\right)$ | $-2$ | $\dfrac{7}{1}<5$ False |
| $C$: $\left(-\dfrac{8}{5},\infty\right)$ | $0$ | $\dfrac{7}{3}<5$ True |

The solution set is $(-\infty,-3)\cup\left(-\dfrac{8}{5},\infty\right)$.

**Vocabulary and Readiness Check**

**1.** $[-7,3)$

**2.** $(-1,5]$

**3.** $(-\infty,0]$

**4.** $(-\infty,-8]$

**5.** $(-\infty,-12)\cup[-10,\infty)$

**6.** $(-\infty,-3]\cup(4,\infty)$

**Exercise Set 8.4**

**1.** $(x+1)(x+5)>0$

$x+1=0$ or $x+5=0$

$x=-1$ or $x=-5$

| Region | Test Point | $(x+1)(x+5)>0$ Result |
|---|---|---|
| $A$: $(-\infty,-5)$ | $-6$ | $(-5)(-1)>0$ True |
| $B$: $(-5,-1)$ | $-2$ | $(-1)(3)>0$ False |
| $C$: $(-1,\infty)$ | $0$ | $(1)(5)>0$ True |

Solution: $(-\infty,-5)\cup(-1,\infty)$

**3.** $(x-3)(x+4)\le 0$

$x-3=0$ or $x+4=0$

$x=3$ or $x=-4$

| Region | Test Point | $(x-3)(x+4)\le 0$ Result |
|---|---|---|
| $A$: $(-\infty,-4]$ | $-5$ | $(-8)(-1)\le 0$ False |
| $B$: $[-4,3]$ | $0$ | $(-3)(4)\le 0$ True |
| $C$: $[3,\infty)$ | $4$ | $(1)(8)\le 0$ False |

Solution: $[-4,3]$

**5.** $x^2-7x+10\le 0$

$(x-5)(x-2)\le 0$

$x-5=0$ or $x-2=0$

$x=5$ or $x=2$

| Region | Test Point | $(x-5)(x-2)\le 0$ Result |
|---|---|---|
| $A$: $(-\infty,2]$ | $0$ | $(-5)(-2)\le 0$ False |
| $B$: $[2,5]$ | $3$ | $(-2)(1)\le 0$ True |
| $C$: $[5,\infty)$ | $6$ | $(1)(4)\le 0$ False |

Solution: $[2,5]$

**7.**     $3x^2 + 16 < -5$

$3x^2 + 16x + 5 < 0$

$(3x + 1)(x + 5) < 0$

$3x + 1 = 0 \quad$ or $\quad x + 5 = 0$

$x = -\dfrac{1}{3} \quad$ or $\qquad x = -5$

| Region | Test Point | $(3x + 1)(x + 5) < 0$ Result |
|---|---|---|
| $A: (-\infty, -5)$ | $-6$ | $(-17)(-1) < 0$ False |
| $B: \left(-5, -\dfrac{1}{3}\right)$ | $-1$ | $(-2)(4) < 0$ True |
| $C: \left(-\dfrac{1}{3}, \infty\right)$ | $0$ | $(1)(5) < 0$ False |

Solution: $\left(-5, -\dfrac{1}{3}\right)$

**9.** $(x - 6)(x - 4)(x - 2) > 0$

$x - 6 = 0 \quad$ or $\quad x - 4 = 0 \quad$ or $\quad x - 2 = 0$

$x = 6 \quad$ or $\qquad x - 4 \quad$ or $\qquad x = 2$

| Region | Test Point | $(x - 6)(x - 4)(x - 2) > 0$ Result |
|---|---|---|
| $A: (-\infty, 2)$ | $0$ | $(-6)(-4)(-2) > 0$ False |
| $B: (2, 4)$ | $3$ | $(-3)(-1)(1) > 0$ True |
| $C: (4, 6)$ | $5$ | $(-1)(1)(3) > 0$ False |
| $D: (6, \infty)$ | $7$ | $(1)(3)(5) > 0$ True |

Solution: $(2, 4) \cup (6, \infty)$

**11.** $x(x-1)(x+4) \le 0$

$x = 0$ or $x - 1 = 0$ or $x + 4 = 0$

$x = 1$ or $x = -4$

| Region | Test Point | $x(x-1)(x+4) \le 0$ Result |
|--------|-----------|-------------------------|
| A: $(-\infty, -4]$ | $-5$ | $-5(-6)(-1) \le 0$ True |
| B. $[-4, 0]$ | $-1$ | $-1(-2)(3) \le 0$ False |
| C: $[0, 1]$ | $\dfrac{1}{2}$ | $\dfrac{1}{2}\left(-\dfrac{1}{2}\right)\left(\dfrac{9}{2}\right) \le 0$ True |
| D: $[1, \infty)$ | $2$ | $2(1)(6) \le 0$ False |

Solution: $(-\infty, -4] \cup [0, 1]$

**13.**

$$(x^2 - 9)(x^2 - 4) > 0$$

$$(x+3)(x-3)(x+2)(x-2) > 0$$

$x + 3 = 0$ or $x - 3 = 0$ or $x + 2 = 0$ or $x - 2 = 0$

$x = -3$ or $x = 3$ or $x = -2$ or $x = 2$

| Region | Test Point | $(x+3)(x-3)(x+2)(x-2) > 0$ Result |
|--------|-----------|--------------------------------|
| A: $(-\infty, -3)$ | $-4$ | $(-1)(-7)(-2)(-6) > 0$ True |
| B: $(-3, -2)$ | $-\dfrac{5}{2}$ | $\left(\dfrac{1}{2}\right)\left(-\dfrac{11}{2}\right)\left(-\dfrac{1}{2}\right)\left(-\dfrac{9}{2}\right) > 0$ False |
| C: $(-2, 2)$ | $0$ | $(3)(-3)(2)(-2) > 0$ True |
| D: $(2, 3)$ | $\dfrac{5}{2}$ | $\left(\dfrac{11}{2}\right)\left(-\dfrac{1}{2}\right)\left(\dfrac{9}{2}\right)\left(\dfrac{1}{2}\right) > 0$ False |
| E: $(3, \infty)$ | $4$ | $(7)(1)(6)(2) > 0$ True |

Solution: $(-\infty, -3) \cup (-2, 2) \cup (3, \infty)$

**15.** $\dfrac{x+7}{x-2} < 0$

$x + 7 = 0 \quad$ or $\quad x - 2 = 0$

$x = -7 \quad$ or $\quad x = 2$

| Region | Test Point | $\dfrac{x+7}{x-2} < 0$ False |
|---|---|---|
| $A: (-\infty, -7)$ | $-8$ | $\dfrac{-1}{-10} < 0$ False |
| $B: (-7, 2)$ | $0$ | $\dfrac{7}{-2} < 0$ True |
| $C: (2, \infty)$ | $3$ | $\dfrac{10}{1} < 0$ False |

Solution: $(-7, 2)$

**17.** $\dfrac{5}{x+1} > 0$

$x + 1 = 0$

$x = -1$

| Region | Test Point | $\dfrac{5}{x+1} > 0$ Result |
|---|---|---|
| $A: (-\infty, -1)$ | $-2$ | $\dfrac{5}{-1} > 0$ False |
| $B: (-1, \infty)$ | $0$ | $\dfrac{5}{1} > 0$ True |

Solution: $(-1, \infty)$

**19.** $\dfrac{x+1}{x-4} \geq 0$

$x + 1 = 0 \quad$ or $\quad x - 4 = 0$

$x = -1 \quad$ or $\quad x = 4$

| Region | Test Point | $\dfrac{x+1}{x-4} \geq 0$ Result |
|---|---|---|
| $A: (-\infty, -1]$ | $-2$ | $\dfrac{-1}{-6} \geq 0$ True |
| $B: [-1, 4)$ | $0$ | $\dfrac{1}{-4} \geq 0$ False |
| $C: (4, \infty)$ | $5$ | $\dfrac{6}{1} \geq 0$ True |

Solution: $(-\infty, -1] \cup (4, \infty)$

**21.** $\dfrac{3}{x-2} < 4$

The denominator is equal to 0 when $x - 2 = 0$, or $x = 2$.

$\dfrac{3}{x-2} = 4$

$3 = 4x - 8$

$11 = 4x$

$\dfrac{11}{4} = x$

| Region | Test Point | $\dfrac{3}{x-2} < 4$ Result |
|---|---|---|
| $A: (-\infty, 2)$ | $0$ | $\dfrac{3}{-2} < 4$ True |
| $B: \left(2, \dfrac{11}{4}\right)$ | $\dfrac{5}{2}$ | $\dfrac{3}{\frac{1}{2}} = 6 < 4$ False |
| $C: \left(\dfrac{11}{4}, \infty\right)$ | $4$ | $\dfrac{3}{2} < 4$ True |

Solution: $(-\infty, 2) \cup \left(\dfrac{11}{4}, \infty\right)$

**23.** $\dfrac{x^2+6}{5x} \geq 1$

The denominator is equal to 0 when $5x = 0$, or $x = 0$.

$$\dfrac{x^2+6}{5x} = 1$$
$$x^2 + 6 = 5x$$
$$x^2 - 5x + 6 = 0$$
$$(x-2)(x-3) = 0$$
$$x - 2 = 0 \quad \text{or} \quad x - 3 = 0$$
$$x = 2 \quad \text{or} \quad x = 3$$

| Region | Test Point | $\dfrac{x^2+6}{5x} \geq 1$ Result |
|---|---|---|
| $A$: $(-\infty, 0)$ | $-1$ | $\dfrac{7}{-5} \geq 1$ False |
| $B$: $(0, 2]$ | $1$ | $\dfrac{7}{5} \geq 1$ True |
| $C$: $[2, 3]$ | $\dfrac{5}{2}$ | $\dfrac{\frac{49}{4}}{\frac{25}{2}} = \dfrac{49}{50} \geq 1$ False |
| $D$: $[3, \infty)$ | $4$ | $\dfrac{22}{20} \geq 1$ True |

Solution: $(0, 2] \cup [3, \infty)$

**25.** $(x-8)(x+7) > 0$
$$x - 8 = 0 \quad \text{or} \quad x + 7 = 0$$
$$x = 8 \quad \text{or} \quad x = -7$$

| Region | Test Point | $(x-8)(x+7) > 0$ Result |
|---|---|---|
| $A$: $(-\infty, -7)$ | $-8$ | $(-16)(-1) > 0$ True |
| $B$: $(-7, 8)$ | $0$ | $(-8)(7) > 0$ False |
| $C$: $(8, \infty)$ | $9$ | $(1)(16) > 0$ True |

Solution: $(-\infty, -7) \cup (8, \infty)$

**27.** $(2x-3)(4x+5) \leq 0$
$$2x - 3 = 0 \quad \text{or} \quad 4x + 5 = 0$$
$$x = \dfrac{3}{2} \quad \text{or} \quad x = -\dfrac{5}{4}$$

| Region | Test Point | $(2x-3)(4x+5) \leq 0$ Result |
|---|---|---|
| $A$: $\left(-\infty, -\dfrac{5}{4}\right]$ | $-2$ | $(-7)(-3) \leq 0$ False |
| $B$: $\left[-\dfrac{5}{4}, \dfrac{3}{2}\right]$ | $0$ | $(-3)(5) \leq 0$ True |
| $C$: $\left[\dfrac{3}{2}, \infty\right)$ | $2$ | $(1)(13) \leq 0$ False |

Solution: $\left[-\dfrac{5}{4}, \dfrac{3}{2}\right]$

**29.** $\quad x^2 > x$
$$x^2 - x > 0$$
$$x(x-1) > 0$$
$$x = 0 \quad \text{or} \quad x - 1 = 0$$
$$x = 1$$

| Region | Test Point | $x(x-1) > 0$ Result |
|---|---|---|
| $A$: $(-\infty, 0)$ | $-1$ | $-1(-2) > 0$ True |
| $B$: $(0, 1)$ | $\dfrac{1}{2}$ | $\dfrac{1}{2}\left(-\dfrac{1}{2}\right) > 0$ False |
| $C$: $(1, \infty)$ | $2$ | $2(1) > 0$ True |

Solution: $(-\infty, 0) \cup (1, \infty)$

**31.** $(2x - 8)(x + 4)(x - 6) \leq 0$

$2x - 8 = 0$   or   $x + 4 = 0$   or   $x - 6 = 0$

    $x = 4$   or      $x = -4$   or      $x = 6$

| Region | Test Point | $(2x - 8)(x + 4)(x - 6) \leq 0$ Result |
|---|---|---|
| $A$: $(-\infty, -4]$ | $-5$ | $(-18)(-1)(-11) \leq 0$ True |
| $B$: $[-4, 4]$ | $0$ | $(-8)(4)(-6) \leq 0$ False |
| $C$: $[4, 6]$ | $5$ | $(2)(9)(-1) \leq 0$ True |
| $D$: $[6, \infty)$ | $7$ | $(6)(11)(1) \leq 0$ False |

Solution: $(-\infty, -4] \cup [4, 6]$

**33.**        $6x^2 - 5x \geq 6$

     $6x^2 - 5x - 6 \geq 0$

  $(3x + 2)(2x - 3) \geq 0$

  $3x + 2 = 0$    or    $2x - 3 = 0$

     $x = -\dfrac{2}{3}$   or      $x = \dfrac{3}{2}$

| Region | Test Point | $(3x + 2)(2x - 3) \geq 0$ Result |
|---|---|---|
| $A$: $\left(-\infty, -\dfrac{2}{3}\right]$ | $-1$ | $(-1)(-5) \geq 0$ True |
| $B$: $\left[-\dfrac{2}{3}, \dfrac{3}{2}\right]$ | $0$ | $(2)(-3) \geq 0$ False |
| $C$: $\left[\dfrac{3}{2}, \infty\right)$ | $2$ | $(8)(1) \geq 0$ True |

Solution: $\left(-\infty, -\dfrac{2}{3}\right] \cup \left[\dfrac{3}{2}, \infty\right)$

**35.**    $4x^3 + 16x^2 - 9x - 36 > 0$

     $4x^2(x + 4) - 9(x + 4) > 0$

         $(x + 4)(4x^2 - 9) > 0$

  $(x + 4)(2x + 3)(2x - 3) > 0$

  $x + 4 = 0$    or    $2x + 3 = 0$    or    $2x - 3 = 0$

     $x = -4$   or      $x = -\dfrac{3}{2}$   or      $x = \dfrac{3}{2}$

| Region | Test Point | $(x+4)(2x+3)(2x-3) > 0$ |
|--------|------------|-------------------------|
| $A$: $(-\infty, -4)$ | $-5$ | $(-1)(-7)(-13) > 0$<br>False |
| $B$: $\left(-4, -\dfrac{3}{2}\right)$ | $-3$ | $(1)(-3)(-9) > 0$<br>True |
| $C$: $\left(-\dfrac{3}{2}, \dfrac{3}{2}\right)$ | $0$ | $(4)(3)(-3) > 0$<br>False |
| $D$: $\left(\dfrac{3}{2}, \infty\right)$ | $4$ | $(8)(11)(5) > 0$<br>True |

Solution: $\left(-4, -\dfrac{3}{2}\right) \cup \left(\dfrac{3}{2}, \infty\right)$

**37.**
$$x^4 - 26x^2 + 25 \geq 0$$
$$(x^2 - 25)(x^2 - 1) \geq 0$$
$$(x+5)(x-5)(x+1)(x-1) \geq 0$$
$$x = -5 \quad \text{or} \quad x = 5 \quad \text{or} \quad x = -1 \quad \text{or} \quad x = 1$$

| Region | Test Point | $(x+5)(x-5)(x+1)(x-1) \geq 0$<br>Result |
|--------|------------|------------------------------------------|
| $A$: $(-\infty, -5]$ | $-6$ | $(-1)(-11)(-5)(-7) \geq 0$<br>True |
| $B$: $[-5, -1]$ | $-2$ | $(3)(-7)(-1)(-3) \geq 0$<br>False |
| $C$: $[-1, 1]$ | $0$ | $(5)(-5)(1)(-1) \geq 0$<br>True |
| $D$: $[1, 5]$ | $2$ | $(7)(-3)(3)(1) \geq 0$<br>False |
| $E$: $[5, \infty)$ | $6$ | $(11)(1)(7)(5) \geq 0$<br>True |

Solution: $(-\infty, -5] \cup [-1, 1] \cup [5, \infty)$

**39.** $(2x-7)(3x+5) > 0$

$2x - 7 = 0$  or  $3x + 5 = 0$

$x = \dfrac{7}{2}$  or  $x = -\dfrac{5}{3}$

| Region | Test Point | $(2x-7)(3x+5) > 0$ |
|---|---|---|
| $A: \left(-\infty, -\dfrac{5}{3}\right)$ | $-2$ | $(-11)(-1) > 0$<br>True |
| $B: \left(-\dfrac{5}{3}, \dfrac{7}{2}\right)$ | $0$ | $(-7)(5) > 0$<br>False |
| $C: \left(\dfrac{7}{2}, \infty\right)$ | $4$ | $(1)(17) > 0$<br>True |

Solution: $\left(-\infty, -\dfrac{5}{3}\right) \cup \left(\dfrac{7}{2}, \infty\right)$

**41.** $\dfrac{x}{x-10} < 0$

$x = 0$  or  $x - 10 = 0$

$x = 10$

| Region | Test Point | $\dfrac{x}{x-10} < 0$<br>Result |
|---|---|---|
| $A: (-\infty, 0)$ | $-1$ | $\dfrac{-1}{-11} < 0$<br>False |
| $B: (0, 10)$ | $5$ | $\dfrac{5}{-5} < 0$<br>True |
| $C: (10, \infty)$ | $11$ | $\dfrac{11}{1} < 0$<br>False |

Solution: $(0, 10)$

**43.** $\dfrac{x-5}{x+4} \geq 0$

$x - 5 = 0$  or  $x + 4 = 0$

$x = 5$  or  $x = -4$

| Region | Test Point | $\dfrac{x-5}{x+4} \geq 0$ Result |
|---|---|---|
| $A$: $(-\infty, -4)$ | $-5$ | $\dfrac{-10}{-1} \geq 0$ True |
| $B$: $(-4, 5]$ | $0$ | $\dfrac{-5}{4} \geq 0$ False |
| $C$: $[5, \infty)$ | $6$ | $\dfrac{1}{10} \geq 0$ True |

Solution: $(-\infty, -4) \cup [5, \infty)$

**45.** $\dfrac{x(x+6)}{(x-7)(x+1)} \geq 0$

$x = 0$ or $x + 6 = 0$ or $x - 7 = 0$ or $x + 1 = 0$
$\qquad\qquad x = -6$ or $\qquad x = 7$ or $\qquad x = -1$

| Region | Test Point | $\dfrac{x(x+6)}{(x-7)(x+1)} \geq 0$ Result |
|---|---|---|
| $A$: $(-\infty, -6]$ | $-7$ | $\dfrac{-7(-1)}{(-14)(-6)} \geq 0$ True |
| $B$: $[-6, -1)$ | $-3$ | $\dfrac{-3(3)}{(-10)(-2)} \geq 0$ False |
| $C$: $(-1, 0]$ | $-\dfrac{1}{2}$ | $\dfrac{-\frac{1}{2}\left(\frac{11}{2}\right)}{\left(-\frac{15}{2}\right)\left(\frac{1}{2}\right)} \geq 0$ True |
| $D$: $[0, 7)$ | $2$ | $\dfrac{2(8)}{(-5)(3)} \geq 0$ False |
| $E$: $(7, \infty)$ | $8$ | $\dfrac{8(14)}{(1)(9)} \geq 0$ True |

Solution: $(-\infty, -6] \cup (-1, 0] \cup (7, \infty)$

**47.** $\dfrac{-1}{x-1} > -1$

The denominator is equal to 0 when $x - 1 = 0$, or $x = 1$.

$$\dfrac{-1}{x-1} = -1$$
$$-1 = -1(x-1)$$
$$-1 = -x+1$$
$$x = 2$$

| Region | Test Point | $\dfrac{-1}{x-1} > -1$ Result |
|---|---|---|
| $A$: $(-\infty, 1)$ | 0 | $\dfrac{-1}{-1} > -1$ True |
| $B$: $(1, 2)$ | $\dfrac{3}{2}$ | $\dfrac{-1}{\frac{1}{2}} = -2 > -1$ False |
| $C$: $(2, \infty)$ | 3 | $\dfrac{-1}{2} > -1$ True |

Solution: $(-\infty, 1) \cup (2, \infty)$

**49.** $\dfrac{x}{x+4} \le 2$

The denominator is equal to 0 when $x + 4 = 0$, or $x = -4$.

$$\dfrac{x}{x+4} = 2$$
$$x = 2x+8$$
$$-x = 8$$
$$x = -8$$

| Region | Test Point | $\dfrac{x}{x+4} \le 2$ Result |
|---|---|---|
| $A$: $(-\infty, -8]$ | $-9$ | $\dfrac{-9}{-5} \le 2$ True |
| $B$: $[-8, -4)$ | $-6$ | $\dfrac{-6}{-2} \le 2$ False |
| $C$: $(-4, \infty)$ | 0 | $\dfrac{0}{4} \le 2$ True |

Solution: $(-\infty, -8] \cup (-4, \infty)$

**51.** $\dfrac{z}{z-5} \ge 2z$

The denominator is equal to 0 when $z - 5 = 0$, or $z = 5$.

$$\dfrac{z}{z-5} = 2z$$
$$z = 2z(z-5)$$
$$z = 2z^2 - 10z$$
$$0 = 2z^2 - 11z$$
$$0 = z(2z - 11)$$
$$z = 0 \quad \text{or} \quad 2z - 11 = 0$$
$$z = \dfrac{11}{2}$$

| Region | Test Point | $\dfrac{z}{z-5} \ge 2z$ Result |
|---|---|---|
| $A$: $(-\infty, 0]$ | $-1$ | $\dfrac{-1}{-6} \ge -2$ True |
| $B$: $[0, 5)$ | $1$ | $\dfrac{1}{-4} \ge 2$ False |
| $C$: $\left(5, \dfrac{11}{2}\right]$ | $\dfrac{21}{4}$ | $\dfrac{\left(\frac{21}{4}\right)}{\left(\frac{1}{4}\right)} \ge \dfrac{21}{2}$ $21 \ge \dfrac{21}{2}$ True |
| $D$: $\left[\dfrac{11}{2}, \infty\right)$ | $6$ | $\dfrac{6}{1} \ge 12$ False |

Solution: $(-\infty, 0] \cup \left(5, \dfrac{11}{2}\right]$

**53.** $\dfrac{(x+1)^2}{5x} > 0$

The denominator is equal to 0 when $5x = 0$, or $x = 0$.

$$\dfrac{(x+1)^2}{5x} = 0$$
$$(x+1)^2 = 0$$
$$x + 1 = 0$$
$$x = -1$$

| Region | Test Point | $\dfrac{(x+1)^2}{5x} > 0$ Result |
|---|---|---|
| $A$: $(-\infty, -1)$ | $-2$ | $\dfrac{1}{-10} > 0$ False |
| $B$: $(-1, 0)$ | $-\dfrac{1}{2}$ | $\dfrac{\left(\frac{1}{4}\right)}{\left(-\frac{5}{2}\right)} > 0$ False |
| $C$: $(0, \infty)$ | $1$ | $\dfrac{4}{5} > 0$ True |

Solution: $(0, \infty)$

**55.** $g(x) = |x| + 2$

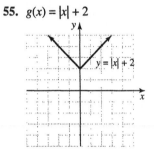

**57.** $F(x) = |x| - 1$

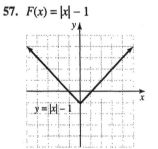

**59.** $F(x) = x^2 - 3$

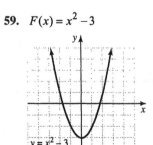

**61.** $H(x) = x^2 + 1$

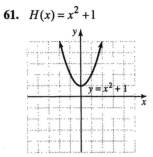

**63.** Answers may vary

**65.** Let $x$ = the number. Then

$\dfrac{1}{x}$ = the reciprocal of the number.

$$x - \dfrac{1}{x} < 0$$

$$\dfrac{x^2 - 1}{x} < 0$$

$$\dfrac{(x+1)(x-1)}{x} < 0$$

$x + 1 = 0$ or $x - 1 = 0$ or $x = 0$
$\qquad x = -1$ or $\qquad x = 1$

| Region | Test Point | $\dfrac{(x+1)(x-1)}{x} < 0$ Result |
|--------|------------|-----------|
| A: $(-\infty, -1)$ | $-2$ | $\dfrac{(-1)(-3)}{-2} < 0$ True |
| B: $(-1, 0)$ | $-\dfrac{1}{2}$ | $\dfrac{\left(\frac{1}{2}\right)\left(-\frac{3}{2}\right)}{\left(-\frac{1}{2}\right)} < 0$ False |
| C: $(0, 1)$ | $\dfrac{1}{2}$ | $\dfrac{\left(\frac{3}{2}\right)\left(-\frac{1}{2}\right)}{\left(\frac{1}{2}\right)} < 0$ True |
| D: $(1, \infty)$ | $2$ | $\dfrac{(3)(1)}{2} < 0$ False |

Any number less than $-1$ or between 0 and 1 and its reciprocal satisfy the conditions.

**67.** $P(x) = -2x^2 + 26x - 44$

$$-2x^2 + 26x - 44 > 0$$
$$-2(x^2 + 13x - 22) > 0$$
$$-2(x - 11)(x - 2) > 0$$
$x - 11 = 0$ or $x - 2 = 0$
$\qquad x = 11$ or $\qquad x = 2$

| Region | Test Point | $-2(x-11)(x-2) > 0$ Result |
|--------|------------|-----------|
| A: $(0, 2)$ | $1$ | $-2(-10)(-3) > 0$ False |
| B: $(2, 11)$ | $3$ | $-2(-8)(1) > 0$ True |
| C: $(11, \infty)$ | $12$ | $-2(1)(10) > 0$ False |

The company makes a profit when $x$ is between 2 and 11.

**69.**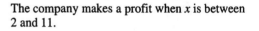

**71.**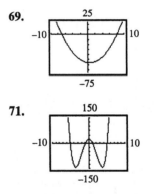

**The Bigger Picture**

**1.** $|x - 8| = |2x + 1|$

$x - 8 = 2x + 1$ or $x - 8 = -(2x + 1)$
$-9 = x$ $\qquad\qquad x - 8 = -2x - 1$
$\qquad\qquad\qquad\qquad 3x = 7$
$\qquad\qquad\qquad\qquad x = \dfrac{7}{3}$

**2.** $0 < -x + 7 < 3$
$-7 < -x < -4$
$7 > x > 4$
$4 < x < 7$
Solution: $(4, 7)$

**3.** $\sqrt{3x-11}+3=x$

$\qquad \sqrt{3x-11}=x-3$

$\qquad 3x-11=(x-3)^2$

$\qquad 3x-11=x^2-6x+9$

$\qquad 0=x^2-9x+20$

$\qquad 0=(x-4)(x-5)$

$\qquad x-4=0 \quad$ or $\quad x-5=0$

$\qquad x=4 \qquad\qquad x=5$

The solutions are 4 and 5.

**4.** $x(3x+1)=1$

$\qquad 3x^2+x-1=0$

$\qquad a=3,\ b=1,\ c=-1$

$\qquad x=\dfrac{-1\pm\sqrt{1^2-4(3)(-1)}}{2(3)}$

$\qquad =\dfrac{-1\pm\sqrt{1+12}}{6}$

$\qquad =\dfrac{-1\pm\sqrt{13}}{6}$

The solutions are $\dfrac{-1+\sqrt{13}}{6}$ and $\dfrac{-1-\sqrt{13}}{6}$.

**5.** $\dfrac{x+2}{x-7}\le 0$

$x-7=0$, so $x=7$ makes the denominator 0.

$\qquad \dfrac{x+2}{x-7}=0$

$\qquad x+2=0$

$\qquad x=-2$

| Region | Test Point | $\dfrac{x+2}{x-7}\le 0$ Result |
|---|---|---|
| $A$: $(-\infty, -2]$ | $-3$ | $\dfrac{-1}{-10}\le 0$ False |
| $B$: $[-2, 7)$ | $0$ | $\dfrac{2}{-7}\le 0$ |
| $C$: $(7, \infty)$ | $8$ | $\dfrac{10}{1}\le 0$ False |

Solution: $[-2, 7)$

**6.** $x(x-6)+4=x^2-2(3-x)$

$\qquad x^2-6x+4=x^2-6+2x$

$\qquad -6x+4=-6+2x$

$\qquad 10=8x$

$\qquad \dfrac{5}{4}=x$

The solution is $\dfrac{5}{4}$.

**7.** $x(5x-36)=-7$

$\qquad 5x^2-36x+7=0$

$\qquad a=5,\ b=-36,\ c=7$

$\qquad x=\dfrac{-(-36)\pm\sqrt{(-36)^2-4(5)(7)}}{2(5)}$

$\qquad =\dfrac{36\pm\sqrt{1156}}{10}$

$\qquad =\dfrac{36\pm 34}{10}$

$x=\dfrac{36+34}{10}=\dfrac{70}{10}=7 \quad$ or $\quad x=\dfrac{36-34}{10}=\dfrac{2}{10}=\dfrac{1}{5}$

The solutions are 7 and $\dfrac{1}{5}$.

**8.** $2x^2-4\ge 7x$

Solve $2x^2-4=7x$.

$\qquad 2x^2-7x-4=0$

$\qquad (2x+1)(x-4)=0$

$\qquad 2x+1=0 \quad$ or $\quad x-4=0$

$\qquad 2x=-1 \qquad\qquad x=4$

$\qquad x=-\dfrac{1}{2}$

| Region | Test Point | $2x^2-4\ge 7x$ Result |
|---|---|---|
| $A$: $\left(-\infty, -\dfrac{1}{2}\right]$ | $-1$ | $2-4\ge -7$ True |
| $B$: $\left[-\dfrac{1}{2}, 4\right]$ | $0$ | $-4\ge 0$ False |
| $C$: $[4, \infty)$ | $5$ | $50-4\ge 35$ True |

Solution: $\left(-\infty, -\dfrac{1}{2}\right]\cup[4, \infty)$

**9.** $\left|\dfrac{x-7}{3}\right| > 5$

$\dfrac{x-7}{3} > 5$    or    $\dfrac{x-7}{3} < -5$

$x - 7 > 15$   or   $x - 7 < -15$

$x > 22$   or     $x < -8$

Solution: $(-\infty,\ -8) \cup (22,\ \infty)$

**10.** $2(x-5) + 4 < 1 + 7(x-5) - x$

$2x - 10 + 4 < 1 + 7x - 35 - x$

$2x - 6 < 6x - 34$

$28 < 4x$

$7 < x$

Solution: $(7,\ \infty)$

## Section 8.5

### Practice Exercises

**1.** $f(x) = x^2$ and $g(x) = x^2 - 4$

Construct a table of values for $f(x)$ and $g(x)$.

| $x$ | $f(x) = x^2$ | $g(x) = x^2 - 4$ |
|---|---|---|
| $-2$ | 4 | 0 |
| $-1$ | 1 | $-3$ |
| 0 | 0 | $-4$ |
| 1 | 1 | $-3$ |
| 2 | 4 | 0 |

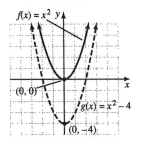

**2. a.** $f(x) = x^2 - 5$

The graph of $f(x)$ is obtained by shifting the graph of $y = x^2$ downward 5 units.

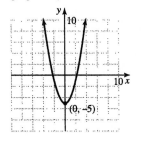

**b.** $g(x) = x^2 + 3$

The graph of $g(x)$ is obtained by shifting the graph of $y = x^2$ upward 3 units.

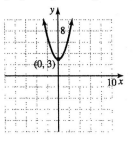

**3.** $f(x) = x^2$ and $g(x) = (x+6)^2$

Plot points. Notice that the graph of $g(x)$ is the graph of $f(x)$ shifted 6 units to the left.

| $x$ | $f(x) = x^2$ | $x$ | $g(x) = (x+6)^2$ |
|---|---|---|---|
| $-2$ | 4 | $-8$ | 4 |
| $-1$ | 1 | $-7$ | 1 |
| 0 | 0 | $-6$ | 0 |
| 1 | 1 | $-5$ | 1 |
| 2 | 4 | $-4$ | 4 |

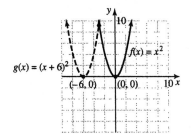

**4. a.** $G(x) = (x+4)^2$

The graph of $G(x)$ is obtained by shifting the graph of $y = x^2$ to the left 4 units.

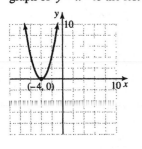

(−4, 0)

**b.** $H(x) = (x-7)^2$

The graph of $H(x)$ is obtained by shifting the graph of $y = x^2$ to the right 7 units.

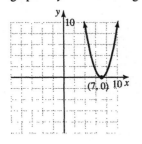

(7, 0)

**5.** $f(x) = (x+2)^2 + 2$

The graph of $f(x)$ is the graph of $y = x^2$ shifted 2 units to the left and 2 units upward. The vertex is then (−2, 2), and the axis of symmetry is $x = -2$.

| $x$ | $f(x) = (x+2)^2 + 2$ |
|-----|-----|
| −4 | 6 |
| −3 | 3 |
| −1 | 3 |
| 0 | 6 |

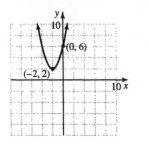

(0, 6)

(−2, 2)

**6.** $f(x) = x^2$, $g(x) = 4x^2$, and $h(x) = \frac{1}{4}x^2$

Comparing tables of values, we see that for each $x$-value, the corresponding value of $g(x)$ is four times that of $f(x)$. Similarly, the value of $h(x)$ is one quarter the value of $f(x)$.

| $x$ | $f(x) = x^2$ | $g(x) = 4x^2$ | $h(x) = \frac{1}{4}x^2$ |
|-----|-----|-----|-----|
| −2 | 4 | 16 | 1 |
| −1 | 1 | 4 | $\frac{1}{4}$ |
| 0 | 0 | 0 | 0 |
| 1 | 1 | 4 | $\frac{1}{4}$ |
| 2 | 4 | 16 | 1 |

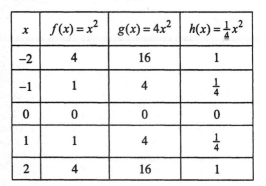

$f(x) = x^2$     $g(x) = 4x^2$

$h(x) = \frac{1}{4}x^2$

**7.** $f(x) = -\frac{1}{2}x^2$

Because $a = -\frac{1}{2}$, a negative value, this parabola opens downward. Since $\left| -\frac{1}{2} \right| = \frac{1}{2} < 1$, the parabola is wider than the graph of $y = x^2$. The vertex is (0, 0), and the axis of symmetry is the $y$-axis.

| $x$ | $f(x) = -\frac{1}{2}x^2$ |
|-----|-----|
| −2 | −2 |
| −1 | $-\frac{1}{2}$ |
| 0 | 0 |
| 1 | $-\frac{1}{2}$ |
| 2 | −2 |

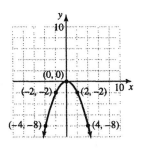

8. $h(x) = \dfrac{1}{3}(x-4)^2 - 3$

This graph is the same as $y = x^2$ shifted 4 units to the right and 3 units downward, and it is wider because $a$ is $\dfrac{1}{3}$. The vertex is $(4, -3)$, and the axis of symmetry is $x = 4$.

| $x$ | $h(x) = \frac{1}{3}(x-4)^2 - 3$ |
|---|---|
| 2 | $-\dfrac{5}{3}$ |
| 3 | $-\dfrac{8}{3}$ |
| 4 | $-3$ |
| 5 | $-\dfrac{8}{3}$ |
| 6 | $-\dfrac{5}{3}$ |

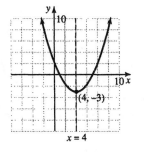

**Graphing Calculator Explorations**

1.

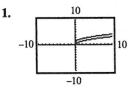

2.

3.

4.

5.

6.

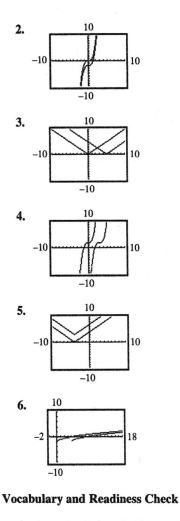

**Vocabulary and Readiness Check**

1. A <u>quadratic</u> function is one that can be written in the form $f(x) = ax^2 + bx + c,\ a \neq 0$.

2. The graph of a quadratic function is a <u>parabola</u> opening <u>upward</u> or <u>downward</u>.

3. If $a > 0$, the graph of the quadratic function opens <u>upward</u>.

4. If $a < 0$, the graph of the quadratic function opens <u>downward</u>.

5. The vertex of a parabola is the <u>lowest</u> point if $a > 0$.

6. The vertex of a parabola is the <u>highest</u> point if $a < 0$.

7. $f(x) = x^2$; vertex: $(0, 0)$

**8.** $f(x) = -5x^2$; vertex: (0, 0)

**9.** $g(x) = (x-2)^2$; vertex: (2, 0)

**10.** $g(x) = (x+5)^2$; vertex: (-5, 0)

**11.** $f(x) = 2x^2 + 3$; vertex: (0, 3)

**12.** $h(x) = x^2 - 1$; vertex: (0, -1)

**13.** $g(x) = (x+1)^2 + 5$; vertex: (-1, 5)

**14.** $h(x) = (x-10)^2 - 7$; vertex: (10, -7)

## Exercise Set 8.5

**1.** $f(x) = x^2 - 1$

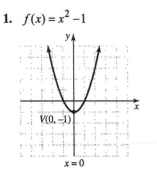

**3.** $h(x) = x^2 + 5$

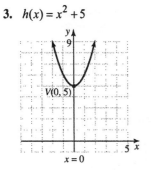

**5.** $g(x) = x^2 + 7$

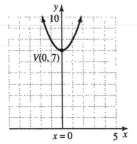

**7.** $f(x) = (x-5)^2$

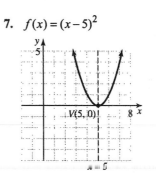

**9.** $h(x) = (x+2)^2$

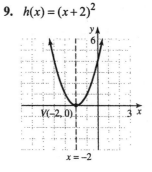

**11.** $G(x) = (x+3)^2$

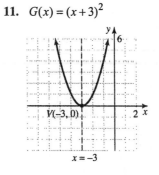

**13.** $f(x) = (x-2)^2 + 5$

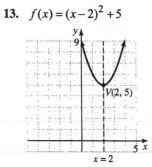

**15.** $h(x) = (x+1)^2 + 4$

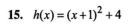

**17.** $g(x) = (x+2)^2 - 5$

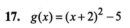

**19.** $g(x) = -x^2$

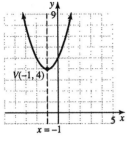

**21.** $h(x) = \frac{1}{3}x^2$

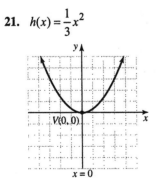

**23.** $H(x) = 2x^2$

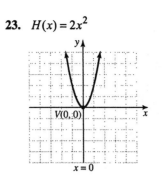

**25.** $f(x) = 2(x-1)^2 + 3$

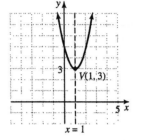

**27.** $h(x) = -3(x+3)^2 + 1$

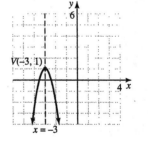

**29.** $H(x) = \frac{1}{2}(x-6)^2 - 3$

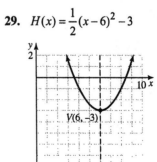

**31.** $f(x) = -(x-2)^2$

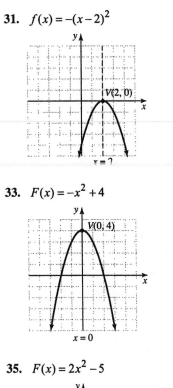

**33.** $F(x) = -x^2 + 4$

**35.** $F(x) = 2x^2 - 5$

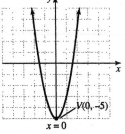

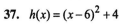

**37.** $h(x) = (x-6)^2 + 4$

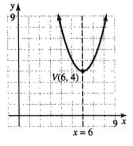

**39.** $F(x) = \left(x + \dfrac{1}{2}\right)^2 - 2$

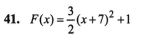

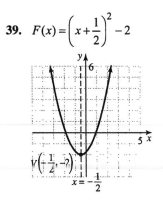

**41.** $F(x) = \dfrac{3}{2}(x+7)^2 + 1$

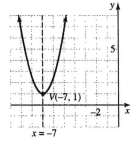

**43.** $f(x) = \dfrac{1}{4}x^2 - 9$

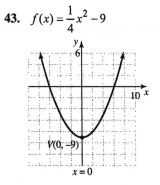

**45.** $G(x) = 5\left(x + \dfrac{1}{2}\right)^2$

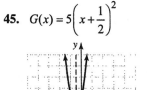

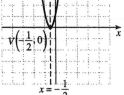

**47.** $h(x) = -(x-1)^2 - 1$

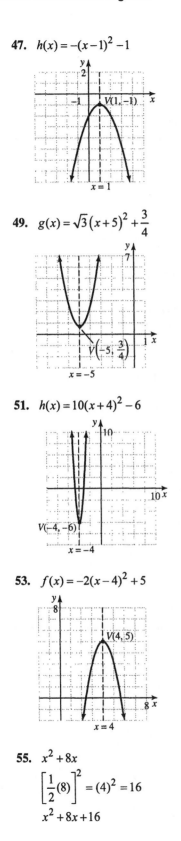

**49.** $g(x) = \sqrt{3}(x+5)^2 + \dfrac{3}{4}$

**51.** $h(x) = 10(x+4)^2 - 6$

**53.** $f(x) = -2(x-4)^2 + 5$

**55.** $x^2 + 8x$

$$\left[\frac{1}{2}(8)\right]^2 = (4)^2 = 16$$

$$x^2 + 8x + 16$$

**57.** $z^2 - 16z$

$$\left[\frac{1}{2}(-16)\right]^2 = (-8)^2 = 64$$

$$z^2 - 16z + 64$$

**59.** $y^2 + y$

$$\left[\frac{1}{2}(1)\right]^2 = \left(\frac{1}{2}\right)^2 = \frac{1}{4}$$

$$y^2 + y + \frac{1}{4}$$

**61.**
$$x^2 + 4x = 12$$
$$x^2 + 4x + \left(\frac{4}{2}\right)^2 = 12 + 4$$
$$x^2 + 4x + 4 = 16$$
$$(x+2)^2 = 16$$
$$x+2 = \pm\sqrt{16}$$
$$x+2 = \pm 4$$
$$x = -2 \pm 4$$
$$x = -6 \text{ or } 2$$

**63.**
$$z^2 + 10z - 1 = 0$$
$$z^2 + 10z = 1$$
$$z^2 + 10z + \left(\frac{10}{2}\right)^2 = 1 + 25$$
$$z^2 + 10z + 25 = 26$$
$$(z+5)^2 = 26$$
$$z+5 = \pm\sqrt{26}$$
$$z = -5 \pm \sqrt{26}$$

**65.**
$$z^2 - 8z = 2$$
$$z^2 - 8z + \left(\frac{-8}{2}\right)^2 = 2 + 16$$
$$z^2 - 8z + 16 = 18$$
$$(z-4)^2 = 18$$
$$z-4 = \pm\sqrt{18}$$
$$z-4 = \pm 3\sqrt{2}$$
$$z = 4 \pm 3\sqrt{2}$$

**67.** $f(x) = -213(x - 0.1)^2 + 3.6$
$a = -213 < 0$, so $f(x)$ opens downward.
The vertex is $(0.1, 3.6)$. The correct answer is **c**.

**69.** $f(x) = 5(x-2)^2 + 3$

**71.** $f(x) = 5[x - (-3)]^2 + 6$

$\qquad = 5(x+3)^2 + 6$

**73.** $y = f(x) + 1$

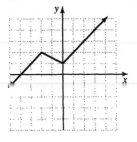

**75.** $y = f(x-3)$

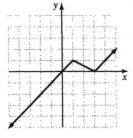

**77.** $y = f(x+2) + 2$

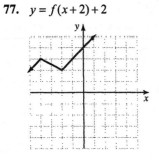

**79.** $f(x) = 668.7x^2 - 2990.7x + 938$

  **a.** $x = 2004 - 1985 = 19$

$f(19) = 668.7(19)^2 - 2990.7(19) + 938$

$\qquad = 185{,}515.4$

There were approximately 185,515 thousand subscribers.

  **b.** $x = 2007 - 1985 = 22$

$f(22) = 668.7(22)^2 - 2990.7(22) + 938$

$\qquad = 258{,}793.4$

There were approximately 258,793 thousand subscribers.

**Section 8.6**

**Practice Exercises**

**1.** $g(x) = x^2 - 2x - 3$

Write in the form $y = (x-h)^2 + k$ by completing the square.

$$y = x^2 - 2x - 3$$
$$y + 3 = x^2 - 2x$$
$$y + 3 + \left(\frac{-2}{2}\right)^2 = x^2 - 2x + \left(\frac{-2}{2}\right)^2$$
$$y + 4 = x^2 - 2x + 1$$
$$y = (x-1)^2 - 4$$

The vertex is at (1, −4).
Let $g(x) = 0$.

$$0 = x^2 - 2x - 3$$
$$0 = (x-3)(x+1)$$
$$x - 3 = 0 \quad \text{or} \quad x + 1 = 0$$
$$x = 3 \qquad\qquad x = -1$$

The $x$-intercepts are (3, 0) and (−1, 0).
Let $x = 0$.

$$g(0) = 0^2 - 2(0) - 3 = -3$$

The $y$-intercept is (0, −3).

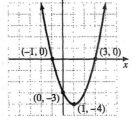

**2.** $g(x) = 4x^2 + 4x + 3$

Replace $g(x)$ with $y$ and complete the square to write the equation in the form $y = a(x-h)^2 + k$.

$$y = 4x^2 + 4x + 3$$
$$y - 3 = 4x^2 + 4x = 4(x^2 + x)$$
$$y - 3 + 4\left(\frac{1}{2}\right)^2 = 4\left[x^2 + x + \left(\frac{1}{2}\right)^2\right]$$
$$y - 3 + 1 = 4\left(x^2 + x + \frac{1}{4}\right)$$
$$y = 4\left(x + \frac{1}{2}\right)^2 + 2$$

$a = 4$, $h = -\dfrac{1}{2}$, and $k = 2$.

The parabola opens upward with vertex $\left(-\dfrac{1}{2}, 2\right)$, and has an axis of symmetry $x = -\dfrac{1}{2}$.

Let $x = 0$.

$g(0) = 4(0)^2 + 4(0) + 3 = 3$

The $y$-intercept is $(0, 3)$. There are no $x$-intercepts.

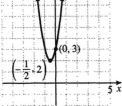

3. $g(x) = -x^2 + 5x + 6$

Write $g(x)$ in the form $a(x - h)^2 + k$ by completing the square. Replace $g(x)$ with $y$.

$y = -x^2 + 5x + 6$

$y - 6 = -x^2 + 5x$

$y - 6 = -1(x^2 - 5x)$

$y - 6 - \left(\dfrac{-5}{2}\right)^2 = -1\left[x^2 - 5x + \left(\dfrac{-5}{2}\right)^2\right]$

$y - 6 - \dfrac{25}{4} = -1\left(x^2 - 5x + \dfrac{25}{4}\right)$

$y - \dfrac{49}{4} = -\left(x - \dfrac{5}{2}\right)^2$

$y = -\left(x - \dfrac{5}{2}\right)^2 + \dfrac{49}{4}$

Since $a = -1$, the parabola opens downward with vertex $\left(\dfrac{5}{2}, \dfrac{49}{4}\right)$ and axis of symmetry $x = \dfrac{5}{2}$.

Let $x = 0$.

$y = -0^2 + 5(0) + 6 = 6$

The $y$-intercept is $(0, 6)$. Let $y = 0$.

$0 = -x^2 + 5x + 6$

$0 = x^2 - 5x - 6$

$0 = (x - 6)(x + 1)$

$x - 6 = 0$ or $x + 1 = 0$

$\quad x = 6 \qquad\qquad x = -1$

The $x$-intercepts are $(6, 0)$ and $(-1, 0)$.

4. $g(x) = x^2 - 2x - 3$

$a = 1$, $b = -2$, and $c = -3$

$\dfrac{-b}{2a} = \dfrac{-(-2)}{2(1)} = \dfrac{2}{2} = 1$

The $x$-value of the vertex is 1.

$g(1) = 1^2 - 2(1) - 3 = 1 - 2 - 3 = -4$

The vertex is $(1, -4)$.

5. $h(t) = -16t^2 + 24t$

Find the vertex of $h(t)$ to find its maximum value.

$a = -16$, $b = 24$, and $c = 0$

$\dfrac{-b}{2a} = \dfrac{-24}{2(-16)} = \dfrac{3}{4}$

The $t$-value of the vertex is $\dfrac{3}{4}$.

$h\left(\dfrac{3}{4}\right) = -16\left(\dfrac{3}{4}\right)^2 + 24\left(\dfrac{3}{4}\right)$

$\qquad = -16\left(\dfrac{9}{16}\right) + 18$

$\qquad = -9 + 18$

$\qquad = 9$

The vertex is $\left(\dfrac{3}{4}, 9\right)$. Thus, the ball reaches its maximum height of 9 feet in $\dfrac{3}{4}$ second.

**Vocabulary and Readiness Check**

1. If a quadratic function is in the form $f(x) = a(x - h)^2 + k$, the vertex of its graph is <u>$(h, k)$</u>.

2. The graph of $f(x) = ax^2 + bx + c$, $a \neq 0$ is a parabola whose vertex has $x$-value of <u>$\dfrac{-b}{2a}$</u>.

| | Parabola Opens | Vertex Location | Number of x-intercept(s) | Number of y-intercept(s) |
|---|---|---|---|---|
| 3. | up | Q I | 0 | 1 |
| 4. | up | Q III | 2 | 1 |
| 5. | down | Q II | 2 | 1 |
| 6. | down | Q IV | 0 | 1 |
| 7. | up | x-axis | 1 | 1 |
| 8. | down | x-axis | 1 | 1 |
| 9. | down | Q III | 0 | |
| 10. | down | Q I | 2 | |
| 11. | up | Q IV | 2 | |
| 12. | up | Q II | 0 | |

**Exercise Set 8.6**

1. $f(x) = x^2 + 8x + 7$

$-\dfrac{b}{2a} = \dfrac{-8}{2(1)} = -4$ and

$\begin{aligned} f(-4) &= (-4)^2 + 8(-4) + 7 \\ &= 16 - 32 + 7 \\ &= -9 \end{aligned}$

Thus, the vertex is (–4, –9).

3. $f(x) = -x^2 + 10x + 5$

$-\dfrac{b}{2a} = \dfrac{-10}{2(-1)} = 5$ and

$\begin{aligned} f(5) &= -(5)^2 + 10(5) + 5 \\ &= -25 + 50 + 5 \\ &= 30 \end{aligned}$

Thus, the vertex is (5, 30).

5. $f(x) = 5x^2 - 10x + 3$

$-\dfrac{b}{2a} = \dfrac{-(-10)}{2(5)} = 1$ and

$\begin{aligned} f(1) &= 5(1)^2 - 10(1) + 3 \\ &= 5 - 10 + 3 \\ &= -2 \end{aligned}$

Thus, the vertex is (1, –2).

**7.** $f(x) = -x^2 + x + 1$

$$-\frac{b}{2a} = \frac{-1}{2(-1)} = \frac{1}{2} \text{ and}$$

$$f\left(\frac{1}{2}\right) = -\left(\frac{1}{2}\right)^2 + \left(\frac{1}{2}\right) + 1$$
$$= -\frac{1}{4} + \frac{1}{2} + 1$$
$$= \frac{5}{4}$$

Thus, the vertex is $\left(\frac{1}{2}, \frac{5}{4}\right)$.

**9.** $f(x) = x^2 - 4x + 3$

$$-\frac{b}{2a} = \frac{-(-4)}{2(1)} = 2 \text{ and}$$

$$f(2) = (2)^2 - 4(2) + 3 = -1$$

The vertex is $(2, -1)$, so the graph is D.

**11.** $f(x) = x^2 - 2x - 3$

$$-\frac{b}{2a} = \frac{-(-2)}{2(1)} = 1 \text{ and}$$

$$f(1) = (1)^2 - 2(1) - 3 = -4$$

The vertex is $(1, -4)$, so the graph is B.

**13.** $f(x) = x^2 + 4x - 5$

$$-\frac{b}{2a} = \frac{-4}{2(1)} = -2 \text{ and}$$

$$f(-2) = (-2)^2 + 4(-2) - 5 = -9$$

Thus, the vertex is $(-2, -9)$.
The graph opens upward ($a = 1 > 0$).

$$x^2 + 4x - 5 = 0$$
$$(x+5)(x-1) = 0$$
$$x + 5 = 0 \quad \text{or} \quad x - 1 = 0$$
$$x = -5 \quad \text{or} \quad x = 1$$

$x$-intercepts: $(-5, 0)$ and $(1, 0)$.
$f(0) = -5$, so the $y$-intercept is $(0, -5)$.

**15.** $f(x) = -x^2 + 2x - 1$

$$-\frac{b}{2a} = \frac{-2}{2(-1)} = 1 \text{ and}$$

$$f(1) = -(1)^2 + 2(1) - 1 = 0$$

Thus, the vertex is $(1, 0)$.
The graph opens downward ($a = -1 < 0$).

$$-x^2 + 2x - 1 = 0$$
$$x^2 - 2x + 1 = 0$$
$$(x-1)^2 = 0$$
$$x - 1 = 0$$
$$x = 1$$

$x$-intercept: $(1, 0)$.
$f(0) = -1$, so the $y$-intercept is $(0, -1)$.

**17.** $f(x) = x^2 - 4$

$$-\frac{b}{2a} = \frac{-0}{2(1)} = 0 \text{ and}$$

$$f(0) = (0)^2 - 4 = -4$$

Thus, the vertex is $(0, -4)$.
The graph opens upward ($a = 1 > 0$).

$$x^2 - 4 = 0$$
$$(x+2)(x-2) = 0$$
$$x + 2 = 0 \quad \text{or} \quad x - 2 = 0$$
$$x = -2 \quad \text{or} \quad x = 2$$

$x$-intercepts: $(-2, 0)$ and $(2, 0)$.
$f(0) = -4$, so the $y$-intercept is $(0, -4)$.

**19.** $f(x) = 4x^2 + 4x - 3$

$-\dfrac{b}{2a} = \dfrac{-4}{2(4)} = -\dfrac{1}{2}$ and

$f\left(-\dfrac{1}{2}\right) = 4\left(-\dfrac{1}{2}\right)^2 + 4\left(-\dfrac{1}{2}\right) - 3 = -4$

Thus, the vertex is $\left(-\dfrac{1}{2}, -4\right)$.

The graph opens upward $(a = 4 > 0)$.

$4x^2 + 4x - 3 = 0$

$(2x+3)(2x-1) = 0$

$2x+3 = 0$  or  $2x-1 = 0$

$x = -\dfrac{3}{2}$  or  $x = \dfrac{1}{2}$

$x$-intercepts: $\left(-\dfrac{3}{2}, 0\right)$ and $\left(\dfrac{1}{2}, 0\right)$.

$f(0) = -3$, so the $y$-intercept is $(0, -3)$.

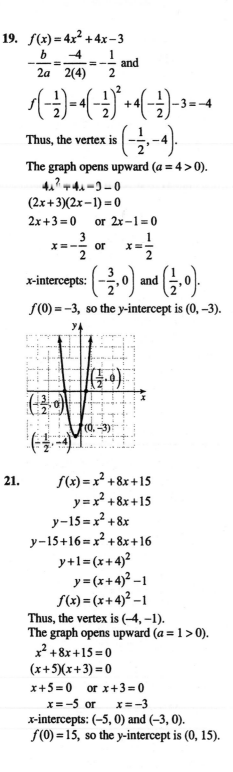

**21.**    $f(x) = x^2 + 8x + 15$

$y = x^2 + 8x + 15$

$y - 15 = x^2 + 8x$

$y - 15 + 16 = x^2 + 8x + 16$

$y + 1 = (x+4)^2$

$y = (x+4)^2 - 1$

$f(x) = (x+4)^2 - 1$

Thus, the vertex is $(-4, -1)$.

The graph opens upward $(a = 1 > 0)$.

$x^2 + 8x + 15 = 0$

$(x+5)(x+3) = 0$

$x+5 = 0$  or  $x+3 = 0$

$x = -5$  or  $x = -3$

$x$-intercepts: $(-5, 0)$ and $(-3, 0)$.

$f(0) = 15$, so the $y$-intercept is $(0, 15)$.

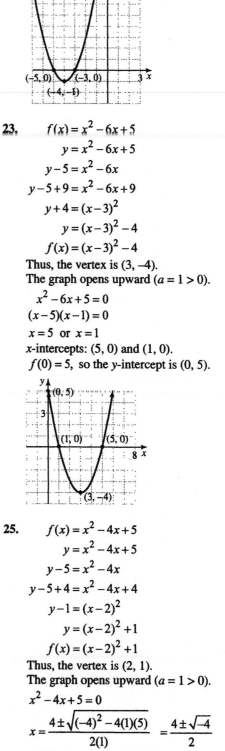

**23.**    $f(x) = x^2 - 6x + 5$

$y = x^2 - 6x + 5$

$y - 5 = x^2 - 6x$

$y - 5 + 9 = x^2 - 6x + 9$

$y + 4 = (x-3)^2$

$y = (x-3)^2 - 4$

$f(x) = (x-3)^2 - 4$

Thus, the vertex is $(3, -4)$.

The graph opens upward $(a = 1 > 0)$.

$x^2 - 6x + 5 = 0$

$(x-5)(x-1) = 0$

$x = 5$ or $x = 1$

$x$-intercepts: $(5, 0)$ and $(1, 0)$.

$f(0) = 5$, so the $y$-intercept is $(0, 5)$.

**25.**    $f(x) = x^2 - 4x + 5$

$y = x^2 - 4x + 5$

$y - 5 = x^2 - 4x$

$y - 5 + 4 = x^2 - 4x + 4$

$y - 1 = (x-2)^2$

$y = (x-2)^2 + 1$

$f(x) = (x-2)^2 + 1$

Thus, the vertex is $(2, 1)$.

The graph opens upward $(a = 1 > 0)$.

$x^2 - 4x + 5 = 0$

$x = \dfrac{4 \pm \sqrt{(-4)^2 - 4(1)(5)}}{2(1)} = \dfrac{4 \pm \sqrt{-4}}{2}$

which give non-real solutions.

Hence, there are no $x$-intercepts.

$f(0) = 5$, so the $y$-intercept is $(0, 5)$.

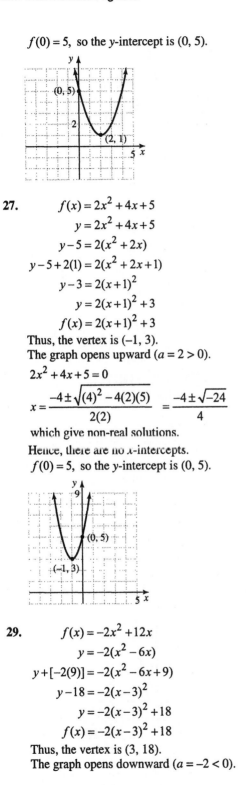

**27.**
$$f(x) = 2x^2 + 4x + 5$$
$$y = 2x^2 + 4x + 5$$
$$y - 5 = 2(x^2 + 2x)$$
$$y - 5 + 2(1) = 2(x^2 + 2x + 1)$$
$$y - 3 = 2(x + 1)^2$$
$$y = 2(x + 1)^2 + 3$$
$$f(x) = 2(x + 1)^2 + 3$$

Thus, the vertex is $(-1, 3)$.
The graph opens upward ($a = 2 > 0$).
$$2x^2 + 4x + 5 = 0$$
$$x = \frac{-4 \pm \sqrt{(4)^2 - 4(2)(5)}}{2(2)} = \frac{-4 \pm \sqrt{-24}}{4}$$
which give non-real solutions.
Hence, there are no $x$-intercepts.
$f(0) = 5$, so the $y$-intercept is $(0, 5)$.

**29.**
$$f(x) = -2x^2 + 12x$$
$$y = -2(x^2 - 6x)$$
$$y + [-2(9)] = -2(x^2 - 6x + 9)$$
$$y - 18 = -2(x - 3)^2$$
$$y = -2(x - 3)^2 + 18$$
$$f(x) = -2(x - 3)^2 + 18$$

Thus, the vertex is $(3, 18)$.
The graph opens downward ($a = -2 < 0$).

$$-2x^2 + 12x = 0$$
$$-2x(x - 6) = 0$$
$$x = 0 \text{ or } x - 6 = 0$$
$$x = 6$$
$x$-intercepts: $(0, 0)$ and $(6, 0)$
$f(0) = 0$, so the $y$-intercept is $(0, 0)$.

**31.** $f(x) = x^2 + 1$
$$x = -\frac{b}{2a} = -\frac{0}{2(1)} = 0$$
$$f(0) = (0)^2 + 1 = 1$$
Thus, the vertex is $(0, 1)$.
The graph opens upward ($a = 1 > 0$).
$$x^2 + 1 = 0$$
$$x^2 = -1$$
which give non-real solutions.
Hence, there are no $x$-intercepts.
$f(0) = 1$, so the $y$-intercept is $(0, 1)$.

**33.**
$$f(x) = x^2 - 2x - 15$$
$$y = x^2 - 2x - 15$$
$$y + 15 = x^2 - 2x$$
$$y + 15 + 1 = x^2 - 2x + 1$$
$$y + 16 = (x - 1)^2$$
$$y = (x - 1)^2 - 16$$
$$f(x) = (x - 1)^2 - 16$$

Thus, the vertex is $(1, -16)$.
The graph opens upward ($a = 1 > 0$).

$x^2 - 2x - 15 = 0$

$(x - 5)(x + 3) = 0$

$x = 5$  or  $x = -3$

$x$-intercepts: $(-3, 0)$ and $(5, 0)$.

$f(0) = -15$  so the $y$-intercept is $(0, -15)$.

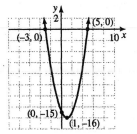

**35.**  $f(x) = -5x^2 + 5x$

$x = -\dfrac{b}{2a} = \dfrac{-5}{2(-5)} = \dfrac{1}{2}$ and

$f\left(\dfrac{1}{2}\right) = -5\left(\dfrac{1}{2}\right)^2 + 5\left(\dfrac{1}{2}\right) = -\dfrac{5}{4} + \dfrac{5}{2} = \dfrac{5}{4}$

Thus, the vertex is $\left(\dfrac{1}{2}, \dfrac{5}{4}\right)$.

The graph opens downward ($a = -5 < 0$).

$-5x^2 + 5x = 0$

$-5x(x - 1) = 0$

$x = 0$  or  $x - 1 = 0$

$\qquad\qquad\quad x = 1$

$x$-intercepts:  $(0, 0)$ and $(1, 0)$

$f(0) = 0$,  so the $y$-intercept is $(0, 0)$.

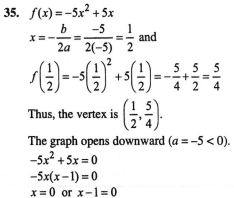

**37.**  $f(x) = -x^2 + 2x - 12$

$x = -\dfrac{b}{2a} = \dfrac{-2}{2(-1)} = 1$ and

$f(1) = -(1)^2 + 2(1) - 12 = -11$

Thus, the vertex is $(1, -11)$.

The graph opens downward ($a = -1 < 0$).

$-x^2 + 2x - 12 = 0$

$x^2 - 2x + 12 = 0$

$x = \dfrac{2 \pm \sqrt{(-2)^2 - 4(1)(12)}}{2(1)} = \dfrac{2 \pm \sqrt{-44}}{2}$

which yields non-real solutions.

Hence, there are no $x$-intercepts.

$f(0) = -12$  so the $y$-intercept is $(0, -12)$.

**39.**  $f(x) = 3x^2 - 12x + 15$

$x = -\dfrac{b}{2a} = \dfrac{-(-12)}{2(3)} = \dfrac{12}{6} = 2$ and

$f(2) = 3(2)^2 - 12(2) + 15$

$\qquad = 12 - 24 + 15$

$\qquad = 3$

Thus, the vertex is $(2, 3)$.

The graph opens upward ($a = 3 > 0$).

$3x^2 - 12x + 15 = 0$

$x^2 - 4x + 5 = 0$

$x = \dfrac{4 \pm \sqrt{(-4)^2 - 4(1)(5)}}{2(1)} = \dfrac{4 \pm \sqrt{-4}}{2}$

which yields non-real solutions.

Hence, there are no $x$-intercepts.

$f(0) = 15$,  so the $y$-intercept is $(0, 15)$.

**41.** $f(x) = x^2 + x - 6$

$x = -\dfrac{b}{2a} = \dfrac{-1}{2(1)} = -\dfrac{1}{2}$ and

$f\left(-\dfrac{1}{2}\right) = \left(-\dfrac{1}{2}\right)^2 + \left(-\dfrac{1}{2}\right) - 6$

$\qquad = \dfrac{1}{4} - \dfrac{1}{2} - 6$

$\qquad = -\dfrac{25}{4}$

Thus, the vertex is $\left(-\dfrac{1}{2}, -\dfrac{25}{4}\right)$.

The graph opens upward ($a = 1 > 0$).

$x^2 + x - 6 = 0$

$(x+3)(x-2) = 0$

$x = -3$ or $x = 2$

$x$-intercepts: $(-3, 0)$ and $(2, 0)$.

$f(0) = -6$ so the $y$-intercept is $(0, -6)$.

**43.** $f(x) = -2x^2 - 3x + 35$

$x = -\dfrac{b}{2a} = \dfrac{-(-3)}{2(-2)} = -\dfrac{3}{4}$ and

$f\left(-\dfrac{3}{4}\right) = -2\left(-\dfrac{3}{4}\right)^2 - 3\left(-\dfrac{3}{4}\right) + 35$

$\qquad = -\dfrac{9}{8} + \dfrac{9}{4} + 35$

$\qquad = \dfrac{289}{8}$

Thus, the vertex is $\left(-\dfrac{3}{4}, \dfrac{289}{8}\right)$.

The graph opens downward ($a = -2 < 0$).

$-2x^2 - 3x + 35 = 0$

$2x^2 + 3x - 35 = 0$

$(2x-7)(x+5) = 0$

$2x - 7 = 0$ or $x + 5 = 0$

$\qquad x = \dfrac{7}{2}$ or $\qquad x = -5$

$x$-intercepts: $(-5, 0)$ and $\left(\dfrac{7}{2}, 0\right)$.

$f(0) = 35$ so the $y$-intercept is $(0, 35)$.

**45.** $h(t) = -16t^2 + 96t$

$t = -\dfrac{b}{2a} = \dfrac{-96}{2(-16)} = \dfrac{96}{32} = 3$ and

$h(3) = -16(3)^2 + 96(3)$

$\qquad = -144 + 288$

$\qquad = 144$

The maximum height is 144 feet.

**47.** $C(x) = 2x^2 - 800x + 92,000$

**a.** $x = -\dfrac{b}{2a} = \dfrac{-(-800)}{2(2)} = 200$

200 bicycles are needed to minimize the cost.

**b.** $C(200) = 2(200)^2 - 800(200) + 92,000$

$\qquad\qquad = 12,000$

The minimum cost is \$12,000.

**49.** Let $x =$ one number. Then

$60 - x =$ the other number.

$f(x) = x(60 - x)$

$\qquad = 60x - x^2$

$\qquad = -x^2 + 60x$

The maximum will occur at the vertex.

$x = -\dfrac{b}{2a} = \dfrac{-60}{2(-1)} = 30$

$60 - x = 60 - 30 = 30$

The numbers are 30 and 30.

**51.** Let $x =$ one number. Then

$10 + x =$ the other number.

$f(x) = x(10 + x)$

$\qquad = 10x + x^2$

$\qquad = x^2 + 10x$

The minimum will occur at the vertex.

$x = -\dfrac{b}{2a} = \dfrac{-10}{2(1)} = -5$

$10 + x = 10 + (-5) = 5$

The numbers are $-5$ and $5$.

53. Let $x =$ width. Then $40 - x =$ the length.
    Area = length · width
    $A(x) = (40 - x)x$
    $\quad\quad = 40x - x^2$
    $\quad\quad = -x^2 + 40x$
    The maximum will occur at the vertex.
    $x = -\dfrac{b}{2a} = \dfrac{-40}{2(-1)} = 20$
    $40 - x = 40 - 20 = 20$
    The maximum area will occur when the length
    and width are 20 units each.

55. $f(x) = x^2 + 2$

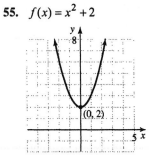

57. $g(x) = x + 2$

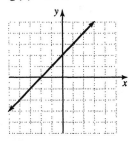

59. $f(x) = (x + 5)^2 + 2$

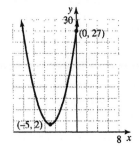

61. $f(x) = 3(x - 4)^2 + 1$

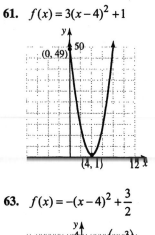

63. $f(x) = -(x - 4)^2 + \dfrac{3}{2}$

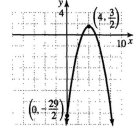

65. $f(x) = 2x^2 - 5$
    Since $a = 2 > 0$, the graph opens upward; thus,
    $f(x)$ has a minimum value.

67. $F(x) = 3 - \dfrac{1}{2}x^2$

    Since $a = -\dfrac{1}{2} < 0$, the graph opens downward;
    thus, $F(x)$ has a maximum value.

69. $f(x) = x^2 + 10x + 15$
    $x = -\dfrac{b}{2a} = \dfrac{-10}{2(1)} = -5$ and
    $f(-5) = (-5)^2 + 10(-5) + 15 = -10$
    Thus, the vertex is $(-5, -10)$.
    The graph opens upward ($a = 1 > 0$).
    $f(0) = 15$ so the $y$-intercept is $(0, 15)$.
    $x^2 + 10x + 15 = 0$
    $x = \dfrac{-10 \pm \sqrt{(10)^2 - 4(1)(15)}}{2(1)}$
    $\quad = \dfrac{-10 \pm \sqrt{40}}{2}$
    $\quad \approx -8.2 \text{ or } -1.8$
    The $x$-intercepts are approximately $(-8.2, 0)$ and
    $(-1.8, 0)$.

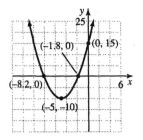

**71.** $f(x) = 3x^2 - 6x + 7$

$x = -\dfrac{b}{2a} = \dfrac{-(-6)}{2(3)} = 1$ and

$f(1) = 3(1)^2 - 6(1) + 7 = 4$

Thus, the vertex is $(1, 4)$.

The graph opens upward $(a = 3 > 0)$.

$f(0) = 7$ so the $y$-intercept is $(0, 7)$.

$3x^2 - 6x + 7 = 0$

$x = \dfrac{6 \pm \sqrt{(-6)^2 - 4(3)(7)}}{2(3)} = \dfrac{6 \pm \sqrt{-48}}{6}$

which yields non-real solutions.

Hence, there are no $x$-intercepts.

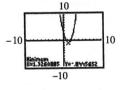

**73.** $f(x) = 2.3x^2 - 6.1x + 3.2$

$x = \dfrac{-(-6.1)}{2(2.3)} \approx 1.33$

$f(1.33) \approx -0.84$

minimum $\approx -0.84$

Alternative solution:

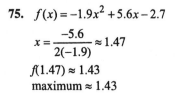

**75.** $f(x) = -1.9x^2 + 5.6x - 2.7$

$x = \dfrac{-5.6}{2(-1.9)} \approx 1.47$

$f(1.47) \approx 1.43$

maximum $\approx 1.43$

Alternate solution:

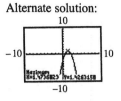

**77.** $f(x) = -96x^2 + 1018x + 28,824$

**a.** It will have a maximum; answer may vary (e.g., since $a = -96 < 0$).

**b.** $x = -\dfrac{b}{2a} = \dfrac{-1018}{2(-96)} \approx 5.3$

$2000 + 5 = 2005$

In the year 2005.

**c.** $f(5.3) = -96(5.3)^2 + 1018(5.3) + 28,824$

$= 31,522.76$

The maximum number of McDonald's is predicted to be about 31,523.

**79.**

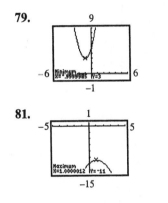

**81.**

**Chapter 8 Vocabulary Check**

1. The <u>discriminant</u> helps us find the number and type of solutions of a quadratic equation.

2. If $a^2 = b$, then $a = \pm\sqrt{b}$.

3. The graph of $f(x) = ax^2 + bx + c$ where $a$ is not 0 is a parabola whose vertex has $x$-value of $\dfrac{-b}{2a}$.

4. A <u>quadratic inequality</u> is an inequality that can be written so that one side is a quadratic expression and the other side is 0.

5. The process of writing a quadratic equation so that one side is a perfect square trinomial is called <u>completing the square</u>.

6. The graph of $f(x) = x^2 + k$ has vertex <u>(0, k)</u>.

7. The graph of $f(x) = (x-h)^2$ has vertex <u>(h, 0)</u>.

8. The graph of $f(x) = (x-h)^2 + k$ has vertex <u>(h, k)</u>.

9. The formula $x = \dfrac{-b \pm \sqrt{b^2 - 4ac}}{2a}$ is called the <u>quadratic formula</u>.

10. A <u>quadratic</u> equation is one that can be written in the form $ax^2 + bx + c = 0$ where $a$, $b$, and $c$ are real numbers and $a$ is not 0.

## Chapter 8 Review

1. $x^2 - 15x + 14 = 0$
 $(x-14)(x-1) = 0$
 $x - 14 = 0$   or   $x - 1 = 0$
   $x = 14$  or     $x = 1$
 The solutions are 1 and 14.

2.          $7a^2 = 29a + 30$
 $7a^2 - 29a - 30 = 0$
 $(7a+6)(a-5) = 0$
 $7a + 6 = 0$   or   $a - 5 = 0$
   $7a = -6$  or     $a = 5$
   $a = -\dfrac{6}{7}$

 The solutions are $-\dfrac{6}{7}$ and 5.

3. $4m^2 = 196$
  $m^2 = 49$
  $m = \pm\sqrt{49}$
  $m = \pm 7$
 The solutions are $-7$ and 7.

4. $(5x-2)^2 = 2$
   $5x - 2 = \pm\sqrt{2}$
    $5x = 2 \pm \sqrt{2}$
     $x = \dfrac{2 \pm \sqrt{2}}{5}$

 The solutions are $\dfrac{2+\sqrt{2}}{5}$ and $\dfrac{2-\sqrt{2}}{5}$.

5.      $z^2 + 3z + 1 = 0$
      $z^2 + 3z = -1$
 $z^2 + 3z + \left(\dfrac{3}{2}\right)^2 = -1 + \dfrac{9}{4}$
    $\left(z + \dfrac{3}{2}\right)^2 = \dfrac{5}{4}$
      $z + \dfrac{3}{2} = \pm\sqrt{\dfrac{5}{4}}$
      $z + \dfrac{3}{2} = \pm\dfrac{\sqrt{5}}{2}$
        $z = -\dfrac{3}{2} \pm \dfrac{\sqrt{5}}{2} = \dfrac{-3 \pm \sqrt{5}}{2}$

 The solutions are $\dfrac{-3+\sqrt{5}}{2}$ and $\dfrac{-3-\sqrt{5}}{2}$.

6.        $(2x+1)^2 = x$
    $4x^2 + 4x + 1 = x$
      $4x^2 + 3x = -1$
       $x^2 + \dfrac{3}{4}x = -\dfrac{1}{4}$
 $x^2 + \dfrac{3}{4}x + \left(\dfrac{\frac{3}{4}}{2}\right)^2 = -\dfrac{1}{4} + \dfrac{9}{64}$
       $\left(x + \dfrac{3}{8}\right)^2 = -\dfrac{7}{64}$
        $x + \dfrac{3}{8} = \pm\sqrt{-\dfrac{7}{64}}$
        $x + \dfrac{3}{8} = \pm\dfrac{i\sqrt{7}}{8}$
          $x = -\dfrac{3}{8} \pm \dfrac{i\sqrt{7}}{8} = \dfrac{-3 \pm i\sqrt{7}}{8}$

 The solutions are $\dfrac{-3+i\sqrt{7}}{8}$ and $\dfrac{-3-i\sqrt{7}}{8}$.

**7.**
$$A = P(1+r)^2$$
$$2717 = 2500(1+r)^2$$
$$\frac{2717}{2500} = (1+r)^2$$
$$(1+r)^2 = 1.0868$$
$$1+r = \pm\sqrt{1.0868}$$
$$1+r = \pm 1.0425$$
$$r = -1 \pm 1.0425$$
$$= 0.0425 \text{ or } -2.0425 \text{ (disregard)}$$
The interest rate is 4.25%.

**8.** Let $x$ = distance traveled.
$$a^2 + b^2 = c^2$$
$$x^2 + x^2 = (150)^2$$
$$2x^2 = 22,500$$
$$x^2 = 11,250$$
$$x = \pm 75\sqrt{2} \approx \pm 106.1$$
Disregard the negative. The ships each traveled $75\sqrt{2} \approx 106.1$ miles.

**9.** Two complex but not real solutions exist.

**10.** Two real solutions exist.

**11.** Two real solutions exist.

**12.** One real solution exists.

**13.** $x^2 - 16x + 64 = 0$
$a = 1, b = -16, c = 64$
$$x = \frac{16 \pm \sqrt{(-16)^2 - 4(1)(64)}}{2(1)}$$
$$= \frac{16 \pm \sqrt{256 - 256}}{2}$$
$$= \frac{16 \pm \sqrt{0}}{2}$$
$$= 8$$
The solution is 8.

**14.** $x^2 + 5x = 0$
$a = 1, b = 5, c = 0$
$$x = \frac{-5 \pm \sqrt{(5)^2 - 4(1)(0)}}{2(1)}$$
$$= \frac{-5 \pm \sqrt{25}}{2}$$
$$= \frac{-5 \pm 5}{2}$$
$$= 0 \text{ or } -5$$
The solutions are –5 and 0.

**15.**
$$2x^2 + 3x = 5$$
$$2x^2 + 3x - 5 = 0$$
$$a = 2, b = 3, c = -5$$
$$x = \frac{-3 \pm \sqrt{(3)^2 - 4(2)(-5)}}{2(2)}$$
$$= \frac{-3 \pm \sqrt{49}}{4}$$
$$= \frac{-3 \pm 7}{4}$$
$$= 1 \text{ or } -\frac{5}{2}$$

The solutions are $-\frac{5}{2}$ and $1$.

**16.**
$$9a^2 + 4 = 2a$$
$$9a^2 - 2a + 4 = 0$$
$$a = \frac{2 \pm \sqrt{(-2)^2 - 4(9)(4)}}{2(9)}$$
$$= \frac{2 \pm \sqrt{-140}}{18}$$
$$= \frac{2 \pm i\sqrt{4 \cdot 35}}{18}$$
$$= \frac{2 \pm 2i\sqrt{35}}{18}$$
$$= \frac{1 \pm i\sqrt{35}}{9}$$

The solutions are $\dfrac{1 + i\sqrt{35}}{9}$ and $\dfrac{1 - i\sqrt{35}}{9}$.

**17.**
$$6x^2 + 7 = 5x$$
$$6x^2 - 5x + 7 = 0$$
$$a = 6, b = -5, c = 7$$
$$x = \frac{5 \pm \sqrt{(-5)^2 - 4(6)(7)}}{2(6)}$$
$$= \frac{5 \pm \sqrt{25 - 168}}{12}$$
$$= \frac{5 \pm \sqrt{-143}}{12}$$
$$= \frac{5 \pm i\sqrt{143}}{12}$$

The solutions are $\dfrac{5 + i\sqrt{143}}{12}$ and $\dfrac{5 - i\sqrt{143}}{12}$.

**18.**
$$(2x - 3)^2 = x$$
$$4x^2 - 12x + 9 - x = 0$$
$$4x^2 - 13x + 9 = 0$$
$$a = 4, b = -13, c = 9$$
$$x = \frac{13 \pm \sqrt{(-13)^2 - 4(4)(9)}}{2(4)}$$
$$= \frac{13 \pm \sqrt{169 - 144}}{8}$$
$$= \frac{13 \pm \sqrt{25}}{8}$$
$$= \frac{13 \pm 5}{8}$$
$$= \frac{9}{4} \text{ or } 1$$

The solutions are $1$ and $\dfrac{9}{4}$.

**19.** $d(t) = -16t^2 + 30t + 6$

    **a.** $d(1) = -16(1)^2 + 30(1) + 6$
$$= -16 + 30 + 6$$
$$= 20 \text{ feet}$$

    **b.**
$$-16t^2 + 30t + 6 = 0$$
$$8t^2 - 15t - 3 = 0$$
$$a = 8, b = -15, c = -3$$
$$t = \frac{15 \pm \sqrt{(-15)^2 - 4(8)(-3)}}{2(8)}$$
$$= \frac{15 \pm \sqrt{225 + 96}}{16}$$
$$= \frac{15 \pm \sqrt{321}}{16}$$

Disregarding the negative, we have
$$t = \frac{15 + \sqrt{321}}{16} \text{ seconds}$$
$$\approx 2.1 \text{ seconds.}$$

**20.** Let $x = $ length of the legs. Then
$x + 6 = $ length of the hypotenuse.
$$x^2 + x^2 = (x + 6)^2$$
$$2x^2 = x^2 + 12x + 36$$
$$x^2 - 12x - 36 = 0$$
$$a = 1, b = -12, c = -36$$
$$x = \frac{12 \pm \sqrt{(-12)^2 - 4(1)(-36)}}{2(1)}$$
$$= \frac{12 \pm \sqrt{144 + 144}}{2}$$
$$= \frac{12 \pm \sqrt{144 \cdot 2}}{2}$$
$$= \frac{12 \pm 12\sqrt{2}}{2}$$
$$= 6 \pm 6\sqrt{2}$$

Disregard the negative. The length of each leg is $\left(6 + 6\sqrt{2}\right)$ cm.

**21.**
$$x^3 = 27$$
$$x^3 - 27 = 0$$
$$(x-3)(x^2 + 3x + 9) = 0$$
$$x - 3 = 0 \text{ or } x^2 + 3x + 9 = 0$$
$$x = 3 \qquad a = 1, b = 3, c = 9$$
$$x = \frac{-3 \pm \sqrt{(3)^2 - 4(1)(9)}}{2(1)}$$
$$= \frac{-3 \pm \sqrt{9 - 36}}{2}$$
$$= \frac{-3 \pm \sqrt{-27}}{2}$$
$$= \frac{-3 \pm 3i\sqrt{3}}{2}$$

The solutions are 3, $\dfrac{-3 + 3i\sqrt{3}}{2}$, and $\dfrac{-3 - 3i\sqrt{3}}{2}$.

**22.**
$$y^3 = -64$$
$$y^3 + 64 = 0$$
$$(y+4)(y^2 - 4y + 16) = 0$$
$$y + 4 = 0 \quad \text{or } y^2 - 4y + 16 = 0$$
$$y = -4 \qquad a = 1, b = -4, c = 16$$
$$y = \frac{4 \pm \sqrt{(-4)^2 - 4(1)(16)}}{2(1)}$$
$$= \frac{4 \pm \sqrt{16 - 64}}{2}$$
$$= \frac{4 \pm \sqrt{-48}}{2}$$
$$= \frac{4 \pm 4i\sqrt{3}}{2}$$
$$= 2 \pm 2i\sqrt{3}$$

The solutions are –4, $2 + 2i\sqrt{3}$, and $2 - 2i\sqrt{3}$.

**23.**
$$\frac{5}{x} + \frac{6}{x-2} = 3$$
$$x(x-2)\left(\frac{5}{x} + \frac{6}{x-2}\right) = 3x(x-2)$$
$$5(x-2) + 6x = 3x^2 - 6x$$
$$5x - 10 + 6x = 3x^2 - 6x$$
$$0 = 3x^2 - 17x + 10$$
$$0 = (3x-2)(x-5)$$
$$3x - 2 = 0 \text{ or } x - 5 = 0$$
$$x = \frac{2}{3} \text{ or } \quad x = 5$$

The solutions are $\dfrac{2}{3}$ and 5.

**24.**
$$x^4 - 21x^2 - 100 = 0$$
$$(x^2 - 25)(x^2 + 4) = 0$$
$$(x+5)(x-5)(x^2 + 4) = 0$$
$$x + 5 = 0 \quad \text{or } x - 5 = 0 \text{ or } x^2 + 4 = 0$$
$$x = -5 \text{ or } \quad x = 5 \text{ or } \quad x^2 = -4$$
$$x = \pm 2i$$

The solutions are –5, 5 –2*i*, and 2*i*.

**25.** $x^{2/3} - 6x^{1/3} + 5 = 0$

Let $y = x^{1/3}$. Then $y^2 = x^{2/3}$ and
$$y^2 - 6y + 5 = 0$$
$$(y-5)(y-1) = 0$$
$$y - 5 = 0 \quad \text{or } y - 1 = 0$$
$$y = 5 \quad \text{or } \quad y = 1$$
$$x^{1/3} = 5 \quad \text{or } x^{1/3} = 1$$
$$x = 125 \text{ or } \quad x = 1$$

The solutions are 1 and 125.

**26.**  $5(x+3)^2 - 19(x+3) = 4$

$5(x+3)^2 - 19(x+3) - 4 = 0$

Let $y = x + 3$. Then $y^2 = (x+3)^2$ and

$5y^2 - 19y - 4 = 0$

$(5y+1)(y-4) = 0$

$5y + 1 = 0$    or $y - 4 = 0$

$y = -\dfrac{1}{5}$    or        $y = 4$

$x + 3 = -\dfrac{1}{5}$    or  $x + 3 = 4$

$x = -\dfrac{16}{5}$    or        $x = 1$

The solutions are $-\dfrac{16}{5}$ and 1.

**27.**                    $a^6 - a^2 = a^4 - 1$

$a^6 - a^4 - a^2 + 1 = 0$

$a^4(a^2 - 1) - 1(a^2 - 1) = 0$

$(a^2 - 1)(a^4 - 1) = 0$

$(a+1)(a-1)(a^2+1)(a^2-1) = 0$

$(a+1)(a-1)(a^2+1)(a+1)(a-1) = 0$

$(a+1)^2(a-1)^2(a^2+1) = 0$

$(a+1)^2 = 0$ or $(a-1)^2 = 0$ or $a^2 + 1 = 0$

$a + 1 = 0$ or    $a - 1 = 0$ or    $a^2 = -1$

$a = -1$ or        $a = 1$ or        $a = \pm i$

The solutions are $-1$, 1, $-i$, and $i$.

**28.**  $y^{-2} + y^{-1} = 20$

$\dfrac{1}{y^2} + \dfrac{1}{y} = 20$

$1 + y = 20y^2$

$0 = 20y^2 - y - 1$

$0 = (5y+1)(4y-1)$

$5y + 1 = 0$    or $4y - 1 = 0$

$y = -\dfrac{1}{5}$ or        $y = \dfrac{1}{4}$

The solutions are $-\dfrac{1}{5}$ and $\dfrac{1}{4}$.

**29.** Let $x$ = time for Jerome alone. Then $x - 1$ = time for Tim alone.

$\dfrac{1}{x} + \dfrac{1}{x-1} = \dfrac{1}{5}$

$5(x-1) + 5x = x(x-1)$

$5x - 5 + 5x = x^2 - x$

$0 = x^2 - 11x + 5$

$a = 1, b = -11, c = 5$

$x = \dfrac{11 \pm \sqrt{(-11)^2 - 4(1)(5)}}{2(1)}$

$= \dfrac{11 \pm \sqrt{101}}{2}$

$\approx 0.475$ (disregard) or 10.525

Jerome: 10.5 hours
Tim: 9.5 hours

**30.** Let $x$ = the number; then

$\dfrac{1}{x}$ = the reciprocal of the number.

$x - \dfrac{1}{x} = -\dfrac{24}{5}$

$5x\left(x - \dfrac{1}{x}\right) = 5x\left(-\dfrac{24}{5}\right)$

$5x^2 - 5 = -24x$

$5x^2 + 24x - 5 = 0$

$(5x-1)(x+5) = 0$

$5x - 1 = 0$ or $x + 5 = 0$

$x = \dfrac{1}{5}$ or        $x = -5$

Disregard the positive value as extraneous. The number is $-5$.

**31.**        $2x^2 - 50 \le 0$

$2(x^2 - 25) \le 0$

$2(x+5)(x-5) \le 0$

$x + 5 = 0$    or $x - 5 = 0$

$x = -5$ or        $x = 5$

| Region | Test Point | $2(x+5)(x-5) \le 0$ Result |
|--------|------------|---------------------------|
| $A$: $(-\infty, -5]$ | $-6$ | $2(-1)(-11) \le 0$ False |
| $B$: $[-5, 5]$ | $0$ | $2(5)(-5) \le 0$ True |
| $C$: $[5, \infty)$ | $6$ | $2(11)(1) \le 0$ False |

Solution: $[-5, 5]$

**32.**
$$\frac{1}{4}x^2 < \frac{1}{16}$$
$$x^2 < \frac{1}{4}$$
$$x^2 - \frac{1}{4} < 0$$
$$\left(x + \frac{1}{2}\right)\left(x - \frac{1}{2}\right) < 0$$
$$x + \frac{1}{2} = 0 \quad \text{or} \quad x - \frac{1}{2} = 0$$
$$x = -\frac{1}{2} \quad \text{or} \quad x = \frac{1}{2}$$

| Region | Test Point | $\left(x + \frac{1}{2}\right)\left(x - \frac{1}{2}\right) < 0$ Result |
|--------|------------|------------------------|
| A: $\left(-\infty, -\frac{1}{2}\right)$ | −1 | $\left(-\frac{1}{2}\right)\left(-\frac{3}{2}\right) < 0$ False |
| B: $\left(-\frac{1}{2}, \frac{1}{2}\right)$ | 0 | $\left(\frac{1}{2}\right)\left(-\frac{1}{2}\right) < 0$ True |
| C: $\left(\frac{1}{2}, \infty\right)$ | 1 | $\left(\frac{3}{2}\right)\left(\frac{1}{2}\right) < 0$ False |

Solution: $\left(-\frac{1}{2}, \frac{1}{2}\right)$

**33.**  $\dfrac{x-5}{x-6} < 0$

$x - 5 = 0$  or  $x - 6 = 0$

$x = 5$  or  $x = 6$

| Region | Test Point | $\dfrac{x-5}{x-6} < 0$ Result |
|--------|-----------|------------------------------|
| $A$: $(-\infty, 5)$ | $0$ | $\dfrac{-5}{-6} < 0$ False |
| $B$: $(5, 6)$ | $\dfrac{11}{2}$ | $\dfrac{\frac{1}{2}}{-\frac{1}{2}} < 0$ True |
| $C$: $(6, \infty)$ | $7$ | $\dfrac{2}{1} < 0$ False |

Solution: $(5, 6)$

**34.**  $(x^2 - 16)(x^2 - 1) > 0$

$(x+4)(x-4)(x+1)(x-1) > 0$

$x + 4 = 0$  or  $x - 4 = 0$  or  $x + 1 = 0$  or  $x - 1 = 0$

$x = -4$  or  $x = 4$  or  $x = -1$  or  $x = 1$

| Region | Test Point | $(x+4)(x-4)(x+1)(x-1) > 0$ Result |
|--------|-----------|-----------------------------------|
| $A$: $(-\infty, -4)$ | $-5$ | $(-1)(-9)(-4)(-6) > 0$ True |
| $B$: $(-4, -1)$ | $-2$ | $(2)(-6)(-1)(-3) > 0$ False |
| $C$: $(-1, 1)$ | $0$ | $(4)(-4)(1)(-1) > 0$ True |
| $D$: $(1, 4)$ | $2$ | $(6)(-2)(3)(1) > 0$ False |
| $E$: $(4, \infty)$ | $5$ | $(9)(1)(6)(4) > 0$ True |

Solution: $(-\infty, -4) \cup (-1, 1) \cup (4, \infty)$

**35.** $\dfrac{(4x+3)(x-5)}{x(x+6)} > 0$

$4x+3=0,\ x-5=0,\ x=0,\ \text{or } x+6=0$

$x=-\dfrac{3}{4},\ x=5,\ x=0,\ \text{or } x=-6$

| Region | Test Point | $\dfrac{(4x+3)(x-5)}{x(x+6)} > 0$ Result |
|---|---|---|
| $A$: $(-\infty, -6)$ | $-7$ | $\dfrac{(-25)(-12)}{-7(-1)} > 0$ True |
| $B$: $\left(-6, -\dfrac{3}{4}\right)$ | $-3$ | $\dfrac{(-9)(-8)}{-3(3)} > 0$ False |
| $C$: $\left(-\dfrac{3}{4}, 0\right)$ | $-\dfrac{1}{2}$ | $\dfrac{(1)\left(-\frac{11}{2}\right)}{-\frac{1}{2}\left(\frac{11}{2}\right)} > 0$ True |
| $D$: $(0, 5)$ | $1$ | $\dfrac{(7)(-4)}{1(7)} > 0$ False |
| $E$: $(5, \infty)$ | $6$ | $\dfrac{(27)(1)}{6(12)} > 0$ True |

Solution: $(-\infty, -6) \cup \left(-\dfrac{3}{4}, 0\right) \cup (5, \infty)$

**36.** $(x+5)(x-6)(x+2) \le 0$

$x+5=0 \quad \text{or } x-6=0 \text{ or } x+2=0$

$x=-5 \quad \text{or} \quad x=6 \text{ or} \quad x=-2$

| Region | Test Point | $(x+5)(x-6)(x+2) \le 0$ Result |
|---|---|---|
| $A$: $(-\infty, -5]$ | $-6$ | $(-1)(-12)(-4) \le 0$ True |
| $B$: $[-5, -2]$ | $-3$ | $(2)(-9)(-1) \le 0$ False |
| $C$: $[-2, 6]$ | $0$ | $(5)(-6)(2) \le 0$ True |
| $D$: $[6, \infty)$ | $7$ | $(12)(1)(9) \le 0$ False |

Solution: $(-\infty, -5] \cup [-2, 6]$

**37.** $x^3 + 3x^2 - 25x - 75 > 0$

$x^2(x+3) - 25(x+3) > 0$

$(x+3)(x^2 - 25) > 0$

$(x+3)(x+5)(x-5) > 0$

$x+3=0 \quad \text{or } x+5=0 \quad \text{or } x-5=0$

$x=-3 \text{ or} \quad x=-5 \text{ or} \quad x=5$

| Region | Test Point | $(x+3)(x+5)(x-5) > 0$ Result |
|---|---|---|
| $A$: $(-\infty, -5)$ | $-6$ | $(-3)(-1)(-11) > 0$ False |
| $B$: $(-5, -3)$ | $-4$ | $(-1)(1)(-9) > 0$ True |
| $C$: $(-3, 5)$ | $0$ | $(3)(5)(-5) > 0$ False |
| $D$: $(5, \infty)$ | $6$ | $(9)(11)(1) > 0$ True |

Solution: $(-5, -3) \cup (5, \infty)$

**38.** $\dfrac{x^2 + 4}{3x} \le 1$

The denominator equals 0 when $3x = 0$, or $x = 0$.

$$\dfrac{x^2 + 4}{3x} = 1$$

$$x^2 + 4 = 3x$$

$$x^2 - 3x + 4 = 0$$

$$x = \dfrac{3 \pm \sqrt{(-3)^2 - 4(1)(4)}}{2(1)} = \dfrac{3 \pm \sqrt{-7}}{2}$$

which yields non-real solutions.

| Region | Test Point | $\dfrac{x^2+4}{3x} \le 1$ Result |
|---|---|---|
| A: $(-\infty, 0)$ | $-1$ | $\dfrac{5}{-3} \le 1$ True |
| B: $(0, \infty)$ | $1$ | $\dfrac{5}{3} \le 1$ False |

Solution: $(\infty, 0)$

**39.** $\dfrac{(5x+6)(x-3)}{x(6x-5)} < 0$

$x = -\dfrac{6}{5}$ or $x = 3$ or $x = 0$ or $x = \dfrac{5}{6}$

| Region | Test Point | $\dfrac{(5x+6)(x-3)}{x(6x-5)} < 0$ Result |
|---|---|---|
| A: $\left(-\infty, -\dfrac{6}{5}\right)$ | $-2$ | $\dfrac{(-4)(-5)}{-2(-17)} < 0$ False |
| B: $\left(-\dfrac{6}{5}, 0\right)$ | $-1$ | $\dfrac{(1)(-4)}{-1(-11)} < 0$ True |
| C: $\left(0, \dfrac{5}{6}\right)$ | $\dfrac{1}{2}$ | $\dfrac{\left(\frac{17}{2}\right)\left(-\frac{5}{2}\right)}{\frac{1}{2}(-2)} < 0$ False |
| D: $\left(\dfrac{5}{6}, 3\right)$ | $2$ | $\dfrac{(16)(-1)}{2(7)} < 0$ True |
| E: $(3, \infty)$ | $4$ | $\dfrac{(26)(1)}{4(19)} < 0$ False |

Solution: $\left(-\dfrac{6}{5}, 0\right) \cup \left(\dfrac{5}{6}, 3\right)$

**40.** $\dfrac{3}{x-2} > 2$

The denominator is equal to 0 when $x - 2 = 0$, or $x = 2$.

$\dfrac{3}{x-2} = 2$

$3 = 2(x-2)$

$3 = 2x - 4$

$7 = 2x$

$\dfrac{7}{2} = x$

| Region | Test Point | $\dfrac{3}{x-2} > 2$ Result |
|---|---|---|
| A: $(-\infty, 2)$ | $0$ | $\dfrac{3}{-2} > 2$ False |
| B: $\left(2, \dfrac{7}{2}\right)$ | $3$ | $\dfrac{3}{1} > 2$ True |
| C: $\left(\dfrac{7}{2}, \infty\right)$ | $5$ | $\dfrac{3}{3} > 2$ False |

Solution: $\left(2, \dfrac{7}{2}\right)$

**41.** $f(x) = x^2 - 4$

Vertex: $(0, -4)$

Axis of symmetry: $x = 0$

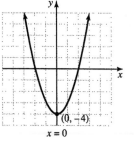

**42.** $g(x) = x^2 + 7$

Vertex: (0, 7)

Axis of symmetry: $x = 0$

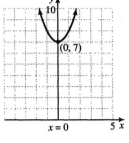

**43.** $H(x) = 2x^2$

Vertex: (0, 0)

Axis of symmetry: $x = 0$

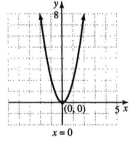

**44.** $h(x) = -\dfrac{1}{3}x^2$

Vertex: (0, 0)

Axis of symmetry: $x = 0$

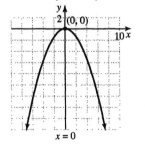

**45.** $F(x) = (x-1)^2$

Vertex: (1, 0)

Axis of symmetry: $x = 1$

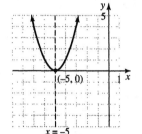

**46.** $G(x) = (x+5)^2$

Vertex: (−5, 0)

Axis of symmetry: $x = -5$

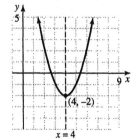

**47.** $f(x) = (x-4)^2 - 2$

Vertex: (4, −2)

Axis of symmetry: $x = 4$

**48.** $f(x) = -3(x-1)^2 + 1$

Vertex: $(1, 1)$

Axis of symmetry: $x = 1$

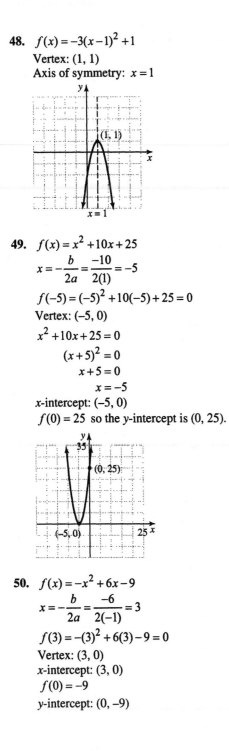

**49.** $f(x) = x^2 + 10x + 25$

$x = -\dfrac{b}{2a} = \dfrac{-10}{2(1)} = -5$

$f(-5) = (-5)^2 + 10(-5) + 25 = 0$

Vertex: $(-5, 0)$

$x^2 + 10x + 25 = 0$

$(x+5)^2 = 0$

$x + 5 = 0$

$x = -5$

$x$-intercept: $(-5, 0)$

$f(0) = 25$ so the $y$-intercept is $(0, 25)$.

**50.** $f(x) = -x^2 + 6x - 9$

$x = -\dfrac{b}{2a} = \dfrac{-6}{2(-1)} = 3$

$f(3) = -(3)^2 + 6(3) - 9 = 0$

Vertex: $(3, 0)$

$x$-intercept: $(3, 0)$

$f(0) = -9$

$y$-intercept: $(0, -9)$

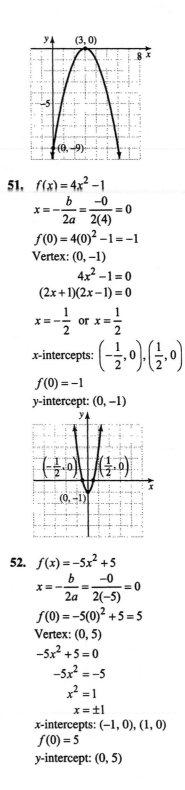

**51.** $f(x) = 4x^2 - 1$

$x = -\dfrac{b}{2a} = \dfrac{-0}{2(4)} = 0$

$f(0) = 4(0)^2 - 1 = -1$

Vertex: $(0, -1)$

$4x^2 - 1 = 0$

$(2x+1)(2x-1) = 0$

$x = -\dfrac{1}{2}$ or $x = \dfrac{1}{2}$

$x$-intercepts: $\left(-\dfrac{1}{2}, 0\right), \left(\dfrac{1}{2}, 0\right)$

$f(0) = -1$

$y$-intercept: $(0, -1)$

**52.** $f(x) = -5x^2 + 5$

$x = -\dfrac{b}{2a} = \dfrac{-0}{2(-5)} = 0$

$f(0) = -5(0)^2 + 5 = 5$

Vertex: $(0, 5)$

$-5x^2 + 5 = 0$

$-5x^2 = -5$

$x^2 = 1$

$x = \pm 1$

$x$-intercepts: $(-1, 0), (1, 0)$

$f(0) = 5$

$y$-intercept: $(0, 5)$

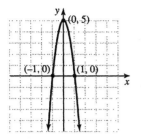

**53.** $f(x) = -3x^2 - 5x + 4$

$$x = -\frac{b}{2a} = \frac{-(-5)}{2(-3)} = -\frac{5}{6}$$

$$f\left(-\frac{5}{6}\right) = -3\left(-\frac{5}{6}\right)^2 - 5\left(-\frac{5}{6}\right) + 4 = \frac{73}{12}$$

Vertex: $\left(-\frac{5}{6}, \frac{73}{12}\right)$

The graph opens downward ($a = -3 < 0$).

$f(0) = 4 \Rightarrow$ $y$-intercept: (0, 4)

$$-3x^2 - 5x + 4 = 0$$

$$x = \frac{5 \pm \sqrt{(-5)^2 - 4(-3)(4)}}{2(-3)}$$

$$= \frac{5 \pm \sqrt{73}}{-6}$$

$$\approx -2.2573 \text{ or } 0.5907$$

$x$-intercepts: $(-2.3, 0)$, $(0.6, 0)$

**54.** $h(t) = -16t^2 + 120t + 300$

**a.**
$$350 = -16t^2 + 120t + 300$$
$$16t^2 - 120t + 50 = 0$$
$$8t^2 - 60t + 25 = 0$$
$$a = 8, b = -60, c = 25$$

$$t = \frac{60 \pm \sqrt{(-60)^2 - 4(8)(25)}}{2(8)}$$

$$= \frac{60 \pm \sqrt{2800}}{16}$$

$$\approx 0.4 \text{ second and } 7.1 \text{ seconds}$$

**b.** The object will be at 350 feet on the way up and on the way down.

**55.** Let $x$ = one number; then
$420 - x$ = the other number.
Let $f(x)$ represent their product.

$$f(x) = x(420 - x)$$
$$= 420x - x^2$$
$$= -x^2 + 420x$$

$$x = -\frac{b}{2a} = \frac{-420}{2(-1)} = 210;$$
$$420 - x = 420 - 210 = 210$$

Therefore, the numbers are both 210.

**56.** $y = a(x - h)^2 + k$

vertex $(-3, 7)$ gives $y = a(x + 3)^2 + 7$.
Passing through the origin gives

$$0 = a(0 + 3)^2 + 7$$
$$-7 = 9a$$
$$-\frac{7}{9} = a$$

Thus, $y = -\frac{7}{9}(x + 3)^2 + 7$.

**57.** $x^2 - x - 30 = 0$
$$(x + 5)(x - 6) = 0$$
$$x + 5 = 0 \quad \text{or} \quad x - 6 = 0$$
$$x = -5 \quad \text{or} \quad x = 6$$
The solutions are $-5$ and $6$.

**58.**
$$10x^2 = 3x + 4$$
$$10x^2 - 3x - 4 = 0$$
$$(5x-4)(2x+1) = 0$$
$$5x - 4 = 0 \text{ or } 2x + 1 = 0$$
$$5x = 4 \text{ or } \quad 2x = -1$$
$$x = \frac{4}{5} \text{ or } \quad x = -\frac{1}{2}$$
The solutions are $-\frac{1}{2}$ and $\frac{4}{5}$.

**59.**
$$9y^2 = 36$$
$$y^2 = 4$$
$$y = \pm\sqrt{4}$$
$$y = \pm 2$$
The solutions are $-2$ and $2$.

**60.**
$$(9n+1)^2 = 9$$
$$9n + 1 = \pm\sqrt{9}$$
$$9n + 1 = \pm 3$$
$$9n = -1 \pm 3$$
$$n = \frac{-1 \pm 3}{9} = \frac{2}{9}, -\frac{4}{9}$$
The solutions are $-\frac{4}{9}$ and $\frac{2}{9}$.

**61.**
$$x^2 + x + 7 = 0$$
$$x^2 + x = -7$$
$$x^2 + x + \left(\frac{1}{2}\right)^2 = -7 + \frac{1}{4}$$
$$\left(x + \frac{1}{2}\right)^2 = -\frac{27}{4}$$
$$x + \frac{1}{2} = \pm\sqrt{-\frac{27}{4}}$$
$$x + \frac{1}{2} = \pm\frac{i\sqrt{9 \cdot 3}}{2}$$
$$x + \frac{1}{2} = \pm\frac{3i\sqrt{3}}{2}$$
$$x = -\frac{1}{2} \pm \frac{3i\sqrt{3}}{2} = \frac{-1 \pm 3i\sqrt{3}}{2}$$
The solutions are $\frac{-1 + 3i\sqrt{3}}{2}$ and $\frac{-1 - 3i\sqrt{3}}{2}$.

**62.**
$$(3x-4)^2 = 10x$$
$$9x^2 - 24x + 16 = 10x$$
$$9x^2 - 34x = -16$$
$$x^2 - \frac{34}{9}x = -\frac{16}{9}$$
$$x^2 - \frac{34}{9}x + \left(\frac{-\frac{34}{9}}{2}\right)^2 = -\frac{16}{9} + \frac{289}{81}$$
$$\left(x - \frac{17}{9}\right)^2 = \frac{145}{81}$$
$$x - \frac{17}{9} = \pm\sqrt{\frac{145}{81}}$$
$$x - \frac{17}{9} = \pm\frac{\sqrt{145}}{9}$$
$$x = \frac{17 \pm \sqrt{145}}{9}$$
The solutions are $\frac{17 + \sqrt{145}}{9}$ and $\frac{17 - \sqrt{145}}{9}$.

**63.** $x^2 + 11 = 0$
$$a = 1, b = 0, c = 11$$
$$x = \frac{0 \pm \sqrt{(0)^2 - 4(1)(11)}}{2(1)}$$
$$= \frac{\pm\sqrt{-44}}{2}$$
$$= \frac{\pm 2i\sqrt{11}}{2}$$
$$= \pm i\sqrt{11}$$
The solutions are $-i\sqrt{11}$ and $i\sqrt{11}$.

**64.**
$$(5a-2)^2 - a = 0$$
$$25a^2 - 20a + 4 - a = 0$$
$$25a^2 - 21a + 4 = 0$$
$$a = \frac{21 \pm \sqrt{(-21)^2 - 4(25)(4)}}{2(25)}$$
$$= \frac{21 \pm \sqrt{441 - 400}}{50}$$
$$= \frac{21 \pm \sqrt{41}}{50}$$
The solutions are $\frac{21 + \sqrt{41}}{50}$ and $\frac{21 - \sqrt{41}}{50}$.

**65.** $\dfrac{7}{8} = \dfrac{8}{x^2}$

$7x^2 = 64$

$x^2 = \dfrac{64}{7}$

$x = \pm\sqrt{\dfrac{64}{7}}$

$x = \pm\dfrac{8}{\sqrt{7}} = \pm\dfrac{8\cdot\sqrt{7}}{\sqrt{7}\cdot\sqrt{7}} = \pm\dfrac{8\sqrt{7}}{7}$

The solutions are $-\dfrac{8\sqrt{7}}{7}$ and $\dfrac{8\sqrt{7}}{7}$.

**66.** $x^{2/3} - 6x^{1/3} = -8$

$x^{2/3} - 6x^{1/3} + 8 = 0$

Let $y = x^{1/3}$. Then $y^2 = x^{2/3}$ and

$y^2 - 6y + 8 = 0$

$(y-4)(y-2) = 0$

$y - 4 = 0$   or   $y - 2 = 0$

$y = 4$   or   $y = 2$

$x^{1/3} = 4$   or   $x^{1/3} = 2$

$x = 64$   or   $x = 8$

The solutions are 8 and 64.

**67.** $(2x-3)(4x+5) \ge 0$

$2x - 3 = 0$   or   $4x + 5 = 0$

$x = \dfrac{3}{2}$   or   $x = -\dfrac{5}{4}$

| Region | Test Point | $(2x-3)(4x+5) \ge 0$ Result |
|---|---|---|
| $A: \left(-\infty, -\dfrac{5}{4}\right]$ | $-2$ | $(-7)(-3) \ge 0$ True |
| $B: \left[-\dfrac{5}{4}, \dfrac{3}{2}\right]$ | $0$ | $(-3)(5) \ge 0$ False |
| $C: \left[\dfrac{3}{2}, \infty\right)$ | $3$ | $(3)(17) \ge 0$ True |

Solution: $\left(-\infty, -\dfrac{5}{4}\right] \cup \left[\dfrac{3}{2}, \infty\right)$

**68.** $\dfrac{x(x+5)}{4x-3} \ge 0$

$x = 0$ or $x + 5 = 0$   or   $4x - 3 = 0$

$x = -5$   or   $x = \dfrac{3}{4}$

| Region | Test Point | $\dfrac{x(x+5)}{4x-3} \ge 0$ Result |
|---|---|---|
| $A: (-\infty, -5]$ | $-6$ | $\dfrac{-6(-1)}{-27} \ge 0$ False |
| $B: [-5, 0]$ | $-1$ | $\dfrac{-1(4)}{-7} \ge 0$ True |
| $C: \left[0, \dfrac{3}{4}\right)$ | $\dfrac{1}{2}$ | $\dfrac{\frac{1}{2}\left(\frac{11}{2}\right)}{-1} \ge 0$ False |
| $D: \left(\dfrac{3}{4}, \infty\right)$ | $1$ | $\dfrac{1(6)}{1} \ge 0$ True |

Solution: $[-5, 0] \cup \left(\dfrac{3}{4}, \infty\right)$

**69.** $\dfrac{3}{x-2} > 2$

The denominator is equal to 0 when $x - 2 = 0$, or $x = 2$.

$\dfrac{3}{x-2} = 2$

$3 = 2(x-2)$

$3 = 2x - 4$

$7 = 2x$

$\dfrac{7}{2} = x$

| Region | Test Point | $\dfrac{3}{x-2} > 2$ Result |
|--------|-----------|------------------|
| $A: (-\infty, 2)$ | 0 | $\dfrac{3}{-2} > 2$ False |
| $B: \left(2, \dfrac{7}{2}\right)$ | 3 | $\dfrac{3}{1} > 2$ True |
| $C: \left(\dfrac{7}{2}, \infty\right)$ | 5 | $\dfrac{3}{3} > 2$ False |

Solution: $\left(2, \dfrac{7}{2}\right)$

**70.** $y = 6.46x^2 + 1236.5x + 7289$

    **a.** $x = 2000 - 1980 = 20$

$$y = 6.46(20)^2 + 1236.5(20) + 7289$$
$$= 34,603 \text{ thousand}$$

The passenger traffic was approximately 34,603,000.

    **b.** Let $y = 60,000$.

$$60,000 = 6.46x^2 + 1236.5x + 7289$$
$$0 = 6.46x^2 + 1236.5x - 52,711$$
$$x = \frac{-1236.5 \pm \sqrt{1236.5^2 - 4(6.46)(-52,711)}}{2(6.46)}$$

Choosing the positive root, $x \approx 36$, we see that there will be 60,000,000 passengers in $1980 + 36 = 2016$.

## Chapter 8 Test

**1.** 
$$5x^2 - 2x = 7$$
$$5x^2 - 2x - 7 = 0$$
$$(5x - 7)(x + 1) = 0$$
$$5x - 7 = 0 \quad \text{or} \quad x + 1 = 0$$
$$x = \frac{7}{5} \quad \text{or} \quad x = -1$$

The solutions are $-1$ and $\dfrac{7}{5}$.

**2.** 
$$(x+1)^2 = 10$$
$$x + 1 = \pm\sqrt{10}$$
$$x = -1 \pm \sqrt{10}$$

The solutions are $-1 + \sqrt{10}$ and $-1 - \sqrt{10}$.

**3.** $m^2 - m + 8 = 0$
$$a = 1, b = -1, c = 8$$
$$m = \frac{1 \pm \sqrt{(-1)^2 - 4(1)(8)}}{2(1)}$$
$$= \frac{1 \pm \sqrt{1 - 32}}{2}$$
$$= \frac{1 \pm \sqrt{-31}}{2}$$
$$= \frac{1 \pm i\sqrt{31}}{2}$$

The solutions are $\dfrac{1 + i\sqrt{31}}{2}$ and $\dfrac{1 - i\sqrt{31}}{2}$.

**4.** $u^2 - 6u + 2 = 0$
$$a = 1, b = -6, c = 2$$
$$u = \frac{-(-6) \pm \sqrt{(-6)^2 - 4(1)(2)}}{2(1)}$$
$$= \frac{6 \pm \sqrt{36 - 8}}{2}$$
$$= \frac{6 \pm \sqrt{28}}{2}$$
$$= \frac{6 \pm 2\sqrt{7}}{2}$$
$$= 3 \pm \sqrt{7}$$

The solutions are $3 + \sqrt{7}$ and $3 - \sqrt{7}$.

**5.** 
$$7x^2 + 8x + 1 = 0$$
$$(7x + 1)(x + 1) = 0$$
$$7x + 1 = 0 \quad \text{or} \quad x + 1 = 0$$
$$7x = -1 \qquad\qquad x = -1$$
$$x = -\frac{1}{7}$$

The solutions are $-\dfrac{1}{7}$ and $-1$.

**6.**   $y^2 - 3y = 5$
$y^2 - 3y - 5 = 0$
$a = 1, b = -3, c = -5$

$$y = \frac{3 \pm \sqrt{(-3)^2 - 4(1)(-5)}}{2(1)}$$

$$= \frac{3 \pm \sqrt{9 + 20}}{2}$$

$$= \frac{3 \pm \sqrt{29}}{2}$$

The solutions are $\dfrac{3 + \sqrt{29}}{2}$ and $\dfrac{3 - \sqrt{29}}{2}$.

**7.**   $\dfrac{4}{x+2} + \dfrac{2x}{x-2} = \dfrac{6}{x^2 - 4}$

$$\frac{4}{x+2} + \frac{2x}{x-2} = \frac{6}{(x+2)(x-2)}$$

$$4(x-2) + 2x(x+2) = 6$$

$$4x - 8 + 2x^2 + 4x = 6$$

$$2x^2 + 8x - 14 = 0$$

$$x^2 + 4x - 7 = 0$$

$a = 1, b = 4, c = -7$

$$x = \frac{-4 \pm \sqrt{(4)^2 - 4(1)(-7)}}{2(1)}$$

$$= \frac{-4 \pm \sqrt{16 + 28}}{2}$$

$$= \frac{-4 \pm \sqrt{44}}{2}$$

$$= \frac{-4 \pm 2\sqrt{11}}{2}$$

$$= -2 \pm \sqrt{11}$$

The solutions are $-2 + \sqrt{11}$ and $-2 - \sqrt{11}$.

**8.**   $x^5 + 3x^4 = x + 3$
$x^5 + 3x^4 - x - 3 = 0$
$x^4(x+3) - 1(x+3) = 0$
$(x+3)(x^4 - 1) = 0$
$(x+3)(x^2 + 1)(x^2 - 1) = 0$

$x + 3 = 0$   or $x^2 + 1 = 0$   or $x^2 - 1 = 0$
$x = -3$ or    $x^2 = -1$ or    $x^2 = 1$
                              $x = \pm i$ or    $x = \pm 1$
The solutions are $-3, -1, 1, -i,$ and $i$.

**9.**   $x^6 + 1 = x^4 + x^2$
$x^6 - x^4 - x^2 + 1 = 0$
$x^4(x^2 - 1) - (x^2 - 1) = 0$
$(x^4 - 1)(x^2 - 1) = 0$
$(x^2 + 1)(x^2 - 1)(x+1)(x-1) = 0$
$(x^2 + 1)(x+1)^2(x-1)^2 = 0$

$x^2 + 1 = 0$   or $x + 1 = 0$   or $x - 1 = 0$
$x^2 = -1$          $x = -1$          $x = 1$
$x = \pm i$

The solutions are $-i, i, -1,$ and $1$.

**10.**   $(x+1)^2 - 15(x+1) + 56 = 0$

Let $y = x + 1$. Then $y^2 = (x+1)^2$ and

$y^2 - 15y + 56 = 0$
$(y-8)(y-7) = 0$
    $y = 8$ or     $y = 7$
$x + 1 = 8$ or $x + 1 = 7$
    $x = 7$ or     $x = 6$
The solutions are 6 and 7.

**11.**                    $x^2 - 6x = -2$

$$x^2 - 6x + \left(\frac{-6}{2}\right)^2 = 2 + 9$$

$$x^2 - 6x + 9 = 7$$

$$(x-3)^2 = 7$$

$$x - 3 = \pm\sqrt{7}$$

$$x = 3 \pm \sqrt{7}$$

The solutions are $3 + \sqrt{7}$ and $3 - \sqrt{7}$.

**12.**
$$2a^2 + 5 = 4a$$
$$2a^2 - 4a = -5$$
$$a^2 - 2a = -\frac{5}{2}$$
$$a^2 - 2a + \left(\frac{-2}{2}\right)^2 = -\frac{5}{2} + 1$$
$$a^2 - 2a + 1 = -\frac{3}{2}$$
$$(a-1)^2 = -\frac{3}{2}$$
$$a - 1 = \pm\sqrt{-\frac{3}{2}} = \pm\frac{i\sqrt{3}}{\sqrt{2}}$$
$$a - 1 = \pm\frac{i\sqrt{6}}{2}$$
$$a = 1 \pm \frac{i\sqrt{6}}{2} \quad \text{or} \quad \frac{2 \pm i\sqrt{6}}{2}$$

The solutions are $\dfrac{2 + i\sqrt{6}}{2}$ and $\dfrac{2 - i\sqrt{6}}{2}$.

**13.**
$$2x^2 - 7x > 15$$
$$2x^2 - 7x - 15 > 0$$
$$(2x + 3)(x - 5) > 0$$
$$2x + 3 = 0 \quad \text{or} \quad x - 5 = 0$$
$$x = -\frac{3}{2} \quad \text{or} \quad x = 5$$

| Region | Test Point | $(2x + 3)(x - 5) > 0$ Result |
|---|---|---|
| $A: \left(-\infty, -\dfrac{3}{2}\right)$ | $-2$ | $(-1)(-7) > 0$ True |
| $B: \left(-\dfrac{3}{2}, 5\right)$ | $0$ | $(3)(-5) > 0$ False |
| $C: (5, \infty)$ | $6$ | $(15)(1) > 0$ True |

Solution: $\left(-\infty, -\dfrac{3}{2}\right) \cup (5, \infty)$

**14.**
$$(x^2 - 16)(x^2 - 25) \geq 0$$
$$(x + 4)(x - 4)(x + 5)(x - 5) \geq 0$$
$$x + 4 = 0 \quad \text{or } x - 4 = 0 \quad \text{or } x + 5 = 0 \quad \text{or } x - 5 = 0$$
$$x = -4 \text{ or } \quad x = 4 \text{ or } \quad x = -5 \text{ or } \quad x = 5$$

| Region | Test Point | $(x + 4)(x - 4)(x + 5)(x - 5) \geq 0$ Result |
|---|---|---|
| $A$: $(-\infty, -5]$ | $-6$ | $(-2)(-10)(-1)(-11) \geq 0$ True |
| $B$: $[-5, -4]$ | $-\dfrac{9}{2}$ | $\left(-\dfrac{1}{2}\right)\left(-\dfrac{17}{2}\right)\left(\dfrac{1}{2}\right)\left(-\dfrac{19}{2}\right) \geq 0$ False |
| $C$: $[-4, 4]$ | $0$ | $(4)(-4)(5)(-5) \geq 0$ True |
| $D$: $[4, 5]$ | $\dfrac{9}{2}$ | $\left(\dfrac{17}{2}\right)\left(\dfrac{1}{2}\right)\left(\dfrac{19}{2}\right)\left(-\dfrac{1}{2}\right) \geq 0$ False |
| $E$: $[5, \infty)$ | $6$ | $(10)(2)(11)(1) \geq 0$ True |

Solution: $(-\infty, -5] \cup [-4, 4] \cup [5, \infty)$

**15.** $\dfrac{5}{x + 3} < 1$

The denominator is equal to 0 when $x + 3 = 0$, or $x = -3$.

$$\dfrac{5}{x + 3} = 1$$
$$5 = x + 3 \text{ so } x = 2$$

| Region | Test Point | $\dfrac{5}{x + 3} < 1$ Result |
|---|---|---|
| $A$: $(-\infty, -3)$ | $-4$ | $\dfrac{5}{-1} < 1$ True |
| $B$: $(-3, 2)$ | $0$ | $\dfrac{5}{3} < 1$ False |
| $C$: $(2, \infty)$ | $3$ | $\dfrac{5}{6} < 1$ True |

Solution: $(-\infty, -3) \cup (2, \infty)$

**16.**
$$\frac{7x-14}{x^2-9} \le 0$$
$$\frac{7(x-2)}{(x+3)(x-3)} \le 0$$
$$x-2=0 \text{ or } x+3=0 \text{ or } x-3=0$$
$$x=2 \text{ or } \quad x=-3 \text{ or } \quad x=3$$

| Region | Test Point | $\dfrac{7(x-2)}{(x+3)(x-3)} \le 0$ Result |
|--------|-----------|-------------------------------------------|
| $A$: $(-\infty, -3)$ | $-4$ | $\dfrac{7(-6)}{(-1)(-7)} \le 0$ True |
| $B$: $(-3, 2]$ | $0$ | $\dfrac{7(-2)}{(3)(-3)} \le 0$ False |
| $C$: $[2, 3)$ | $\dfrac{5}{2}$ | $\dfrac{7\left(\frac{1}{2}\right)}{\left(\frac{11}{2}\right)\left(-\frac{1}{2}\right)} \le 0$ True |
| $D$: $(3, \infty)$ | $4$ | $\dfrac{7(2)}{(7)(1)} \le 0$ False |

Solution: $(-\infty, -3) \cup [2, 3)$

**17.** $f(x) = 3x^2$
Vertex: $(0, 0)$

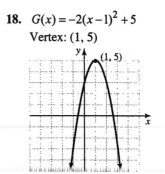

**18.** $G(x) = -2(x-1)^2 + 5$
Vertex: $(1, 5)$

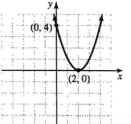

**19.** $h(x) = x^2 - 4x + 4$
$$x = -\frac{b}{2a} = \frac{-(-4)}{2(1)} = 2$$
$$h(2) = (2)^2 - 4(2) + 4 = 0$$
Vertex: $(2, 0)$
$$h(0) = 4 \Rightarrow y\text{-intercept: } (0, 4)$$
$x$-intercept: $(2, 0)$

**20.** $F(x) = 2x^2 - 8x + 9$
$$x = -\frac{b}{2a} = \frac{-(-8)}{2(2)} = 2$$
$$F(2) = 2(2)^2 - 8(2) + 9 = 1$$
Vertex: $(2, 1)$
$$F(0) = 9 \Rightarrow y\text{-intercept: } (0, 9)$$
$$2x^2 - 8x + 9 = 0$$
$$a = 2, b = -8, c = 9$$
$$x = \frac{8 \pm \sqrt{(-8)^2 - 4(2)(9)}}{2(2)}$$
$$= \frac{8 \pm \sqrt{-8}}{4}$$
which yields non-real solutons.
Therefore, there are no $x$-intercepts.

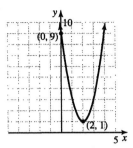

**21.** Let $t$ = time for Sandy alone. Then
$t - 2$ = time for Dave alone.

$$\frac{1}{t} + \frac{1}{t-2} = \frac{1}{4}$$
$$4(t-2) + 4t = t(t-2)$$
$$4t - 8 + 4t = t^2 - 2t$$
$$0 = t^2 - 10t + 8$$
$$a = 1, b = -10, c = 8$$
$$t = \frac{10 \pm \sqrt{(-10)^2 - 4(1)(8)}}{2(1)}$$
$$= \frac{10 \pm \sqrt{68}}{2}$$
$$= \frac{10 \pm 2\sqrt{17}}{2}$$
$$= 5 \pm \sqrt{17}$$
$$\approx 9.12 \text{ or } 0.88 \text{ (discard)}$$

It takes her about 9.12 hours.

**22.** $s(t) = -16t^2 + 32t + 256$

   **a.**   $t = -\dfrac{b}{2a} = \dfrac{-32}{2(-16)} = 1$

        $s(1) = -16(1)^2 + 32(1) + 256 = 272$
        Vertex: $(1, 272)$
        The maximum height is 272 feet.

   **b.**   $-16t^2 + 32t + 256 = 0$
$$t^2 - 2t - 16 = 0$$
$$a = 1, b = -2, c = -16$$
$$t = \frac{2 \pm \sqrt{(-2)^2 - 4(1)(-16)}}{2(1)}$$
$$= \frac{2 \pm \sqrt{68}}{2}$$
$$= \frac{2 \pm 2\sqrt{17}}{2}$$
$$= 1 \pm \sqrt{17}$$
$$\approx -3.12 \text{ and } 5.12$$

        Disregard the negative. The stone will hit
        the water in about 5.12 seconds.

**23.**
$$a^2 + b^2 = c^2$$
$$x^2 + (x+8)^2 = (20)^2$$
$$x^2 + (x^2 + 16x + 64) = 400$$
$$2x^2 + 16x - 336 = 0$$
$$x^2 + 8x - 168 = 0$$
$$a = 1, b = 8, c = -168$$
$$x = \frac{-8 \pm \sqrt{(8)^2 - 4(1)(-168)}}{2(1)}$$
$$\frac{-8 \pm \sqrt{736}}{2}$$
$$\approx -17.565 \text{ or } 9.565$$

Disregard the negative.
$$x \approx 9.6$$
$$x + 8 \approx 9.6 + 8 = 17.6$$
$$17.6 + 9.6 = 27.2$$
$$27.2 - 20 = 7.2$$

They would save about 7 feet.

## Chapter 8 Cumulative Review

**1. a.**   $5 + y \geq 7$

   **b.**   $11 \neq z$

   **c.**   $20 < 5 - 2x$

**2.** $|3x - 2| = -5$ which is impossible. Thus, there is
no solution, or $\varnothing$.

3. $m = \dfrac{5-3}{2-0} = \dfrac{2}{2} = 1$

   Plot the given points and draw a line through them.

4. $\begin{cases} -6x + y = 5 \ (1) \\ 4x - 2y = 6 \ (2) \end{cases}$

   Multiply E1 by 2 and add to E2.

   $-12x + 2y = 10$

   $\underline{\hphantom{-12x+}4x - 2y = 6\hphantom{0}}$

   $-8x \hphantom{+2y} = 16$

   $x = -2$

   Replace $x$ with $-2$ in E1.

   $-6(-2) + y = 5$

   $12 + y = 5$

   $y = -7$

   The solution is $(-2, -7)$.

5. $\begin{cases} x - 5y = -12 \ (1) \\ -x + y = 4 \hphantom{-12} (2) \end{cases}$

   Add E1 and E2.

   $-4y = -8$

   $y = 2$

   Replace $y$ with 2 in E1.

   $x - 5(2) = -12$

   $x - 10 = -12$

   $x = -2$

   The solution is $(-2, 2)$.

6. a. $(a^{-2}bc^3)^{-3} = (a^{-2})^{-3} b^{-3} (c^3)^{-3}$

   $= a^6 b^{-3} c^{-9}$

   $= \dfrac{a^6}{b^3 c^9}$

   b. $\left( \dfrac{a^{-4}b^2}{c^3} \right)^{-2} = \dfrac{(a^{-4})^{-2}(b^2)^{-2}}{(c^3)^{-2}}$

   $= \dfrac{a^8 b^{-4}}{c^{-6}}$

   $= \dfrac{a^8 c^6}{b^4}$

   c. $\left( \dfrac{3a^8 b^2}{12a^5 b^5} \right)^{-2} = \left( \dfrac{a^3}{4b^3} \right)^{-2}$

   $= \dfrac{(a^3)^{-2}}{4^{-2}(b^3)^{-2}}$

   $= \dfrac{4^2 a^{-6}}{b^{-6}}$

   $= \dfrac{16b^6}{a^6}$

7. a. $(2x-7)(3x-4) = 6x^2 - 8x - 21x + 28$

   $= 6x^2 - 29x + 28$

   b. $(3x^2 + y)(5x^2 - 2y)$

   $= 15x^4 - 6x^2 y + 5x^2 y - 2y^2$

   $= 15x^4 - x^2 y - 2y^2$

8. a. $(4a-3)(7a-2) = 28a^2 - 8a - 21a + 6$

   $= 28a^2 - 29a + 6$

   b. $(2a+b)(3a-5b)$

   $= 6a^2 - 10ab + 3ab - 5b^2$

   $= 6a^2 - 7ab - 5b^2$

9. a. $8x^2 + 4 = 4(2x^2 + 1)$

   b. $5y - 2z^4$ is a prime polynomial.

   c. $6x^2 - 3x^3 + 12x^4 = 3x^2(2 - x + 4x^2)$

10. a. $9x^3 + 27x^2 - 15x = 3x(3x^2 + 9x - 5)$

    b. $2x(3y-2) - 5(3y-2)$
    $= (3y-2)(2x-5)$

    c. $2xy + 6x - y - 3 = 2x(y+3) - 1(y+3)$
    $= (y+3)(2x-1)$

**11.** $x^2 - 12x + 35 = (x-5)(x-7)$

**12.** $x^2 - 2x - 48 = (x+6)(x-8)$

**13.** $3a^2x - 12abx + 12b^2x = 3x(a^2 - 4ab + 4b^2)$
$$= 3x(a - 2b)(a - 2b)$$
$$= 3x(a - 2b)^2$$

**14.** $2ax^2 - 12axy + 18ay^2 = 2a(x^2 - 6xy + 9y^2)$
$$= 2a(x - 3y)(x - 3y)$$
$$= 2a(x - 3y)^2$$

**15.** $3(x^2 + 4) + 5 = -6(x^2 + 2x) + 13$
$$3x^2 + 12 + 5 = -6x^2 - 12x + 13$$
$$9x^2 + 12x + 4 = 0$$
$$(3x + 2)^2 = 0$$
$$3x + 2 = 0$$
$$3x = -2$$
$$x = -\frac{2}{3}$$
The solutions is $-\frac{2}{3}$.

**16.** $2(a^2 + 2) - 8 = -2a(a-2) - 5$
$$2a^2 + 4 - 8 = -2a^2 + 4a - 5$$
$$4a^2 - 4a + 1 = 0$$
$$(2a - 1)^2 = 0$$
$$2a - 1 = 0$$
$$2a = 1$$
$$a = \frac{1}{2}$$
The solution is $\frac{1}{2}$.

**17.** $x^3 = 4x$
$$x^3 - 4x = 0$$
$$x(x^2 - 4) = 0$$
$$x(x + 2)(x - 2) = 0$$
$$x = 0 \text{ or } x + 2 = 0 \text{ or } x - 2 = 0$$
$$x = -2 \text{ or } \quad x = 2$$
The solutions are –2, 0, and 2.

**18.** $f(x) = x^2 + x - 12$
$$x = -\frac{b}{2a} = \frac{-1}{2(1)} = -\frac{1}{2}$$
$$f\left(-\frac{1}{2}\right) = \left(-\frac{1}{2}\right)^2 + \left(-\frac{1}{2}\right) - 12$$
$$= \frac{1}{4} - \frac{1}{2} - 12$$
$$= -\frac{49}{4}$$
Vertex: $\left(-\frac{1}{2}, -\frac{49}{4}\right)$

$$x^2 + x - 12 = 0$$
$$(x + 4)(x - 3) = 0$$
$$x + 4 = 0 \quad \text{or} \quad x - 3 = 0$$
$$x = -4 \qquad x = 3$$
*x*-intercepts: (–4, 0), (3, 0)
$$f(0) = 0^2 + 0 - 12 = -12$$
*y*-intercept: (0, –12)

**19.** $\dfrac{2x^2}{10x^3 - 2x^2} = \dfrac{2x^2}{2x^2(5x-1)} = \dfrac{1}{5x-1}$

**20.** $\dfrac{x^2 - 4x + 4}{2 - x} = \dfrac{(x-2)^2}{-(x-2)} = \dfrac{x-2}{-1} = 2 - x$

**21.** $\dfrac{2x-1}{2x^2 - 9x - 5} + \dfrac{x+3}{6x^2 - x - 2}$
$$= \frac{2x-1}{(2x+1)(x-5)} + \frac{x+3}{(2x+1)(3x-2)}$$
$$= \frac{(2x-1)(3x-2) + (x+3)(x-5)}{(2x+1)(x-5)(3x-2)}$$
$$= \frac{(6x^2 - 4x - 3x + 2) + (x^2 - 5x + 3x - 15)}{(2x+1)(x-5)(3x-2)}$$
$$= \frac{7x^2 - 9x - 13}{(2x+1)(x-5)(3x-2)}$$

**22.** $\dfrac{a+1}{a^2-6a+8}-\dfrac{3}{16-a^2}$

$=\dfrac{a+1}{(a-4)(a-2)}-\dfrac{3}{(4+a)(4-a)}$

$=\dfrac{a+1}{(a-4)(a-2)}+\dfrac{3}{(4+a)(a-4)}$

$=\dfrac{(a+1)(a+4)+3(a-2)}{(a-4)(a-2)(a+4)}$

$=\dfrac{(a^2+4a+a+4)+3a-6}{(a-4)(a-2)(a+4)}$

$=\dfrac{a^2+8a-2}{(a-4)(a-2)(a+4)}$

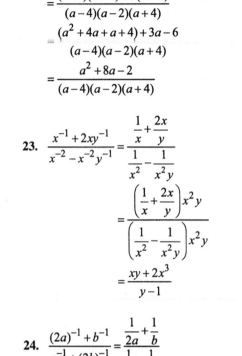

**23.** $\dfrac{x^{-1}+2xy^{-1}}{x^{-2}-x^{-2}y^{-1}}=\dfrac{\dfrac{1}{x}+\dfrac{2x}{y}}{\dfrac{1}{x^2}-\dfrac{1}{x^2y}}$

$=\dfrac{\left(\dfrac{1}{x}+\dfrac{2x}{y}\right)x^2y}{\left(\dfrac{1}{x^2}-\dfrac{1}{x^2y}\right)x^2y}$

$=\dfrac{xy+2x^3}{y-1}$

**24.** $\dfrac{(2a)^{-1}+b^{-1}}{a^{-1}+(2b)^{-1}}=\dfrac{\dfrac{1}{2a}+\dfrac{1}{b}}{\dfrac{1}{a}+\dfrac{1}{2b}}$

$=\dfrac{\left(\dfrac{1}{2a}+\dfrac{1}{b}\right)2ab}{\left(\dfrac{1}{a}+\dfrac{1}{2b}\right)2ab}$

$=\dfrac{b+2a}{2b+a}$

$=\dfrac{2a+b}{a+2b}$

**25.** $\dfrac{3x^5y^2-15x^3y-x^2y-6x}{x^2y}$

$=\dfrac{3x^5y^2}{x^2y}-\dfrac{15x^3y}{x^2y}-\dfrac{x^2y}{x^2y}-\dfrac{6x}{x^2y}$

$=3x^3y-15x-1-\dfrac{6}{xy}$

**26.** $x+3\overline{\smash{\big)}\,x^3-3x^2-10x+24}$ with quotient $x^2-6x+8$

$\underline{x^3+3x^2}$

$-6x^2-10x$

$\underline{-6x^2-18x}$

$8x+24$

$\underline{8x+24}$

$0$

Answer: $x^2-6x+8$

**27.** $P(x)=2x^3-4x^2+5$

   **a.** $P(2)=2(2)^3-4(2)^2+5$

           $=2(8)-4(4)+5$

           $=16-16+5$

           $=5$

   **b.**

| 2| | 2 | $-4$ | 0 | 5 |
|---|---|---|---|---|---|
| | | | 4 | 0 | 0 |
| | | 2 | 0 | 0 | 5 |

     Thus, $P(2)=5$.

**28.** $P(x)=4x^3-2x^2+3$

   **a.** $P(-2)=4(-2)^3-2(-2)^2+3$

            $=4(-8)-2(4)+3$

            $=-32-8+3$

            $=-37$

   **b.**

| $-2$| | 4 | $-2$ | 0 | 3 |
|---|---|---|---|---|---|
| | | | $-8$ | 20 | $-40$ |
| | | 4 | $-10$ | 20 | $-37$ |

     Thus, $P(-2)=-37$.

**29.** $\dfrac{4x}{5}+\dfrac{3}{2}=\dfrac{3x}{10}$

$10\left(\dfrac{4x}{5}+\dfrac{3}{2}\right)=10\left(\dfrac{3x}{10}\right)$

$2(4x)+5(3)=3x$

$8x+15=3x$

$5x=-15$

$x=-3$

The solution is $-3$.

**30.**
$$\frac{x+3}{x^2+5x+6} = \frac{3}{2x+4} - \frac{1}{x+3}$$
$$\frac{x+3}{(x+3)(x+2)} = \frac{3}{2(x+2)} - \frac{1}{x+3}$$
$$2(x+3) = 3(x+3) - 2(x+2)$$
$$2x+6 = 3x+9 - 2x - 4$$
$$2x+6 = x+5$$
$$x = -1$$

**31.** Let $x$ = the number.
$$\frac{9-x}{19+x} = \frac{1}{3}$$
$$3(9-x) = 1(19+x)$$
$$27 - 3x = 19 + x$$
$$-4x = -8$$
$$x = 2$$
The number is 2.

**32.** Let $t$ = time to roof the house together.
$$\frac{1}{24} + \frac{1}{40} = \frac{1}{t}$$
$$120t\left(\frac{1}{24} + \frac{1}{40}\right) = 120t\left(\frac{1}{t}\right)$$
$$5t + 3t = 120$$
$$8t = 120$$
$$t = \frac{120}{8} = 15$$

It would take them 15 hours to roof the house working together.

**33.** $y = kx$
$$5 = k(30)$$
$$k = \frac{5}{30} = \frac{1}{6} \text{ and } y = \frac{1}{6}x$$

**34.** $y = \frac{k}{x}$
$$8 = \frac{k}{14}$$
$$k = 8(14) = 112 \text{ and } y = \frac{112}{x}$$

**35. a.** $\sqrt{(-3)^2} = |-3| = 3$

**b.** $\sqrt{x^2} = |x|$

**c.** $\sqrt[4]{(x-2)^4} = |x-2|$

**d.** $\sqrt[3]{(-5)^3} = -5$

**e.** $\sqrt[5]{(2x-7)^5} = 2x-7$

**f.** $\sqrt{25x^2} = \sqrt{25} \cdot \sqrt{x^2} = 5|x|$

**g.** $\sqrt{x^2+2x+1} = \sqrt{(x+1)^2} = |x+1|$

**36. a.** $\sqrt{(-2)^2} = |-2| = 2$

**b.** $\sqrt{y^2} = |y|$

**c.** $\sqrt[4]{(a-3)^4} = |a-3|$

**d.** $\sqrt[3]{(-6)^3} = -6$

**e.** $\sqrt[5]{(3x-1)^5} = 3x-1$

**37. a.** $\sqrt[8]{x^4} = x^{4/8} = x^{1/2} = \sqrt{x}$

**b.** $\sqrt[6]{25} = (25)^{1/6}$
$$= (5^2)^{1/6} = 5^{2/6} = 5^{1/3} = \sqrt[3]{5}$$

**c.** $\sqrt[4]{r^2 s^6} = (r^2 s^6)^{1/4}$
$$= r^{2/4} s^{6/4}$$
$$= r^{1/2} s^{3/2}$$
$$= (rs^3)^{1/2} = \sqrt{rs^3}$$

**38. a.** $\sqrt[4]{5^2} = 5^{2/4} = 5^{1/2} = \sqrt{5}$

**b.** $\sqrt[12]{x^3} = x^{3/12} = x^{1/4} = \sqrt[4]{x}$

**c.** $\sqrt[6]{x^2 y^4} = (x^2 y^4)^{1/6}$
$$= x^{2/6} y^{4/6}$$
$$= x^{1/3} y^{2/3}$$
$$= (xy^2)^{1/3} = \sqrt[3]{xy^2}$$

**39. a.** $\sqrt{25x^3} = \sqrt{25x^2 \cdot x} = 5x\sqrt{x}$

**b.** $\sqrt[3]{54x^6 y^8} = \sqrt[3]{27x^6 y^6 \cdot 2y^2}$
$$= 3x^2 y^2 \sqrt[3]{2y^2}$$

c. $\sqrt[4]{81z^{11}} = \sqrt[4]{81z^8 \cdot z^3} = 3z^2\sqrt[4]{z^3}$

**40. a.** $\sqrt{64a^5} = \sqrt{64a^4 \cdot a} = 8a^2\sqrt{a}$

   **b.** $\sqrt[3]{24a^7b^9} = \sqrt[3]{8a^6b^9 \cdot 3a} = 2a^2b^3\sqrt[3]{3a}$

   **c.** $\sqrt[4]{48x^9} = \sqrt[4]{16x^8 \cdot 3x} = 2x^2\sqrt[4]{3x}$

**41. a.** $\dfrac{2}{\sqrt{5}} = \dfrac{2 \cdot \sqrt{5}}{\sqrt{5} \cdot \sqrt{5}} = \dfrac{2\sqrt{5}}{5}$

   **b.** $\dfrac{2\sqrt{16}}{\sqrt{9x}} = \dfrac{2 \cdot 4}{3\sqrt{x}} = \dfrac{8 \cdot \sqrt{x}}{3\sqrt{x} \cdot \sqrt{x}} = \dfrac{8\sqrt{x}}{3x}$

   **c.** $\sqrt[3]{\dfrac{1}{2}} = \dfrac{\sqrt[3]{1}}{\sqrt[3]{2}} = \dfrac{1}{\sqrt[3]{2}} = \dfrac{1 \cdot \sqrt[3]{2^2}}{\sqrt[3]{2} \cdot \sqrt[3]{2^2}} = \dfrac{\sqrt[3]{4}}{2}$

**42. a.** $\left(\sqrt{3}-4\right)\left(2\sqrt{3}+2\right)$
$= \sqrt{3} \cdot 2\sqrt{3} + 2\sqrt{3} - 4 \cdot 2\sqrt{3} - 4 \cdot 2$
$= 2(3) + 2\sqrt{3} - 8\sqrt{3} - 8$
$= 6 - 6\sqrt{3} - 8$
$= -2 - 6\sqrt{3}$

   **b.** $\left(\sqrt{5}-x\right)^2 = \left(\sqrt{5}\right)^2 - 2 \cdot \sqrt{5} \cdot x + x^2$
$= 5 - 2x\sqrt{5} + x^2$

   **c.** $\left(\sqrt{a}+b\right)\left(\sqrt{a}-b\right) = \left(\sqrt{a}\right)^2 - b^2$
$= a - b^2$

**43.** $\sqrt{2x+5} + \sqrt{2x} = 3$
$\sqrt{2x+5} = 3 - \sqrt{2x}$
$\left(\sqrt{2x+5}\right)^2 = \left(3-\sqrt{2x}\right)^2$
$2x + 5 = 9 - 6\sqrt{2x} + 2x$
$-4 = -6\sqrt{2x}$
$(-4)^2 = \left(-6\sqrt{2x}\right)^2$
$16 = 36(2x)$
$16 = 72x$
$x = \dfrac{16}{72} = \dfrac{2}{9}$

The solution is $\dfrac{2}{9}$.

**44.** $\sqrt{x-2} = \sqrt{4x+1} - 3$
$\left(\sqrt{x-2}\right)^2 = \left(\sqrt{4x+1}-3\right)^2$
$x - 2 = (4x+1) - 6\sqrt{4x+1} + 9$
$6\sqrt{4x+1} = 3x + 12$
$2\sqrt{4x+1} = x + 4$
$\left(2\sqrt{4x+1}\right)^2 = (x+4)^2$
$4(4x+1) = x^2 + 8x + 16$
$16x + 4 = x^2 + 8x + 16$
$0 = x^2 - 8x + 12$
$0 = (x-6)(x-2)$
$x - 6 = 0 \text{ or } x - 2 = 0$
$x = 6 \text{ or } \quad x = 2$
The solutions are 2 and 6.

**45. a.** $\dfrac{2+i}{1-i} = \dfrac{(2+i) \cdot (1+i)}{(1-i) \cdot (1+i)}$
$= \dfrac{2 + 2i + 1i + i^2}{1^2 - i^2}$
$= \dfrac{2 + 3i - 1}{1+1}$
$= \dfrac{1+3i}{2} \text{ or } \dfrac{1}{2} + \dfrac{3}{2}i$

   **b.** $\dfrac{7}{3i} = \dfrac{7 \cdot (-3i)}{3i \cdot (-3i)} = \dfrac{-21i}{-9i^2} = \dfrac{-21i}{9} = -\dfrac{7}{3}i$

**46. a.** $3i(5-2i) = 15i - 6i^2$
$= 15i + 6$
$= 6 + 15i$

   **b.** $(6-5i)^2 = 6^2 - 2(6)(5i) + (5i)^2$
$= 36 - 60i + 25i^2$
$= 36 - 60i - 25$
$= 11 - 60i$

   **c.** $\left(\sqrt{3}+2i\right)\left(\sqrt{3}-2i\right) = \left(\sqrt{3}\right)^2 - (2i)^2$
$= 3 - 4i^2$
$= 3 + 4$
$= 7$

**47.** $(x+1)^2 = 12$

$$x+1 = \pm\sqrt{12}$$
$$x+1 = \pm 2\sqrt{3}$$
$$x = -1 \pm 2\sqrt{3}$$

The solutions are $-1+2\sqrt{3}$ and $-1-2\sqrt{3}$.

**48.** $(y-1)^2 = 24$

$$y-1 = \pm\sqrt{24}$$
$$y-1 = \pm 2\sqrt{6}$$
$$y = 1 \pm 2\sqrt{6}$$

The solutions are $1+2\sqrt{6}$ and $1-2\sqrt{6}$.

**49.** $x - \sqrt{x} - 6 = 0$

Let $y = \sqrt{x}$. Then $y^2 = x$ and

$$y^2 - y - 6 = 0$$
$$(y-3)(y+2) = 0$$
$$y - 3 = 0 \text{ or } y + 2 = 0$$
$$y = 3 \text{ or } \quad y = -2$$
$$\sqrt{x} = 3 \text{ or } \quad \sqrt{x} = -2 \text{ (can't happen)}$$
$$x = 9$$

The solution is 9.

**50.** $\quad\quad\quad m^2 = 4m + 8$

$$m^2 - 4m - 8 = 0$$
$$a = 1, b = -4, c = -8$$
$$x = \frac{4 \pm \sqrt{(-4)^2 - 4(1)(-8)}}{2(1)}$$
$$= \frac{4 \pm \sqrt{16 + 32}}{2}$$
$$= \frac{4 \pm \sqrt{48}}{2}$$
$$= \frac{4 \pm 4\sqrt{3}}{2}$$
$$= 2 \pm 2\sqrt{3}$$

The solutions are $2 + 2\sqrt{3}$ and $2 - 2\sqrt{3}$.

# Chapter 9

**Practice Exercises**

**1.** $f(x) = x + 2$; $g(x) = 3x + 5$

  **a.** $(f + g)(x) = f(x) + g(x)$
  $= (x + 2) + (3x + 5)$
  $= 4x + 7$

  **b.** $(f - g)(x) = f(x) - g(x)$
  $= (x + 2) - (3x + 5)$
  $= x + 2 - 3x - 5$
  $= -2x - 3$

  **c.** $(f \cdot g)(x) = f(x) \cdot g(x)$
  $= (x + 2)(3x + 5)$
  $= 3x^2 + 6x + 5x + 10$
  $= 3x^2 + 11x + 10$

  **d.** $\left(\dfrac{f}{g}\right)(x) = \dfrac{f(x)}{g(x)} = \dfrac{x + 2}{3x + 5}$, where $x \neq -\dfrac{5}{3}$.

**2.** $f(x) = x^2 + 1$; $g(x) = 3x - 5$

  **a.** $(f \circ g)(4) = f(g(4)) = f(7) = 50$
  $(g \circ f)(4) = g(f(4)) = g(17) = 46$

  **b.** $(f \circ g)(x) = f(g(x))$
  $= f(3x - 5)$
  $= (3x - 5)^2 + 1$
  $= 9x^2 - 30x + 26$
  $(g \circ f)(x) = g(f(x))$
  $= g(x^2 + 1)$
  $= 3(x^2 + 1) - 5$
  $= 3x^2 - 2$

**3.** $f(x) = x^2 + 5$; $g(x) = x + 3$

  **a.** $(f \circ g)(x) = f(g(x))$
  $= f(x + 3)$
  $= (x + 3)^2 + 5$
  $= x^2 + 6x + 14$

  **b.** $(g \circ f)(x) = g(f(x))$
  $= g(x^2 + 5)$
  $= (x^2 + 5) + 3$
  $= x^2 + 8$

**4.** $f(x) = 3x$; $g(x) = x - 4$; $h(x) = |x|$

  **a.** $F(x) = |x - 4|$
  $F(x) = (h \circ g)(x)$
  $= h(g(x))$
  $= h(x - 4)$
  $= |x - 4|$

  **b.** $G(x) = 3x - 4$
  $G(x) = (g \circ f)(x)$
  $= g(f(x))$
  $= g(3x)$
  $= 3x - 4$

**Vocabulary and Readiness Check**

1. C

2. E

3. F

4. A

5. D

6. B

**Exercise Set 9.1**

**1. a.** $(f + g)(x) = (x - 7) + (2x + 1) = 3x - 6$

  **b.** $(f - g)(x) = (x - 7) - (2x + 1)$
  $= x - 7 - 2x - 1$
  $= -x - 8$

  **c.** $(f \cdot g)(x) = (x - 7)(2x + 1) = 2x^2 - 13x - 7$

  **d.** $\left(\dfrac{f}{g}\right)(x) = \dfrac{x - 7}{2x + 1}$, where $x \neq -\dfrac{1}{2}$.

**3. a.** $(f + g)(x) = (x^2 + 1) + 5x = x^2 + 5x + 1$

  **b.** $(f - g)(x) = (x^2 + 1) - 5x = x^2 - 5x + 1$

472

**c.** $(f \cdot g)(x) = (x^2 + 1)(5x) = 5x^3 + 5x$

**d.** $\left(\dfrac{f}{g}\right)(x) = \dfrac{x^2 + 1}{5x}$, where $x \neq 0$

**5. a.** $(f + g)(x) = \sqrt{x} + x + 5$

**b.** $(f - g)(x) = \sqrt{x} - (x + 5) = \sqrt{x} - x - 5$

**c.** $(f \cdot g)(x) = \sqrt{x}(x + 5)$
$= x\sqrt{x} + 5\sqrt{x}$

**d.** $\left(\dfrac{f}{g}\right)(x) = \dfrac{\sqrt{x}}{x + 5}$; where $x \neq -5$.

**7. a.** $(f + g)(x) = -3x + 5x^2$ or $5x^2 - 3x$

**b.** $(f - g)(x) = -3x - 5x^2$ or $-5x^2 - 3x$

**c.** $(f \cdot g)(x) = (-3x)(5x^2) = -15x^3$

**d.** $\left(\dfrac{f}{g}\right)(x) = \dfrac{-3x}{5x^2}$
$= -\dfrac{3}{5x}$, where $x \neq 0$.

**9.** $(f \circ g)(2) = f(g(2))$
$= f(-4)$
$= (-4)^2 - 6(-4) + 2$
$= 16 + 24 + 2$
$= 42$

**11.** $(g \circ f)(-1) = g(f(-1))$
$= g(9)$
$= -2(9)$
$= -18$

**13.** $(g \circ h)(0) = g(h(0))$
$= g(0)$
$= -2(0)$
$= 0$

**15.** $(f \circ g)(x) = f(g(x))$
$= f(5x)$
$= (5x)^2 + 1$
$= 25x^2 + 1$

$(g \circ f)(x) = g(f(x))$
$= g(x^2 + 1)$
$= 5(x^2 + 1)$
$= 5x^2 + 5$

**17.** $(f \circ g)(x) = f(g(x))$
$= f(x + 7)$
$= 2(x + 7) - 3$
$= 2x + 14 - 3$
$= 2x + 11$
$(g \circ f)(x) = g(f(x))$
$= g(2x - 3)$
$= (2x - 3) + 7$
$= 2x + 4$

**19.** $(f \circ g)(x) = f(g(x))$
$= f(-2x)$
$= (-2x)^3 + (-2x) - 2$
$= -8x^3 - 2x - 2$
$(g \circ f)(x) = g(f(x))$
$= g(x^3 + x - 2)$
$= -2(x^3 + x - 2)$
$= -2x^3 - 2x + 4$

**21.** $(f \circ g)(x) = f(g(x))$
$= f(10x - 3)$
$= |10x - 3|$
$(g \circ f)(x) = g(f(x)) = g(|x|) = 10|x| - 3$

**23.** $(f \circ g)(x) = f(g(x)) = f(-5x + 2) = \sqrt{-5x + 2}$
$(g \circ f)(x) = g(f(x)) = g\left(\sqrt{x}\right) = -5\sqrt{x} + 2$

**25.** $H(x) = (g \circ h)(x)$
$= g(h(x))$
$= g(x^2 + 2)$
$= \sqrt{x^2 + 2}$

**27.** $F(x) = (h \circ f)(x)$
$= h(f(x))$
$= h(3x)$
$= (3x)^2 + 2$
$= 9x^2 + 2$

**29.** $G(x) = (f \circ g)(x)$
   $= f(g(x))$
   $= f\left(\sqrt{x}\right)$
   $= 3\sqrt{x}$

**31.** Answers may vary. For example, $g(x) = x + 2$ and $f(x) = x^2$.

**33.** Answers may vary. For example, $g(x) = x + 5$ and $f(x) = \sqrt{x} + 2$.

**35.** Answers may vary. For example, $g(x) = 2x - 3$ and $f(x) = \dfrac{1}{x}$.

**37.** $x = y + 2$
   $y = x - 2$

**39.** $x = 3y$
   $y = \dfrac{x}{3}$

**41.** $x = -2y - 7$
   $2y = -x - 7$
   $y = -\dfrac{x + 7}{2}$

**43.** $(f + g)(2) = f(2) + g(2) = 7 + (-1) = 6$

**45.** $(f \circ g)(2) = f(g(2)) = f(-1) = 4$

**47.** $(f \cdot g)(7) = f(7) \cdot g(7) = 1 \cdot 4 = 4$

**49.** $\left(\dfrac{f}{g}\right)(-1) = \dfrac{f(-1)}{g(-1)} = \dfrac{4}{-4} = -1$

**51.** Answers may vary.

**53.** Profit is equal to the revenue minus the cost; $P(x) = R(x) - C(x)$

**Section 9.2**

**Practice Exercises**

**1. a.** $f = \{(4, -3), (3, -4), (2, 7), (5, 0)\}$
   $f$ is one-to-one since each $y$-value corresponds to only one $x$-value.

   **b.** $g = \{(8, 4), (-2, 0), (6, 4), (2, 6)\}$
   $g$ is not one-to-one because the $y$-value 4 in (8, 4) and (6, 4) corresponds to two different $x$-values.

   **c.** $h = \{(2, 4), (1, 3), (4, 6), (-2, 4)\}$
   $h$ is not one-to-one because the $y$-value 4 in (2, 4) and (-2, 4) corresponds to two different $x$-values.

**d.**

| Year | 1950 | 1963 | 1968 | 1975 | 1997 | 2002 |
|------|------|------|------|------|------|------|
| **Federal Minimum Wage** | $0.75 | $1.25 | $1.60 | $2.10 | $5.15 | $5.15 |

This function is not one-to-one because the wage $5.15 corresponds to two different years.

**e.** The function represented by the graph is not one-to-one because the *y*-value 2 in (2, 2) and (3, 2) corresponds to two different *x*-values.

**f.** The function represented by the diagram is not one-to-one because the score 509 corresponds to two different states.

**2.** Graphs **a**, **b**, and **c** all pass the vertical line test, so only these graphs are functions. But, of these, only **b** and **c** pass the horizontal line test, so only **b** and **c** are graphs of one-to-one functions.

**3.** $f(x) = \{(3, 4), (-2, 0), (2, 8), (6, 6)\}$

Switching the coordinates of each ordered pair gives $f^{-1}(x) = \{(4, 3), (0, -2), (8, 2), (6, 6)\}$

**4.** $f(x) = 6 - x$
Replace $f(x)$ with $y$.
$y = 6 - x$
Interchange $x$ and $y$.
$x = 6 - y$
Solve for $y$.
$x = 6 - y$
$y = 6 - x$
Replace $y$ with $f^{-1}(x)$.
$f^{-1}(x) = 6 - x$

**5.** $f(x) = 5x + 2$
Replace $f(x)$ with $y$.
$y = 5x + 2$
Interchange $x$ and $y$.
$x = 5y + 2$
Solve for $y$.
$\quad x = 5y + 2$
$x - 2 = 5y$
$\dfrac{x - 2}{5} = y$

Replace $y$ with $f^{-1}(x)$.

$f^{-1}(x) = \dfrac{x - 2}{5}$

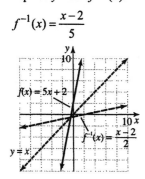

**6. a.** $f(x) = 2x - 3$

$y = 2x - 3$

$x = 2y - 3$

$x + 3 = 2y$

$\dfrac{x + 3}{2} = y$

$f^{-1}(x) = \dfrac{x + 3}{2}$

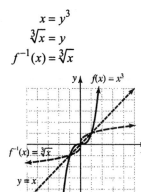

**b.** $f(x) = x^3$

$y = x^3$

$x = y^3$

$\sqrt[3]{x} = y$

$f^{-1}(x) = \sqrt[3]{x}$

**7.** $f(x) = 4x - 1; \quad f^{-1}(x) = \dfrac{x+1}{4}$

$(f \circ f^{-1})(x) = f(f^{-1}(x))$

$= f\left(\dfrac{x+1}{4}\right)$

$= 4\left(\dfrac{x+1}{4}\right) - 1$

$= x + 1 - 1$

$= x$

$(f^{-1} \circ f)(x) = f^{-1}(f(x))$

$= f^{-1}(4x - 1)$

$= \dfrac{(4x-1) + 1}{4}$

$= \dfrac{4x - 1 + 1}{4}$

$= \dfrac{4x}{4}$

$= x$

Since $f \circ f^{-1} = x$ and $f^{-1} \circ f = x$, it

$f(x) = 4x - 1, \quad f^{-1}(x) = \dfrac{x+1}{4}.$

## Vocabulary and Readiness Check

1. If $f(2) = 11$, the corresponding ordered pair is <u>(2, 11)</u>.

2. The symbol $f^{-1}$ means <u>the inverse of $f$</u>.

3. If (7, 3) is an ordered pair solution of $f(x)$, and $f(x)$ has an inverse, then an ordered pair solution of $f^{-1}(x)$ is <u>(3, 7)</u>.

4. To tell whether a graph is the graph of a function, use the <u>vertical</u> line test.

5. To tell whether the graph of a function is also a one-to-one function, use the <u>horizontal</u> line test.

6. The graphs of $f$ and $f^{-1}$ are symmetric about the <u>$y = x$</u> line.

7. Two functions are inverse of each other if $(f \circ f^{-1})(x) = \underline{x}$ and $(f^{-1} \circ f)(x) = \underline{x}$.

## Exercise Set 9.2

1. $f = \{(-1, -1), (1, 1), (0, 2), (2, 0)\}$
   is a one-to-one function.
   $f^{-1} = \{(-1, -1), (1, 1), (2, 0), (0, 2)\}$

3. $h = \{(10, 10)\}$
   is a one-to-one function.
   $h^{-1} = \{(10, 10)\}$

**5.** $f = \{(11,12),(4,3),(3,4),(6,6)\}$

is a one-to-one function.

$f^{-1} = \{(12,11),(3,4),(4,3),(6,6)\}$

**7.** This function is not one-to-one because there are two pairs of two months with the same output: (January, 4.6) and (February, 4.6); (March, 4.4) and (April, 4.4).

**9.** This function is one-to-one.

| Rank in Population (input) | 1 | 19 | 35 | 4 | 48 |
|---|---|---|---|---|---|
| State (output) | California | Maryland | Nevada | Florida | North Dakota |

**11.** $f(x) = x^3 + 2$

    **a.** $f(1) = 1^3 + 2 = 3$

    **b.** $f^{-1}(3) = 1$

**13.** $f(x) = x^3 + 2$

    **a.** $f(-1) = (-1)^3 + 2 = 1$

    **b.** $f^{-1}(1) = -1$

**15.** The graph represents a one-to-one function because it passes the horizontal line test.

**17.** The graph does not represent a one-to-one function because it does not pass the horizontal line test.

**19.** The graph represents a one-to-one function because it passes the horizontal line test.

**21.** The graph does not represent a one-to-one function because it does not pass the horizontal line test.

**23.**
$$f(x) = x + 4$$
$$y = x + 4$$
$$x = y + 4$$
$$y = x - 4$$
$$f^{-1}(x) = x - 4$$

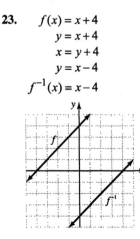

**25.** $f(x) = 2x - 3$
$$y = 2x - 3$$
$$x = 2y - 3$$
$$2y = x + 3$$
$$y = \frac{x+3}{2}$$
$$f^{-1}(x) = \frac{x+3}{2}$$

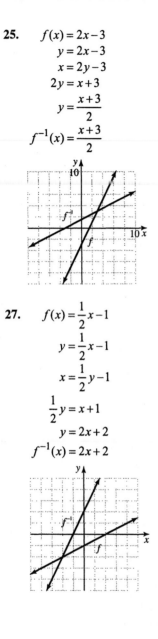

**27.** $f(x) = \frac{1}{2}x - 1$
$$y = \frac{1}{2}x - 1$$
$$x = \frac{1}{2}y - 1$$
$$\frac{1}{2}y = x + 1$$
$$y = 2x + 2$$
$$f^{-1}(x) = 2x + 2$$

**29.** $f(x) = x^3$
$$y = x^3$$
$$x = y^3$$
$$y = \sqrt[3]{x}$$
$$f^{-1}(x) = \sqrt[3]{x}$$

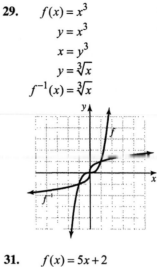

**31.** $f(x) = 5x + 2$
$$y = 5x + 2$$
$$x = 5y + 2$$
$$5y = x - 2$$
$$y = \frac{x-2}{5}$$
$$f^{-1}(x) = \frac{x-2}{5}$$

**33.** $f(x) = \frac{x-2}{5}$
$$y = \frac{x-2}{5}$$
$$x = \frac{y-2}{5}$$
$$5x = y - 2$$
$$y = 5x + 2$$
$$f^{-1}(x) = 5x + 2$$

**35.** $f(x) = \sqrt[3]{x}$
$$y = \sqrt[3]{x}$$
$$x = \sqrt[3]{y}$$
$$x^3 = y$$
$$f^{-1}(x) = x^3$$

**37.** $f(x) = \dfrac{5}{3x+1}$

$$y = \dfrac{5}{3x+1}$$

$$x = \dfrac{5}{3y+1}$$

$$3y+1 = \dfrac{5}{x}$$

$$3y = \dfrac{5}{x} - 1$$

$$3y = \dfrac{5-x}{x}$$

$$y = \dfrac{5-x}{3x}$$

$$f^{-1}(x) = \dfrac{5-x}{3x}$$

**39.** $f(x) = (x+2)^3$

$$y = (x+2)^3$$

$$x = (y+2)^3$$

$$\sqrt[3]{x} = y+2$$

$$\sqrt[3]{x} - 2 = y$$

$$f^{-1}(x) = \sqrt[3]{x} - 2$$

**41.**

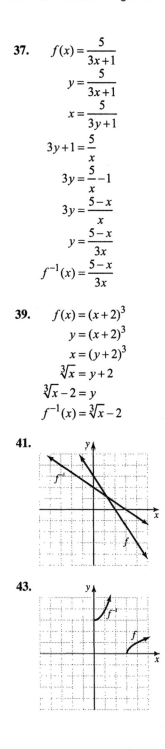

**43.**

**45.**

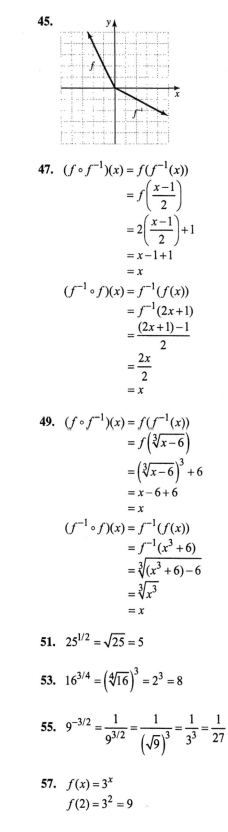

**47.** $(f \circ f^{-1})(x) = f(f^{-1}(x))$

$$= f\left(\dfrac{x-1}{2}\right)$$

$$= 2\left(\dfrac{x-1}{2}\right) + 1$$

$$= x - 1 + 1$$

$$= x$$

$(f^{-1} \circ f)(x) = f^{-1}(f(x))$

$$= f^{-1}(2x+1)$$

$$= \dfrac{(2x+1)-1}{2}$$

$$= \dfrac{2x}{2}$$

$$= x$$

**49.** $(f \circ f^{-1})(x) = f(f^{-1}(x))$

$$= f\left(\sqrt[3]{x-6}\right)$$

$$= \left(\sqrt[3]{x-6}\right)^3 + 6$$

$$= x - 6 + 6$$

$$= x$$

$(f^{-1} \circ f)(x) = f^{-1}(f(x))$

$$= f^{-1}(x^3 + 6)$$

$$= \sqrt[3]{(x^3 + 6) - 6}$$

$$= \sqrt[3]{x^3}$$

$$= x$$

**51.** $25^{1/2} = \sqrt{25} = 5$

**53.** $16^{3/4} = \left(\sqrt[4]{16}\right)^3 = 2^3 = 8$

**55.** $9^{-3/2} = \dfrac{1}{9^{3/2}} = \dfrac{1}{\left(\sqrt{9}\right)^3} = \dfrac{1}{3^3} = \dfrac{1}{27}$

**57.** $f(x) = 3^x$

$$f(2) = 3^2 = 9$$

**59.**  $f(x) = 3^x$

   $f\left(\dfrac{1}{2}\right) = 3^{1/2} \approx 1.73$

**61.** $f(2) = 9$

    **a.**  $(2, 9)$

    **b.**  $(9, 2)$

**63. a.**  $\left(-2, \dfrac{1}{4}\right), \left(-1, \dfrac{1}{2}\right), (0,1), (1,2), (2,5)$

    **b.**  $\left(\dfrac{1}{4}, -2\right), \left(\dfrac{1}{2}, -1\right), (1,0), (2,1), (5,2)$

    **c, d.**

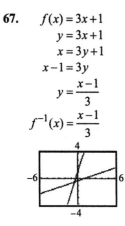

**65.** Answers may vary.

**67.**  $f(x) = 3x + 1$

       $y = 3x + 1$

       $x = 3y + 1$

       $x - 1 = 3y$

       $y = \dfrac{x-1}{3}$

    $f^{-1}(x) = \dfrac{x-1}{3}$

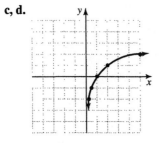

**69.** $f(x) = \sqrt[3]{x+1}$

$y = \sqrt[3]{x+1}$

$x = \sqrt[3]{y+1}$

$x^3 = y+1$

$y = x^3 - 1$

$f^{-1}(x) = x^3 - 1$

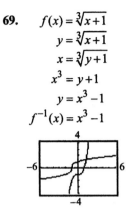

## Section 9.3

### Practice Exercises

**1.**

| $f(x) = 2^x$ | $x$ | 0 | 1 | 2 | 3 | $-1$ | $-2$ |
|---|---|---|---|---|---|---|---|
| | $f(x)$ | 1 | 2 | 4 | 8 | $\frac{1}{2}$ | $\frac{1}{4}$ |

| $g(x) = 7^x$ | $x$ | 0 | 1 | 2 | 3 | $-1$ | $-2$ |
|---|---|---|---|---|---|---|---|
| | $g(x)$ | 1 | 7 | 49 | 343 | $\frac{1}{7}$ | $\frac{1}{49}$ |

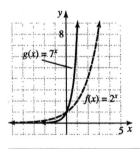

**2.**

| $f(x) = \left(\frac{1}{3}\right)^x$ | $x$ | 0 | 1 | 2 | 3 | $-1$ | $-2$ |
|---|---|---|---|---|---|---|---|
| | $f(x)$ | 1 | $\frac{1}{3}$ | $\frac{1}{9}$ | $\frac{1}{27}$ | 3 | 9 |

| $g(x) = \left(\frac{1}{5}\right)^x$ | $x$ | 0 | 1 | 2 | 3 | $-1$ | $-2$ |
|---|---|---|---|---|---|---|---|
| | $g(x)$ | 1 | $\frac{1}{5}$ | $\frac{1}{25}$ | $\frac{1}{125}$ | 5 | 25 |

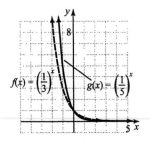

$f(x) = \left(\frac{1}{3}\right)^x$          $g(x) = \left(\frac{1}{5}\right)^x$

**3.** $f(x) = 2^{x+3}$

| $y = 2^{x+3}$ | $x$ | 0 | $-1$ | $-2$ | $-3$ | $-4$ | $-5$ |
|---|---|---|---|---|---|---|---|
| | $y$ | 8 | 4 | 2 | 1 | $\frac{1}{2}$ | $\frac{1}{4}$ |

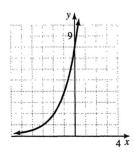

**4. a.** $3^x = 9$

Write 9 as a power of 3, $9 = 3^2$.

$3^x = 3^2$, thus, $x = 2$.

**b.** $8^x = 16$

Write 8 and 16 as powers of 2.

$8 = 2^3$ and $16 = 2^4$.

$$8^x = 16$$
$$(2^3)^x = 2^4$$
$$2^{3x} = 2^4$$
$$3x = 4$$
$$x = \frac{4}{3}$$

**c.** $125^x = 25^{x-2}$

Write 125 and 25 as powers of 5.

$125 = 5^3$ and $25 = 5^2$.

$125^x = 25^{x-2}$

$(5^3)^x = (5^2)^{x-2}$

$5^{3x} = 5^{2x-4}$

$3x = 2x - 4$

$x = -4$

**5.** $P = \$3000$, $r = 7\% = 0.07$, $n = 2$, and $t = 4$.

$$A = P\left(1 + \frac{r}{n}\right)^{nt}$$

$$A = 3000\left(1 + \frac{0.07}{2}\right)^{2(4)}$$

$$= 3000(1.035)^8$$

$$\approx 3950.43$$

Thus, the amount $A$ owed is approximately $3950.43.

**6.** $p(n) = 100(2.7)^{-0.05n}$, $n = 10$ sheets of glass.

$p(10) = 100(2.7)^{-0.05(10)} = 100(2.7)^{-0.5} \approx 60.86$

Thus, approximately 60.86% of the light passes through.

**Graphing Calculator Explorations**

**1.**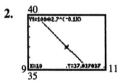

The expected percent after 2 days is 81.98%.

**2.**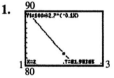

The expected percent after 10 days is 37.04%.

**3.**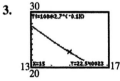

The expected percent after 15 days is 22.54%.

**4.**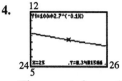

The expected percent after 25 days is 8.35%.

**Vocabulary and Readiness Check**

**1.** A function such as $f(x) = 2^x$ is an <u>exponential</u> function; **C.**

**2.** If $7^x = 7^y$, then <u>$x = y$</u>; **B.**

**3.** Yes, the function passes both the vertical- and horizontal-line tests.

**4.** The function has no $x$-intercept.

**5.** The function has a $y$-intercept of <u>(0, 1)</u>.

**6.** The domain of this function, in interval notation, is <u>$(-\infty, \infty)$</u>.

**7.** The range of this function, in interval notation, is <u>$(0, \infty)$</u>.

**Exercise Set 9.3**

**1.** $y = 4^x$

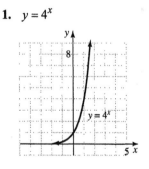

**3.** $y = 2^x + 1$

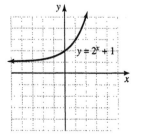

**5.** $y = \left(\dfrac{1}{4}\right)^x$

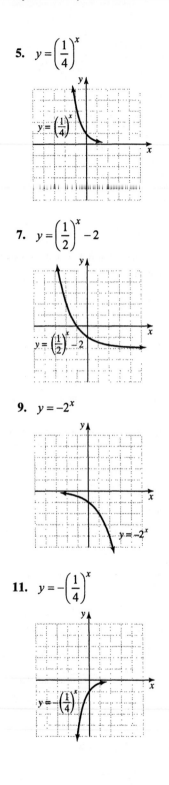

**7.** $y = \left(\dfrac{1}{2}\right)^x - 2$

**9.** $y = -2^x$

**11.** $y = -\left(\dfrac{1}{4}\right)^x$

**13.** $f(x) = 2^{x+1}$

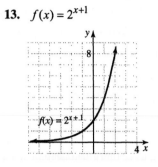

**15.** $f(x) = 4^{x-2}$

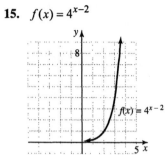

**17.** C

**19.** B

**21.** $3^x = 27$
$3^x = 3^3$
$x = 3$
The solution is 3.

**23.** $16^x = 8$
$(2^4)^x = 2^3$
$2^{4x} = 2^3$
$4x = 3$
$x = \dfrac{3}{4}$

The solution is $\dfrac{3}{4}$.

**25.** $32^{2x-3} = 2$
$(2^5)^{2x-3} = 2^1$
$2^{10x-15} = 2^1$
$10x - 15 = 1$
$10x = 16$
$x = \dfrac{8}{5}$

The solution is $\dfrac{8}{5}$.

**27.** $\dfrac{1}{4} = 2^{3x}$

$2^{-2} = 2^{3x}$

$3x = -2$

$x = -\dfrac{2}{3}$

The solution is $-\dfrac{2}{3}$.

**29.** $5^x = 625$

$5^x = 5^4$

$x = 4$

The solution is 4.

**31.** $4^x = 8$

$(2^2)^x = 2^3$

$2^{2x} = 2^3$

$2x = 3$

$x = \dfrac{3}{2}$

The solution is $\dfrac{3}{2}$.

**33.** $27^{x+1} = 9$

$(3^3)^{x+1} = 3^2$

$3^{3x+3} = 3^2$

$3x + 3 = 2$

$3x = -1$

$x = -\dfrac{1}{3}$

The solution is $-\dfrac{1}{3}$.

**35.** $81^{x-1} = 27^{2x}$

$(3^4)^{x-1} = (3^3)^{2x}$

$3^{4x-4} = 3^{6x}$

$4x - 4 = 6x$

$-4 = 2x$

$x = -2$

The solution is $-2$.

**37.** $y = 30(2.7)^{-0.004t}$, $t = 50$

$y = 30(2.7)^{-(0.004)(50)}$

$= 30(2.7)^{-0.2}$

$\approx 24.6$

Approximately 24.6 pounds of uranium will remain after 50 days.

**39.** $y = 260(2.7)^{0.025t}$, $t = 10$

$y = 260(2.7)^{0.025(10)}$

$= 260(2.7)^{0.25}$

$\approx 333$

There should be about 333 bison in the park in 10 years.

**41.** $y = 5(2.7)^{-0.15t}$, $t = 10$

$y = 5(2.7)^{-0.15(10)}$

$= 5(2.7)^{-1.5}$

$\approx 1.1$

After 10 seconds there will be about 1.1 grams.

**43.** $p(h) = 760(2.7)^{-0.145h}$

  **a.** $p(1) = 760(2.7)^{-0.145(1)} \approx 658.1$

     The pressure is 658.1 Pascals at a height of 1 kilometer.

  **b.** $p(10) = 760(2.7)^{-0.145(10)}$

     $= 760(2.7)^{-1.45}$

     $\approx 180.0$

     The pressure is 180.0 Pascals at a height of 10 kilometers.

**45.** $y = 84,949(1.096)^x$

  **a.** $x = 2000 - 1995 = 5$

     $y = 84,949(1.096)^5 \approx 134,342$

     134,342 American students studied abroad in 2000.

  **b.** $x = 2020 - 1995 = 25$

     $y = 84,949(1.096)^{25} \approx 840,276$

     840,276 American students would be studying abroad in 2020.

**47.** $A = P\left(1+\dfrac{r}{n}\right)^{nt}$

$t = 3$, $P = 6000$, $r = 0.08$, and $n = 12$

$A = 6000\left(1+\dfrac{0.08}{12}\right)^{12(3)}$

$= 6000\left(1+\dfrac{0.08}{12}\right)^{36}$

$\approx 7621.42$

Erica would owe \$7621.42 after 3 years.

**49.** $A = P\left(1+\dfrac{r}{n}\right)^{nt}$

$P = 2000$

$r = 0.06$, $n = 2$, and $t = 12$

$A = 2000\left(1+\dfrac{0.06}{2}\right)^{2(12)}$

$= 2000(1.03)^{24}$

$\approx 4065.59$

Janina has approximately \$4065.59 in her savings account.

**51.** $y = 18(1.24)^x$

$x = 2010 - 1994 = 16$

$y = 18(1.24)^{16} \approx 562$

There will be approximately 562 million cellular phone users in 2010.

**53.** $5x - 2 = 18$

$5x = 20$

$x = 4$

The solution is 4.

**55.** $3x - 4 = 3(x+1)$

$3x - 4 = 3x + 3$

$-4 = 3$

This is a false statement. The solution set is $\varnothing$.

**57.** $x^2 + 6 = 5x$

$x^2 - 5x + 6 = 0$

$(x-2)(x-3) = 0$

$x = 2$ or $x = 3$

The solutions are 2 and 3.

**59.** $2^x = 8$

$2^3 = 8$

$x = 3$

**61.** $5^x = \dfrac{1}{5}$

$5^{-1} = \dfrac{1}{5}$

$x = -1$

**63.** Answers may vary

**65.** $y = \left|3^x\right|$

**67.** $y = 3^{|x|}$

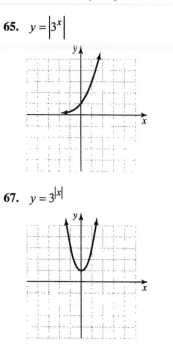

**69.**

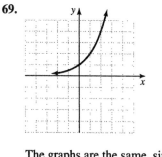

The graphs are the same, since $\left(\dfrac{1}{2}\right)^{-x} = 2^x$.

**71.**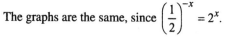

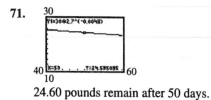

24.60 pounds remain after 50 days.

**73.**

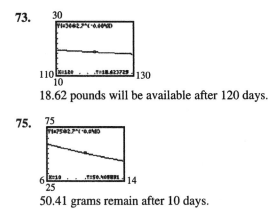

18.62 pounds will be available after 120 days.

**75.**

50.41 grams remain after 10 days.

## Section 9.4

**Practice Exercises**

**1. a.** $\log_3 81 = 4$ means $3^4 = 81$.

   **b.** $\log_5 \dfrac{1}{5} = -1$ means $5^{-1} = \dfrac{1}{5}$.

   **c.** $\log_7 \sqrt{7} = \dfrac{1}{2}$ means $7^{1/2} = \sqrt{7}$.

   **d.** $\log_{13} y = 4$ means $13^4 = y$.

**2. a.** $4^3 = 64$ means $\log_4 64 = 3$.

   **b.** $6^{1/3} = \sqrt[3]{6}$ means $\log_6 \sqrt[3]{6} = \dfrac{1}{3}$.

   **c.** $5^{-3} = \dfrac{1}{125}$ means $\log_5 \dfrac{1}{125} = -3$.

   **d.** $\pi^7 = z$ means $\log_\pi z = 7$.

**3. a.** $\log_3 9 = 2$ because $3^2 = 9$.

   **b.** $\log_2 \dfrac{1}{8} = -3$ because $2^{-3} = \dfrac{1}{8}$.

   **c.** $\log_{49} 7 = \dfrac{1}{2}$ because $49^{1/2} = 7$.

**4. a.** $\log_5 \dfrac{1}{25} = x$

   $\log_5 \dfrac{1}{25} = x$ means $5^x = \dfrac{1}{25}$. Solve $5^x = \dfrac{1}{25}$.

$$5^x = \dfrac{1}{25}$$
$$5^x = 5^{-2}$$

Since the bases are the same, by the uniqueness of $b^x$, we have that $x = -2$. The solution is $-2$ or the solution set is $\{-2\}$.

   **b.** $\log_x 8 = 3$
$$x^3 = 8$$
$$x^3 = 2^3$$
$$x = 2$$

   **c.** $\log_6 x = 2$
$$6^2 = x$$
$$36 = x$$

   **d.** $\log_{13} 1 = x$
$$13^x = 1$$
$$13^x = 13^0$$
$$x = 0$$

   **e.** $\log_h 1 = x$
$$h^x = 1$$
$$h^x = h^0$$
$$x = 0$$

**5. a.** From Property 2, $\log_5 5^4 = 4$.

   **b.** From Property 2, $\log_9 9^{-2} = -2$.

   **c.** From Property 3, $6^{\log_6 5} = 5$.

   **d.** From Property 3, $7^{\log_7 4} = 4$.

**6.** $y = \log_7 x$ means that $7^y = x$. Find some ordered pair solutions that satisfy $7^y = x$.

| $x = 7^y$ | $y$ |
|-----------|-----|
| 1 | 0 |
| 7 | 1 |
| $\frac{1}{7}$ | $-1$ |
| $\frac{1}{49}$ | $-2$ |

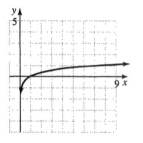

**7.** $y = \log_{1/4} x$ means that $\left(\frac{1}{4}\right)^y = x$. Find some ordered-pair solutions that satisfy $\left(\frac{1}{4}\right)^y = x$.

| $x = \left(\frac{1}{4}\right)^y$ | $y$ |
|-----------|-----|
| 1 | 0 |
| $\frac{1}{4}$ | 1 |
| 4 | $-1$ |
| 16 | $-2$ |

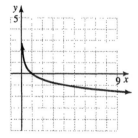

**Vocabulary and Readiness Check**

1. A function, such as $y = \log_2 x$ is a <u>logarithmic</u> function; **B**.

2. If $y = \log_2 x$, then <u>$2^y = x$</u>; **C**.

3. Yes, the function passes both the horizontal- and vertical-line tests.

4. The function has an $x$-intercept of <u>(1, 0)</u>.

5. The function has no $y$-intercept.

6. The domain of this function, in interval notation, is <u>$(0, \infty)$</u>.

7. The range of this function, in interval notation, is <u>$(-\infty, \infty)$</u>.

**Exercise Set 9.4**

1. $\log_6 36 = 2$
   $6^2 = 36$

3. $\log_3 \frac{1}{27} = -3$
   $3^{-3} = \frac{1}{27}$

5. $\log_{10} 1000 = 3$
   $10^3 = 1000$

7. $\log_9 x = 4$
   $9^4 = x$

9. $\log_\pi \frac{1}{\pi^2} = -2$
   $\pi^{-2} = \frac{1}{\pi^2}$

11. $\log_7 \sqrt{7} = \frac{1}{2}$
    $7^{1/2} = \sqrt{7}$

13. $\log_{0.7} 0.343 = 3$
    $0.7^3 = 0.343$

**15.** $\log_3 \dfrac{1}{81} = -4$

$3^{-4} = \dfrac{1}{81}$

**17.** $2^4 = 16$

$\log_2 16 = 4$

**19.** $10^2 = 100$

$\log_{10} 100 = 2$

**21.** $\pi^3 = x$

$\log_\pi x = 3$

**23.** $10^{-1} = \dfrac{1}{10}$

$\log_{10} \dfrac{1}{10} = -1$

**25.** $4^{-2} = \dfrac{1}{16}$

$\log_4 \dfrac{1}{16} = -2$

**27.** $5^{1/2} = \sqrt{5}$

$\log_5 \sqrt{5} = \dfrac{1}{2}$

**29.** $\log_2 8 = 3$ since $2^3 = 8$.

**31.** $\log_3 \dfrac{1}{9} = -2$ since $3^{-2} = \dfrac{1}{9}$.

**33.** $\log_{25} 5 = \dfrac{1}{2}$ since $25^{1/2} = 5$.

**35.** $\log_{1/2} 2 = -1$ since $\left(\dfrac{1}{2}\right)^{-1} = 2$.

**37.** $\log_6 1 = 0$ since $6^0 = 1$.

**39.** $\log_{10} 100 = \log_{10} 10^2 = 2$

**41.** $\log_3 81 = \log_3 3^4 = 4$

**43.** $\log_4 \dfrac{1}{64} = \log_4 4^{-3} = -3$

**45.** $\log_3 9 = x$

$3^x = 9$

$3^x = 3^2$

$x = 2$

**47.** $\log_3 x = 4$

$x = 3^4 = 81$

**49.** $\log_x 49 = 2$

$x^2 = 49$

$x = \pm 7$

We discard the negative base.

$x = 7$

**51.** $\log_2 \dfrac{1}{8} = x$

$2^x = \dfrac{1}{8}$

$2^x = 2^{-3}$

$x = -3$

**53.** $\log_3 \dfrac{1}{27} = x$

$\dfrac{1}{27} = 3^x$

$3^{-3} = 3^x$

$-3 = x$

**55.** $\log_8 x = \dfrac{1}{3}$

$x = 8^{1/3} = 2$

**57.** $\log_4 16 = x$

$4^x = 16$

$4^x = 4^2$

$x = 2$

**59.** $\log_{3/4} x = 3$

$\left(\dfrac{3}{4}\right)^3 = x$

$\dfrac{27}{64} = x$

**61.** $\log_x 100 = 2$

$x^2 = 100$

$x = \pm 10$

We discard the negative base.

$x = 10$

**63.** $\log_2 2^4 = x$
$$2^x = 2^4$$
$$x = 4$$

**65.** $3^{\log_3 5} = x$
$$5 = x$$

**67.** $\log_x \dfrac{1}{7} = \dfrac{1}{2}$
$$x^{1/2} = \dfrac{1}{7}$$
$$x = \dfrac{1}{49}$$

**69.** $\log_5 5^3 = 3$

**71.** $2^{\log_2 3} = 3$

**73.** $\log_9 9 = 1$

**75.** $y = \log_3 x$
$y = 0:$
$\log_3 x = 0$
$$x = 3^0 = 1$$
$(1, 0)$ is the only $x$-intercept. No $y$-intercept exists.

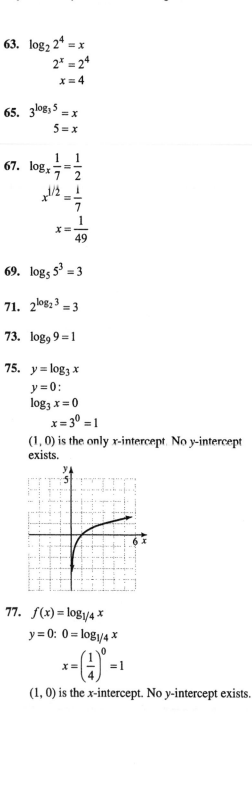

**77.** $f(x) = \log_{1/4} x$
$y = 0:\ 0 = \log_{1/4} x$
$$x = \left(\dfrac{1}{4}\right)^0 = 1$$
$(1, 0)$ is the $x$-intercept. No $y$-intercept exists.

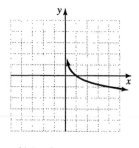

**79.** $f(x) = \log_5 x$
$y = 0:\ 0 = \log_5 x$
$$x = 5^0 = 1$$
$(1, 0)$ is the $x$-intercept. No $y$-intercept exists.

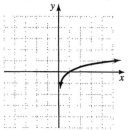

**81.** $f(x) = \log_{1/16} x$
$y = 0:$
$0 = \log_{1/6} x$
$$x = \left(\dfrac{1}{6}\right)^0 = 1$$
$(1, 0)$ is the $x$-intercept. No $y$-intercept exists.

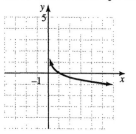

**83.** $\dfrac{x+3}{3+x} = \dfrac{x+3}{x+3} = 1$

**85.** $\dfrac{x^2 - 8x + 16}{2x - 8} = \dfrac{(x-4)^2}{2(x-4)} = \dfrac{x-4}{2}$

**87.** $\dfrac{2}{x} + \dfrac{3}{x^2} = \dfrac{2x}{x^2} + \dfrac{3}{x^2} = \dfrac{2x+3}{x^2}$

**89.** $\dfrac{m^2}{m+1} - \dfrac{1}{m+1} = \dfrac{m^2-1}{m+1}$

$\qquad = \dfrac{(m+1)(m-1)}{m+1}$

$\qquad = m-1$

**91.** $f(x) = \log_5 x;\ \ f^{-1}(x) = g(x) = 5^x$

**a.** $(2, 25)$ implies $g(2) = 25$.

**b.** Since $f^{-1}(x) = g(x),\ (25, 2)$ is a solution of $f(x)$.

**c.** $(25, 2)$ implies $f(25) = 2$.

**93.** Answers may vary

**95.** $\log_7(5x-2) = 1$

$\qquad 5x - 2 = 7^1$

$\qquad\quad 5x = 9$

$\qquad\quad\ x = \dfrac{9}{5}$

**97.** $\log_3\left(\log_5 125\right) = \log_3(3) = 1$

**99.** $y = 4^x;\ y = \log_4 x$

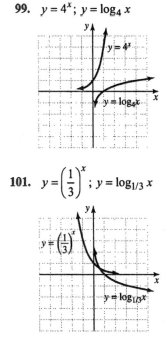

**101.** $y = \left(\dfrac{1}{3}\right)^x;\ y = \log_{1/3} x$

**103.** Answers may vary

**105.** $\log_{10}(1-k) = \dfrac{-0.3}{H},\ H = 8$

$\qquad \log_{10}(1-k) = \dfrac{-0.3}{8} = -0.0375$

$\qquad\qquad 1 - k = 10^{-0.0375}$

$\qquad 1 - 10^{-0.0375} = k$

$\qquad\qquad\quad k \approx 0.0827$

The rate of decay is 0.0827.

**Section 9.5**

**Practice Exercises**

**1. a.** $\log_8 5 + \log_8 3 = \log_8(5 \cdot 3) = \log_8 15$

**b.** $\log_2 \dfrac{1}{3} + \log_2 18 = \log_2\left(\dfrac{1}{3} \cdot 18\right) = \log_2 6$

**c.** $\log_5(x-1) + \log_5(x+1) = \log_5[(x+1)(x+1)]$
$\qquad\qquad\qquad\qquad\qquad\qquad = \log_5(x^2-1)$

**2. a.** $\log_5 18 - \log_5 6 = \log_5 \dfrac{18}{6} = \log_5 3$

**b.** $\log_6 x - \log_6 3 = \log_6 \dfrac{x}{3}$

**c.** $\log_4(x^2+1) - \log_4(x^2+3) = \log_4 \dfrac{x^2+1}{x^2+3}$

**3. a.** $\log_7 x^8 = 8\log_7 x$

**b.** $\log_5 \sqrt[4]{7} = \log_5 7^{1/4} = \dfrac{1}{4}\log_5 7$

**4. a.** $2\log_5 4 + 5\log_5 2 = \log_5 4^2 + \log_5 2^5$
$\qquad\qquad\qquad\qquad = \log_5 16 + \log_5 32$
$\qquad\qquad\qquad\qquad = \log_5(16 \cdot 32)$
$\qquad\qquad\qquad\qquad = \log_5 512$

**b.** $2\log_8 x - \log_8(x+3) = \log_8 x^2 - \log_8(x+3)$
$\qquad\qquad\qquad\qquad\qquad = \log_8 \dfrac{x^2}{x+3}$

**c.** $\log_7 12 + \log_7 5 - \log_7 4$
$= \log_7 (12 \cdot 5) - \log_7 4$
$= \log_7 60 - \log_7 4$
$= \log_7 \dfrac{60}{4}$
$= \log_7 15$

**5. a.** $\log_5 \dfrac{4 \cdot 3}{7} = \log_5 (4 \cdot 3) - \log_5 7$
$= \log_5 4 + \log_5 3 - \log_5 7$

**b.** $\log_4 \dfrac{a^2}{b^5} = \log_4 a^2 - \log_4 b^5$
$= 2\log_4 a - 5\log_4 b$

**6.** $\log_b 5 = 0.83$ and $\log_b 3 = 0.56$

**a.** $\log_b 15 = \log_b (3 \cdot 5)$
$= \log_b 3 + \log_b 5$
$= 0.56 + 0.83$
$= 1.39$

**b.** $\log_b 25 = \log_b 5^2 = 2\log_b 5 = 2(0.83) = 1.66$

**c.** $\log_b \sqrt{3} = \log_b 3^{1/2}$
$= \dfrac{1}{2} \log_b 3$
$= \dfrac{1}{2}(0.56)$
$= 0.28$

**Vocabulary and Readiness Check**

**1.** $\log_b 12 + \log_b 3 = \log_b (12 \cdot 3) = \log_b \underline{36}$; **a.**

**2.** $\log_b 12 - \log_b 3 = \log_b \dfrac{12}{3} = \log_b \underline{4}$; **c.**

**3.** $7\log_b 2 = \underline{\log_b 2^7}$; **b.**

**4.** $\log_b 1 = \underline{0}$; **c.**

**5.** $b^{\log_b x} = \underline{x}$; **a.**

**6.** $\log_5 5^2 = \underline{2}$; **b.**

**Exercise Set 9.5**

**1.** $\log_5 2 + \log_5 7 = \log_5 (2 \cdot 7) = \log_5 14$

**3.** $\log_4 9 + \log_4 x = \log_4 9x$

**5.** $\log_6 x + \log_6 (x+1) = \log_6 [x(x+1)]$
$= \log_6 (x^2 + x)$

**7.** $\log_{10} 5 + \log_{10} 2 + \log_{10} (x^2 + 2)$
$= \log_{10} \left[ 5 \cdot 2 \left( x^2 + 2 \right) \right]$
$= \log_{10} \left( 10x^2 + 20 \right)$

**9.** $\log_5 12 - \log_5 4 = \log_5 \dfrac{12}{4} = \log_5 3$

**11.** $\log_3 8 - \log_3 2 = \log_3 \dfrac{8}{2} = \log_3 4$

**13.** $\log_2 x - \log_2 y = \log_2 \dfrac{x}{y}$

**15.** $\log_2 (x^2 + 6) - \log(x^2 + 1) = \log_2 \dfrac{x^2 + 6}{x^2 + 1}$

**17.** $\log_3 x^2 = 2\log_3 x$

**19.** $\log_4 5^{-1} = -\log_4 5$

**21.** $\log_5 \sqrt{y} = \log_5 y^{1/2} = \dfrac{1}{2}\log_5 y$

**23.** $\log_2 5 + \log_2 x^3 = \log_2 5x^3$

**25.** $3\log_4 2 + \log_4 6 = \log_4 2^3 + \log_4 6$
$= \log_4 8 + \log_4 6$
$= \log_4 (8 \cdot 6)$
$= \log_4 48$

**27.** $3\log_5 x + 6\log_5 z = \log_5 x^3 + \log_5 z^6$
$= \log_5 x^3 z^6$

**29.** $\log_4 2 + \log_4 10 - \log_4 5 = \log_4 (2 \cdot 10) - \log_4 5$
$= \log_4 \dfrac{20}{5}$
$= \log_4 4$
$= 1$

**31.** $\log_7 6 + \log_7 3 - \log_7 4 = \log_7 (6 \cdot 3) - \log_7 4$
$$= \log_7 \frac{18}{4}$$
$$= \log_7 \frac{9}{2}$$

**33.** $\log_{10} x - \log_{10}(x+1) + \log_{10}(x^2 - 2)$
$$= \log_{10} \frac{x}{x+1} + \log_{10}(x^2 - 2)$$
$$= \log_{10} \frac{x(x^2 - 2)}{x+1}$$
$$= \log_{10} \frac{x^3 - 2x}{x+1}$$

**35.** $3\log_2 x + \frac{1}{2}\log_2 x - 2\log_2(x+1)$
$$= \log_2 x^3 + \log_2 x^{1/2} - \log_2(x+1)^2$$
$$= \log_2 (x^3 \cdot x^{1/2}) - \log_2(x+1)^2$$
$$= \log_2 x^{7/2} - \log_2(x+1)^2$$
$$= \log_2 \frac{x^{7/2}}{(x+1)^2}$$

**37.** $2\log_8 x - \frac{2}{3}\log_8 x + 4\log_8 x = \left(2 - \frac{2}{3} + 4\right)\log_8 x$
$$= \frac{16}{3}\log_8 x$$
$$= \log_8 x^{16/3}$$

**39.** $\log_3 \frac{4y}{5} = \log_3 4y - \log_3 5$
$$= \log_3 4 + \log_3 y - \log_3 5$$

**41.** $\log_4 \frac{2}{9z} = \log_4 2 - \log_4 9z$
$$= \log_4 2 - (\log_4 9 + \log_4 z)$$
$$= \log_4 2 - \log_4 9 - \log_4 z$$

**43.** $\log_2 \frac{x^3}{y} = \log_2 x^3 - \log_2 y$
$$= 3\log_2 x - \log_2 y$$

**45.** $\log_b \sqrt{7x} = \log_b (7x)^{1/2}$
$$= \frac{1}{2}\log_b (7x)$$
$$= \frac{1}{2}\left[\log_b 7 + \log_b x\right]$$
$$= \frac{1}{2}\log_b 7 + \frac{1}{2}\log_b x$$

**47.** $\log_6 x^4 y^5 = \log_6 x^4 + \log_6 y^5$
$$= 4\log_6 x + 5\log_6 y$$

**49.** $\log_5 x^3(x+1) = \log_5 x^3 + \log_5(x+1)$
$$= 3\log_5 x + \log_5(x+1)$$

**51.** $\log_6 \frac{x^2}{x+3} = \log_6 x^2 - \log_6(x+3)$
$$= 2\log_6 x - \log_6(x+3)$$

**53.** $\log_b 15 = \log_b(5 \cdot 3)$
$$= \log_b 5 + \log_b 3$$
$$= 0.7 + 0.5$$
$$= 1.2$$

**55.** $\log_b \frac{5}{3} = \log_b 5 - \log_b 3 = 0.7 - 0.5 = 0.2$

**57.** $\log_b \sqrt{5} = \log_b 5^{1/2} = \frac{1}{2}\log_b 5 = \frac{1}{2}(0.7) = 0.35$

**59.** $\log_b 8 = \log_b 2^3 = 3\log_b 2 = 3(0.43) = 1.29$

**61.** $\log_b \frac{3}{9} = \log_b 3 - \log_b 9$
$$= \log_b 3 - \log_b 3^2$$
$$= \log_b 3 - 2\log_b 3$$
$$= -\log_b 3$$
$$= -0.68$$

**63.** $\log_b \sqrt{\frac{2}{3}} = \log_b \left(\frac{2}{3}\right)^{1/2}$
$$= \frac{1}{2}\log_b \frac{2}{3}$$
$$= \frac{1}{2}\left(\log_b 2 - \log_b 3\right)$$
$$= \frac{1}{2}(0.43 - 0.68)$$
$$= \frac{1}{2}(-0.25)$$
$$= -0.125$$

**65.** $y = 10^x$ and $y = \log_{10} x$

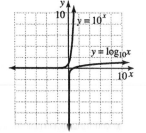

**67.** $\log_{10} \dfrac{1}{10} = x$

$\log_{10} 10^{-1} = x$

$-1 = x$

**69.** $\log_7 \sqrt{7} = x$

$\log_7 7^{1/2} = x$

$\dfrac{1}{2} = x$

**71.** $\log_9 \dfrac{21}{3} = \log_9 7 = \log_9 21 - \log_9 3$

The correct answers are **a** and **d**.

**73.** $\log_3 (x + y) = \log_3 x + \log_3 y$ is false.

**75.** $\log_7 \dfrac{14}{8} = \log_7 14 - \log_7 8$ is true.

**77.** $(\log_3 6) \cdot (\log_3 4) = \log_3 24$ is false.

**Integrated Review**

**1.** $(f + g)(x) = x - 6 + x^2 + 1 = x^2 + x - 5$

**2.** $(f - g)(x) = x - 6 - (x^2 + 1) = -x^2 + x - 7$

**3.** $(f \cdot g)(x) = (x - 6)(x^2 + 1) = x^3 - 6x^2 + x - 6$

**4.** $\left(\dfrac{f}{g}\right)(x) = \dfrac{x - 6}{x^2 + 1}$

**5.** $(f \circ g)(x) = f(g(x)) = f(3x - 1) = \sqrt{3x - 1}$

**6.** $(g \circ f)(x) = g(f(x)) = g\left(\sqrt{x}\right) = 3\sqrt{x} - 1$

**7.** one-to-one; inverse:

$\{(6, -2), (8, 4), (-6, 2), (3, 3)\}$

**8.** not one-to-one

**9.** not one-to-one

**10.** one-to-one

**11.** not one-to-one

**12.** $f(x) = 3x$

$y = 3x$

$x = 3y$

$y = \dfrac{x}{3}$

$f^{-1}(x) = \dfrac{x}{3}$

**13.** $f(x) = x + 4$

$y = x + 4$

$x = y + 4$

$y = x - 4$

$f^{-1}(x) = x - 4$

**14.** $f(x) = 5x - 1$

$y = 5x - 1$

$x = 5y - 1$

$5y = x + 1$

$y = \dfrac{x + 1}{5}$

$f^{-1}(x) = \dfrac{x + 1}{5}$

**15.** $f(x) = 3x + 2$

$y = 3x + 2$

$x = 3y + 2$

$3y = x - 2$

$y = \dfrac{x - 2}{3}$

$f^{-1}(x) = \dfrac{x - 2}{3}$

**16.** $y = \left(\dfrac{1}{2}\right)^x$

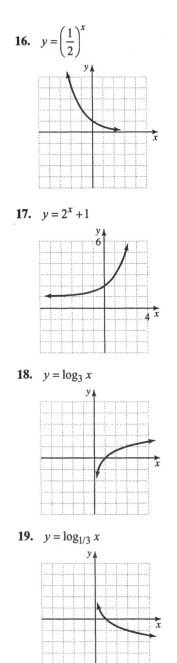

**17.** $y = 2^x + 1$

**18.** $y = \log_3 x$

**19.** $y = \log_{1/3} x$

**20.** $2^x = 8$

$2^x = 2^3$

$x = 3$

The solution is 3.

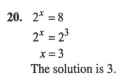

**21.** $9 = 3^{x-5}$

$3^2 = 3^{x-5}$

$2 = x - 5$

$7 = x$

The solution is 7.

**22.** $4^{x-1} = 8^{x+2}$

$(2^2)^{x-1} = (2^3)^{x+2}$

$2^{2x-2} = 2^{3x+6}$

$2x - 2 = 3x + 6$

$-8 = x$

The solution is –8.

**23.** $25^x = 125^{x-1}$

$(5^2)^x = (5^3)^{x-1}$

$5^{2x} = 5^{3x-3}$

$2x = 3x - 3$

$3 = x$

The solution is 3.

**24.** $\log_4 16 = x$

$4^x = 16$

$4^x = 4^2$

$x = 2$

The solution is 2.

**25.** $\log_{49} 7 = x$

$49^x = 7$

$(7^2)^x = 7$

$7^{2x} = 7$

$2x = 1$

$x = \dfrac{1}{2}$

The solution is $\dfrac{1}{2}$.

**26.** $\log_2 x = 5$

$2^5 = x$

$32 = x$

The solution is 32.

**27.** $\log_x 64 = 3$

$x^3 = 64$

$x^3 = 4^3$

$x = 4$

The solution is 4.

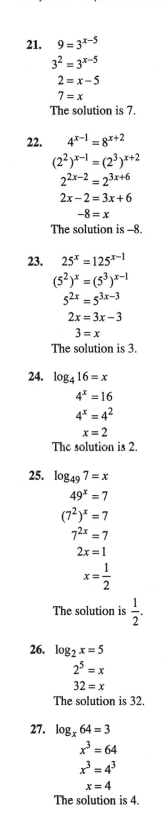

**28.** $\log_x \dfrac{1}{125} = -3$

$$x^{-3} = \dfrac{1}{125}$$

$$x^{-3} = 5^{-3}$$

$$x = 5$$

The solution is 5.

**29.** $\log_3 x = -2$

$$3^{-2} = x$$

$$x = \dfrac{1}{3^2} = \dfrac{1}{9}$$

The solution is $\dfrac{1}{9}$.

**30.** $5\log_2 x = \log_2 x^5$

**31.** $x\log_2 5 = \log_2 5^x$

**32.** $3\log_5 x - 5\log_5 y = \log_5 x^3 - \log_5 y^5 = \log_5 \dfrac{x^3}{y^5}$

**33.** $9\log_5 x + 3\log_5 y = \log_5 x^9 + \log_5 y^3$
$$= \log_5 x^9 y^3$$

**34.** $\log_2 x + \log_2 (x-3) - \log_2 (x^2 + 4)$
$$= \log_2 [x(x-3)] - \log_2 (x^2 + 4)$$
$$= \log_2 (x^2 - 3x) - \log_2 (x^2 + 4)$$
$$= \log_2 \dfrac{x^2 - 3x}{x^2 + 4}$$

**35.** $\log_3 y - \log_3 (y+2) + \log_3 (y^3 + 11)$
$$= \log_3 \dfrac{y}{y+2} + \log_3 (y^3 + 11)$$
$$= \log_3 \dfrac{y(y^3 + 11)}{y+2}$$
$$= \log_3 \dfrac{y^4 + 11y}{y+2}$$

**36.** $\log_7 \dfrac{9x^2}{y} = \log_7 9x^2 - \log_7 y$
$$= \log_7 9 + \log_7 x^2 - \log_7 y$$
$$= \log_7 9 + 2\log_7 x - \log_7 y$$

**37.** $\log_6 \dfrac{5y}{z^2} = \log_6 5y - \log_6 z^2$
$$= \log_6 5 + \log_6 y - 2\log_6 z$$

**Section 9.6**

**Practice Exercises**

**1.** To four decimal places, $\log 15 \approx 1.1761$.

**2. a.** $\log \dfrac{1}{100} = \log 10^{-2} = 2$

   **b.** $\log 100,000 = \log 10^5 = 5$

   **c.** $\log \sqrt[5]{10} = \log 10^{1/5} = \dfrac{1}{5}$

   **d.** $\log 0.001 = \log 10^{-3} = -3$

**3.** $\log x = 3.4$
$$x = 10^{3.4}$$
$$x \approx 2511.8864$$

**4.** $a = 450$ micrometers
   $T = 4.2$ seconds
   $B = 3.6$
$$R = \log \left( \dfrac{a}{T} \right) + B$$
$$= \log \left( \dfrac{450}{4.2} \right) + 3.6$$
$$\approx 2.0 + 3.6$$
$$= 5.6$$
   The earthquake had a magnitude of 5.6 on the Richter scale.

**5.** To four decimal places, $\ln 13 \approx 2.5649$.

**6. a.** $\ln e^4 = 4$

   **b.** $\ln \sqrt[3]{e} = \ln e^{1/3} = \dfrac{1}{3}$

**7.** $\ln 5x = 8$
$$e^8 = 5x$$
$$\dfrac{e^8}{5} = x$$
$$x = \dfrac{1}{5} e^8 \approx 596.1916$$

**8.** $P = \$2400$
$r = 6\% = 0.06$
$t = 4$ years
$A = Pe^{rt} = 2400e^{0.06(4)} = 2400e^{0.24} \approx 3051.00$
The total amount of money owed is \$3051.00.

**9.** $\log_8 5 = \dfrac{\log 5}{\log 8} \approx \dfrac{0.6989700043}{0.903089987} \approx 0.773976$
To four decimal places, $\log_8 5 \approx 0.7740$.

## Vocabulary and Readiness Check

**1.** The base of $\log 7$ is $\underline{10}$; **c.**

**2.** The base of $\ln 7$ is $\underline{e}$; **a.**

**3.** $\log_{10} 10^7 = \underline{7}$; **b.**

**4.** $\log_7 1 = \underline{0}$; **d.**

**5.** $\log_e e^5 = \underline{5}$; **b.**

**6.** $\ln e^5 = \underline{5}$; **b.**

**7.** $\log_2 7 = \dfrac{\log 7}{\log 2} = \dfrac{\ln 7}{\ln 2}$; **a** and **b**.

## Exercise Set 9.6

**1.** $\log 8 \approx 0.9031$

**3.** $\log 2.31 \approx 0.3636$

**5.** $\ln 2 \approx 0.6931$

**7.** $\ln 0.0716 \approx -2.6367$

**9.** $\log 12.6 \approx 1.1004$

**11.** $\ln 5 \approx 1.6094$

**13.** $\log 41.5 \approx 1.6180$

**15.** Answers may vary

**17.** $\log 100 = \log 10^2 = 2$

**19.** $\log\left(\dfrac{1}{1000}\right) = \log 10^{-3} = -3$

**21.** $\ln e^2 = 2$

**23.** $\ln \sqrt[4]{e} = \ln e^{1/4} = \dfrac{1}{4}$

**25.** $\log 10^3 = 3$

**27.** $\ln e^{-7} = -7$

**29.** $\log 0.0001 = \log 10^{-4} = -4$

**31.** $\ln \sqrt{e} = \ln e^{1/2} = \dfrac{1}{2}$

**33.** $\ln 2x = 7$
$2x = e^7$
$x = \dfrac{1}{2}e^7 \approx 548.3166$

**35.** $\log x = 1.3$
$x = 10^{1.3} \approx 19.9526$

**37.** $\log 2x = 1.1$
$2x = 10^{1.1}$
$x = \dfrac{10^{1.1}}{2} \approx 6.2946$

**39.** $\ln x = 1.4$
$x = e^{1.4} \approx 4.0552$

**41.** $\ln(3x - 4) = 2.3$
$3x - 4 = e^{2.3}$
$3x = 4 + e^{2.3}$
$x = \dfrac{4 + e^{2.3}}{3} \approx 4.6581$

**43.** $\log x = 2.3$
$x = 10^{2.3} \approx 199.5262$

**45.** $\ln x = -2.3$
$x = e^{-2.3} \approx 0.1003$

**47.** $\log(2x + 1) = -0.5$
$2x + 1 = 10^{-0.5}$
$2x = 10^{-0.5} - 1$
$x = \dfrac{10^{-0.5} - 1}{2} \approx -0.3419$

**49.** $\ln 4x = 0.18$

$$4x = e^{0.18}$$

$$x = \frac{e^{0.18}}{4} \approx 0.2993$$

**51.** $\log_2 3 = \frac{\log 3}{\log 2} \approx 1.5850$

**53.** $\log_{1/2} 5 = \frac{\ln 5}{\ln\left(\frac{1}{2}\right)} \approx 2.3219$

**55.** $\log_4 9 = \frac{\ln 9}{\ln 4} \approx 1.5850$

**57.** $\log_3\left(\frac{1}{6}\right) = \frac{\log\left(\frac{1}{6}\right)}{\log 3} \approx -1.6309$

**59.** $\log_8 6 = \frac{\log 6}{\log 8} \approx 0.8617$

**61.** $R = \log\left(\frac{a}{T}\right) + B$, $a = 200$, $T = 1.6$

$B = 2.1$

$$R = \log\left(\frac{200}{1.6}\right) + 2.1 \approx 4.2$$

The earthquake measures 4.2 on the Richter scale.

**63.** $R = \log\left(\frac{a}{T}\right) + B$, $a = 400$, $T = 2.6$

$B = 3.1$

$$R = \log\left(\frac{400}{2.6}\right) + 3.1 \approx 5.3$$

The earthquake measures 5.3 on the Richter scale.

**65.** $A = Pe^{rt}$, $t = 12$, $P = 1400$, $r = 0.08$

$A = 1400e^{(0.08)12} = 1400e^{0.96} \approx 3656.38$

Dana has $3656.38 after 12 years.

**67.** $A = Pe^{rt}$, $t = 4$, $P = 2000$, $r = 0.06$

$A = 2000e^{(0.06)4} = 2000e^{0.24} \approx 2542.50$

Barbara owes $2542.50 at the end of 4 years.

**69.** $6x - 3(2 - 5x) = 6$

$$6x - 6 + 15x = 6$$

$$21x = 12$$

$$x = \frac{12}{21} = \frac{4}{7}$$

The solution is $\frac{4}{7}$.

**71.** $2x + 3y = 6x$

$$3y = 4x$$

$$x = \frac{3y}{4}$$

**73.** $x^2 + 7x = -6$

$$x^2 + 7x + 6 = 0$$

$$(x + 6)(x + 1) = 0$$

$x + 6 = 0 \quad$ or $\quad x + 1 = 0$

$x = -6 \quad$ or $\qquad x = -1$

The solutions are $-6$ and $-1$.

**75.** $\begin{cases} x + 2y = -4 \\ 3x - y = 9 \end{cases}$

Multiply the second equation by 2, then add.

$$\begin{aligned} x + 2y &= -4 \\ 6x - 2y &= 18 \\ \hline 7x \phantom{- 2y} &= 14 \\ x &= 2 \end{aligned}$$

Replace $x$ with 2 in the first equation.

$$x + 2y = -4$$

$$2 + 2y = -4$$

$$2y = -6$$

$$y = -3$$

The solution is $(2, -3)$.

**77.** ln 50 is larger. Answers may vary

**79.** $f(x) = e^x$

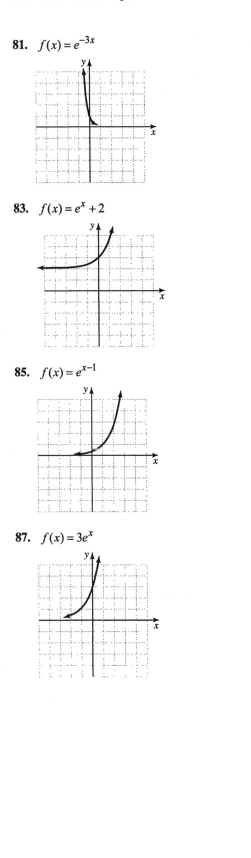

**81.** $f(x) = e^{-3x}$

**83.** $f(x) = e^{x} + 2$

**85.** $f(x) = e^{x-1}$

**87.** $f(x) = 3e^{x}$

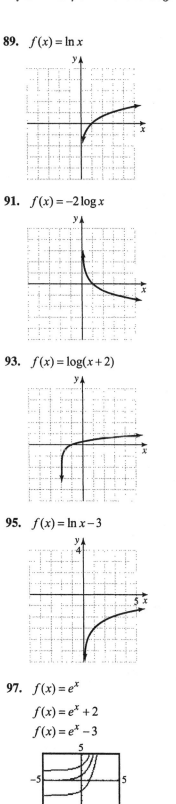

**89.** $f(x) = \ln x$

**91.** $f(x) = -2 \log x$

**93.** $f(x) = \log(x + 2)$

**95.** $f(x) = \ln x - 3$

**97.** $f(x) = e^{x}$

$f(x) = e^{x} + 2$

$f(x) = e^{x} - 3$

Answers may vary

**Section 9.7**

**Practice Exercises**

1.  $5^x = 9$

    $\log 5^x = \log 9$

    $x \log 5 = \log 9$

    $x = \dfrac{\log 9}{\log 5} \approx 1.3652$

    The solution is $\dfrac{\log 9}{\log 5}$, or approximately 1.3652.

2.  $\log_2(x-1) = 5$

    $2^5 = x - 1$

    $32 = x - 1$

    $33 = x$

    Check:   $\log_2(x-1) = 5$

    $\log_2(33-1) \stackrel{?}{=} 5$

    $\log_2 32 \stackrel{?}{=} 5$

    $2^5 = 32$   True

    The solution is 33.

3.  $\log_5 x + \log_5(x+4) = 1$

    $\log_5 x(x+4) = 1$

    $\log_5(x^2 + 4x) = 1$

    $5^1 = x^2 + 4x$

    $0 = x^2 + 4x - 5$

    $0 = (x+5)(x-1)$

    $x + 5 = 0$   or   $x - 1 = 0$

    $x = -5$          $x = 1$

    Since $\log_5(-5)$ is undefined, $-5$ is rejected. The solution is 1.

4.  $\log(x+3) - \log x = 1$

    $\log \dfrac{x+3}{x} = 1$

    $10^1 = \dfrac{x+3}{x}$

    $10x = x + 3$

    $9x = 3$

    $x = \dfrac{1}{3}$

    The solution is $\dfrac{1}{3}$.

5.  $y_0 = 60;\ t = 3$

    $y = y_0 e^{0.916t}$

    $y = 60 e^{0.916(3)} = 60 e^{2.748} \approx 937$

    The population will be approximately 937 rabbits.

6.  $P = \$3000;\ r = 7\% = 0.07;\ n = 12;$
    $A = 2P = \$6000$

    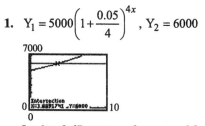

    $6000 = 3000 \left(1 + \dfrac{0.07}{12}\right)^{12t}$

    $2 = \left(1 + \dfrac{0.07}{12}\right)^{12t}$

    $\log 2 = \log \left(1 + \dfrac{0.07}{12}\right)^{12t}$

    $\log 2 = 12t \log \left(1 + \dfrac{0.07}{12}\right)$

    $\dfrac{\log 2}{12 \log \left(1 + \frac{0.07}{12}\right)} = t$

    $9.9 \approx t$

    It takes nearly 10 years to double.

**Graphing Calculator Explorations**

1.  $Y_1 = 5000 \left(1 + \dfrac{0.05}{4}\right)^{4x},\ Y_2 = 6000$

    It takes 3.67 years, or 3 years and 8 months.

2.  $Y_1 = 1000 \left(1 + \dfrac{0.045}{365}\right)^{365x},\ Y_2 = 2000$

    It takes 15.40 years or 15 years and 5 months.

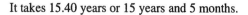

**3.** $Y_1 = 10,000\left(1 + \dfrac{0.06}{12}\right)^{12x}$, $Y_2 = 40,000$

It takes 23.16 years or 23 years and 2 months.

**4.** $Y_1 = 500\left(1 + \dfrac{0.04}{2}\right)^{2x}$, $Y_2 = 800$

It takes 11.87 years or 11 years and 10 months.

**Exercise Set 9.7**

**1.** $3^x = 6$

$\log 3^x = \log 6$

$x \log 3 = \log 6$

$x = \dfrac{\log 6}{\log 3} \approx 1.6309$

**3.** $3^{2x} = 3.8$

$\log 3^{2x} = \log 3.8$

$2x \log 3 = \log 3.8$

$x = \dfrac{\log 3.8}{2 \log 3} \approx 0.6076$

**5.** $2^{x-3} = 5$

$\log 2^{x-3} = \log 5$

$(x-3)\log 2 = \log 5$

$x - 3 = \dfrac{\log 5}{\log 2}$

$x = 3 + \dfrac{\log 5}{\log 2} \approx 5.3219$

**7.** $9^x = 5$

$\log 9^x = \log 5$

$x \log 9 = \log 5$

$x = \dfrac{\log 5}{\log 9} \approx 0.7325$

**9.** $4^{x+7} = 3$

$\log 4^{x+7} = \log 3$

$(x+7)\log 4 = \log 3$

$x + 7 = \dfrac{\log 3}{\log 4}$

$x = -7 + \dfrac{\log 3}{\log 4} \approx -6.2075$

**11.** $7^{3x-4} = 11$

$\log 7^{3x-4} = \log 11$

$(3x-4)\log 7 = \log 11$

$3x - 4 = \dfrac{\log 11}{\log 7}$

$3x = 4 + \dfrac{\log 11}{\log 7}$

$x = \dfrac{1}{3}\left(4 + \dfrac{\log 11}{\log 7}\right) \approx 1.7441$

**13.** $e^{6x} = 5$

$\ln e^{6x} = \ln 5$

$6x = \ln 5$

$x = \dfrac{\ln 5}{6} \approx 0.2682$

**15.** $\log_2(x+5) = 4$

$x + 5 = 2^4$

$x + 5 = 16$

$x = 11$

**17.** $\log_3 x^2 = 4$

$x^2 = 3^4$

$x^2 = 81$

$x = \pm 9$

**19.** $\log_4 2 + \log_4 x = 0$

$\log_4(2x) = 0$

$2x = 4^0$

$2x = 1$

$x = \dfrac{1}{2}$

**21.** $\log_2 6 - \log_2 x = 3$

$$\log_2\left(\frac{6}{x}\right) = 3$$

$$\frac{6}{x} = 2^3$$

$$\frac{6}{x} = 8$$

$$8x = 6$$

$$x = \frac{3}{4}$$

**23.** $\log_4 x + \log_4(x+6) = 2$

$$\log_4 x(x+6) = 2$$

$$x(x+6) = 4^2$$

$$x^2 + 6x = 16$$

$$x^2 + 6x - 16 = 0$$

$$(x+8)(x-2) = 0$$

$x = -8$   or   $x = 2$

We discard −8 as extraneous, the solution is 2.

**25.** $\log_5(x+3) - \log_5 x = 2$

$$\log_5\left(\frac{x+3}{x}\right) = 2$$

$$\frac{x+3}{x} = 5^2$$

$$\frac{x+3}{x} = 25$$

$$x + 3 = 25x$$

$$3 = 24x$$

$$x = \frac{1}{8}$$

**27.** $\log_3(x-2) = 2$

$$x - 2 = 3^2$$

$$x - 2 = 9$$

$$x = 11$$

**29.** $\log_4(x^2 - 3x) = 1$

$$x^2 - 3x = 4$$

$$x^2 - 3x - 4 = 0$$

$$(x-4)(x+1) = 0$$

$x = 4$   or   $x = -1$

**31.** $\ln 5 + \ln x = 0$

$$\ln(5x) = 0$$

$$e^0 = 5x$$

$$1 = 5x$$

$$\frac{1}{5} = x$$

**33.** $3\log x - \log x^2 = 2$

$$3\log x - 2\log x = 2$$

$$\log x = 2$$

$$x = 10^2$$

$$x = 100$$

**35.** $\log_2 x + \log_2(x+5) = 1$

$$\log_2 x(x+5) = 1$$

$$x(x+5) = 2$$

$$x^2 + 5x - 2 = 0$$

$a = 1, b = 5, c = -2$

$$x = \frac{-5 \pm \sqrt{5^2 - 4(1)(-2)}}{2(1)}$$

$$x = \frac{-5 \pm \sqrt{33}}{2}$$

Discard $\dfrac{-5 - \sqrt{33}}{2}$, the solution is $\dfrac{-5 + \sqrt{33}}{2}$.

**37.** $\log_4 x - \log_4(2x-3) = 3$

$$\log_4\left(\frac{x}{2x-3}\right) = 3$$

$$\frac{x}{2x-3} = 4^3$$

$$x = 64(2x-3)$$

$$x = 128x - 192$$

$$192 = 127x$$

$$x = \frac{192}{127}$$

**39.** $\log_2 x + \log_2(3x+1) = 1$

$$\log_2 x(3x+1) = 1$$

$$x(3x+1) = 2$$

$$3x^2 + x - 2 = 0$$

$$(3x-2)(x+1) = 0$$

$3x - 2 = 0$   or   $x + 1 = 0$

$$x = \frac{2}{3} \quad \text{or} \quad x = -1$$

We discard −1 as extraneous, the solution is $\dfrac{2}{3}$.

**41.** $y = y_0 e^{0.043t}$, $y_0 = 83$, $t = 5$

$y = 83e^{0.043(5)} = 83e^{0.215} \approx 103$

There should be 103 wolves in 5 years.

**43.** $y = y_0 e^{0.023t}$, $y_0 = 294,380$, $t = 8$

$y = 294,380e^{0.023(8)} \approx 354,000$

There will be approximately 354,000 inhabitants in 2015.

**45.** $y = y_0 e^{-0.00033t}$

$y_0 = 82,400$, $y = 82,000$

$82,000 = 82,400e^{-0.00033t}$

$\dfrac{82,000}{82,400} = e^{-0.005t}$

$t = \dfrac{\ln\left(\frac{82,000}{82,400}\right)}{-0.00033} \approx 14.7$

It will take approximately 14.7 years to reach 82,000.

**47.** $A = P\left(1 + \dfrac{r}{n}\right)^{nt}$, $P = 600$,

$A = 2(600) = 1200$, $r = 0.07$, $n = 12$

$1200 = 600\left(1 + \dfrac{0.07}{12}\right)^{12t}$

$2 = \left(1 + \dfrac{0.07}{12}\right)^{12t}$

$\log 2 = \log\left(1 + \dfrac{0.07}{12}\right)^{12t}$

$\log 2 = 12t \log\left(1 + \dfrac{0.07}{12}\right)$

$\dfrac{\log 2}{12 \log\left(1 + \frac{0.07}{12}\right)} = t$

$9.9 \approx t$

It takes approximately 9.9 years for the $600 to double.

**49.** $A = P\left(1 + \dfrac{r}{n}\right)^{nt}$, $P = 1200$,

$A = P + I = 1200 + 200 = 1400$

$r = 0.09$, $n = 4$

$1400 = 1200\left(1 + \dfrac{0.09}{4}\right)^{4t}$

$\dfrac{7}{6} = (1.0225)^{4t}$

$\log\dfrac{7}{6} = \log 1.0225^{4t}$

$\log\dfrac{7}{6} = 4t \log 1.0225$

$t = \dfrac{\log\frac{7}{6}}{4 \log 1.0225}$

$t \approx 1.7$

It would take the investment approximately 1.7 years to earn $200.

**51.** $A = P\left(1 + \dfrac{r}{n}\right)^{nt}$, $P = 1000$

$A = 2(1000) = 2000$, $r = 0.08$, $n = 2$

$2000 = 1000\left(1 + \dfrac{0.08}{2}\right)^{2t}$

$2 = (1.04)^{2t}$

$\log 2 = \log 1.04^{2t}$

$\log 2 = 2t \log 1.04$

$t = \dfrac{\log 2}{2 \log 1.04}$

$t \approx 8.8$

It takes 8.8 years to double.

**53.** $w = 0.00185h^{2.67}$, and $h = 35$

$w = 0.00185(35)^{2.67} \approx 24.5$

The expected weight of a boy 35 inches tall is 24.5 pounds.

**55.** $w = 0.00185h^{2.67}$, and $w = 85$

$85 = 0.00185h^{2.67}$

$\dfrac{85}{0.00185} = h^{2.67}$

$h = \left(\dfrac{85}{0.00185}\right)^{1/2.67} \approx 55.7$

The expected height of the boy is 55.7 inches.

**57.** $P = 14.7e^{-0.21x}$, $x = 1$

$P = 14.7e^{-0.21(1)}$

$= 14.7e^{-0.21}$

$\approx 11.9$

The average atmospheric pressure in Denver is approximately 11.9 pounds per square inch.

**59.** $P = 14.7e^{-0.21x}$, $P = 7.5$

$$7.5 = 14.7e^{-0.21x}$$

$$\frac{7.5}{14.7} = e^{-0.21x}$$

$$-0.21x = \ln\left(\frac{7.5}{14.7}\right)$$

$$x = -\frac{1}{0.21}\ln\left(\frac{7.5}{14.7}\right) \approx 3.2$$

The elevation of the jet is approximately 3.2 miles.

**61.** $t = \frac{1}{c}\ln\left(\frac{A}{A-N}\right)$

$$t = \frac{1}{0.09}\ln\left(\frac{75}{75-50}\right)$$

$$t = \frac{1}{0.09}\ln(3)$$

$$t \approx 12.21$$

It will take 12 weeks.

**63.** $t = \frac{1}{c}\ln\left(\frac{A}{A-N}\right)$

$$t = \frac{1}{0.07}\ln\left(\frac{210}{210-150}\right)$$

$$t = \frac{1}{0.07}\ln(3.5)$$

$$t \approx 17.9$$

It will take 18 weeks.

**65.** $\dfrac{x^2 - y + 2z}{3x} = \dfrac{(-2)^2 - 0 + 2(3)}{3(-2)}$

$$= \frac{4+6}{-6}$$

$$= \frac{10}{-6}$$

$$= -\frac{5}{3}$$

**67.** $\dfrac{3z - 4x + y}{x + 2z} = \dfrac{3(3) - 4(-2) + 0}{-2 + 2(3)} = \dfrac{9+8}{-2+6} = \dfrac{17}{4}$

**69.** $f(x) = 5x + 2$

$$y = 5x + 2$$

$$x = 5y + 2$$

$$\frac{x-2}{5} = y$$

$$f^{-1}(x) = \frac{x-2}{5}$$

**71.** $y = 6{,}123{,}106$; $y_0 = 5{,}130{,}632$; $t = 6$

$$y = y_0 e^{kt}$$

$$6{,}123{,}106 = 5{,}130{,}632e^{k(6)}$$

$$\frac{6{,}123{,}106}{5{,}130{,}632} = e^{6k}$$

$$\ln\frac{6{,}123{,}106}{5{,}130{,}632} = 6k$$

$$k = \frac{1}{6}\ln\frac{6{,}123{,}106}{5{,}130{,}632} \approx 0.029$$

The annual rate of population growth was approximately 2.9%.

**73.** Answers may vary

**75.** $Y_1 = e^{0.3x}$, $Y_2 = 8$

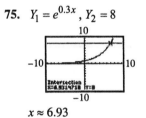

$x \approx 6.93$

**77.** $Y_1 = 2\log(-5.6x + 1.3) + x + 1$, $Y_2 = 0$

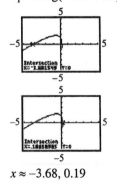

$x \approx -3.68, 0.19$

**79.** $Y_1 = 7^{3x-4} - 11,\ Y_2 = 0$

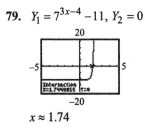

$x \approx 1.74$

**81.** $Y_1 = \ln 5 + \ln x,\ Y_2 = 0$

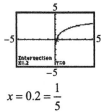

$x = 0.2 = \dfrac{1}{5}$

**The Bigger Picture**

**1.** $\quad 8^x = 2^{x-3}$

$\quad\ 2^{3x} = 2^{x-3}$

$\quad\ 3x = x - 3$

$\quad\ 2x = -3$

$\quad\quad x = -\dfrac{3}{2}$

**2.** $\quad 11^x = 5$

$\quad \log 11^x = \log 5$

$\quad x \log 11 = \log 5$

$\quad\quad\ x = \dfrac{\log 5}{\log 11} \approx 0.6712$

**3.** $-7x + 3 \le -5x + 13$

$\quad\ -10 \le 2x$

$\quad\quad -5 \le x$

The solution is $[-5, \infty)$.

**4.** $\quad -7 \le 3x + 6 \le 0$

$\quad\ -13 \le 3x \le -6$

$\quad -\dfrac{13}{3} \le x \le -2$

The solution is $\left[ -\dfrac{13}{3}, -2 \right]$.

**5.** $|5y + 3| < 3$

$\quad -3 < 5y + 3 < 3$

$\quad\ -6 < 5y < 0$

$\quad -\dfrac{6}{5} < y < 0$

The solution is $\left( -\dfrac{6}{5}, 0 \right)$.

**6.** $(x - 6)(5x + 1) = 0$

$\quad x - 6 = 0 \quad$ or $\quad 5x + 1 = 0$

$\quad\quad x = 6 \quad\quad\quad\ 5x = -1$

$\quad\quad\quad\quad\quad\quad\quad\quad x = -\dfrac{1}{5}$

The solutions are 6 and $-\dfrac{1}{5}$.

**7.** $\log_{13} 8 + \log_{13}(x - 1) = 1$

$\quad\quad\ \log_{13}(8x - 8) = 1$

$\quad\quad\quad\quad 13^1 = 8x - 8$

$\quad\quad\quad\quad\ 21 = 8x$

$\quad\quad\quad\quad \dfrac{21}{8} = x$

**8.** $\left| \dfrac{3x - 1}{4} \right| = 2$

$\quad \dfrac{3x - 1}{4} = 2 \quad$ or $\quad \dfrac{3x - 1}{4} = -2$

$\quad\ 3x - 1 = 8 \quad\quad\quad 3x - 1 = -8$

$\quad\quad\ 3x = 9 \quad\quad\quad\quad\ 3x = -7$

$\quad\quad\quad x = 3 \quad\quad\quad\quad\quad x = -\dfrac{7}{3}$

The solutions are 3 and $-\dfrac{7}{3}$.

**9.** $|7x + 1| > -2$ is a true statement for all $x$, so the solution is $(-\infty, \infty)$.

**10.** $x^2 = 4$

$\quad x = \pm\sqrt{4} = \pm 2$

The solutions are 2 and $-2$.

**11.** $(x + 5)^2 = 3$

$\quad\ x + 5 = \pm\sqrt{3}$

$\quad\quad\quad x = -5 \pm \sqrt{3}$

The solutions are $-5 + \sqrt{3}$ and $-5 - \sqrt{3}$.

**12.** $\log_7(4x^2 - 27x) = 1$

$$7^1 = 4x^2 - 27x$$
$$0 = 4x^2 - 27x - 7$$
$$0 = (4x+1)(x-7)$$

$4x + 1 = 0$    or    $x - 7 = 0$
$4x = -1$          $x = 7$

$$x = -\frac{1}{4}$$

The solutions are $-\frac{1}{4}$ and 7.

**Chapter 9 Vocabulary Check**

1. For each one-to-one function, we can find its <u>inverse</u> function by switching the coordinates of the ordered pairs of the function.

2. The <u>composition</u> of functions $f$ and $g$ is $(f \circ g)(x) = f(g(x))$.

3. A function of the form $f(x) = b^x$ is called an <u>exponential</u> function if $b > 0$, $b$ is not 1, and $x$ is a real number.

4. The graphs of $f$ and $f^{-1}$ are <u>symmetric</u> about the line $y = x$.

5. <u>Natural</u> logarithms are logarithms to base $e$.

6. <u>Common</u> logarithms are logarithms to base 10.

7. To see whether a graph is the graph of a one-to-one function, apply the <u>vertical</u> line test to see if it is a function, and then apply the <u>horizontal</u> line test to see if it is a one-to-one function.

8. A <u>logarithmic</u> function is a function that can be defined by $f(x) = \log_b x$ where $x$ is a positive real number, $b$ is a constant positive real number, and $b$ is not 1.

**Chapter 9 Review**

1. $(f+g)(x) = f(x) + g(x)$
   $= (x-5) + (2x+1)$
   $= x - 5 + 2x + 1$
   $= 3x - 4$

2. $(f-g)(x) = f(x) - g(x)$
   $= (x-5) - (2x+1)$
   $= x - 5 - 2x - 1$
   $= -x - 6$

3. $(f \cdot g)(x) = f(x) \cdot g(x)$
   $= (x-5)(2x+1)$
   $= 2x^2 + x - 10x - 5$
   $= 2x^2 - 9x - 5$

4. $\left(\dfrac{g}{f}\right)(x) = \dfrac{g(x)}{f(x)} = \dfrac{2x+1}{x-5}, x \neq 5$

5. $(f \circ g)(x) = f(g(x))$
   $= f(x+1)$
   $= (x+1)^2 - 2$
   $= x^2 + 2x - 1$

6. $(g \circ f)(x) = g(f(x))$
   $= g(x^2 - 2)$
   $= x^2 - 2 + 1$
   $= x^2 - 1$

7. $(h \circ g)(2) = h(g(2)) = h(3) = 3^3 - 3^2 = 18$

8. $(f \circ f)(x) = f(f(x))$
   $= f(x^2 - 2)$
   $= (x^2 - 2)^2 - 2$
   $= x^4 - 4x^2 + 4 - 2$
   $= x^4 - 4x^2 + 2$

9. $(f \circ g)(-1) = f(g(-1)) = f(0) = 0^2 - 2 = -2$

10. $(h \circ h)(2) = h(h(2)) = h(4) = 4^3 - 4^2 = 48$

11. The function is one-to-one.
    $h^{-1} = \{(14,-9),(8,6),(12,-11),(15,15)\}$

12. The function is not one-to-one.

13. The function is one-to-one.

| Rank in Auto Thefts (Input) | 2 | 4 | 1 | 3 |
|---|---|---|---|---|
| U.S. Region (Output) | West | Midwest | South | Northeast |

14. The function is not one-to-one.

**15.** $f(x) = \sqrt{x+2}$

    **a.** $f(7) = \sqrt{7+2} = \sqrt{9} = 3$

    **b.** $f^{-1}(3) = 7$

**16.** $f(x) = \sqrt{x+2}$

    **a.** $f(-1) = \sqrt{-1+2} = \sqrt{1} = 1$

    **b.** $f^{-1}(1) = -1$

**17.** The graph does not represent a one-to-one function.

**18.** The graph does not represent a one-to-one function.

**19.** The graph does not represent a one-to-one function.

**20.** The graph represents a one-to-one function.

**21.** $\quad f(x) = x - 9$
$$y = x - 9$$
$$x = y - 9$$
$$y = x + 9$$
$$f^{-1}(x) = x + 9$$

**22.** $\quad f(x) = x + 8$
$$y = x + 8$$
$$x = y + 8$$
$$y = x - 8$$
$$f^{-1}(x) = x - 8$$

**23.** $\quad f(x) = 6x + 11$
$$y = 6x + 11$$
$$x = 6y + 11$$
$$6y = x - 11$$
$$y = \frac{x-11}{6}$$
$$f^{-1}(x) = \frac{x-11}{6}$$

**24.** $\quad f(x) = 12x$
$$y = 12x$$
$$x = 12y$$
$$y = \frac{x}{12}$$
$$f^{-1}(x) = \frac{x}{12}$$

**25.** $\quad f(x) = x^3 - 5$
$$y = x^3 - 5$$
$$x = y^3 - 5$$
$$y^3 = x + 5$$
$$y = \sqrt[3]{x+5}$$
$$f^{-1}(x) = \sqrt[3]{x+5}$$

**26.** $\quad f(x) = \sqrt[3]{x+2}$
$$y = \sqrt[3]{x+2}$$
$$x = \sqrt[3]{y+2}$$
$$x^3 = y + 2$$
$$y = x^3 - 2$$
$$f^{-1}(x) = x^3 - 2$$

**27.** $\quad g(x) = \dfrac{12x-7}{6}$
$$y = \frac{12x-7}{6}$$
$$x = \frac{12y-7}{6}$$
$$6x = 12y - 7$$
$$12y = 6x + 7$$
$$y = \frac{6x+7}{12}$$
$$g^{-1}(x) = \frac{6x+7}{12}$$

**28.** $\quad r(x) = \dfrac{13}{2}x - 4$
$$y = \frac{13}{2}x - 4$$
$$x = \frac{13}{2}y - 4$$
$$x + 4 = \frac{13}{2}y$$
$$y = \frac{2(x+4)}{13}$$
$$r^{-1}(x) = \frac{2(x+4)}{13}$$

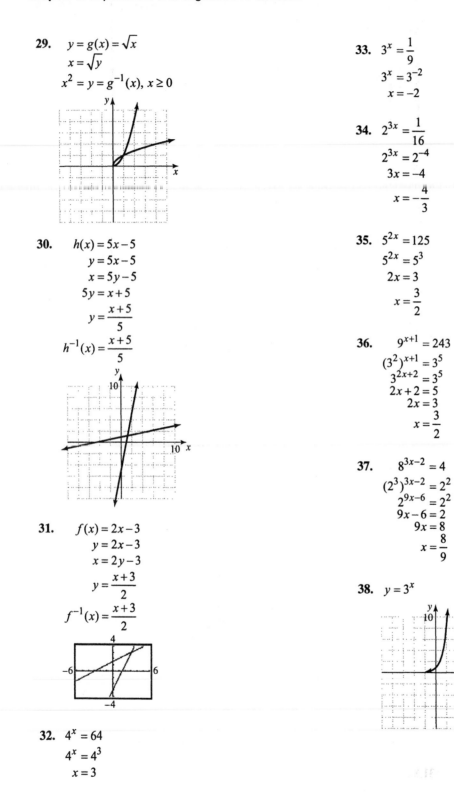

**29.** $y = g(x) = \sqrt{x}$
$x = \sqrt{y}$
$x^2 = y = g^{-1}(x),\ x \geq 0$

**30.** $h(x) = 5x - 5$
$y = 5x - 5$
$x = 5y - 5$
$5y = x + 5$
$y = \dfrac{x+5}{5}$
$h^{-1}(x) = \dfrac{x+5}{5}$

**31.** $f(x) = 2x - 3$
$y = 2x - 3$
$x = 2y - 3$
$y = \dfrac{x+3}{2}$
$f^{-1}(x) = \dfrac{x+3}{2}$

**32.** $4^x = 64$
$4^x = 4^3$
$x = 3$

**33.** $3^x = \dfrac{1}{9}$
$3^x = 3^{-2}$
$x = -2$

**34.** $2^{3x} = \dfrac{1}{16}$
$2^{3x} = 2^{-4}$
$3x = -4$
$x = -\dfrac{4}{3}$

**35.** $5^{2x} = 125$
$5^{2x} = 5^3$
$2x = 3$
$x = \dfrac{3}{2}$

**36.** $9^{x+1} = 243$
$(3^2)^{x+1} = 3^5$
$3^{2x+2} = 3^5$
$2x + 2 = 5$
$2x = 3$
$x = \dfrac{3}{2}$

**37.** $8^{3x-2} = 4$
$(2^3)^{3x-2} = 2^2$
$2^{9x-6} = 2^2$
$9x - 6 = 2$
$9x = 8$
$x = \dfrac{8}{9}$

**38.** $y = 3^x$

**39.** $y = \left(\dfrac{1}{3}\right)^x$

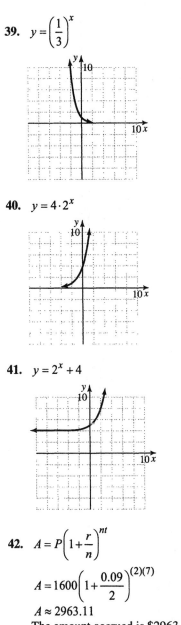

**40.** $y = 4 \cdot 2^x$

**41.** $y = 2^x + 4$

**42.** $A = P\left(1 + \dfrac{r}{n}\right)^{nt}$

$A = 1600\left(1 + \dfrac{0.09}{2}\right)^{(2)(7)}$

$A \approx 2963.11$

The amount accrued is \$2963.11.

**43.** $A = P\left(1 + \dfrac{r}{n}\right)^{nt}$

$A = 800\left(1 + \dfrac{0.07}{4}\right)^{(4)(5)}$

$A \approx 1131.82$

The certificate is worth \$1131.82 at the end of 5 years.

**44.** $y = 4 \cdot 2^x$

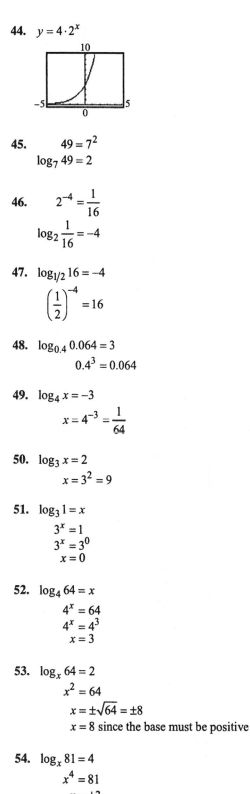

**45.** $\quad 49 = 7^2$

$\log_7 49 = 2$

**46.** $\quad 2^{-4} = \dfrac{1}{16}$

$\log_2 \dfrac{1}{16} = -4$

**47.** $\log_{1/2} 16 = -4$

$\left(\dfrac{1}{2}\right)^{-4} = 16$

**48.** $\log_{0.4} 0.064 = 3$

$0.4^3 = 0.064$

**49.** $\log_4 x = -3$

$x = 4^{-3} = \dfrac{1}{64}$

**50.** $\log_3 x = 2$

$x = 3^2 = 9$

**51.** $\log_3 1 = x$

$3^x = 1$

$3^x = 3^0$

$x = 0$

**52.** $\log_4 64 = x$

$4^x = 64$

$4^x = 4^3$

$x = 3$

**53.** $\log_x 64 = 2$

$x^2 = 64$

$x = \pm\sqrt{64} = \pm 8$

$x = 8$ since the base must be positive

**54.** $\log_x 81 = 4$

$x^4 = 81$

$x = \pm 3$

$x = 3$ since the base must be positive

**55.** $\log_4 4^5 = x$
$x = 5$

**56.** $\log_7 7^{-2} = x$
$x = -2$

**57.** $5^{\log_5 4} = x$
$x = 4$

**58.** $2^{\log_2 9} = x$
$9 = x$

**59.** $\log_2 (3x - 1) = 4$
$3x - 1 = 2^4$
$3x - 1 = 16$
$3x = 17$
$x = \dfrac{17}{3}$

**60.** $\log_3 (2x + 5) = 2$
$2x + 5 = 3^2$
$2x + 5 = 9$
$2x = 4$
$x = 2$

**61.** $\log_4 (x^2 - 3x) = 1$
$x^2 - 3x = 4$
$x^2 - 3x - 4 = 0$
$(x + 1)(x - 4) = 0$
$x = -1$ or $x = 4$

**62.** $\log_8 (x^2 + 7x) = 1$
$x^2 + 7x = 8$
$x^2 + 7x - 8 = 0$
$(x + 8)(x - 1) = 0$
$x = -8$ or $x = 1$

**63.** $y = 2^x$ and $y = \log_2 x$

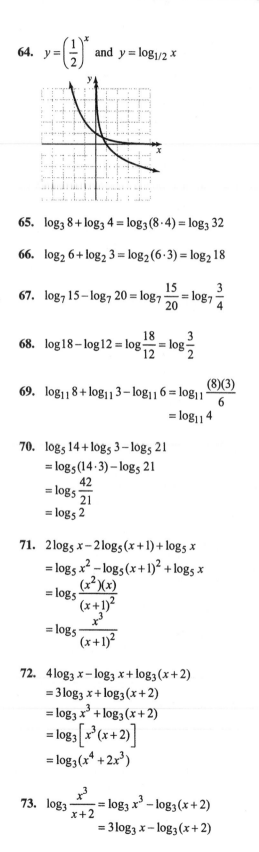

**64.** $y = \left(\dfrac{1}{2}\right)^x$ and $y = \log_{1/2} x$

**65.** $\log_3 8 + \log_3 4 = \log_3 (8 \cdot 4) = \log_3 32$

**66.** $\log_2 6 + \log_2 3 = \log_2 (6 \cdot 3) = \log_2 18$

**67.** $\log_7 15 - \log_7 20 = \log_7 \dfrac{15}{20} = \log_7 \dfrac{3}{4}$

**68.** $\log 18 - \log 12 = \log \dfrac{18}{12} = \log \dfrac{3}{2}$

**69.** $\log_{11} 8 + \log_{11} 3 - \log_{11} 6 = \log_{11} \dfrac{(8)(3)}{6}$
$= \log_{11} 4$

**70.** $\log_5 14 + \log_5 3 - \log_5 21$
$= \log_5 (14 \cdot 3) - \log_5 21$
$= \log_5 \dfrac{42}{21}$
$= \log_5 2$

**71.** $2\log_5 x - 2\log_5 (x + 1) + \log_5 x$
$= \log_5 x^2 - \log_5 (x + 1)^2 + \log_5 x$
$= \log_5 \dfrac{(x^2)(x)}{(x + 1)^2}$
$= \log_5 \dfrac{x^3}{(x + 1)^2}$

**72.** $4\log_3 x - \log_3 x + \log_3 (x + 2)$
$= 3\log_3 x + \log_3 (x + 2)$
$= \log_3 x^3 + \log_3 (x + 2)$
$= \log_3 \left[ x^3 (x + 2) \right]$
$= \log_3 (x^4 + 2x^3)$

**73.** $\log_3 \dfrac{x^3}{x + 2} = \log_3 x^3 - \log_3 (x + 2)$
$= 3\log_3 x - \log_3 (x + 2)$

**74.** $\log_4 \dfrac{x+5}{x^2} = \log_4(x+5) - \log_4 x^2$

$\qquad = \log_4(x+5) - 2\log_4 x$

**75.** $\log_2 \dfrac{3x^2 y}{z} = \log_2(3x^2 y) - \log_2 z$

$\qquad = \log_2 3 + \log_2 x^2 + \log_2 y - \log_2 z$

$\qquad = \log_2 3 + 2\log_2 x + \log_2 y - \log_2 z$

**76.** $\log_7 \dfrac{yz^3}{x} = \log_7(yz^3) - \log_7 x$

$\qquad = \log_7 y + \log_7 z^3 - \log_7 x$

$\qquad = \log_7 y + 3\log_7 z - \log_7 x$

**77.** $\log_b 50 = \log_b(5)(5)(2)$

$\qquad = \log_b(5) + \log_b(5) + \log_b(2)$

$\qquad = 0.83 + 0.83 + 0.36$

$\qquad = 2.02$

**78.** $\log_b \dfrac{4}{5} = \log_b 4 - \log_b 5$

$\qquad = \log_b 2^2 - \log_b 5$

$\qquad = 2\log_b 2 - \log_b 5$

$\qquad = 2(0.36) - 0.83$

$\qquad = 0.72 - 0.83$

$\qquad = -0.11$

**79.** $\log 3.6 \approx 0.5563$

**80.** $\log 0.15 \approx -0.8239$

**81.** $\ln 1.25 \approx 0.2231$

**82.** $\ln 4.63 \approx 1.5326$

**83.** $\log 1000 = \log 10^3 = 3$

**84.** $\log \dfrac{1}{10} = \log 10^{-1} = -1$

**85.** $\ln \dfrac{1}{e} = \ln e^{-1} = -1$

**86.** $\ln e^4 = 4$

**87.** $\ln(2x) = 2$

$\qquad 2x = e^2$

$\qquad x = \dfrac{e^2}{2}$

**88.** $\ln(3x) = 1.6$

$\qquad 3x = e^{1.6}$

$\qquad x = \dfrac{e^{1.6}}{3}$

**89.** $\ln(2x-3) = -1$

$\qquad 2x - 3 = e^{-1}$

$\qquad x = \dfrac{e^{-1}+3}{2}$

**90.** $\ln(3x+1) = 2$

$\qquad 3x + 1 = e^2$

$\qquad 3x = e^2 - 1$

$\qquad x = \dfrac{e^2 - 1}{3}$

**91.** $\quad \ln \dfrac{I}{I_0} = -kx$

$\ln \dfrac{0.03 I_0}{I_0} = -2.1x$

$\qquad \ln 0.03 = -2.1x$

$\qquad \dfrac{\ln 0.03}{-2.1} = x$

$\qquad x \approx 1.67$

The depth is 1.67 millimeters.

**92.** $\quad \ln \dfrac{I}{I_0} = -kx$

$\ln \dfrac{0.02 I_0}{I_0} = -3.2x$

$\qquad \ln 0.02 = -3.2x$

$\qquad \dfrac{\ln 0.02}{-3.2} = x$

$\qquad x \approx 1.22$

2% of the original radioactivity will penetrate at a depth of approximately 1.22 millimeters.

**93.** $\log_5 1.6 = \dfrac{\log 1.6}{\log 5} \approx 0.2920$

**94.** $\log_3 4 = \dfrac{\log 4}{\log 3} \approx 1.2619$

**95.** $A = Pe^{rt}$

$A = 1450e^{(0.06)(5)}$

$A \approx 1957.30$

The accrued amount is \$1957.30.

**96.** $A = Pe^{rt}$

$A = 940e^{0.11(3)} = 940e^{0.33} \approx 1307.51$

The investment grows to \$1307.51.

**97.** $3^{2x} = 7$

$\log 3^{2x} = \log 7$

$2x \log 3 = \log 7$

$x = \dfrac{\log 7}{2 \log 3} \approx 0.8856$

**98.** $6^{3x} = 5$

$\log 6^{3x} = \log 5$

$3x \log 6 = \log 5$

$x = \dfrac{\log 5}{3 \log 6} \approx 0.2994$

**99.** $3^{2x+1} = 6$

$\log 3^{2x+1} = \log 6$

$(2x+1) \log 3 = \log 6$

$2x = \dfrac{\log 6}{\log 3} - 1$

$x = \dfrac{1}{2}\left(\dfrac{\log 6}{\log 3} - 1\right) \approx 0.3155$

**100.** $4^{3x+2} = 9$

$\log 4^{3x+2} = \log 9$

$(3x+2) \log 4 = \log 9$

$3x = \dfrac{\log 9}{\log 4} - 2$

$x = \dfrac{1}{3}\left(\dfrac{\log 9}{\log 4} - 2\right) \approx -0.1383$

**101.** $5^{3x-5} = 4$

$\log 5^{3x-5} = \log 4$

$(3x-5) \log 5 = \log 4$

$3x = \dfrac{\log 4}{\log 5} + 5$

$x = \dfrac{1}{3}\left(\dfrac{\log 4}{\log 5} + 5\right) \approx 1.9538$

**102.** $8^{4x-2} = 3$

$\log 8^{4x-2} = \log 3$

$(4x-2) \log 8 = \log 3$

$4x = \dfrac{\log 3}{\log 8} + 2$

$x = \dfrac{1}{4}\left(\dfrac{\log 3}{\log 8} + 2\right) \approx 0.6321$

**103.** $2 \cdot 5^{x-1} = 1$

$\log(2 \cdot 5^{x-1}) = \log 1$

$\log 2 + (x-1) \log 5 = 0$

$(x-1) \log 5 = -\log 2$

$x = -\dfrac{\log 2}{\log 5} + 1 \approx 0.5693$

**104.** $3 \cdot 4^{x+5} = 2$

$4^{x+5} = \dfrac{2}{3}$

$\log 4^{x+5} = \log \dfrac{2}{3}$

$(x+5) \log 4 = \log \dfrac{2}{3}$

$x = \dfrac{\log\left(\frac{2}{3}\right)}{\log 4} - 5 \approx -5.2925$

**105.** $\log_5 2 + \log_5 x = 2$

$\log_5 2x = 2$

$2x = 5^2$

$2x = 25$

$x = \dfrac{25}{2}$

**106.** $\log_3 x + \log_3 10 = 2$

$\log_3(10x) = 2$

$10x = 3^2$

$10x = 9$

$x = \dfrac{9}{10}$

**107.** $\log(5x) - \log(x+1) = 4$

$$\log\frac{5x}{x+1} = 4$$

$$\frac{5x}{x+1} = 10^4$$

$$\frac{5x}{x+1} = 10,000$$

$$5x = 10,000x + 10,000$$

$$x = -1.0005$$

no solution, or $\varnothing$

**108.** $\ln(3x) - \ln(x-3) = 2$

$$\ln\left(\frac{3x}{x-3}\right) = 2$$

$$\frac{3x}{x-3} = e^2$$

$$3x = e^2 x - 3e^2$$

$$3x - e^2 x = -3e^2$$

$$(3 - e^2)x = -3e^2$$

$$x = \frac{3e^2}{e^2 - 3}$$

**109.** $\log_2 x + \log_2 2x - 3 = 1$

$$\log_2(x \cdot 2x) = 4$$

$$2x^2 = 2^4$$

$$2x^2 = 16$$

$$x^2 = 8$$

$$x = \pm 2\sqrt{2}$$

$-2\sqrt{2}$ is rejected since $\log_2\left(-2\sqrt{2}\right)$ is undefined. The solution is $2\sqrt{2}$.

**110.** $-\log_6(4x+7) + \log_6 x = 1$

$$\log_6\frac{x}{4x+7} = 1$$

$$\frac{x}{4x+7} = 6$$

$$x = 6(4x+7)$$

$$x = 24x + 42$$

$$x = -\frac{42}{23}$$

$-\frac{42}{23}$ is rejected since $\log_6\left(-\frac{42}{23}\right)$ is undefined. There is no solution, or $\varnothing$.

**111.** $y = y_0 e^{kt}$

$$y = 155,000e^{0.06(4)}$$
$$\approx 197,044$$

There will be 197,044 ducks after 4 weeks.

**112.** $y = y_0 e^{kt}$

$$y = 2,971,650e^{-0.00129(8)}$$
$$= 2,971,650e^{-0.01032}$$
$$\approx 2,941,140$$

The population of Armenia in the year 2015 will be approximately 2,941,140.

**113.** $y = y_0 e^{kt}$

$$1,500,000,000 = 1,321,851,888e^{0.00606t}$$

$$\frac{1,500,000,000}{1,321,851,888} = e^{0.00606t}$$

$$\ln\frac{1,500,000,000}{1,321,851,888} = \ln e^{0.00606t}$$

$$\ln\frac{1,500,000,000}{1,321,851,888} = 0.00606t$$

$$t = \frac{1}{0.00606}\ln\frac{1,500,000,000}{1,321,851,888}$$

$$t \approx 20.9$$

It will take approximately 20.9 years.

**114.** $y = y_0 e^{kt}$

$$2(33,390,141) = 33,390,141e^{0.009t}$$

$$2 = e^{0.009t}$$

$$\ln 2 = \ln e^{0.009t}$$

$$\ln 2 = 0.009t$$

$$t = \frac{\ln 2}{0.009}$$

$$t \approx 77.0$$

It will take approximately 77.0 years.

**115.** $y = y_0 e^{kt}$

$$2(24,821,286) = 24,821,286e^{0.018t}$$

$$2 = e^{0.018t}$$

$$\ln 2 = \ln e^{0.018t}$$

$$\ln 2 = 0.018t$$

$$t = \frac{\ln 2}{0.018}$$

$$t \approx 38.5$$

It will take approximately 38.5 years.

**116.**
$$A = P\left(1 + \frac{r}{n}\right)^{nt}$$
$$10{,}000 = 5000\left(1 + \frac{0.08}{4}\right)^{4t}$$
$$2 = (1.02)^{4t}$$
$$\log 2 = \log 1.02^{4t}$$
$$\log 2 = 4t \log 1.02$$
$$t = \frac{\log 2}{4 \log 1.02} \approx 8.8$$
It will take 8.8 years.

**117.**
$$A = P\left(1 + \frac{r}{n}\right)^{nt}$$
$$10{,}000 = 6000\left(1 + \frac{0.06}{12}\right)^{12t}$$
$$\frac{5}{3} = (1.005)^{12t}$$
$$\log \frac{5}{3} = \log 1.005^{12t}$$
$$\log \frac{5}{3} = 12t \log 1.005$$
$$t = \frac{1}{12}\left(\frac{\log\left(\frac{5}{3}\right)}{\log(1.005)}\right) \approx 8.5$$
It was invested for approximately 8.5 years.

**118.** $Y_1 = e^x$, $Y_2 = 2$

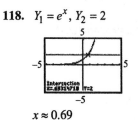

$x \approx 0.69$

**119.** $Y_1 = 10^{0.3x}$, $Y_2 = 7$

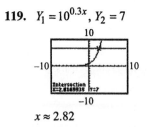

$x \approx 2.82$

**120.**
$$3^x = \frac{1}{81}$$
$$3^x = 3^{-4}$$
$$x = -4$$

**121.**
$$7^{4x} = 49$$
$$7^{4x} = 7^2$$
$$4x = 2$$
$$x = \frac{1}{2}$$

**122.**
$$8^{3x-2} = 32$$
$$(2^3)^{(3x-2)} = 2^5$$
$$2^{9x-6} = 2^5$$
$$9x - 6 = 5$$
$$9x = 11$$
$$x = \frac{11}{9}$$

**123.**
$$\log_4 4 = x$$
$$4^x = 4^1$$
$$x = 1$$

**124.**
$$\log_3 x = 4$$
$$3^4 = x$$
$$81 = x$$

**125.**
$$\log_5 (x^2 - 4x) = 1$$
$$5^1 = x^2 - 4x$$
$$0 = x^2 - 4x - 5$$
$$0 = (x - 5)(x + 1)$$
$$x - 5 = 0 \quad \text{or} \quad x + 1 = 0$$
$$x = 5 \qquad\qquad x = -1$$
Both check, so the solutions are 5 and −1.

**126.**
$$\log_4 (3x - 1) = 2$$
$$4^2 = 3x - 1$$
$$16 + 1 = 3x$$
$$\frac{17}{3} = x$$

**127.**
$$\ln x = -3.2$$
$$e^{\ln x} = e^{-3.2}$$
$$x = e^{-3.2}$$

**128.**
$$\log_5 x + \log_5 10 = 2$$
$$\log_5 (10x) = 2$$
$$5^2 = 10x$$
$$\frac{25}{10} = x$$
$$\frac{5}{2} = x$$

**129.** $\ln x - \ln 2 = 1$

$$\ln \frac{x}{2} = 1$$

$$e^{\ln \frac{x}{2}} = e^1$$

$$\frac{x}{2} = e$$

$$x = 2e$$

**130.** $\log_6 x - \log_6 (4x+7) = 1$

$$\log_6 \frac{x}{4x+7} = 1$$

$$6^1 = \frac{x}{4x+7}$$

$$24x + 42 = x$$

$$23x = -42$$

$$x = -\frac{42}{23}$$

$-\dfrac{42}{23}$ is rejected since $\log_6\left(-\dfrac{42}{23}\right)$ is undefined.

There is no solution, or $\varnothing$.

## Chapter 9 Test

**1.** $f(x) = x$ and $g(x) = 2x - 3$

$(f \cdot g)(x) = f(x) \cdot g(x) = x(2x-3) = 2x^2 - 3x$

**2.** $f(x) = x$ and $g(x) = 2x - 3$

$(f - g)(x) = f(x) - g(x)$

$\qquad = x - (2x-3)$

$\qquad = -x + 3$

$\qquad = 3 - x$

**3.** $(f \circ h)(0) = f(h(0)) = f(5) = 5$

**4.** $(g \circ f)(x) = g(f(x)) = g(x) = x - 7$

**5.** $(g \circ h)(x) = g(h(x))$

$\qquad = g(x^2 - 6x + 5)$

$\qquad = x^2 - 6x + 5 - 7$

$\qquad = x^2 - 6x - 2$

**6.** $f(x) = 7x - 14, \; f^{-1}(x) = \dfrac{x+14}{7}$

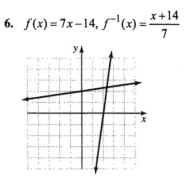

**7.** The graph represents a one-to-one function.

**8.** The graph does not represent a one-to-one function.

**9.** $y = 6 - 2x$ is one-to-one.

$\qquad x = 6 - 2y$

$\qquad 2y = -x + 6$

$\qquad y = \dfrac{-x+6}{2}$

$f^{-1}(x) = \dfrac{-x+6}{2}$

**10.** $f = \{(0,0),(2,3),(-1,5)\}$ is one-to-one.

$f^{-1} = \{(0,0),(3,2),(5,-1)\}$

**11.** The function is not one-to-one.

**12.** $\log_3 6 + \log_3 4 = \log_3 (6 \cdot 4) = \log_3 24$

**13.** $\log_5 x + 3\log_5 x - \log_5 (x+1)$

$\qquad = 4\log_5 x - \log_5 (x+1)$

$\qquad = \log_5 x^4 - \log_5 (x+1)$

$\qquad = \log_5 \dfrac{x^4}{x+1}$

**14.** $\log_6 \dfrac{2x}{y^3} = \log_6 2x - \log_6 y^3$

$\qquad\qquad = \log_6 2 + \log_6 x - 3\log_6 y$

**15.** $\log_b \left(\dfrac{3}{25}\right) = \log_b 3 - \log_b 25$

$\qquad\qquad = \log_b 3 - \log_b 5^2$

$\qquad\qquad = \log_b 3 - 2\log_b 5$

$\qquad\qquad = 0.79 - 2(1.16)$

$\qquad\qquad = -1.53$

**16.** $\log_7 8 = \dfrac{\ln 8}{\ln 7} \approx 1.0686$

**17.** $8^{x-1} = \dfrac{1}{64}$

$8^{x-1} = 8^{-2}$

$x - 1 = -2$

$x = -1$

**18.** $3^{2x+5} = 4$

$\log 3^{2x+5} = \log 4$

$(2x+5)\log 3 = \log 4$

$2x = \dfrac{\log 4}{\log 3} - 5$

$x = \dfrac{1}{2}\left(\dfrac{\log 4}{\log 3} - 5\right)$

$x \approx -1.8691$

**19.** $\log_3 x = -2$

$x = 3^{-2}$

$x = \dfrac{1}{9}$

**20.** $\ln \sqrt{e} = x$

$\ln e^{1/2} = x$

$\dfrac{1}{2} = x$

**21.** $\log_8 (3x - 2) = 2$

$3x - 2 = 8^2$

$3x - 2 = 64$

$3x = 66$

$x = \dfrac{66}{3} = 22$

**22.** $\log_5 x + \log_5 3 = 2$

$\log_5 (3x) = 2$

$3x = 5^2$

$3x = 25$

$x = \dfrac{25}{3}$

**23.** $\log_4 (x+1) - \log_4 (x-2) = 3$

$\log_4 \dfrac{x+1}{x-2} = 3$

$\dfrac{x+1}{x-2} = 4^3$

$\dfrac{x+1}{x-2} = 64$

$x + 1 = 64x - 128$

$129 = 63x$

$\dfrac{129}{63} = x$

$\dfrac{43}{21} = x$

**24.** $\ln(3x + 7) = 1.31$

$3x + 7 = e^{1.31}$

$3x = e^{1.31} - 7$

$x = \dfrac{e^{1.31} - 7}{3} \approx -1.0979$

**25.** $y = \left(\dfrac{1}{2}\right)^x + 1$

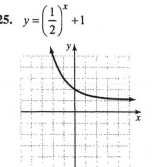

**26.** $y = 3^x$ and $y = \log_3 x$

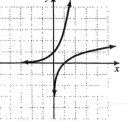

**27.** $A = \left(1 + \dfrac{r}{n}\right)^{nt}$, $P = 4000$, $t = 3$, $r = 0.09$,

and $n = 12$

$$A = 4000\left(1 + \dfrac{0.09}{12}\right)^{12(3)}$$
$$= 4000(1.0075)^{36}$$
$$\approx 5234.58$$

$5234.58 will be in the account.

**28.** $A = \left(1 + \dfrac{r}{n}\right)^{nt}$, $P = 2000$, $A = 3000$

$r = 0.07$, $n = 2$

$$3000 = 2000\left(1 + \dfrac{0.07}{2}\right)^{2t}$$
$$1.5 = (1.035)^{2t}$$
$$\log 1.5 = \log 1.035^{2t}$$
$$\log 1.5 = 2t \log 1.035$$
$$t = \dfrac{\log 1.5}{2 \log 1.035} \approx 5.9$$

It would take 6 years.

**29.** $y = y_0 e^{kt}$

$$y = 57{,}000 e^{0.026(5)}$$
$$= 57{,}000 e^{0.13}$$
$$\approx 64{,}913$$

There will be approximately 64,913 prairie dogs 5 years from now.

**30.**
$$y = y_0 e^{kt}$$
$$1000 = 400 e^{0.062(t)}$$
$$2.5 = e^{0.062t}$$
$$\ln 2.5 = \ln e^{0.062t}$$
$$0.062t = \ln 2.5$$
$$t = \dfrac{\ln 2.5}{0.062} \approx 14.8$$

It will take the naturalists approximately 15 years to reach their goal.

**31.** $\log(1 + k) = \dfrac{0.3}{D}$, $D = 56$

$$\log(1 + k) = \dfrac{0.3}{56}$$
$$1 + k = 10^{0.3/56}$$
$$k = -1 + 10^{0.3/56}$$
$$k \approx 0.012$$

The rate of population increase is approximately 1.2%.

## Chapter 9 Cumulative Review

**1. a.** $(-8)(-1) = 8$

   **b.** $(-2)\dfrac{1}{6} = -\dfrac{1}{3}$

   **c.** $-1.2(0.3) = -0.36$

   **d.** $0(-11) = 0$

   **e.** $\left(\dfrac{1}{5}\right)\left(-\dfrac{10}{11}\right) = -\dfrac{2}{11}$

   **f.** $(7)(1)(-2)(-3) = 42$

   **g.** $8(-2)(0) = 0$

**2.** $\dfrac{1}{3}(x - 2) = \dfrac{1}{4}(x + 1)$
$$4(x - 2) = 3(x + 1)$$
$$4x - 8 = 3x + 3$$
$$x = 11$$

**3.** $y = x^2$

**4.** $y = f(x) = -3x + 4$, $m = -3$

Perpendicular line: $m = \dfrac{1}{3}$, through $(-2, 6)$

$$y - y_1 = m(x - x_1)$$
$$y - 6 = \dfrac{1}{3}[x - (-2)]$$
$$y - 6 = \dfrac{1}{3}x + \dfrac{2}{3}$$
$$y = \dfrac{1}{3}x + \dfrac{20}{3}$$
$$f(x) = \dfrac{1}{3}x + \dfrac{20}{3}$$

**5.** Equation 2 is twice the opposite of equation 1 and equation 3 is one-half of equation 1. Therefore, the system is dependent. The solution is $\{(x, y, z) | x - 5y - 2z = 6\}$.

**6.** The angles labeled $y°$ and $(x-40)°$ are alternate interior angles, so $y = x - 40$. The angles labeled $x°$ and $y°$ are supplementary, so $x + y = 180$.

$$\begin{cases} y = x - 40 \\ x + y = 180 \end{cases}$$

Replace $y$ with $x - 40$ in the second equation.

$$x + (x - 40) = 180$$
$$2x = 220$$
$$x = 110$$
$$y = x - 40 = 110 - 40 = 70$$

**7. a.** $\dfrac{x^7}{x^4} = x^{7-4} = x^3$

**b.** $\dfrac{5^8}{5^2} = 5^{8-2} = 5^6$

**c.** $\dfrac{20x^6}{4x^5} = \dfrac{20}{4}x^{6-5} = 5x^1 = 5x$

**d.** $\dfrac{12y^{10}z^7}{14y^8z^7} = \dfrac{12}{14}y^{10-8}z^{7-7} = \dfrac{6}{7}y^2z^0 = \dfrac{6y^2}{7}$

**8. a.** $(4a^3)^2 = 4^2(a^3)^2 = 16a^6$

**b.** $\left(-\dfrac{2}{3}\right)^3 = \dfrac{(-2)^3}{3^3} = \dfrac{-8}{27} = -\dfrac{8}{27}$

**c.** $\left(\dfrac{4a^5}{b^3}\right)^3 = \dfrac{4^3(a^5)^3}{(b^3)^3} = \dfrac{64a^{15}}{b^9}$

**d.** $\left(\dfrac{3^{-2}}{x}\right)^{-3} = \dfrac{(3^{-2})^{-3}}{x^{-3}} = \dfrac{3^6}{x^{-3}} = 729x^3$

**e.** $(a^{-2}b^3c^{-4})^{-2} = (a^{-2})^{-2}(b^3)^{-2}(c^{-4})^{-2}$
$= a^4b^{-6}c^8$
$= \dfrac{a^4c^8}{b^6}$

**9. a.** $C(100) = \dfrac{2.6(100)+10,000}{100}$
$= 102.60$
The cost is \$102.60 per disc for 100 discs.

**b.** $C(1000) = \dfrac{2.6(1000)+10,000}{1000}$
$= 12.60$
The cost is \$12.60 per disc for 1000 discs.

**10. a.** $(3x-1)^2 = (3x)^2 - 2(3x)(1) + 1^2$
$= 9x^2 - 6x + 1$

**b.** $\left(\dfrac{1}{2}x+3\right)\left(\dfrac{1}{2}x-3\right) = \left(\dfrac{1}{2}x\right)^2 - 3^2$
$= \dfrac{1}{4}x^2 - 9$

**c.** $(2x-5)(6x+7) = 12x^2 + 14x - 30x - 35$
$= 12x^2 - 16x - 35$

**11. a.** $\dfrac{x}{4} + \dfrac{5x}{4} = \dfrac{6x}{4} = \dfrac{3x}{2}$

**b.** $\dfrac{5}{7z^2} + \dfrac{x}{7z^2} = \dfrac{5+x}{7z^2}$

**c.** $\dfrac{x^2}{x+7} - \dfrac{49}{x+7} = \dfrac{x^2-49}{x+7}$
$= \dfrac{(x+7)(x-7)}{x+7}$
$= x - 7$

**d.** $\dfrac{x}{3y^2} - \dfrac{x+1}{3y^2} = \dfrac{x-x-1}{3y^2} = -\dfrac{1}{3y^2}$

**12.** $\dfrac{5}{x-2} + \dfrac{3}{x^2+4x+4} - \dfrac{6}{x+2}$
$= \dfrac{5}{x-2} + \dfrac{3}{(x+2)^2} - \dfrac{6}{x+2}$
$= \dfrac{5(x+2)^2 + 3(x-2) - 6(x-2)(x+2)}{(x-2)(x+2)(x+2)}$
$= \dfrac{-x^2+23x+38}{(x-2)(x+2)^2}$

**13.**

$$
x^2-1\overline{\smash{\big)}\,3x^4+2x^3\phantom{+3x^2}-8x+6}
$$

quotient: $3x^2+2x+3$

$$
\underline{3x^4\phantom{+2x^3}-3x^2}
$$
$$
2x^3+3x^2-8x
$$
$$
\underline{2x^3\phantom{+3x^2}-2x}
$$
$$
3x^2-6x+6
$$
$$
\underline{3x^2\phantom{-6x}-3}
$$
$$
-6x+9
$$

Solution: $3x^2+2x+3+\dfrac{-6x+9}{x^2-1}$

**14. a.** $\dfrac{\frac{a}{5}}{\frac{a-1}{10}}=\dfrac{a}{5}\cdot\dfrac{10}{a-1}=\dfrac{2a}{a-1}$

**b.** $\dfrac{\frac{3}{2+a}+\frac{6}{2-a}}{\frac{5}{a+2}-\frac{1}{a-2}}=\dfrac{\frac{3}{a+2}-\frac{6}{a-2}}{\frac{5}{a+2}-\frac{1}{a-2}}$

Multiply the numerator and the denominator by $(a+2)(a-2)$.

$$
\dfrac{3(a-2)-6(a+2)}{5(a-2)-1(a+2)}=\dfrac{3a-6-6a-12}{5a-10-a-2}
$$
$$
=\dfrac{-3a-18}{4a-12}
$$

**c.** $\dfrac{x^{-1}+y^{-1}}{xy}=\dfrac{\frac{1}{x}+\frac{1}{y}}{xy}=\dfrac{\left(\frac{1}{x}+\frac{1}{y}\right)xy}{(xy)(xy)}=\dfrac{y+x}{x^2y^2}$

**15.**

$$
\dfrac{2x}{2x-1}+\dfrac{1}{x}=\dfrac{1}{2x-1}
$$
$$
(2x-1)x\left(\dfrac{2x}{2x-1}+\dfrac{1}{x}\right)=(2x-1)x\left(\dfrac{1}{2x-1}\right)
$$
$$
2x^2+2x-1=x
$$
$$
2x^2+x-1=0
$$
$$
(2x-1)(x+1)=0
$$
$$
2x-1=0 \quad\text{or}\quad x+1=0
$$
$$
2x=1 \qquad\qquad x=-1
$$
$$
x=\dfrac{1}{2}
$$

$x=\dfrac{1}{2}$ makes the denominator $2x-1$ zero, so the only solution is $x=-1$.

**16.** $\dfrac{x^3-8}{x-2}=\dfrac{(x-2)(x^2+2x+4)}{(x-2)}$

$\phantom{\dfrac{x^3-8}{x-2}}=x^2+2x+4$

**17.** Use distance = (rate)(time). Let $c$ be the speed of the current.

| | d | r | t |
|---|---|---|---|
| Upstream | 72 | $30-c$ | $1.5t$ |
| Downstream | 72 | $30+c$ | $t$ |

Upstream: $72=1.5t(30-c)$ or $t=\dfrac{72}{1.5(30-c)}$

Downstream: $72=t(30+c)$ or $t=\dfrac{72}{30+c}$

$$
\dfrac{72}{1.5(30-c)}=\dfrac{72}{30+c}
$$
$$
72(30+c)=72(1.5)(30-c)
$$
$$
2160+72c=3240-108c
$$
$$
180c=1080
$$
$$
c=6
$$

The speed of the current is 6 miles per hour.

**18.**

$$
2\,\underline{|\,8 \quad -12 \quad -7}
$$
$$
\phantom{2\,|\,8}\quad 16 \quad\ \ 8
$$
$$
\overline{\phantom{2\,|\,}8 \quad\ \ 4 \quad\ \ 1}
$$

Solution: $8x+4+\dfrac{1}{x-2}$

**19. a.** $\sqrt[4]{81}=\sqrt[4]{3^4}=3$

**b.** $\sqrt[5]{-243}=\sqrt[5]{(-3)^5}=-3$

**c.** $-\sqrt{25}=-\sqrt{5^2}=-5$

**d.** $\sqrt[4]{-81}$ is not a real number.

**e.** $\sqrt[3]{64x^3}=\sqrt[3]{4^3x^3}=4x$

**20.**
$$\frac{1}{a+5} = \frac{1}{3a+6} - \frac{a+2}{a^2+7a+10}$$
$$\frac{1}{a+5} = \frac{1}{3(a+2)} - \frac{a+2}{(a+2)(a+5)}$$
$$3(a+2) = a+5 - 3(a+2)$$
$$3a+6 = a+5 - 3a - 6$$
$$5a = -7$$
$$a = -\frac{7}{5}$$

**21. a.** $\sqrt{x} \cdot \sqrt[4]{x} = x^{1/2} \cdot x^{1/4} = x^{3/4} = \sqrt[4]{x^3}$

**b.** $\dfrac{\sqrt{x}}{\sqrt[3]{x}} = \dfrac{x^{1/2}}{x^{1/3}} = x^{\frac{1}{2}-\frac{1}{3}} = x^{1/6} = \sqrt[6]{x}$

**c.** $\sqrt[3]{3} \cdot \sqrt{2} = 3^{1/3} \cdot 2^{1/2}$
$$= 3^{2/6} \cdot 2^{3/6}$$
$$= 9^{1/6} \cdot 8^{1/6}$$
$$= 72^{1/6}$$
$$= \sqrt[6]{72}$$

**22.** $y = kx$
$$\frac{1}{2} = 12k$$
$$k = \frac{1}{24}, \ y = \frac{1}{24}x$$

**23. a.** $\sqrt{3}\left(5+\sqrt{30}\right) = 5\sqrt{3} + \sqrt{90} = 5\sqrt{3} + 3\sqrt{10}$

**b.** $\left(\sqrt{5}-\sqrt{6}\right)\left(\sqrt{7}+1\right) = \sqrt{35} + \sqrt{5} - \sqrt{42} - \sqrt{6}$

**c.** $\left(7\sqrt{x}+5\right)\left(3\sqrt{x}-\sqrt{5}\right)$
$$= 21x - 7\sqrt{5x} + 15\sqrt{x} - 5\sqrt{5}$$

**d.** $\left(4\sqrt{3}-1\right)^2$
$$= \left(4\sqrt{3}\right)^2 - 2\left(4\sqrt{3}\right)(1) + 1^2$$
$$= 16\cdot3 - 8\sqrt{3} + 1$$
$$= 49 - 8\sqrt{3}$$

**e.** $\left(\sqrt{2x}-5\right)\left(\sqrt{2x}+5\right) = \left(\sqrt{2x}\right)^2 - 5^2$
$$= 2x - 25$$

**f.** $\left(\sqrt{x-3}+5\right)^2 = \left(\sqrt{x-3}\right)^2 + 2\sqrt{x-3}(5) + 5^2$
$$= x - 3 + 10\sqrt{x-3} + 25$$
$$= x + 22 + 10\sqrt{x-3}$$

**24. a.** $\sqrt[4]{81} = \sqrt[4]{3^4} = 3$

**b.** $\sqrt[3]{-27} = \sqrt[3]{(-3)^3} = -3$

**c.** $\sqrt{\dfrac{9}{64}} = \sqrt{\left(\dfrac{3}{8}\right)^2} = \dfrac{3}{8}$

**d.** $\sqrt[4]{x^{12}} = x^3$

**e.** $\sqrt[3]{-125y^6} = -5y^2$

**25.** $\dfrac{\sqrt[4]{x}}{\sqrt[4]{81y^5}} = \dfrac{\sqrt[4]{x}}{\sqrt[4]{81y^5}} \cdot \dfrac{\sqrt[4]{y^3}}{\sqrt[4]{y^3}} = \dfrac{\sqrt[4]{xy^3}}{3y^2}$

**26. a.** $a^{1/4}\left(a^{3/4} - a^{7/4}\right) = a^{4/4} - a^{8/4} = a - a^2$

**b.** $\left(x^{1/2}-3\right)\left(x^{1/2}+5\right)$
$$= x^{2/2} + 5x^{1/2} - 3x^{1/2} - 15$$
$$= x + 2x^{1/2} - 15$$

**27.** $\sqrt{4-x} = x-2$
$$\left(\sqrt{4-x}\right)^2 = (x-2)^2$$
$$4-x = x^2 - 4x + 4$$
$$0 = x^2 - 3x$$
$$0 = x(x-3)$$
$$x = 0 \quad \text{or} \quad x-3 = 0$$
$$x = 3$$
$x = 0$ does not check, so the only solution is $x = 3$.

**28. a.** $\sqrt{\dfrac{54}{6}} = \sqrt{9} = 3$

**b.**
$$\frac{\sqrt{108a^2}}{3\sqrt{3}} = \frac{1}{3}\sqrt{\frac{108a^2}{3}}$$
$$= \frac{1}{3}\sqrt{36a^2}$$
$$= \frac{1}{3}(6a)$$
$$= 2a$$

**c.**
$$\frac{3\sqrt[3]{81a^5b^{10}}}{\sqrt[3]{3b^4}} = 3\sqrt[3]{\frac{81a^5b^{10}}{3b^4}}$$
$$= 3\sqrt[3]{27a^5b^6}$$
$$= 9ab^2\sqrt[3]{a^2}$$

**29.**
$$3x^2 - 9x + 8 = 0$$
$$x^2 - 3x + \frac{8}{3} = 0$$
$$x^2 - 3x = -\frac{8}{3}$$
$$x^2 - 3x + \left(\frac{-3}{2}\right)^2 = -\frac{8}{3} + \left(\frac{-3}{2}\right)^2$$
$$x^2 - 3x + \frac{9}{4} = -\frac{8}{3} + \frac{9}{4}$$
$$\left(x - \frac{3}{2}\right)^2 = -\frac{5}{12}$$
$$x - \frac{3}{2} = \pm\sqrt{-\frac{5}{12}}$$
$$x - \frac{3}{2} = \pm\frac{i\sqrt{5}}{2\sqrt{3}}$$
$$x - \frac{3}{2} = \pm\frac{i\sqrt{15}}{6}$$
$$x = \frac{3}{2} \pm \frac{i\sqrt{15}}{6}$$
$$= \frac{9}{6} \pm \frac{i\sqrt{15}}{6}$$
$$= \frac{9 \pm i\sqrt{15}}{6}$$

The solutions are $\dfrac{9 + i\sqrt{15}}{6}$ and $\dfrac{9 - i\sqrt{15}}{6}$.

**30. a.**
$$\frac{\sqrt{20}}{3} + \frac{\sqrt{5}}{4} = \frac{2\sqrt{5}}{3} + \frac{\sqrt{5}}{4}$$
$$= \frac{8\sqrt{5} + 3\sqrt{5}}{12}$$
$$= \frac{11\sqrt{5}}{12}$$

**b.**
$$\sqrt[3]{\frac{24x}{27}} - \frac{\sqrt[3]{3x}}{2} = \frac{2\sqrt[3]{3x}}{3} - \frac{\sqrt[3]{3x}}{2}$$
$$= \frac{4\sqrt[3]{3x} - 3\sqrt[3]{3x}}{6}$$
$$= \frac{\sqrt[3]{3x}}{6}$$

**31.**
$$\frac{3x}{x-2} - \frac{x+1}{x} = \frac{6}{x(x-2)}$$
$$3x(x) - (x+1)(x-2) = 6$$
$$3x^2 - x^2 + x + 2 = 6$$
$$2x^2 + x - 4 = 0$$
$$a = 2, b = 1, c = -4$$
$$x = \frac{-1 \pm \sqrt{1^2 - 4(2)(-4)}}{2(2)} = \frac{-1 \pm \sqrt{33}}{4}$$

**32.**
$$\sqrt[3]{\frac{27}{m^4n^8}} = \frac{\sqrt[3]{27}}{\sqrt[3]{m^4n^8}}$$
$$= \frac{3}{mn^2\sqrt[3]{mn^2}}$$
$$= \frac{3 \cdot \sqrt[3]{m^2n}}{mn^2\sqrt[3]{mn^2} \cdot \sqrt[3]{m^2n}}$$
$$= \frac{3\sqrt[3]{m^2n}}{m^2n^3}$$

**33.** $x^2 - 4x \le 0$
$$x(x-4) = 0$$
$$x = 0, x = 4$$

| Region | Test Point | $x(x-4) \le 0$ | Result |
|--------|------------|----------------|--------|
| $x < 0$ | $x = -1$ | $(-1)(-5) \le 0$ | False |
| $0 < x < 4$ | $x = 2$ | $2(-2) \le 0$ | True |
| $x > 4$ | $x = 5$ | $5(1) \le 0$ | False |

Solution: [0, 4]

**34.**
$$c^2 = a^2 + b^2$$
$$8^2 = 4^2 + b^2$$
$$64 = 16 + b^2$$
$$48 = b^2$$
$$\pm 4\sqrt{3} = b$$

$b > 0$ so the length is $4\sqrt{3}$ inches.

**35.** $F(x) = (x-3)^2 + 1$

**36. a.** $i^8 = (i^2)^4 = (-1)^4 = 1$

**b.** $i^{21} = i(i^{20}) = i$

**c.** $i^{42} = i^2(i^{40}) = i^2 = -1$

**d.** $i^{-13} = \dfrac{1}{i^{13}} = \dfrac{1}{i(i^{12})} = \dfrac{1}{i} = \dfrac{i}{i^2} = -i$

**37.** $f(x) = x - 1$ and $g(x) = 2x - 3$

**a.** $(f+g)(x) = f(x) + g(x)$
$$= x - 1 + 2x - 3$$
$$= 3x - 4$$

**b.** $(f-g)(x) = f(x) - g(x)$
$$= x - 1 - (2x - 3)$$
$$= -x + 2$$

**c.** $(f \cdot g)(x) = f(x) \cdot g(x)$
$$= (x-1)(2x-3)$$
$$= 2x^2 - 5x + 3$$

**d.** $\left(\dfrac{f}{g}\right)(x) = \dfrac{f(x)}{g(x)} = \dfrac{x-1}{2x-3}$, where $x \neq \dfrac{3}{2}$.

**38.** $4x^2 + 8x - 1 = 0$
$$x^2 + 2x - \frac{1}{4} = 0$$
$$x^2 + 2x = \frac{1}{4}$$
$$x^2 + 2x + \left(\frac{2}{2}\right)^2 = \frac{1}{4} + \left(\frac{2}{2}\right)^2$$
$$x^2 + 2x + 1 = \frac{1}{4} + 1$$
$$(x+1)^2 = \frac{5}{4}$$
$$x + 1 = \pm\sqrt{\frac{5}{4}}$$
$$x + 1 = \pm\frac{\sqrt{5}}{2}$$
$$x = -1 \pm \frac{\sqrt{5}}{2}$$
$$= \frac{-2 \pm \sqrt{5}}{2}$$

The solutions are $\dfrac{-2+\sqrt{5}}{2}$ and $\dfrac{-2-\sqrt{5}}{2}$.

**39.** $f(x) = x + 3$
$$y = x + 3$$
$$x = y + 3$$
$$y = x - 3$$
$$f^{-1}(x) = x - 3$$

**40.** $\left(x - \dfrac{1}{2}\right)^2 = \dfrac{x}{2}$
$$x^2 - x + \frac{1}{4} = \frac{1}{2}x$$
$$x^2 - \frac{3}{2}x + \frac{1}{4} = 0$$
$$4x^2 - 6x + 1 = 0$$
$$a = 4, b = -6, c = 1$$
$$x = \frac{-(-6) \pm \sqrt{(-6)^2 - 4(4)(1)}}{2(4)}$$
$$= \frac{6 \pm \sqrt{20}}{8}$$
$$= \frac{6 \pm 2\sqrt{5}}{8}$$
$$= \frac{3 \pm \sqrt{5}}{4}$$

The solutions are $\dfrac{3+\sqrt{5}}{4}$ and $\dfrac{3-\sqrt{5}}{4}$.

**41. a.** $\log_4 16 = \log_4 4^2 = 2$

**b.** $\log_{10} \dfrac{1}{10} = \log_{10} 10^{-1} = -1$

**c.** $\log_9 3 = \log_9 9^{1/2} = \dfrac{1}{2}$

**42.** $f(x) = -(x+1)^2 + 1$

Vertex: $(-1, 1)$

Axis of symmetry: $x = -1$

# Chapter 10

**1.** $x = \frac{1}{2}y^2$;  $a = \frac{1}{2}$, $h = 0$, $k = 0$; vertex: $(0, 0)$

| $x$ | $y$ |
|-----|-----|
| 2 | −2 |
| $\frac{1}{2}$ | −1 |
| 0 | 0 |
| $\frac{1}{2}$ | 1 |
| 2 | 2 |

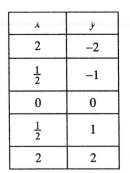

**2.** $x = -2(y + 4)^2 - 1$;  $a = -2$, $h = -1$, $k = -4$;
vertex: $(-1, -4)$

| $x$ | $y$ |
|-----|-----|
| −9 | −6 |
| 3 | −5 |
| −1 | −4 |
| −3 | −3 |
| −9 | −2 |

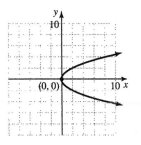

**3.**
$$y = -x^2 + 4x + 6$$
$$y - 6 = -x^2 + 4x$$
$$y - 6 = -(x^2 - 4x)$$
$$y - 6 - (+4) = -(x^2 - 4x + 4)$$
$$y - 10 = -(x - 2)^2$$
$$y = -(x - 2)^2 + 10$$
$a = -1$, $h = 2$, $k = 10$
vertex: $(2, 10)$

| $x$ | $y$ |
|-----|-----|
| −1 | 1 |
| 0 | 6 |
| 1 | 9 |
| 2 | 10 |
| 3 | 9 |
| 4 | 6 |
| 5 | 1 |

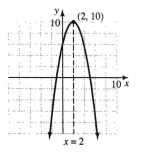

**4.** $x = 3y^2 + 6y + 4$
Find the vertex.
$$y = \frac{-b}{2a} = \frac{-6}{2(3)} = -1$$
$$x = 3(-1)^2 + 6(-1) + 4 = 3 - 6 + 4 = 1$$
vertex: $(1, -1)$
The axis of symmetry is the line $y = -1$.
Since $a > 0$, the parabola opens to the right.
$$x = 3(0)^2 + 6(0) + 4 = 4$$
The $x$-intercept is $(4, 0)$.

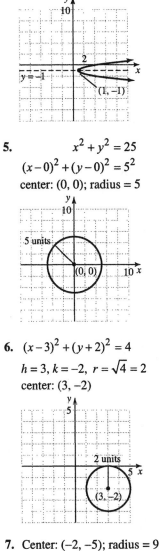

**5.**

$$x^2 + y^2 = 25$$

$$(x - 0)^2 + (y - 0)^2 = 5^2$$

center: (0, 0); radius = 5

**6.** $(x - 3)^2 + (y + 2)^2 = 4$

$h = 3,\ k = -2,\ r = \sqrt{4} = 2$

center: (3, -2)

**7.** Center: (-2, -5); radius = 9

$$(x - h)^2 + (y - k)^2 = r^2$$

$h = -2,\ k = -5,$ and $r = 9.$

The equation is $(x + 2)^2 + (y + 5)^2 = 81.$

**8.**

$$x^2 + y^2 + 6x - 2y = 6$$

$$(x^2 + 6x) + (y^2 - 2y) = 6$$

$$(x^2 + 6x + 9) + (y^2 - 2y + 1) = 6 + 9 + 1$$

$$(x + 3)^2 + (y - 1)^2 = 16$$

Center: (-3, 1); radius = $\sqrt{16} = 4$

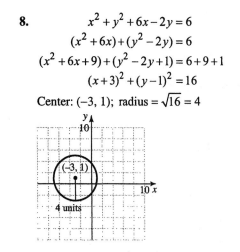

## Graphing Calculator Explorations

**1.** $x^2 + y^2 = 55$

$$y^2 = 55 - x^2$$

$$y = \pm\sqrt{55 - x^2}$$

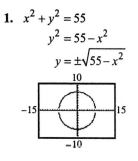

**2.** $x^2 + y^2 = 20$

$$y^2 = 20 - x^2$$

$$y = \pm\sqrt{20 - x^2}$$

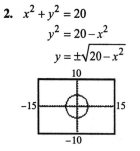

**3.** $5x^2 + 5y^2 = 50$

$$5y^2 = 50 - 5x^2$$

$$y^2 = 10 - x^2$$

$$y = \pm\sqrt{10 - x^2}$$

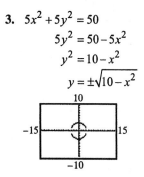

**4.** $6x^2 + 6y^2 = 105$
$$6y^2 = 105 - 6x^2$$
$$y^2 = 17.5 - x^2$$
$$y = \pm\sqrt{17.5 - x^2}$$

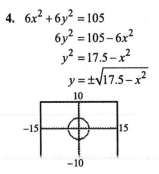

**5.** $2x^2 + 2y^2 - 34 = 0$
$$2y^2 = 34 - 2x^2$$
$$y^2 = 17 - x^2$$
$$y = \pm\sqrt{17 - x^2}$$

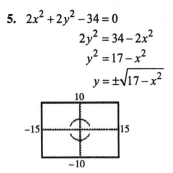

**6.** $4x^2 + 4y^2 - 48 = 0$
$$4y^2 = 48 - 4x^2$$
$$y^2 = 12 - x^2$$
$$y = \pm\sqrt{12 - x^2}$$

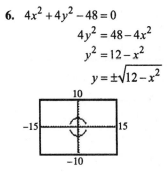

**7.** $7x^2 + 7y^2 - 89 = 0$
$$7y^2 = 89 - 7x^2$$
$$y^2 = \frac{89 - 7x^2}{7}$$
$$y = \pm\sqrt{\frac{89 - 7x^2}{7}}$$

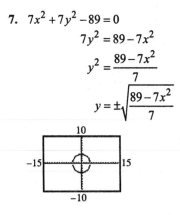

**8.** $3x^2 + 3y^2 - 35 = 0$
$$3y^2 = 35 - 3x^2$$
$$y^2 = \frac{35 - 3x^2}{3}$$
$$y = \pm\sqrt{\frac{35 - 3x^2}{3}}$$

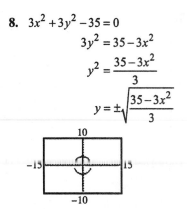

**Vocabulary and Readiness Check**

1. The circle, parabola, ellipse, and hyperbola are called the conic sections.

2. For a parabola that opens upward the lowest point is the vertex.

3. A circle is the set of all points in a plane that are the same distance from a fixed point. The fixed point is called the center.

4. The midpoint of a diameter of a circle is the center.

5. The distance from the center of a circle to any point of the circle is called the radius.

6. Twice a circle's radius is its diameter.

7. $y = x^2 - 7x + 5$; $a = 1$, upward

8. $y = -x^2 + 16$; $a = -1$, downward

9. $x = -y^2 - y + 2$; $a = -1$, to the left

10. $x = 3y^2 + 2y - 5$; $a = 3$, to the right

11. $y = -x^2 + 2x + 1$; $a = -1$, downward

12. $x = -y^2 + 2y - 6$; $a = -1$, to the left

**Exercise Set 10.1**

**1.** $x = 3y^2$

$x = 3(y - 0)^2 + 0$

Vertex: (0, 0)

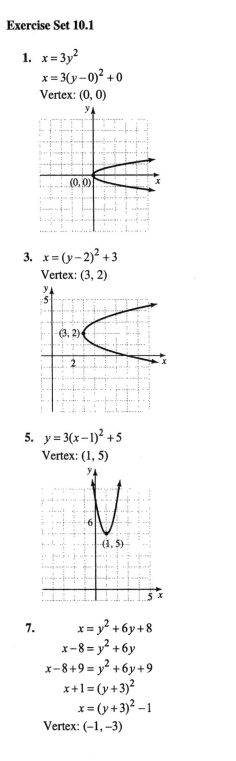

**3.** $x = (y - 2)^2 + 3$

Vertex: (3, 2)

**5.** $y = 3(x - 1)^2 + 5$

Vertex: (1, 5)

**7.** $x = y^2 + 6y + 8$

$x - 8 = y^2 + 6y$

$x - 8 + 9 = y^2 + 6y + 9$

$x + 1 = (y + 3)^2$

$x = (y + 3)^2 - 1$

Vertex: (−1, −3)

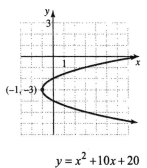

(−1, −3)

**9.** $y = x^2 + 10x + 20$

$y - 20 = x^2 + 10x$

$y - 20 + 25 = x^2 + 10x + 25$

$y + 5 = (x + 5)^2$

$y = (x + 5)^2 - 5$

Vertex: (−5, −5)

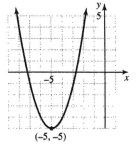

(−5, −5)

**11.** $x = -2y^2 + 4y + 6$

$x - 6 = -2(y^2 - 2y)$

$x - 6 + [-2(1)] = -2(y^2 - 2y + 1)$

$x - 8 = -2(y - 1)^2$

$x = -2(y - 1)^2 + 8$

Vertex: (8, 1)

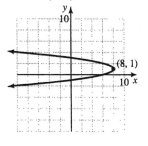

(8, 1)

**13.** $x^2 + y^2 = 9$

$(x-0)^2 + (y-0)^2 = 3^2$

Center: (0, 0), radius $r = 3$.

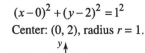

**15.** $x^2 + (y-2)^2 = 1$

$(x-0)^2 + (y-2)^2 = 1^2$

Center: (0, 2), radius $r = 1$.

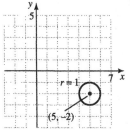

**17.** $(x-5)^2 + (y+2)^2 = 1$

$(x-5)^2 + (y+2)^2 = 1^2$

Center: (5, –2), radius $r = 1$.

**19.** $x^2 + y^2 + 6y = 0$

$x^2 + (y^2 + 6y) = 0$

$x^2 + (y^2 + 6y + 9) = 9$

$(x-0)^2 + (y+3)^2 = 3^2$

Center: (0, –3), radius $r = 3$.

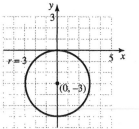

**21.** $x^2 + y^2 + 2x - 4y = 4$

$(x^2 + 2x) + (y^2 - 4y) = 4$

$(x^2 + 2x + 1) + (y^2 - 4y + 4) = 4 + 1 + 4$

$(x+1)^2 + (y-2)^2 = 9$

Center: (–1, 2), radius $r = \sqrt{9} = 3$.

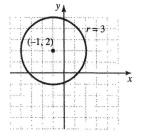

**23.** $x^2 + y^2 - 4x - 8y - 2 = 0$

$(x^2 - 4x) + (y^2 - 8y) = 2$

$(x^2 - 4x + 4) + (y^2 - 8y + 16) = 2 + 4 + 16$

$(x-2)^2 + (y-4)^2 = 22$

Center: (2, 4), radius $r = \sqrt{22}$.

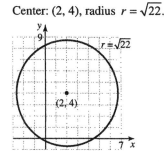

**25.** Center $(h, k) = (2, 3)$ and radius $r = 6$.

$(x-h)^2 + (y-k)^2 = r^2$

$(x-2)^2 + (y-3)^2 = 6^2$

$(x-2)^2 + (y-3)^2 = 36$

**27.** Center $(h, k) = (0, 0)$ and radius $r = \sqrt{3}$.

$$(x - h)^2 + (y - k)^2 = r^2$$
$$(x - 0)^2 + (y - 0)^2 = \left(\sqrt{3}\right)^2$$
$$x^2 + y^2 = 3$$

**29.** Center $(h, k) = (-5, 4)$ and radius $r = 3\sqrt{5}$.

$$(x - h)^2 + (y - k)^2 = r^2$$
$$[x - (-5)]^2 + (y - 4)^2 = \left(3\sqrt{5}\right)^2$$
$$(x + 5)^2 + (y - 4)^2 = 45$$

**31.** The radius is $\sqrt{10}$.

**33.** $x = y^2 - 3$

$x = (y - 0)^2 - 3$
Vertex: $(-3, 0)$

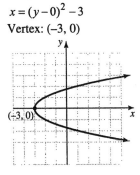

**35.** $y = (x - 2)^2 - 2$
Vertex: $(2, -2)$

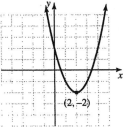

**37.** $x^2 + y^2 = 1$
Center: $(0, 0)$, radius $r = \sqrt{1} = 1$

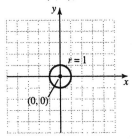

**39.** $x = (y + 3)^2 - 1$
Vertex: $(-1, -3)$

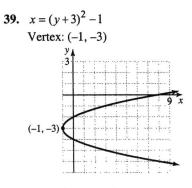

**41.** $(x - 2)^2 + (y - 2)^2 = 16$
Center: $(2, 2)$, radius $r = \sqrt{16} = 4$

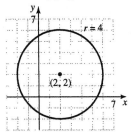

**43.** $x = -(y - 1)^2$
Vertex: $(0, 1)$

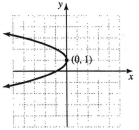

**45.** $(x - 4)^2 + y^2 = 7$
Center: $(4, 0)$, radius $r = \sqrt{7}$

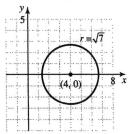

**47.** $y = 5(x+5)^2 + 3$
Vertex: (–5, 3)

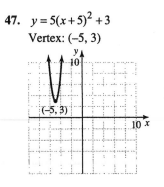

**49.** $\dfrac{x^2}{8} + \dfrac{y^2}{8} = 2$

$8\left(\dfrac{x^2}{8} + \dfrac{y^2}{8}\right) = 8(2)$

$x^2 + y^2 = 16$

Center: (0, 0), radius $r = \sqrt{16} = 4$

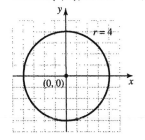

**51.** $y = x^2 + 7x + 6$
$y - 6 = x^2 + 7x$
$y - 6 + \dfrac{49}{4} = x^2 + 7x + \dfrac{49}{4}$
$y + \dfrac{25}{4} = \left(x + \dfrac{7}{2}\right)^2$
$y = \left(x + \dfrac{7}{2}\right)^2 - \dfrac{25}{4}$

Vertex: $\left(-\dfrac{7}{2}, -\dfrac{25}{4}\right)$

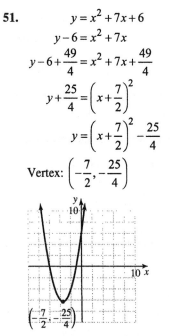

**53.** $x^2 + y^2 + 2x + 12y - 12 = 0$
$(x^2 + 2x) + (y^2 + 12y) = 12$
$(x^2 + 2x + 1) + (y^2 + 12y + 36) = 12 + 1 + 36$
$(x+1)^2 + (y+6)^2 = 49$
Center: (–1, –6), radius $r = \sqrt{49} = 7$

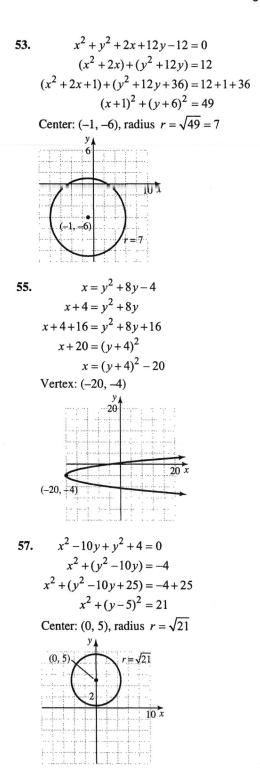

**55.** $x = y^2 + 8y - 4$
$x + 4 = y^2 + 8y$
$x + 4 + 16 = y^2 + 8y + 16$
$x + 20 = (y+4)^2$
$x = (y+4)^2 - 20$
Vertex: (–20, –4)

**57.** $x^2 - 10y + y^2 + 4 = 0$
$x^2 + (y^2 - 10y) = -4$
$x^2 + (y^2 - 10y + 25) = -4 + 25$
$x^2 + (y-5)^2 = 21$
Center: (0, 5), radius $r = \sqrt{21}$

**59.**
$$x = -3y^2 + 30y$$
$$x = -3(y^2 - 10y)$$
$$x + [-3(25)] = -3(y^2 - 10y + 25)$$
$$x - 75 = -3(y - 5)^2$$
$$x = -3(y - 5)^2 + 75$$

Vertex: (75, 5)

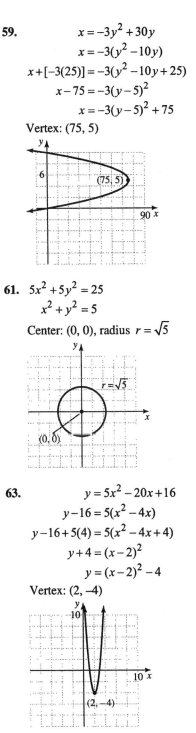

**61.** $5x^2 + 5y^2 = 25$
$$x^2 + y^2 = 5$$

Center: (0, 0), radius $r = \sqrt{5}$

**63.**
$$y = 5x^2 - 20x + 16$$
$$y - 16 = 5(x^2 - 4x)$$
$$y - 16 + 5(4) = 5(x^2 - 4x + 4)$$
$$y + 4 = (x - 2)^2$$
$$y = (x - 2)^2 - 4$$

Vertex: (2, –4)

**65.** $y = -3x + 3$

**67.** $x = -2$

**69.** $\dfrac{\sqrt{5}}{\sqrt{8}} = \dfrac{\sqrt{5}}{2\sqrt{2}} = \dfrac{\sqrt{5} \cdot \sqrt{2}}{2\sqrt{2} \cdot \sqrt{2}} = \dfrac{\sqrt{10}}{2 \cdot 2} = \dfrac{\sqrt{10}}{4}$

**71.** $\dfrac{10}{\sqrt{5}} = \dfrac{10 \cdot \sqrt{5}}{\sqrt{5} \cdot \sqrt{5}} = \dfrac{10\sqrt{5}}{5} = 2\sqrt{5}$

**73. a.** radius $= \dfrac{1}{2}$(diameter) $= \dfrac{1}{2}$(135 meters)
$$= 67.5 \text{ meters}$$

**b.** The wheel is at ground level or 0 meters.

**c.** The height of the center is equal to the radius or 67.5 meters.

**d.** The coordinates of the center are (0, 67.5).

**e.** $h = 0$, $k = 67.5$, and $r = 67.5$.
$$(x - h)^2 + (y - k)^2 = r^2$$
$$x^2 + (y - 67.5)^2 = 67.5^2$$

**75. a.** radius $= \dfrac{1}{2}$(diameter) $= \dfrac{1}{2}$(153 meters)
$$= 76.5 \text{ meters}$$

**b.** height $-$ diameter
$$= 160 - 153$$
$$= 7 \text{ meters from the ground}$$

**c.**  height from ground + radius
$$= 7 + 76.5$$
$$= 83.5 \text{ meters from the ground}$$

**d.**  Center: (0, 83.5)

**e.**  $h = 0$, $k = 83.5$, and $r = 76.5$.
$$(x - h)^2 + (y - k)^2 = r^2$$
$$x^2 + (y - 83.5)^2 = 76.5^2$$

**77.**  diameter = 20 cm; center: (0, 0)

**a.**

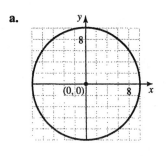

**b.**  $h = 0$, $k = 0$, and $r = \dfrac{1}{2}(20) = 10$
$$(x - h)^2 + (y - k)^2 = r^2$$
$$x^2 + y^2 = 100$$

**c.**  $h = 0$, $k = 0$, and the radius is the distance from the fountain or 5 feet.
$$x^2 + y^2 = 25$$

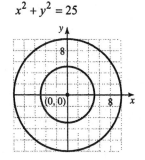

**79.**  $5x^2 + 5y^2 = 25$
$$5y^2 = 25 - 5x^2$$
$$y^2 = 5 - x^2$$
$$y = \pm\sqrt{5 - x^2}$$

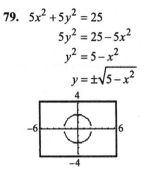

**81.**  $y = 5x^2 - 20x + 16$

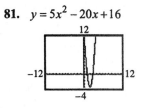

## Section 10.2

### Practice Exercises

**1.**  $\dfrac{x^2}{25} + \dfrac{y^2}{4} = 1$

The equation is an ellipse with $a = 5$ and $b = 2$. The center is (0, 0). The $x$-intercepts are (5, 0) and (−5, 0). The $y$-intercepts are (2, 0) and (−2, 0).

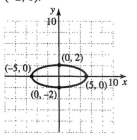

**2.**  $9x^2 + 4y^2 = 36$
$$\frac{9x^2}{36} + \frac{4y^2}{36} = \frac{36}{36}$$
$$\frac{x^2}{4} + \frac{y^2}{9} = 1$$

This is an equation of an ellipse with $a = 2$ and $b = 3$. The ellipse has center (0, 0), $x$-intercepts (2, 0) and (−2, 0), and $y$-intercepts (3, 0) and (−3, 0).

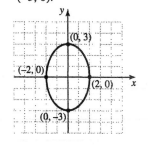

**3.**  $\dfrac{(x - 4)^2}{49} + \dfrac{(y + 1)^2}{81} = 1$

This ellipse has center (4, −1). $a = 7$ and $b = 9$. Find four points on the ellipse.

$(4 + 7, -1) = (11, -1)$
$(4 - 7, -1) = (-3, -1)$
$(4, -1 + 9) = (4, 8)$
$(4, -1 - 9) = (4, -10)$

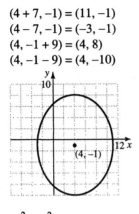

**4.**  $\dfrac{x^2}{9} - \dfrac{y^2}{16} = 1$

This is a hyperbola with $a = 3$ and $b = 4$. It has center $(0, 0)$ and $x$-intercepts $(3, 0)$ and $(-3, 0)$. The asymptotes pass through $(3, 4)$, $(3, -4)$, $(-3, 4)$, and $(-3, -4)$.

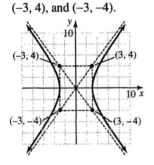

**5.**  $9y^2 - 25x^2 = 225$

$\dfrac{9y^2}{225} - \dfrac{25x^2}{225} = \dfrac{225}{225}$

$\dfrac{y^2}{25} - \dfrac{x^2}{9} = 1$

This is a hyperbola with $a = 3$ and $b = 5$. The center is at $(0, 0)$ with $y$-intercepts $(0, 5)$ and $(0, -5)$. The asymptotes pass through $(3, 5)$, $(3, -5)$, $(-3, 5)$, and $(-3, -5)$.

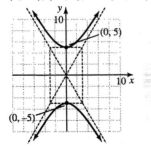

**Graphing Calculator Explorations**

**1.**  $10x^2 + y^2 = 32$

$y^2 = 32 - 10x^2$

$y = \pm\sqrt{32 - 10x^2}$

**2.**  $x^2 + 6y^2 = 35$

$6y^2 = 35 - x^2$

$y^2 = \dfrac{35 - x^2}{6}$

$y = \pm\sqrt{\dfrac{35 - x^2}{6}}$

**3.**  $20x^2 + 5y^2 = 100$

$5y^2 = 100 - 20x^2$

$y^2 = 20 - 4x^2$

$y = \pm\sqrt{20 - 4x^2}$

**4.**  $4y^2 + 12x^2 = 48$

$4y^2 = 48 - 12x^2$

$y^2 = 12 - 3x^2$

$y = \pm\sqrt{12 - 3x^2}$

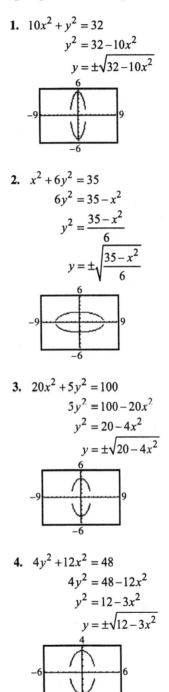

5. $7.3x^2 + 15.5y^2 = 95.2$
$$15.5y^2 = 95.2 - 7.3x^2$$
$$y^2 = \frac{95.2 - 7.3x^2}{15.5}$$
$$y = \pm\sqrt{\frac{95.2 - 7.3x^2}{15.5}}$$

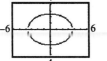

6. $18.8x^2 + 36.1y^2 = 205.8$
$$36.1y^2 = 205.8 - 18.8x^2$$
$$y^2 = \frac{205.8 - 18.8x^2}{36.1}$$
$$y = \pm\sqrt{\frac{205.8 - 18.8x^2}{36.1}}$$

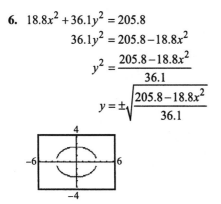

**Vocabulary and Readiness Check**

1. A <u>hyperbola</u> is the set of points in a plane such that the absolute value of the differences of their distances from two fixed points is constant.

2. An <u>ellipse</u> is the set of points in a plane such that the sum of their distances from two fixed points is constant.

3. The two fixed points are each called a <u>focus</u>.

4. The point midway between the foci is called the <u>center</u>.

5. The graph of $\frac{x^2}{a^2} - \frac{y^2}{b^2} = 1$ is a <u>hyperbola</u> with center <u>(0, 0)</u> and x-intercepts of <u>(a, 0) and (-a, 0)</u>.

6. The graph of $\frac{x^2}{b^2} + \frac{y^2}{a^2} = 1$ is an <u>ellipse</u> with center <u>(0, 0)</u> and x-intercepts of <u>(b, 0) and (-b, 0)</u>.

7. $\frac{x^2}{16} + \frac{y^2}{4} = 1$ is an ellipse.

8. $\frac{x^2}{16} - \frac{y^2}{4} = 1$ is a hyperbola.

9. $x^2 - 5y^2 = 3$ is a hyperbola.

10. $-x^2 + 5y^2 = 3$ or $5y^2 - x^2 = 3$ is a hyperbola.

11. $-\frac{y^2}{25} + \frac{x^2}{36} = 1$ or $\frac{x^2}{36} - \frac{y^2}{25} = 1$ is a hyperbola.

12. $\frac{y^2}{25} + \frac{x^2}{36} = 1$ is an ellipse.

**Exercise Set 10.2**

1. $\frac{x^2}{4} + \frac{y^2}{25} = 1$
$$\frac{x^2}{2^2} + \frac{y^2}{5^2} = 1$$
Center: (0, 0)
x-intercepts: (−2, 0), (2, 0)
y-intercepts: (0, −5), (0, 5)

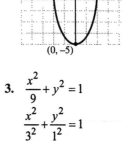

3. $\frac{x^2}{9} + y^2 = 1$
$$\frac{x^2}{3^2} + \frac{y^2}{1^2} = 1$$
Center: (0, 0)
x-intercepts: (−3, 0), (3, 0)
y-intercepts: (0, −1), (0, 1)

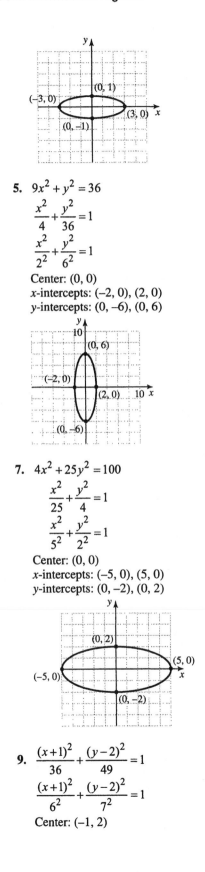

**5.** $9x^2 + y^2 = 36$

$$\frac{x^2}{4} + \frac{y^2}{36} = 1$$

$$\frac{x^2}{2^2} + \frac{y^2}{6^2} = 1$$

Center: (0, 0)
x-intercepts: (–2, 0), (2, 0)
y-intercepts: (0, –6), (0, 6)

**7.** $4x^2 + 25y^2 = 100$

$$\frac{x^2}{25} + \frac{y^2}{4} = 1$$

$$\frac{x^2}{5^2} + \frac{y^2}{2^2} = 1$$

Center: (0, 0)
x-intercepts: (–5, 0), (5, 0)
y-intercepts: (0, –2), (0, 2)

**9.** $\dfrac{(x+1)^2}{36} + \dfrac{(y-2)^2}{49} = 1$

$$\frac{(x+1)^2}{6^2} + \frac{(y-2)^2}{7^2} = 1$$

Center: (–1, 2)

Other points:
$(-1-6,\,2) = (-7,\,2)$
$(-1+6,\,2) = (5,\,2)$
$(-1,\,2-7) = (-1,\,-5)$
$(-1,\,2+7) = (-1,\,9)$

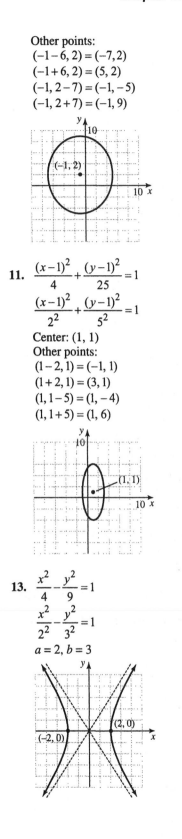

**11.** $\dfrac{(x-1)^2}{4} + \dfrac{(y-1)^2}{25} = 1$

$$\frac{(x-1)^2}{2^2} + \frac{(y-1)^2}{5^2} = 1$$

Center: (1, 1)
Other points:
$(1-2,\,1) = (-1,\,1)$
$(1+2,\,1) = (3,\,1)$
$(1,\,1-5) = (1,\,-4)$
$(1,\,1+5) = (1,\,6)$

**13.** $\dfrac{x^2}{4} - \dfrac{y^2}{9} = 1$

$$\frac{x^2}{2^2} - \frac{y^2}{3^2} = 1$$

$a = 2,\ b = 3$

**15.** $\dfrac{y^2}{25} - \dfrac{x^2}{16} = 1$

$\dfrac{y^2}{5^2} - \dfrac{x^2}{4^2} = 1$

$a = 4,\ b = 5$

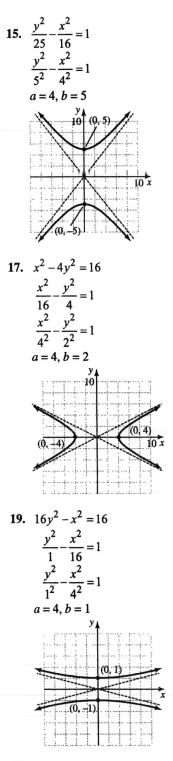

**17.** $x^2 - 4y^2 = 16$

$\dfrac{x^2}{16} - \dfrac{y^2}{4} = 1$

$\dfrac{x^2}{4^2} - \dfrac{y^2}{2^2} = 1$

$a = 4,\ b = 2$

**19.** $16y^2 - x^2 = 16$

$\dfrac{y^2}{1} - \dfrac{x^2}{16} = 1$

$\dfrac{y^2}{1^2} - \dfrac{x^2}{4^2} = 1$

$a = 4,\ b = 1$

**21.** Answers may vary

**23.** $y = x^2 + 4$

Parabola; vertex (0, 4), opens upward

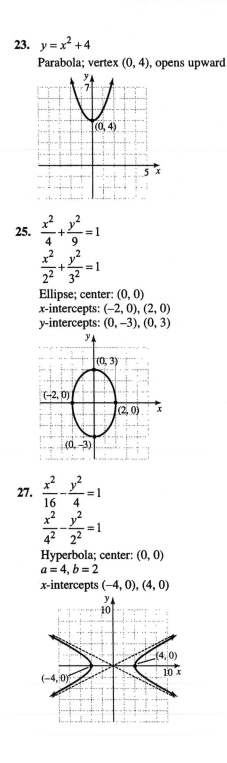

**25.** $\dfrac{x^2}{4} + \dfrac{y^2}{9} = 1$

$\dfrac{x^2}{2^2} + \dfrac{y^2}{3^2} = 1$

Ellipse; center: (0, 0)
$x$-intercepts: (–2, 0), (2, 0)
$y$-intercepts: (0, –3), (0, 3)

**27.** $\dfrac{x^2}{16} - \dfrac{y^2}{4} = 1$

$\dfrac{x^2}{4^2} - \dfrac{y^2}{2^2} = 1$

Hyperbola; center: (0, 0)
$a = 4,\ b = 2$
$x$-intercepts (–4, 0), (4, 0)

**29.** $x^2 + y^2 = 16$

Circle; center: (0, 0), radius: $r = \sqrt{16} = 4$

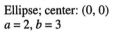

**31.** $x = -y^2 + 6y$

Parabola: $y = \dfrac{-b}{2a} = \dfrac{-6}{2(-1)} = 3$

$x = -(3)^2 + 6(3) = -9 + 18 = 9$

Vertex: (9, 3), opens to the left

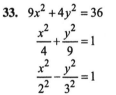

**33.** $9x^2 + 4y^2 = 36$

$\dfrac{x^2}{4} + \dfrac{y^2}{9} = 1$

$\dfrac{x^2}{2^2} - \dfrac{y^2}{3^2} = 1$

Ellipse; center: (0, 0)

$a = 2, b = 3$

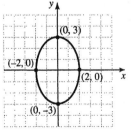

**35.** $y^2 = x^2 + 16$

$y^2 - x^2 = 16$

$\dfrac{y^2}{16} - \dfrac{x^2}{16} = 1$

$\dfrac{y^2}{4^2} - \dfrac{x^2}{4^2} = 1$

Hyperbola; center: (0, 0)

$a = 4, b = 4$

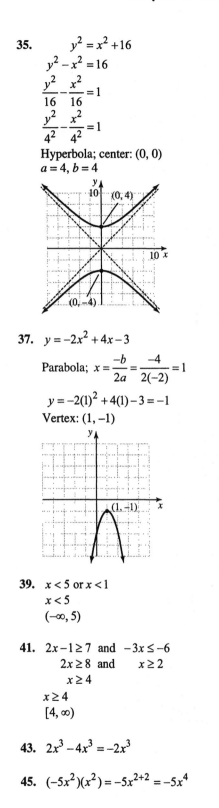

**37.** $y = -2x^2 + 4x - 3$

Parabola; $x = \dfrac{-b}{2a} = \dfrac{-4}{2(-2)} = 1$

$y = -2(1)^2 + 4(1) - 3 = -1$

Vertex: (1, –1)

**39.** $x < 5$ or $x < 1$

$x < 5$

$(-\infty, 5)$

**41.** $2x - 1 \geq 7$ and $-3x \leq -6$

$\quad 2x \geq 8$ and $\quad x \geq 2$

$\quad\quad x \geq 4$

$x \geq 4$

$[4, \infty)$

**43.** $2x^3 - 4x^3 = -2x^3$

**45.** $(-5x^2)(x^2) = -5x^{2+2} = -5x^4$

**47.** $\dfrac{x^2}{100} + \dfrac{y^2}{49} = 1$

$\sqrt{100} = 10$, so the distance between the
$x$-intercepts is $10 + 10 = 20$ units.
$\sqrt{49} = 7$, so the distance between the
$y$-intercepts is $7 + 7 = 14$ units.
The distance between the $x$-intercepts is longer
by $20 - 14 = 6$ units.

**49.** $x^2 + 4y^2 = 36$

$\dfrac{x^2}{36} + \dfrac{y^2}{9} = 1$

$\sqrt{36} = 6$, so the distance between the
$x$-intercepts is $6 + 6 = 12$ units.
$\sqrt{9} = 3$, so the distance between the
$y$-intercepts is $3 + 3 = 6$ units.
The distance between the $x$-intercepts is longer
by $12 - 6 = 6$ units.

**51.** Circles: B, F
Ellipses: C, E, H
Hyperbolas: A, D, G

**53.** A: $c^2 = 36 + 13 = 49;\ c = \sqrt{49} = 7$

B: $c^2 = 1 - 1 = 0;\ c = \sqrt{0} = 0$

C: $c^2 = |25 - 16| = 9;\ c = \sqrt{9} = 3$

D: $c^2 = 39 + 25 = 64;\ c = \sqrt{64} = 8$

E: $c^2 = |81 - 17| = 64;\ c = \sqrt{64} = 8$

F: $c^2 = |36 - 36| = 0;\ c = \sqrt{0} = 0$

G: $c^2 = 65 + 16 = 81;\ c = \sqrt{81} = 9$

H: $c^2 = |144 - 140| = 4;\ c = \sqrt{4} = 2$

**55.** A: $e = \dfrac{7}{6}$

B: $e = \dfrac{0}{2} = 0$

C: $e = \dfrac{3}{5}$

D: $e = \dfrac{8}{5}$

E: $e = \dfrac{8}{9}$

F: $e = \dfrac{0}{6} = 0$

G: $e = \dfrac{9}{4}$

H: $e = \dfrac{2}{12} = \dfrac{1}{6}$

**57.** They are equal to 0.

**59.** Answers may vary

**61.** $a = 130{,}000{,}000 \Rightarrow a^2 = (130{,}000{,}000)^2$
$\qquad\qquad\qquad\qquad = 1.69 \times 10^{16}$

$b = 125{,}000{,}000 \Rightarrow b^2 = (125{,}000{,}000)^2$
$\qquad\qquad\qquad\qquad = 1.5625 \times 10^{16}$

Thus, the equation is

$\dfrac{x^2}{1.69 \times 10^{16}} + \dfrac{y^2}{1.5625 \times 10^{16}} = 1$.

**63.** $9x^2 + 4y^2 = 36$

$4y^2 = 36 - 9x^2$

$y^2 = \dfrac{36 - 9x^2}{4}$

$y = \pm\sqrt{\dfrac{36 - 9x^2}{4}} = \pm\dfrac{\sqrt{36 - 9x^2}}{2}$

**65.** $\dfrac{(x-1)^2}{4} - \dfrac{(y+1)^2}{25} = 1$

Center: $(1, -1)$
$a = 2,\ b = 5$

**67.** $\dfrac{y^2}{16} - \dfrac{(x+3)^2}{9} = 1$

Center: $(-3, 0)$
$a = 3,\ b = 4$

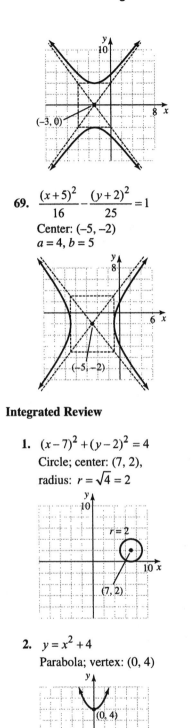

**69.** $\dfrac{(x+5)^2}{16} - \dfrac{(y+2)^2}{25} = 1$

Center: (–5, –2)

$a = 4, b = 5$

## Integrated Review

**1.** $(x-7)^2 + (y-2)^2 = 4$

Circle; center: (7, 2),

radius: $r = \sqrt{4} = 2$

**2.** $y = x^2 + 4$

Parabola; vertex: (0, 4)

**3.** $y = x^2 + 12x + 36$

Parabola; $x = \dfrac{-b}{2a} = \dfrac{-12}{2(1)} = -6$

$y = (-6)^2 + 12(-6) + 36 = 0$

Vertex: (–6, 0)

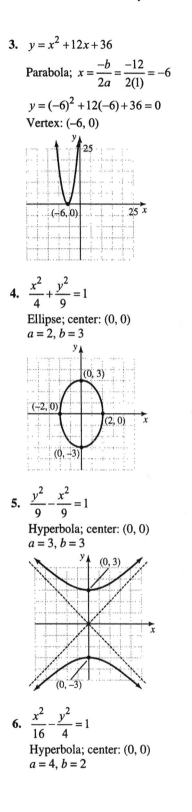

**4.** $\dfrac{x^2}{4} + \dfrac{y^2}{9} = 1$

Ellipse; center: (0, 0)

$a = 2, b = 3$

**5.** $\dfrac{y^2}{9} - \dfrac{x^2}{9} = 1$

Hyperbola; center: (0, 0)

$a = 3, b = 3$

**6.** $\dfrac{x^2}{16} - \dfrac{y^2}{4} = 1$

Hyperbola; center: (0, 0)

$a = 4, b = 2$

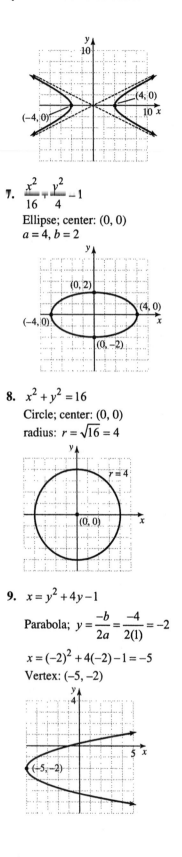

**7.** $\dfrac{x^2}{16} + \dfrac{y^2}{4} = 1$

Ellipse; center: (0, 0)
$a = 4, b = 2$

**8.** $x^2 + y^2 = 16$
Circle; center: (0, 0)
radius: $r = \sqrt{16} = 4$

**9.** $x = y^2 + 4y - 1$

Parabola; $y = \dfrac{-b}{2a} = \dfrac{-4}{2(1)} = -2$

$x = (-2)^2 + 4(-2) - 1 = -5$
Vertex: (−5, −2)

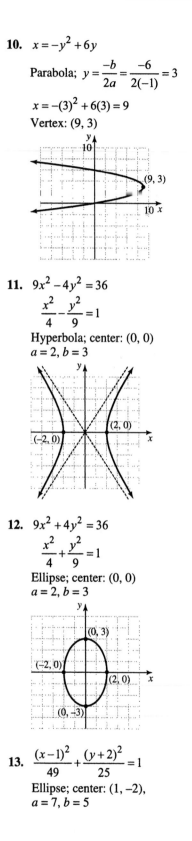

**10.** $x = -y^2 + 6y$

Parabola; $y = \dfrac{-b}{2a} = \dfrac{-6}{2(-1)} = 3$

$x = -(3)^2 + 6(3) = 9$
Vertex: (9, 3)

**11.** $9x^2 - 4y^2 = 36$

$\dfrac{x^2}{4} - \dfrac{y^2}{9} = 1$

Hyperbola; center: (0, 0)
$a = 2, b = 3$

**12.** $9x^2 + 4y^2 = 36$

$\dfrac{x^2}{4} + \dfrac{y^2}{9} = 1$

Ellipse; center: (0, 0)
$a = 2, b = 3$

**13.** $\dfrac{(x-1)^2}{49} + \dfrac{(y+2)^2}{25} = 1$

Ellipse; center: (1, −2),
$a = 7, b = 5$

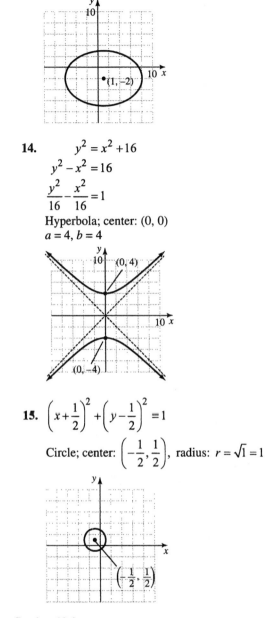

**14.**
$$y^2 = x^2 + 16$$
$$y^2 - x^2 = 16$$
$$\frac{y^2}{16} - \frac{x^2}{16} = 1$$
Hyperbola; center: (0, 0)
$a = 4, b = 4$

**15.** $\left(x + \frac{1}{2}\right)^2 + \left(y - \frac{1}{2}\right)^2 = 1$

Circle; center: $\left(-\frac{1}{2}, \frac{1}{2}\right)$, radius: $r = \sqrt{1} = 1$

**Section 10.3**

**Practice Exercises**

**1.** $\begin{cases} x^2 - 4y = 4 \\ x + y = -1 \end{cases}$

Solve $x + y = -1$ for $y$.
$y = -x - 1$
Replace $y$ with $-x - 1$ in the first equation and
solve for $x$.

$$x^2 - 4(-x - 1) = 4$$
$$x^2 + 4x + 4 = 4$$
$$x^2 + 4x = 0$$
$$x(x + 4) = 0$$
$x = 0$ or $x = -4$
Let $x = 0$,          Let $x = -4$,
$y = -0 - 1 = -1$      $y = -(-4) - 1 = 3$
The solutions are (0, −1) and (−4, 3).

**2.** $\begin{cases} y = -\sqrt{x} \\ x^2 + y^2 = 20 \end{cases}$

Substitute $-\sqrt{x}$ for $y$ in the second equation.
$$x^2 + \left(-\sqrt{x}\right)^2 = 20$$
$$x^2 + x = 20$$
$$x^2 + x - 20 = 0$$
$$(x + 5)(x - 4) = 0$$
$x = -5$ or $x = 4$
Let $x = -5$.
$y = -\sqrt{-5}$     Not a real number
Let $x = 4$.
$y = -\sqrt{4} = -2$
The solution is (4, −2).

**3.** $\begin{cases} x^2 + y^2 = 9 \\ x - y = 5 \end{cases}$

Solve the second equation for $x$.
$x = y + 5$
Let $x = y + 5$ in the first equation.
$$(y + 5)^2 + y^2 = 9$$
$$y^2 + 10y + 25 + y^2 = 9$$
$$2y^2 + 10y + 16 = 0$$
$$y^2 + 5y + 8 = 0$$
By the quadratic formula,
$$y = \frac{-5 \pm \sqrt{5^2 - 4(1)(8)}}{2(1)} = \frac{-5 \pm \sqrt{-7}}{2}$$

$\sqrt{-7}$ is not a real number. There is no real
solution, or $\varnothing$.

**4.** $\begin{cases} x^2 + 4y^2 = 16 \\ x^2 - y^2 = 1 \end{cases}$

Add the opposite of the second equation to the first.

$x^2 + 4y^2 = 16$
$\underline{-x^2 \phantom{.}+ y^2 = -1}$
$0 + 5y^2 = 15$
$\phantom{0 + 5}y^2 = 3$
$\phantom{0 + 5}y = \pm\sqrt{3}$

Let $y = \sqrt{3}$.            Let $y = -\sqrt{3}$.

$x^2 - \left(\sqrt{3}\right)^2 = 1$       $x^2 - \left(-\sqrt{3}\right)^2 = 1$

$\phantom{x^2 -}x^2 - 3 = 1$          $\phantom{x^2 -}x^2 - 3 = 1$

$\phantom{x^2 -}x^2 = 4$                 $\phantom{x^2 -}x^2 = 4$

$\phantom{x^2 -}x = \pm 2$              $\phantom{x^2 -}x = \pm 2$

The solutions are $\left(2, \sqrt{3}\right), \left(2, -\sqrt{3}\right),$

$\left(-2, \sqrt{3}\right),$ and $\left(-2, -\sqrt{3}\right).$

**Exercise Set 10.3**

**1.** $\begin{cases} x^2 + y^2 = 25 \quad (1) \\ 4x + 3y = 0 \quad (2) \end{cases}$

Solve E2 for y.
$3y = -4x$
$y = -\dfrac{4x}{3}$

Substitute into E1.

$x^2 + \left(-\dfrac{4x}{3}\right)^2 = 25$

$x^2 + \dfrac{16x^2}{9} = 25$

$9\left(x^2 + \dfrac{16x^2}{9}\right) = 9(25)$

$9x^2 + 16x^2 = 225$

$25x^2 = 225$

$x^2 = 9$

$x = \pm\sqrt{9} = \pm 3$

$x = 3: y = -\dfrac{4(3)}{3} = -4$

$x = -3: y = -\dfrac{4(-3)}{3} = 4$

The solutions are $(3, -4)$ and $(-3, 4)$.

**3.** $\begin{cases} x^2 + 4y^2 = 10 \quad (1) \\ \phantom{x^2 + 4}y = x \quad (2) \end{cases}$

Substitute x for y in E1.

$x^2 + 4x^2 = 10$

$5x^2 = 10$

$x^2 = 2$

$x = \pm\sqrt{2}$

Substitute these values into E2.

$x = \sqrt{2} : y = x = \sqrt{2}$
$x = -\sqrt{2} : y = x = -\sqrt{2}$

The solutions are $\left(\sqrt{2}, \sqrt{2}\right)$ and $\left(-\sqrt{2}, -\sqrt{2}\right).$

**5.** $\begin{cases} y^2 = 4 - x \quad (1) \\ x - 2y = 4 \quad (2) \end{cases}$

Solve E2 for x.
$x = 2y + 4$

Substitute into E1.

$y^2 = 4 - (2y + 4)$

$y^2 = -2y$

$y^2 + 2y = 0$

$y(y + 2) = 0$

$y = 0$ or $y + 2 = 0$
$\phantom{y = 0 \text{ or } }y = -2$

Substitute these values into the equation
$x = 2y + 4$.

$y = 0 : x = 2(0) + 4 = 4$
$y = -2 : x = 2(-2) + 4 = 0$

The solutions are $(4, 0)$ and $(0, -2)$.

**7.** $\begin{cases} x^2 + y^2 = 9 \quad (1) \\ 16x^2 - 4y^2 = 64 \quad (2) \end{cases}$

Multiply E1 by 4 and add to E2.

$4x^2 + 4y^2 = 36$
$\underline{16x^2 - 4y^2 = 64}$
$20x^2 \phantom{- 4y^2} = 100$
$\phantom{20}x^2 = 5$
$\phantom{20}x = \pm\sqrt{5}$

Substitute 5 for $x^2$ into E1.

$5 + y^2 = 9$

$y^2 = 4$

$y = \pm 2$

The solutions are $\left(-\sqrt{5}, -2\right), \left(-\sqrt{5}, 2\right),$

$\left(\sqrt{5}, -2\right),$ and $\left(\sqrt{5}, 2\right).$

**9.** $\begin{cases} x^2 + 2y^2 = 2 & (1) \\ x - y = 2 & (2) \end{cases}$

Solve E2 for $x$: $x = y + 2$

Substitute into E1.

$$(y+2)^2 + 2y^2 = 2$$
$$y^2 + 4y + 4 + 2y^2 = 2$$
$$3y^2 + 4y + 2 = 0$$
$$y = \frac{-4 \pm \sqrt{(4)^2 - 4(3)(2)}}{2(3)} = \frac{-4 \pm \sqrt{-8}}{6}$$

There are no real solutions. The solution is $\varnothing$.

**11.** $\begin{cases} y = x^2 - 3 & (1) \\ 4x - y = 6 & (2) \end{cases}$

Substitute $x^2 - 3$ for $y$ in E2.

$$4x - (x^2 - 3) = 6$$
$$4x - x^2 + 3 = 6$$
$$0 = x^2 - 4x + 3$$
$$0 = (x-3)(x-1)$$
$$x - 3 = 0 \text{ or } x - 1 = 0$$
$$x = 3 \text{ or } \quad x = 1$$

Substitute these values into E1.

$$x = 3: y = (3)^2 - 3 = 6$$
$$x = 1: y = (1)^2 - 3 = -2$$

The solutions are $(3, 6)$ and $(1, -2)$.

**13.** $\begin{cases} y = x^2 & (1) \\ 3x + y = 10 & (2) \end{cases}$

Substitute $x^2$ for $y$ in E2.

$$3x + x^2 = 10$$
$$x^2 + 3x - 10 = 0$$
$$(x+5)(x-2) = 0$$
$$x + 5 = 0 \quad \text{or } x - 2 = 0$$
$$x = -5 \text{ or } \quad x = 2$$

Substitute these values into E1.

$$x = -5: y = (-5)^2 = 25$$
$$x = 2: y = (2)^2 = 4$$

The solutions are $(-5, 25)$ and $(2, 4)$.

**15.** $\begin{cases} y = 2x^2 + 1 & (1) \\ x + y = -1 & (2) \end{cases}$

Substitute $2x^2 + 1$ for $y$ in E2.

$$x + 2x^2 + 1 = -1$$
$$2x^2 + x + 2 = 0$$
$$x = \frac{-1 \pm \sqrt{(1)^2 - 4(2)(2)}}{2(2)} = \frac{-1 \pm \sqrt{-15}}{4}$$

There are no real solutions. The solution is $\varnothing$.

**17.** $\begin{cases} y = x^2 - 4 & (1) \\ y = x^2 - 4x & (2) \end{cases}$

Substitute $x^2 - 4$ for $y$ in E2.

$$x^2 - 4 = x^2 - 4x$$
$$-4 = -4x$$
$$1 = x$$

Substitute this value into E1.

$$y = (1)^2 - 4 = -3$$

The solution is $(1, -3)$.

**19.** $\begin{cases} 2x^2 + 3y^2 = 14 & (1) \\ -x^2 + y^2 = 3 & (2) \end{cases}$

Multiply E2 by 2 and add to E1.

$$2x^2 + 3y^2 = 14$$
$$\underline{-2x^2 + 2y^2 = 6}$$
$$5y^2 = 20$$
$$y^2 = 4$$
$$y = \pm 2$$

Substitute 4 for $y^2$ into E2.

$$-x^2 + 4 = 3$$
$$-x^2 = -1$$
$$x^2 = 1$$
$$x = \pm 1$$

The solutions are $(-1, -2)$, $(-1, 2)$, $(1, -2)$, and $(1, 2)$.

**21.** $\begin{cases} x^2 + y^2 = 1 & (1) \\ x^2 + (y+3)^2 = 4 & (2) \end{cases}$

Multiply E1 by $-1$ and add to E2.

$$-x^2 - y^2 = -1$$
$$\underline{x^2 + (y+3)^2 = 4}$$
$$(y+3)^3 - y^2 = 3$$
$$y^2 + 6y + 9 - y^2 = 3$$
$$6y = -6$$
$$y = -1$$

Replace $y$ with $-1$ in E1.

$$x^2 + (-1)^2 = 1$$
$$x^2 = 0$$
$$x = 0$$

The solution is $(0, -1)$.

**23.** $\begin{cases} y = x^2 + 2 & (1) \\ y = -x^2 + 4 & (2) \end{cases}$

Add E1 and E2.

$$y = x^2 + 2$$
$$\underline{y = -x^2 + 4}$$
$$2y = 6$$
$$y = 3$$

Substitute this value into E1.

$$3 = x^2 + 2$$
$$1 = x^2$$
$$\pm 1 = x$$

The solutions are $(-1, 3)$ and $(1, 3)$.

**25.** $\begin{cases} 3x^2 + y^2 = 9 & (1) \\ 3x^2 - y^2 = 9 & (2) \end{cases}$

Add E1 and E2.

$$3x^2 + y^2 = 9$$
$$\underline{3x^2 - y^2 = 9}$$
$$6x^2 \quad\;\; = 18$$
$$x^2 = 3$$
$$x = \pm\sqrt{3}$$

Substitute 3 for $x^2$ in E1.

$$3(3) + y^2 = 9$$
$$y^2 = 0$$
$$y = 0$$

The solutions are $\left(-\sqrt{3}, 0\right)$, $\left(\sqrt{3}, 0\right)$.

**27.** $\begin{cases} x^2 + 3y^2 = 6 & (1) \\ x^2 - 3y^2 = 10 & (2) \end{cases}$

Solve E2 for $x^2$: $x^2 = 3y^2 + 10$.
Substitute into E1.

$$(3y^2 + 10) + 3y^2 = 6$$
$$6y^2 = -4$$
$$y^2 = -\frac{2}{3}$$

There are no real solutions. The solution is $\varnothing$.

**29.** $\begin{cases} x^2 + y^2 = 36 & (1) \\ y = \dfrac{1}{6}x^2 - 6 & (2) \end{cases}$

Solve E1 for $x^2$: $x^2 = 36 - y^2$.
Substitute into E2.

$$y = \frac{1}{6}(36 - y^2) - 6$$
$$y = 6 - \frac{1}{6}y^2 - 6$$
$$6y = -y^2$$
$$y^2 + 6y = 0$$
$$y(y+6) = 0$$
$$y = 0 \;\text{ or }\; y = -6$$

Substitute these values into the equation $x^2 = 36 - y^2$.

$$y = 0: x^2 = 36 - (0)^2$$
$$x^2 = 36$$
$$x = \pm 6$$
$$y = -6: x^2 = 36 - (6)^2$$
$$x^2 = 0$$
$$x = 0$$

The solutions are $(-6, 0)$, $(6, 0)$ and $(0, -6)$.

**31.** $x > -3$

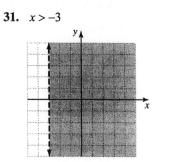

**33.** $y < 2x - 1$

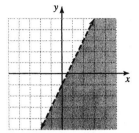

**35.** $P = x + (2x - 5) + (5x - 20) = (8x - 25)$ inches

**37.** $P = 2(x^2 + 3x + 1) + 2(x^2)$
$= 2x^2 + 6x + 2 + 2x^2$
$= (4x^2 + 6x + 2)$ meters

**39.** Answers may vary

**41.** There are 0, 1, 2, 3, or 4 possible real solutions. Answers may vary

**43.** Let $x$ and $y$ represent the numbers.
$$\begin{cases} x^2 + y^2 = 130 \\ x^2 - y^2 = 32 \end{cases}$$
Add the equations.
$$\begin{aligned} x^2 + y^2 &= 130 \\ x^2 - y^2 &= 32 \\ \hline 2x^2 \phantom{+y^2} &= 162 \\ x^2 &= 81 \\ x &= \pm 9 \end{aligned}$$
Replace $x^2$ with 81 in the first equation.
$$\begin{aligned} 81 + y^2 &= 130 \\ y^2 &= 49 \\ y &= \pm 7 \end{aligned}$$
The numbers are –9 and –7, –9 and 7, 9 and –7, and 9 and 7.

**45.** Let $x$ and $y$ be the length and width.
$$\begin{cases} xy = 285 \\ 2x + 2y = 68 \end{cases}$$
Solve the first equation for $y$: $y = \dfrac{285}{x}$.

Substitute into the second equation.

$$2x + 2\left(\frac{285}{x}\right) = 68$$
$$x + \frac{285}{x} = 34$$
$$x^2 + 285 = 34x$$
$$x^2 - 34x + 285 = 0$$
$$(x - 19)(x - 15) = 0$$
$$x = 19 \text{ or } x = 15$$
Using $x = 19$, $y = \dfrac{285}{x} = \dfrac{285}{19} = 15$.

Using $x = 15$, $y = \dfrac{285}{x} = \dfrac{285}{15} = 19$.

The dimensions are 19 cm by 15 cm.

**47.** $\begin{cases} p = -0.01x^2 - 0.2x + 9 \\ p = 0.01x^2 - 0.1x + 3 \end{cases}$
Substitute.
$$\begin{aligned} -0.01x^2 - 0.2x + 9 &= 0.01x^2 - 0.1x + 3 \\ 0 &= 0.02x^2 + 0.1x - 6 \\ 0 &= x^2 + 5x - 300 \\ 0 &= (x + 20)(x - 15) \end{aligned}$$
$x + 20 = 0$    or $x - 15 = 0$
   $x = -20$ or      $x = 15$
Disregard the negative.
$$p = -0.01(15)^2 - 0.2(15) + 9$$
$$p = 3.75$$
The equilibrium quantity is 15,000 compact discs, and the corresponding price is $3.75.

**49.** $\begin{cases} x^2 + 4y^2 = 10 \\ y = x \end{cases}$

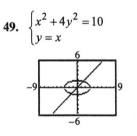

**51.** $\begin{cases} y = x^2 + 2 \\ y = -x^2 + 4 \end{cases}$

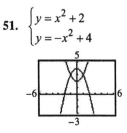

**Section 10.4**

**Practice Exercises**

1.  $\dfrac{x^2}{36} + \dfrac{y^2}{16} \geq 1$

    First graph the ellipse $\dfrac{x^2}{36} + \dfrac{y^2}{16} = 1$ as a solid

    curve. Choose (0, 0) as a test point.

    $\dfrac{x^2}{36} + \dfrac{y^2}{16} \geq 1$

    $\dfrac{0^2}{36} + \dfrac{0^2}{16} \geq 1$

    $\qquad 0 \geq 1 \quad$ False

    The solution set is the region that does not
    contain (0, 0).

    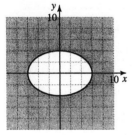

2.  $16y^2 > 9x^2 + 144$

    The related equation is $16y^2 = 9x^2 + 144$.

    $16y^2 - 9x^2 = 144$

    $\dfrac{y^2}{9} - \dfrac{x^2}{16} = 1$

    Graph the hyperbola as a dashed curve.
    Choose (0, 0), (0, 4), and (0, −4) as test points.

    (0, 0): $16(0)^2 > 9(0)^2 + 144$

    $\qquad\quad 0 > 144 \quad$ False

    (0, 4): $16(4)^2 > 9(0)^2 + 144$

    $\qquad\quad 256 > 144 \quad$ True

    (0, −4): $16(-4)^2 > 9(0)^2 + 144$

    $\qquad\quad\; 256 > 144 \quad$ True

    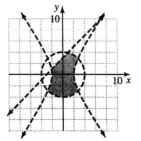

3.  $\begin{cases} y \geq x^2 \\ y \leq -3x + 2 \end{cases}$

    Solve the related system $\begin{cases} y = x^2 \\ y = -3x + 2 \end{cases}$.

    Substitute $-3x + 2$ for $y$ in the first equation.

    $\qquad x^2 = -3x + 2$

    $x^2 + 3x - 2 = 0$

    $x = \dfrac{-3 \pm \sqrt{3^2 - 4(1)(-2)}}{2(1)}$

    $\;\; = \dfrac{-3 \pm \sqrt{17}}{2}$

    $\;\; \approx 0.56 \text{ or } -3.56$

    $y = -3x + 2 \approx -3(0.56) + 2 = 0.32$

    $y \approx -3(-3.56) + 2 = 12.68$

    The points of intersection are approximately
    (0.56, 0.32) and (−3.56, 12.68).

    Graph $y = x^2$ and $y = -3x + 2$ as solid curves.

    The region of the solution set is above the
    parabola but below the line.

    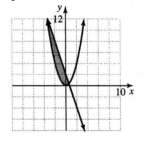

4.  $\begin{cases} x^2 + y^2 < 16 \\ \dfrac{x^2}{4} - \dfrac{y^2}{9} < 1 \\ y < x + 3 \end{cases}$

    Graph $x^2 + y^2 = 16$, $\dfrac{x^2}{4} - \dfrac{y^2}{9} = 1$, and $y = x + 3$.

    The test point (0, 0) gives true statements for all
    three inequalities; thus, the innermost region is
    the solution set.

    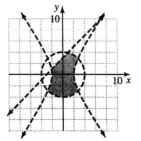

**Exercise Set 10.4**

**1.** $y < x^2$

First graph the parabola as a dashed curve.

| Test Point | $y < x^2$; Result |
|---|---|
| (0, 1) | $1 < 0^2$; False |

Shade the region which does not contain (0, 1).

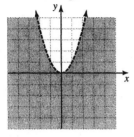

**3.** $x^2 + y^2 \geq 16$

First graph the circle as a solid curve.

| Test Point | $x^2 + y^2 \geq 16$; Result |
|---|---|
| (0, 0) | $0^2 + 0^2 \geq 16$; False |

Shade the region which does not contain (0, 0).

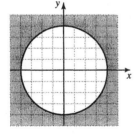

**5.** $\dfrac{x^2}{4} - y^2 < 1$

First graph the hyperbola as a dashed curve.

| Test Point | $\dfrac{x^2}{4} - y^2 < 1$; Result |
|---|---|
| (–4, 0) | $\dfrac{(-4)^2}{4} - 0^2 < 1$; False |
| (0, 0) | $\dfrac{(0)^2}{4} - 0^2 < 1$; True |
| (4, 0) | $\dfrac{(4)^2}{4} - 0^2 < 1$; False |

Shade the region containing (0, 0).

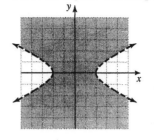

**7.** $y > (x-1)^2 - 3$

First graph the parabola as a dashed curve.

| Test Point | $y > (x-1)^2 - 3$; Result |
|---|---|
| (0, 0) | $0 > (0-1)^2 - 3$; True |

Shade the region containing (0, 0).

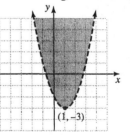

**9.** $x^2 + y^2 \leq 9$

First graph the circle as a solid curve.

| Test Point | $x^2 + y^2 \leq 9$; Result |
|---|---|
| (0, 0) | $0^2 + 0^2 \leq 9$; True |

Shade the region containing (0, 0).

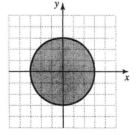

**11.** $y > -x^2 + 5$

First graph the parabola as a dashed curve.

| Test Point | $y > -x^2 + 5$; Result |
|---|---|
| $(0, 0)$ | $0 > -(0)^2 + 5$; False |

Shade the region which does not contain $(0, 0)$.

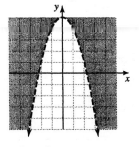

**13.** $\dfrac{x^2}{4} + \dfrac{y^2}{9} \le 1$

First graph the ellipse as a solid curve.

| Test Point | $\dfrac{x^2}{4} + \dfrac{y^2}{9} \le 1$; Result |
|---|---|
| $(0, 0)$ | $\dfrac{(0)^2}{4} + \dfrac{(0)^2}{9} \le 1$; True |

Shade the region containing $(0, 0)$.

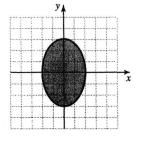

**15.** $\dfrac{y^2}{4} - x^2 \le 1$

First graph the hyperbola as solid curves.

| Test Point | $\dfrac{y^2}{4} - x^2 \le 1$; Result |
|---|---|
| $(0, -4)$ | $\dfrac{(-4)^2}{4} - 0^2 \le 1$; False |
| $(0, 0)$ | $\dfrac{(0)^2}{4} - 0^2 \le 1$; True |
| $(0, 4)$ | $\dfrac{(4)^2}{4} - 0^2 \le 1$; False |

Shade the region containing $(0, 0)$.

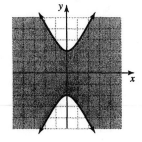

**17.** $y < (x-2)^2 + 1$

First graph the parabola as a dashed curve.

| Test Point | $y < (x-2)^2 + 1$; Result |
|---|---|
| $(0, 0)$ | $0 < (0-2)^2 + 1$; True |

Shade the region containing $(0, 0)$.

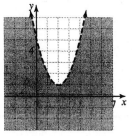

**19.** $y \le x^2 + x - 2$

First graph the parabola as a solid curve.

| Test Point | $y \le x^2 + x - 2$; Result |
|---|---|
| $(0, 0)$ | $0 \le (0)^2 + (0) - 2$; False |

Shade the region which does not contain $(0, 0)$.

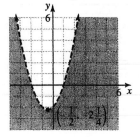

**21.** $\begin{cases} 4x + 3y \geq 12 \\ x^2 + y^2 < 16 \end{cases}$

First graph $4x + 3y = 12$ as a solid line.

| Test Point | $4x + 3y \geq 12$; Result |
|---|---|
| (0, 0) | $4(0) + 3(0) \geq 12$; False |

Shade the region which does not contain (0, 0). Next, graph the circle $x^2 + y^2 = 16$ as a dashed curve.

| Test Point | $x^2 + y^2 < 16$; Result |
|---|---|
| (0, 0) | $0^2 + 0^2 < 16$; True |

Shade the region containing (0, 0). The solution to the system is the intersection.

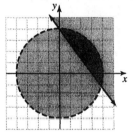

**23.** $\begin{cases} x^2 + y^2 \leq 9 \\ x^2 + y^2 \geq 1 \end{cases}$

First graph the circle with radius 3 as a solid curve.

| Test Point | $x^2 + y^2 \leq 9$; Result |
|---|---|
| (0, 0) | $0^2 + 0^2 \leq 9$; True |

Shade the region containing (0, 0). Next, graph the circle with 1 as a dashed curve.

| Test Point | $x^2 + y^2 \geq 1$; Result |
|---|---|
| (0, 0) | $0^2 + 0^2 \geq 1$; False |

Shade the region which does not contain (0, 0). The solution to the system is the intersection.

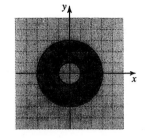

**25.** $\begin{cases} y > x^2 \\ y \geq 2x + 1 \end{cases}$

First graph the parabola as a dashed curve.

| Test Point | $y > x^2$; Result |
|---|---|
| (0, 1) | $1 > 0^2$; True |

Shade the region containing (0, 1). Next, graph $y = 2x + 1$ as a solid line.

| Test Point | $y \geq 2x + 1$; Result |
|---|---|
| (0, 0) | $0 \geq 2(0) + 1$; False |

Shade the region which does not contain (0, 0). The solution to the system is the intersection.

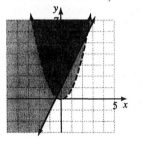

**27.** $\begin{cases} x^2 + y^2 > 9 \\ y > x^2 \end{cases}$

First graph the circle as a dashed curve.

| Test Point | $x^2 + y^2 > 9$; Result |
|---|---|
| (0, 0) | $0^2 + 0^2 > 9$; False |

Shade the region which does not contain (0, 0). Next, graph the parabola as a dashed curve.

| Test Point | $y > x^2$; Result |
|------------|-------------------|
| (0, 1)     | $1 > 0^2$; True   |

Shade the region containing (0, 1). The solution to the system is the intersection.

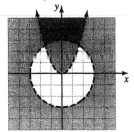

**29.** $\begin{cases} \dfrac{x^2}{4} + \dfrac{y^2}{9} \geq 1 \\ x^2 + y^2 \geq 4 \end{cases}$

First graph the ellipse as a solid curve.

| Test Point | $\dfrac{x^2}{4} + \dfrac{y^2}{9} \geq 1$; Result |
|------------|--------------------------------------------------|
| (0, 0)     | $\dfrac{0^2}{4} + \dfrac{0^2}{9} \geq 1$; False  |

Shade the region which does not contain (0, 0). Next, graph the circle as a solid curve.

| Test Point | $x^2 + y^2 \geq 4$; Result |
|------------|----------------------------|
| (0, 0)     | $0^2 + 0^2 \geq 4$; False  |

Shade the region which does not contain (0, 0). The solution to the system is the intersection.

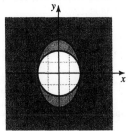

**31.** $\begin{cases} x^2 - y^2 \geq 1 \\ y \geq 0 \end{cases}$

First graph the hyperbola as solid curves.

| Test Point | $x^2 - y^2 \geq 1$; Result |
|------------|----------------------------|
| (−2, 0)    | $(-2)^2 - 0^2 \geq 1$; True |
| (0, 0)     | $0^2 - 0^2 \geq 1$; False   |
| (2, 0)     | $2^2 - 0^2 \geq 1$; True    |

Shade the region which does not contain (0, 0). Next, graph $y = 0$ as a solid line.

| Test Point | $y > 0$; Result |
|------------|-----------------|
| (0, 1)     | $1 \geq 0$; True |

Shade the region containing (0, 1). The solution to the system is the intersection.

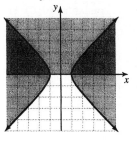

**33.** $\begin{cases} x + y \geq 1 \\ 2x + 3y < 1 \\ x > -3 \end{cases}$

First graph $x + y = 1$ as a solid line.

| Test Point | $x + y \geq 1$; Result |
|------------|------------------------|
| (0, 0)     | $0 + 0 \geq 1$; False   |

Shade the region which does not contain (0, 0). Next, graph $2x + 3y = 1$ as a dashed line.

| Test Point | $2x + 3y < 1$; Result |
|------------|-----------------------|
| (0, 0)     | $2(0) + 3(0) < 1$; True |

Shade the region containing (0, 0). Now graph the line $x = -3$ as a dashed line.

| Test Point | $x > -3$; Result |
|------------|------------------|
| (0, 0)     | $0 > -3$; True   |

Shade the region containing (0, 0). The solution to the system is the intersection.

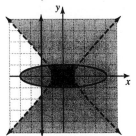

35. $\begin{cases} x^2 - y^2 < 1 \\ \dfrac{x^2}{16} + y^2 \le 1 \\ x \ge -2 \end{cases}$

First graph the hyperbola as dashed curves.

| Test Point | $x^2 - y^2 < 1$; Result |
|------------|-------------------------|
| $(-2, 0)$  | $(-2)^2 - 0^2 < 1$; False |
| $(0, 0)$   | $0^2 - 0^2 < 1$; True |
| $(2, 0)$   | $2^2 - 0^2 < 1$; False |

Shade the region containing $(0, 0)$. Next, graph the ellipse as a solid curve.

| Test Point | $\dfrac{x^2}{16} + y^2 \le 1$; Result |
|------------|---------------------------------------|
| $(0, 0)$   | $\dfrac{0^2}{16} + 0^2 \le 1$; True |

Shade the region containing $(0, 0)$. Now graph the line $x = -2$ as a solid line.

| Test Point | $x \ge -2$; Result |
|------------|--------------------|
| $(0, 0)$   | $0 \ge -2$; True |

Shade the region containing $(0, 0)$. The solution to the system is the intersection.

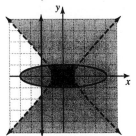

37. This is not a function because a vertical line can cross the graph in more than one place.

39. This is a function because a vertical line can cross the graph in no more than one place.

41. $f(x) = 3x^2 - 2$
$f(-1) = 3(-1)^2 - 2 = 3 - 2 = 1$

43. $f(x) = 3x^2 - 2$
$f(a) = 3(a)^2 - 2 = 3a^2 - 2$

45. Answers may vary

47. $\begin{cases} y \le x^2 \\ y \ge x + 2 \\ x \ge 0 \\ y \ge 0 \end{cases}$

First graph $y = x^2$ as a solid curve.

| Test Point | $y \le x^2$; Result |
|------------|---------------------|
| $(0, 1)$   | $1 \le 0^2$; False |

Shade the region which does not contain $(0, 1)$. Next, graph $y = x + 2$ as a solid line.

| Test Point | $y \ge x + 2$; Result |
|------------|-----------------------|
| $(0, 0)$   | $0 \ge 0 + 2$; False |

Shade the region which does not contain $(0, 0)$. Next graph the line $x = 0$ as a solid line, and shade to the right. Now graph the line $y = 0$ as a solid line, and shade above. The solution to the system is the intersection.

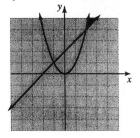

**Chapter 10 Vocabulary Check**

1.  A <u>circle</u> is the set of all points in a plane that are the same distance from a fixed point, called the <u>center</u>.

2.  A <u>nonlinear system of equations</u> is a system of equations at least one of which is not linear.

3.  An <u>ellipse</u> is the set of points on a plane such that the sum of the distances of those points from two fixed points is a constant.

4.  In a circle, the distance from the center to a point of the circle is called its <u>radius</u>.

5.  A <u>hyperbola</u> is the set of points in a plane such that the absolute value of the difference of the distance from two fixed points is constant.

**Chapter 10 Review**

1.  center (–4, 4), radius 3
    $$[x-(-4)]^2+(y-4)^2=3^2$$
    $$(x+4)^2+(y-4)^2=9$$

2.  center (5, 0), radius 5
    $$(x-5)^2+(y-0)^2=5^2$$
    $$(x-5)^2+y^2=25$$

3.  center (–7, –9), radius $\sqrt{11}$
    $$[x-(-7)]^2+[y-(-9)]^2=\left(\sqrt{11}\right)^2$$
    $$(x+7)^2+(y+9)^2=11$$

4.  center (0, 0), radius $\dfrac{7}{2}$
    $$(x-0)^2+(y-0)^2=\left(\dfrac{7}{2}\right)^2$$
    $$x^2+y^2=\dfrac{49}{4}$$

5.  $x^2+y^2=7$
    Circle; center (0, 0), radius $r=\sqrt{7}$
    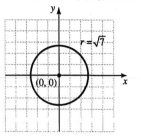

6.  $x=2(y-5)^2+4$
    Parabola; vertex: (4, 5)
    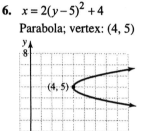

7.  $x=-(y+2)^2+3$
    Parabola; vertex: (3, –2)
    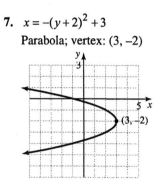

8.  $(x-1)^2+(y-2)^2=4$
    Circle; center (1, 2), radius $r=\sqrt{4}=2$
    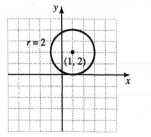

**9.** $y = -x^2 + 4x + 10$

Parabola; $x = \dfrac{-b}{2a} = \dfrac{-4}{2(-1)} = 2$

$y = -(2)^2 + 4(2) + 10 = 14$

Vertex: (2, 14)

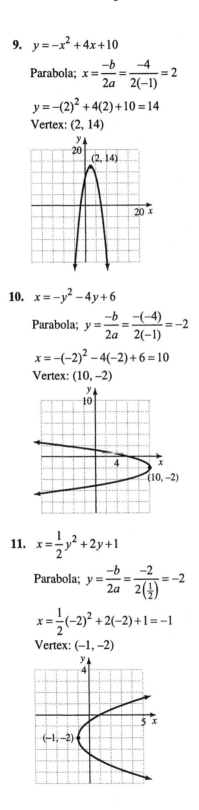

**10.** $x = -y^2 - 4y + 6$

Parabola; $y = \dfrac{-b}{2a} = \dfrac{-(-4)}{2(-1)} = -2$

$x = -(-2)^2 - 4(-2) + 6 = 10$

Vertex: (10, −2)

**11.** $x = \dfrac{1}{2}y^2 + 2y + 1$

Parabola; $y = \dfrac{-b}{2a} = \dfrac{-2}{2\left(\frac{1}{2}\right)} = -2$

$x = \dfrac{1}{2}(-2)^2 + 2(-2) + 1 = -1$

Vertex: (−1, −2)

**12.** $y = -3x^2 + \dfrac{1}{2}x + 4$

Parabola; $x = \dfrac{-b}{2a} = \dfrac{-\frac{1}{2}}{2(-3)} = \dfrac{1}{12}$

$y = -3\left(\dfrac{1}{12}\right)^2 + \dfrac{1}{2}\left(\dfrac{1}{12}\right) + 4 = \dfrac{193}{48}$

Vertex: $\left(\dfrac{1}{12}, \dfrac{193}{48}\right)$

**13.**
$$x^2 + y^2 + 2x + y = \dfrac{3}{4}$$
$$(x^2 + 2x) + (y^2 + y) = \dfrac{3}{4}$$
$$(x^2 + 2x + 1) + \left(y^2 + y + \dfrac{1}{4}\right) = \dfrac{3}{4} + 1 + \dfrac{1}{4}$$
$$(x+1)^2 + \left(y + \dfrac{1}{2}\right)^2 = 2$$

Circle; center $\left(-1, -\dfrac{1}{2}\right)$, radius $r = \sqrt{2}$

**14.**
$$x^2 + y^2 - 3y = \dfrac{7}{4}$$
$$x^2 + \left(y^2 - 3y + \dfrac{9}{4}\right) = \dfrac{7}{4} + \dfrac{9}{4}$$
$$x^2 + \left(y - \dfrac{3}{2}\right)^2 = 4$$

Circle; center $\left(0, \dfrac{3}{2}\right)$, radius $r = \sqrt{4} = 2$

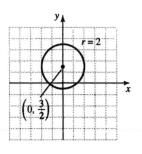

**15.**
$$4x^2 + 4y^2 + 16x + 8y = 1$$
$$(x^2 + 4x) + (y^2 + 2y) = \frac{1}{4}$$
$$(x^2 + 4x + 4) + (y^2 + 2y + 1) = \frac{1}{4} + 4 + 1$$
$$(x+2)^2 + (y+1)^2 = \frac{21}{4}$$

Circle; center $(-2, -1)$, radius $r = \sqrt{\dfrac{21}{4}} = \dfrac{\sqrt{21}}{2}$

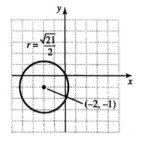

**16.** $x^2 + \dfrac{y^2}{4} = 1$

Center: $(0, 0)$; $a = 1$, $b = 2$

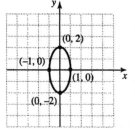

**17.** $x^2 - \dfrac{y^2}{4} = 1$

Center: $(0, 0)$; $a = 1$, $b = 2$

**18.** $\dfrac{x^2}{5} + \dfrac{y^2}{5} = 1$

$x^2 + y^2 = 5$

Center: $(0, 0)$; radius $r = \sqrt{5}$

**19.** $\dfrac{x^2}{5} - \dfrac{y^2}{5} = 1$

Center: $(0, 0)$; $a = \sqrt{5}$, $b = \sqrt{5}$

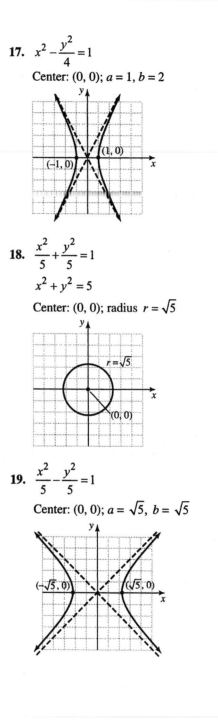

**20.** $-5x^2 + 25y^2 = 125$

$$\frac{y^2}{5} - \frac{x^2}{25} = 1$$

Center: $(0, 0)$; $a = 5$, $b = \sqrt{5}$

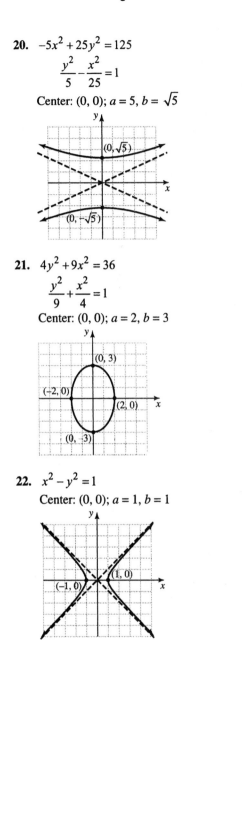

**21.** $4y^2 + 9x^2 = 36$

$$\frac{y^2}{9} + \frac{x^2}{4} = 1$$

Center: $(0, 0)$; $a = 2$, $b = 3$

**22.** $x^2 - y^2 = 1$

Center: $(0, 0)$; $a = 1$, $b = 1$

**23.** $\dfrac{(x+3)^2}{9} + \dfrac{(y-4)^2}{25} = 1$

Center: $(-3, 4)$; $a = 3$, $b = 5$

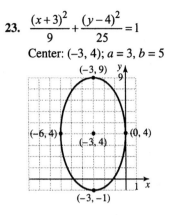

**24.** $y^2 = x^2 + 9$

$y^2 - x^2 = 9$

$$\frac{y^2}{9} - \frac{x^2}{9} = 1$$

Center: $(0, 0)$; $a = 3$, $b = 3$

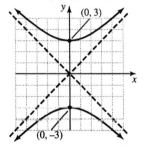

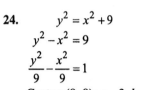

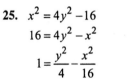

**25.** $x^2 = 4y^2 - 16$

$16 = 4y^2 - x^2$

$$1 = \frac{y^2}{4} - \frac{x^2}{16}$$

Center: $(0, 0)$; $a = 4$, $b = 2$

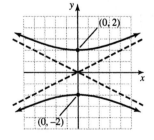

**26.** $100 - 25x^2 = 4y^2$

$$100 = 25x^2 + 4y^2$$

$$1 = \frac{x^2}{4} + \frac{y^2}{25}$$

Center: $(0, 0)$; $a = 2$, $b = 5$

**27.** $\begin{cases} y = 2x - 4 & (1) \\ y^2 = 4x & (2) \end{cases}$

Substitute $2x - 4$ for $y$ in E2.

$$(2x - 4)^2 = 4x$$

$$4x^2 - 16x + 16 = 4x$$

$$4x^2 - 20x + 16 = 0$$

$$x^2 - 5x + 4 = 0$$

$$(x - 4)(x - 1) = 0$$

$x = 4$ or $x = 1$

Use these values in E1.

$x = 4: y = 2(4) - 4 = 4$

$x = 1: y = 2(1) - 4 = -2$

The solutions are $(4, 4)$ and $(1, -2)$.

**28.** $\begin{cases} x^2 + y^2 = 4 & (1) \\ x - y = 4 & (2) \end{cases}$

Solve E2 for $x$: $x = y + 4$.

Substitute into E1.

$$(y + 4)^2 + y^2 = 4$$

$$(y^2 + 8y + 16) + y^2 = 4$$

$$2y^2 + 8y + 12 = 0$$

$$y^2 + 4y + 6 = 0$$

$$y = \frac{-4 \pm \sqrt{(4)^2 - 4(1)(6)}}{2(1)} = \frac{-4 \pm \sqrt{-8}}{2}$$

There are no real solutions. The solution is $\varnothing$.

**29.** $\begin{cases} y = x + 2 & (1) \\ y = x^2 & (2) \end{cases}$

Substitute $x + 2$ for $y$ in E2.

$$x + 2 = x^2$$

$$0 = x^2 - x - 2$$

$$0 = (x - 2)(x + 1)$$

$x = 2$ or $x = -1$

Use these values in E1.

$x = 2: y = 2 + 2 = 4$

$x = -1: y = -1 + 2 = 1$

The solutions are $(2, 4)$ and $(-1, 1)$.

**30.** $\begin{cases} x^2 + 4y^2 = 16 & (1) \\ x^2 + y^2 = 4 & (2) \end{cases}$

Multiply E2 by $-1$ and add to E1.

$$x^2 + 4y^2 = 16$$

$$\underline{-x^2 - y^2 = -4}$$

$$3y^2 = 12$$

$$y^2 = 4$$

$$y = \pm 2$$

Replace $y^2$ with 4 in E2.

$$x^2 + 4 = 4$$

$$x^2 = 0$$

$$x = 0$$

The solutions are $(0, 2)$ and $(0, -2)$.

**31.** $\begin{cases} 4x - y^2 = 0 & (1) \\ 2x^2 + y^2 = 16 & (2) \end{cases}$

Solve E1 for $y^2$: $y^2 = 4x$.

Substitute into E2.

$$2x^2 + 4x = 16$$

$$2x^2 + 4x - 16 = 0$$

$$x^2 + 2x - 8 = 0$$

$$(x + 4)(x - 2) = 0$$

$x = -4$ or $x = 2$

Use these values in the equation $y^2 = 4x$.

$x = -4: y^2 = 4(-4)$

$\qquad y^2 = -16$ (no real solutions)

$x = 2: y^2 = 4(2)$

$\qquad y^2 = 8$

$\qquad y = \pm\sqrt{8} = \pm 2\sqrt{2}$

The solutions are $\left(2, -2\sqrt{2}\right)$ and $\left(2, 2\sqrt{2}\right)$.

**32.** $\begin{cases} x^2 + 2y = 9 & (1) \\ 5x - 2y = 5 & (2) \end{cases}$

Add E1 and E2.

$$x^2 + 2y = 9$$
$$\underline{5x - 2y = 5}$$
$$x^2 + 5x = 14$$

$$x^2 + 5x - 14 = 0$$
$$(x + 7)(x - 2) = 0$$
$$x = -7 \text{ or } x = 2$$

Use these values in E1.

$$x = -7 : (-7)^2 + 2y = 9$$
$$49 + 2y = 9$$
$$2y = -40$$
$$y = -20$$

$$x = 2 : (2)^2 + 2y = 9$$
$$4 + 2y = 9$$
$$2y = 5$$
$$y = \frac{5}{2}$$

The solutions are $(-7, -20)$ and $\left(2, \frac{5}{2}\right)$.

**33.** $\begin{cases} y = 3x^2 + 5x - 4 & (1) \\ y = 3x^2 - x + 2 & (2) \end{cases}$

Substitute.

$$3x^2 + 5x - 4 = 3x^2 - x + 2$$
$$6x = 6$$
$$x = 1$$

Use this value in E1.

$$y = 3(1)^2 + 5(1) - 4 = 4$$

The solution is $(1, 4)$.

**34.** $\begin{cases} x^2 - 3y^2 = 1 & (1) \\ 4x^2 + 5y^2 = 21 & (2) \end{cases}$

Multiply E1 by $-4$ and add to E2.

$$-4x^2 + 12y^2 = -4$$
$$\underline{4x^2 + 5y^2 = 21}$$
$$17y^2 = 17$$
$$y^2 = 1$$
$$y = \pm 1$$

Replace $y^2$ with 1 in E1.

$$x^2 - 3(1) = 1$$
$$x^2 = 4$$
$$x = \pm 2$$

The solutions are $(-2, -1)$, $(-2, 1)$, $(2, -1)$ and $(2, 1)$.

**35.** Let $x$ and $y$ be the length and width.

$$\begin{cases} xy = 150 \\ 2x + 2y = 50 \end{cases}$$

Solve the first equation for $y$: $y = \dfrac{150}{x}$.

Substitute into E2.

$$2x + 2\left(\frac{150}{x}\right) = 50$$
$$x + \frac{150}{x} = 25$$
$$x^2 + 150 = 25x$$

$$x^2 - 25x + 150 = 0$$
$$(x - 15)(x - 10) = 0$$
$$x = 15 \text{ or } x = 10$$

Substitute these values into E1.

$$15y = 150 \qquad\qquad 10y = 150$$
$$y = 10 \qquad\qquad\quad y = 15$$

The room is 15 feet by 10 feet.

**36.** Four real solutions are possible.

**37.** $y \le -x^2 + 3$

Graph $y = -x^2 + 3$ as a solid curve.

| Test Point | $y \le -x^2 + 3$; Result |
|------------|--------------------------|
| $(0, 0)$ | $0 \le -(0)^2 + 3$; True |

Shade the region containing $(0, 0)$.

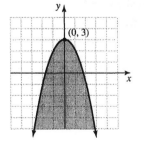

**38.** $x^2 + y^2 < 9$

First graph the circle as a dashed curve.

| Test Point | $x^2 + y^2 < 9$; Result |
|------------|-------------------------|
| $(0, 0)$ | $0^2 + 0^2 < 9$; True |

Shade the region containing $(0, 0)$.

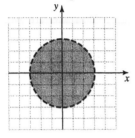

**39.** $\begin{cases} 2x \le 4 \\ x + y \ge 1 \end{cases}$

First graph $2x = 4$, or $x = 2$, as a solid line, and shade to the left of the line. Next, graph $x + y = 1$ as a solid line.

| Test Point | $x + y \ge 1$; Result |
|------------|-----------------------|
| $(0, 0)$ | $0 + 0 \ge 1$; False |

Shade the region which does not contain $(0, 0)$. The solution to the system is the intersection.

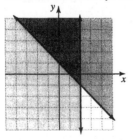

**40.** $\dfrac{x^2}{4} + \dfrac{y^2}{9} \ge 1$

First graph the ellipse as a solid curve.

| Test Point | $\dfrac{x^2}{4} + \dfrac{y^2}{9} \ge 1$; Result |
|------------|-------------------------------------------------|
| $(0, 0)$ | $\dfrac{(0)^2}{4} + \dfrac{(0)^2}{9} \ge 1$; False |

Shade the region that does not contain $(0, 0)$.

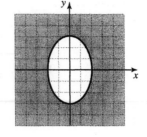

**41.** $\begin{cases} x^2 + y^2 < 4 \\ x^2 - y^2 \le 1 \end{cases}$

First graph the first circle as a dashed curve.

| Test Point | $x^2 + y^2 < 4$; Result |
|------------|-------------------------|
| $(0, 0)$ | $0^2 + 0^2 < 4$; True |

Shade the region containing $(0, 0)$. Next, graph the hyperbola as a solid curve.

| Test Point | $x^2 - y^2 \le 1$; Result |
|------------|---------------------------|
| $(-2, 0)$ | $(-2)^2 - 0^2 \le 1$; False |
| $(0, 0)$ | $0^2 - 0^2 \le 1$; True |
| $(2, 0)$ | $2^2 - 0^2 \le 1$; False |

Shade the region containing $(0, 0)$. The solution to the system is the intersection.

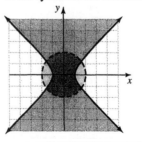

**42.** $\begin{cases} x^2 + y^2 \le 16 \\ x^2 + y^2 \ge 4 \end{cases}$

First graph the first circle as a solid curve.

| Test Point | $x^2 + y^2 \le 16$; Result |
|------------|----------------------------|
| $(0, 0)$ | $0^2 + 0^2 \le 16$; True |

Shade the region containing (0, 0). Next, graph
the second circle as a solid curve.

| Test Point | $x^2 + y^2 \geq 4$;  Result |
|------------|----------------------------|
| (0, 0) | $0^2 + 0^2 \geq 4$;  False |

Shade the region which does not contain (0, 0).
The solution to the system is the intersection.

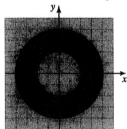

**43.** center: (−7, 8); radius = 5

$$(x-h)^2 + (y-k)^2 = r^2$$
$$(x+7)^2 + (y-8)^2 = 25$$

**44.**
$$3x^2 + 6x + 3y^2 = 9$$
$$x^2 + 2x + y^2 = 3$$
$$x^2 + 2x + 1 + y^2 = 3 + 1$$
$$(x+1)^2 + y^2 = 4$$

This is a circle with center (−1, 0) and radius 2.

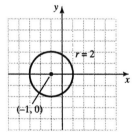

**45.**  $y = x^2 + 6x + 9$

$$y = (x+3)^2$$

This is a parabola that opens upward with vertex
(−3, 0).

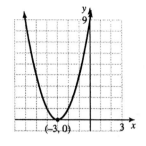

**46.**  $x = y^2 + 6y + 9$

$$x = (y+3)^2$$

This is a parabola that opens to the right with
vertex (0, −3).

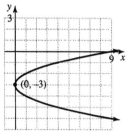

**47.**  $\dfrac{y^2}{4} - \dfrac{x^2}{16} = 1$

This is a hyperbola with center (0, 0), $a = 4$ and
$b = 2$.

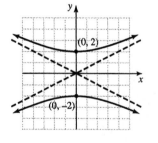

**48.**  $\dfrac{y^2}{4} + \dfrac{x^2}{16} = 1$

This is an ellipse with center (0, 0), $a = 4$ and
$b = 2$. The intercepts are (4, 0), (−4, 0), (0, 2),
and (0, −2).

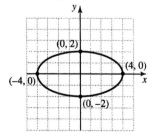

**49.** $\dfrac{(x-2)^2}{4}+(y-1)^2=1$

This is an ellipse with center (2, 1), $a = 2$ and $b = 1$.

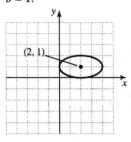

**50.**        $y^2 = x^2 + 6$

$y^2 - x^2 = 6$

$\dfrac{y^2}{6} - \dfrac{x^2}{6} = 1$

This is a hyperbola with center (0, 0), $a = \sqrt{6}$ and $b = \sqrt{6}$.

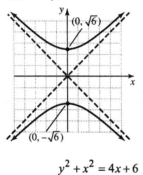

**51.**        $y^2 + x^2 = 4x + 6$

$y^2 + (x^2 - 4x) = 6$

$y^2 + (x^2 - 4x + 4) = 6 + 4$

$y^2 + (x-2)^2 = 10$

This is a circle with center (2, 0) and radius $\sqrt{10}$.

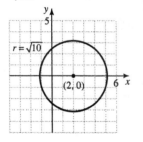

**52.**        $x^2 + y^2 - 8y = 0$

$x^2 + y^2 - 8y + 16 = 16$

$x^2 + (y-4)^2 = 16$

This is a circle with center (0, 4) and radius $\sqrt{16} = 4$.

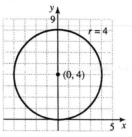

**53.** $6(x-2)^2 + 9(y+5)^2 = 36$

$\dfrac{(x-2)^2}{6} + \dfrac{(y+5)^2}{4} = 1$

This is an ellipse with center (2, −5), $a = \sqrt{6}$, and $b = 2$.

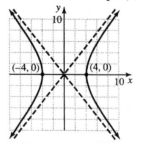

**54.** $\dfrac{x^2}{16} - \dfrac{y^2}{25} = 1$

This is a hyperbola with center (0, 0), $a = 4$, $b = 5$, and $x$-intercepts (4, 0) and (−4, 0).

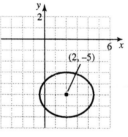

**55.** $\begin{cases} y = x^2 - 5x + 1 & (1) \\ y = -x + 6 & (2) \end{cases}$

Substitute $-x + 6$ for $y$ in E2.

$$-x+6 = x^2 - 5x + 1$$
$$0 = x^2 - 4x - 5$$
$$0 = (x-5)(x+1)$$
$$x = 5 \text{ or } x = -1$$

Use these values in E2.
$$x = 5: y = -(5) + 6 = 1$$
$$x = -1: y = -(-1) + 6 = 7$$

The solutions are (5, 1) and (−1, 7).

**56.** $\begin{cases} x^2 + y^2 = 10 & (1) \\ 9x^2 + y^2 = 18 & (2) \end{cases}$

Multiply E1 by −1 and add to E2.
$$-x^2 - y^2 = -10$$
$$\underline{9x^2 + y^2 = 18}$$
$$8x^2 \qquad\;\; = 8$$
$$x^2 = 1$$
$$x = \pm 1$$

Replace $x^2$ with 1 in E1.
$$1 + y^2 = 10$$
$$y^2 = 9$$
$$y = \pm 3$$

The solutions are (−1, −3), (−1, 3), (1, −3) and (1, 3).

**57.** $x^2 - y^2 < 1$

First graph the hyperbola as dashed curves.

| Test Point | $x^2 - y^2 < 1$; Result |
|------------|--------------------------|
| (−2, 0) | $(-2)^2 - 0^2 < 1$; False |
| (0, 0) | $0^2 - 0^2 < 1$; True |
| (2, 0) | $2^2 - 0^2 < 1$; False |

Shade the region containing (0, 0).

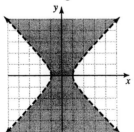

**58.** $\begin{cases} y > x^2 \\ x + y \geq 3 \end{cases}$

First graph the parabola as a dashed curve.

| Test Point | $y > x^2$; Result |
|------------|-------------------|
| (0, 1) | $1 > 0^2$; True |

Shade the region containing (0, 1). Next, graph $x + y = 3$ as a solid line.

| Test Point | $x + y \geq 3$; Result |
|------------|------------------------|
| (0, 0) | $0 + 0 \geq 3$; False |

Shade the region which does not contain (0, 0). The solution to the system is the overlapping region.

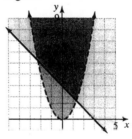

**Chapter 10 Test**

**1.** $x^2 + y^2 = 36$

Circle; center: (0, 0), radius $r = \sqrt{36} = 6$

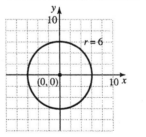

**2.** $x^2 - y^2 = 36$

$\dfrac{x^2}{36} - \dfrac{y^2}{36} = 1$

Hyperbola; center: $(0, 0)$, $a = 6$, $b = 6$

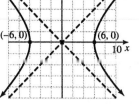

**3.** $16x^2 + 9y^2 = 144$

$\dfrac{x^2}{9} + \dfrac{y^2}{16} = 1$

Ellipse; center: $(0, 0)$, $a = 3$, $b = 4$

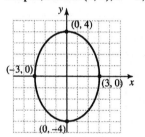

**4.** $y = x^2 - 8x + 16$

$y = (x - 4)^2$

Parabola; vertex: $(4, 0)$

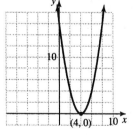

**5.** $x^2 + y^2 + 6x = 16$

$(x^2 + 6x) + y^2 = 16$

$(x^2 + 6x + 9) + y^2 = 16 + 9$

$(x + 3)^2 + y^2 = 25$

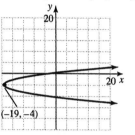

**6.** $x = y^2 + 8y - 3$

$x + 16 = (y^2 + 8y + 16) - 3$

$x = (y + 4)^2 - 19$

Parabola; vertex: $(-4, -19)$

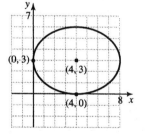

**7.** $\dfrac{(x-4)^2}{16} + \dfrac{(y-3)^2}{9} = 1$

Ellipse: center: $(4, 3)$, $a = 4$, $b = 3$

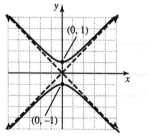

**8.** $y^2 - x^2 = 1$

Hyperbola: center: $(0, 0)$, $a = 1$, $b = 1$

562

**9.** $\begin{cases} x^2 + y^2 = 26 & (1) \\ x^2 - 2y^2 = 23 & (2) \end{cases}$

Solve E1 for $x^2$: $x^2 = 26 - y^2$.
Substitute into E2.
$$(26 - y^2) - 2y^2 = 23$$
$$-3y^2 = -3$$
$$y^2 = 1$$
$$y = \pm 1$$
Replace $y^2$ with 1 in E1.
$$x^2 + 1 = 26$$
$$x^2 = 25$$
$$x = \pm 5$$
The solutions are $(-5, -1)$, $(-5, 1)$, $(5, -1)$, and $(5, 1)$.

**10.** $\begin{cases} y = x^2 - 5x + 6 & (1) \\ y = 2x & (2) \end{cases}$

Substitute $2x$ for $y$ in E1.
$$2x = x^2 - 5x + 6$$
$$0 = x^2 - 7x + 6$$
$$0 = (x - 6)(x - 1)$$
$x = 6$ or $x = 1$
Use these values in E2.
$x = 6: y = 2(6) = 12$
$x = 1: y = 2(1) = 2$
The solutions are $(1, 2)$ and $(6, 12)$.

**11.** $\begin{cases} 2x + 5y \geq 10 \\ y \geq x^2 + 1 \end{cases}$

First graph $2x + 5y = 10$ as a solid line.

| Test Point | $2x + 5y \geq 10$; Result |
|---|---|
| $(0, 0)$ | $2(0) + 5(0) \geq 10$; False |

Shade the region which does not contain $(0, 0)$.
Next, graph $y = x^2 + 1$ as a solid curve.

| Test Point | $y \geq x^2 + 1$; Result |
|---|---|
| $(0, 0)$ | $0 \geq 0^2 + 1$; False |

Shade the region which does not contain $(0, 0)$.
The solution to the system is the intersection.

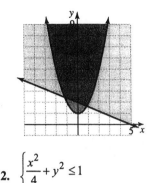

**12.** $\begin{cases} \dfrac{x^2}{4} + y^2 \leq 1 \\ x + y > 1 \end{cases}$

First graph the ellipse as a solid curve.

| Test Point | $\dfrac{x^2}{4} + y^2 \leq 1$; Result |
|---|---|
| $(0, 0)$ | $\dfrac{0^2}{4} + 0^2 \leq 1$; True |

Shade the region containing $(0, 0)$. Next, graph $x + y = 1$ as a dashed line.

| Test Point | $x + y > 1$; Result |
|---|---|
| $(0, 0)$ | $0 + 0 > 1$; False |

Shade the region which does not contain $(0, 0)$.
The solution to the system is the intersection.

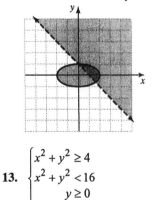

**13.** $\begin{cases} x^2 + y^2 \geq 4 \\ x^2 + y^2 < 16 \\ y \geq 0 \end{cases}$

First graph the circle $x^2 + y^2 = 4$ as a solid curve.

| Test Point | $x^2 + y^2 \geq 4$; Result |
|---|---|
| $(0, 0)$ | $0^2 + 0^2 \geq 4$; False |

Shade the region which does not contain $(0, 0)$.

Next graph the circle $x^2 + y^2 = 16$ as a dashed curve.

| Test Point | $x^2 + y^2 < 16$; Result |
|------------|--------------------------|
| $(0, 0)$   | $0^2 + 0^2 < 16$; True   |

Shade the region containing $(0, 0)$. Now graph the inequality $y \geq 0$ by shading the region above the $x$-axis. The solution to the system is the intersection.

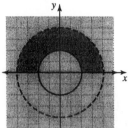

**14.** $100x^2 + 225y^2 = 22,500$

$$\frac{x^2}{225} + \frac{y^2}{100} = 1$$

$a = \sqrt{225} = 15$
$b = \sqrt{100} = 10$
Width = 15 + 15 = 30 feet
Height = 10 feet

## Chapter 10 Cumulative Review

**1.** $4 \cdot (9y) = (4 \cdot 9)y = 36y$

**2.** $3x + 4 > 1$ and $2x - 5 \leq 9$
$\quad\quad 3x > -3$ and $\quad\quad 2x \leq 14$
$\quad\quad\; x > -1$ and $\quad\quad\;\; x \leq 7$
$\quad -1 < x \leq 7$
$\quad (-1, 7]$

**3.** $x = -2y$
$\quad y = -\dfrac{1}{2}x$

| $x$ | $y = -\frac{1}{2}x$ |
|-----|---------------------|
| $-2$ | $1$ |
| $0$ | $0$ |
| $4$ | $-2$ |

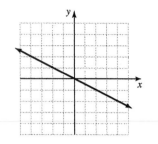

**4.** $(3, 2), (1, -4)$

$$m = \frac{-4 - 2}{1 - 3} = \frac{-6}{-2} = 3$$

**5.** $\begin{cases} 3x + \dfrac{y}{2} = 2 \;\; (1) \\ 6x + y = 5 \;\; (2) \end{cases}$

Multiply E1 by $-2$ and add to E2.
$\quad -6x - y = -4$
$\quad\;\; \underline{6x + y = 5}$
$\quad\quad\quad\quad 0 = 1$

This is a false statement. Therefore, the solution is $\varnothing$.

**6.** Let $x$ = speed of one plane. Then
$\quad x + 25$ = speed of the other plane.
$\quad d_{\text{plane 1}} + d_{\text{plane 2}} = 650$ miles
$\quad\quad 2x + 2(x + 25) = 650$
$\quad\quad\; 2x + 2x + 50 = 650$
$\quad\quad\quad\quad\quad\; 4x = 600$
$\quad\quad\quad\quad\quad\;\; x = 150$
$x + 25 = 150 + 25 = 175$
The planes are traveling at 150 mph and 175 mph.

**7. a.** $(5x^2)^3 = 5^3(x^2)^3 = 125x^6$

**b.** $\left(\dfrac{2}{3}\right)^3 = \dfrac{2^3}{3^3} = \dfrac{8}{27}$

**c.** $\left(\dfrac{3p^4}{q^5}\right)^2 = \dfrac{3^2(p^4)^2}{(q^5)^2} = \dfrac{9p^8}{q^{10}}$

**d.** $\left(\dfrac{2^{-3}}{y}\right)^{-2} = \dfrac{(2^{-3})^{-2}}{y^{-2}}$
$\quad\quad\quad\quad\quad = 2^6 y^2$
$\quad\quad\quad\quad\quad = 64y^2$

**e.** $(x^{-5}y^2z^{-1})^7 = (x^{-5})^7(y^2)^7(z^{-1})^7$
$$= x^{-35}y^{14}z^{-7}$$
$$= \frac{y^{14}}{x^{35}z^7}$$

**8. a.** $\dfrac{4^8}{4^3} = 4^{8-3} = 4^5$

**b.** $\dfrac{y^{11}}{y^5} = y^{11-5} = y^6$

**c.** $\dfrac{32x^7}{4x^6} = \dfrac{32}{4}x^{7-6} = 8x$

**d.** $\dfrac{18a^{12}b^6}{12a^8b^6} = \dfrac{18}{12}a^{12-8}b^{6-6} = \dfrac{3}{2}a^4b^0 = \dfrac{3a^4}{2}$

**9.** $2x^2 = \dfrac{17}{3}x + 1$
$$3(2x^2) = 3\left(\dfrac{17}{3}x + 1\right)$$
$$6x^2 = 17x + 3$$
$$6x^2 - 17x - 3 = 0$$
$$(6x + 1)(x - 3) = 0$$
$$6x + 1 = 0 \quad \text{or} \quad x - 3 = 0$$
$$6x = -1 \quad \text{or} \quad x = 3$$
$$x = -\dfrac{1}{6}$$

The solutions are $-\dfrac{1}{6}$ and 3.

**10. a.** $3y^2 + 14y + 15 = (3y + 5)(y + 3)$

**b.** $20a^5 + 54a^4 + 10a^3$
$$= 2a^3(10a^2 + 27a + 5)$$
$$= 2a^3(2a + 5)(5a + 1)$$

**c.** $(y-3)^2 - 2(y-3) - 8$
Let $u = y - 3$. Then $u^2 = (y-3)^2$ and
$$u^2 - 2u - 8 = (u-4)(u+2)$$
$$= [(y-3)-4][(y-3)+2]$$
$$= (y-7)(y-1)$$

**11.** $\dfrac{7}{x-1} + \dfrac{10x}{x^2-1} - \dfrac{5}{x+1}$
$$= \dfrac{7}{x-1} + \dfrac{10x}{(x+1)(x-1)} - \dfrac{5}{x+1}$$
$$= \dfrac{7(x+1) + 10x - 5(x-1)}{(x+1)(x-1)}$$
$$= \dfrac{7x + 7 + 10x - 5x + 5}{(x+1)(x-1)}$$
$$= \dfrac{12x + 12}{(x+1)(x-1)}$$
$$= \dfrac{12(x+1)}{(x+1)(x-1)}$$
$$= \dfrac{12}{x-1}$$

**12.** $\dfrac{2}{3a-15} - \dfrac{a}{25-a^2}$
$$= \dfrac{2}{3(a-5)} + \dfrac{a}{a^2-25}$$
$$= \dfrac{2}{3(a-5)} + \dfrac{a}{(a+5)(a-5)}$$
$$= \dfrac{2(a+5) + 3a}{3(a+5)(a-5)}$$
$$= \dfrac{2a + 10 + 3a}{3(a+5)(a-5)}$$
$$= \dfrac{5a + 10}{3(a+5)(a-5)}$$

**13. a.** $\dfrac{\frac{2x}{27y^2}}{\frac{6x^2}{9}} = \dfrac{2x}{27y^2} \cdot \dfrac{9}{6x^2} = \dfrac{1}{3y^2} \cdot \dfrac{1}{3x} = \dfrac{1}{9xy^2}$

**b.** $\dfrac{\frac{5x}{x+2}}{\frac{10}{x-2}} = \dfrac{5x}{x+2} \cdot \dfrac{x-2}{10} = \dfrac{x(x-2)}{2(x+2)}$

**c.** $\dfrac{\frac{x}{y^2}+\frac{1}{y}}{\frac{y}{x^2}+\frac{1}{x}} = \dfrac{\left(\frac{x}{y^2}+\frac{1}{y}\right)x^2y^2}{\left(\frac{y}{x^2}+\frac{1}{x}\right)x^2y^2}$
$$= \dfrac{x^3 + x^2y}{y^3 + xy^2}$$
$$= \dfrac{x^2(x+y)}{y^2(y+x)}$$
$$= \dfrac{x^2}{y^2}$$

**14. a.** $(a^{-1} - b^{-1})^{-1} = \left( \dfrac{1}{a} - \dfrac{1}{b} \right)^{-1}$

$$= \left( \dfrac{b-a}{ab} \right)^{-1}$$

$$= \dfrac{ab}{b-a}$$

**b.** $\dfrac{2 - \frac{1}{x}}{4x - \frac{1}{x}} = \dfrac{\left( 2 - \frac{1}{x} \right) x}{\left( 4x - \frac{1}{x} \right) x}$

$$= \dfrac{2x - 1}{4x^2 - 1}$$

$$= \dfrac{2x - 1}{(2x+1)(2x-1)}$$

$$= \dfrac{1}{2x+1}$$

**15.**
$$
\require{enclose}
\begin{array}{r}
2x - 5 \\[-2pt]
x+2 \enclose{longdiv}{2x^2 - x - 10} \\
\underline{2x^2 + 4x} \\
-5x - 10 \\
\underline{-5x - 10} \\
0
\end{array}
$$

Answer: $2x - 5$

**16.** $\dfrac{2}{x+3} = \dfrac{1}{x^2-9} - \dfrac{1}{x-3}$

$\dfrac{2}{x+3} = \dfrac{1}{(x+3)(x-3)} - \dfrac{1}{x-3}$

$2(x-3) = 1 - 1(x+3)$

$2x - 6 = 1 - x - 3$

$2x - 6 = -x - 2$

$3x = 4$

$x = \dfrac{4}{3}$

**17.**
$$
\begin{array}{r|rrrrrrr}
4 & 4 & -25 & 35 & 0 & 17 & 0 & 0 \\
  &   & 16 & -36 & -4 & -16 & 4 & 16 \\
\hline
  & 4 & -9 & -1 & -4 & 1 & 4 & 16
\end{array}
$$

Thus, $P(4) = 16$.

**18.** $y = \dfrac{k}{x}$

$3 = \dfrac{k}{\frac{2}{3}}$

$k = 3\left( \dfrac{2}{3} \right) = 2$

Thus, the equation is $y = \dfrac{2}{x}$.

**19.** $\dfrac{2x}{x-3} + \dfrac{6-2x}{x^2-9} = \dfrac{x}{x+3}$

$\dfrac{2x}{x-3} + \dfrac{-2(x-3)}{(x+3)(x-3)} = \dfrac{x}{x+3}$

$\dfrac{2x}{x-3} - \dfrac{2}{x+3} = \dfrac{x}{x+3}$

$\dfrac{2x}{x-3} = \dfrac{x}{x+3} + \dfrac{2}{x+3}$

$\dfrac{2x}{x-3} = \dfrac{x+2}{x+3}$

$2x(x+3) = (x+2)(x-3)$

$2x^2 + 6x = x^2 - x - 6$

$x^2 + 7x + 6 = 0$

$(x+6)(x+1) = 0$

$x + 6 = 0 \quad \text{or} \quad x + 1 = 0$

$x = -6 \quad \text{or} \quad x = -1$

The solutions are $-6$ and $-1$.

**20. a.** $\sqrt[5]{-32} = -2$ because $(-2)^5 = -32$.

**b.** $\sqrt[4]{625} = 5$ because $5^4 = 625$.

**c.** $-\sqrt{36} = -6$ because $6^2 = 36$.

**d.** $-\sqrt[3]{-27x^3} = -(-3x) = 3x$

**e.** $\sqrt{144y^2} = 12y$

**21.** Let $t$ = time it will take together.

$$\frac{1}{4}+\frac{1}{5}=\frac{1}{t}$$

$$20t\left(\frac{1}{4}+\frac{1}{5}\right)=20t\left(\frac{1}{t}\right)$$

$$5t+4t=20$$

$$9t=20$$

$$t=\frac{20}{9}=2\frac{2}{9}$$

It will take them $2\frac{2}{9}$ hours. No, they can not finish before the movie starts.

**22. a.** $\dfrac{\sqrt{32}}{\sqrt{4}}=\sqrt{\dfrac{32}{4}}=\sqrt{8}=\sqrt{4\cdot2}=2\sqrt{2}$

**b.** $\dfrac{\sqrt[3]{240y^2}}{5\sqrt[3]{3y^{-4}}}=\dfrac{1}{5}\sqrt[3]{\dfrac{240y^2}{3y^{-4}}}$

$$=\frac{1}{5}\sqrt[3]{80y^6}$$

$$=\frac{1}{5}\sqrt[3]{8y^6\cdot10}$$

$$=\frac{2y^3\sqrt[3]{10}}{5}$$

**c.** $\dfrac{\sqrt[5]{64x^9y^2}}{\sqrt[5]{2x^2y^{-8}}}=\sqrt[5]{\dfrac{64x^9y^2}{2x^2y^{-8}}}$

$$=\sqrt[5]{32x^7y^{10}}$$

$$=\sqrt[5]{32x^5y^{10}\cdot x^2}$$

$$=2xy^2\sqrt[5]{x^2}$$

**23. a.** $\sqrt[3]{1}=1$

**b.** $\sqrt[3]{-64}=-4$

**c.** $\sqrt[3]{\dfrac{8}{125}}=\dfrac{\sqrt[3]{8}}{\sqrt[3]{125}}=\dfrac{2}{5}$

**d.** $\sqrt[3]{x^6}=x^2$

**e.** $\sqrt[3]{-27x^9}=-3x^3$

**24. a.** $\sqrt{5}\left(2+\sqrt{15}\right)=2\sqrt{5}+\sqrt{5}\cdot\sqrt{15}$

$$=2\sqrt{5}+\sqrt{75}$$

$$=2\sqrt{5}+5\sqrt{3}$$

**b.** $\left(\sqrt{3}-\sqrt{5}\right)\left(\sqrt{7}-1\right)$

$$=\sqrt{3}\cdot\sqrt{7}-\sqrt{3}\cdot1-\sqrt{5}\cdot\sqrt{7}+\sqrt{5}\cdot1$$

$$=\sqrt{21}-\sqrt{3}-\sqrt{35}+\sqrt{5}$$

**c.** $\left(2\sqrt{5}-1\right)^2=\left(2\sqrt{5}\right)^2-2\cdot2\sqrt{5}\cdot1+1^2$

$$=4(5)-4\sqrt{5}+1$$

$$=21-4\sqrt{5}$$

**d.** $\left(3\sqrt{2}+5\right)\left(3\sqrt{2}-5\right)=\left(3\sqrt{2}\right)^2-5^2$

$$=9(2)-25$$

$$=18-25$$

$$=-7$$

**25. a.** $z^{2/3}(z^{1/3}-z^5)=z^{2/3+1/3}-z^{2/3+5}$

$$=z^{3/3}-z^{2/3+15/3}$$

$$=z-z^{17/3}$$

**b.** $(x^{1/3}-5)(x^{1/3}+2)$

$$=x^{1/3}\cdot x^{1/3}+2x^{1/3}-5x^{1/3}-5(2)$$

$$=x^{2/3}-3x^{1/3}-10$$

**26.** $\dfrac{-2}{\sqrt{3}+3}=\dfrac{-2\left(\sqrt{3}-3\right)}{\left(\sqrt{3}+3\right)\left(\sqrt{3}-3\right)}$

$$=\frac{-2\left(\sqrt{3}-3\right)}{\left(\sqrt{3}\right)^2-3^2}$$

$$=\frac{-2\left(\sqrt{3}-3\right)}{3-9}$$

$$=\frac{-2\left(\sqrt{3}-3\right)}{-6}$$

$$=\frac{\sqrt{3}-3}{3}$$

**27. a.** $\dfrac{\sqrt{20}}{\sqrt{5}}=\sqrt{\dfrac{20}{5}}=\sqrt{4}=2$

**b.** $\dfrac{\sqrt{50x}}{2\sqrt{2}}=\dfrac{1}{2}\sqrt{\dfrac{50x}{2}}=\dfrac{1}{2}\sqrt{25x}=\dfrac{5\sqrt{x}}{2}$

**c.**　$\dfrac{7\sqrt[3]{48x^4y^8}}{\sqrt[3]{6y^2}} = 7\sqrt[3]{\dfrac{48x^4y^8}{6y^2}}$

$\qquad\qquad = 7\sqrt[3]{8x^4y^6}$

$\qquad\qquad = 7\sqrt[3]{8x^3y^6 \cdot x}$

$\qquad\qquad = 7 \cdot 2xy^2\sqrt[3]{x}$

$\qquad\qquad = 14xy^2\sqrt[3]{x}$

**d.**　$\dfrac{2\sqrt[4]{32a^9b^6}}{\sqrt[4]{a^{-1}b^2}} = 2\sqrt[4]{\dfrac{32a^9b^6}{a^{-1}b^2}}$

$\qquad\qquad = 2\sqrt[4]{32a^9b^4}$

$\qquad\qquad = 2\sqrt[4]{16a^8b^4 \cdot 2a}$

$\qquad\qquad = 2 \cdot 2a^2b\sqrt[4]{2a}$

$\qquad\qquad = 4a^2b\sqrt[4]{2a}$

**28.**　$\sqrt{2x-3} = x-3$

$\quad \left(\sqrt{2x-3}\right)^2 = (x-3)^2$

$\qquad 2x-3 = x^2-6x+9$

$\qquad\quad 0 = x^2-8x+12$

$\qquad\quad 0 = (x-6)(x-2)$

$x-6=0$ or $x-2=0$

$\quad x=6$ or $\quad\;\; x=2$

Discard 2 as an extraneous solution. The solution is 6.

**29. a.**　$\dfrac{\sqrt{45}}{4} - \dfrac{\sqrt{5}}{3} = \dfrac{3\sqrt{5}}{4} - \dfrac{\sqrt{5}}{3}$

$\qquad\qquad = \dfrac{9\sqrt{5}-4\sqrt{5}}{12}$

$\qquad\qquad = \dfrac{5\sqrt{5}}{12}$

**b.**　$\sqrt[3]{\dfrac{7x}{8}} + 2\sqrt[3]{7x} = \dfrac{\sqrt[3]{7x}}{2} + 2\sqrt[3]{7x}$

$\qquad\qquad = \dfrac{\sqrt[3]{7x}}{2} + \dfrac{4\sqrt[3]{7x}}{2}$

$\qquad\qquad = \dfrac{5\sqrt[3]{7x}}{2}$

**30.**　$9x^2 - 6x = -4$

$\quad 9x^2 - 6x + 4 = 0$

$\quad a=9, b=-6, c=4$

$\quad b^2 - 4ac = (-6)^2 - 4(9)(4)$

$\qquad\qquad = 36 - 144$

$\qquad\qquad = -108$

Two complex but not real solutions

**31.**　$\sqrt{\dfrac{7x}{3y}} = \dfrac{\sqrt{7x}}{\sqrt{3y}} = \dfrac{\sqrt{7x} \cdot \sqrt{3y}}{\sqrt{3y} \cdot \sqrt{3y}} = \dfrac{\sqrt{21xy}}{3y}$

**32.**　$\dfrac{4}{x-2} - \dfrac{x}{x+2} = \dfrac{16}{x^2-4}$

$\quad \dfrac{4}{x-2} - \dfrac{x}{x+2} = \dfrac{16}{(x+2)(x-2)}$

$\quad 4(x+2) - x(x-2) = 16$

$\qquad 4x+8-x^2+2x = 16$

$\qquad\qquad 0 = x^2-6x+8$

$\qquad\qquad 0 = (x-4)(x-2)$

$x-4=0$ or $x-2=0$

$\quad x=4$ or $\quad\;\; x=2$

Discard the solution 2 as extraneous. The solution is 4.

**33.**　$\sqrt{2x-3} = 9$

$\quad \left(\sqrt{2x-3}\right)^2 = 9^2$

$\qquad 2x-3 = 81$

$\qquad\quad 2x = 84$

$\qquad\quad\; x = 42$

The solution is 42.

**34.**　$x^3 + 2x^2 - 4x \ge 8$

$\quad x^3 + 2x^2 - 4x - 8 \ge 0$

$\quad x^2(x+2) - 4(x+2) \ge 0$

$\qquad (x+2)(x^2-4) \ge 0$

$\quad (x+2)(x+2)(x-2) \ge 0$

$\qquad\quad (x+2)^2(x-2) \ge 0$

$(x+2)^2 = 0$　or　$x-2=0$

$\quad x+2=0$　or　$\quad x=2$

$\qquad x=-2$

| Region | Test Point | $(x+2)^2(x-2) \geq 0$ Result |
|---|---|---|
| A: $(-\infty, -2)$ | $-3$ | $(-1)^2(-5) \geq 0$ False |
| B: $(-2, 2)$ | $0$ | $(2)^2(-2) \geq 0$ False |
| C: $(2, \infty)$ | $3$ | $(5)^2(1) \geq 0$ True |

Solution: $[2, \infty)$

**35. a.** $i^7 = i^4 \cdot i^3 = 1 \cdot (-i) = -i$

**b.** $i^{20} = (i^4)^5 = 1^5 = 1$

**c.** $i^{46} = i^{44} \cdot i^2 = (i^4)^{11} \cdot (-1) = 1^{11}(-1) = -1$

**d.** $i^{-12} = \dfrac{1}{i^{12}} = \dfrac{1}{(i^4)^3} = \dfrac{1}{1^3} = 1$

**36.** $f(x) = (x+2)^2 - 1$

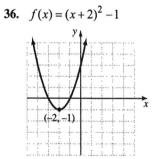

**37.**
$$p^2 + 2p = 4$$
$$p^2 + 2p + \left(\frac{2}{2}\right)^2 = 4 + 1$$
$$p^2 + 2p + 1 = 5$$
$$(p+1)^2 = 5$$
$$p + 1 = \pm\sqrt{5}$$
$$p = -1 \pm \sqrt{5}$$
The solutions are $-1 + \sqrt{5}$ and $-1 - \sqrt{5}$.

**38.** $f(x) = -x^2 - 6x + 4$
The maximum will occur at the vertex.
$$x = \frac{-b}{2a} = \frac{-(-6)}{2(-1)} = -3$$
$$f(-3) = -(-3)^2 - 6(-3) + 4 = 13$$
The maximum value is 13.

**39.**
$$\frac{1}{4}m^2 - m + \frac{1}{2} = 0$$
$$4\left(\frac{1}{4}m^2 - m + \frac{1}{2}\right) = 4(0)$$
$$m^2 - 4m + 2 = 0$$
$$a = 1, b = -4, c = 2$$
$$m = \frac{-(-4) \pm \sqrt{(-4)^2 - 4(1)(2)}}{2(1)}$$
$$= \frac{4 \pm \sqrt{16 - 8}}{2}$$
$$= \frac{4 \pm \sqrt{8}}{2}$$
$$= \frac{4 \pm 2\sqrt{2}}{2}$$
$$= 2 \pm \sqrt{2}$$
The solutions are $2 + \sqrt{2}$ and $2 - \sqrt{2}$.

**40.**
$$f(x) = \frac{x+1}{2}$$
$$y = \frac{x+1}{2}$$
$$x = \frac{y+1}{2}$$
$$2x = y + 1$$
$$2x - 1 = y$$
$$f^{-1}(x) = 2x - 1$$

**41.**
$$p^4 - 3p^2 - 4 = 0$$
$$(p^2 - 4)(p^2 + 1) = 0$$
$$(p+2)(p-2)(p^2 + 1) = 0$$
$$p + 2 = 0 \quad \text{or } p - 2 = 0 \text{ or } p^2 + 1 = 0$$
$$p = -2 \text{ or} \quad p = 2 \text{ or} \quad p^2 = -1$$
$$p = \pm i$$
The solutions are $-2$, $2$, $-i$, and $i$.

**42.** $f(x) = x^2 - 3x + 2$
$g(x) = -3x + 5$

    **a.** $(f \circ g)(x) = f[g(x)]$
$= f(-3x + 5)$
$= (-3x + 5)^2 - 3(-3x + 5) + 2$
$= 9x^2 - 30x + 25 + 9x - 15 + 2$
$= 9x^2 - 21x + 12$

    **b.** $(f \circ g)(-2) = f[g(-2)]$
$= f[-3(-2) + 5]$
$= f(11)$
$= (11)^2 - 3(11) + 2$
$= 121 - 33 + 2$
$= 90$

    **c.** $(g \circ f)(x) = g[f(x)]$
$= g(x^2 - 3x + 2)$
$= -3(x^2 - 3x + 2) + 5$
$= -3x^2 + 9x - 6 + 5$
$= -3x^2 + 9x - 1$

    **d.** $(g \circ f)(5) = g[f(5)]$
$= g[(5)^2 - 3(5) + 2]$
$= g(12)$
$= -3(12) + 5$
$= -36 + 5$
$= -31$

**43.** $\dfrac{x+2}{x-3} \le 0$

$x + 2 = 0 \quad$ or $\quad x - 3 = 0$
$x = -2 \quad$ or $\quad x = 3$

| Region | Test Point | $\dfrac{x+2}{x-3} \le 0$ Result |
|---|---|---|
| A: $(-\infty, -2)$ | $-3$ | $\dfrac{-1}{-6} \le 0$ ; False |
| B: $(-2, 3)$ | $0$ | $\dfrac{2}{-3} \le 0$ ; True |
| C: $(3, \infty)$ | $4$ | $\dfrac{6}{1} \le 0$ ; False |

Solution: $[-2, 3)$

**44.** $4x^2 + 9y^2 = 36$

$\dfrac{x^2}{9} + \dfrac{y^2}{4} = 1$

Ellipse: center $(0, 0)$, $a = 3$, $b = 2$

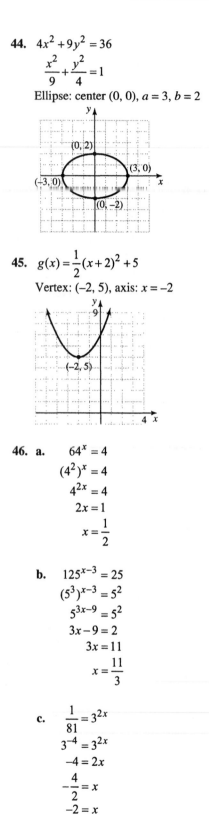

**45.** $g(x) = \dfrac{1}{2}(x+2)^2 + 5$

Vertex: $(-2, 5)$, axis: $x = -2$

**46. a.** $\quad 64^x = 4$
$(4^2)^x = 4$
$4^{2x} = 4$
$2x = 1$
$x = \dfrac{1}{2}$

    **b.** $\quad 125^{x-3} = 25$
$(5^3)^{x-3} = 5^2$
$5^{3x-9} = 5^2$
$3x - 9 = 2$
$3x = 11$
$x = \dfrac{11}{3}$

    **c.** $\quad \dfrac{1}{81} = 3^{2x}$
$3^{-4} = 3^{2x}$
$-4 = 2x$
$-\dfrac{4}{2} = x$
$-2 = x$

**47.** $f(x) = x^2 - 4x - 12$

$x = \dfrac{-b}{2a} = \dfrac{-(-4)}{2(1)} = 2$

$f(2) = (2)^2 - 4(2) - 12 = -16$

Vertex: $(2, -16)$

**48.** $\begin{cases} x + 2y < 8 \\ \quad y \geq x^2 \end{cases}$

First, graph $x + 2y = 8$ as a dashed line.

| Test Point | $x + 2y < 8$; Result |
|------------|----------------------|
| $(0, 0)$   | $0 + 2(0) < 8$; True |

Shade the region containing $(0, 0)$. Next, graph the parabola $y = x^2$ as a solid curve.

| Test Point | $y \geq x^2$; Result |
|------------|----------------------|
| $(0, 1)$   | $1 \geq 0^2$; True   |

Shade the region containing $(0, 1)$. The solution to the system is the intersection.

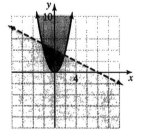

**49.** $(2, -5), (1, -4)$

$\begin{aligned} d &= \sqrt{[-4 - (-5)]^2 + (1 - 2)^2} \\ &= \sqrt{1^2 + (-1)^2} \\ &= \sqrt{2} \approx 1.414 \end{aligned}$

**50.** $\begin{cases} x^2 + y^2 = 36 & (1) \\ \quad\quad y = x + 6 & (2) \end{cases}$

Substitute $x + 6$ for $y$ in E1.

$x^2 + (x + 6)^2 = 36$

$x^2 + (x^2 + 12x + 36) = 36$

$2x^2 + 12x = 0$

$2x(x + 6) = 0$

$2x = 0$ or $x + 6 = 0$

$x = 0$ or $\quad x = -6$

Use these values in E2 to find $y$.

$x = 0: y = 0 + 6 = 6$

$x = -6: y = -6 + 6 = 0$

The solutions are $(0, 6)$ and $(-6, 0)$.

# Chapter 11

**Section 11.1**

**Practice Problems**

1. $a_n = 5 + n^2$

   $a_1 = 5 + 1^2 = 5 + 1 = 6$

   $a_2 = 5 + 2^2 = 5 + 4 = 9$

   $a_3 = 5 + 3^2 = 5 + 9 = 14$

   $a_4 = 5 + 4^2 = 5 + 16 = 21$

   $a_5 = 5 + 5^2 = 5 + 25 = 30$

   Thus, the first five terms of the sequence are 6, 9, 14, 21, and 30.

2. $a_n = \dfrac{(-1)^n}{5n}$

   a. $a_1 = \dfrac{(-1)^1}{5(1)} = -\dfrac{1}{5}$

   b. $a_4 = \dfrac{(-1)^4}{5(4)} = \dfrac{1}{20}$

   c. $a_{30} = \dfrac{(-1)^{30}}{5(30)} = \dfrac{1}{150}$

   d. $a_{19} = \dfrac{(-1)^{19}}{5(19)} = -\dfrac{1}{95}$

3. a. $1, 3, 5, 7, \ldots$

   These numbers are the first four odd natural numbers, so a general term might be $a_n = (2n - 1)$.

   b. $3, 9, 27, 81, \ldots$

   These numbers are all powers of 3 ($3 = 3^1$, $9 = 3^2$, $27 = 3^3$, and $81 = 3^4$), so a general term might be $a_n = 3^n$.

   c. $\dfrac{1}{2}, \dfrac{2}{3}, \dfrac{3}{4}, \dfrac{4}{5}, \ldots$

   The numerators are the first four natural numbers and each denominator is one greater than the numerator, so a general term might be $a_n = \dfrac{n}{n+1}$.

   d. $-\dfrac{1}{2}, -\dfrac{1}{3}, -\dfrac{1}{4}, -\dfrac{1}{5}, \ldots$

   The denominators are consecutive natural numbers beginning with 2 and each term is negative, so a general term might be

   $$a_n = -\dfrac{1}{n+1}.$$

4. $v_n = 3950(0.8)^n$

   $v_3 = 3950(0.8)^3$

   $\quad = 3950(0.512)$

   $\quad = 2022.4$

   The value of the copier after three years is $2022.40.

**Vocabulary and Readiness Check**

1. The $n$th term of the sequence $a_n$ is called the <u>general</u> term.

2. A <u>finite</u> sequence is a function whose domain is $\{1, 2, 3, 4, \ldots, n\}$ where $n$ is some natural number.

3. An <u>infinite</u> sequence is a function whose domain is $\{1, 2, 3, 4, \ldots\}$.

4. $a_n = 7^n$

   $a_1 = 7^1 = 7$

5. $a_n = \dfrac{(-1)^n}{n}$

   $a_1 = \dfrac{(-1)^1}{1} = -1$

6. $a_n = (-1)^n \cdot n^4$

   $a_1 = (-1)^1 \cdot 1^4 = -1$

**Exercise Set 11.1**

1. $a_n = n + 4$

   $a_1 = 1 + 4 = 5$

   $a_2 = 2 + 4 = 6$

   $a_3 = 3 + 4 = 7$

   $a_4 = 4 + 4 = 8$

   $a_5 = 5 + 4 = 9$

   Thus, the first five terms of the sequence $a_n = n + 4$ are 5, 6, 7, 8, 9.

**3.** $a_n = (-1)^n$

$a_1 = (-1)^1 = -1$
$a_2 = (-1)^2 = 1$
$a_3 = (-1)^3 = -1$
$a_4 = (-1)^4 = 1$
$a_5 = (-1)^5 = -1$

Thus, the first five terms of the sequence $a_n = (-1)^n$ are $-1, 1, -1, 1, -1$.

**5.** $a_n = \dfrac{1}{n+3}$

$a_1 = \dfrac{1}{1+3} = \dfrac{1}{4}$
$a_2 = \dfrac{1}{2+3} = \dfrac{1}{5}$
$a_3 = \dfrac{1}{3+3} = \dfrac{1}{6}$
$a_4 = \dfrac{1}{4+3} = \dfrac{1}{7}$
$a_5 = \dfrac{1}{5+3} = \dfrac{1}{8}$

Thus, the first five terms of the sequence $a_n = \dfrac{1}{n+3}$ are $\dfrac{1}{4}, \dfrac{1}{5}, \dfrac{1}{6}, \dfrac{1}{7}, \dfrac{1}{8}$.

**7.** $a_n = 2n$

$a_1 = 2(1) = 2$
$a_2 = 2(2) = 4$
$a_3 = 2(3) = 6$
$a_4 = 2(4) = 8$
$a_5 = 2(5) = 10$

Thus, the first five terms of the sequence $a_n = 2n$ are $2, 4, 6, 8, 10$.

**9.** $a_n = -n^2$

$a_1 = -1^2 = -1$
$a_2 = -2^2 = -4$
$a_3 = -3^2 = -9$
$a_4 = -4^2 = -16$
$a_5 = -5^2 = -25$

Thus, the first five terms of the sequence $a_n = n^2$ are $-1, -4, -8, -16, -25$.

**11.** $a_n = 2^n$

$a_1 = 2^1 = 2$
$a_2 = 2^2 = 4$
$a_3 = 2^3 = 8$
$a_4 = 2^4 = 16$
$a_5 = 2^5 = 32$

Thus, the first five terms of the sequence $a_n = 2^n$ are $2, 4, 8, 16, 32$.

**13.** $a_n = 2n + 5$

$a_1 = 2(1) + 5 = 2 + 5 = 7$
$a_2 = 2(2) + 5 = 4 + 5 = 9$
$a_3 = 2(3) + 5 = 6 + 5 = 11$
$a_4 = 2(4) + 5 = 8 + 5 = 13$
$a_5 = 2(5) + 5 = 10 + 5 = 15$

Thus, the first five terms of the sequence $a_n = 2n + 5$ are $7, 9, 11, 13, 15$.

**15.** $a_n = (-1)^n n^2$

$a_1 = (-1)^1 (1)^2 = -1(1) = -1$
$a_2 = (-1)^2 (2)^2 = 1(4) = 4$
$a_3 = (-1)^3 (3)^2 = -1(9) = -9$
$a_4 = (-1)^4 (4)^2 = 1(16) = 16$
$a_5 = (-1)^5 (5)^2 = -1(25) = -25$

Thus, the first five terms of the sequence $a_n = (-1)^n n^2$ are $-1, 4, -9, 16, -25$.

**17.** $a_n = 3n^2$

$a_5 = 3(5)^2 = 3(25) = 75$

**19.** $a_n = 6n - 2$

$a_{20} = 6(20) - 2 = 120 - 2 = 118$

**21.** $a_n = \dfrac{n+3}{n}$

$a_{15} = \dfrac{15+3}{15} = \dfrac{18}{15} = \dfrac{6}{5}$

**23.** $a_n = (-3)^n$

$a_6 = (-3)^6 = 729$

84941968

**25.** $a_n = \dfrac{n-2}{n+1}$

$a_6 = \dfrac{6-2}{6+1} = \dfrac{4}{7}$

**27.** $a_n = \dfrac{(-1)^n}{n}$

$a_8 = \dfrac{(-1)^8}{8} = \dfrac{1}{8}$

**29.** $a_n = -n^2 + 5$

$a_{10} = -10^2 + 5 = -100 + 5 = -95$

**31.** $a_n = \dfrac{(-1)^n}{n+6}$

$a_{19} = \dfrac{(-1)^{19}}{19+6} = -\dfrac{1}{25}$

**33.** 3, 7, 11, 15, or $4(1)-1$, $4(2)-1$, $4(3)-1$, $4(4)-1$. In general, $a_n = 4n-1$.

**35.** $-2, -4, -8, -16$, or $-2, -2^2, -2^3, -2^4$

In general, $a_n = -2^n$.

**37.** $\dfrac{1}{3}, \dfrac{1}{9}, \dfrac{1}{27}, \dfrac{1}{81}$, or $\dfrac{1}{3}, \dfrac{1}{3^2}, \dfrac{1}{3^3}, \dfrac{1}{3^4}$

In general, $a_n = \dfrac{1}{3^n}$.

**39.** $a_n = 32n - 16$

$a_2 = 32(2) - 16 = 64 - 16 = 48$ ft
$a_3 = 32(3) - 16 = 96 - 16 = 80$ ft
$a_4 = 32(4) - 16 = 128 - 16 = 112$ ft

**41.** 0.10, 0.20, 0.40, or 0.10, 0.10(2), $0.10(2)^2$

In general, $a_n = 0.10(2)^{n-1}$

$a_{14} = 0.10(2)^{13} = \$819.20$

**43.** $a_n = 75(2)^{n-1}$

$a_6 = 75(2)^5 = 75(32) = 2400$ cases
$a_1 = 75(2)^0 = 75(1) = 75$ cases

**45.** $a_n = \dfrac{1}{2}a_{n-1}$ for $n > 1, a_1 = 800$

In 2000, $n = 1$ and $a_1 = 800$.

In 2001, $n = 2$ and $a_2 = \dfrac{1}{2}(800) = 400$.

In 2002, $n = 3$ and $a_3 = \dfrac{1}{2}(400) = 200$.

In 2003, $n = 4$ and $a_4 = \dfrac{1}{2}(200) = 100$.

In 2004, $n = 5$ and $a_5 = \dfrac{1}{2}(100) = 50$.

The population estimate for 2004 is 50 sparrows. Continuing the sequence:

In 2005, $n = 6$ and $a_6 = \dfrac{1}{2}(50) = 25$.

In 2006, $n = 7$ and $a_7 = \dfrac{1}{2}(25) \approx 12$.

In 2007, $n = 8$ and $a_8 = \dfrac{1}{2}(12) = 6$.

In 2008, $n = 9$ and $a_9 = \dfrac{1}{2}(6) = 3$.

In 2009, $n = 10$ and $a_{10} = \dfrac{1}{2}(3) \approx 1$.

In 2010, $n = 11$ and $a_{11} = \dfrac{1}{2}(1) \approx 0$.

The population is estimated to become extinct in 2010.

**47.** $f(x) = (x-1)^2 + 3$

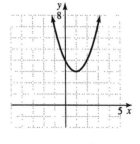

**49.** $f(x) = 2(x+4)^2 + 2$

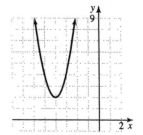

**51.** $(-4, -1)$ and $(-7, -3)$

$$d = \sqrt{\left[-7 - (-4)\right]^2 + \left[-3 - (-1)\right]^2}$$
$$= \sqrt{(-7 + 4)^2 + (-3 + 1)^2}$$
$$= \sqrt{(-3)^2 + (-2)^2}$$
$$= \sqrt{9 + 4}$$
$$= \sqrt{13} \text{ units}$$

**53.** $(2, -7)$ and $(-3, -3)$

$$d = \sqrt{(-3 - 2)^2 + \left[-3 - (-7)\right]^2}$$
$$= \sqrt{(-5)^2 + (-3 + 7)^2}$$
$$= \sqrt{(-5)^2 + (4)^2}$$
$$= \sqrt{25 + 16}$$
$$= \sqrt{41} \text{ units}$$

**55.** $a_n = \dfrac{1}{\sqrt{n}}$

$$a_1 = \frac{1}{\sqrt{1}} = \frac{1}{1} = 1$$

$$a_2 = \frac{1}{\sqrt{2}} \approx 0.7071$$

$$a_3 = \frac{1}{\sqrt{3}} \approx 0.5774$$

$$a_4 = \frac{1}{\sqrt{4}} = \frac{1}{2} = 0.5$$

$$a_5 = \frac{1}{\sqrt{5}} \approx 0.4472$$

Thus, the first five terms of the sequence

$a_n = \dfrac{1}{\sqrt{n}}$ are $1, 0.7071, 0.5774, 0.5, 0.4472$.

**57.** $a_n = \left(1 + \dfrac{1}{n}\right)^n$

$$a_1 = \left(1 + \frac{1}{1}\right)^1 = (2)^1 = 2$$

$$a_2 = \left(1 + \frac{1}{2}\right)^2 = \left(\frac{3}{2}\right)^2 = 2.25$$

$$a_3 = \left(1 + \frac{1}{3}\right)^3 = \left(\frac{4}{3}\right)^3 \approx 2.3704$$

$$a_4 = \left(1 + \frac{1}{4}\right)^4 = \left(\frac{5}{4}\right)^4 \approx 2.4414$$

$$a_5 = \left(1 + \frac{1}{5}\right)^5 = \left(\frac{6}{5}\right)^5 \approx 2.4883$$

Thus, the first five terms of the sequence

$a_n = \left(1 + \dfrac{1}{n}\right)^n$ are $2, 2.25, 2.3704, 2.4414,$

$2.4883$.

### Section 11.2

### Practice Problems

**1.** $a_1 = 4$
$a_2 = 4 + 5 = 9$
$a_3 = 9 + 5 = 14$
$a_4 = 14 + 5 = 19$
$a_5 = 19 + 5 = 24$
The first five terms are 4, 9, 14, 19, 24.

**2. a.** $a_n = a_1 + (n - 1)d$
Here, $a_1 = 2$ and $d = -3$.
$a_n = 2 + (n - 1)(-3) = 2 - 3n + 3 = 5 - 3n$

**b.** $a_n = 5 - 3n$
$a_{12} = 5 - 3 \cdot 12 = 5 - 36 = -31$

**3.** Since the sequence is arithmetic, the ninth term is $a_9 = a_1 + (9 - 1)d = a_1 + 8d$.
$a_1$ is the first term of the sequence, so $a_1 = 3$. $d$ is the constant difference, so
$d = a_2 - a_1 = 9 - 3 = 6$. Thus,
$a_9 = a_1 + 8d = 3 + 8 \cdot 6 = 51$.

**4.** We need to find $a_1$ and $d$. The given facts, $a_3 = 23$ and $a_8 = 63$, lead to a system of linear equations.
$$\begin{cases} a_3 = a_1 + (3 - 1)d \\ a_8 = a_1 + (8 - 1)d \end{cases} \text{ or } \begin{cases} 23 = a_1 + 2d \\ 63 = a_1 + 7d \end{cases}$$
We solve the system by elimination. Multiply both sides of the second equation by $-1$.
$$\begin{cases} 23 = a_1 + 2d \\ -1(63) = -1(a_1 + 7d) \end{cases} \text{ or } \begin{cases} 23 = a_1 + 2d \\ \underline{-63 = -a_1 - 7d} \\ \phantom{-63 =} -40 = -5d \\ \phantom{-63 == } 8 = d \end{cases}$$
To find $a_1$, let $d = 8$ in $23 = a_1 + 2d$.
$23 = a_1 + 2(8)$
$23 = a_1 + 16$
$7 = a_1$
Thus, $a_1 = 7$ and $d = 8$, so
$a_n = 7 + (n - 1)(8) = 7 + 8n - 8 = -1 + 8n$ and
$a_6 = -1 + 8 \cdot 6 = 47$.

**5.** The first term, $a_1$, is 57,000, and $d$ is 2200.
$$a_n = 57{,}000 + (n-1)(2200)$$
$$= 54{,}800 + 2200n$$
$$a_3 = 54{,}800 + 2200 \cdot 3 = 61{,}400$$
The salary for the third year is $61,400.

**6.** $a_1 = 8$
$$a_2 = 8(-3) = -24$$
$$a_3 = -24(-3) = 72$$
$$a_4 = 72(-3) = -216$$
The first four terms are 8, −24, 72, and −216.

**7.** $a_n = a_1 r^{n-1}$

Here, $a_1 = 64$ and $r = \dfrac{1}{4}$.

Evaluate $a_n$ for $n = 7$.
$$a_7 = 64\left(\frac{1}{4}\right)^{7-1}$$
$$= 64\left(\frac{1}{4}\right)^{6}$$
$$= 64\left(\frac{1}{4096}\right)$$
$$= \frac{1}{64}$$

**8.** Since the sequence is geometric and $a_1 = -3$, the seventh term must be $a_1 r^{7-1}$, or $-3r^6$. $r$ is the common ratio of terms, so $r$ must be $\dfrac{6}{-3}$, or −2.
$$a_7 = -3r^6$$
$$a_7 = -3(-2)^6 = -192$$

**9.** Notice that $\dfrac{27}{4} \div \dfrac{9}{2} = \dfrac{3}{2}$, so $r = \dfrac{3}{2}$.
$$a_2 = a_1\left(\frac{3}{2}\right)^{2-1}$$
$$\frac{9}{2} = a_1\left(\frac{3}{2}\right)^1, \quad \text{or} \quad a_1 = 3$$

The first term is 3, and the common ration is $\dfrac{3}{2}$.

**10.** Since the culture is reduced by one-half each day, the population sizes are modeled by a geometric sequence. Here, $a_1 = 4800$ and $r = \dfrac{1}{2}$.
$$a_n = a_1 r^{n-1} = 4800\left(\frac{1}{2}\right)^{n-1}$$
$$a_7 = 4800\left(\frac{1}{2}\right)^{7-1} = 75$$

The bacterial culture should measure 75 units at the beginning of day 7.

**Vocabulary and Readiness Check**

**1.** A <u>geometric</u> sequence is one in which each term (after the first) is obtained by multiplying the preceding term by a constant $r$. The constant $r$ is called the common <u>ratio</u>.

**2.** An <u>arithmetic</u> sequence is one in which each term (after the first) differs from the preceding term by a constant amount $d$. The constant $d$ is called the common <u>difference</u>.

**3.** The general term of an arithmetic sequence is $a_n = a_1 + (n-1)d$ where $a_1$ is the <u>first</u> term and $d$ is the common <u>difference</u>.

**4.** The general term of a geometric sequence is $a_n = a_1 r^{n-1}$ where $a_1$ is the <u>first</u> term and $r$ is the common <u>ratio</u>.

**Exercise Set 11.2**

**1.** $a_n = a_1 + (n-1)d$
$a_1 = 4; \; d = 2$
$a_1 = 4$
$a_2 = 4 + (2-1)2 = 6$
$a_3 = 4 + (3-1)2 = 8$
$a_4 = 4 + (4-1)2 = 10$
$a_5 = 4 + (5-1)2 = 12$
The first five terms are 4, 6, 8, 10, 12.

**3.** $a_n = a_1 + (n-1)d$
$a_1 = 6, \; d = -2$
$a_1 = 6$
$a_2 = 6 + (2-1)(-2) = 4$
$a_3 = 6 + (3-1)(-2) = 2$
$a_4 = 6 + (4-1)(-2) = 0$
$a_5 = 6 + (5-1)(-2) = -2$
The first five terms are 6, 4, 2, 0, −2.

**5.** $a_n = a_1 r^{n-1}$

$a_1 = 1, r = 3$

$a_1 = 1(3)^{1-1} = 1$

$a_2 = 1(3)^{2-1} = 3$

$a_3 = 1(3)^{3-1} = 9$

$a_4 = 1(3)^{4-1} = 27$

$a_5 = 1(3)^{5-1} = 81$

The first five terms are 1, 3, 9, 27, 81.

**7.** $a_n = a_1 r^{n-1}$

$a_1 = 48, r = \dfrac{1}{2}$

$a_1 = 48\left(\dfrac{1}{2}\right)^{1-1} = 48$

$a_2 = 48\left(\dfrac{1}{2}\right)^{2-1} = 24$

$a_3 = 48\left(\dfrac{1}{2}\right)^{3-1} = 12$

$a_4 = 48\left(\dfrac{1}{2}\right)^{4-1} = 6$

$a_5 = 48\left(\dfrac{1}{2}\right)^{5-1} = 3$

The first five terms are 48, 24, 12, 6, 3.

**9.** $a_n = a_1 + (n-1)d$

$a_1 = 12, d = 3$

$a_n = 12 + (n-1)3$

$a_8 = 12 + 7(3) = 12 + 21 = 33$

**11.** $a_n = a_1 r^{n-1}$

$a_1 = 7, d = -5$

$a_n = a_1 r^{n-1}$

$a_4 = 7(-5)^3 = 7(-125) = -875$

**13.** $a_n = a_1 + (n-1)d$

$a_1 = -4, d = -4$

$a_n = -4 + (n-1)(-4)$

$a_{15} = -4 + 14(-4) = -4 - 56 = -60$

**15.** 0, 12, 24

$a_1 = 0$ and $d = 12$

$a_n = 0 + (n-1)12$

$a_9 = 8(12) = 96$

**17.** 20, 18, 16

$a_1 = 20$ and $d = -2$

$a_n = 20 + (n-1)(-2)$

$a_{25} = 20 + 24(-2) = 20 - 48 = -28$

**19.** 2, −10, 50

$a_1 = 2$ and $r = -5$

$a_n = 2(-5)^{n-1}$

$a_5 = 2(-5)^4 = 2(625) = 1250$

**21.** $a_4 = 19, a_{15} = 52$

$\begin{cases} a_4 = a_1 + (4-1)d \\ a_{15} = a_1 + (15-1)d \end{cases}$ or

$\begin{cases} 19 = a_1 + 3d \\ 52 = a_1 + 14d \end{cases}$

$\begin{cases} -19 = -a_1 - 3d \\ 52 = a_1 + 14d \end{cases}$

Adding yields $33 = 11d$ or $d = 3$. Then
$a_1 = 19 - 3(3) = 10$.

$a_n = 10 + (n-1)3$

$\quad = 10 + 3n - 3$

$\quad = 7 + 3n$

and $a_8 = 7 + 3(8)$

$\qquad = 7 + 24$

$\qquad = 31$

**23.** $a_2 = -1, a_4 = 5$

$\begin{cases} a_2 = a_1 + (2-1)d \\ a_4 = a_1 + (4-1)d \end{cases}$ or

$\begin{cases} -1 = a_1 + d \\ 5 = a_1 + 3d \end{cases}$

$\begin{cases} 1 = -a_1 - d \\ 5 = a_1 + 3d \end{cases}$

Adding yields $6 = 2d$ or $d = 3$. Then
$a_1 = -1 - 3 = -4$.

$a_n = -4 + (n-1)3$

$\quad = -4 + 3n - 3$

$\quad = -7 + 3n$

and $a_9 = -7 + 3(9)$

$\qquad = -7 + 27$

$\qquad = 20$

**25.** $a_2 = -\dfrac{4}{3}$ and $a_3 = \dfrac{8}{3}$

Notice that $\dfrac{8}{3} \div \dfrac{-4}{3} = \dfrac{8}{3} \cdot -\dfrac{3}{4} = -2$, so $r = -2$.

Then

$a_2 = a_1(-2)^{2-1}$

$-\dfrac{4}{3} = a_1(-2)$

$\dfrac{2}{3} = a_1$

The first term is $\dfrac{2}{3}$ and the common ratio is $-2$.

**27.** Answers may vary

**29.** $2, 4, 6$ is an arithmetic sequence.

$a_1 = 2$ and $d = 2$

**31.** $5, 10, 20$ is a geometric sequence.

$a_1 = 5$ and $r = 2$

**33.** $\dfrac{1}{2}, \dfrac{1}{10}, \dfrac{1}{50}$ is a geometric sequence.

$a_1 = \dfrac{1}{2}$ and $r = \dfrac{1}{5}$

**35.** $x, 5x, 25x$ is a geometric sequence.

$a_1 = x$ and $r = 5$

**37.** $p, p+4, p+8$ is an arithmetic sequence.

$a_1 = p$ and $d = 4$

**39.** $a_1 = 14$ and $d = \dfrac{1}{4}$

$a_n = 14 + (n-1)\dfrac{1}{4}$

$a_{21} = 14 + 20\left(\dfrac{1}{4}\right) = 14 + 5 = 19$

**41.** $a_1 = 3$ and $r = -\dfrac{2}{3}$

$a_n = 3\left(-\dfrac{2}{3}\right)^{n-1}$

$a_4 = 3\left(-\dfrac{2}{3}\right)^3 = 3\left(-\dfrac{8}{27}\right) = -\dfrac{8}{9}$

**43.** $\dfrac{3}{2}, 2, \dfrac{5}{2}, ...$

$a_1 = \dfrac{3}{2}$ and $d = \dfrac{1}{2}$

$a_n = \dfrac{3}{2} + (n-1)\dfrac{1}{2}$

$a_{15} = \dfrac{3}{2} + 14\left(\dfrac{1}{2}\right) = \dfrac{17}{2}$

**45.** $24, 8, \dfrac{8}{3}, ...$

$a_1 = 24$ and $r = \dfrac{1}{3}$

$a_n = 24\left(\dfrac{1}{3}\right)^{n-1}$

$a_6 = 24\left(\dfrac{1}{3}\right)^5 = 24\left(\dfrac{1}{243}\right) = \dfrac{8}{81}$

**47.** $a_3 = 2$, $a_{17} = -40$

$\begin{cases} a_3 = a_1 + (3-1)d \\ a_{17} = a_1 + (17-1)d \end{cases}$ or

$\begin{cases} 2 = a_1 + 2d \\ -40 = a_1 + 16d \end{cases}$

$\begin{cases} -2 = -a_1 - 2d \\ -40 = a_1 + 16d \end{cases}$

Adding yields $-42 = 14d$ or $d = -3$. Then

$a_1 = 2 - 2(-3) = 8$.

$a_n = 8 + (n-1)(-3) = 8 - 3n + 3 = 11 - 3n$

and

$a_{10} = 11 - 3(10) = 11 - 30 = -19$

**49.** $54, 58, 62$

$a_1 = 54$ and $d = 4$

$a_n = 54 + (n-1)4$

$a_{20} = 54 + 19(4) = 54 + 76 = 130$

The general term of the sequence is

$a_n = 4n + 50$. There are 130 seats in the

twentieth row.

**51.** $a_1 = 6$ and $r = 3$

$a_n = 6(3)^{n-1} = 2 \cdot 3 \cdot (3)^{n-1} = 2(3)^n$

The general term of the sequence is

$a_n = 6(3)^{n-1}$ or $a_n = 2(3)^n$.

**53.** $a_1 = 486$ and $r = \dfrac{1}{3}$

Initial Height $= a_1 = 486\left(\dfrac{1}{3}\right)^{1-1} = 486$

Rebound 1 $= a_2 = 486\left(\dfrac{1}{3}\right)^{2-1} = 162$

Rebound 2 $= a_3 = 486\left(\dfrac{1}{3}\right)^{3-1} = 54$

Rebound 3 $= a_4 = 486\left(\dfrac{1}{3}\right)^{4-1} = 18$

Rebound 4 $= a_5 = 486\left(\dfrac{1}{3}\right)^{5-1} = 6$

The first five terms of the sequence are 486, 162, 54, 18, 6.

The general term is $a_n = 486\left(\dfrac{1}{3}\right)^{n-1}$ or

$a_n = \dfrac{486}{3^{n-1}}$. Since $a_6 = 2$ and $a_7 = \dfrac{2}{3}$, $a_7$ is the

first term less than 1. Since $a_7$ corresponds to the 6th bounce, it takes 6 bounces for the ball to rebound less than 1 foot.

**55.** $a_1 = 4000$ and $d = 125$

$a_n = 4000 + (n-1)125$ or

$a_n = 3875 + 125n$

$a_{12} = 4000 + 11(125) = 5375$

His salary for his last month of training is $5375.

**57.** $a_1 = 400$ and $r = \dfrac{1}{2}$

12 hours $= 4(3 \text{ hours})$, so we seek the fourth term after $a_1$, namely $a_5$.

$a_n = a_1 r^{n-1}$

$a_5 = 400\left(\dfrac{1}{2}\right)^4 = \dfrac{400}{16} = 25$

25 grams of the radioactive material remain after 12 hours.

**59.** $\dfrac{1}{3(1)} + \dfrac{1}{3(2)} + \dfrac{1}{3(3)} = \dfrac{1}{3} + \dfrac{1}{6} + \dfrac{1}{9}$

$\qquad = \dfrac{6}{18} + \dfrac{3}{18} + \dfrac{2}{18}$

$\qquad = \dfrac{11}{18}$

**61.** $3^0 + 3^1 + 3^2 + 3^3 = 1 + 3 + 9 + 27 = 40$

**63.** $\dfrac{8-1}{8+1} + \dfrac{8-2}{8+2} + \dfrac{8-3}{8+3} = \dfrac{7}{9} + \dfrac{6}{10} + \dfrac{5}{11}$

$\qquad = \dfrac{770}{990} + \dfrac{594}{990} + \dfrac{450}{990}$

$\qquad = \dfrac{1814}{990}$

$\qquad = \dfrac{907}{495}$

**65.** $a_1 = \$11,782.40$

$r = 0.5$

$a_2 = (11,782.40)(0.5) = \$5891.20$

$a_3 = (5891.20)(0.5) = \$2945.60$

$a_4 = (2945.60)(0.5) = \$1472.80$

The first four terms of the sequence are $11,782.40, $5891.20, $2945.60, $1472.80.

**67.** $a_1 = 19.652$ and $d = -0.034$

$a_2 = 19.652 - 0.034 = 19.618$

$a_3 = 19.618 - 0.034 = 19.584$

$a_4 = 19.584 - 0.034 = 19.550$

**69.** Answers may vary

**Section 11.3**

**Practice Problems**

**1. a.** $\displaystyle\sum_{i=0}^{4} \dfrac{i-3}{4} = \dfrac{0-3}{4} + \dfrac{1-3}{4} + \dfrac{2-3}{4} + \dfrac{3-3}{4} + \dfrac{4-3}{4}$

$\qquad = \left(-\dfrac{3}{4}\right) + \left(-\dfrac{2}{4}\right) + \left(-\dfrac{1}{4}\right) + 0 + \dfrac{1}{4}$

$\qquad = -\dfrac{5}{4}$, or $-1\dfrac{1}{4}$

**b.** $\displaystyle\sum_{i=2}^{5} 3^i = 3^2 + 3^3 + 3^4 + 3^5$

$\qquad = 9 + 27 + 81 + 243$

$\qquad = 360$

**2. a.** Since the difference of each term and the preceding term is 5, the terms correspond to the first six terms of the arithmetic sequence $a_n = 5 + (n-1)5 = 5n$. Thus, in summation notation,

$5 + 10 + 15 + 20 + 25 + 30 = \displaystyle\sum_{i=1}^{6} 5i.$

**b.** Since each term is the product of the preceding term and $\frac{1}{5}$, these terms correspond to the first four terms of the geometric sequence $a_n = \frac{1}{5}\left(\frac{1}{5}\right)^{n-1} = \left(\frac{1}{5}\right)^n$.

In summation notation,

$$\frac{1}{5} + \frac{1}{25} + \frac{1}{125} + \frac{1}{625} = \sum_{i=1}^{4}\left(\frac{1}{5}\right)^i.$$

**3.** $S_4 = \sum_{i=1}^{4} \frac{2+3i}{i^2}$

$= \frac{2+3\cdot1}{1^2} + \frac{2+3\cdot2}{2^2} + \frac{2+3\cdot3}{3^2} + \frac{2+3\cdot4}{4^2}$

$= \frac{5}{1} + \frac{8}{4} + \frac{11}{9} + \frac{14}{16}$

$= 5 + 2 + \frac{11}{9} + \frac{7}{8}$

$= \frac{655}{72}$, or $9\frac{7}{72}$

**4.** $S_5 = \sum_{i=1}^{5} i(2i-1)$

$= 1(2\cdot1-1) + 2(2\cdot2-1) + 3(2\cdot3-1)$
$\quad + 4(2\cdot4-1) + 5(2\cdot5-1)$

$= 1 + 6 + 15 + 28 + 45$

$= 95$

There are 95 plants after 5 years.

**Vocabulary and Readiness Check**

1. A series is an <u>infinite</u> series if it is the sum of all the terms of the sequence.

2. A series is a <u>finite</u> series if it is the sum of a finite number of terms.

3. A shorthand notation for denoting a series when the general term of the sequence is known is called <u>summation</u> notation.

4. In the notation $\sum_{i=1}^{7}(5i-2)$, the $\Sigma$ is the Greek uppercase letter <u>sigma</u> and the $i$ is called the <u>index of summation</u>.

5. The sum of the first $n$ terms of a sequence is a finite series known as a <u>partial sum</u>.

**6.** For the notation in Exercise 4 above, the beginning value of $i$ is <u>1</u> and the ending value of $i$ is <u>7</u>.

**Exercise Set 11.3**

**1.** $\sum_{i=1}^{4}(i-3) = (1-3)+(2-3)+(3-3)+(4-3)$

$= -2 + (-1) + 0 + 1$

$= -2$

**3.** $\sum_{i=4}^{7}(2i+4) = [2(4)+4]+[2(5)+4]+[2(6)+4]$
$\quad\quad +[2(7)+4]$

$= 12 + 14 + 16 + 18$

$= 60$

**5.** $\sum_{i=2}^{4}(i^2-3) = (2^2-3)+(3^2-3)+(4^2-3)$

$= 1 + 6 + 13$

$= 20$

**7.** $\sum_{i=1}^{3}\left(\frac{1}{i+5}\right) = \frac{1}{1+5} + \frac{1}{2+5} + \frac{1}{3+5}$

$= \frac{1}{6} + \frac{1}{7} + \frac{1}{8}$

$= \frac{28}{168} + \frac{24}{168} + \frac{21}{168}$

$= \frac{73}{168}$

**9.** $\sum_{i=1}^{3}\frac{1}{6i} = \frac{1}{6(1)} + \frac{1}{6(2)} + \frac{1}{6(3)}$

$= \frac{1}{6} + \frac{1}{12} + \frac{1}{18}$

$= \frac{6+3+2}{36}$

$= \frac{11}{36}$

**11.** $\sum_{i=2}^{6} 3i = 3(2)+3(3)+3(4)+3(5)+3(6)$

$= 6 + 9 + 12 + 15 + 18$

$= 60$

**13.** $\displaystyle\sum_{i=3}^{5} i(i+2) = 3(3+2) + 4(4+2) + 5(5+2)$

$$= 15 + 24 + 35$$
$$= 74$$

**15.** $\displaystyle\sum_{i=1}^{5} 2^i = 2^1 + 2^2 + 2^3 + 2^4 + 2^5$

$$= 2 + 4 + 8 + 16 + 32$$
$$= 62$$

**17.** $\displaystyle\sum_{i=1}^{4} \frac{4i}{i+3} = \frac{4(1)}{1+3} + \frac{4(2)}{2+3} + \frac{4(3)}{3+3} + \frac{4(4)}{4+3}$

$$= 1 + \frac{8}{5} + 2 + \frac{16}{7}$$
$$= \frac{105}{35} + \frac{56}{35} + \frac{80}{35}$$
$$= \frac{241}{35}$$

**19.** $1 + 3 + 5 + 7 + 9$

$a_1 = 1,\ d = 2$

$a_n = 1 + (n-1)2 = 2n - 1$

$$\sum_{i=1}^{5} (2i - 1)$$

**21.** $4 + 12 + 36 + 108 = 4 + 4(3) + 4(3)^2 + 4(3)^3$

$$= \sum_{i=1}^{4} 4(3)^{i-1}$$

**23.** $12 + 9 + 6 + 3 + 0 + (-3)$

$a_1 = 12,\ d = -3$

$a_n = 12 + (n-1)(-3) = -3n + 15$

$$\sum_{i=1}^{6} (-3i + 15)$$

**25.** $12 + 4 + \dfrac{4}{3} + \dfrac{4}{9} = \dfrac{4}{3^{-1}} + \dfrac{4}{3^0} + \dfrac{4}{3} + \dfrac{4}{3^2}$

$$= \sum_{i=1}^{4} \frac{4}{3^{i-2}}$$

**27.** $1 + 4 + 9 + 16 + 25 + 36 + 49$

$= 1^2 + 2^2 + 3^2 + 4^2 + 5^2 + 6^2 + 7^2$

$$= \sum_{i=1}^{7} i^2$$

**29.** $a_n = (n+2)(n-5)$

$S_2 = \displaystyle\sum_{i=1}^{2} (i+2)(i-5)$

$$= (1+2)(1-5) + (2+2)(2-5)$$
$$= 3(-4) + 4(-3)$$
$$= -12 - 12$$
$$= -24$$

**31.** $a_n = (-1)^n$

$S_6 = \displaystyle\sum_{i=1}^{6} (-1)^i$

$$= (-1)^1 + (-1)^2 + (-1)^3 + (-1)^4 + (-1)^5$$
$$+ (-1)^6$$
$$= -1 + 1 + (-1) + 1 + (-1) + 1$$
$$= 0$$

**33.** $a_n = (n+3)(n+1)$

$S_4 = \displaystyle\sum_{i=1}^{4} (i+3)(i+1)$

$$= (1+3)(1+1) + (2+3)(2+1) + (3+3)(3+1)$$
$$+ (4+3)(4+1)$$
$$= 4(2) + 5(3) + 6(4) + 7(5)$$
$$= 8 + 15 + 24 + 35$$
$$= 82$$

**35.** $a_n = -2n$

$S_4 = \displaystyle\sum_{i=1}^{4} (-2i)$

$$= -2(1) + (-2)(2) + (-2)(3) + (-2)(4)$$
$$= -2 - 4 - 6 - 8$$
$$= -20$$

**37.** $a_n = -\dfrac{n}{3}$

$S_3 = \displaystyle\sum_{i=1}^{3} -\frac{i}{3} = -\frac{1}{3} - \frac{2}{3} - \frac{3}{3} = -2$

**39.** $1, 2, 3, \ldots, 10$

$a_n = n$

$$S_{10} = \sum_{i=1}^{10} i = 1 + 2 + 3 + \ldots + 10 = 55$$

A total of 55 trees were planted.

**41.** $a_1 = 6$ and $r = 2$

$a_n = 6 \cdot 2^{n-1}$

$a_5 = 6 \cdot 2^4 = 6 \cdot 16 = 96$

There will be 96 fungus units at the beginning of the 5th day.

**43.** The general term of the sequence is

$a_n = 50(2)^n$, where $n$ represents the number of 12-hr periods.

$a_4 = 50(2)^4 = 50(16) = 800$

There are 800 bacteria after 48 hours.

**45.** $a_n = (n+1)(n+2)$

$a_4 = (4+1)(4+2) = 5(6) = 30$

30 opossums were killed in the fourth month.

$$S_4 = \sum_{i=1}^{4} (i+1)(i+2)$$
$$= 2(3) + (3)(4) + (4)(5) + (5)(6)$$
$$= 6 + 12 + 20 + 30$$
$$= 68$$

68 opossums were killed in the four months.

**47.** $a_n = 100(0.5)^n$

$a_4 = 100(0.5)^4 = 6.25$

The decay in the fourth year is 6.25 pounds.

$$S_4 = \sum_{i=1}^{4} 100(0.5)^i$$
$$= 100(0.5)^1 + 100(0.5)^2 + 100(0.5)^3$$
$$\quad + 100(0.5)^4$$
$$= 100(0.5) + 100(0.25) + 100(0.125)$$
$$\quad + 100(0.0625)$$
$$= 50 + 25 + 12.5 + 6.25$$
$$= 93.75$$

The decay over the four years is 93.75 pounds.

**49.** $a_1 = 40$ and $r = \dfrac{4}{5}$

$a_5 = 40\left(\dfrac{4}{5}\right)^4 = 16.384$

The length of the fifth swing is approximately 16.4 inches.

$$S_5 = \sum_{i=1}^{5} 40\left(\dfrac{4}{5}\right)^{i-1}$$

$$= 40\left(\dfrac{4}{5}\right)^0 + 40\left(\dfrac{4}{5}\right)^1 + 40\left(\dfrac{4}{5}\right)^2 + 40\left(\dfrac{4}{5}\right)^3$$
$$\quad + 40\left(\dfrac{4}{5}\right)^4$$

$$= 40 + 32 + 25.6 + 20.48 + 16.384$$
$$= 134.464$$

The pendulum swings about 134.5 inches in five swings.

**51.** $\dfrac{5}{1-\frac{1}{2}} = \dfrac{5}{\frac{1}{2}} = 5 \cdot \dfrac{2}{1} = 10$

**53.** $\dfrac{\frac{1}{3}}{1-\frac{1}{10}} = \dfrac{\frac{1}{3}}{\frac{9}{10}} = \dfrac{1}{3} \cdot \dfrac{10}{9} = \dfrac{10}{27}$

**55.** $\dfrac{3(1-2^4)}{1-2} = \dfrac{3(1-16)}{-1} = \dfrac{3(-15)}{-1} = \dfrac{-45}{-1} = 45$

**57.** $\dfrac{10}{2}(3+15) = \dfrac{10}{2}(18) = \dfrac{180}{2} = 90$

**59. a.** $\displaystyle\sum_{i=1}^{7} (i + i^2)$

$$= (1+1^2) + (2+2^2) + (3+3^2) + (4+4^2)$$
$$\quad + (5+5^2) + (6+6^2) + (7+7^2)$$
$$= 2 + 6 + 12 + 20 + 30 + 42 + 56$$

**b.** $\displaystyle\sum_{i=1}^{7} i + \sum_{i=1}^{7} i^2$

$$= (1+2+3+4+5+6+7)$$
$$\quad + (1+4+9+16+25+36+49)$$

**c.** Answers may vary

**d.** True; answers may vary.

**Integrated Review**

1. $a_n = n - 3$
$a_1 = 1 - 3 = -2$
$a_2 = 2 - 3 = -1$
$a_3 = 3 - 3 = 0$
$a_4 = 4 - 3 = 1$
$a_5 = 5 - 3 = 2$
Therefore, the first five terms are $-2, -1, 0, 1, 2$.

2. $a_n = \dfrac{7}{1+n}$
$a_1 = \dfrac{7}{1+1} = \dfrac{7}{2}$
$a_2 = \dfrac{7}{1+2} = \dfrac{7}{3}$
$a_3 = \dfrac{7}{1+3} = \dfrac{7}{4}$
$a_4 = \dfrac{7}{1+4} = \dfrac{7}{5}$
$a_5 = \dfrac{7}{1+5} = \dfrac{7}{6}$
The first five terms are $\dfrac{7}{2}, \dfrac{7}{3}, \dfrac{7}{4}, \dfrac{7}{5}$, and $\dfrac{7}{6}$.

3. $a_n = 3^{n-1}$
$a_1 = 3^{1-1} = 3^0 = 1$
$a_2 = 3^{2-1} = 3^1 = 3$
$a_3 = 3^{3-1} = 3^2 = 9$
$a_4 = 3^{4-1} = 3^3 = 27$
$a_5 = 3^{5-1} = 3^4 = 81$
The first five terms are $1, 3, 9, 27$, and $81$.

4. $a_n = n^2 - 5$
$a_1 = 1^2 - 5 = 1 - 5 = -4$
$a_2 = 2^2 - 5 = 4 - 5 = -1$
$a_3 = 3^2 - 5 = 9 - 5 = 4$
$a_4 = 4^2 - 5 = 16 - 5 = 11$
$a_5 = 5^2 - 5 = 25 - 5 = 20$
The first five terms are $-4, -1, 4, 11$, and $20$.

5. $(-2)^n$; $a_6$
$a_6 = (-2)^6 = 64$

6. $-n^2 + 2$; $a_4$
$a_4 = -(4)^2 + 2 = -16 + 2 = -14$

7. $\dfrac{(-1)^n}{n}$; $a_{40}$
$a_{40} = \dfrac{(-1)^{40}}{40} = \dfrac{1}{40}$

8. $\dfrac{(-1)^n}{2n}$; $a_{41}$
$a_{41} = \dfrac{(-1)^{41}}{2(41)} = \dfrac{-1}{82} = -\dfrac{1}{82}$

9. $a_1 = 7$; $d = -3$
$a_1 = 7$
$a_2 = 7 - 3 = 4$
$a_3 = 4 - 3 = 1$
$a_4 = 1 - 3 = -2$
$a_5 = -2 - 3 = -5$
The first five terms are $7, 4, 1, -2, -5$.

10. $a_1 = -3$; $r = 5$
$a_1 = -3$
$a_2 = -3(5) = -15$
$a_3 = -15(5) = -75$
$a_4 = -75(5) = -375$
$a_5 = -375(5) = -1875$
The first five terms are $-3, -15, -75, -375,$
$-1875$.

11. $a_1 = 45$; $r = \dfrac{1}{3}$
$a_1 = 45$
$a_2 = 45\left(\dfrac{1}{3}\right) = 15$
$a_3 = 15\left(\dfrac{1}{3}\right) = 5$
$a_4 = 5\left(\dfrac{1}{3}\right) = \dfrac{5}{3}$
$a_5 = \dfrac{5}{3}\left(\dfrac{1}{3}\right) = \dfrac{5}{9}$
The first five terms are $45, 15, 5, \dfrac{5}{3}, \dfrac{5}{9}$.

**12.** $a_1 = -12; \; d = 10$

$a_1 = -12$

$a_2 = -12 + 10 = -2$

$a_3 = -2 + 10 = 8$

$a_4 = 8 + 10 = 18$

$a_5 = 18 + 10 = 28$

The first five terms are $-12, -2, 8, 18, 28$.

**13.** $a_1 = 20; \; d = 9$

$a_n = a_1 + (n-1)d$

$a_{10} = 20 + (10-1)9$

$\quad = 20 + 81$

$\quad = 101$

**14.** $a_1 = 64; \; r = \dfrac{3}{4}$

$a_n = a_1 r^{n-1}$

$a_6 = 64\left(\dfrac{3}{4}\right)^{6-1}$

$\quad = 64\left(\dfrac{3}{4}\right)^5$

$\quad = 64\left(\dfrac{243}{1024}\right)$

$\quad = \dfrac{243}{16}$

**15.** $a_1 = 6; \; r = \dfrac{-12}{6} = -2$

$a_n = a_1 r^{n-1}$

$a_7 = 6(-2)^{7-1} = 6(-2)^6 = 6(64) = 384$

**16.** $a_1 = -100; \; d = -85 - (-100) = 15$

$a_n = a_1 + (n-1)d$

$a_{20} = -100 + (20-1)(15)$

$\quad = -100 + (19)(15)$

$\quad = -100 + 285$

$\quad = 185$

**17.** $a_4 = -5, \; a_{10} = -35$

$a_n = a_1 + (n-1)d$

$\begin{cases} a_4 = a_1 + (4-1)d \\ a_{10} = a_1 + (10-1)d \end{cases}$

$\begin{cases} -5 = a_1 + 3d \\ -35 = a_1 + 9d \end{cases}$

Multiply eq. 2 by $-1$, then add the equations.

$\begin{cases} \qquad\quad -5 = a_1 + 3d \\ (-1)(-35) = -1(a_1 + 9d) \end{cases}$

$\begin{cases} -5 = a_1 + 3d \\ 35 = -a_1 - 9d \end{cases}$

$30 = -6d$

$-5 = d$

To find $a_1$, let $d = -5$ in

$-5 = a_1 + 3d$

$-5 = a_1 + 3(-5)$

$10 = a_1$

Thus, $a_1 = 10$ and $d = -5$, so

$a_n = 10 + (n-1)(-5) = -5n + 15$

$a_5 = -5(5) + 15 = -10$

**18.** $a_4 = 1; \; a_7 = \dfrac{1}{125}$

$a_n = a_1 r^{n-1}$

$a_4 = a_1 r^{4-1}$ so $1 = a_1 r^3$

$a_7 = a_1 r^{71}$ so $\dfrac{1}{125} = a_1 r^6$

Since $a_1 r^6 = (a_1 r^3) r^3$, $\dfrac{1}{125} = 1 \cdot r^3$ and $r = \dfrac{1}{5}$.

$a_5 = a_4 \cdot r$ so $a_5 = 1 \cdot \dfrac{1}{5} = \dfrac{1}{5}$

**19.** $\displaystyle\sum_{i=1}^{4} 5i = 5(1) + 5(2) + 5(3) + 5(4)$

$\quad = 5 + 10 + 15 + 20$

$\quad = 50$

**20.** $\displaystyle\sum_{i=1}^{7} (3i + 2)$

$= (3(1) + 2) + (3(2) + 2) + (3(3) + 2)$

$\quad + (3(4) + 2) + (3(5) + 2) + (3(6) + 2)$

$\quad + (3(7) + 2)$

$= 5 + 8 + 11 + 14 + 17 + 20 + 23$

$= 98$

**21.** $\sum_{i=3}^{7} 2^{i-4}$

$= 2^{3-4} + 2^{4-4} + 2^{5-4} + 2^{6-4} + 2^{7-4}$

$= 2^{-1} + 2^{0} + 2^{1} + 2^{2} + 2^{3}$

$= \dfrac{1}{2} + 1 + 2 + 4 + 8$

$= 15\dfrac{1}{2}$

$= \dfrac{31}{2}$

**22.** $\sum_{i=2}^{5} \dfrac{i}{i+1} = \dfrac{2}{2+1} + \dfrac{3}{3+1} + \dfrac{4}{4+1} + \dfrac{5}{5+1}$

$= \dfrac{2}{3} + \dfrac{3}{4} + \dfrac{4}{5} + \dfrac{5}{6}$

$= \dfrac{61}{20}$

**23.** $S_3 = \sum_{i=1}^{3} i(i-4)$

$= 1(1-4) + 2(2-4) + 3(3-4)$

$= -3 - 4 - 3$

$= -10$

**24.** $S_{10} = \sum_{i=1}^{10} (-1)^i (i+1)$

$= (-1)^1 (1+1) + (-1)^2 (2+1)$
$\quad + (-1)^3 (3+1) + (-1)^4 (4+1)$
$\quad + (-1)^5 (5+1) + (-1)^6 (6+1)$
$\quad + (-1)^7 (7+1) + (-1)^8 (8+1)$
$\quad + (-1)^9 (9+1) + (-1)^{10} (10+1)$
$= -2 + 3 - 4 + 5 - 6 + 7 - 8 + 9 - 10 + 11$
$= 5$

## Section 11.4

### Practice Problems

**1.** 2, 9, 16, 23, 30
Use the formula for $S_n$ of an arithmetic sequence, replacing $n$ with 5, $a_1$ with 2, and $a_n$ with 30.

$S_n = \dfrac{n}{2}(a_1 + a_n)$

$S_5 = \dfrac{5}{2}(2 + 30) = \dfrac{5}{2}(32) = 80$

**2.** Because 1, 2, 3, ..., 50 is an arithmetic sequence, use the formula for $S_n$ with $n = 50$, $a_1 = 1$, and $a_n = 50$.

$S_n = \dfrac{n}{2}(a_1 + a_n)$

$S_5 = \dfrac{50}{2}(1 + 50) = 25(51) = 1275$

**3.** The list 6, 7, ..., 15 is the first 10 terms of an arithmetic sequence. Use the formula for $S_n$ with $n = 10$, $a_1 = 6$, and $a_n = 15$.

$S_{10} = \dfrac{10}{2}(6 + 15) = 5(21) = 105$

There are a total of 105 blocks of ice.

**4.** 32, 8, 2, $\dfrac{1}{2}$, $\dfrac{1}{8}$

Use the formula for the partial sum $S_n$ of the terms of a geometric sequence. Here, $n = 5$, the first term $a_1 = 32$, and the common ratio $r = \dfrac{1}{4}$.

$S_n = \dfrac{a_1(1 - r^n)}{1 - r}$

$S_5 = \dfrac{32\left[1 - \left(\frac{1}{4}\right)^5\right]}{1 - \frac{1}{4}}$

$= \dfrac{32\left(1 - \frac{1}{1024}\right)}{\frac{3}{4}}$

$= \dfrac{32 - \frac{1}{32}}{\frac{3}{4}}$

$= \dfrac{\frac{1023}{32}}{\frac{3}{4}}$

$= \dfrac{1023}{32} \cdot \dfrac{4}{3}$

$= \dfrac{341}{8}$

$= 42\dfrac{5}{8}$

**5.** The donations are modeled by the first seven terms of a geometric sequence. Evaluate $S_n$ when $n = 7$, $a_1 = 250{,}000$, and $r = 0.8$.

$S_7 = \dfrac{250{,}000[1 - (0.8)^7]}{1 - 0.8} = 987{,}856$

The total amount donated during the seven years is \$987,856.

**6.** $7, \dfrac{7}{4}, \dfrac{7}{16}, \dfrac{7}{64}, \ldots$

For this geometric sequence $r = \dfrac{1}{4}$. Since $|r| < 1$, use the formula for $S_\infty$ of a geometric sequence with $a_1 = 7$ and $r = \dfrac{1}{4}$.

$$S_\infty = \dfrac{a_1}{1-r} = \dfrac{7}{1-\dfrac{1}{4}} = \dfrac{7}{\dfrac{3}{4}} = \dfrac{28}{3} = 9\dfrac{1}{3}$$

**7.** We must find the sum of the terms of an infinite geometric sequence whose first term, $a_1$, is 36 and whose common ratio, $r$, is 0.96. Since $|r| < 1$, we may use the formula for $S_\infty$.

$$S_\infty = \dfrac{a_1}{1-r} = \dfrac{36}{1-0.96} = \dfrac{36}{0.04} = 900$$

The ball travels a total distance of 900 inches before it comes to a rest.

**Vocabulary and Readiness Check**

**1.** Each term after the first is 5 more than the preceding term; the sequence is <u>arithmetic</u>.

**2.** Each term after the first is 2 times the preceding term; the sequence is <u>geometric</u>.

**3.** Each term after the first is $-3$ times the preceding term; the sequence is <u>geometric</u>.

**4.** Each term after the first is 2 more than the preceding term; the sequence is <u>arithmetic</u>.

**5.** Each term after the first is 7 more than the preceding term; the sequence is <u>arithmetic</u>.

**6.** Each term after the first is $-1$ times the preceding term; the sequence is <u>geometric</u>.

**Exercise Set 11.4**

**1.** $1, 3, 5, 7, \ldots$

$d = 2;\ a_6 = 1 + (6-1)(2) = 11$

$$S_6 = \dfrac{6}{2}(1+11) = 3(12) = 36$$

**3.** $4, 12, 36, \ldots$

$a_1 = 4, r = 3, n = 5$

$$S_5 = \dfrac{4(1-3^5)}{1-3} = 484$$

**5.** $3, 6, 9, \ldots$

$d = 3;\ a_6 = 3 + (6-1)(3) = 18$

$$S_6 = \dfrac{6}{2}(3+18) = 3(21) = 63$$

**7.** $2, \dfrac{2}{5}, \dfrac{2}{25}, \ldots$

$a_1 = 2, r = \dfrac{1}{5}, n = 4$

$$S_4 = \dfrac{2\left[1-\left(\tfrac{1}{5}\right)^4\right]}{1-\tfrac{1}{5}} = 2.496$$

**9.** $1, 2, 3, \ldots, 10$

The first term is 1 and the tenth term is 10.

$$S_{10} = \dfrac{10}{2}(1+10) = 5(11) = 55$$

**11.** $1, 2, 3, 7$

The first term is 1 and the fourth term is 7.

$$S_4 = \dfrac{4}{2}(1+7) = 2(8) = 16$$

**13.** $12, 6, 3, \ldots$

$a_1 = 12,\ r = \dfrac{1}{2}$

$$S_\infty = \dfrac{12}{1-\tfrac{1}{2}} = \dfrac{12}{\tfrac{1}{2}} = 12 \cdot \dfrac{2}{1} = 24$$

**15.** $\dfrac{1}{10}, \dfrac{1}{100}, \dfrac{1}{1000}, \ldots$

$a_1 = \dfrac{1}{10},\ r = \dfrac{1}{10}$

$$S_\infty = \dfrac{\tfrac{1}{10}}{1-\tfrac{1}{10}} = \dfrac{\tfrac{1}{10}}{\tfrac{9}{10}} = \dfrac{1}{10} \cdot \dfrac{10}{9} = \dfrac{1}{9}$$

**17.** $-10, -5, -\dfrac{5}{2}, \ldots$

$a_1 = -10,\ r = \dfrac{1}{2}$

$$S_\infty = \dfrac{-10}{1-\tfrac{1}{2}} = \dfrac{-10}{\tfrac{1}{2}} = -10 \cdot \dfrac{2}{1} = -20$$

**19.** $2, -\dfrac{1}{4}, \dfrac{1}{32}, ...$

$a_1 = 2, \quad r = -\dfrac{1}{8}$

$S_\infty = \dfrac{2}{1 - \left(-\frac{1}{8}\right)} = \dfrac{2}{\frac{9}{8}} = 2 \cdot \dfrac{8}{9} = \dfrac{16}{9}$

**21.** $\dfrac{2}{3}, -\dfrac{1}{3}, \dfrac{1}{6}, ...$

$a_1 = \dfrac{2}{3}, \quad r = -\dfrac{1}{2}$

$S_\infty = \dfrac{\frac{2}{3}}{1 - \left(-\frac{1}{2}\right)} = \dfrac{\frac{2}{3}}{\frac{3}{2}} = \dfrac{2}{3} \cdot \dfrac{2}{3} = \dfrac{4}{9}$

**23.** $-4, 1, 6, ..., 41$

The first term is $-4$ and the tenth term is $41$.

$S_{10} = \dfrac{10}{2}(-4 + 41) = 5(37) = 185$

**25.** $3, \dfrac{3}{2}, \dfrac{3}{4}, ...$

$a_1 = 3, r = \dfrac{1}{2}, n = 7$

$S_7 = \dfrac{3\left[1 - \left(\frac{1}{2}\right)^7\right]}{1 - \frac{1}{2}} = \dfrac{381}{64}$

**27.** $-12, 6, -3, ...$

$a_1 = -12, r = -\dfrac{1}{2}, n = 5$

$S_5 = \dfrac{-12\left[1 - \left(-\frac{1}{2}\right)^5\right]}{1 - \left(-\frac{1}{2}\right)} = -\dfrac{33}{4} = -8.25$

**29.** $\dfrac{1}{2}, \dfrac{1}{4}, 0, ..., -\dfrac{17}{4}$

The first term is $\dfrac{1}{2}$ and the twentieth term is

$-\dfrac{17}{4}$.

$S_{20} = \dfrac{20}{2}\left(\dfrac{1}{2} - \dfrac{17}{4}\right) = 10\left(\dfrac{-15}{4}\right) = -\dfrac{75}{2}$

**31.** $a_1 = 8, r = -\dfrac{2}{3}, n = 3$

$S_3 = \dfrac{8\left[1 - \left(-\frac{2}{3}\right)^3\right]}{1 - \left(-\frac{2}{3}\right)} = \dfrac{56}{9}$

**33.** The first five terms are 4000, 3950, 3900, 3850, 3800.

$a_1 = 4000, d = -50, n = 12$

$a_{12} = 4000 + 11(-50) = 3450$

3450 cars will be sold in month 12.

$S_{12} = \dfrac{12}{2}(4000 + 3450) = 44,700$

44,700 cars will be sold in the first year.

**35.** Firm $A$:
The first term is 22,000 and the tenth term is 31,000.

$S_{10} = \dfrac{10}{2}(22,000 + 31,000)$
$\quad\quad = \$265,000$

Firm $B$:
The first term is 20,000 and the tenth term is 30,800.

$S_{10} = \dfrac{10}{2}(20,000 + 30,800)$
$\quad\quad = \$254,000$

Thus, Firm $A$ is making the more profitable offer.

**37.** $a_1 = 30,000, r = 1.10, n = 4$

$a_4 = 30,000(1.10)^{4-1} = 39,930$
She made \$39,930 during her fourth year of business.

$S_4 = \dfrac{30,000(1 - 1.10^4)}{1 - 1.10} = 139,230$
She made \$139,230 during the first four years of business.

**39.** $a_1 = 30, r = 0.9, n = 5$

$a_5 = 30(0.9)^{5-1} = 19.683$
Approximately 20 minutes to assemble the first computer.

$S_5 = \dfrac{30(1 - 0.9^5)}{1 - 0.9} = 122.853$
Approximately 123 minutes to assemble the first 5 computers.

**41.** $a_1 = 20, r = \dfrac{4}{5}$

$$S_\infty = \dfrac{20}{1 - \dfrac{4}{5}} = 100$$

We double the number (to account for the flight up as well as down) and subtract 20 (since the first bounce was preceded by only a downward flight). Thus, the ball travels $2(100) - 20 = 180$ feet.

**43.** Player $A$:
The first term is 1 and the ninth term is 9.

$$S_9 = \dfrac{9}{2}(1+9) = 45 \text{ points}$$

Player $B$:
The first term is 10 and the sixth term is 15.

$$S_6 = \dfrac{6}{2}(10+15) = 75 \text{ points}$$

**45.** The first term is 200 and the twentieth is
$200 - 19(5) = 105$.

$$S_{20} = \dfrac{20}{2}(200+105) = 3050$$

Thus, $3050 rent is paid for 20 days during the holiday rush.

**47.** $a_1 = 0.01, r = 2, n = 30$

$$S_3 = \dfrac{0.01\left[1 - 2^{30}\right]}{1 - 2} = 10,737,418.23$$

He would pay $10,737,418.23 in room and board for the 30 days.

**49.** $6 \cdot 5 \cdot 4 \cdot 3 \cdot 2 \cdot 1 = 720$

**51.** $\dfrac{3 \cdot 2 \cdot 1}{2 \cdot 1} = \dfrac{3 \cdot \cancel{2} \cdot \cancel{1}}{\cancel{2} \cdot \cancel{1}} = 3$

**53.** $(x+5)^2 = x^2 + 2 \cdot x \cdot 5 + 5^2 = x^2 + 10x + 25$

**55.** $(2x-1)^3 = (2x-1)^2(2x-1)$
$$= (4x^2 - 4x + 1)(2x-1)$$
$$= 8x^3 - 4x^2 + 2x - 8x^2 + 4x - 1$$
$$= 8x^3 - 12x^2 + 6x - 1$$

**57.** $0.\overline{888} = 0.8 + 0.08 + 0.008 + \cdots$
$$= \dfrac{8}{10} + \dfrac{8}{100} + \dfrac{8}{1000} + \cdots$$

This is a geometric series with $a_1 = \dfrac{8}{10}, r = \dfrac{1}{10}$.

$$S_\infty = \dfrac{\dfrac{8}{10}}{1 - \dfrac{1}{10}} = \dfrac{\dfrac{8}{10}}{\dfrac{9}{10}} = \dfrac{8}{10} \cdot \dfrac{10}{9} = \dfrac{8}{9}$$

**59.** Answers may vary.

## Section 11.5

**Practice Problems**

**1.** $(p+r)^7$

The $n = 7$ row of Pascal's triangle is

1    7    21    35    35    21    7    1

Using the $n = 7$ row of Pascal's triangle as the coefficients, $(p + r)^7$ can be expanded as

$p^7 + 7p^6r + 21p^5r^2 + 35p^4r^3 + 35p^3r^4 + 21p^2r^5 + 7pr^6 + r^7$

**2. a.**  $\dfrac{6!}{7!} = \dfrac{6 \cdot 5 \cdot 4 \cdot 3 \cdot 2 \cdot 1}{7 \cdot 6 \cdot 5 \cdot 4 \cdot 3 \cdot 2 \cdot 1} = \dfrac{1}{7}$

**b.**  $\begin{aligned} \dfrac{8!}{4!2!} &= \dfrac{8 \cdot 7 \cdot 6 \cdot 5 \cdot 4!}{4! \cdot 2 \cdot 1} \\ &= \dfrac{8 \cdot 7 \cdot 6 \cdot 5}{2 \cdot 1} \\ &= 4 \cdot 7 \cdot 6 \cdot 5 \\ &= 840 \end{aligned}$

**c.**  $\dfrac{5!}{4!1!} = \dfrac{5 \cdot 4 \cdot 3 \cdot 2 \cdot 1}{4 \cdot 3 \cdot 2 \cdot 1 \cdot 1} = 5$

**d.**  $\dfrac{9!}{9!0!} = \dfrac{9!}{9! \cdot 1} = 1$

**3.** $(a+b)^9$

Let $n = 9$ in the binomial formula.

$$(a+b)^9 = a^9 + \frac{9}{1!}a^8b + \frac{9 \cdot 8}{2!}a^7b^2 + \frac{9 \cdot 8 \cdot 7}{3!}a^6b^3 + \frac{9 \cdot 8 \cdot 7 \cdot 6}{4!}a^5b^4 + \frac{9 \cdot 8 \cdot 7 \cdot 6 \cdot 5}{5!}a^4b^5 + \frac{9 \cdot 8 \cdot 7 \cdot 6 \cdot 5 \cdot 4}{6!}a^3b^6$$

$$+ \frac{9 \cdot 8 \cdot 7 \cdot 6 \cdot 5 \cdot 4 \cdot 3}{7!}a^2b^7 + \frac{9 \cdot 8 \cdot 7 \cdot 6 \cdot 5 \cdot 4 \cdot 3 \cdot 2}{8!}ab^8 + b^9$$

$$= a^9 + 9a^8b + 36a^7b^2 + 84a^6b^3 + 126a^5b^4 + 126a^4b^5 + 84a^3b^6 + 36a^2b^7 + 9ab^8 + b^9$$

**4.** $(a+5b)^3$

Replace $b$ with $5b$ in the binomial formula.

$$\begin{aligned} (a+5b)^3 &= a^3 + \frac{3}{1!}a^2(5b) + \frac{3 \cdot 2}{2!}a(5b)^2 + (5b)^3 \\ &= a^3 + 3a^2(5b) + 3a(25b^2) + 125b^3 \\ &= a^3 + 15a^2b + 75ab^2 + 125b^3 \end{aligned}$$

5.  $(3x-2y)^3$

Let $a = 3x$ and $b = -2y$ in the binomial formula.

$$(3x-2y)^3 = (3x)^3 + \frac{3}{1!}(3x)^2(-2y) + \frac{3\cdot 2}{2!}(3x)(-2y)^2 + (-2y)^3$$
$$= 27x^3 + 3(9x^2)(-2y) + 3(3x)(4y^2) - 8y^3$$
$$= 27x^3 - 54x^2 y + 36xy^2 - 8y^3$$

6.  $(x-4y)^{11}$

Use the formula with $n = 11$, $a = x$, $b = -4y$, and $r + 1 = 7$. Notice that, since $r + 1 = 7$, $r = 6$.

$$\frac{n!}{r!(n-r)!}a^{n-r}b^r = \frac{11!}{6!5!}x^5(-4y)^6$$
$$= 462x^5(4096y^6)$$
$$= 1,892,352x^5 y^6$$

**Vocabulary and Readiness Check**

1.  $0! = \underline{1}$

2.  $1! = \underline{1}$

3.  $4! = 4 \cdot 3 \cdot 2 \cdot 1 = \underline{24}$

4.  $2! = 2 \cdot 1 = \underline{2}$

5.  $3!0! = 3 \cdot 2 \cdot 1 \cdot 1 = \underline{6}$

6.  $0!2! = 1 \cdot 2 \cdot 1 = \underline{2}$

**Exercise Set 11.5**

1.  $(m+n)^3 = m^3 + 3m^2 n + 3mn^2 + n^3$

3.  $(c+d)^5 = c^5 + 5c^4 d + 10c^3 d^2 + 10c^2 d^3 + 5cd^4 + d^5$

5.  $(y-x)^5 = [y+(-x)]^5$
    $$= y^5 - 5y^4 x + 10y^3 x^2 - 10y^2 x^3 + 5yx^4 - x^5$$

7.  Answers may vary

9.  $\frac{8!}{7!} = \frac{8 \cdot 7!}{7!} = 8$

11. $\frac{7!}{5!} = \frac{7 \cdot 6 \cdot 5!}{5!} = 7 \cdot 6 = 42$

13. $\frac{10!}{7!2!} = \frac{10 \cdot 9 \cdot 8 \cdot 7!}{7!2!} = \frac{10 \cdot 9 \cdot 8}{2 \cdot 1} = 360$

**15.**  $\dfrac{8!}{6!0!} = \dfrac{8\cdot 7\cdot 6!}{6!1} = 8\cdot 7 = 56$

**17.** Let $n = 7$ in the binomial theorem.

$(a+b)^7 = a^7 + \dfrac{7}{1!}a^6 b + \dfrac{7\cdot 6}{2!}a^5 b^2 + \dfrac{7\cdot 6\cdot 5}{3!}a^4 b^3 + \dfrac{7\cdot 6\cdot 5\cdot 4}{4!}a^3 b^4 + \dfrac{7\cdot 6\cdot 5\cdot 4\cdot 3}{5!}a^2 b^5 + \dfrac{7\cdot 6\cdot 5\cdot 4\cdot 3\cdot 2}{6!}ab^6 + b^7$

$\quad = a^7 + 7a^6 b + 21a^5 b^2 + 35a^4 b^3 + 35a^3 b^4 + 21a^2 b^5 + 7ab^6 + b^7$

**19.** Let $b = 2b$ and $n = 5$ in the binomial theorem.

$(a+2b)^5 = a^5 + \dfrac{5}{1!}a^4(2b) + \dfrac{5\cdot 4}{2!}a^3(2b)^2 + \dfrac{5\cdot 4\cdot 3}{3!}a^2(2b)^3 + \dfrac{5\cdot 4\cdot 3\cdot 2}{4!}a(2b)^4 + (2b)^5$

$\quad = a^5 + 10a^4 b + 40a^3 b^2 + 80a^2 b^3 + 80ab^4 + 32b^5$

**21.** Let $a = q$, $b = r$, and $n = 9$ in the binomial theorem.

$(q+r)^2 = q^9 + \dfrac{9}{1!}q^8 r + \dfrac{9\cdot 8}{2!}q^7 r^2 + \dfrac{9\cdot 8\cdot 7}{3!}q^6 r^3 + \dfrac{9\cdot 8\cdot 7\cdot 6}{4!}q^5 r^4 + \dfrac{9\cdot 8\cdot 7\cdot 6\cdot 5}{5!}q^4 r^5 + \dfrac{9\cdot 8\cdot 7\cdot 6\cdot 5\cdot 4}{6!}q^3 r^6$

$\quad + \dfrac{9\cdot 8\cdot 7\cdot 6\cdot 5\cdot 4\cdot 3}{7!}q^2 r^7 + \dfrac{9\cdot 8\cdot 7\cdot 6\cdot 5\cdot 4\cdot 3\cdot 2}{8!}qr^8 + r^9$

$\quad = q^9 + 9q^8 r + 36q^7 r^2 + 84q^6 r^3 + 126q^5 r^4 + 126q^4 r^5 + 84q^3 r^6 + 36q^2 r^7 + 9qr^8 + r^9$

**23.** Let $a = 4a$ and $n = 5$ in the binomial theorem.

$(4a+b)^5 = (4a)^5 + \dfrac{5}{1!}(4a)^4 b + \dfrac{5\cdot 4}{2!}(4a)^3 b^2 + \dfrac{5\cdot 4\cdot 3}{3!}(4a)^2 b^3 + \dfrac{5\cdot 4\cdot 3\cdot 2}{4!}(4a)b^4 + b^5$

$\quad = 1024a^5 + 1280a^4 b + 640a^3 b^2 + 160a^2 b^3 + 20ab^4 + b^5$

**25.** Let $a = 5a$, $b = -2b$, and $n = 4$ in the binomial theorem.

$(5a-2b)^4 = (5a)^4 + \dfrac{4}{1!}(5a)^3(-2b) + \dfrac{4\cdot 3}{2!}(5a)^2(-2b)^2 + \dfrac{4\cdot 3\cdot 2}{3!}(5a)(-2b)^3 + (-2b)^4$

$\quad = 625a^4 - 1000a^3 b + 600a^2 b^2 - 160ab^3 + 16b^4$

**27.** Let $a = 2a$, $b = 3b$, and $n = 3$ in the binomial theorem.

$(2a+3b)^3 = (2a)^3 + \dfrac{3}{1!}(2a)^2(3b) + \dfrac{3\cdot 2}{2!}(2a)(3b)^2 + (3b)^3$

$\quad = 8a^3 + 36a^2 b + 54ab^2 + 27b^3$

**29.** Let $a = x$, $b = 2$, and $n = 5$ in the binomial theorem.

$(x+2)^5 = x^5 + \dfrac{5}{1!}x^4(2) + \dfrac{5\cdot 4}{2!}x^3(2)^2 + \dfrac{5\cdot 4\cdot 3}{3!}x^2(2)^3 + \dfrac{5\cdot 4\cdot 3\cdot 2}{4!}x(2)^4 + (2)^5$

$\quad = x^5 + 10x^4 + 40x^3 + 80x^2 + 80x + 32$

**31.** 5th term of $(c-d)^5$ corresponds to $r = 4$:

$\dfrac{5!}{4!(5-4)!}c^{5-4}(-d)^4 = 5cd^4$

**33.** 8th term of $(2c+d)^7$ corresponds to $r = 7$:

$\dfrac{7!}{7!(7-7)!}(2c)^{7-7}(d)^7 = d^7$

**35.** 4th term of $(2r-s)^5$ corresponds to $r = 3$:

$$\frac{5!}{3!(5-3)!}(2r)^{5-3}(-s)^3 = -40r^2s^3$$

**37.** 3rd term of $(x+y)^4$ corresponds to $r = 2$: $\frac{4!}{2!(4-2)!}(x)^{4-2}(y)^2 = 6x^2y^2$

**39.** 2nd term of $(a+3b)^{10}$ corresponds to $r = 1$: $\frac{10!}{1!(10-1)!}(a)^{10-1}(3b)^1 = 30a^9b$

**41.** $f(x) = |x|$

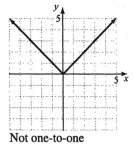

Not one-to-one

**43.** $H(x) = 2x+3$

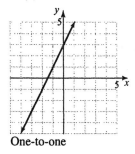

One-to-one

**45.** $f(x) = x^2 + 3$

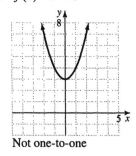

Not one-to-one

**47.** $(\sqrt{x}+\sqrt{3})^5$

Use the binomial theorem with $n = 5$, $a = \sqrt{x}$, , and $b = \sqrt{3}$.

$$\left(\sqrt{x}+\sqrt{3}\right)^5 = \left(\sqrt{x}\right)^5 + 5\left(\sqrt{x}\right)^4\left(\sqrt{3}\right) + 10\left(\sqrt{x}\right)^3\left(\sqrt{3}\right)^2 + 10\left(\sqrt{x}\right)^2\left(\sqrt{3}\right)^3 + 5\left(\sqrt{x}\right)\left(\sqrt{3}\right)^4 + \left(\sqrt{3}\right)^5$$

$$= x^2\sqrt{x} + 5\sqrt{3}x^2 + 30x\sqrt{x} + 30\sqrt{3}x + 45\sqrt{x} + 9\sqrt{3}$$

**49.** $\dbinom{9}{5} = \dfrac{9!}{5!(9-5)!}$

$= \dfrac{9!}{5!4!}$

$= \dfrac{9 \cdot 8 \cdot 7 \cdot 6 \cdot 5 \cdot 4 \cdot 3 \cdot 2 \cdot 1}{(5 \cdot 4 \cdot 3 \cdot 2 \cdot 1) \cdot (4 \cdot 3 \cdot 2 \cdot 1)}$

$= 126$

**51.** $\dbinom{8}{2} = \dfrac{8!}{2!(8-2)!}$

$= \dfrac{8!}{2!6!}$

$= \dfrac{8 \cdot 7 \cdot 6 \cdot 5 \cdot 4 \cdot 3 \cdot 2 \cdot 1}{(2 \cdot 1) \cdot (6 \cdot 5 \cdot 4 \cdot 3 \cdot 2 \cdot 1)}$

$= 28$

**53.** Answers may vary.

## Chapter 11 Vocabulary Check

1. A <u>finite sequence</u> is a function whose domain is the set of natural numbers {1, 2, 3, ..., $n$}, where $n$ is some natural number.

2. The <u>factorial of $n$</u>, written $n!$, is the product of the first $n$ consecutive natural numbers.

3. An <u>infinite sequence</u> is a function whose domain is the set of natural numbers.

4. A <u>geometric sequence</u> is a sequence in which each term (after the first) is obtained by multiplying the preceding term by a constant amount $r$. The constant $r$ is called the <u>common ratio</u> of the sequence.

5. A sum of the terms of a sequence is called a <u>series</u>.

6. The $n$th term of the sequence $a_n$ is called the <u>general term</u>.

7. An <u>arithmetic sequence</u> is a sequence in which each term (after the first) differs from the preceding term by a constant amount $d$. The constant $d$ is called the <u>common difference</u> of the sequence.

8. A triangle array of the coefficients of the terms of the expansions of $(a+b)^n$ is called <u>Pascal's triangle</u>.

## Chapter 11 Review

1. $a_n = -3n^2$

$a_1 = -3(1)^2 = -3$
$a_2 = -3(2)^2 = -12$
$a_3 = -3(3)^2 = -27$
$a_4 = -3(4)^2 = -48$
$a_5 = -3(5)^2 = -75$

2. $a_n = n^2 + 2n$

$a_1 = 1^2 + 2(1) = 3$
$a_2 = 2^2 + 2(2) = 8$
$a_3 = 3^2 + 2(3) = 15$
$a_4 = 4^2 + 2(4) = 24$
$a_5 = 5^2 + 2(5) = 35$

3. $a_n = \dfrac{(-1)^n}{100}$

$a_{100} = \dfrac{(-1)^{100}}{100} = \dfrac{1}{100}$

4. $a_n = \dfrac{2n}{(-1)^2}$

$a_{50} = \dfrac{2(50)}{(-1)^2} - 100$

5. $\dfrac{1}{6 \cdot 1}, \dfrac{1}{6 \cdot 2}, \dfrac{1}{6 \cdot 3}, \cdots$

In general, $a_n = \dfrac{1}{6n}$.

6. $-1, 4, -9, 16, \ldots$

$a_n = (-1)^n n^2$

7. $a_n = 32n - 16$

$a_5 = 32(5) - 16 = 144$ feet
$a_6 = 32(6) - 16 = 176$ feet
$a_7 = 32(7) - 16 = 208$ feet

8. $a_n = 100(2)^{n-1}$

$10,000 = 100(2)^{n-1}$
$100 = 2^{n-1}$
$\log 100 = (n-1)\log 2$
$\quad n = \dfrac{\log 100}{\log 2} + 1 \approx 7.6$

Eighth day culture will be at least 10,000.
Since $n = 1$ corresponds to the end of the first
day, the original amount corresponds to $n = 0$.

$$a_0 = 100(2)^{-1} = 100\left(\frac{1}{2}\right) = 50$$

The original measure of the culture was 50.

9. 2006: $a_1 = 660,000$

 2007: $a_2 = 660,000(2) = 1,320,000$

 2008: $a_3 = 1,320,000(2) = 2,640,000$

 2009: $a_4 = 2,640,000(2) = 5,280,000$

 2010: $a_5 = 5,280,000(2) = 10,560,000$

 There will be 10,560,000 acres of infested trees
 in 2010.

10. $a_n = 50 + (n-1)8$

 $a_1 = 50$

 $a_2 = 50 + 8 = 58$

 $a_3 = 50 + 2(8) = 66$

 $a_4 = 50 + 3(8) = 74$

 $a_5 = 50 + 4(8) = 82$

 $a_6 = 50 + 5(8) = 90$

 $a_7 = 50 + 6(8) = 98$

 $a_8 = 50 + 7(8) = 106$

 $a_9 = 50 + 8(8) = 114$

 $a_{10} = 50 + 9(8) = 122$

 There are 122 seats in the tenth row.

11. $a_1 = -2, r = \frac{2}{3}$

 $a_1 = -2$

 $a_2 = -2\left(\frac{2}{3}\right) = -\frac{4}{3}$

 $a_3 = \left(-\frac{4}{3}\right)\left(\frac{2}{3}\right) = -\frac{8}{9}$

 $a_4 = \left(-\frac{8}{9}\right)\left(\frac{2}{3}\right) = -\frac{16}{27}$

 $a_5 = \left(-\frac{16}{27}\right)\left(\frac{2}{3}\right) = -\frac{32}{81}$

12. $a_n = 12 + (n-1)(-1.5)$

 $a_1 = 12$

 $a_2 = 12 + (1)(-1.5) = 10.5$

 $a_3 = 12 + 2(-1.5) = 9$

 $a_4 = 12 + 3(-1.5) = 7.5$

 $a_5 = 12 + 4(-1.5) = 6$

13. $a_n = -5 + (n-1)^4$

 $a_{30} = 5 + (30-1)4 = 111$

14. $a_n = 2 + (n-1)\frac{3}{4}$

 $a_{11} = 2 + 10\left(\frac{3}{4}\right) = \frac{19}{2}$

15. 12, 7, 2,...

 $a_1 = 12, \ d = -5, n = 20$

 $a_{20} = 12 + (20-1)(-5) = -83$

16. $a_n = a_1 r^{n-1}, \ a_1 = 4, \ r = \frac{3}{2}$

 $a_6 = 4\left(\frac{3}{2}\right)^{6-1} = \frac{243}{8}$

17. $a_4 = 18, \ a_{20} = 98$

 $\begin{cases} a_4 = a_1 + (4-1)d \\ a_{20} = a_1 + (20-1)d \end{cases}$

 $\begin{cases} 18 = a_1 + 3d \\ 98 = a_1 + 19d \end{cases}$

 $\begin{cases} -18 = -a_1 - 3d \\ \ \ 98 = a_1 + 19d \end{cases}$

 Adding yields $80 = 16d$ or $d = 5$.
 Then $a_1 = 18 - 3(5) = 3$.

18. $a_3 = -48, \ a_4 = 192$

 $r = \frac{a_4}{a_3} = \frac{192}{-48} = -4$

 $a_3 = a_1 r^{3-1}$

 $-48 = a_1(-4)^2$

 $-48 = 16a_1$

 $-3 = a_1$

 $r = -4, \ a_1 = -3$

19. $\frac{3}{10}, \frac{3}{10^2}, \frac{3}{10^3},...$

 In general, $a_n = \frac{3}{10^n}$

20. 50, 58, 66, ...

 $a_n = 50 + (n-1)8$ or $a_n = 42 + 8n$

594

**21.** $\frac{8}{3}$, 4, 6, ...

Geometric; $a_1 = \frac{8}{3}$,

$r = \frac{4}{\frac{8}{3}} = 4 \cdot \frac{3}{8} = \frac{12}{8} = \frac{3}{2}$

**22.** $-10.5$, $-6.1$, $-1.7$
Arithmetic; $a_1 = -10.5$,
$d = -6.1 - (-10.5) = 4.4$

**23.** $7x$, $-14x$, $28x$
Geometric; $a_1 = 7x$, $r = -2$

**24.** neither

**25.** $a_1 = 8$, $r = 0.75$
$a_1 = 8$
$a_2 = 8(0.75) = 6$
$a_3 = 8(0.75)^2 = 4.5$
$a_4 = 8(0.75)^3 \approx 3.4$
$a_5 = 8(0.75)^4 \approx 2.5$
$a_6 = 8(0.75)^5 \approx 1.9$
Yes, a ball that rebounds to a height of 2.5 feet after the fifth bounce is good, since $2.5 \geq 1.9$.

**26.** $a_1 = 25$, $d = -4$
$a_n = a_1 + (n-1)d$
$a_n = 25 + (n-1)(-4) = 29 - 4n$
$a_7 = 25 + 6(-4) = 1$
Continuing the progression as far as possible leaves 1 can in the top row.

**27.** $a_1 = 1$, $r = 2$
$a_n = 2^{n-1}$
$a_{10} = 2^9 = 512$
$a_{30} = 2^{29} = 536,870,912$
You save \$512 on the tenth day and \$536,870,912 on the thirtieth day.

**28.** $a_n = a_1 r^{n-1}$, $a_1 = 30$, $r = 0.7$
$a_5 = 30(0.7)^4 = 7.203$
The length is 7.203 inches on the fifth swing.

**29.** $a_1 = 900$, $d = 150$
$a_n = 900 + (n-1)150 = 150_n + 750$
$a_6 = 900 + (6-1)150 = 1650$
Her salary is \$1650 per month at the end of training.

**30.** $\frac{1}{512}$, $\frac{1}{256}$, $\frac{1}{128}$, ...

first fold: $a_1 = \frac{1}{256}$, $r = 2$

$a_{15} = \frac{1}{256}(2)^{15-1} = 64$

After 15 folds, the thickness is 64 inches.

**31.** $\displaystyle\sum_{i=1}^{5}(2i-1) = [2(1)-1] + [2(2)-1] + [2(3)-1]$
$\qquad\qquad\qquad + [2(4)-1] + [2(5)-1]$
$\qquad = 1 + 3 + 5 + 7 + 9$
$\qquad = 25$

**32.** $\displaystyle\sum_{i=1}^{5} i(i+2) = 1(1+2) + 2(2+2) + 3(3+2)$
$\qquad\qquad\qquad + 4(4+2) + 5(5+2)$
$\qquad = 3 + 8 + 15 + 24 + 35$
$\qquad = 85$

**33.** $\displaystyle\sum_{i=2}^{4} \frac{(-1)^i}{2i} = \frac{(-1)^2}{2(2)} + \frac{(-1)^3}{2(3)} + \frac{(-1)^4}{2(4)}$
$\qquad = \frac{1}{4} - \frac{1}{6} + \frac{1}{8}$
$\qquad = \frac{5}{24}$

**34.** $\displaystyle\sum_{i=3}^{5} 5(-1)^{i-1} = 5(-1)^{3-1} + 5(-1)^{4-1} + 5(-1)^{5-1}$
$\qquad = 5(1) + 5(-1) + 5(1)$
$\qquad = 5 - 5 + 5$
$\qquad = 5$

**35.** $a_n = (n-3)(n+2)$
$S_4 = \displaystyle\sum_{i=1}^{4}(i-3)(i+2)$
$\qquad = (1-3)(1+2) + (2-3)(2+2)$
$\qquad\qquad + (3-3)(3+2) + (4-3)(4+2)$
$\qquad = -6 - 4 + 0 + 6$
$\qquad = -4$

**36.** $a_n = n^2$

$$S_6 = \sum_{i=1}^{6} i^2$$
$$= (1)^2 + (2)^2 + (3)^2 + (4)^2 + (5)^2 + (6)^2$$
$$= 91$$

**37.** $a_n = -8 + (n-1)3 = 3n - 11$

$$S_5 = \sum_{i=1}^{5} (3i - 11)$$
$$= [3(1) - 11] + [3(2) - 11] + [3(3) - 11]$$
$$\quad + [3(4) - 11] + [3(5) - 11]$$
$$= -8 - 5 - 2 + 1 + 4$$
$$= -10$$

**38.** $a_n = 5(4)^{n-1}$

$$S_3 = \sum_{i=1}^{3} 5(4)^{i-1} = 5(4)^0 + 5(4)^1 + 5(4)^2 = 105$$

**39.** $1 + 3 + 9 + 27 + 81 + 243$
$$= 3^0 + 3^1 + 3^2 + 3^3 + 3^4 + 3^5$$
$$= \sum_{i=1}^{6} 3^{i-1}$$

**40.** $6 + 2 + (-2) + (-6) + (-10) + (-14) + (-18)$

$a_1 = 6,\ d = -4$
$a_n = 6 + (n-1)(-4)$
$$\sum_{i=1}^{7} [6 + (i-1)(-4)]$$

**41.** $\dfrac{1}{4} + \dfrac{1}{16} + \dfrac{1}{64} + \dfrac{1}{256} = \dfrac{1}{4^1} + \dfrac{1}{4^2} + \dfrac{1}{4^3} + \dfrac{1}{4^4}$

$$= \sum_{i=1}^{4} \frac{1}{4^i}$$

**42.** $1 + \left(-\dfrac{3}{2}\right) + \dfrac{9}{4} = \left(-\dfrac{3}{2}\right)^0 + \left(-\dfrac{3}{2}\right)^1 + \left(-\dfrac{3}{2}\right)^2$

$$= \sum_{i=1}^{3} \left(-\frac{3}{2}\right)^{i-1}$$

**43.** $a_1 = 20,\ r = 2$

$a_n = 20(2)^n$ represents the number of yeast, where $n$ represents the number of 8-hour periods. Since $48 = 6(8)$ here, $n = 6$.

$a_6 = 20(2)^6 = 1280$

There are 1280 yeast after 48 hours.

**44.** $a_n = n^2 + 2n - 1$

$$a_4 = (4)^2 + 2(4) - 1 = 23$$

$$S_4 = \sum_{i=1}^{4} (i^2 + 2i - 1)$$
$$= (1 + 2 - 1) + (4 + 4 - 1) + (9 + 6 - 1)$$
$$\quad + (16 + 8 - 1)$$
$$= 46$$

23 cranes are born in the fourth year and 46 cranes are born in the first four years.

**45.** For Job $A$: $a_1 = 39,500,\ d = 2200$;
$a_5 = 39,500 + (5-1)2200 = \$48,330$
For Job $B$: $a_1 = 41,000,\ d = 1400$
$a_5 = 41,000 + (5-1)1400 = \$46,600$
For the fifth year, Job $A$ has a higher salary.

**46.** $a_n = 200(0.5)^n$

$a_3 = 200(0.5)^3 = 25$

$$S_3 = \sum_{i=1}^{3} 200(0.5)^i$$
$$= 200(0.5) + 200(0.5)^2 + 200(0.5)^3$$
$$= 175$$

25 kilograms decay in the third year and 175 kilograms decay in the first three years.

**47.** $15, 19, 23, \ldots$
$a_1 = 15,\ d = 4,\ a_6 = 15 + (6-1)4 = 35$
$$S_6 = \frac{6}{2}[15 + 35] = 150$$

**48.** $5, -10, 20, \ldots$
$a_1 = 5,\ r = -2$
$$S_n = \frac{a_1(1 - r^n)}{1 - r}$$
$$S_9 = \frac{5(1 - (-2)^9)}{1 - (-2)} = 855$$

**49.** $a_1 = 1, d = 2, n = 30, a_{30} = 1 + (30-1)2 = 59$

$$S_{30} = \frac{30}{2}[1+59] = 900$$

**50.** 7, 14, 21, 28, ...

$a_n = 7 + (n-1)7$

$a_{20} = 7 + (20-1)7 = 140$

$$S_{20} = \frac{20}{2}(7+140) = 1470$$

**51.** 8, 5, 2, ...

$a_1 = 8, d = -3, n = 20$

$a_{20} = 8 + (20-1)(-3) = -49$

$$S_{20} = \frac{20}{2}[8+(-49)]$$
$$= -410$$

**52.** $\frac{3}{4}, \frac{9}{4}, \frac{27}{4}, ...$

$a_1 = \frac{3}{4}, r = 3$

$$S_8 = \frac{\frac{3}{4}(1-3^8)}{1-3} = 2460$$

**53.** $a_1 = 6, r = 5$

$$S_4 = \frac{6(1-5^4)}{1-5} = 936$$

**54.** $a_1 = -3, d = -6$

$a_n = -3 + (n-1)(-6)$

$a_{100} = -3 + (100-1)(-6) = -597$

$$S_{100} = \frac{100}{2}(-3+(-597)) = -30,000$$

**55.** $5, \frac{5}{2}, \frac{5}{4}, ...$

$a_1 = 5, r = \frac{1}{2}$

$$S_\infty = \frac{5}{1-\frac{1}{2}} = 10$$

**56.** $18, -2, \frac{2}{9}, ...$

$a_1 = 18, r = -\frac{1}{9}$

$$S_\infty = \frac{18}{1+\frac{1}{9}} = \frac{81}{5}$$

**57.** $-20, -4, -\frac{4}{5}, ...$

$a_1 = -20, r = \frac{1}{5}$

$$S_\infty = \frac{-20}{1-\frac{1}{5}} = -25$$

**58.** 0.2, 0.02, 0.002, ...

$a_1 = 0.2 = \frac{1}{5}, r = \frac{1}{10}$

$$S_\infty = \frac{\frac{1}{5}}{1-\frac{1}{10}} = \frac{2}{9}$$

**59.** $a_1 = 20,000, r = 1.15, n = 4$

$a_4 = 20,000(1.15)^{4-1} = 30,418$

$$S_4 = \frac{20,000(1-1.15^4)}{1-1.15} = 99,868$$

He earned \$30,418 during the fourth year and \$99,868 over the four years.

**60.** $a_n = 40(0.8)^{n-1}$

$a_4 = 40(0.8)^{4-1} = 20.48$

$$S_4 = \frac{40(1-0.8^4)}{1-0.8} = 118.08$$

He takes 20 minutes to assemble the fourth television and 118 minutes to assemble the first four televisions.

**61.** $a_1 = 100, d = -7, n = 7$

$a_7 = 100 + (7-1)(-7) = 58$

$$S_7 = \frac{7}{2}(100+58) = 553$$

The rent for the seventh day is \$58 and the rent for 7 days is \$553.

**62.** $a_1 = 15, r = 0.8$

$S_\infty = \dfrac{15}{1-0.8} = 75$ feet downward

$a_1 = 15(0.8) = 12, r = 0.8$

$S_\infty = \dfrac{12}{1-0.8} = 60$ feet upward

The total distance is 135 feet.

**63.** 1800, 600, 200,...

$a_1 = 1800, r = \dfrac{1}{3}, n = 6$

$S_6 = 1800 \dfrac{\left(1 - \left(\frac{1}{3}\right)^6\right)}{1 - \frac{1}{3}} \approx 2696$

Approximately 2696 mosquitoes were killed during the first six days after the spraying.

**64.** 1800, 600, 200, ...

For which $n$ is $a_n < 1$?

$a_n = 1800\left(\dfrac{1}{3}\right)^{n-1} < 1$

$\left(\dfrac{1}{3}\right)^{n-1} < \dfrac{1}{1800}$

$(n-1)\log\dfrac{1}{3} < \log\dfrac{1}{1800}$

$(n-1)\log 3^{-1} < \log 1800^{-1}$

$(n-1)(-\log 3) < -\log 1800$

$n - 1 > \dfrac{-\log 1800}{-\log 3}$

$n > 1 + \dfrac{\log 1800}{\log 3}$

$n > 7.8$

No longer effective on the 8th day

$S_8 = \dfrac{1800\left(1 - \left(\frac{1}{3}\right)^8\right)}{1 - \frac{1}{3}} \approx 2700$

About 2700 mosquitoes were killed.

**65.** $0.5\overline{55} = 0.5 + 0.05 + 0.005 + \cdots$

$a_1 = 0.5, r = 0.1$

$S_\infty = \dfrac{0.5}{1 - 0.1} = \dfrac{0.5}{0.9} = \dfrac{5}{9}$

**66.** 27, 30, 33, ...

$$a_n = 27 + (n-1)(3)$$
$$a_{20} = 27 + (20-1)(3) = 84$$
$$S_{20} = \frac{20}{2}(27 + 84) = 1110$$

There are 1110 seats in the theater.

**67.** $(x+z)^5 = x^5 + 5x^4z + 10x^3z^2 + 10x^2z^3 + 5xz^4 + z^5$

**68.** $(y-r)^6 = y^6 + 6y^5(-r) + 15y^4(-r)^2 + 20y^3(-r)^3 + 15y^2(-r)^4 + 6y(-r)^5 + (-r)^6$
$$= y^6 - 6y^5r + 15y^4r^2 - 20y^3r^3 + 15y^2r^4 - 6yr^5 + r^6$$

**69.** $(2x+y)^4 = (2x)^4 + 4(2x)^3y + 6(2x)^2y^2 + 4(2x)y^3 + y^4$
$$= 16x^4 + 32x^3y + 24x^2y^2 + 8xy^3 + y^4$$

**70.** $(3y-z)^4 = (3y)^4 + 4(3y)^3(-z) + 6(3y)^2(-z)^2 + 4(3y)(-z)^3 + (-z)^4$
$$= 81y^4 - 108y^3z + 54y^2z^2 - 12yz^3 + z^4$$

**71.** $(b+c)^8 = b^8 + \dfrac{8}{1!}b^7c + \dfrac{8\cdot7}{2!}b^6c^2 + \dfrac{8\cdot7\cdot6}{3!}b^5c^3 + \dfrac{8\cdot7\cdot6\cdot5}{4!}b^4c^4 + \dfrac{8\cdot7\cdot6\cdot5\cdot4}{5!}b^3c^5$
$$+ \dfrac{8\cdot7\cdot6\cdot5\cdot4\cdot3}{6!}b^2c^6 + \dfrac{8\cdot7\cdot6\cdot5\cdot4\cdot3\cdot2}{7!}bc^7 + c^8$$
$$= b^8 + 8b^7c + 28b^6c^2 + 56b^5c^3 + 70b^4c^4 + 56b^3c^5 + 28b^2c^6 + 8bc^7 + c^8$$

**72.** $(x-w)^7 = x^7 + \dfrac{7}{1!}x^6(-w) + \dfrac{7\cdot6}{2!}x^5(-w)^2 + \dfrac{7\cdot6\cdot5}{3!}x^4(-w)^3 + \dfrac{7\cdot6\cdot5\cdot4}{4!}x^3(-w)^4 + \dfrac{7\cdot6\cdot5\cdot4\cdot3}{5!}x^2(-w)^5$
$$+ \dfrac{7\cdot6\cdot5\cdot4\cdot3\cdot2}{6!}x(-w)^6 + (-w)^7$$
$$= x^7 - 7x^6w + 21x^5w^2 - 35x^4w^3 + 35x^3w^4 - 21x^2w^5 + 7xw^6 - w^7$$

**73.** $(4m-n)^4 = (4m)^4 + \dfrac{4}{1!}(4m)^3(-n) + \dfrac{4\cdot3}{2!}(4m)^2(-n)^2 + \dfrac{4\cdot3\cdot2}{3!}(4m)(-n)^3 + (-n)^4$
$$= 256m^4 - 256m^3n + 96m^2n^2 - 16mn^3 + n^4$$

**74.** $(p-2r)^5 = p^5 + \dfrac{5}{1!}p^4(-2r) + \dfrac{5\cdot4}{2!}p^3(-2r)^2 + \dfrac{5\cdot4\cdot3}{3!}p^2(-2r)^3 + \dfrac{5\cdot4\cdot3\cdot2}{4!}p(-2r)^4 + (-2r)^5$
$$= p^5 - 10p^4r + 40p^3r^2 - 80p^2r^3 + 80pr^4 - 32r^5$$

**75.** The 4th term corresponds to $r = 3$.

$$\frac{7!}{3!(7-3)!}a^{7-3}b^3 = 35a^4b^3$$

**76.** The 11th term corresponds to $r = 10$.

$$\frac{10!}{10!0!}y^{10-10}(2z)^{10} = 1024z^{10}$$

## Chapter 11 Test

1. $a_n = \dfrac{(-1)^n}{n+4}$

   $a_1 = \dfrac{(-1)^1}{1+4} = -\dfrac{1}{5}$

   $a_2 = \dfrac{(-1)^2}{2+4} = \dfrac{1}{6}$

   $a_3 = \dfrac{(-1)^3}{3+4} = -\dfrac{1}{7}$

   $a_4 = \dfrac{(-1)^4}{4+4} = \dfrac{1}{8}$

   $a_5 = \dfrac{(-1)^5}{5+4} = -\dfrac{1}{9}$

2. $a_n = 10 + 3(n-1)$

   $a_{80} = 10 + 3(80-1) = 247$

3. $\dfrac{2}{5}, \dfrac{2}{25}, \dfrac{2}{125}, \dots$

   In general, $a_n = \dfrac{2}{5}\left(\dfrac{1}{5}\right)^{n-1}$ or $a_n = \dfrac{2}{5^n}$.

4. $(-1)^1 9 \cdot 1,\ (-1)^2 9 \cdot 2, \dots, a_n = (-1)^n 9n$

5. $a_n = 5(2)^{n-1}, S_5 = \dfrac{5(1-2^5)}{1-2} = 155$

6. $a_n = 18 + (n-1)(-2)$

   $a_1 = 18, a_{30} = 18 + (30-1)(-2) = -40$

   $S_{30} = \dfrac{30}{2}[18 - 40] = -330$

7. $a_1 = 24, \ r = \dfrac{1}{6}$

   $S_\infty = \dfrac{24}{1-\frac{1}{6}} = \dfrac{144}{5}$

8. $\dfrac{3}{2}, -\dfrac{3}{4}, \dfrac{3}{8}, \dots$

   $a_1 = \dfrac{3}{2}, \ r = -\dfrac{1}{2}$

   $S_\infty = \dfrac{\frac{3}{2}}{1-\left(-\frac{1}{2}\right)} = 1$

**9.** $\displaystyle\sum_{i=1}^{4} i(i-2) = 1(1-2) + 2(2-2) + 3(3-2) + 4(4-2)$
$\qquad\qquad\qquad = -1 + 0 + 3 + 8 - 20 + 40 - 80$
$\qquad\qquad\qquad = 10$

**10.** $\displaystyle\sum_{i=2}^{4} 5(2)^i (-1)^{i-1} = 5(2)^2 (-1)^{2-1} + 5(2)^3 (-1)^{3-1} + 5(2)^4 (-1)^{4-1} = -20 + 40 - 80 = -60$

**11.** $(a-b)^6 = a^6 - 6a^5 b + 15a^4 b^2 - 20a^3 b^3 + 15a^2 b^4 - 6ab^5 + b^6$

**12.** $(2x+y)^5 = (2x)^5 + \dfrac{5}{1!}(2x)^4 y + \dfrac{5\cdot4}{2!}(2x)^3 y^2 + \dfrac{5\cdot4\cdot3}{3!}(2x)^2 y^3 + \dfrac{5\cdot4\cdot3\cdot2}{4!}(2x)y^4 + y^5$
$\qquad\qquad = 32x^5 + 80x^4 y + 80x^3 y^2 + 40x^2 y^3 + 10xy^4 + y^5$

**13.** $a_n = 250 + 75(n-1)$
$a_{10} = 250 + 75(10-1) = 925$
There were 925 people in the town at the beginning of the tenth year.
$a_1 = 250 + 75(1-1) = 250$
There were 250 people in the town at the beginning of the first year.

**14.** $1, 3, 5, \ldots$
$a_1 = 1, d = 2, n = 8$
$a_8 = 1 + (8-1)2 = 15$
$1 + 3 + 5 + 7 + 9 + 11 + 13 + 15$
$S_8 = \dfrac{8}{2}[1+15] = 64$
There were 64 shrubs planted in the 8 rows.

**15.** $a_1 = 80, r = \dfrac{3}{4}, n = 4$
$a_4 = 80\left(\dfrac{3}{4}\right)^{4-1} = 33.75$
The arc length is 33.75 cm on the 4th swing.
$S_4 = \dfrac{80\left(1 - \left(\frac{3}{4}\right)^4\right)}{1 - \frac{3}{4}} = 218.75$
The total of the arc lengths is 218.75 cm for the first 4 swings.

**16.** $a_1 = 80, r = \dfrac{3}{4}$
$S_\infty = \dfrac{80}{1 - \frac{3}{4}} = 320$
The total of the arc lengths is 320 cm before the pendulum comes to rest.

**17.**  16, 48, 80,...

$a_{10} = 16 + (10-1)32 = 304$

He falls 304 feet during the 10th second.

$S_{10} = \dfrac{10}{2}[16 + 304] = 1600$

He falls 1600 feet during the first 10 seconds.

**18.**  $0.4\overline{2}\overline{4}\overline{2} = 0.42 + 0.0042 + 0.000042$

$a_1 = 0.42 = \dfrac{42}{100}, \ r = 0.01 = \dfrac{1}{100}$

$S_\infty = \dfrac{\frac{42}{100}}{1 - \frac{1}{100}} = \dfrac{42}{100} \cdot \dfrac{100}{99} = \dfrac{14}{33}$

Thus, $0.4\overline{2}\overline{4}\overline{2} = \dfrac{14}{33}$.

## Chapter 11 Cumulative Review

**1.  a.**  $\dfrac{20}{-4} = -5$

**b.**  $\dfrac{-9}{-3} = 3$

**c.**  $-\dfrac{3}{8} \div 3 = -\dfrac{3}{8} \cdot \dfrac{1}{3} = -\dfrac{1}{8}$

**d.**  $\dfrac{-40}{10} = -4$

**e.**  $\dfrac{-1}{10} \div \dfrac{-2}{5} = \dfrac{1}{10} \cdot \dfrac{5}{2} = \dfrac{1}{4}$

**f.**  $\dfrac{8}{0}$ is undefined.

**2.  a.**  $3a - (4a+3) = 3a - 4a - 3 = -a - 3$

**b.**  $(5x-3) + (2x+6) = 7x + 3$

**c.**  $4(2x-5) - 3(5x+1) = 8x - 20 - 15x - 3$
$= -7x - 23$

**3.**  Let $x$ = the original price, then
$x - 0.08x = 2162$
$0.92x = 2162$
$x = 2350$
The original price is $2350.

**4.**  Let $x$ = the price before taxes, then
$x + 0.06x = 344.50$
$1.06x = 344.50$
$x = 325$
The price before taxes was $325.

**5.**  $3y - 2x = 7$
$3y = 2x + 7$
$y = \dfrac{1}{3}(2x+7)$
$y = \dfrac{2x}{3} + \dfrac{7}{3}$

**6.**  If the line is to be parallel, then the slope has to be the same as the slope of the given line.

Therefore, $m = \dfrac{3}{2}$.

$(y-(-2)) = \dfrac{3}{2}(x-3)$

$y + 2 = \dfrac{3}{2}(x-3)$

$y = \dfrac{3}{2}x - \dfrac{13}{2}$

$f(x) = \dfrac{3}{2}x - \dfrac{13}{2}$

**7.  a.**  $(3x^6)(5x) = 3 \cdot 5 x^{6+1} = 15x^7$

**b.**  $(-2.4x^3 p^2)(4xp^{10}) = -2.4 \cdot 4 x^{3+1} p^{2+10}$
$= -9.6x^4 p^{12}$

**8.**  $y^3 + 5y^2 - y = 5$
$y^3 + 5y^2 - y - 5 = 0$
$(y^3 + 5y^2) + (-y-5) = 0$
$y^2(y+5) - 1(y+5) = 0$
$(y^2-1)(y+5) = 0$
$(y+1)(y-1)(y+5) = 0$
$y = -5, -1, 1$

**9.**  $-2 \underline{| \ 1 \quad -2 \quad -11 \quad 5 \quad 34}$
$\underline{\quad\quad -2 \quad 8 \quad 6 \quad -22}$
$\quad 1 \quad -4 \quad -3 \quad 11 \quad 12$

Answer: $x^3 - 4x^2 - 3x + 11 + \dfrac{12}{x+2}$

**10.** $\dfrac{5}{3a-6} - \dfrac{a}{a-2} + \dfrac{3+2a}{5a-10}$

$= \dfrac{5}{3(a-2)} - \dfrac{a}{a-2} + \dfrac{3+2a}{5(a-2)}$

$= \dfrac{5 \cdot 5 - 3 \cdot 5a + 3(3+2a)}{3 \cdot 5(a-2)}$

$= \dfrac{25 - 15a + 9 + 6a}{15(a-2)}$

$= \dfrac{34 - 9a}{15(a-2)}$

**11. a.** $\sqrt{50} = \sqrt{2}\sqrt{25} = 5\sqrt{2}$

**b.** $\sqrt[3]{24} = \sqrt[3]{8}\sqrt[3]{3} = 2\sqrt[3]{3}$

**c.** $\sqrt{26} = \sqrt{26}$

**d.** $\sqrt[4]{32} = \sqrt[4]{16}\sqrt[4]{2} = 2\sqrt[4]{2}$

**12.** $\sqrt{3x+6} - \sqrt{7x-6} = 0$

$\sqrt{3x+6} = \sqrt{7x-6}$

$\left(\sqrt{3x+6}\right)^2 = \left(\sqrt{7x-6}\right)^2$

$3x+6 = 7x-6$

$-4x = -12$

$x - 3$

**13.** $2420 = 2000(1+r)^2$

$\dfrac{2420}{2000} = (1+r)^2$

$\dfrac{121}{100} = (1+r)^2$

$\pm\sqrt{\dfrac{121}{100}} = 1+r$

$\pm\dfrac{11}{10} = 1+r$

$-1 \pm \dfrac{11}{10} = r$

Discard the negative value.

$r = -1 + \dfrac{11}{10} = \dfrac{1}{10} = 0.10$

The interest rate is 10%.

**14. a.** $\sqrt[3]{\dfrac{4}{3x}} = \dfrac{\sqrt[3]{4}}{\sqrt[3]{3x}} = \left(\dfrac{\sqrt[3]{9x^2}}{\sqrt[3]{9x^2}}\right) = \dfrac{\sqrt[3]{36x^2}}{3x}$

**b.** $\dfrac{\sqrt{2}+1}{\sqrt{2}-1} = \dfrac{\sqrt{2}+1}{\sqrt{2}-1} \cdot \left(\dfrac{\sqrt{2}+1}{\sqrt{2}+1}\right)$

$= \dfrac{2 + 2\sqrt{2} + 1}{2-1}$

$= 3 + 2\sqrt{2}$

**15.** $(x-3)^2 - 3(x-3) - 4 = 0$

$x^2 - 6x + 9 - 3x + 9 - 4 = 0$

$x^2 - 9x + 14 = 0$

$(x-2)(x-7) = 0$

$x = 2, 7$

**16.** $\dfrac{10}{(2x+4)^2} - \dfrac{1}{2x+4} = 3$

$10 - (2x+4) = 3(2x+4)^2$

$10 - 2x - 4 = 3(4x^2 + 16x + 16)$

$-2x + 6 = 12x^2 + 48x + 48$

$12x^2 + 50x + 42 = 0$

$6x^2 + 25x + 21 - 0$

$(6x + 7)(x + 3) = 0$

$x = -\dfrac{7}{6}, -3$

**17.** $\dfrac{5}{x+1} < -2$

$x + 1 = 0$

$x = -1$

Solve $\dfrac{5}{x+1} = -2.$

$(x+1)\dfrac{5}{x+1} = (x+1)(-2)$

$5 = -2x - 2$

$7 = -2x$

$-\dfrac{7}{2} = x$

| Region | Test Point | $\dfrac{5}{x+1} < -2$; Result |
|---|---|---|
| $\left(-\infty, -\dfrac{7}{2}\right)$ | $x = -6$ | $\dfrac{5}{-5} < -2$; False |
| $\left(-\dfrac{7}{2}, -1\right)$ | $x = -2$ | $\dfrac{5}{-1} < -2$; True |
| $(-1, \infty)$ | $x = 4$ | $\dfrac{5}{5} < -2$; False |

The solution set is $\left(-\dfrac{7}{2}, -1\right)$.

**18.** $f(x) = (x+2)^2 - 6$

Axis of symmetry: $x = -2$

vertex: $(-2, -6)$

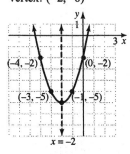

**19.** $f(t) = -16t^2 + 20t$

The maximum height occurs at the vertex.

$t = \dfrac{-20}{2(-16)} = \dfrac{5}{8}$

$f\left(\dfrac{5}{8}\right) = -16\left(\dfrac{5}{8}\right)^2 + 20\left(\dfrac{5}{8}\right) = \dfrac{25}{4}$

The maximum height of $\dfrac{25}{4}$ feet occurs at

$\dfrac{5}{8}$ second.

**20.** $f(x) = x^2 + 3x - 18$

$a = 1, b = 3, c = -18$

$x = \dfrac{-3}{2(1)} = -\dfrac{3}{2}$

$f\left(-\dfrac{3}{2}\right) = \left(-\dfrac{3}{2}\right)^2 + 3\left(\dfrac{3}{2}\right) - 18 = -\dfrac{81}{4}$

The vertex is $\left(-\dfrac{3}{2}, -\dfrac{81}{4}\right)$.

**21. a.** $(f \circ g)(2) = f(g(2)) = f(5) = 5^2 = 25$
$(g \circ f)(2) = g(f(2)) = g(4) = 4 + 3 = 7$

**b.** $(f \circ g)(x) = f(x+3)$
$= (x+3)^2$
$= x^2 + 6x + 9$
$(g \circ f)(x) = g(x^2) = x^2 + 3$

**22.** $f(x) = -2x + 3$
$y = -2x + 3$
$x = -2y + 3$
$x - 3 = -2y$
$\dfrac{x-3}{-2} = y$

$f^{-1}(x) = -\dfrac{x-3}{2}$ or $f^{-1}(x) = \dfrac{3-x}{2}$

**23.** $f^{-1} = \{(1,0),\ (7,-2),\ (-6,3),\ (4,4)\}$

**24. a.** $(f \circ g)(2) = f(g(2)) = f(3) = 3^2 - 2 = 7$
$(g \circ f)(2) = g(f(2)) = g(2) = 2 + 1 = 3$

**b.** $(f \circ g)(x) = f(x+1)$
$= (x+1)^2 - 2$
$= x^2 + 2x - 1$
$(g \circ f)(x) = g(x^2 - 2) = x^2 - 2 + 1 = x^2 - 1$

**25. a.** $2^x = 16$
$2^x = 2^4$
$x = 4$

**b.** $9^x = 27$
$(3^2)^x = 3^3$
$2x = 3$
$x = \dfrac{3}{2}$

**c.** $4^{x+3} = 8^x$
$(2^2)^{x+3} = (2^3)^x$
$2^{2x+6} = 2^{3x}$
$2x + 6 = 3x$
$x = 6$

**26. a.** $\log_2 32 = x$

$\qquad 2^x = 32$

$\qquad 2^x = 2^5$

$\qquad x = 5$

**b.** $\log_4 \dfrac{1}{64} = x$

$\qquad 4^x = \dfrac{1}{64}$

$\qquad 4^x = 4^{-3}$

$\qquad x = -3$

**c.** $\log_{\frac{1}{2}} x = 5$

$\qquad \left(\dfrac{1}{2}\right)^5 = x$

$\qquad x = \dfrac{1}{32}$

**27. a.** $\log_3 3^2 = 2$

**b.** $\log_7 7^{-1} = -1$

**c.** $5^{\log_5 3} = 3$

**d.** $2^{\log_2 6} = 6$

**28. a.** $\qquad 4^x = 64$

$\qquad \left(2^2\right)^x = 2^6$

$\qquad 2x = 6$

$\qquad x = 3$

**b.** $\qquad 8^x = 32$

$\qquad \left(2^3\right)^x = 2^5$

$\qquad 3x = 5$

$\qquad x = \dfrac{5}{3}$

**c.** $\qquad 9^{x+4} = 243^x$

$\qquad (3^2)^{x+4} = (3^5)^x$

$\qquad 3^{2x+8} = 3^{5x}$

$\qquad 2x + 8 = 5x$

$\qquad 8 = 3x$

$\qquad x = \dfrac{8}{3}$

**29. a.** $\log_{11} 10 + \log_{11} 3 = \log_{11}(10 \cdot 3) = \log_{11} 30$

**b.** $\log_3 \dfrac{1}{2} + \log_3 12 = \log_3 \left(\dfrac{1}{2} \cdot 12\right) = \log_3 6$

**c.** $\log_2(x+2) + \log_2 x = \log_2[(x+2)x]$

$\qquad\qquad\qquad\qquad\qquad = \log_2(x^2 + 2x)$

**30. a.** $\log 100,000 = \log_{10} 10^5 = 5$

**b.** $\log 10^{-3} = \log_{10} 10^{-3} = -3$

**c.** $\ln \sqrt[5]{e} = \ln e^{1/5} = \dfrac{1}{5}$

**d.** $\ln e^4 = 4$

**31.** $A = Pe^{rt}$

$\qquad A = 1600e^{0.09(5)} \approx 2509.30$

$\qquad$ \$2509.30 is owed after 5 years.

**32. a.** $\log_6 5 + \log_6 4 = \log_6(5 \cdot 4) = \log_6 20$

**b.** $\log_8 12 - \log_8 4 = \log_8 \dfrac{12}{4} = \log_8 3$

**c.** $2\log_2 x + 3\log_2 x - 2\log_2(x-1)$

$\qquad = 5\log_2 x - \log_2(x-1)^2$

$\qquad = \log_2 x^5 - \log_2(x-1)^2$

$\qquad = \log_2 \dfrac{x^5}{(x-1)^2}$

**33.** $\qquad 3^x = 7$

$\qquad \log 3^x = \log 7$

$\qquad x \log 3 = \log 7$

$\qquad x = \dfrac{\log 7}{\log 3} \approx 1.7712$

**34.** $10,000 = 5000\left(1 + \dfrac{0.02}{4}\right)^{4t}$

$\qquad\quad 2 = (1.005)^{4t}$

$\qquad\quad \ln 2 = \ln 1.005^{4t}$

$\qquad\quad \ln 2 = 4t \ln(1.005)$

$\qquad\qquad t = \dfrac{\ln 2}{4\ln 1.005} \approx 34.7$

$\qquad$ It takes 34.7 years.

**35.** $\log_4(x-2) = 2$

$$4^2 = x-2$$
$$x-2 = 16$$
$$x = 18$$

**36.** $\log_4 10 - \log_4 x = 2$

$$\log_4 \frac{10}{x} = 2$$
$$4^2 = \frac{10}{x}$$
$$16 = \frac{10}{x}$$
$$16x = 10$$
$$x = \frac{5}{8}$$

**37.** $\dfrac{x^2}{16} - \dfrac{y^2}{25} = 1$

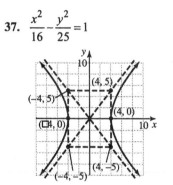

**38.** $(8, 5), (-2, 4)$

$$d = \sqrt{(-2-8)^2 + (4-5)^2} = \sqrt{101} \text{ units}$$

**39.** $\begin{cases} y = \sqrt{x} \\ x^2 + y^2 = 6 \end{cases}$

Replace $y$ with $\sqrt{x}$ in the first equation.

$$(x)^2 + (\sqrt{x})^2 = 6$$
$$x^2 + x - 6 = 0$$
$$(x+3)(x-2) = 0$$
$$x = -3 \text{(discard) or } x = 2$$
$$x = 2: \ y = \sqrt{x} = \sqrt{2}$$
$$\left(2, \sqrt{2}\right)$$

**40.** $\begin{cases} x^2 + y^2 = 36 \\ x - y = 6 \Rightarrow x = y+6 \end{cases}$

Replace $x$ with $y + 6$ in the first equation.

$$(y+6)^2 + y^2 = 36$$
$$2y^2 + 12y = 0$$
$$2y(y+6) = 0$$

$y = 0$  or  $y = -6$
$x = 0+6 = 6$    $x = -6+6 = 0$
$(0, -6); (6, 0)$

**41.** $\dfrac{x^2}{9} + \dfrac{y^2}{16} \le 1$

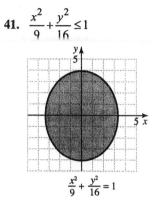

$$\frac{x^2}{9} + \frac{y^2}{16} = 1$$

**42.**

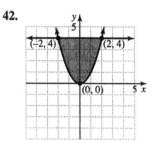

**43.** $a_n = n^2 - 1$

$$a_1 = 1^2 - 1 = 0$$
$$a_2 = 2^2 - 1 = 3$$
$$a_3 = 3^2 - 1 = 8$$
$$a_4 = 4^2 - 1 = 15$$
$$a_5 = 5^2 - 1 = 24$$

**44.** $a_n = \dfrac{n}{n+4}$

$$a_8 = \frac{8}{8+4} = \frac{8}{12} = \frac{2}{3}$$

**45.** $a_1 = 2, \ d = 9 - 2 = 7$

$$a_{11} = 2 + (11-1)(7) = 72$$

**46.** $a_1 = 2, \ r = \dfrac{10}{2} = 5$

$$a_6 = 2(5)^{6-1} = 2(5)^5 = 6250$$

**47. a.** $\displaystyle\sum_{i=0}^{6}\frac{i-2}{2}=\frac{0-2}{2}+\frac{1-2}{2}+\frac{2-2}{2}+\frac{3-2}{2}+\frac{4-2}{2}+\frac{5-2}{2}+\frac{6-2}{2}$

$$=-1-\frac{1}{2}+0+\frac{1}{2}+1+\frac{3}{2}+2$$

$$=\frac{7}{2}$$

**b.** $\displaystyle\sum_{i=3}^{5}2^{i}=2^{3}+2^{4}+2^{5}=8+16+32=56$

**48. a.** $\displaystyle\sum_{i=0}^{4}i(i+1)=0(0+1)+1(1+1)+2(2+1)+3(3+1)+4(4+1)$

$$=0+2+6+12+20$$

$$=40$$

**b.** $\displaystyle\sum_{i=0}^{3}2^{i}=2^{0}+2^{1}+2^{2}+2^{3}=1+2+4+8=15$

**49.** $a_1=1,\ a_{30}=30$

$$S_n=\frac{n}{2}(a_1+a_n)=\frac{30}{2}(1+30)=465$$

**50.** $(x-y)^6$ where $a=x,\ b=-y,\ n=6,$ and $r=2$.

$$\frac{6!}{2!(6-2)!}x^{6-2}y^2-15x^4y^2$$

The third term in the expansion of $(x-y)^6$ is $15x^4y^2$.

# Appendices

**1.** $\sqrt{216} = \sqrt{36 \cdot 6} = \sqrt{36} \cdot \sqrt{6} = 6\sqrt{6}$

**2.** $\dfrac{\left(4 - \sqrt{16}\right) - (-7 - 20)}{-2(1-4)^2} = \dfrac{(4-4) - (-27)}{-2(-3)^2}$

$= \dfrac{0 + 27}{-2(9)}$

$= \dfrac{27}{-18}$

$= -\dfrac{3}{2}$

**3.** $\left(\dfrac{1}{125}\right)^{-1/3} = 125^{1/3} = \sqrt[3]{125} = \sqrt[3]{5^3} = 5$

**4.** $(-9x)^{-2} = \dfrac{1}{(-9x)^2} = \dfrac{1}{(-9)^2 x^2} = \dfrac{1}{81x^2}$

**5.** $\dfrac{\dfrac{5}{x} - \dfrac{7}{3x}}{\dfrac{9}{8x} - \dfrac{1}{x}} = \dfrac{24x\left(\dfrac{5}{x} - \dfrac{7}{3x}\right)}{24x\left(\dfrac{9}{8x} - \dfrac{1}{x}\right)}$

$= \dfrac{24x\left(\dfrac{5}{x}\right) - 24x\left(\dfrac{7}{3x}\right)}{24x\left(\dfrac{9}{8x}\right) - 24x\left(\dfrac{1}{x}\right)}$

$= \dfrac{24 \cdot 5 - 8 \cdot 7}{3 \cdot 9 - 24}$

$= \dfrac{120 - 56}{27 - 24}$

$= \dfrac{64}{3}$

**6.** $\dfrac{6^{-1}a^2b^{-3}}{3^{-2}a^{-5}b^2} = \dfrac{3^2 a^{2-(-5)}b^{-3-2}}{6^1} = \dfrac{9a^7b^{-5}}{6} = \dfrac{3a^7}{2b^5}$

**7.** $\left(\dfrac{64c^{4/3}}{a^{-2/3}b^{5/6}}\right)^{1/2} = \dfrac{64^{1/2}c^{\frac{4}{3} \cdot \frac{1}{2}}}{a^{-\frac{2}{3} \cdot \frac{1}{2}}b^{\frac{5}{6} \cdot \frac{1}{2}}}$

$= \dfrac{8c^{2/3}}{a^{-1/3}b^{5/12}}$

$= \dfrac{8a^{1/3}c^{2/3}}{b^{5/12}}$

**8.** $3x^2y - 27y^3 = 3y(x^2 - 9y^2)$

$= 3y[x^2 - (3y)^2]$

$= 3y(x + 3y)(x - 3y)$

**9.** $16y^3 - 2 = 2(8y^3 - 1)$

$= 2[(2y)^3 - 1^3]$

$= 2(2y - 1)[(2y)^2 + 2y \cdot 1 + 1^2]$

$= 2(2y - 1)(4y^2 + 2y + 1)$

**10.** $x^2y - 9y - 3x^2 + 27 = y(x^2 - 9) - 3(x^2 - 9)$

$= (x^2 - 9)(y - 3)$

$= (x + 3)(x - 3)(y - 3)$

**11.** $(4x^3y - 3x - 4) - (9x^3y + 8x + 5)$

$= 4x^3y - 3x - 4 - 9x^3y - 8x - 5$

$= 4x^3y - 9x^3y - 3x - 8x - 4 - 5$

$= -5x^3y - 11x - 9$

**12.** $(6m + n)^2 = (6m)^2 + 2(6m)(n) + n^2$

$= 36m^2 + 12mn + n^2$

**13.** $(2x - 1)(x^2 - 6x + 4)$

$= 2x(x^2 - 6x + 4) - 1(x^2 - 6x + 4)$

$= 2x^3 - 12x^2 + 8x - x^2 + 6x - 4$

$= 2x^3 - 13x^2 + 14x - 4$

**14.** $\dfrac{3x^2 - 12}{x^2 + 2x - 8} \div \dfrac{6x + 18}{x + 4} = \dfrac{3x^2 - 12}{x^2 + 2x - 8} \cdot \dfrac{x + 4}{6x + 18}$

$= \dfrac{3(x^2 - 4)}{(x + 4)(x - 2)} \cdot \dfrac{x + 4}{6(x + 3)}$

$= \dfrac{3(x + 2)(x - 2)(x + 4)}{(x + 4)(x - 2) \cdot 6(x + 3)}$

$= \dfrac{x + 2}{2(x + 3)}$

**15.** $\dfrac{2x^2+7}{2x^4-18x^2}-\dfrac{6x+7}{2x^4-18x^2}=\dfrac{(2x^2+7)-(6x+7)}{2x^4-18x^2}$

$=\dfrac{2x^2+7-6x-7}{2x^4-18x^2}$

$=\dfrac{2x^2-6x}{2x^2(x^2-9)}$

$=\dfrac{2x(x-3)}{2x^2(x+3)(x-3)}$

$=\dfrac{1}{x(x+3)}$

**16.** $\dfrac{3}{x^2-x-6}+\dfrac{2}{x^2-5x+6}$

$=\dfrac{3}{(x-3)(x+2)}+\dfrac{2}{(x-2)(x-3)}$

$=\dfrac{3(x-2)}{(x-3)(x+2)(x-2)}+\dfrac{2(x+2)}{(x-2)(x-3)(x+2)}$

$=\dfrac{3(x-2)+2(x+2)}{(x-3)(x+2)(x-2)}$

$=\dfrac{3x-6+2x+4}{(x-3)(x+2)(x-2)}$

$=\dfrac{5x-2}{(x-3)(x+2)(x-2)}$

**17.** $\sqrt{125x^3}-3\sqrt{20x^3}=\sqrt{25x^2\cdot 5x}-3\sqrt{4x^2\cdot 5x}$

$=5x\sqrt{5x}-3\cdot 2x\sqrt{5x}$

$=5x\sqrt{5x}-6x\sqrt{5x}$

$=(5x-6x)\sqrt{5x}$

$=-x\sqrt{5x}$

**18.** $\left(\sqrt{5}+5\right)\left(\sqrt{5}-5\right)=\left(\sqrt{5}\right)^2-5^2=5-25=-20$

**19.**
$$
\begin{array}{r}
2x^2-x-2 \\
2x+1\overline{)4x^3+0x^2-5x+0} \\
\underline{4x^3+2x^2}\phantom{-5x+0} \\
-2x^2-5x\phantom{+0} \\
\underline{-2x^2\phantom{0}-x}\phantom{+0} \\
-4x+0 \\
\underline{-4x-2} \\
2
\end{array}
$$

$(4x^3-5x)\div(2x+1)=2x^2-x-2+\dfrac{2}{2x+1}$

**20.** $9(x+2)=5[11-2(2-x)+3]$

$9x+18=5(11-4+2x+3)$

$9x+18=5(2x+10)$

$9x+18=10x+50$

$9x-10x=50-18$

$-x=32$

$x=-32$

**21.** $|6x-5|-3=-2$

$|6x-5|=1$

$6x-5=-1$  or  $6x-5=1$

$6x=4$  or  $6x=6$

$x=\dfrac{4}{6}$  or  $x=1$

$x=\dfrac{2}{3}$

Both solutions check.

**22.** $3n(7n-20)=96$

$21n^2-60n=96$

$21n^2-60n-96=0$

$3(7n^2-20n-32)=0$

$3(7n+8)(n-4)=0$

$7n+8=0$  or  $n-4=0$

$n-\dfrac{8}{7}$  or  $n-4$

Both solutions check.

**23.** $-3<2(x-3)\le 4$

$-3<2x-6\le 4$

$-3+6<2x-6+6\le 4+6$

$3<2x\le 10$

$\dfrac{3}{2}<\dfrac{2x}{2}\le\dfrac{10}{2}$

$\dfrac{3}{2}<x\le 5$

$\left(\dfrac{3}{2},5\right]$

**24.** $|3x+1|>5$

$3x+1<-5$  or  $3x+1>5$

$3x<-6$        $3x>4$

$x<-2$          $x>\dfrac{4}{3}$

$(-\infty,-2)\cup\left(\dfrac{4}{3},\infty\right)$

**25.**
$$\frac{x^2+8}{x}-1=\frac{2(x+4)}{x}$$

$$x\left(\frac{x^2+8}{x}-1\right)=x\left(\frac{2(x+4)}{x}\right)$$

$$x^2+8-x=2(x+4)$$

$$x^2-x+8=2x+8$$

$$x^2-3x=0$$

$$x(x-3)=0$$

$$x=0 \quad \text{or} \quad x-3=0$$

$$x=3$$

The only solution is 3.

**26.**
$$y^2-3y=5$$

$$y^2-3y-5=0$$

$$y=\frac{-(-3)\pm\sqrt{(-3)^2-4(1)(-5)}}{2(1)}$$

$$y=\frac{3\pm\sqrt{9+20}}{2}$$

$$y=\frac{3\pm\sqrt{29}}{2}$$

**27.**
$$x=\sqrt{x-2}+2$$

$$x-2=\sqrt{x-2}$$

$$(x-2)^2=\left(\sqrt{x-2}\right)^2$$

$$x^2-4x+4=x-2$$

$$x^2-5x+6=0$$

$$(x-2)(x-3)=0$$

$$x-2=0 \quad \text{or} \quad x-3=0$$

$$x=2 \quad \text{or} \quad x=3$$

**28.**
$$2x^2-7x>15$$

$$2x^2-7x-15>0$$

$$(2x+3)(x-5)>0$$

$$2x+3=0 \quad \text{or} \quad x-5=0$$

$$x=-\frac{3}{2} \quad \text{or} \quad x=5$$

| Region | Test Point | $2x^2-7x>15$ Result |
|--------|------------|---------------------|
| $\left(-\infty,-\frac{3}{2}\right)$ | $-3$ | $39>15$ True |
| $\left(-\frac{3}{2},5\right)$ | $0$ | $0>15$ False |
| $(5,\infty)$ | $6$ | $30>15$ True |

$$\left(-\infty,-\frac{3}{2}\right)\cup(5,\infty)$$

**29.**
$$\begin{cases} \dfrac{x}{2}+\dfrac{y}{4}=-\dfrac{3}{4} \\ x+\dfrac{3}{4}y=-4 \end{cases}$$

$$\begin{cases} -8\left(\dfrac{x}{2}+\dfrac{y}{4}\right)=-8\left(-\dfrac{3}{4}\right) \\ 4\left(x+\dfrac{3}{4}y\right)=4(-4) \end{cases}$$

$$\begin{aligned} -4x-2y&=6 \\ 4x+3y&=-16 \\ \hline y&=-10 \end{aligned}$$

Let $y=-10$ in the second equation.

$$x+\frac{3}{4}y=-4$$

$$x+\frac{3}{4}(-10)=-4$$

$$x-\frac{15}{2}=-\frac{8}{2}$$

$$x=\frac{7}{2}$$

The solution is $\left(\frac{7}{2},-10\right)$.

**30.** $4x+6y=7$

$$6y=-4x+7$$

$$y=-\frac{2}{3}x+\frac{7}{6}$$

slope $=-\dfrac{2}{3}$, $y$-intercept $\left(0,\dfrac{7}{6}\right)$

Plot points: $\left(0,\dfrac{7}{6}\right),\left(\dfrac{7}{4},0\right),\left(-3,\dfrac{19}{6}\right)$

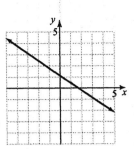

**31.** $2x - y > 5$

Graph $2x - y = 5$ with a dashed line because the inequality is $>$.

| $x$ | $2x - y = 5$ | $y$ |
|---|---|---|
| 0 | $2(0) - y = 5$ | $-5$ |
| 1 | $2(1) - y = 5$ | $-3$ |
| 3 | $2(3) - y = 5$ | $1$ |

Test point $(0, 0)$:  $2(0) - 0 \overset{?}{>} 5$

$\qquad\qquad\qquad 0 > 5$  False

Shade the region that does not include $(0, 0)$.

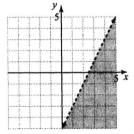

**32.** $y = -3$

The graph of $y = -3$ is a horizontal line with a $y$-intercept of $(0, -3)$.

**33.** $g(x) = -|x + 2| - 1$

| $x$ | $g(x) = -|x + 2| - 1$ | $g(x)$ |
|---|---|---|
| $-5$ | $-|-5 + 2| - 1 = -4$ | $-4$ |
| $-4$ | $-|-4 + 2| - 1 = -3$ | $-3$ |
| $-3$ | $-|-3 + 2| - 1 = -2$ | $-2$ |
| $-2$ | $-|-2 + 2| - 1 = -1$ | $-1$ |
| $-1$ | $-|-1 + 2| - 1 = -2$ | $-2$ |
| $0$ | $-|0 + 2| - 1 = -3$ | $-3$ |
| $1$ | $-|1 + 2| - 1 = -4$ | $-4$ |

Domain: All real numbers, $(-\infty, \infty)$
Range: $(-\infty, -1]$

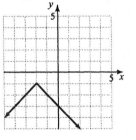

**34.** $h(x) - x^2 - 4x + 4$

$x$-intercept: Let $h(x) = 0$ and solve for $x$.

$0 = x^2 - 4x + 4$
$0 = (x - 2)^2$
$x - 2 = 0$
$x = 2$

$x$-intercept: $(2, 0)$
$y$-intercept: Let $x = 0$.

$h(0) = 0^2 - 4(0) + 4 = 4$

$y$-intercept: $(0, 4)$
$x$-coordinate of vertex:

$$-\frac{b}{2a} = -\frac{-4}{2(1)} = 2$$

vertex: $(2, 0)$

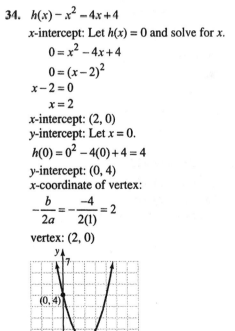

**35.** $f(x) = \begin{cases} -\dfrac{1}{2}x & \text{if} \quad x \le 0 \\ 2x-3 & \text{if} \quad x > 0 \end{cases}$

If $x \le 0$

| $x$ | $-\frac{1}{2}x$ | $f(x)$ |
|-----|-----------------|--------|
| 0 | $-\frac{1}{2}(0)$ | 0 |
| $-2$ | $-\frac{1}{2}(-2)$ | 1 |
| $-4$ | $-\frac{1}{2}(-4)$ | 2 |

If $x > 0$

| $x$ | $2x-3$ | $f(x)$ |
|-----|--------|--------|
| 1 | $2(1)-3$ | $-1$ |
| 2 | $2(2)-3$ | 1 |
| 3 | $2(3)-3$ | 3 |

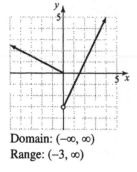

Domain: $(-\infty, \infty)$
Range: $(-3, \infty)$

**36.** through $(4, -2)$ and $(6, -3)$

$\text{slope} = m = \dfrac{y_2 - y_1}{x_2 - x_1} = \dfrac{-3-(-2)}{6-4} = \dfrac{-1}{2}$

$y - y_1 = m(x - x_1)$

$y - (-2) = -\dfrac{1}{2}(x - 4)$

$y + 2 = -\dfrac{1}{2}x + 2$

$y = -\dfrac{1}{2}x$

$f(x) = -\dfrac{1}{2}x$

**37.** through $(-1, 2)$ and perpendicular to $3x - y = 4$
Find the slope of $3x - y = 4$ by writing the equation in slope-intercept form.
$3x - y = 4$
$\quad -y = -3x + 4$
$\quad\quad y = 3x - 4$
The slope is 3. The slope of a line perpendicular to this line is $-\dfrac{1}{3}$.

Substitute $m = -\dfrac{1}{3}$ and $(x_1, y_1) = (-1, 2)$ in the equation:

$y - y_1 = m(x - x_1)$

$y - 2 = -\dfrac{1}{3}[x - (-1)]$

$y - 2 = -\dfrac{1}{3}(x + 1)$

$y - 2 = -\dfrac{1}{3}x - \dfrac{1}{3}$

$y = -\dfrac{1}{3}x + \dfrac{5}{3}$

$f(x) = -\dfrac{1}{3}x + \dfrac{5}{3}$

**38.** $(x_1, y_1) = (-6, 3); \quad (x_2, y_2) = (-8, -7)$

$d = \sqrt{(x_2 - x_1)^2 + (y_2 - y_1)^2}$

$\quad = \sqrt{[-8-(-6)]^2 + (-7-3)^2}$

$\quad = \sqrt{(-2)^2 + (-10)^2}$

$\quad = \sqrt{4 + 100}$

$\quad = \sqrt{104}$

$\quad = 2\sqrt{26}$ units

**39.** $(x_1, y_1) = (-2, -5); \quad (x_2, y_2) = (-6, 12)$

$\text{midpoint} = \left( \dfrac{x_1 + x_2}{2}, \dfrac{y_1 + y_2}{2} \right)$

$\quad = \left( \dfrac{-2 + (-6)}{2}, \dfrac{-5 + 12}{2} \right)$

$\quad = \left( \dfrac{-8}{2}, \dfrac{7}{2} \right)$

$\quad = \left( -4, \dfrac{7}{2} \right)$

**40.** $\sqrt{\dfrac{9}{y}} = \dfrac{\sqrt{9}}{\sqrt{y}} = \dfrac{\sqrt{9}}{\sqrt{y}} \cdot \dfrac{\sqrt{y}}{\sqrt{y}} = \dfrac{\sqrt{9} \cdot \sqrt{y}}{\sqrt{y} \cdot \sqrt{y}} = \dfrac{3\sqrt{y}}{y}$

**41.** $\dfrac{4-\sqrt{x}}{4+2\sqrt{x}} = \dfrac{4-\sqrt{x}}{4+2\sqrt{x}} \cdot \dfrac{4-2\sqrt{x}}{4-2\sqrt{x}}$

$\qquad = \dfrac{\left(4-\sqrt{x}\right)\left(4-2\sqrt{x}\right)}{\left(4+2\sqrt{x}\right)\left(4-2\sqrt{x}\right)}$

$\qquad = \dfrac{16-12\sqrt{x}+2x}{16-4x}$

$\qquad = \dfrac{2\left(8-6\sqrt{x}+x\right)}{2(8-2x)}$

$\qquad = \dfrac{8-6\sqrt{x}+x}{8-2x}$

**42.** Let $x$ = population of New York, then
$x + 1.3$ = Seoul's population, and
$2x - 10.2$ = Tokyo's population.
$x + (x+1.3) + (2x-10.2) = 78.3$
$\qquad\qquad\qquad 4x - 8.9 = 78.3$
$\qquad\qquad\qquad\quad\ 4x = 87.2$
$\qquad\qquad\qquad\qquad x = 21.8$

$x + 1.3 = 23.1$
$2x - 10.2 = 33.4$
The populations are as follows:
New York: 21.8 million; Seoul: 23.1 million;
Tokyo: 33.4 million

**43.** Subtract the area of the small square from the area of the large square.
$x^2 - (2y)^2 = (x+2y)(x-2y)$

**44.** Let $x$ = the number.

$(x+1) \cdot \left(2 \cdot \dfrac{1}{x}\right) = \dfrac{12}{5}$

$\qquad \dfrac{2}{x}(x+1) = \dfrac{12}{5}$

$5x\left[\dfrac{2}{x}(x+1)\right] = 5x\left(\dfrac{12}{5}\right)$

$\qquad 10(x+1) = x \cdot 12$

$\qquad 10x + 10 = 12x$

$\qquad\qquad 10 = 2x$

$\qquad\qquad\ 5 = x$

The number is 5.

**45.** $W = \dfrac{k}{V}$

Find $k$ by substituting $W = 20$ and $V = 12$.

$20 = \dfrac{k}{12}$

$240 = k$

Write the inverse relation equation.

$W = \dfrac{240}{V}$

Let $V = 15$ and find $W$.

$W = \dfrac{240}{15}$

$W = 16$

**46.** Use the Pythagorean Theorem.
$c^2 = a^2 + b^2$
$20^2 = x^2 + (x+8)^2$
$400 = x^2 + x^2 + 16x + 64$
$\quad\ 0 = 2x^2 + 16x - 336$
$\quad\ 0 = 2(x^2 + 8x - 168)$

$x = \dfrac{-8 \pm \sqrt{8^2 - 4(1)(-168)}}{2(1)}$

$x = \dfrac{-8 \pm \sqrt{736}}{2}$

$x \approx -17.6$ or $x \approx 9.6$
Discard a negative distance.
$x + 8 + x = 9.6 + 8 + 9.6 = 27.2$
$27.2 - 20 = 7.2$ or about 7
A person saves about 7 feet.

**47. a.** Find the vertex.

$\quad s(t) = -16t^2 + 32t + 256$

$\quad$ $t$-value: $\dfrac{-b}{2a} = \dfrac{-32}{2(-16)} = 1$

$\quad$ $s(t)$-value:

$\quad s(1) = -16(1)^2 + 32(1) + 256 = 272$

$\quad$ The maximum height is 272 feet.

$\quad$ **b.** Let $s(t) = 0$ and solve for $t$.

$\qquad 0 = -16t^2 + 32t + 256$

$\qquad 0 = -16(t^2 - 2t - 16)$

$\qquad t = \dfrac{-(-2) \pm \sqrt{(-2)^2 - 4(1)(-16)}}{2(1)}$

$\qquad t = \dfrac{2 \pm \sqrt{68}}{2}$

$\qquad t = \dfrac{2 \pm 2\sqrt{17}}{2}$

$\qquad t = 1 \pm \sqrt{17}$

$\qquad t \approx -3.12$ or $t \approx 5.12$
$\qquad$ Discard a negative time.
$\qquad$ The stone will hit the water in
$\qquad$ approximately 5.12 seconds.

**48.** Let $x$ = amount of 10% solution to add to mixture.

| solution | amount of solution | amount of fructose |
|---|---|---|
| 10% | $x$ | $0.10x$ |
| 20% | $20 - x$ | $0.20(20 - x)$ |
| 17.5% | 20 | $0.175(20)$ |

$$0.10x + 0.20(20 - x) = 0.175(20)$$
$$0.10x + 4 - 0.20x = 3.5$$
$$-0.10x = -0.5$$
$$x = 5$$

$20 - x = 15$
Therefore, mix 5 gallons of 10% solution with 15 gallons of 20% solution.

**49.** $-\sqrt{-8} = -\sqrt{4 \cdot (-1) \cdot 2} = -\sqrt{4} \cdot \sqrt{-1} \cdot \sqrt{2} = -2i\sqrt{2}$

**50.** $(12 - 6i) - (12 - 3i) = 12 - 6i - 12 + 3i$
$$= 12 - 12 - 6i + 3i$$
$$= 0 - 3i$$
$$= -3i$$

**51.** $(4 + 3i)^2 = (4 + 3i)(4 + 3i)$
$$= 16 + 12i + 12i + 9i^2$$
$$= 16 + 24i - 9$$
$$= 7 + 24i$$

**52.** $\dfrac{1 + 4i}{1 - i} = \dfrac{1 + 4i}{1 - i} \cdot \dfrac{1 + i}{1 + i}$
$$= \dfrac{(1 + 4i)(1 + i)}{(1 - i)(1 + i)}$$
$$= \dfrac{1 + 5i + 4i^2}{1 - i^2}$$
$$= \dfrac{1 + 5i - 4}{1 - (-1)}$$
$$= \dfrac{-3 + 5i}{2}$$
$$= -\dfrac{3}{2} + \dfrac{5}{2}i$$

**53.** $g(x) = x - 7$ and $h(x) = x^2 - 6x + 5$

$(g \circ h)(x) = (x^2 - 6x + 5) - 7 = x^2 - 6x - 2$

**54.** $f(x) = 6 - 2x$ is a one-to-one function since there is only one $f(x)$ value for each $x$-value.

Inverse:
$$y = 6 - 2x \qquad \Rightarrow \qquad x = 6 - 2y$$
$$x + 2y = 6$$
$$2y = -x + 6$$
$$y = \dfrac{-x + 6}{2}$$
$$f^{-1}(x) = \dfrac{-x + 6}{2}$$

**55.** $\log_5 x + 3\log_5 x - \log_5(x + 1)$
$$= \log_5 x + \log_5 x^3 - \log_5(x + 1)$$
$$= \log_5 x \cdot x^3 - \log_5(x + 1)$$
$$= \log_5 x^4 - \log_5(x + 1)$$
$$= \log_5 \dfrac{x^4}{x + 1}$$

**56.** $8^{x-1} = \dfrac{1}{64}$
$$(2^3)^{x-1} = \dfrac{1}{2^6}$$
$$2^{3(x-1)} = 2^{-6}$$
$$3(x - 1) = -6$$
$$3x - 3 = -6$$
$$3x = -3$$
$$x = -1$$

**57.** $3^{2x+5} = 4$
$$\log 3^{2x+5} = \log 4$$
$$(2x + 5)\log 3 = \log 4$$
$$2x + 5 = \dfrac{\log 4}{\log 3}$$
$$2x = \dfrac{\log 4}{\log 3} - 5$$
$$x = \dfrac{1}{2}\left(\dfrac{\log 4}{\log 3} - 5\right)$$
$$x \approx -1.8691$$

**58.** $\log_8(3x - 2) = 2$
$$8^2 = 3x - 2$$
$$64 = 3x - 2$$
$$66 = 3x$$
$$22 = x$$

**59.** $\log_4(x+1) - \log_4(x-2) = 3$

$$\log_4 \frac{x+1}{x-2} = 3$$

$$4^3 = \frac{x+1}{x-2}$$

$$64 = \frac{x+1}{x-2}$$

$$64(x-2) = x+1$$

$$64x - 128 = x+1$$

$$63x = 129$$

$$x = \frac{129}{63} = \frac{43}{21}$$

**60.** $\ln\sqrt{e} = x$

$$\ln e^{1/2} = x$$

$$\frac{1}{2}\ln e = x$$

$$\frac{1}{2} = x$$

**61.** $y = \left(\frac{1}{2}\right)^x + 1$

| $x$ | $\left(\frac{1}{2}\right)^x + 1$ | $y$ |
|---|---|---|
| $-3$ | $\left(\frac{1}{2}\right)^{-3} + 1 = 9$ | $9$ |
| $-2$ | $\left(\frac{1}{2}\right)^{-2} + 1 = 5$ | $5$ |
| $-1$ | $\left(\frac{1}{2}\right)^{-1} + 1 = 3$ | $3$ |
| $0$ | $\left(\frac{1}{2}\right)^0 + 1 = 2$ | $2$ |
| $1$ | $\left(\frac{1}{2}\right)^1 + 1 = 1\frac{1}{2}$ | $1\frac{1}{2}$ |
| $2$ | $\left(\frac{1}{2}\right)^2 + 1 = 1\frac{1}{4}$ | $1\frac{1}{4}$ |
| $3$ | $\left(\frac{1}{2}\right)^3 + 1 = 1\frac{1}{8}$ | $1\frac{1}{8}$ |

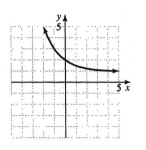

**62.** Let $y_0 = 57,000$, $k = 0.026$, $t = 5$.

$y = y_0 e^{kt}$

$y = 57,000 e^{0.026(5)}$

$y \approx 64,913$

In 5 years, there will be 64,913 prairie dogs.

**63.** $x^2 - y^2 = 36$

$x^2 - y^2 = 6^2$

hyperbola, with $x$-intercepts $(-6, 0)$, $(6, 0)$

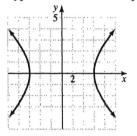

**64.** $16x^2 + 9y^2 = 144$

$$\frac{16x^2}{144} + \frac{9y^2}{144} = \frac{144}{144}$$

$$\frac{x^2}{9} + \frac{y^2}{16} = 1$$

Ellipse, $x$-intercepts $(-3, 0)$, $(3, 0)$

$y$-intercepts $(0, -4)$, $(0, 4)$

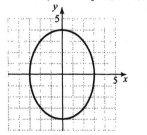

**65.**
$$x^2 + y^2 + 6x = 16$$
$$(x^2 + 6x + 9) + y^2 = 16 + 9$$
$$(x+3)^2 + y^2 = 25$$
$$[x - (-3)]^2 + (y-0)^2 = 5^2$$
circle with center $(-3, 0)$ and radius 5

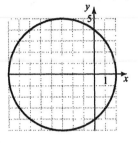

**66.** $\begin{cases} x^2 + y^2 = 26 \\ x^2 - 2y^2 = 23 \end{cases}$

Multiply equation (2) by $-1$ and add the equations.

$$x^2 + y^2 = 26$$
$$\underline{-x^2 + 2y^2 = -23}$$
$$3y^2 = 3$$
$$y^2 = 1$$
$$y = \pm 1$$

Substitute $y = -1$ and $y = 1$ into equation (1).

$$x^2 + (-1)^2 = 26$$
$$x^2 = 25$$
$$x = \pm 5$$

$$x^2 + 1^2 = 26$$
$$x^2 = 25$$
$$x = \pm 5$$

The solutions are $(-5, -1)$, $(-5, 1)$, $(5, -1)$, $(5, 1)$.

**67.** $a_n = \dfrac{(-1)^n}{n+4}$

$$a_1 = \frac{(-1)^1}{1+4} = -\frac{1}{5}$$
$$a_2 = \frac{(-1)^2}{2+4} = \frac{1}{6}$$
$$a_3 = \frac{(-1)^3}{3+4} = -\frac{1}{7}$$
$$a_4 = \frac{(-1)^4}{4+4} = \frac{1}{8}$$
$$a_5 = \frac{(-1)^5}{5+4} = -\frac{1}{9}$$

The first five terms are $-\dfrac{1}{5}, \dfrac{1}{6}, -\dfrac{1}{7}, \dfrac{1}{8}, -\dfrac{1}{9}$.

**68.** $a_n = 5(2)^{n-1}$

$$a_1 = 5(2)^{1-1} = 5(2)^0 = 5$$
$$r = 2$$
$$n = 5$$
$$S_n = \frac{a_1(1 - r^n)}{1-r}$$
$$S_5 = \frac{5(1 - 2^5)}{1-2} = \frac{5(1-32)}{-1} = 155$$

**69.** Sequence $\dfrac{3}{2}, -\dfrac{3}{4}, \dfrac{3}{8}, \ldots$

$$a_1 = \frac{3}{2}, \ r = -\frac{1}{2}$$
$$S_\infty = \frac{a_1}{1-r} = \frac{\frac{3}{2}}{1 - \left(-\frac{1}{2}\right)} = \frac{\frac{3}{2}}{\frac{3}{2}} = 1$$

**70.** $\displaystyle\sum_{i=1}^{4} i(i-2) = 1(1-2) + 2(2-2) + 3(3-2) + 4(4-2)$
$$= 1(-1) + 2(0) + 3(1) + 4(2)$$
$$= -1 + 0 + 3 + 8$$
$$= 10$$

**71.** $(2x+y)^5 = \binom{5}{0}(2x)^5 + \binom{5}{1}(2x)^4(y) + \binom{5}{2}(2x)^3(y)^2 + \binom{5}{3}(2x)^2(y)^3 + \binom{5}{4}(2x)^1(y)^4 + \binom{5}{5}y^5$

$\qquad = 2^5 x^5 + 5 \cdot 2^4 x^4 y + 10 \cdot 2^3 x^3 y^2 + 10 \cdot 2^2 x^2 y^3 + 5 \cdot 2xy^4 + y^5$

$\qquad = 32x^5 + 80x^4 y + 80x^3 y^2 + 40x^2 y^3 + 10xy^4 + y^5$

## Appendix B.3 Exercise Set

**1.** $V = lwh$

$\qquad = (6 \text{ in.})(4 \text{ in.})(3 \text{ in.})$

$\qquad = 72 \text{ cu in.}$

$\quad SA = 2lh + 2wh + 2lw$

$\qquad = 2(6 \text{ in.})(3 \text{ in.}) + 2(4 \text{ in.})(3 \text{ in.}) + 2(6 \text{ in.})(4 \text{ in.})$

$\qquad = 36 \text{ sq in.} + 24 \text{ sq in.} + 48 \text{ sq in.}$

$\qquad = 108 \text{ sq in.}$

**3.** $V = s^3 = (8 \text{ cm})^3 = 512 \text{ cu cm}$

$\quad SA = 6s^2 = 6(8 \text{ cm})^2 = 384 \text{ sq cm}$

**5.** $V = \dfrac{1}{3}\pi r^2 h$

$\qquad = \dfrac{1}{3}\pi(2 \text{ yd})^2(3 \text{ yd})$

$\qquad = 4\pi \text{ cu yd}$

$\qquad \approx 4\left(\dfrac{22}{7}\right) \text{ cu yd}$

$\qquad \approx 12.57 \text{ cu yd}$

$\quad SA = \pi r\sqrt{r^2 + h^2} + \pi r^2$

$\qquad = \pi(2 \text{ yd})\sqrt{(2 \text{ yd})^2 + (3 \text{ yd})^2} + \pi(2 \text{ yd})^2$

$\qquad = \pi(2 \text{ yd})\left(\sqrt{13} \text{ yd}\right) + \pi(4 \text{ sq yd})$

$\qquad = \left(2\sqrt{13} + 4\right)\pi \text{ sq yd}$

$\qquad \approx 3.14\left(2\sqrt{13} + 4\right) \text{ sq yd}$

$\qquad \approx 35.20 \text{ sq yd}$

7. $V = \dfrac{4}{3}\pi r^3$

$\quad = \dfrac{4}{3}\pi (5 \text{ in.})^3$

$\quad = \dfrac{500}{3}\pi \text{ cu in.}$

$\quad \approx \dfrac{500}{3}\left(\dfrac{22}{7}\right) \text{ cu in.}$

$\quad = 523\dfrac{17}{21} \text{ cu in.}$

$SA = 4\pi r^2$

$\quad = 4\pi (5 \text{ in.})^2$

$\quad = 100\pi \text{ sq in.}$

$\quad \approx 100\left(\dfrac{22}{7}\right) \text{ sq in.}$

$\quad = 314\dfrac{2}{7} \text{ sq in.}$

9. $V = \dfrac{1}{3}s^2 h = \dfrac{1}{3}(6 \text{ cm})^2 (4 \text{ cm}) = 48 \text{ cu cm}$

$SA = B + \dfrac{1}{2}pl$

$\quad = (6 \text{ cm})^2 + \dfrac{1}{2}(24 \text{ cm})(5 \text{ cm})$

$\quad = 36 \text{ sq cm} + 60 \text{ sq cm}$

$\quad = 96 \text{ sq cm}$

11. $V = s^3$

$\quad = \left(1\dfrac{1}{3} \text{ in.}\right)^3$

$\quad = \left(\dfrac{4}{3} \text{ in.}\right)^3$

$\quad = \dfrac{64}{27} \text{ cu in.}$

$\quad = 2\dfrac{10}{27} \text{ cu in.}$

13. $SA = 2lh + 2wh + 2lw$

$\quad = 2(2 \text{ ft})(1.4 \text{ ft}) + 2(2 \text{ ft})(3 \text{ ft}) + 2(1.4 \text{ ft})(3 \text{ ft})$

$\quad = 5.6 \text{ sq ft} + 12 \text{ sq ft} + 8.4 \text{ sq ft}$

$\quad = 26 \text{ sq ft}$

15. $V = \dfrac{1}{3}s^2 h$

$\quad = \dfrac{1}{3}(5 \text{ in.})^2 (1.3 \text{ in.})$

$\quad = \dfrac{1}{3}(25 \text{ sq in.})\left(\dfrac{13}{10} \text{ in.}\right)$

$\quad = \dfrac{65}{6} \text{ cu in.}$

$\quad = 10\dfrac{5}{6} \text{ cu in.}$

17. $V = \dfrac{1}{3}s^2 h = \dfrac{1}{3}(12 \text{ cm})^2 (20 \text{ cm}) = 960 \text{ cu cm}$

19. $SA = 4\pi r^2 = 4\pi (7 \text{ in.})^2 = 196\pi \text{ sq in.}$

21. $V = (2 \text{ ft})\left(2\dfrac{1}{2} \text{ ft}\right)\left(1\dfrac{1}{2} \text{ ft}\right) = 7\dfrac{1}{2} \text{ cu ft}$

23. $V = \dfrac{1}{3}\pi r^2 h$

$\quad \approx \dfrac{1}{3}\left(\dfrac{22}{7}\right)(2 \text{ cm})^2 (3 \text{ cm})$

$\quad = \dfrac{88}{7} \text{ cu cm}$

$\quad = 12\dfrac{4}{7} \text{ cu cm}$

## Appendix C Exercise Set

1. $f(x) = 3|x|$
   Find and plot ordered-pair solutions.

| $x$ | $f(x) = 3\vert x\vert$ |
|-----|------------------------|
| $-1$ | $3\vert{-1}\vert = 3$ |
| $0$ | $3\vert 0\vert = 0$ |
| $1$ | $3\vert 1\vert = 3$ |

**3.** $f(x) = \frac{1}{4}|x|$

Find and plot ordered-pair solutions.

| $x$ | $f(x) = \frac{1}{4}|x|$ |
|-----|------|
| –4 | 1 |
| 0 | 0 |
| 4 | 1 |

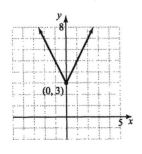

**5.** $g(x) = 2|x| + 3$
Write in the form $g(x) = a|x - h| + k$.
$g(x) = 2|x - 0| + 3$

- vertex is $(h, k) = (0, 3)$

- since $a > 0$, V-shape opens up

- since $|a| = |2| = 2 > 1$, the graph is narrower than $y = |x|$

| $x$ | $g(x) = 2|x| + 3$ |
|-----|------|
| –1 | $2|-1| + 3 = 5$ |
| 0 | $2|0| + 3 = 3$ |
| 1 | $2|1| + 3 = 5$ |

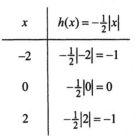

**7.** $h(x) = -\frac{1}{2}|x|$

- vertex is $(h, k) = (0, 0)$

- since $a < 0$, V-shape opens down

- since $|a| = \left|-\frac{1}{2}\right| = \frac{1}{2} < 1$, the graph is wider than $y = |x|$

| $x$ | $h(x) = -\frac{1}{2}|x|$ |
|-----|------|
| –2 | $-\frac{1}{2}|-2| = -1$ |
| 0 | $-\frac{1}{2}|0| = 0$ |
| 2 | $-\frac{1}{2}|2| = -1$ |

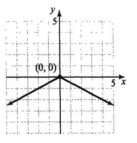

**9.** $f(x) = 4|x - 1|$
Write in the form $f(x) = a|x - h| + k$.
$f(x) = 4|x - 1| + 0$

- vertex is $(h, k) = (1, 0)$

- since $a > 0$, V-shape opens up

- since $|a| = |4| = 4 > 1$, the graph is narrower than $y = |x|$

| $x$ | $f(x) = 4|x - 1|$ |
|-----|------|
| –2 | $4|-2 - 1| = 12$ |
| 0 | $4|0 - 1| = 4$ |
| 2 | $4|2 - 1| = 4$ |

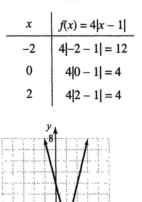

**11.** $g(x) = -\frac{1}{3}|x| - 2$

Write in the form $g(x) = a|x - h| + k$.

$g(x) = -\frac{1}{3}|x - 0| + (-2)$

- vertex is $(h, k) = (0, -2)$

- since $a < 0$, V-shape opens down

- since $|a| = \left|-\frac{1}{3}\right| = \frac{1}{3} < 1$, the graph is wider than $y = |x|$

| $x$ | $g(x) = -\frac{1}{3}|x| - 2$ |
|---|---|
| $-3$ | $-\frac{1}{3}|-3| - 2 = -3$ |
| $0$ | $-\frac{1}{3}|0| - 2 = -2$ |
| $3$ | $-\frac{1}{3}|3| - 2 = -3$ |

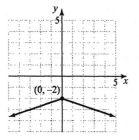

**13.** $f(x) = -2|x - 3| + 4$
This function is already written in the form
$f(x) = a|x - h| + k$.

- vertex is $(h, k) = (3, 4)$

- since $a < 0$, V-shape opens down

- since $|a| = |-2| = 2 > 1$, the graph is narrower than $y = |x|$

| $x$ | $f(x) = -2|x - 3| + 4$ |
|---|---|
| $-1$ | $-2|-1 - 3| + 4 = -4$ |
| $1$ | $-2|1 - 3| + 4 = 0$ |
| $4$ | $-2|4 - 3| + 4 = 2$ |

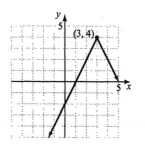

**15.** $f(x) = \frac{2}{3}|x + 2| - 5$

Write in the form $f(x) = a|x - h| + k$.

$f(x) = \frac{2}{3}|x - (-2)| + (-5)$

- vertex is $(h, k) = (-2, -5)$

- since $a > 0$, V-shape opens up

- since $|a| = \left|\frac{2}{3}\right| = \frac{2}{3} < 1$, the graph is wider than $y = |x|$

| $x$ | $f(x) = \frac{2}{3}|x + 2| - 5$ |
|---|---|
| $-5$ | $\frac{2}{3}|-5 + 2| - 5 = -3$ |
| $-2$ | $\frac{2}{3}|-2 + 2| - 5 = -5$ |
| $1$ | $\frac{2}{3}|1 + 2| - 5 = -3$ |

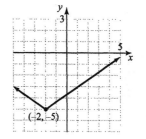

**Appendix D**

**Vocabulary and Readiness Check**

**1.** $\begin{vmatrix} 7 & 2 \\ 0 & 8 \end{vmatrix} = 56$

**2.** $\begin{vmatrix} 6 & 0 \\ 1 & 2 \end{vmatrix} = 12$

**3.** $\begin{vmatrix} -4 & 2 \\ 0 & 8 \end{vmatrix} = -32$

**4.** $\begin{vmatrix} 5 & 0 \\ 3 & -5 \end{vmatrix} = -25$

**5.** $\begin{vmatrix} -2 & 0 \\ 3 & -10 \end{vmatrix} = 20$

**6.** $\begin{vmatrix} -1 & 4 \\ 0 & -18 \end{vmatrix} = 18$

**Appendix D Exercise Set**

**1.** $\begin{vmatrix} 3 & 5 \\ -1 & 7 \end{vmatrix} = ad - bc = 3(7) - 5(-1) = 21 + 5 = 26$

**3.** $\begin{vmatrix} 9 & -2 \\ 4 & -3 \end{vmatrix} = ad - bc$
$= 9(-3) - (-2)(4)$
$= -27 + 8$
$= -19$

**5.** $\begin{vmatrix} -2 & 9 \\ 4 & -18 \end{vmatrix} = ad - bc$
$= -2(-18) - 9(4)$
$= 36 - 36$
$= 0$

**7.** $\begin{vmatrix} \frac{3}{4} & \frac{5}{2} \\ -\frac{1}{6} & \frac{7}{3} \end{vmatrix} = ad - bc$
$= \left(\frac{3}{4}\right)\left(\frac{7}{3}\right) - \left(\frac{5}{2}\right)\left(-\frac{1}{6}\right)$
$= \frac{7}{4} + \frac{5}{12}$
$= \frac{21}{12} + \frac{5}{12}$
$= \frac{26}{12}$
$= \frac{13}{6}$

**9.** $\begin{cases} 2y - 4 = 0 \\ x + 2y = 5 \end{cases}$ or $\begin{cases} 0x + 2y = 4 \\ 1x + 2y = 5 \end{cases}$
$D = \begin{vmatrix} 0 & 2 \\ 1 & 2 \end{vmatrix} = 0 - 2 = -2$
$D_x = \begin{vmatrix} 4 & 2 \\ 5 & 2 \end{vmatrix} = 8 - 10 = -2$

$D_y = \begin{vmatrix} 0 & 4 \\ 1 & 5 \end{vmatrix} = 0 - 4 = -4$
$x = \frac{D_x}{D} = \frac{-2}{-2} = 1$
$y = \frac{D_y}{D} = \frac{-4}{-2} = 2$
The solution is (1, 2).

**11.** $\begin{cases} 3x + y = 1 \\ 2y = 2 - 6x \end{cases}$ or $\begin{cases} 3x + 1y = 1 \\ 6x + 2y = 2 \end{cases}$
$D = \begin{vmatrix} 3 & 1 \\ 6 & 2 \end{vmatrix} = 6 - 6 = 0$

Since $D = 0$, Cramer's Rule cannot be used. Notice that equation (2) is equation (1) multiplied by 2.
The solution is $\{(x, y) | 3x + y = 1\}$.

**13.** $\begin{cases} 5x - 2y = 27 \\ -3x + 5y = 18 \end{cases}$
$D = \begin{vmatrix} 5 & -2 \\ -3 & 5 \end{vmatrix} = 25 - 6 = 19$
$D_x = \begin{vmatrix} 27 & -2 \\ 18 & 5 \end{vmatrix} = 135 + 36 = 171$
$D_y = \begin{vmatrix} 5 & 27 \\ -3 & 18 \end{vmatrix} = 90 + 81 = 171$
$x = \frac{D_x}{D} = \frac{171}{19} = 9$ and $y = \frac{D_y}{D} = \frac{171}{19} = 9$
The solution is (9, 9).

**15.** $\begin{cases} 2x - 5y = 4 \\ x + 2y = -7 \end{cases}$
$D = \begin{vmatrix} 2 & -5 \\ 1 & 2 \end{vmatrix} = 4 + 5 = 9$
$D_x = \begin{vmatrix} 4 & -5 \\ -7 & 2 \end{vmatrix} = 8 - 35 = -27$
$D_y = \begin{vmatrix} 2 & 4 \\ 1 & -7 \end{vmatrix} = -14 - 4 = -18$
$x = \frac{D_x}{D} = \frac{-27}{9} = -3$ and $y = \frac{D_y}{D} = \frac{-18}{9} = -2$
The solution is (-3, -2).

**17.** $\begin{cases} \dfrac{2}{3}x - \dfrac{3}{4}y = -1 \\ -\dfrac{1}{6}x + \dfrac{3}{4}y = \dfrac{5}{2} \end{cases}$

$D = \begin{vmatrix} \dfrac{2}{3} & -\dfrac{3}{4} \\ -\dfrac{1}{6} & \dfrac{3}{4} \end{vmatrix} = \dfrac{1}{2} - \dfrac{1}{8} = \dfrac{3}{8}$

$D_x = \begin{vmatrix} -1 & -\dfrac{3}{4} \\ \dfrac{5}{2} & \dfrac{3}{4} \end{vmatrix} = -\dfrac{3}{4} + \dfrac{15}{8} = \dfrac{9}{8}$

$D_y = \begin{vmatrix} \dfrac{2}{3} & -1 \\ -\dfrac{1}{6} & \dfrac{5}{2} \end{vmatrix} = \dfrac{10}{6} - \dfrac{1}{6} = \dfrac{9}{6}$

$x = \dfrac{D_x}{D} = \dfrac{\frac{9}{8}}{\frac{3}{8}} = 3$ and $y = \dfrac{D_y}{D} = \dfrac{\frac{9}{6}}{\frac{3}{8}} = 4$

The solution is (3, 4).

**19.** Expand by first row.

$\begin{vmatrix} 2 & 1 & 0 \\ 0 & 5 & -3 \\ 4 & 0 & 2 \end{vmatrix} = 2\begin{vmatrix} 5 & -3 \\ 0 & 2 \end{vmatrix} - 1\begin{vmatrix} 0 & -3 \\ 4 & 2 \end{vmatrix} + 0\begin{vmatrix} 0 & 5 \\ 4 & 0 \end{vmatrix}$

$= 2(10 - 0) - 1(0 + 12) + 0$

$= 20 - 12$

$= 8$

**21.** Expand by third column.

$\begin{vmatrix} 4 & -6 & 0 \\ -2 & 3 & 0 \\ 4 & -6 & 1 \end{vmatrix} = 0\begin{vmatrix} -2 & 3 \\ 4 & -6 \end{vmatrix} - 0\begin{vmatrix} 4 & -6 \\ 4 & -6 \end{vmatrix} + 1\begin{vmatrix} 4 & -6 \\ -2 & 3 \end{vmatrix}$

$= 0 - 0 + 1(12 - 12)$

$= 0$

**23.** Expand by first row.

$\begin{vmatrix} 1 & 0 & 4 \\ 1 & -1 & 2 \\ 3 & 2 & 1 \end{vmatrix} = 1\begin{vmatrix} -1 & 2 \\ 2 & 1 \end{vmatrix} - 0\begin{vmatrix} 1 & 2 \\ 3 & 1 \end{vmatrix} + 4\begin{vmatrix} 1 & -1 \\ 3 & 2 \end{vmatrix}$

$= 1(-1 - 4) - 0 + 4(2 + 3)$

$= -5 + 20$

$= 15$

**25.** Expand by first row.

$\begin{vmatrix} 3 & 6 & -3 \\ -1 & -2 & 3 \\ 4 & -1 & 6 \end{vmatrix} = 3\begin{vmatrix} -2 & 3 \\ -1 & 6 \end{vmatrix} - 6\begin{vmatrix} -1 & 3 \\ 4 & 6 \end{vmatrix} - 3\begin{vmatrix} -1 & -2 \\ 4 & -1 \end{vmatrix}$

$= 3(-12 + 3) - 6(-6 - 12) - 3(1 + 8)$

$= -27 + 108 - 27$

$= 54$

**27.** $\begin{cases} 3x \qquad + z = -1 \\ -x - 3y + z = 7 \\ \qquad 3y + z = 5 \end{cases}$

$D = \begin{vmatrix} 3 & 0 & 1 \\ -1 & -3 & 1 \\ 0 & 3 & 1 \end{vmatrix} = 3\begin{vmatrix} -3 & 1 \\ 3 & 1 \end{vmatrix} - 0\begin{vmatrix} -1 & 1 \\ 0 & 1 \end{vmatrix} + 1\begin{vmatrix} -1 & -3 \\ 0 & 3 \end{vmatrix}$

$\qquad = 3(-3 - 3) - 0 + 1(-3 - 0)$

$\qquad = -18 - 3$

$\qquad = -21$

$D_x = \begin{vmatrix} -1 & 0 & 1 \\ 7 & -3 & 1 \\ 5 & 3 & 1 \end{vmatrix}$

$\quad = -1\begin{vmatrix} -3 & 1 \\ 3 & 1 \end{vmatrix} - 0\begin{vmatrix} 7 & 1 \\ 5 & 1 \end{vmatrix} + 1\begin{vmatrix} 7 & -3 \\ 5 & 3 \end{vmatrix}$

$\quad = -1(-3 - 3) - 0 + 1|21 + 15|$

$\quad = 6 + 36$

$\quad = 42$

$D_y = \begin{vmatrix} 3 & -1 & 1 \\ -1 & 7 & 1 \\ 0 & 5 & 1 \end{vmatrix} = 3\begin{vmatrix} 7 & 1 \\ 5 & 1 \end{vmatrix} + 1\begin{vmatrix} -1 & 1 \\ 5 & 1 \end{vmatrix} + 0\begin{vmatrix} -1 & 1 \\ 7 & 1 \end{vmatrix}$

$\qquad = 3(7 - 5) + 1(-1 - 5) + 0$

$\qquad = 6 - 6$

$\qquad = 0$

$D_z = \begin{vmatrix} 3 & 0 & -1 \\ -1 & -3 & 7 \\ 0 & 3 & 5 \end{vmatrix}$

$\quad = 3\begin{vmatrix} -3 & 7 \\ 3 & 5 \end{vmatrix} - 0\begin{vmatrix} -1 & 7 \\ 0 & 5 \end{vmatrix} - 1\begin{vmatrix} -1 & -3 \\ 0 & 3 \end{vmatrix}$

$\quad = 3(-15 - 21) - 0 - 1(-3 - 0)$

$\quad = -108 + 3$

$\quad = -105$

$x = \dfrac{D_x}{D} = \dfrac{42}{-21} = -2, \quad y = \dfrac{D_y}{D} = \dfrac{0}{-21} = 0,$

$z = \dfrac{D_z}{D} = \dfrac{-105}{-21} = 5$

The solution is (-2, 0, 5).

**29.** $\begin{cases} x + y + z = 8 \\ 2x - y - z = 10 \\ x - 2y + 3z = 22 \end{cases}$

$$D = \begin{vmatrix} 1 & 1 & 1 \\ 2 & -1 & -1 \\ 1 & -2 & 3 \end{vmatrix}$$

$$= 1\begin{vmatrix} -1 & -1 \\ -2 & 3 \end{vmatrix} - 1\begin{vmatrix} 2 & -1 \\ 1 & 3 \end{vmatrix} + 1\begin{vmatrix} 2 & -1 \\ 1 & -2 \end{vmatrix}$$

$$= 1(-3-2) - 1(6+1) + 1(-4+1)$$

$$= -5 - 7 - 3$$

$$= -15$$

$$D_x = \begin{vmatrix} 8 & 1 & 1 \\ 10 & -1 & -1 \\ 22 & -2 & 3 \end{vmatrix}$$

$$= 8\begin{vmatrix} -1 & -1 \\ -2 & 3 \end{vmatrix} - 10\begin{vmatrix} 1 & 1 \\ -2 & 3 \end{vmatrix} + 22\begin{vmatrix} 1 & 1 \\ -1 & -1 \end{vmatrix}$$

$$= 8(-3-2) - 10(3+2) + 22(-1+1)$$

$$= -40 - 50 + 0$$

$$= -90$$

$$D_y = \begin{vmatrix} 1 & 8 & 1 \\ 2 & 10 & -1 \\ 1 & 22 & 3 \end{vmatrix}$$

$$= 1\begin{vmatrix} 10 & -1 \\ 22 & 3 \end{vmatrix} - 8\begin{vmatrix} 2 & -1 \\ 1 & 3 \end{vmatrix} + 1\begin{vmatrix} 2 & 10 \\ 1 & 22 \end{vmatrix}$$

$$= 1(30+22) - 8(6+1) + 1(44-10)$$

$$= 52 - 56 + 34$$

$$= 30$$

$$D_z = \begin{vmatrix} 1 & 1 & 8 \\ 2 & -1 & 10 \\ 1 & -2 & 22 \end{vmatrix}$$

$$= 1\begin{vmatrix} -1 & 10 \\ -2 & 22 \end{vmatrix} - 1\begin{vmatrix} 2 & 10 \\ 1 & 22 \end{vmatrix} + 8\begin{vmatrix} 2 & -1 \\ 1 & -2 \end{vmatrix}$$

$$= 1(-22+20) - 1(44-10) + 8(-4+1)$$

$$= -2 - 34 - 24$$

$$= -60$$

$$x = \frac{D_x}{D} = \frac{-90}{-15} = 6, \quad y = \frac{D_y}{D} = \frac{30}{-15} = -2,$$

$$z = \frac{D_z}{D} = \frac{-60}{-15} = 4$$

The solution is (6, –2, 4).

**31.** $\begin{cases} 2x + 2y + z = 1 \\ -x + y + 2z = 3 \\ x + 2y + 4z = 0 \end{cases}$

$$D = \begin{vmatrix} 2 & 2 & 1 \\ -1 & 1 & 2 \\ 1 & 2 & 4 \end{vmatrix} = 2\begin{vmatrix} 1 & 2 \\ 2 & 4 \end{vmatrix} - 2\begin{vmatrix} -1 & 2 \\ 1 & 4 \end{vmatrix} + 1\begin{vmatrix} -1 & 1 \\ 1 & 2 \end{vmatrix}$$

$$= 2(4-4) - 2(-4-2) + 1(-2-1)$$

$$= 0 + 12 - 3$$

$$= 9$$

$$D_x = \begin{vmatrix} 1 & 2 & 1 \\ 3 & 1 & 2 \\ 0 & 2 & 4 \end{vmatrix} = 1\begin{vmatrix} 1 & 2 \\ 2 & 4 \end{vmatrix} - 3\begin{vmatrix} 2 & 1 \\ 2 & 4 \end{vmatrix} + 0$$

$$= 1(4-4) - 3(8-2)$$

$$= -18$$

$$D_y = \begin{vmatrix} 2 & 1 & 1 \\ -1 & 3 & 2 \\ 1 & 0 & 4 \end{vmatrix} = 2\begin{vmatrix} 3 & 2 \\ 0 & 4 \end{vmatrix} - 1\begin{vmatrix} -1 & 2 \\ 1 & 4 \end{vmatrix} + 1\begin{vmatrix} -1 & 3 \\ 1 & 0 \end{vmatrix}$$

$$= 2(12-0) - 1(-4-2) + 1(0-3)$$

$$= 24 + 6 - 3$$

$$= 27$$

$$D_z = \begin{vmatrix} 2 & 2 & 1 \\ -1 & 1 & 3 \\ 1 & 2 & 0 \end{vmatrix} = 2\begin{vmatrix} 1 & 3 \\ 2 & 0 \end{vmatrix} - 2\begin{vmatrix} -1 & 3 \\ 1 & 0 \end{vmatrix} + 1\begin{vmatrix} -1 & 1 \\ 1 & 2 \end{vmatrix}$$

$$= 2(0-6) - 2(0-3) + 1(-2-1)$$

$$= -12 + 6 - 3$$

$$= -9$$

$$x = \frac{D_x}{D} = \frac{-18}{9} = -2, \quad y = \frac{D_y}{D} = \frac{27}{9} = 3,$$

$$z = \frac{D_z}{D} = \frac{-9}{9} = -1$$

The solution is (–2, 3, –1).

**33.** $\begin{cases} x - 2y + z = -5 \\ 3y + 2z = 4 \\ 3x - y = -2 \end{cases}$

$$D = \begin{vmatrix} 1 & -2 & 1 \\ 0 & 3 & 2 \\ 3 & -1 & 0 \end{vmatrix} = 1\begin{vmatrix} 3 & 2 \\ -1 & 0 \end{vmatrix} + 2\begin{vmatrix} 0 & 2 \\ 3 & 0 \end{vmatrix} + 1\begin{vmatrix} 0 & 3 \\ 3 & -1 \end{vmatrix}$$

$$= 1(0+2) + 2(0-6) + 1(0-9)$$

$$= 2 - 12 - 9$$

$$= -19$$

$$D_x = \begin{vmatrix} -5 & -2 & 1 \\ 4 & 3 & 2 \\ -2 & -1 & 0 \end{vmatrix}$$

$$= -5 \begin{vmatrix} 3 & 2 \\ -1 & 0 \end{vmatrix} + 2 \begin{vmatrix} 4 & 2 \\ -2 & 0 \end{vmatrix} + 1 \begin{vmatrix} 4 & 3 \\ -2 & -1 \end{vmatrix}$$

$$= -5(0+2) + 2(0+4) + 1(-4+6)$$

$$= -10 + 8 + 2$$

$$= 0$$

$$D_y = \begin{vmatrix} 1 & -5 & 1 \\ 0 & 4 & 2 \\ 3 & -2 & 0 \end{vmatrix} = 1 \begin{vmatrix} 4 & 2 \\ -2 & 0 \end{vmatrix} + 5 \begin{vmatrix} 0 & 2 \\ 3 & 0 \end{vmatrix} + 1 \begin{vmatrix} 0 & 4 \\ 3 & -2 \end{vmatrix}$$

$$= 1(0+4) + 5(0-6) + 1(0-12)$$

$$= 4 - 30 - 12$$

$$= -38$$

$$D_z = \begin{vmatrix} 1 & -2 & -5 \\ 0 & 3 & 4 \\ 3 & -1 & -2 \end{vmatrix}$$

$$= 1 \begin{vmatrix} 3 & 4 \\ -1 & -2 \end{vmatrix} + 2 \begin{vmatrix} 0 & 4 \\ 3 & -2 \end{vmatrix} - 5 \begin{vmatrix} 0 & 3 \\ 3 & -1 \end{vmatrix}$$

$$= 1(-6+4) + 2(0-12) - 5(0-9)$$

$$= -2 - 24 + 45$$

$$= 19$$

$$x = \frac{D_x}{D} = \frac{0}{-19} = 0, \quad y = \frac{D_y}{D} = \frac{-38}{-19} = 2,$$

$$z = \frac{D_z}{D} = \frac{19}{-19} = -1$$

The solution is $(0, 2, -1)$.

**35.**  $\begin{vmatrix} 1 & x \\ 2 & 7 \end{vmatrix} = -3$

$$(1)(7) - x \cdot 2 = -3$$

$$7 - 2x = -3$$

$$-2x = -10$$

$$x = 5$$

**37.** 0; answers may vary

## Appendix E

### Viewing Window and Interpreting Window Settings Exercise Set

**1.** Yes, since every coordinate is between $-10$ and $10$.

**3.** No, since $-11$ is less than $-10$.

**5.** Answers may vary. Any values such that Xmin $< -90$, Ymin $< -80$, Xmax $> 55$, and Ymax $> 80$.

**7.** Answers may vary. Any values such that Xmin $< -11$, Ymin $< -5$, Xmax $> 7$, and Ymax $> 2$.

**9.** Answers may vary. Any values such that Xmin $< 50$, Ymin $< -50$, Xmax $> 200$, and Ymax $> 200$.

**11.**  Xmin $= -12$      Ymin $= -12$
     Xmax $= 12$      Ymax $= 12$
     Xscl $= 3$      Yscl $= 3$

**13.**  Xmin $= -9$      Ymin $= -12$
     Xmax $= 9$      Ymax $= 12$
     Xscl $= 1$      Yscl $= 2$

**15.**  Xmin $= -10$      Ymin $= -25$
     Xmax $= 10$      Ymax $= 25$
     Xscl $= 2$      Yscl $= 5$

**17.**  Xmin $= -10$      Ymin $= -30$
     Xmax $= 10$      Ymax $= 30$
     Xscl $= 1$      Yscl $= 3$

**19.**  Xmin $= -20$      Ymin $= -30$
     Xmax $= 30$      Ymax $= 50$
     Xscl $= 5$      Yscl $= 10$

### Graphing Equations and Square Viewing Window Exercise Set

**1.** Setting A:

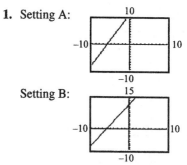

Setting B:

Setting B shows all intercepts.

3. Setting A:

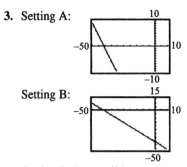

Setting B:

Setting B shows all intercepts.

5. Setting A:

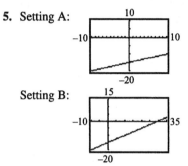

Setting B:

Setting B shows all intercepts.

7. $3x = 5y$

$y = \dfrac{3}{5}x$

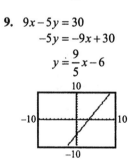

9. $9x - 5y = 30$

$\quad -5y = -9x + 30$

$\quad\quad y = \dfrac{9}{5}x - 6$

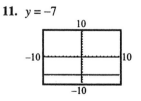

11. $y = -7$

13. $x + 10y = -5$

$\quad 10y = -x - 5$

$\quad\quad y = -\dfrac{1}{10}x - \dfrac{1}{2}$

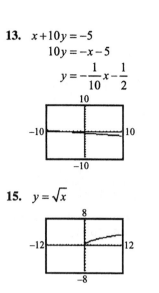

15. $y = \sqrt{x}$

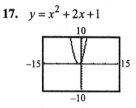

17. $y = x^2 + 2x + 1$

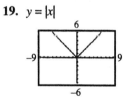

19. $y = |x|$

21. $x + 2y = 30$

$\quad 2y = -x + 30$

$\quad\quad y = -\dfrac{1}{2}x + 15$

Standard window:

Adjusted window:

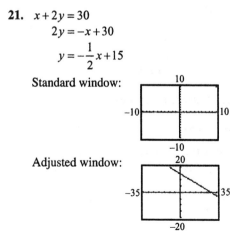